Kirk-Othmer

ENCYCLOPEDIA OF CHEMICAL TECHNOLOGY

Second Edition

VOLUME 8

Electron Tube Materials
to
Ferrites

Kirk-Othmer

ENCYCLOPEDIA OF CHEMICAL TECHNOLOGY

Second completely revised edition

VOLUME 8

**Electron Tube Materials
to
Ferrites**

CONTENTS

EDITORIAL STAFF FOR VOLUME 8

Eva A. Parolla

Frances L. Dankberg   Joseph J. Kerstein   Anna Klingsberg
Joan C. Mooney   Lynda L. Strauss   Martha Windholz

CONTRIBUTORS TO VOLUME 8

Ralph F. Anderson, *International Minerals & Chemical Corporation, Bioferm Division,* Fermentation

W. C. Ault, *U.S. Department of Agriculture,* Fatty acids (Analysis and standards; Fatty acids from tall oil; Manufacture; Polybasic acids; Branched-chain acids)

D. A. Barsness, *General Electric Company,* Embedding

R. J. Bondley, *General Electric Company,* Electron tube materials

H. M. Briggs, *South Dakota State University,* Feeds, animal

D. L. Caldwell, *The Lummus Company,* Ethylene

Myron A. Coler, *Markite Corporation,* Electrophoretic deposition

H. M. Crooks, Jr., *Parke, Davis & Company,* Epinephrine

George I. de Becze, *Schenley Distillers, Inc.,* Enzymes, industrial

E. W. Eckey, *E. W. Eckey Research Laboratory,* Ester interchange

George Economos, *Allen-Bradley Company,* Ferrites

Edward U. Elam, *Tennessee Eastman Company,* Esters, organic

A. L. Friedberg, *University of Illinois,* Enamels, porcelain or vitreous

W. C. Griffin, *Atlas Chemical Industries, Inc.,* Emulsions

E. F. Izard, *E. I. du Pont de Nemours & Co., Inc.,* Ester interchange

Haydn Jones, *Hizone Laboratories, Wilmette, Illinois,* Embalming fluids

M. Lapkin, *Olin Mathieson Chemical Corporation,* Epoxides

Ernest Le Monnier, *Celanese Corporation of America,* Ethanoic acid (Acetic acid; Acetic anhydride)

G. A. Lescisin, *Union Carbide Corporation, Chemicals Division,* Ethanol

Charles E. Leyes, *Newark College of Engineering,* Esterification

I. Lichtenstein, *The Lummus Company,* Ethylene

Victor Lindner, *U.S. Army, Picatinny Arsenal,* Explosives (Propellants)

F. A. Lowenheim, *M & T Chemicals, Inc.,* Electroplating

Arnold P. Lurie, *Eastman Kodak Company,* Ethane; Ethers; Ethanoic acid (Halogenated derivatives)

F. J. Modic, *General Electric Company,* Embedding

F. A. Norris, *Swift & Company,* Fats and fatty oils

C. A. Pentz, Jr., *Union Carbide Corporation, Chemicals Division,* Ethanol

E. H. Pryde, *U.S. Department of Agriculture,* Fatty acids (Industrially important reactions; Economic aspects)

Wm. H. Rinkenbach, *Consulting Chemist,* Explosives (in part)

L. M. Roberts, *Research-Cottrell, Inc.,* Electrostatic precipitation

E. G. Rochow, *Harvard University,* Elements—periodic system

E. G. Scheibel, *The Cooper Union for the Advancement of Science and Art,* Extraction

Henry C. Schultze, *Union Carbide Corporation,* Ethylene oxide

Ferris C. Standiford, *W. L. Badger Associates, Inc.,* Evaporation

A. B. Walker, *Research-Cottrell, Inc.,* Electrostatic precipitation

John G. Wallace, *E. I. du Pont de Nemours & Co., Inc.,* Epoxidation

Joseph R. Weschler, *Ciba Products Company,* Epoxy resins

E. J. Wickson, *Enjay Laboratories,* Fatty acids (Trialkylacetic acids)

ABBREVIATIONS AND SYMBOLS

A	ampere(s)
A	anion (eg, HA)
Å	angstrom unit(s)
AATCC	American Association of Textile Chemists and Colorists
abs	absolute
ac	alternating current
ac-	alicylic (eg, ac-derivatives of tetrahydronaphthalene)
accel(d)	accelerate(d)
acceln	acceleration
ACS	American Chemical Society
addn	addition
AGA	American Gas Association
Ah	ampere-hour(s)
AIChE	American Institute of Chemical Engineers
AIME	American Institute of Mining and Metallurgical Engineers
AIP	American Institute of Physics
alc	alcohol(ic)
alk	alkaline (not alkali)
Alk	alkyl
A-min	ampere-minute(s)
amt	amount (noun)
anhyd	anhydrous
API	American Petroleum Institute
app	apparatus
approx	approximate(ly)
aq	aqueous
ar-	aromatic (eg, ar-vinylaniline)
Ar	aryl
as-	asymmetric(al) (eg, as-trichlorobenzene)
ASA	American Standards Association
ASHRAE	American Society of Heating, Refrigeration and Air-Conditioning Engineers
ASM	American Society for Metals
ASME	American Society of Mechanical Engineers
ASTM	American Society for Testing and Materials
atm	atmosphere(s), atmospheric
at. no.	atomic number
at. wt	atomic weight
av	average
b	barn(s)
b (as in b_{11})	boiling (at 11 mm Hg)
bbl	barrel(s)
BC	body-centered
Bé	Baumé
Bhn	Brinell hardness number
bp	boiling point
BP	*British Pharmacopoeia* (General Medical Council in London)
Btu	British thermal unit(s)
bu	bushel(s)
C	Celsius (centigrade); coulomb(s)
C-	denoting attachment to carbon (eg, C-acetylindoline)
CA	Chemical Abstracts
ca	circa, approximately

cal	calorie(s)	db	dry-bulb
calcd	calculated	dB	decibel(s)
cfm,		dc	direct current
ft³/min	cubic foot (feet) per minute	dec,	
cg	centigram(s)	decomp	decompose(s)
cgs	centimeter-gram-second	decompd	decomposed
Ci	curie(s)	decompn	decomposition
CI	Colour Index (number);	den	denier(s)
	the CI numbers given	den/fil	denier(s) per filament
	in *ECT*, 2nd ed., are	deriv	derivative
	from the new *Colour*	detd	determined
	Index (1956) and	detn	determination
	Suppl. (1963), *Soc.*	diam	diameter
	Dyers Colourists,	dielec	dielectric (adj.)
	Bradford, England,	dil	dilute
	and *AATCC*, U.S.A.	DIN	Deutsche Industrienormen
cif	cost, insurance, freight	distd	distilled
cl	car lots	distn	distillation
cm	centimeter(s)	dl	deciliter(s)
coeff	coefficient	*dl-*, DL	racemic
compd,		dm	decimeter(s)
cpd	compound (noun)	dp	dewpoint
compn	composition	dyn	dyne(s)
concd	concentrated	*e*	electron; base of natural
concn	concentration		logarithms
cond	conductivity	ed.	edited, edition, editor
const	constant	elec	electric(al)
cont	continued	emf	electromotive force
cor	corrected	emu	electromagnetic unit(s)
cp	chemically pure	en	entropy unit(s)
cP	centipoise(s)	eng	engineering
cpd,		equil	equilibrium(s)
compd	compound (noun)	equiv	equivalent
cps	cycles per second	esp	especially
crit	critical	est(d)	estimate(d)
cryst	crystalline	estn	estimation
crystd	crystallized	esu	electrostatic unit(s)
crystn	crystallization	eV	electron volt(s)
cSt	centistokes	expt(l)	experiment(al)
cʋ	cubic	ext(d)	extract(ed)
d	density (conveniently,	extn	extraction
	specific gravity)	F	Fahrenheit; farad(s)
d	differential operator	*F*	faraday constant
d-	*dextro-*, dextrorotatory	FC	face-centered
D	Debye unit(s)	Fed, fedl	federal (eg, Fed Spec)
D-	denoting configurational	fl oz	fluid ounce(s)
	relationship (as to	fob	free on board
	*dextro-*glyceraldehyde)	fp	freezing point

frz	freezing	IUPAC	International Union of Pure and Applied Chemistry
ft	foot (feet)		
ft³/min, cfm	cubic foot (feet) per minute	J	joule(s)
ft-lb	foot-pound(s)	K	Kelvin
g	gram(s)	K	dissociation constant
g	gravitational acceleration	kbar	kilobar(s)
G	gauss(es)	kc	kilocycle(s)
G	Gibbs free energy	kcal	kilogram-calorie(s)
gal	gallon(s)	keV	kilo electron volt(s)
gal/min, gpm	gallon(s) per minute	kg	kilogram(s)
g/den	gram(s) per denier	kG	kilogauss(es)
gem-	geminal (attached to the same atom)	kJ	kilojoule(s)
		kV	kilovolt(s)
g-mol	gram-molecular (as in g-mol wt)	kVA	kilovolt-ampere(s)
		kW	kilowatt(s)
g-mole	gram-mole(s)	kWh	kilowatt-hour(s)
G-Oe	gauss-oersted(s)	l	liter(s)
gpm, gal/min	gallon(s) per minute	*l-*	*levo-*, levorotatory
		L-	denoting configurational relationship (as to *levo*-glyceraldehyde)
gr	grain(s)		
h, hr	hour(s)	lb	pound(s)
hl	hectoliter(s)	LC_{50}	concentration lethal to 50% of the animals tested
hp	horsepower(s)		
hr, h	hour(s)		
hyd	hydrated, hydrous	lcl	less than car lots
hyg	hygroscopic	LD_{50}	dose lethal to 50% of the animals tested
Hz	hertz(es)		
i, insol	insoluble	liq	liquid
^{i} (eg, Pr^i)	iso (eg, isopropyl)	lm	lumen
i-	inactive (eg, *i*-methionine)	ln	logarithm (natural)
IACS	International Annealed Copper Standard	log	logarithm (common)
		m	meter(s)
ibp	initial boiling point	*m-*	meta (eg, *m*-xylene)
ICC	Interstate Commerce Commission	M	metal
		M	molar (as applied to concentration; not molal)
ICT	International Critical Tables		
		mA	milliampere(s)
ID	inner diameter	mAh	milliampere-hour(s)
in.	inch(es)	manuf	manufacture
insol, i	insoluble	manufd, mfd	manufactured
IPT	Institute of Petroleum Technologists		
		manufg, mfg	manufacturing
ISO	International Organization for Standardization	max	maximum
IU	International Unit(s)	Mc	megacycle(s)

MCA	Manufacturing Chemists' Association
mcal	millicalorie(s)
mech	mechanical
meq	milliequivalent(s)
MeV	million electron volt(s)
mfd, manufd	manufactured
mfg, manufg	manufacturing
mg	milligram(s)
min	minimum; minute(s)
misc	miscellaneous
mixt	mixture
ml	milliliter(s)
MLD	minimum lethal dose
mm	millimeter(s)
mM	millimole(s)
mo(s)	month(s)
mol	molecule, molecular
mol wt	molecular weight
mp	melting point
mph	miles per hour
MR	molar refraction
mV	millivolt(s)
mμ	millimicron(s)
^{n} (eg, Bu^n), n-	normal (eg, normal butyl)
n (as, n_D^{20})	index of refraction (for 20°C and sodium light)
n-, ^{n}	normal (eg, n-butyl; Bu^n)
N	normal (as applied to concentration)
N-	denoting attachment to nitrogen (eg, N-methylaniline)
neg	negative (adj.)
NF	*National Formulary* (American Pharmaceutical Association)
NMR	nuclear magnetic resonance
NND	*New and Nonofficial Drugs* (American Medical Association)
no.	number
NOIBN	not otherwise indexed by name (ICC specification for shipping containers)

o-	ortho (eg, o-xylene)
O-	denoting attachment to oxygen (eg, O-acetyl-hydroxylamine)
Ω	ohm(s)
Ω-cm	ohm-centimeter(s)
OD	outer diameter
Oe	oersted(s)
owf	on weight of fiber
oz	ounce(s)
p-	para (eg, p-xylene)
P	poise(s)
pdr	powder
PhI	*Pharmacopoeia Internationalis*, 2 vols. and Suppl., World Health Organization, Geneva, 1951, 1955, and 1959
phr	parts per hundred of rubber or resin
pos	positive (adj.)
powd	powdered
ppm	parts per million
ppt(d)	precipitate(d)
pptn	precipitation
Pr. (no.)	Foreign prototype (number); dyestuff designation used in *AATCC Year Books* for dyes not listed in the old *Colour Index* (1924 ed.; 1928 Suppl.); obsolete since new *Colour Index* was published (1956 ed.; 1963 Suppl.)
prepd	prepared
prepn	preparation
psi	pound(s) per square inch
psia	pound(s) per square inch absolute
psig	pound(s) per square inch gage
pt	point
pts	parts
qual	qualitative
quant	quantitative
qv	which see (quod vide)
r	roentgen

R	univalent hydrocarbon radical (or hydrogen); Rankine		sp	specific
			sp, spp	species (sing. and pl.)
			spec	specification
rep	roentgen(s) equivalent physical		sp gr	specific gravity
			sq	square
resp	respectively		St	stokes
rh	relative humidity		STP	standard temperature and pressure (760 mm Hg, 0°C)
RI	Ring Index (number); from *The Ring Index*, Reinhold Publishing Corp., N.Y., 1940			
			subl	sublime(s), subliming
			SUs	Saybolt Universal second(s)
rms	root mean square			
rpm	revolutions per minute		*sym, s-*	symmetrical (eg, *sym*-dichloroethylene)
rps	revolutions per second			
RRI	Revised Ring Index (number); from *The Ring Index*, 2nd ed., American Chemical Society, Washington, D.C., 1960		t, temp	temperature
			^{t} (eg, Bu^t), *t-, tert-*	tertiary (eg, tertiary butyl)
			t-, tert-, ^{t}	tertiary (eg, *t*-butyl)
			TAPPI	Technical Association of the Pulp and Paper Industry
RT	room temperature			
s, sol	soluble			
^{s} (eg, Bu^s), *sec-*	secondary (eg, secondary butyl)		tech	technical
			temp, t	temperature
s-, sym-	symmetrical (eg, *s*-dichloroethylene)		*tert-, t-,* ^{t}	tertiary (eg, *tert*-butyl)
			theoret	theoretical
S-	denoting attachment to sulfur (eg, *S*-methylcysteine)		Twad	Twaddell
			USP	(*The*) *United States Pharmacopeia* (Mack Publishing Co., Easton, Pa.)
SAE	Society of Automotive Engineers			
satd	saturated		uv	ultraviolet
satn	saturation		V	volt(s)
SCF	standard cubic foot (feet) 760 mm Hg, 63°F)		*v-, vic-*	vicinal (attached to adjacent atoms)
Sch	Schultz number (designation for dyes from *Farbstofftabellen*, 4 vols., Akademie Verlag, Leipzig, 1931–1939)		var	variety
			vic-, v-	vicinal (attached to adjacent atoms)
			vol	volume(s) (not volatile)
sec	second(s)		v s, v sol	very soluble
			vs	versus
sec-, ^{s}	secondary (eg, *sec*-butyl; Bu^s)		W	watt(s)
			Wh	watt-hour(s)
SFs	Saybolt Furol second(s)		wt	weight
sl s, sl sol	slightly soluble		xu (ca 10^{-11} cm)	x unit(s)
sol, s	soluble		yd	yard(s)
soln	solution		yr	year(s)
soly	solubility			

Quantities

Some standard abbreviations (prefixes) for very small and very large quantities are as follows:

deci (10^{-1})	d		deka (10^{1})	dk
centi (10^{-2})	c		hecto (10^{2})	h
milli (10^{-3})	m		kilo (10^{3})	k
micro (10^{-6})	μ		mega (10^{6})	M
nano (10^{-9})	n		giga (10^{9})	G (or B)
pico (10^{-12})	p		tera (10^{12})	T
femto (10^{-15})	f			
atto (10^{-18})	a			

E continued

ELECTRON TUBE MATERIALS

Electron tubes comprise (*1*) an evacuated or partially gas-filled envelope containing (*2*) a source of electrons, and (*3*) one or more electrodes to collect or control the flow of electrons within the device. Electron tubes can perform many functions such as amplification, rectification, generation, detection, switching, and displaying.

The design and construction of an electron tube involves a knowledge of the sciences of metallurgy, physics, electricity, and chemistry. However, it is the electron tube materials, in the final analysis, that set the ultimate limit to the power capability and performance of the device. An understanding of the properties of the elements, their behavior in vacuum tube environments, and the reactions that occur either during processing or during the life of an electron tube fall within the scope of the chemical disciplines. These materials of construction utilize the particular or unique properties of many elements of the periodic table.

The chemist's contribution to electron tube manufacture is closely related to the quality control activities in (a) preparation of electron tube materials, including cleaning and processing; (b) quality control of purchased or unprocessed metals and materials through analyses to check conformation to specifications; and (c) analysis for contaminants whenever trouble is encountered.

Although extreme purity of the metals and materials from which the electron tube is constructed is highly desirable, it is actually the nature of the impurities, even in minute quantities, that largely determines the quality and usability of the construction materials. Traces of certain foreign elements may be harmless or in some instances even beneficial, whereas equal amounts of other foreign elements may render the material completely useless for vacuum and high-temperature environments. The detection, identification, and quantitative determination of these impurities broadly challenge the methods and techniques of analytical chemistry. In general, impurities harmful to thermionic emitters and vacuum devices are those which break down under heat, electron bombardment, or chemical combinations, thereby releasing chlorine or halogens, sulfur or sulfur compounds, carbon monoxide or carbon dioxide, oxygen, hydrocarbons, water vapor; or high vapor pressure constituents which contribute to interelectrode leakage by condensation on insulators. The role of the more prevalent elements is discussed element by element. Since the cathode dominates the overall performance of electron devices, a special section is devoted to the chemistry and

1

physics of this critical component. This article briefly describes those phases of electron tube manufacture necessary to explain the functions and uses of the various materials involved.

Elements Used in Electron Tubes

Aluminum in the elemental state is rarely used in electron devices. However, the oxide of aluminum is widely accepted as a high-quality ceramic insulation due to its low dielectric loss factor, its excellent insulating properties at elevated temperatures, and its high mechanical strength. Single crystal aluminum oxide, or sapphire, is used as a "window" in microwave devices because of its high transparency to microwave energy. In this application, the crystal is usually cut perpendicular to the optic axis, so that the crystal has symmetry in the plane of the incident wave.

Finely powdered aluminum oxide is used to insulate tungsten heaters in indirectly heated cathodes. The coating is applied by spraying, dipping, or cataphoresis (see Electrophoretic deposition). It is then sintered to the tungsten wire by heating the assembly in hydrogen to a temperature of 1600–1800°C. This oxide is also often found as an ingredient in high-melting-point glasses.

Aluminum-clad iron sheet is used as anode material in receiving tubes and other low-power devices. A thin layer of aluminum is pressure bonded to sheet iron. When this sheet is heated in vacuum, the aluminum alloys with the iron to produce a darkened surface having high thermal emissivity.

Barium aluminate (1) is widely used as the active material in refractory metal matrix cathodes. Nickel–aluminum alloys have been used as the base metal for oxide cathodes. However, these aluminum alloys have fallen into disfavor because of their tendency toward formation of high interface resistance between the oxide coating and the base metal under certain operating conditions.

Argon, the most abundant of the noble gases, has many uses in electron tubes and other tube manufacture. It is used as a filling gas in thyratrons and voltage regulator tubes; and in tube manufacture, it furnishes a protective atmosphere around the tungsten electrode in the tungsten–inert gas (TIG) welding process.

Barium in the elemental state is used as a chemical getter (see below) in electron tubes. Barium oxide is the most widely used constituent in coatings used as electron sources in thermionic emitters. The oxide is also used as an ingredient in special glasses or ceramic compositions.

Beryllium in elemental form (2) because of its low **Z** number is fairly transparent to high-energy electrons and x rays; because of this property it has been used as a window in x-ray tubes. The oxide of beryllium is unique in its unusually high thermal conductivity (about the same as brass). This property, together with its excellent electrical insulation, makes it useful in applications where a component must be cooled by thermal conduction to a heat sink, and still be electrically insulated from the sink. Alloys of beryllium, particularly copper–beryllium alloys, are used for secondary emission cathodes because of their high secondary electron yield.

Calcium in elemental form has been used as a chemical getter in vacuum devices. Calcium carbonate, in amounts ranging from 3 to 15% is mixed with barium and strontium carbonates to form the triple carbonate emission mixes for oxide-coated cathodes.

Carbon, as graphite, has many uses in electron tubes. It is used as an anode material in high-power devices such as ignitrons and mercury rectifiers. Its high thermal emissivity makes it valuable as a coating for grids and other tube elements; coatings of graphite are used to suppress secondary emission from parts subject to electron bombardment. Slurries of carbon with a suitable binder are used as the conductive coatings on the vacuum side of glass envelopes, such as in cathode-ray tubes.

Cesium (qv) is used in photoelectric cells where it appears as cesium on silver oxide. These cells are most sensitive in the red portion of the visible spectrum. Cesium vapor is used in thermionic converters for the direct conversion of heat to electrical energy (see Thermoelectric devices).

Chromium in electron tubes is usually alloyed with iron or nickel, such as in the 300 or 400 series of stainless steels (3). The chrome–iron alloys, in the range of 16–30% chromium, have a lower thermal coefficient of expansion than iron alone, and are widely used as sealing metals in soft glass or ceramic seals. The chrome alloys are oxidation-resistant and are impervious to hydrogen ions when in contact with water. This property makes them useful for water jackets and cooling coils when one surface is exposed to the vacuum chamber.

The nickel–chromium–iron alloys, such as the 18-8 variety of stainless steel, are practically nonmagnetic. Thus the presence of stainless steel does not alter the magnetic field configuration in devices requiring precise fields for the focusing or confining of the flow of electrons.

When the 18-8 series must be welded, Type 304 low-carbon or Type 347 niobium stabilized steels are preferred, since carbon is not precipitated at the grain boundaries of the weld zone, with the subsequent formation of cracks or the lowering of the resistance to corrosion.

The alkali metals, especially cesium, can be released in vacuum by the reaction of their dichromates with powdered aluminum. The reaction is exothermic and is triggered by applying heat, usually by high-frequency induction, to a metal container in which a pellet of the mixed powders is enclosed.

Cobalt, in alloys of nickel and iron, is widely used as a sealing alloy in the fabrication of glass to metal seals. The composition, which contains 17–18% cobalt, 28–29% nickel, and a balance of iron, is known commercially as Kovar (registered trade name, Westinghouse) (4). As Kovar exactly matches the thermal expansion of certain Pyrex glasses the seals are strainfree. The low thermal expansion properties of these glasses make them resistant to thermal shock and high thermal gradients.

Copper, due to its high electrical and high thermal conductivity, is a necessary constituent of microwave tubes. Oxygenfree, high-conductivity copper (OFHC brand copper) is universally specified as it does not become embrittled when heated to high temperatures in hydrogen atmospheres. Copper-clad metals are often used where the physical or mechanical properties of the underlying metal are required, as well as the high electrical conductivity of copper. At microwave frequencies the depth of penetration of the electric currents is very low, so that a layer of copper, 0.001–0.002 in. thick, is all that is required to achieve full electrical conductivity.

Brazing alloys of copper and silver, or copper and gold, are used in fabricating vacuum tubes (5). The eutectic alloy containing 78% silver and 28% copper melts at 779°C. An alloy containing 37.5% gold and 62.5% copper melts at 990°C. The gold–copper alloys are used in high-temperature environments because they have a lower vapor pressure than the silver alloys, and in addition are not permeable to oxygen as are the high-silver alloys.

Gold is used as a plating metal in electron tubes. On external surfaces, since gold does not oxidize, the function of gold is to ensure a low contact resistance to the circuits. Inside the vacuum chamber, control grids are often gold-plated to suppress primary emission. Gold alloys, particularly with copper or nickel, melt in the 900–1100°C range and are used for high-temperature brazes since they readily wet tungsten or molybdenum.

Helium has several important uses in electron devices. Its main contribution is in processing, although this gas has been used in voltage reference tubes. As a protective atmosphere for tungsten arc-welding techniques it provides a higher energy arc than argon and is useful in welding the refractory elements.

Helium has been universally applied in the detection of leaks in all types of vacuum apparatus (6). The device under test is connected to a mass spectrometer and evacuated. The joints and seals being tested are flooded with helium. A sensitive mass spectrometer peaked on helium can detect and locate leaks smaller than 1 μl/day.

The high sensitivity of this method is due to (1) the low molar mass of the helium ion, which allows it to diffuse through a leak at a greater rate than any other gas except hydrogen; (2) the low residual helium concentration in the atmosphere (less than one part in 200,000 parts of air); (3) there being no possibility that an ion due to any other gas will give an indication that can be mistaken for helium.

Hydrogen is the most prevalent of the residual gases found in electron tubes. This is not unexpected, since nearly all tube components are subjected to a hydrogen atmosphere at some stage of manufacture, either during the annealing, brazing, oxide reduction phase, or when hydrogen-ion penetration occurs during plating or acid cleaning.

Hydrogen is used as the filling gas in switch tubes such as hydrogen thyratrons. Hydrogen when mixed with nitrogen in an amount sufficient to make it incapable of forming an explosive mixture with air, is used as a protective atmosphere during bakeout and processing.

The hydrides of titanium or zirconium are used in the active metal processes for the fabrication of ceramic seals (7). The absorption or giving up of hydrogen, depending upon the temperature, makes these metals usable as reservoirs for controlling the gas pressure in hydrogen thyratrons.

Indium is usually found as one of the constituents of the lower-temperature brazing alloys. These alloys are valuable in step brazing, since the silver–copper alloy containing about 15% indium melts about 75°C lower than the eutectic alloy of silver and copper alone.

Transparent conducting surfaces on glass can be formed by spraying a solution of an indium compound on a heated glass substrate.

Iron is used extensively as the vacuum envelope in industrial tubes, such as mercury-vapor rectifiers, thryatrons, ignitrons, and metal receiving tubes. Alloys of iron with nickel, chromium, or cobalt form the basis for most glass or ceramic seal alloys. The composition of these alloys can be tailored to yield a specific thermal coefficient of expansion from essentially zero, for 36% nickel–iron, up to nearly 13×10^{-6} per °C where they approach the expansion of pure iron. The chrome–iron alloys have a nearly linear coefficient of expansion, whereas the nickel–iron or nickel–iron–cobalt alloys vary with temperature, particularly in the 300–500°C range. This latter type of expansion is similar to that of glass (see Fig. 1).

Lead in the form of its oxide is one of the elements found in many types of glass.

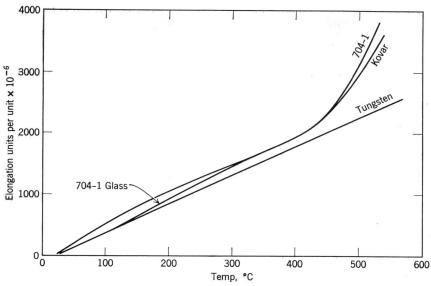

Fig. 1. Thermal expansion characteristics of Kovar and 704-1 Pyrex glass as compared to the linear expansion of tungsten.

These glasses are characterized by their high electrical resistivity at elevated temperatures and are superior to the soda–lime glasses in this respect.

Elemental lead, or lead alloys containing a small percent of silver have been used in the titanium hydride processes for joining metals to nonmetals such as ceramic or high melting point glasses. Many low-power microwave tubes are evacuated, processed, and finally sealed together inside a vacuum bell jar by this process. The lead solder, as it solidifies, furnishes the final closure for the tube envelope.

Magnesium has been used as a flash getter for the chemical cleanup of residual gases in electron tubes. Magnesium silicate in the form of forsterite, $2MgO.SiO_2$, is an important low-dielectric-loss ceramic used in microwave tube envelopes and metal–ceramic seals. Small amounts of magnesium oxide are often used in aluminum oxide ceramics, since it aids in forming a vacuum-proof ceramic body.

Manganese in trace amounts is found in nickel used for oxide cathodes. Powdered manganese metal mixed with powdered molybdenum in the ratio of about 20% manganese to 80% molybdenum is the basis for forming metalized layers on ceramics, prior to brazing the ceramic to a structural metal (8). In a hydrogen atmosphere and at temperatures ranging from 1250–1600°C, these metallic powders react with the ceramic and sinter together, forming a tightly adherent metal surface to which a structural metal can be brazed in a subsequent assembly process.

Mercury vapor is used as the ionizing gas in thyratrons, ignitrons, and mercury pool rectifiers. In tube processing, high vacuum can be attained by mercury diffusion pumps (9). These pumps involve no mechanical motion, but depend upon diffusion of residual gases into a high velocity stream of mercury vapor (10).

Although oil diffusion pumps are now widely used, mercury vapor pumps still have many advocates; because mercury is a well-defined substance that does not break down or fractionate when heated in vacuum, it does not creep on the walls of vacuum plumbing, and is not deleterious to most thermionic emitters.

Molybdenum has many desirable physical properties that fulfill the requirements imposed by vacuum environments and electron tubes. It is a refractory element with a melting point of 2620°C, and can safely be used in vacuum up to about 1600°C before its vapor pressure, or rate of evaporation, becomes excessive (11). It is non-magnetic, can be sealed to glass to form hermetic seals, and can be drawn into fine wires which are widely used for control grids in space charge tubes because of its strength at elevated temperatures. Molybdenum is also specified where a superior structural metal for vacuum environments is needed.

Nickel is the base metal used in practically all barium oxide coated thermionic emitters (12). Because of the ease with which nickel can be formed or drawn, it is used as a structural metal, or drawn into wire for grids. Anodes for low-power tubes are often made from carbonized nickel to aid in heat dissipation by radiation (13). The carbon surfaces are formed by pyrolytic deposition of carbon from a hydrocarbon vapor.

Nickel is also valuable because of the alloys it forms with iron, cobalt, copper, gold, and chromium, all of which have electronic applications.

Niobium is added to stainless steel to prevent carbon precipitation at the grain boundaries during welding. The element is used in metal-to-ceramic seals, since it has almost identical thermal-expansion properties as alumina ceramics (14).

A niobium–ruthenium alloy has been used as a very high temperature brazing alloy to join tungsten filaments to molybdenum or other tungsten structures (15).

Palladium is used in high-temperature brazing alloys, as in the palladium–cobalt or palladium–chromium series (16). It is also added in small amounts to silver-brazing alloys to inhibit the intergranular penetration of silver into the nickel–iron alloys. Palladium is unique in that it is readily permeable to hydrogen when heated to temperatures above 500°C. This property has been utilized to obtain very pure hydrogen by diffusing the gas through heated thin-wall palladium tubes (17). These tubes, or membranes, when sealed to an evacuated chamber, can be used to admit hydrogen into the device with the exclusion of other gases. Similarly, they can be used to remove residual hydrogen from the device, the direction of flow depending upon the differential concentration of hydrogen.

Platinum has a thermal coefficient of expansion of about 8×10^{-6} per °C. It thus makes excellent seals to soft glass. The main deterrent to its use is its high cost.

Platinum-clad tungsten wires are used for the grids in space-charge tubes employing thoriated tungsten cathodes, as the platinum coating suppresses primary electron emission from the grids, even though they run hot, because of their proximity to the cathode (18).

Potassium in the form of its oxide is often used in glass compositions.

Rhenium is a relatively new element used in electron tubes (19). It is next to tungsten in melting point, and has been investigated for use in thermionic emission sources. Thus far, its primary use has been as an alloying element with tungsten or molybdenum in amounts up to about 25%. Its presence adds ductility to these refractory elements, and greatly reduces the fragility of filaments or heaters in indirectly heated cathodes.

Silicon, in the form of silica, is an essential constituent of nearly all glass (20). Pure fused silica has excellent insulating and dielectric properties and is used for tube spacers or supports where a superior material is indicated. Since it has a practically zero thermal coefficient of expansion, it will not crack under extreme thermal gradients.

Fused silica is transparent to ultraviolet radiation, and has been used as a window in photoelectric tubes sensitive to this portion of the spectrum. Elemental silicon, in small but carefully controlled amounts, is added to nickel to act as a reducing agent for barium oxide in thermionic cathodes.

Silver is the chief constituent of the low-temperature brazing alloys. Elemental silver is the best conductor of electricity, and this property is often utilized in silver-plated or silver-clad structures found in microwave tubes (21).

Thorium and thorium oxide are used in thermionic emitters. Thorium is chemically active, and is used as a nonflash getter for residual gas in electron tubes. These nonflash getters can be placed in higher temperature environments than the more common barium getters (22).

Thorium in tungsten imparts nonsag properties to tungsten wire filaments.

Tantalum is a highly refractory metal which in a pure state is ductile and easy to fabricate by resistance welding (23). It is nonmagnetic, and can be applied to critical magnetic regions as it does not perturb the magnetic fields. Used as an anode material, it can be run hot enough to dissipate considerable energy through radiation due to its high melting point and low vapor pressure. The metal is chemically active and when heated reacts with many gases. For this reason, it must be processed in vacuum or in one of the inactive gases such as argon or helium. Its property of readily reducing barium oxide to liberate barium metal has been utilized in getters that can be flashed electrically.

When alloyed with tungsten it forms a material that does not readily anneal, and thus finds applications in high-temperature springs. The thermal expansion of tantalum is slightly lower than that of alumina. This property is used to advantage in pin seals in alumina ceramics, since the pins are under compression when the seal cools after brazing.

Titanium is a relatively new element used in electronic devices. Its high chemical activity is utilized in getter applications. At temperatures above 700°C, it reacts with most gases to form thermally stable compounds. Hydrogen is the exception. Below 400°C, titanium absorbs hydrogen, but above 500°C, the hydrogen is liberated in the atomic state. The high stability of the compounds titanium forms makes it useful in ion pumps for the production of ultrahigh vacuum.

Titanium finds wide application as the active metal in the sealing techniques used in joining metals to ceramic or other nonmetals (24). It matches the thermal expansion of modified forsterite ceramics and yields reliable vacuum-proof structures.

Tungsten, the most refractory element, is used almost exclusively for filaments and high-temperature applications such as cathode heaters (25). Porous tungsten furnishes the body for matrix or dispenser cathodes. Its low thermal expansion makes it suitable for sealing to the high-melting-point glasses such as Pyrex (26,27).

Tungsten is the target metal for x-ray tubes. It can be drawn into very fine wires and is then used for planar grids in close-spaced microwave tubes. Tungsten–rhenium alloy wires in combination with tungsten are used in thermocouples for the measurement of very high temperatures. Tungsten has a high temperature coefficient of resistance, and this property is utilized in resistance gauges for measuring vacuum, particularly in the range of $10-100\mu$.

Yttrium is finding applications as an alloying addition to steel to give it increased resistance to oxidation. The chrome–iron–yttrium alloys have potential as a structural metal in ceramic seals for high-temperature environments.

Yttrium oxide is a promising addition to other refractory oxides for obtaining specific high-temperature qualities.

Zirconium is similar to titanium in its properties, and has similar uses in electron tubes (28). It is employed in the active metal in sealing processes, usually as the hydride, for joining metals to ceramics. Because its vapor pressure is lower than that of titanium, zirconium is the preferred metal when high-temperature solders are employed.

Small amounts of zirconium, usually less than 2%, are often added to the base metal in thermionic cathodes for the purpose of reducing the barium compounds.

Cathodes

The source of electrons is the cathode, and the electrode to which the electrons flow is usually the anode. However, in certain electron tubes the term anode is often applied to an electrode used to accelerate or shape a beam of electrons. In a well-designed beam-forming system the accelerating or modulating anode collects little or no current. Instead, the bulk of the current in the beam impinges upon a structure known as the collector.

THEORY OF ELECTRON EMISSION

According to modern concepts of metals in the solid state the metallic bond, which is responsible for the cohesion of metals and gives rise to the crystal structure characteristics of metals, consists of a spatial array of ions built up by regular repetition in three dimensions. The metal lattice consists of close-packed positive nuclei surrounded by bands of negative electrons. If vacancies exist in the outer or valence bands, electrons are relatively free to move from one atom to another in random motion with thermal velocities.

In the presence of an externally applied potential difference, the electrons acquire an additional velocity in the direction of and proportional to the electric field, thus defining the conductivity of the metal. Normally, these free electrons do not escape from the body of the metal because of a potential energy barrier at the boundary or surface of the metal.

Although there is no attachment of consequence between the free electrons and individual atoms in a metal, there is a strong attachment between the free electrons and the metal as a whole. An electron escaping from the surface of a conductor has only positive charges tending to pull it back to the metal and none pulling it out. Thus a definite amount of kinetic energy, usually measured in electron volts and called the "work function," must be acquired by any one of the highest energyfree electrons to enable it to overcome the attractive force. The work function of metals ranges from 1.5 to 7 eV. The energy required to release an electron from metals may be supplied in a number of different ways: (*1*) thermionic emission; (*2*) field emission; (*3*) secondary emission; or (*4*) photoelectric emission.

Thermionic Emission. Thermionic emission occurs when the temperature of a metal is raised to the point where the kinetic energy of some electrons becomes great enough to enable them to surmount the potential energy barrier and escape from the surface of the metal. The temperature–electron current relationship is described by

Richardson's (29) equation. The more familiar expression for the emitted current is Dushman's (30) modification of the Richardson equation which states that

$$J = A_0 T^2 \exp\left(-E_{\mathrm{W}} e 10^7 / KT\right)$$

where J = thermionic current density, A/cm^2

A_0 = semiempirical constant, theoretically equal to 120 for pure metals, $(A/\mathrm{cm}^2)/(^\circ\mathrm{K})^2$

T = absolute temperature, $^\circ\mathrm{K}$

K = Boltzmann's universal gas constant $(1.372 \times 10^{-16} \mathrm{\ erg}/^\circ\mathrm{K})$

e = electronic charge, C $(1.6 \times 10^{-19} \mathrm{\ esu})$

E_{W} = work function, an empirical constant of the emitting surface, eV

The numerator of the exponent, $E_{\mathrm{W}} e 10^7$, describes in ergs per electron the energy an electron inside the hot metal must have in order to escape through the metal surface.

The equation is often written as

$$J = A_0 T^2 \exp\left(-b_0 / T\right)$$

where b ($^\circ\mathrm{K}$), the temperature equivalent of the work function, $= eE_{\mathrm{W}} 10^7 = 11{,}600 E_{\mathrm{W}}$ $^\circ\mathrm{K}$. This can be derived from E_t, the voltage equivalent of temperature, as defined by the relationship $E_t e 10^7 = KT$. The value of the work function b varies approximately linearly with temperature, according to the relation $b = b_0 + aT$, where b_0 = work function at $T = 0^\circ\mathrm{K}$. Tables of emission constants are sometimes given in values of E_{W} and sometimes in b_0.

From the above equations it is clear that the electron emission is a function of temperature. The maximum useful emission is limited by the rate of evaporation of the cathode material. Since the life of the cathode in an electron tube is determined by the evaporation, its design is a compromise between life and temperature. The demands made upon the cathode by the environment to which it is subjected determine the type of materials of its construction.

Field Emission. The presence of an accelerating field at the surface of a thermionic cathode produces an effective reduction of the height of the potential barrier at the surface. If the accelerating potential is sufficiently intense, some electrons will penetrate and escape through the potential barrier that exists at the surface of the metal, even though the cathode is cold so that the thermionic emission is negligible. The variation of the emission current density J (measured in A/cm^2), with the electric field intensity at the surface of the metal is expressed by the Fowler-Nordheim (31) equation as shown below:

$$J = CF^2 \exp\left(-D/F\right)$$

where $C = \dfrac{6.2 \times 10^{-6}}{E_{\mathrm{B}}} \left[E_{\mathrm{M}}/E_{\mathrm{W}}\right]^{1/2}$

$D = 6.8 \times 10^7 E_{\mathrm{W}}^{3/2}$

E_{B} is the potential barrier at the surface of a metal; E_{M}, the Fermi characteristic energy; E_{W}, the work function; and F, the electric field intensity.

Field emission cathodes are usually in the form of needle-sharp points produced from refractory metal wires by electrochemical etching techniques (32,33) (see p. 18).

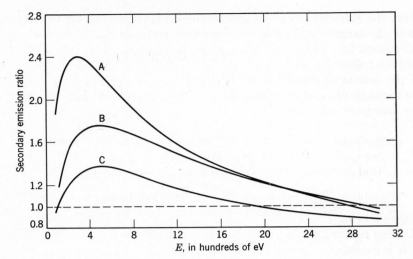

Fig. 2. Secondary emission ratio of various copper alloys as a function of the energy of normal incidence primary electrons. A. Copper–rhodium. B. Copper. C. Copper–gold alloy.

Secondary Emission. When a metal or a dielectric is bombarded from an external source with either electrons or ions, secondary electrons may be emitted from the surface. The secondary-emission ratio is defined as the ratio of the number of secondary electrons per primary electron. The total secondary emission depends upon the number of primary electrons, the velocity of the primary electrons, their angle of incidence, the type of the material, and the physical condition of the surface (34–37).

An incident primary electron gives up its energy to several electrons within the material. The depth of penetration of the primary electron depends upon its energy, the more energetic, the greater the depth. An appreciable emission occurs from a depth of 150 atomic layers for silver, if the incident electrons have energies greater than 50 eV. If the inner electrons do not give up all their energy through collision when moving toward the surface, they are then able to overcome the barrier at the surface and escape as secondary electrons.

Thus, for low-energy primaries, the number of secondaries that are able to overcome the surface attraction is small. For high-energy primaries, more energetic secondaries are produced but at a greater depth below the surface. This increases the probability of collision with a consequent loss of energy of these secondaries. Thus, the secondary emission ratio passes through a maximum, usually around 500 V incident energy. Figure 2 represents the secondary-emission ratio as a function of the energy of the primary beam.

Photoelectric Emission. Radiant energy is transferred to electrons or atoms in discrete energy units of hf ergs where f is the frequency of the incident light in cycles per second and h is Planck's constant (6.542×10^{-27} erg-sec). The energy units, variously called "light quanta" or "photons," in eV are defined by the following relation:

$$E_{\mathrm{ph}}e10^7 = hf$$

where e is the electronic charge and E_{ph} is the light quanta in eV.

Where the light-quantum energy of the incident light is greater than the work function of the target (photo cathode), electrons can escape from the cathode. Since E_{ph} lies between 1.75 and 3.0 eV for visible light, a photoelectric surface must have a work function below this range to be sensitive to visible light. The number of electrons emitted per second is directly proportional to the intensity of the incident light, provided the angle of incidence, wavelength, and polarization remain constant. However, the energy of the electrons after escape is controlled entirely by the light frequency.

The photoelectric yield, in A/W of light energy input, is equal to the quantum yield/E_{ph}. The quantum yield is usually not more than 10%, and is the number of electrons emitted per hundred incident photons.

THERMIONIC CATHODE MATERIALS

Tungsten, being a pure metal emitter, is relatively free from loss of emission due to contaminating residual gases. Because its emission does not depend upon a surface coating, it is similarly very resistant to energetic positive-ion bombardment found in high-voltage tubes. Typical applications of tungsten emitters are in high-voltage x-ray tubes, in diode rectifiers, and in many commercial tubes and vacuum-measuring devices (38).

The melting point of the element tungsten is about 3650°K, the highest of any metal. Similarly, it has the lowest vapor pressure of any metallic element, which allows operation in vacuum in the temperature range 2600–2800°K (39). Its high work function of 4.5 eV requires that it be operated at these very high temperatures to yield useful electron emission.

Because of the high operating temperature of tungsten emitters, it is impractical to heat them by radiation or thermal conduction from an auxiliary heat source. Thus, tungsten cathodes are usually directly heated filaments or thin ribbons (40).

The element tungsten has a high positive temperature coefficient of resistance. The inrush of current to a cold tungsten structure may be as much as ten times that of its final high-temperature operating conditions. In high-reliability and long-life applications it is necessary to restrict the initial current by some type of series impedance to prevent damage to the structure from the resulting magnetic forces (41).

The end of life of a tungsten emitter occurs when a sufficient amount of tungsten has evaporated to alter its electrical characteristics beyond practical limits. For wire, this usually occurs when the cross-section area has been decreased by 15% or more. Thus, the life requirements of the device determine the maximum temperature at which the emitter can be operated. Once this temperature is determined, the size requirements of the cathode can be calculated from the Richardson equation.

Thoriated Tungsten. Pure tungsten wire is processed during manufacture to yield a fibrous structure necessary for ductility. When this fibrous tungsten is heated above 1000°C, crystal growth starts, and the wire ultimately acquires a fragile crystalline structure. This crystal growth can be inhibited by the addition of 1–2% thorium oxide to the powdered tungsten from which the wire is made (42).

In addition to altering the mechanical properties of tungsten, the thorium oxide lowers the work function of the emitting surface (43). The thermionic efficiency of thoriated tungsten can be greatly enhanced by heating it in a hydrocarbon vapor for a brief period to form a carbonized outer shell (44). A subsequent high-temperature flash to about 2500°C, results in a uniform coverage of thorium metal over the tungsten carbide surface. The work function of thoriated tungsten is about 2.8 eV. This surface is subject to deactivation when exposed to adverse environments. However, its increased electron efficiency over pure tungsten makes thoriated tungsten attractive for many tubes of intermediate and high power levels (45).

Tantalum. Tantalum can also be used as a pure metal emitter. It is a refractory metal with a melting point of 2996°C, and a work function of 4.1 eV. At a given temperature its emission may be as much as ten times that of pure tungsten, but its evaporation rate is also much higher. At a temperature that will give the same emission density as tungsten, its evaporation rate is still slightly higher, so that its ultimate life may be shorter (46).

Pure tantalum is very ductile and can be formed or drawn into almost any shape. It does not recrystallize into a brittle phase when welded, and has a great advantage over tungsten in this aspect. Because of this ease of fabrication, tantalum emitters are found in kylstron amplifier tubes used in television transmitters. The cathode is a rugged disc of the metal with a spherical contour to aid in focusing the beam of electrons. It is heated to the required emitting temperature by electron bombardment from an auxiliary tungsten filament (see Fig. 3). In this system, the tantalum cathode is the collector (anode) in the auxiliary heating scheme. The input to the tantalum disc in watts is the product of the current from the tungsten filament and the voltage between the filament and the cathode. If this voltage is very high, in the range of 5000–10,000 V, only a small current from the auxiliary tungsten filament is necessary to obtain the required temperature for the main emitter.

Oxide-Coated Cathodes. In 1904, Wehnelt (47) investigated the emission of electrons from metallic oxides, and found that platinum wires coated with oxides of barium, strontium, or calcium were better electron emitters than platinum alone. Since that time a staggering amount of research and investigational effort has been expended on all types and variations of oxide emitters (48). The modern nickel-base oxide-coated cathode, with a work function of about 1.2 eV, is an efficient source of electrons. It is universally used in receiving tubes and many other lower-voltage commerical electron devices.

The low operating temperature of 1000°K makes it well suited for indirect heating. A hollow sleeve or equivalent structure encompasses an insulated tungsten heater. This allows the cathode to be operated at a different potential from the heater. The cathode sleeve is coated with emission material either on the sides or on an end, depending upon whether the tube is designed for circular or planar geometry.

Coatings comprising a mixture of oxides give higher emission than barium oxide alone. The emitting surfaces are first coated with the alkaline earth carbonates rather than the oxides, as the oxides react with moisture in the atmosphere. The carbonates are decomposed to oxides during subsequent evacuation and out-gassing of the tube's elements. As a final step in the exhaust schedule, the cathode is heated to a temperature of 1200–1400°K to ensure complete conversion of the carbonates to the oxide, the reaction being $BaCO_3 \rightarrow BaO + CO_2$. The carbon dioxide is removed by the vacuum pumps. Double carbonate mixes contain 30–50% barium carbonate, the remainder being strontium carbonate. The triple carbonate mixes contain an addition of 5–15% calcium carbonate. The calcium content is said to decrease the rate of barium evaporation from the cathode surface.

The cathode coatings are applied by spraying a suspension of the carbonates in a rapid drying liquid, such as amyl acetate or acetone. A fugitive binder, such as cellu-

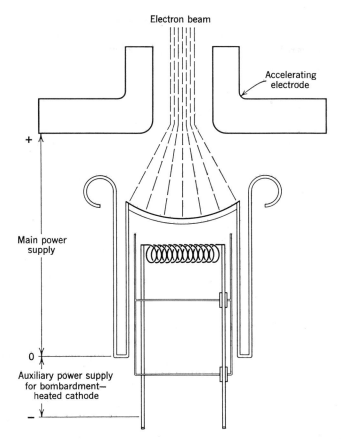

Fig. 3. Electron gun with bombardment-heated cathode.

lose nitrate, is added to the mix to give it sufficient body to withstand assembly and mounting. Other methods of applying emission coatings include brushing, dip or drag coating, electrophoresis (49), and tapes (50).

The tape coating, where applicable, allows placing a known amount of the carbonates on the metal substrate. These tape coatings have uniform thickness and sharply defined edges, as contrasted with the coatings derived from spraying. The tapes are manufactured in one form by applying a suspension of the carbonates over insoluble plastic film. The active layer is transferred from the film to the metal by suitable solvents. In the other form, the entire tape, which is calendered from a suspension of the carbonates in a fugitive plastic, is applied to the metal much like conventional adhesive tape.

After a tube is sealed from the vacuum pumps, an ageing schedule is required to stabilize and bring the cathode to full emission. This activation involves collecting current by one or more of the tube elements. During this period, residual gases are absorbed, either by a chemical getter or by the metal surfaces.

There are several theories concerning the emission from oxide surfaces. It has been well established that an excess of barium metal, either dispersed through the oxide or diffused over the surface, is essential for a low work function (51). This excess barium is produced either by electrolytic reduction of the oxide, or by reaction of the oxide with the base metal, usually nickel. The chemical reaction is produced by the additions of controlled amounts of reducing elements to the nickel melt. Pure nickel alone is passive, and has little or no reducing effect on the oxide. Additions of silicon, magnesium, titanium, zirconium, aluminum, or tungsten result in an active nickel alloy.

The rate of barium production must be in equilibrium with the environment in which the cathode operates. Excessive amounts of the reducing agents may reduce too much oxide, there by shortening the life of the cathode and contaminating the insulators and spacers with evaporated barium, or coating the control grids so that they acquire undesirable primary or secondary emission properties.

Nickel melts containing silicon or equivalent as a reducing element are not recommended for stand-by service, ie, applications where the cathode is held at emitting temperatures, but no emission current is allowed to flow. Under these circumstances, a silica interface layer may form on the nickel surface. This silica layer insulates the oxide from the base metal, thereby spoiling the operating characteristics of the tube. By carefully controlling the type and amount of reducing elements in the nickel melt, it is possible to tailor-make the base metal to yield optimum performance in a particular environment.

The peak or pulsed emission from an oxide cathode can be many times its average dc capability. This stems from the high resistivity of the oxides at emitting temperature. High sustained currents through this semiconducting coating cause I^2R heating, with resultant destruction of the emissive layer. The full-peak emission capability of oxide cathodes can be realized with pulse lengths up to about 10 μsec and low-duty cycles. At pulse lengths longer than a few hundred μsec, the allowable peak emission approaches the continuous current rating of the cathode.

Dispenser Cathodes. The term "dispenser cathode" is applied to a class that gains its electron emission properties by virtue of material dispensed to its surface (52). Forms of the dispenser cathode are identified by such terms as "matrix," "impregnated," "pressed," "extended interface," "L cathode," in many variations or combinations. It has been an objective in the development of these dispenser cathodes to produce a long-life emitter by providing a reservoir of the active material, either from a vapor surrounding the cathode surface or dispensed to the surface via bulk diffusion.

A large reservoir of active material allows dispenser cathodes to be operated at higher temperatures than the oxide-coated cathodes, and thus provides increased emission per unit area. The emitting surfaces are essentially metallic, and as such are resistant to positive-ion bombardment and sparking, since sparking is due to the I^2R heating that occurs in the high-resistance oxide coatings. In contrast, the metallic emitters at high and sustained current levels are actually cooled by electron evaporation—a process analogous to the cooling of water by evaporation. This amount, in W, is equal to the emission current multiplied by the work function in eV. To maintain the cathode at proper temperature, extra power must be supplied to the heater over that required for stand-by conditions.

The first dispenser cathode that was so designated was described by Hull (53). It was designed for use in gaseous discharge tubes. Barium oxide was dispensed to an emitting surface from barium aluminate heated to 1150–1200°C. The operating temperature of the emitting surface was maintained at 850°C. Since the rate of barium oxide evaporation at this temperature is about 6×10^{-11} g/(cm²)(sec), the

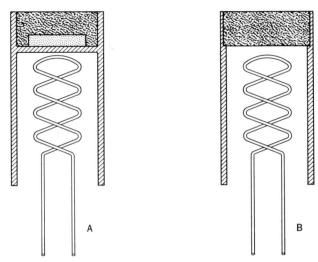

Fig. 4. Dispenser cathode.   A. L-cathode.   B. Pressed or impregnated matrix cathode.

dispensing rate from the evaporator must be equal to this number multiplied by the ratio of the effective cathode to evaporator surface areas.   The true work function ϕ of this cathode equals $1.215 + 4.26 \times 10^{-4}T$ (eV).

Other cathodes deriving their emissive surfaces from external reservoirs include those in which a high work function metal is surrounded by the vapor of an electropositive metal, for example, cesium, potassium, or rubidium (54).   The vapor pressure is controlled by the bulb temperature, and at all times there exists an equilibrium between the condensation of metal vapor and reevaporation.

The work function of a partially covered surface of cesium on tungsten can be approximated by the linear law

$$\phi = \theta\phi_{cs} + (1 - \theta)\phi_w$$

where ϕ_{cs} = the work function of an optimum cesium coverage
   θ = the fractional coverage from optimum
   ϕ_w = the work function of uncoated tungsten

The contact potential of a cesium-coated surface compared to a clean tungsten surface is a function of the cesium coverage.   This property is utilized in the cesium-filled thermionic converter.   Here the work function of the emitting surface can be made high by having a small cesium coverage, while the anode work function is made low by having it run at a lower temperature with a higher coverage.   These differences provide a source of emf for the generation of power by direct conversion of heat energy to electrical energy.

Barium-Tungsten.   The L-cathode (55) is another form of dispenser cathode which dispenses barium from a vapor phase.   Many tubes utilizing electron beams require a planar or concave emitting surface to launch a uniform beam.   The construction of these end-fire emitters is illustrated in Figure 4A.   A source of barium oxide is embedded beneath a porous tungsten cover attached to an otherwise vaportight enclosure.   Barium is produced by the reaction

$$6\ \mathrm{BaO} + \mathrm{W} \rightarrow \mathrm{Ba_4WO_6} + 2\ \mathrm{Ba}$$

The free barium diffuses through the pores of the tungsten cap by migration over pore walls and by molecular streaming or Knudsen flow (56) (so named from Knudsen's derivations of the laws governing the effusion of vapor through a small orifice). Upon reaching the surface, the barium spreads over the surface in a near monolayer. The emission capability is obtained from a work function $\phi = 1.68 + 3.24 \times 10^{-4}T$. This corresponds to an emission density ranging from 0.6 A/cm^2 at 965°C to 10 A/cm^2 at 1190°C. This emission is greater and the evaporation rate is lower than a pure barium–tungsten surface, leading to the conclusion that the surface is a monolayer of barium on oxygen on tungsten, and the surface dipole so formed by this adsorbed layer decreases the electron barrier at the surface.

The tungsten-matrix includes the pressed and impregnated types shown in Figure 4B. In the pressed type, the active material, usually barium aluminate, is mixed with tungsten powder, pressed into a compact, and sintered into a coherent mass. The impregnated matrix differs in that a porous tungsten compact is first formed, and this porous body is then impregnated with molten barium aluminate or a mixture of barium and calcium aluminates. A possible reaction that produces free barium is

$$2\,(3\ BaO.Al_2O_3) + W(s) \rightarrow BaO.WO_3\,(s) + 2(BaO.Al_2O_3)\,(s) + 3\ Ba$$

The work function (eV) of the impregnated-type cathode is (57)

$$\phi = 1.67 + 3.2 \times 10^{-4}T$$

Nickel-matrix cathodes, either pressed or impregnated (58), are fabricated from finely divided nickel powder and alkaline earth carbonates or similar salts. They have an advantage in that they can easily be shaped by machining. They are more resistant to ion bombardment and gas poisoning than oxide-coated emitters. On the negative side, equivalent thermionic emission requires operation at temperatures where nickel readily evaporates (59). Their main field of use has been in magnetrons, where part of the electron cloud is derived from secondary emission from the cathode.

Other thermionic emitters include the refractory-coated cathodes. These were developed for applications requiring a more rugged cathode than the barium oxide-coated types. They normally operate at higher temperatures and have a higher work function, but this lack of efficiency is offset by their stability and resistance to ion bombardment.

Thorium oxide on tungsten (60) is a refractory-coated emitter first used in magnetrons and high-voltage tubes. The thorium oxide is applied to a thickness corresponding to 20 mg/cm^2 by brushing, spraying, or cataphoresis (61).

An accepted model of this cathode is one in which a thin film of thorium on the surface of thoria provides the low-work-function surface. This film is provided by electrolytic decomposition of the thoria. Under pulsed conditions, the effective work function is about $2.6 + 2.4 \times 10^{-4}T$.

Hexaboride cathodes are useful in applications involving higher currents and high voltage. They are stable in air, activate easily, and are particularly useful in demountable vacuum systems since they do not deteriorate upon exposure to air. The hexaborides have a somewhat unusual crystallographic property. The small boron atoms form a three-dimensional framework which surrounds the larger metal atoms, but apparently do not form any valence bonds with them. The valence electrons of the metal are therefore free and impart metallic behavior to the solid.

The strong binding forces between the boron atoms in the cage structure lead to refractory compounds with melting points above 2100°C. When the crystal is heated, a monolayer of metal forms on the surface to yield a low work function emitter. As these surface atoms evaporate they are replaced by diffusion of metal atoms from the interior. Thus, the hexaboride crystal acts in a manner similar to a matrix cathode.

Lanthanum boride, LaB_6, with a work function of about 2.66 eV, is probably the most useful of this class (62). Operating temperature is in the range of 1300–1500°C.

The mounting or supporting of the hexaboride emitters has been a major problem area. There is a strong tendency for the boron atoms to diffuse into interstices of any metal with which it makes contact. This causes a collapse of the boron cage structure and a rapid evaporation of the metal atoms. Carbon, carbonized tantalum, or other refractory elements that do not form borides are required for the supporting structure that holds the active hexaboride.

Tube Construction and Manufacture

Joining Processes. The exacting technologies employed in the construction of electron tubes encompass the broadest number of joining processes. Many of these joining procedures were borrowed from other products and adopted to electron tube assembly. Additional new manufacturing techniques were devised as necessary to meet specific tube requirements. Conversely, certain of these techniques and materials originally developed for the tube industry have also been widely adopted in the manufacture of products totally unrelated to electronic devices.

It was only natural that early tubes resembled electric light bulbs, since lamp machinery could easily be converted to tube processing. These original lamp-manufacturing concepts, with many improvements in automation, are still used in small glass-tube manufacture.

The advent of the glass-sealing alloys such as the nickel–iron and nickel–iron–cobalt series, made the massive metal-to-glass seals practical, and sparked the development of the metal-envelope radio and industrial tubes. The need for increased reliability in welding of the metal envelopes into leakproof structures resulted in the development of the synchronous electronic timers for spot and seam-resistance welders. These synchronous timers, employing ignitron tubes as electronic switches, have wide usage wherever precision resistance welds are essential to the product.

High-conductivity metals and the refractory elements present problems for resistance-welding processes (63). The tungsten inert arc is well suited for welding this type of metal. In addition, this process is rather gentle in that metals can be joined with a minimum of mechanical distortion. The inert arc process does not replace resistance welding, but extends and augments the type of joints and materials that can be reliably fabricated into vacuum proof assemblies.

"Electron beam" welding is a process that promises to extend further the scope of joining metals by fusion (64). A beam of electrons is converged and focused into a spot to melt the metals being fused. The energy in the beam is the product of the beam current and the beam voltage. In the more sophisticated electron beam welders, the beam voltage may be as high as 150 kV.

Electron beam welders are characterized by (a) their ability to melt any known material; (b) extreme local heating; (c) a very great ratio of depth to width penetration of the weld zone; (d) ability to make blind welds by melting through an external or first layer metal, and fusing the underlying metal; (e) ability to weld at the bottom of holes or deep recesses; and (f) the creation of a clean and oxidefree weld, since the fusion is carried out in vacuum.

Lower energies in the beam can be utilized for local heating, with applications for vacuum brazing or evaporating metals for vapor plating or deposition in vacuum chambers.

Machining and Cutting Materials. The electron beam, in addition to its uses for welding, can also be used for machining or cutting metals. For machining, the energy is increased to the point where the metals are literally evaporated by the impact of the beam.

Other machining processes now being used in obtaining complicated shapes include electrical disintegrating methods. These disintegrating processes are limited to shaping metals or materials that are electrical conductors. A spark discharge between a shaped electrode and the metal being machined, erodes the metal away. A fluid, usually a type of dielectric oil forced between the electrode and the work, carries away the products of disintegration. Accuracies of 0.001 in. can be obtained with electrical disintegrating machining processes.

Brittle materials, such as ceramic or glass, can be shaped or drilled by impact grinding. A tool of the desired shape or contour is vibrated against the work, usually at ultrasonic frequencies. A slurry of an abrasive powder, such as boron carbide, is circulated between the tool and the work. Although very little material is removed with each impact of the tool, the great number of strokes per second result in a rapid and accurate machining operation. The tool is vibrated at ultrasonic frequencies by piezoelectric crystals, or more often by utilizing the magnetostriction properties of nickel–iron alloys.

Chemical machining techniques have found many applications in the manufacture of complex and intricate electron tube parts. The ultraprecision that is characteristic of optical processes employed in photoetching techniques is well suited to forming planar grids, and resonant structures for millimeter wave generators. Perhaps the largest usage of chemical machining is found in the manufacture of precision shadow masks for color television display tubes.

Machining is simulated by selectively removing metal by chemicals or by electrolysis (see Electrolytic machining). A mask or pattern resistant to the acid bath or chemical etchant is placed on the sheet of metal from which the part is being machined. Thus, only the exposed areas are attacked by the etching solution.

Extremely accurate and complicated shapes can be cut from sheet metals by these chemical machining methods. It is common practice to develop the mask by photo techniques. A photosensitive resist is applied to the metal sheet, and a pattern or drawing of the part is optically projected on the sensitized surface. This surface is then developed. The exposed areas are soluble and are washed away, leaving a chemical resistant and highly accurate pattern on the metal. The more complicated the shape, the more adaptable it becomes for economical chemical machining processes.

Thick metal sheets can be chemically machined by applying an accurately aligned resist to both sides, and simultaneously dissolving the metal from opposite sides. This procedure results in less undercutting or overcutting than if the entire part were machined from one surface. The undercutting can also be controlled by the velocity of jets of the etchant directed against the masked surface.

Similarly, metal can be removed from nonmasked areas by applying a potential between the sheet being machined and another metal submersed in the electrolyte, a process the exact reverse of electroplating.

Processing.   The chemical and physical treatment to which tube components, tube subassemblies, and eventually the final structure and vacuum envelope are subjected determine to a large extent the quality and reliability of the device.   This treatment is directed toward the removal or elimination of adsorbed gases, volatile materials, and residual chemical compounds that can be decomposed under heat or electron bombardment to degrade the vacuum or impair the cathode emission.

The type of chemical treatment must be compatible with the metal or combination of metals being cleaned and the nature of the contaminant being removed.   Solvents or hot alkaline baths remove the bulk of machine and cutting lubricants.   Acid baths

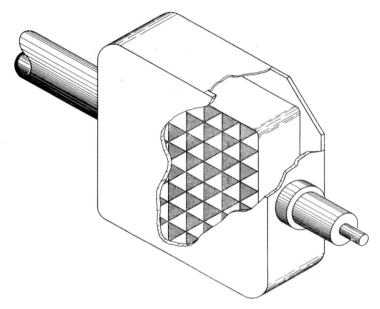

Fig. 5. Cellular construction of sputter ion getter.

are employed in removing oxides.   Electrolytic deplating or electropolishing procedures remove the outer surfaces and sharp projections from metals and are often more effective than acid removal.

Abrasive cleaning, such as sand blast, carborundum, steel shot, or slurries of abrasive powders propelled by high-velocity air, are effective in removing scale or heavy oxide layers from metal envelope tubes after exhaust.   Chemical cleaning of evacuated metal envelope tubes is undesirable because active hydrogen may penetrate the walls and spoil the vacuum.

After chemical cleaning, metal parts are "fired" in hydrogen or in vacuum bell jars.   This high-temperature treatment in hydrogen serves to reduce further metal oxides and to replace other absorbed gases with hydrogen.

Because of hydrogen's mobility through metals, it is one of the easiest gases to be removed during evacuation (65).   Vacuum firing of individual parts before assembly often allows a higher temperature and more thorough out-gassing than can be obtained in the final exhaust.

After assembly the tube undergoes a final evacuation on a high-vacuum system. The schedule consists of an oven bake-out at the highest practical temperature to remove water vapor and adsorbed gas. In devices containing glass, the highest bake-out temperature is set by the softening point of the glass. Tubes constructed with metal envelopes and ceramic seals can be processed at higher temperatures, the upper limit being set by the melting point or vapor pressure of some metal or alloy that is exposed to the vacuum environment.

Bake-out temperatures range between 300 and 450°C for glass tubes. High-temperature ceramic seal development is still in a dynamic stage, and as of 1965 the technology has advanced to the point where metal–ceramic structures employing refractory metals can be processed up to about 1500°C.

The thermionic cathode is a potent source of gas because it runs at high temperature, and in the case of oxide-coated and dispenser cathodes chemical reactions are taking place continually. These slowly released gases are prevented from reaching deleterious levels by a getter.

During the final stages of bake-out, or immediately following bake-out, the cathode activation is begun. Cathode temperature is gradually raised to break down the carbonates in oxide-coated emitters, or to out-gas the cathode structures in other types of emitters. The cathode is raised to a higher temperature than it will be operated during life. On high-voltage tubes it is customary to apply a potential between the cathode and the various tube elements since the impinging high-energy electrons may release gas that could not be liberated by heat alone during bake-out.

Gettering. Gettering is the process by which the purity of the vacuum is maintained in evacuated devices (66). Although it is possible to process tubes and to out-gas the elements to such an extent that no additional buildup of gas pressure occurs during operation, the time required to achieve this state greatly adds to the cost. These stringent exhaust schedules are employed mainly in the manufacture of high-voltage or premium tubes. In high-production and low-cost tubes, gettering permits a reduction in the time required to exhaust the tube, and increases the degree of vacuum over that supplied by the vacuum pumps at the time of seal-off.

The most widely used process makes use of flash getters, that is to say chemically active metals evaporated on the walls of the vacuum enclosure to provide a large area for reaction with the gas. During the time the active metal is being evaporated, the gas cleanup is very rapid. After this dispersal gettering, the metal deposited on the walls continues to adsorb gas molecules that come in contact with it, thus maintaining a high vacuum throughout the life of the device.

Barium is the most prevalent active metal used in flash-type getters (67). The barium is evaporated by either heating a metal tubing containing metallic barium, or by heating a barium compound with a reactive metal to release barium by chemical exchange. In addition to barium, other elements commonly used for flash getters include calcium, strontium, magnesium, and aluminum.

Bulk-contact getters are used in higher-temperature environments or in limited volumes where a getter flash is impractical. The bulk getters, to be effective, must run hot, but are not flashed. Metals, or mixtures of metals used in bulk getters include thorium, titanium, cesium, zirconium, uranium, tantalum, hafnium, niobium, lanthanum, or mixtures of rare earth elements such as misch metal.

To present a maximum surface, the metals are often used in a powdered form, and are applied as a coating on anodes or other tube structures that are heated to the required temperature by either electron bombardment, or by cathode heat.

Ion getters are a recent addition to techniques for attaining and maintaining a very high vacuum (68). These are actually miniature adaptations of ion pumps (69,70). Their operation requires a magnetic field, usually supplied by permanent magnets, and a source of high voltage. These complications limit their use to the large and more costly electron tubes, such as the multimegawatt klystrons.

The construction of ion getters is shown in Figure 5. An anode consisting of a cellular metal grid (titanium metal is very efficient for this structure) is placed between two planar electrodes. This entire structure is immersed in a magnetic field of several thousand gauss. A high voltage, usually less than 10 kV, placed between the grid and the adjacent plates, causes electrons to be emitted by field emission. These electrons describe a spiral path due to the magnetic field, and are effective in producing ions and dissociated molecules by collision. These high-density ion beams bombard the cathode plates where they cause sputtering of the cathode metal. Atoms and metastable particles which strike the sputtered deposits are bound by physisorption or chemisorption.

Vacuums greater than 10^{-9} Torr are readily attained by these ion getters. Pumping speed is independent of pressure below 10^{-5} Torr, and is determined by the size of the interaction space. Small structures, with pumping speeds of 1–5 liter/sec, are adequate for maintaining vacuum in most tubes, since the ion getter must only remove gases liberated after pinch-off.

These ion getters also serve as vacuum gages, since the current to the anode is a function of the gas pressure. Ion getters will remove all gases, including helium and argon, although these noble gases are pumped at a slower rate than the common gases.

Bibliography

"Vacuum Tubes" in *ECT* 1st ed., Vol. 14, pp. 536–549, by J. V. Festa, Sylvania Electric Products, Inc.

1. E. S. Rittner, W. C. Rutledge, and A. H. Ahlert, *J. Appl. Phys.* **28**, 1468–1473 (1957).
2. J. R. Lane, *J. Metals* **10**, 738–742 (Nov. 1958).
3. P. Hidnert, *J. Res. Natl. Bur. Std.* **A**, 1031–1066 (Dec. 1931) (RP 338).
4. A. W. Hull, E. E. Burger, and L. Navias. *J. Appl. Phys.* **12**, 698–707 (Sept. 1941).
5. American Welding Society, *Brazing Manual*, Reinhold Publishing Corp., New York, 1955.
6. W. G. Worcester and E. O. Doughty, *Trans. Am. Inst. Elec. Engrs.* **65**, 946 (1946).
7. R. J. Bondley, *Electronics* **20**, 97–99 (July 1947).
8. H. J. Nolte and R. F. Spurck, *Television Eng.* **1**, 14–18, 39 (Nov. 1950).
9. W. Gaede, *Ann. Physik* **46**, 357 (1915).
10. P. Alexander, *J. Sci. Instr.* **23**, 11 (1946).
11. L. Northcott, *Molybdenum*, Academic Press, Inc., New York, 1956.
12. K. Jackson and R. O. Jenkins, *Metallurgia* **47**, 277–282 (June 1953).
13. T. H. Briggs, *Metals & Alloys* **9**, 303–306 (Nov. 1938).
14. C. R. Tottle, *J. Inst. Metals* **85** (8), 375–378 (April 1957).
15. J. P. Jasiomis and J. E. Clime, *IRE Trans. Electron Devices*, **ED-3**, 162 (July 1956).
16. E. M. Wise, *J. Electrochem. Soc.* **97**, 570–640 (March 1950).
17. E. L. Jossem, *Rev. Sci. Instr.* **11**, 164 (1940).
18. Baker and Company, *Rev. Sci. Instr.* **26**, 645 (June 1955).
19. C. T. Sims, C. M. Craighead, and R. I. Jaffee, *J. Metals* **7**, 168–179 (Jan. 1955).
20. G. W. Morey, *The Properties of Glass*, 2nd ed., Reinhold Publishing Corp., New York, 1954.

21. Reference 5, Chap. 3, pp. 40–43.
22. T. H. Briggs, *Proc. Natl. Conf. Tube Techniques, 3rd,* 117–123 (Sept. 12–14, 1956).
23. L. F. Yntema and A. L. Percy, *Rare Metals Handbook,* Reinhold Publishing Corp., New York, 1954, Chap. 20.
24. J. E. Beggs, *IRE Trans. Component Parts,* **CP-4,** 28–31 (March 1957).
25. H. A. Jones and I. Langmuir, *Gen. Elec. Rev.* **30,** 310–319 (1927).
26. J. H. Partridge, *Glass-to-Metal Seals,* The Society of Glass Technology, Elmfield, Sheffield, England, 1949.
27. A. J. Monack, *Elec. Mfg.* **39,** 96–101, 162–180 (Feb. 1947).
28. A. N. Rogers, *Trans. Electrochem. Soc.* **883,** 205–210 (Oct. 1945).
29. O. W. Richardson, *Cambridge Phil. Soc. Proc.* **11,** 286 (1901).
30. S. Dushman, *Phys. Rev.* **21,** 623 (1923).
31. R. H. Fowler and L. W. Nordheim, *Proc. Roy. Soc. (London) Ser. A* **119,** 173 (1928).
32. W. P. Dyke and J. K. Trolan, *Phys. Rev.* **89,** 799 (1953).
33. W. W. Dolan, W. P. Dyke, and J. K. Trolan, *Phys. Rev.* **91,** 1054 (1953). W. W. Dolan, W. P. Dyke, and J. K. Trolan, *J. Appl. Phys.* **24,** 570–576 (May 1953).
34. O. Hachenberg and W. Brauer, *Advances in Electronics and Electron Physics,* Vol. 11, Academic Press, New York, 1959, p. 413.
35. A. J. Dekker, "Secondary Electronic Emission," in F. Seitz, *Solid State Physics,* Vol. 1, Academic Press, New York, 1958, p. 251.
36. K. G. McKay, *Advances in Electronics,* Vol. 1, Academic Press, New York, 1948, p. 65.
37. H. Bruining, *Physics and Applications of Secondary Electron Emission,* Pergamon Press, London, 1954.
38. D. A. Wright, *Proc. Inst. Elec. Engrs. (London), Pt. III,* **100,** 125–139 (May 1953).
39. R. E. Honig, *RCA Rev.* **18,** 195–204 (June 1957).
40. R. N. Bloomer, *Proc. Inst. Elec. Engrs. (London), Pt. B,* **104,** 153–157 (March 1957).
41. A. A. Halacsy, *Proc. Inst. Elec. Engrs. (London), Pt.1,* **97,** (104), 37–42 (March 1950).
42. I. Langmuir, *J. Franklin Inst.* **217,** 543–569 (May 1934).
43. P. Schneider, *J. Chem. Phys.* **28,** 675–682 (April 1958).
44. M. R. Andrews and S. Dushman, *J. Phys. Chem.* **29,** 462–472 (1925).
45. H. J. Dailey, *Electronics* **21,** 107–109 (Jan. 1948).
46. M. D. Fiske, *Phys. Rev.* **61,** 513 (1942).
47. A. Wehnelt, *Ann. Physik* **14,** 425 (1904).
48. G. Herrmann and S. Wagener, *The Oxide-Coated Cathode,* Chapman and Hall Ltd., London, 1951.
49. M. Benjamin and A. B. Osborn, *Trans. Faraday Soc.* **36,** 287–295 (Jan. 1940).
50. *Electronic Inds. Tele-Tech* **18** (4), 53–55 (April 1959).
51. R. W. Peterson, D. E. Anderson, and W. G. Shepherd, *J. Appl. Phys.* **28,** 22–33 (Jan. 1957).
52. V. L. Stout, in *Fourth National Conference on Tube Techniques, Sept. 10–12, 1958.* (Proceedings published by New York University Press, New York, 1959.)
53. A. W. Hull, *Phys. Rev.* **56,** 86–93 (1939).
54. V. C. Wilson, *J. Appl. Phys.* **30,** 475–481 (1959).
55. H. J. Lemmens, M. J. Jansen, and R. Loosjes, *Phillips Tech. Rev.* **11,** 341 (1950).
56. M. Knudsen, *Ann. Physik* **28,** 75 (1909); **31,** 205 (1910); **32,** 838 (1910).
57. R. Levi, *J. Appl. Phys.* **26,** 639 (1955).
58. G. Mesnard and R. Uzan, *Vide* **9,** 1492–1507 (1954).
59. R. Uzan, *Vide* **9,** 290–296 (1954).
60. G. Mesnard, *Vide* **10,** 347–351 (1955).
61. C. P. Hadley, *Rev. Sci. Instr.* **27,** 177 (1956).
62. J. M. Lafferty, *J. Appl. Phys.* **22,** 303 (1951).
63. T. Perry, H. S. Spacil, and J. Wulff, *Welding J.* (N.Y.) **33,** 442–448s (Sept. 1954).
64. W. L. Wyman, *Welding J.* (N.Y.) **37,** 49s–53s (Feb. 1958).
65. S. Dushman, *Scientific Foundations of Vacuum Technique,* John Wiley & Sons, Inc., New York, 1949, pp. 553–596.
66. S. Wagener, in *Proceedings Fourth National Conference on Tube Techniques, New York, Sept. 10–12, 1958.* (Proceedings published by New York University Press, New York, 1959, pp. 1–19.)
67. P. Della Porta, *Vacuum* **6,** 41–58 (Oct. 1956).

68. A. M. Gurewitsch and W. F. Westendorp, *Rev. Sci. Inst.* **25** (4), 389–390 (April 1954).
69. L. D. Hall, *Science* **128**, 279–285 (Aug. 8, 1958).
70. L. Holland, *J. Sci. Inst.* **36,** 105–116 (March 1959).

General References

Walter H. Kohl, *Materials and Techniques for Electron Tubes*, Reinhold Publishing Corp., New York, 1960.
S. Dushman, *Scientific Foundations of Vacuum Technique*, John Wiley & Sons, Inc., New York, 1959
William C. Dow, *Fundamentals of Engineering Electronics*, John Wiley & Sons, Inc., New York, 1937.
J. Millman and S. Seely, *Electronics*, McGraw-Hill Book Co., Inc., New York, 1941.
Rare Metals Handbook, Reinhold Publishing Corp., New York, 1954.

R. J. BONDLEY
General Electric Company

ELECTROPHORETIC DEPOSITION

Electrokinetic Phenomena and Terminology

Electrophoretic deposits may be obtained by applying a dc electric field between two electrodes immersed in a suitable liquid suspension, which causes a migration of the suspended phase toward one of the electrodes (*electrophoresis*) and the deposition of a coating or form at that electrode.

When particles migrate to the cathode, the process is commonly referred to as *cataphoresis;* when they move toward the anode, as *anaphoresis.* Under certain conditions, eg, with mixed suspensions and superimposed ac fields, deposition may take place at both electrodes simultaneously. (Under certain conditions neither migration nor deposition will take place.)

Electrophoresis is an important example of a larger group of phenomena known as *electrokinetic* phenomena. These phenomena can be broadly but somewhat simply characterized by the observation that when two different materials are in relative motion, an electric potential will tend to be generated; and conversely, when an electric potential is applied to two different materials physically capable of relative motion, they will tend to so move under the influence of the externally applied electric field. Usually, at least one of the materials is an insulator possessing a fairly high dielectric constant.

Electrokinetic phenomena, therefore, include not only the coordinated relative movement of finely suspended solids or immiscible liquid droplets (emulsions) through a liquid suspending medium under the influence of an electric field as in the case of electrophoresis, but also the corresponding movement of charged particles through gases. Moreover, when the solid is held in a rigid position, eg, corresponding to the form of a packed bed or porous medium, with a potential applied across it, and the liquid is free to move, the corresponding coordinated migration of the liquid will take place in the line of the applied field; this phenomenon is known as *electroosmosis*.

This article is concerned primarily with several limited aspects of electrokinesis, specifically, electrophoresis will be considered as a means of bringing the suspended material to the substrate, and, to a lesser extent, electroosmosis as an aid in consolidating the deposit by removal of the entrained suspending liquid. However, it is well to bear in mind that, despite the restricted scope of this article, these facets of phenomena have widespread significance in nature and in technology.   Devices and processes as seemingly diverse as Van de Graaff accelerators, electrostatic paint-spray systems, Cottrell precipitators, and gasoline delivery safety attachments, excepting certain auxiliary effects, are strongly based on electrokinetic phenomena.   Several recognized theories maintain that lightning arises from electrokinetically developed potentials. In a sense, these more general remarks may appear to be a digression in an article devoted to electrophoretic deposition, yet, the subject of electrophoretic deposition has suffered because it has been stressed as a descriptive art rather than a well-established technology, due in part to the fact that it has been most frequently investigated in isolation rather than as an important branch of the larger subject of electrokinesis.

Deposition and Coating

As noted, in this article electrophoretic coating is primarily discussed. However, it should be recognized that coating is only one form of deposition and that electrophoresis in turn is only one of the valuable mechanisms for moving suspended particles toward the appropriate electrode. What occurs at the electrode or in its immediate vicinity after the particles have arrived may be determined by phenomena such as coagulation which are unrelated to electrophoresis per se. As a group, far less is known about these phenomena of deposition other than in a pragmatic way. The manipulation of deposition conditions may involve a good deal of technical art and will naturally depend upon the more immediate purpose. For example, in the concentration of latex by electrophoretic deposition, emphasis will normally be placed on securing substantial mass deposition or enrichment with a minimum expenditure of time, labor, and power costs; hence, the geometric appearance or mechanical properties of the deposit or concentrate are likely to be of little interest. On the other hand, in the manufacture of surgical gloves from latex obtained by electrophoretic deposition such considerations as the yield per kWh are much less important than is the securing of a product which is almost uniformly thin, yet strong, free from pinholes, and of good appearance.

It is often convenient to discuss electrophoretic deposition as if it were a special case of ordinary electroplating and its variants, such as electrowinning, electroanalysis, and electroforming. The conventional copper or zinc plating of steel to protect steel against corrosion finds many parallels in the electrophoretic deposition of paints on automobile parts for similar protection. The electrophoretic concentration of, eg, clay or of the latex mentioned above has a counterpart in electrowinning where the accumulated deposit is of primary interest rather than in its more permanent relation to the collecting electrode. Analogously, the use of electroanalytic techniques for the identification and separation of dissolved metals or the fractional electrowinning processes has counterparts in some of the elegant and sophisticated techniques developed for the electrophoretic fractionations of proteins and other complex biochemical media. The example of the electrophoretic deposition of latex for surgical gloves previously mentioned has its counterpart in electroforming.

Although subsequent comments will emphasize coating phenomena and its applications, they will largely apply to forming as well, since the similarities between the processes of *coating* and *forming* are sufficiently great. Forming can be constructively seen as coating wherein the image (negative) of the substrate but not the substrate itself is retained. Provision must be made to remove the substrate by such means as stripping or selectively dissolving it away. Since, in the case of forming, the production item is the deposit itself, whereas, in the case of coating, the product is the combination of the substrate and its coating, forming usually involves heavier deposits with the frequently attendant aggravated problems of preserving dimensional stabilities, etc.

Despite the many formal resemblances between electrophoretic deposition and electroplating, the analogy should be noted but not pressed too far. As will be indicated later, many of the advantages and limitations of electrophoretic deposition are related to the differences rather than the similarities between it and conventional electroplating.

When electrophoretic deposition is considered as a coating process, it becomes apparent that it is subject to the general considerations of that field. Substantially all coating processes involve the following sequence of steps: (*1*) preparation of the substrate; (*2*) preparation of the coating medium; (*3*) application of the coating; (*4*) cure or aftertreatment of the coating.

In terms of this sequence, electrophoretic deposition is primarily a method of coating application such as brushing, spraying, sputtering, flow coating, flame and plasma-gun coating, or gel coating. As with any specific method of application, electrophoretic coating introduces its own parameters with respect to the formulation of the coating medium. Since in electrophoretic deposition the substrate consists either of an electrode or a porous diaphragm surrounding the attracting electrodes, the choice of substrate is limited to conductors or relatively inert porous media; further limitations are obviously set by the specific deposition phenomena involved.

The frequent failure, even among experts, to appreciate the fact that electrophoretic coating is actually only another coating process (albeit a uniquely interesting one) has led to wasted effort in duplicating or rediscovering or, even worse, the ignoring of pertinent knowledge in other areas of the older general art and technology of coating. Thus, for example, although combinations of flow coating and jet coating have been applied in conjunction with electrophoresis, the most practical applications have involved immersion of the substrate in a suitable bath and its subsequent withdrawal after deposition occurs. This process exhibits many characteristics of conventional dip coating. If the object to be coated has certain types of concavities or other traps which would preclude drainage in ordinary dip coating, the corresponding problem may be anticipated in electrophoretic coating. Similarly, when the bath is not agitated or circulated, settling and other inhomogeneities may prove troublesome, and when agitation is too vigorous and exposed, air may be beaten in, producing foaming and objectionably porous or incomplete deposits. If, in runs of significant duration, allowances are not made for such effects as depletion of solids through electrophoretic deposition or loss of volatiles by evaporation, the characteristics of the suspension, and hence of the deposit, may be adversely affected.

Moreover, electrophoretic coating affords no magic solutions to the problems of cure or aftertreatment of the coating. A satisfactory coating, regardless of method of application, should normally possess significant adhesion, cohesion, and continuity. These properties are usually not achievable without postapplication treatments to the "green" deposit. The aftertreatment may be as simple as allowing the solvent or liquid-suspending agent to evaporate. More commonly, baking, firing, and even chemical reduction of oxides and hydrostatic compaction may be required to develop the ultimate potential properties of the coating. Electrophoretic deposits as a group tend to be more selectively dependent on such aftertreatments.

Background and the Technical Literature

As indicated, the subject of electrophoretic deposition overlaps in the areas of at least three rather distinct fields: (1) the study of electrokinetic phenomena, (2) electroplating, and (3) general coating technology. In turn, each of these subjects has an extensive literature of its own as well as a share in a peripheral literature which also includes a variety of other subjects.

The purpose of this article is to provide the basic information to be expected in a modest encyclopedic treatment of a seemingly rather specialized subject within the vast field of chemical technology. Nevertheless, it is felt that the literature pertinent to this subject is so extensive but yet so uneven in distribution and quality that the bibliography and its selection should be given more direct attention within the text rather than included simply to bolster several of the author's points or provide a convenient means of working off inconvenient details in an aura of diffuse erudition.

Accordingly, a selected bibliography of moderate size has been included (1–107). Most of these references in turn will refer to chains of other references, the majority of which are not duplicated in the present list. Their noninclusion, therefore, reflects a compromise with time, format, and present viewpoint, rather than their lack of merit. The extent of the literature available may be better appreciated when it is noted that the bibliography prepared by Henley published in 1953 (29) contains well over 2000 references and that Abramson's classic book published in 1934 (1) contains some 500 references. In addition, particularly in the field of applications, there is a considerable amount of material of limited availability in the form of classified and proprietary reports and private communications.

Some further words of caution regarding the use of the present list may be helpful: The frequency with which an author's name appears is not necessarily a measure of the value of his contributions; thus, eg, patents may proliferate merely as a result of the Patent Office's suggestion that an application be divided, whereas technical articles may tend to be combined or condensed under editorial exigencies. A number of the references are actually poor in that they may be careless in their use of scientific terminology, eg, confusing colloidal systems and true solutions, or, in obscuring key information by trade designations. Nevertheless, these references are representative of the "state of the art" and recent trends, and thereby represent the best information available on some of the newer industrial developments. Similarly, many patents must be taken with the proverbial "grain of salt" since they may accurately state possible rather than preferred ways of carrying out commercial processes. Commercial operations usually depend more on economics than on feasibility.

In several cases, preliminary or interim reports as well as the corresponding final report have been included to give the reader an idea of the evolutionary way in which many practical problems peculiar to this field are solved.

A major source of confusion in trying to get a "feel" for the literature as a whole arises because the literature reflects highly diverse interests which often lead to excessive provincialism. Many investigators and reporters concerned primarily with the electrophoretic deposition of paints, rubber, and other organic high-polymer systems appear to show surprisingly little interest in the problems of electrodeposition of ceramics, metals, and cermets, and vice versa. Similarly, many who are interested in, eg, the ionographic separation of complex biological media for assay purposes are not interested in processes which permit the simultaneous codeposition of the constituents of an alloy. There is also a frequent prejudice encountered with regard to time of writing; pertinent and still valid earlier contributions are often overlooked or cited in a manner which suggests little familiarity with the work. Consequently, investigators in the overall field are deprived of the maximum information of their colleagues not through lack of interest but because of their unawareness of scientific developments.

Hence, the bibliography should be seen not as uniform and comprehensive, but rather as a fair sampling and a good starting point.

Theory and Practice

Despite the extensiveness of the pertinent literature, there are no unified theories of electrophoretic deposition which will account in a predictive or truly quantitative way for the observed phenomena. This is not so surprising when one considers the diversity and complexity of the systems involved and the fact that even familiar phenomena like the presumably simple gravitational settling of slurries are also not fully accounted for in a quantitative way. When enough ingenuity is used, almost any small body, from a particle of clay to a living ameba, can be made to electrophorese. The systems to be accounted for vary from almost gross slurries through micron and submicron-range suspensions to colloidal "solutions" of large molecules. Incidentally, the noncritical and almost colloquial use of the word "solution" for colloidal systems is a source of considerable mischief. True solutions can be diluted with the corresponding solvent indefinitely, and, unless the solvent or solute interact or are unstable, will also keep indefinitely. In contradistinction, colloidal "solutions" and suspensions tend to become unstable when diluted excessively, exhibit Tyndall cones, and are prone to change after a period of time.

Even the source of the apparent electrical charge on the migrating particle is not self evident. Certainly, concepts such as Helmholtz's double layer and its subsequent elaboration by other investigators and zeta potential calculations have provided a certain amount of intellectual comfort, but are at present of negligible or limited value in predicting the quantitative behavior of practical systems encountered in technological applications. Nevertheless, a number of these concepts and generalized observations may provide helpful qualitative guides.

In order to secure migration of suspended particles under the influence of an electric field, the particles must carry an effective electrical charge, and consequently the liquid phase must carry a corresponding charge of the opposite sign to preserve electrical neutrality. This charge is generally attributed to the sorption of ions or ionizable substances. Thus, in the formation of alkaline earth carbonate suspensions from solutions of their nitrates, preferential adsorption of alkaline earth cations is said to take place on the carbonate particles so that they acquire a positive charge. On the other hand, some synthetic-resin latexes are made up with sodium alkyl sulfates as dispersing agents; the alkyl sulfate ion is apparently adsorbed onto the polymer, giving it a negative charge. In the case of natural rubber latex, the particles may be kept in aqueous suspension by adsorbed proteins, which are capable of yielding either positive or negative protein ions; hence, the rubber particles will be either positively or negatively charged, depending upon the pH of the latex. The isoelectric point of the suspension is the pH at which the degree of positive and negative ionization is the same; the particles will have no net charge and coagulation will tend to take place in most cases at the isoelectric value.

Since the liquid has a charge opposite to that of the dispersed phase, it will tend, as noted previously, to migrate in the opposite direction. This phenomenon is of considerable importance in practical applications. Although the liquid phase is frequently aqueous, it is by no means restricted to water or water solutions. In nonaqueous systems, the counterpart of the isoelectric point may not be describable in terms of a simple pH parameter.

As noted, a number of theories have been proposed to explain the formation of electrophoretic deposits. Apart from considerations of direct-discharge phenomena, other important possible mechanisms are described as follows:

1. It is known that many suspensions will set to comparatively firm structures above a certain fairly definite solids concentration. In any suspension containing charged particles, there are repulsive electrostatic (coulomb) forces, which tend to keep the particles separated, as well as attractive (van der Waals) forces which tend to bring the particles together. The repulsive forces between particles appear to be effective over greater distances than the attractive ones; as a result dilute dispersions, in which the particle separation is relatively large, may be quite fluid. Above a critical concentration, however, the attractive forces begin to prevail, and the suspension will thicken and set. The electrophoretic migration of particles to one electrode and the electroosmosis of liquid in the opposite direction tend to produce a local concentration of the suspension at one of the electrodes. If this concentration exceeds the critical range, a thickened layer of the dispersed phase is produced.

2. In many cases, electrophoretic deposits are obtained by coagulation of a suspension by ions formed at one of the electrodes. Such ions include hydrogen or metal ions at the anode, and hydroxyl ions at the cathode. These ions may neutralize the charge of the dispersed particles, generally by forming an insoluble or little ionized compound with the dispersing agent adsorbed on the particles. For example, if a material is kept in suspension by a sodium soap, the negative fatty acid radical may be adsorbed on the suspended phase, giving it a negative charge and causing it to migrate to the anode. If there is generation of zinc ions (as by anode solution) or hydrogen ions, these ions can form an insoluble zinc soap or the free fatty acid, respectively, causing coagulation of the suspended phase in both cases.

The coagulating ions formed at an electrode will coagulate the suspension in contact with that electrode. The coagulated layer is usually a gel, and may be permeable to the migration of additional coagulating ions, which would normally tend to migrate away from the electrode. When these ions reach the boundary between the deposited layer and the main body of the dispersion, further coagulation will take place. This might explain how thick deposits of nonconductors may be obtained on an electrode. Removal of interstitial liquid from the coagulate by electroosmosis and by migrating ions helps to pack the deposit, and may give it a firm mechanical structure upon removal from the electrophoretic bath.

In some electrophoretic depositions, it is quite likely that both of the above proposed mechanisms and others may be involved.

The particle size of the suspended phase generally falls within the colloidal range, in which the dispersions have a fair degree of stability. The usual methods of preparing colloids and semicolloids are employed in making up the dispersions for electrophoresis. Thus, the precipitation method may be used in preparing alkaline earth carbonate suspensions from soluble salts and vinyl polymer suspensions may be analogously prepared by addition of alcohols to an ester solution of the resin. On the other hand, colloidal graphite is usually formed by size reduction and the addition of a stabilizing agent, whereas synthetic latexes are frequently prepared by emulsion polymerization. The conditions of preparation will naturally determine the charge of the dispersed phase.

It was mentioned that both aqueous and organic media were suited for electrophoretic coating. Aqueous suspensions eliminate the flammability, toxicity, recovery, and cost problems encountered in the use of organic solvents; they are generally more concentrated than organic dispersions and deposition can be effected at much lower voltages and higher rates. However, organic media have at least one major advantage; in contrast with the aqueous systems, there are few or no secondary electrode reactions involved and, hence, substantially higher voltages may be employed to compensate for the lower conductivities.

Just as it is difficult to state precisely where colloidal sizes end and molecular sizes begin, it is equally difficult to delineate sharply between electrophoresis and electrolysis. Actually, both processes may take place simultaneously. In aqueous suspensions, dissolved ions may migrate along with the colloidal particles; the order of magnitude of migration rates is often made deliberately comparable for most colloids and ions. Similarly, at the electrodes, various reactions may take place in parallel with the formation of an electrophoretic deposit such as gas evolution, electrode solution, oxidation, or reduction. The relative potentials of these reactions (taking into account concentration effects, gas overvoltage, passivation, etc) may determine in significant measure which electrode process will prevail. Some of these electrode reactions may be harmful, and have to be suppressed or circumvented. In other cases, the side electrode reactions may be useful, and advantage can be taken of them.

These diverse parallel and sequential reactions and processes frequently favor, as has been noted, the use of so-called diaphragms, usually of porous ceramic, to take maximum advantage of useful effects while minimizing other deleterious competitive effects. Thus, eg, if there is extensive gas evolution at the electrode which would produce a bubble-disrupted deposit, electrophoretic deposition may be made to take place on a porous diaphragm surrounding the electrode so that ions may move through freely but gas evolution is confined to the sequestered electrode.

Some Applications and Observations

Although several examples of the application of electrophoretic deposition have already been mentioned and a large number have been given by implication in the "reference chains," it is thought that a better feeling for the widespread and often unique applicability of electrophoretic deposition might be provided by citing a number of the additional diverse and somewhat overlapping applications which have been used or recommended. In a number of cases, examples have been selected which are illustrative rather than exhaustive.

Fabrication of Cutting Tools (51,52). Cutting tools may be made by the electrophoretic deposition of materials such as tungsten carbide with cobalt as the matrix. This is followed by sintering. Certain advantages have been secured by the incorporation of boron.

Protection of Molybdenum in High-Temperature Service (98). Multilayer coatings, including nickel–chromium compositions, titanium and niobium carbides, as well as cermet compositions of nickel-bonded metal carbides, were effectively deposited on molybdenum to provide oxidation resistance for high-temperature service. Zein was included as the activator. Isostatic pressing within Teflon (polytetrafluorethylene) sleeves preceded the firing of the deposited coatings.

Deposition of Poly(vinyl Chloride), Poly(vinylidene Chloridee), and Polyethylne (15,71). Poly(vinyl chloride) and poly(vinylidene chloride) were deposited from organic suspensions prepared by dissolving the polymer in a vehicle such as butyl acetate followed by adding an organic precipitant liquid, such as ethyl alcohol, until an appropriate suspension was produced. Polyethylene was electrophoretically deposited from aqueous dispersions stabilized by the addition of an "amic-acid" type (monamide of a dibasic acid) of dispersing agent such as polymeric octadecylbutyl-styrene maleamic acid. Improved coherent deposits were obtained by subsequent fusion.

Deposition of Polytetrafluoroethylene (42,43). Very thin films of polytetrafluoro-ethylene to be used as a dry lubricant and/or preservative surface were laid down electrophoretically. Odd shapes and sizes of items difficult to coat thinly by a spray technique were amenable to this electrophoretic technique.

Ceramic-Based Jewelry (9). Uniform, thin deposits of enameling glass frit suspended in alcohol were electrophoretically deposited on a cathode. Decorative techniques may also be carried out by applying an insulating coating on that part of the metallic cathode where no enameling is wanted.

Thoriated Cathodes (47,48). Thorium dioxide was cataphoretically deposited on tungsten employing a nickel anode and using such suspending media as absolute alcohol with small amounts of ionizing agents.

High-Friction Element (83). A high-friction element consisting essentially of a surface of a metallic matrix, such as nickel or copper, and a high-friction material, such as molybdenum disilicide or alumina, was formed by the electrophoretic codeposition of the respective metallic oxides plus the high-friction material followed by reduction in hydrogen to form the metallic matrix.

Low-Friction Element (82). A low-friction element may be prepared by electro-phoretically codepositing a reducible metallic oxide or sulfide with nonreducible lubricating molybdenum disulfide followed by hydrogen reduction to produce a metallic matrix incorporating the molybdenum disulfide.

Barium Titanate for Electronic Components (87). Extremely thin layers of barium titanate for use as piezoelectric units may be electrophoretically deposited from dispersions in diethylene glycol dimethyl ether, nitropropane, or pyridine.

Deposition of Luminescent Materials (89). Thin, extremely even layers of lumines-cent materials, such as copper-activated zinc sulfide, were electrophoretically deposited from a suspending medium containing ionizable electrolyte. This medium consisted mainly of an alcohol miscible with water such as methanol or 2-propanol, a minor amount of water plus an ionizable electrolyte, eg, thorium nitrate.

Electrophoretically Formed Abrasive Articles With Auxiliary Binder (85). Uniform application of grit plus binder was obtained by electrophoretic deposition of such abrasives as silicon carbide or alumina, suspended in an alcohol medium such as 2-propanol followed by electroplating of the metallic binder such as nickel or the electrophoretic codeposition of the metallic oxide followed by reduction in an hydrogen atmosphere.

Borating Copper Wire for Sealing to Glass (77). In order to provide a glass-sealable coating for copper wire, a borate glass frit plus metallic oxide activator such as copper oxide was electrophoretically codeposited on the above wire from a nonaqueous suspending medium such as amyl acetate.

Polytetrafluoroethylene-Surrounded Electrophoretically Deposited Ceramic (79). Insulation of a flexible electrical conductor is accomplished in certain cases by electrophoretic codeposition of a very thin coating of a ceramic plus polytetrafluoroethylene resin followed by a bake to fuse the resin particles to one another and to the ceramic, thus providing an impervious coating. An aqueous suspension of the ceramic and polytetrafluoroethylene plus wetting agents was used.

Nonemitting Electron Tube Control Grid (75). A mossy metallic grid coating which will prevent electron-emitting surfaces from contaminating the control grid surface was formed by electrophoretically depositing oxides of metals such as tantalum, zirconium, or tungsten, followed by vacuum reduction to produce the above-mentioned mossy metallic surface. The deposit was made from an acetone dispersion of the oxides.

Production of Synthetic Fluorphlogopite Mica (45). Sheets of the synthetic mica were formed by electrophoretic deposition of 5–20-μ mica particles from a *n*-amyl alcohol suspension followed by hot pressing the "green" deposits between molybdenum sheets at 2000 psi and 1300°C.

Spectrographic Sources of Europium Oxide and Thorium Fluoride (13). Fine wire sources for permanent magnet spectrographs were successfully formed by electrophoretic deposition of europium oxide or thorium fluoride from 2-propanol suspensions.

Electrophoretic Printing (95). As indicated in one claim, a method of printing has been developed by electrophoretic transfer of material which comprises providing a source sheet having at one surface a fluid phase containing relatively charged mobile particles of a detectable material capable of electrophoretic transfer, etc.

Electrophoretic Painting (4–6,54). Successful coating with excellent uniformity has been reported for paint systems based on aqueous dispersions in which such items as automotive parts are made the active electrode and the containing tank serves as the other electrode.

The examples given above are obviously not complete. As has been pointed out, a substantial portion of the most sophisticated work has been done in connection with medical and biochemical problems (see ref. 2, Chap. 9). Although this area is beyond the scope of this article, future investigators in the "hardware" application field might eliminate much unnecessary trial-and-error efforts by taking advantage of modified Tiselius techniques and the like.

There is reason to believe that almost all, if not all, solid and many liquid materials of reasonable stability can be electrophoretically deposited. Apart from those specifically mentioned above, materials which have been electrophoretically deposited include silicon carbide, iron oxide, boron, dysprosium, gold, niobium, tungsten, diamond powder, silicate glasses, chromium oxide, rhenium, zirconium hydride, thorium carbide, neptunium carbide, plutonium carbide, tantalum oxide, tungsten–uranium oxide composites, molybdenum disulfide, etc (27,28,32,60). A similar large array of typical organic materials, especially high polymers, might be cited.

The scope of utility has also been extended by improved application devices and the employment of analogs of certain electroforming techniques. Thus, multilayer and sandwich structures, etc, have been fabricated (84). By incorporating nuclear fuel materials in a matrix of nonfissionable retaining metal of acceptable nuclear cross section, fuel-element prototype structures have been made.

One of the most attractive features of electrophoretic deposition is that it permits the simultaneous codeposition of quite varied materials from the same codispersion. Moreover, materials tend to deposit in substantially the same proportions as they are present in the dispersion. This permits the incorporation of pigments and extenders along with the binders in the electrophoretic deposition of paints. It similarly allows the incorporation of vulcanizing agents, accelerators, etc, in latex designed for electro-phoretic depositing of rubber. By codepositing from mixed vinylidene chloride and styrene–butadiene latexes, improved elasticity has been secured in the electro-deposit compared with the deposit from the particular poly(vinylidene chloride) latex by itself (16). In a number of inorganic systems, codeposition combined with selective cure permits such variants as introducing nickel, and chromium and aluminum oxides in such proportions as to secure as the ultimate material, after hydrogen reduction, aluminum oxide in a matrix of a desired nickel–chromium alloy.

Further interesting variations may be obtained as indicated by taking advantage of the fact that, with some artfulness in arranging conditions, it is possible to deposit electrophoretically one constituent material dispersed in a plating bath from which a metal is being simultaneously electroplated (17). Just as it becomes more difficult to draw sharp distinctions between true solutions and colloidal dispersions when the molecules of the colloid approach small molecular weights, so it is sometimes difficult to ascertain in the case of mixed electroplated and dispersed solid codeposits whether the dispersed solid has gotten to the electrode solely by electrophoresis or at least in part by simple mechanical entrainment or settling.

Despite these borderline situations, more confusion is caused by failing to appre-ciate certain major differences between electroplating and electrophoretic deposition. One distinction seems to derive from the fact that the dispersed particles behave as if they have a relatively enormous effective ratio of mass to charge compared to simple ions. Thus, in an ordinary electrolytic system, approximately 1 g of hydrogen or 32 g of copper will be discharged per faraday; however, in one example of electrophoretic deposition of aluminum oxide, values of over 2,000,000 g/F have been reported (35). This, of course, favors high relative electrophoretic deposition rates.

In most electrophoretic depositions, the dispersed phase is made up of insulator particles. Even when the dispersed phase is made up of metal, graphite, or other highly conductive particles, the surface of the particles is usually coated or otherwise endowed with an insulator or much less conductive surface. This fact constitutes the basis of one of the most valuable characteristics of electrophoretic coating: if a conductive electrode area is covered with a relatively high-resistive layer, the current "following the path of least resistance" will be directed towards uncoated or more thinly coated areas. Hence, unlike substantially all other coating processes, such as brushing, spraying, ordinary dipping, conventional electroplating, electrophoretic coating tends to be almost self-regulating. This self-regulating ability results in the deposition of coatings of more uniform thickness and greater freedom from pinholes, even in relatively inaccessible regions. This latter characteristic, often referred to as "throwing power," is of extreme value in coating objects which have sharp edges, seams, and recesses which are difficult to see or reach.

It may seem strange that although electrophoresis serves, on the one hand, to separate substances such as proteins or pigments which are rather "close" in their properties, on the other hand, it is also recommended for the simultaneous codeposition of substances which are "far apart" in their properties. The explanation lies in the recognition of one of the most elementary and least appreciated characteristics of electrokinetic phenomena—they are primarily surface phenomena.

A particle of quartz or a droplet of mineral oil coated with a layer of protein will exhibit within wide limits the migration characteristics of the protein surface not the core materials.

Electrophoretic deposition is not a panacea. The "green" or formed deposits are usually, as previously observed, worthless without further treatment. The overall behavior of a dispersion is extremely sensitive to "activators," impurities, or other minor additions which may change the determining surface characteristics. Even though it may be simple, special electrical equipment is needed. Touch-up and in situ applications may be awkward or impossible. If coatings are excessively thick they may crack. If the current density does not fall within a reasonable range for each system, the deposit may be nonuniform or even nonexistent.

Yet, despite the fact that there is often a plethora of art required and a paucity of scientific guidance, coating by electrophoretic deposition not only fills a unique gap by itself, but offers some unusual and unprecedented possibilities when used in cooperation with, and not just in place of, conventional finishing techniques.

Bibliography

"Electrophoretic Deposition" in *ECT* 1st ed., Vol. 5, pp. 606–610, by M. A. Coler, Markite Co. and New York University, and M. Feinleib, Armour Research Foundation, Illinois Institute of Technology.

1. H. A. Abramson, *Electrokinetic Phenomena and Their Application to Biology and Medicine,* The Chemical Catalog Co., Inc., New York, 1934.
2. R. Audubert and S. de Mende, *The Principles of Electrophoresis,* The Macmillan Co., New York, 1960.
3. R. Bahn, *Silikat Tech.* **9,** 299–303 (1958); *Chem. Abstr.* **52,** 19060 (1958).
4. J. R. Berry, *Paint Technol.* **27** (12), 13–18 (1963).
5. *Ibid.,* **28** (1), 24–28 (1964).
6. *Ibid.,* **28** (3), 53–58 (1964).
7. H. Brintzinger, R. Haug, and G. Sachs, *Farbe Lack* **58,** 5–10, 143–150 (1952); *Chem. Abstr.* **46,** 3770, 6401 (1952).
8. J. P. Burden and V. H. Guy, *Trans. Inst. Metal Finishing* **40,** 93–97 (1963).
9. N. F. Cerulli, *Ceram. Bull.* **33,** 373–377 (1954).
10. *Chem. Eng. News* **42,** 100–110 (1964).
11. M. A. Coler and M. Feinleib, "Electrophoretic Deposition" in R. E. Kirk and D. F. Othmer, eds., *Encyclopedia of Chemical Technology,* Vol. 5, 1st ed., Interscience Publishers, Inc., New York, 1950, pp. 606–610.
12. *Corrosion Prevent. & Control* **11,** 19–25 (1964).
13. F. P. Cranston, Jr., and W. J. McCreary, *Rev. Sci. Instr.* **27,** 973 (1956).
14. Dutch Pat. 81,831 (June 15, 1956), N. V. Philips' Gloeilampenfabrieken.
15. M. Feinleib, *Trans. Electrochem. Soc.* **88,** 11–23 (1945).
16. C. G. Fink and M. Feinleib, *J. Electrochem. Soc.* **94,** 309–40 (1948).
17. C. G. Fink and J. D. Prince, *Trans. Electrochem. Soc.* **54,** 315–321 (1928).
18. R. K. Finn, "Electrophoresis," in H. M. Schoen, ed., *New Chemical Engineering Separation Techniques,* Interscience Publishers, a division of John Wiley & Sons, Inc., New York, 1963, Chap. 6.
19. S. R. Finn and C. C. Mell, *Prod. Finishing* **17,** 85–87, 91 (1964).
20. D. J. Fishlock, *Metal Ind.* **93,** 537–538 (1958).
21. Fr. Pat. 938,907 (Oct. 28, 1948), Société Française Radioélectrique.
22. Fr. Pat. 1,005,559 (April 11, 1952), Société Anon. de Commentry-Forchambault & Decazeville.
23. A. Gemant, *Direct Current* **1,** 90–92 (1953).

24. H. L. B. Gould, *Elec. Eng.* **69,** 544–548 (1950).

25. G. W. Gray, "Electrophoresis," *Sci. Am.* **185,** 45–83 (1951).

26. P. F. Grosso (CBS Labs., Stamford, Conn.), "Development of Phosphor Screens for High Resolution Display Devices," *U.S. Dept. of Comm. Office Tech. Serv. AD Rept. 600724* (May 1964).

27. C. P. Gutierrez, J. R. Mosley, and T. C. Wallace, *J. Electrochem. Soc.* **109,** 923–927 (1962).

28. C. P. Gutierrez, J. R. Mosley, and T. C. Wallace (Los Alamos Scientific Lab., New Mexico), "Electrophoretic Deposition: A Versatile Coating Method," *U.S. Dept. Comm. Office Tech. Serv. TID Rept. 11153* (March 1963).

29. A. Henley, ed., *Electrophoresis Bibliography*, American Instrument Co., Inc., Silver Springs, Md., 1953.

30. Hung. Pat. 138,148 (Oct. 15, 1947), Egyesült Izzolámpa és Villamossági R.T.; *Chem. Abstr.* **45,** 483 (1951).

31. Hung. Pat. 139,286 (Feb. 2, 1949), Imre Patai; *Chem. Abstr.* **45,** 483 (1951).

32. *Iron Age* **193,** 80–82 (1964).

33. R. A. Keeler (Vitro Laboratories, W. Orange, N.J.), "Deposition of Glaze Materials on Foam Ceramics by Electrophoresis," *Armed Services Technical Information Agency (ASTIA) Doc. 201971* (Sept. 1958).

34. R. A. Keeler and L. C. Terminello, *Am. Machinist* **163,** 138–139 (1959).

35. G. F. Kinney and J. V. Festa, *Sylvania Technologist* **10,** 48–52 (1957).

36. G. S. Koshurnikov, *Sb. Nauchn. Tr. Leningr. Inst. Tochnoi Mekhan. Optiki, Mat. Mekh. Khim.* **24,** 91–94 (1957); *Chem. Abstr.* **53,** 5701 (1959).

37. G. S. Koshurnikov and I. V. Nemilova, *Sb. Nauchn. Tr. Leningr. Inst. Tochnoi Mekhan. Optiki, Mat. Mekh. Khim.* **24,** 95–102 (1957); *Chem. Abstr.* **53,** 5701 (1959).

38. V. A. Lamb and W. E. Reid, Jr., *Plating* **47,** 291–296 (1960).

39. V. A. Lamb and H. I. Salmon, *Ceram. Bull.* **41,** 781–782 (1962).

40. H. Koelmans and J. Th. G. Overbeek, *Discussions Faraday Soc.* **18,** 52–63 (1954).

41. R. C. Lever, *Paint Technol.* **27** (2), 35–38 (1963).

42. R. W. Logan (General Plastics Corp., Bloomfield, N.J.), "Production of Thin Polytetrafluor-ethylene Resin (Teflon) Coatings by Electrodeposition Methods," *U.S. Dept. Comm. Office Tech. Serv. AD Rept. 402993* (Oct. 1963).

43. R. W. Logan (General Plastics Corp., Bloomfield, N.J.), "Research and Development of Thin Polytetrafluoroethylene (Teflon) Coatings by Electrodeposition," *U.S. Dept. Comm. Office Tech. Serv. AD Rept. 278562* (July 1962).

44. H. J. McDonald, *Ionography; Electrophoresis in Stabilized Media*, The Year Book Publishers, Inc., Chicago, 1955.

45. W. McNeill, J. E. Chrostowski, and T. J. Mackus, *J. Electrochem. Soc.* **108,** 763–767 (1961).

46. K. Meier and H. Ladeburg, *Deut. Farben-Z.* **5,** 413–421 (1951).

47. G. Mesnard, *Compt. Rend.* **230,** 70–72 (1950).

48. G. Mesnard and R. Uzak, *Vide* **5,** 769–776 (1950).

49. J. Muirhead, *Paint Technol.* **28** (5), 34–35 (1964).

50. "Gel Electrophoresis," *Ann. N.Y. Acad. Sci.* **121,** 305–650 (Dec. 28, 1964).

51. M. H. Ortner and K. A. Gebler (Vitro Labs., W. Orange, N.J.), "Fabrication of Cutting Tools by Electrophoretic Deposition," *U.S. Dept. Comm. Office Tech. Serv. AD Rept. 266711* (Oct. 1961).

52. *Ibid., AD Rept. 285514* (July 1962).

53. J. Th. G. Overbeek, "Quantitative Interpretation of the Electrophoretic Velocity of Colloids," in H. Mark and E. J. W. Verwey, eds., *Advances in Colloid Science*, Vol. 3, Interscience Publishers, Inc., New York, 1950, pp. 97–135.

54. A. L. L. Palluel, *Can. Paint & Varnish Mag.* **38,** 44–45, 59–61 (1964).

55. F. Pearlstein, R. Wick, and A. Gallaccio, *J. Electrochem. Soc.* **110,** 843–846 (1963).

56. S. A. Rice and M. Nagasawa, *Polyelectrolyte Solutions*, Academic Press, N. Y., 1961, Chap. 4.

57. F. K. Sautter, *J. Electrochem. Soc.* **110,** 557–560 (1963).

58. F. Scofield, *Ind. Eng. Chem.* **56,** 49–50 (1964).

59. J. J. Shyne, H. N. Barr, W. D. Fletcher, and H. G. Scheible, *Plating* **42,** 1255–1258 (1955).

60. J. J. Shyne and H. G. Scheible, *Electrophoretic Coatings*, in F. A. Lowenheim, ed., *Modern Electroplating*, 2nd ed., John Wiley & Sons, Inc., New York, 1963, Chap. 34.

61. C. R. Smith, "Electrodeposited Dispersion-Hardened Alloys—Key to High Temperature Strength in Clad Pieces," *U.S. Dept. Comm. Office Tech. Serv. PB Rept. 181502.*
62. L. C. Terminello, *Mill & Factory* **66**, 85–86 (1960).
63. S. A. Troelstra, *Philips Tech. Rev.* **12**, 293–303 (1951).
64. W. D. Turner and M. A. Coler, *Ind. Eng. Chem.* **30**, 1282–1284 (1938).
65. U.S. Pat. 2,138,938 (Dec. 6, 1938), A. W. Plensler (to Resistelite Corp.).
66. U.S. Pat. 2,251,992 (Aug. 12, 1941), L. E. Flory and G. A. Morton (to Radio Corporation of America).
67. U.S. Pat. 2,385,313 (Sept. 18, 1945), E. A. Thurber and L. A. Wooten (to Bell Telephone Laboratories, Inc.).
68. U.S. Pat. 2,421,652 (June 3, 1947), P. Robinson and S. O. Dorst (to Sprague Electric Co.).
69. U.S. Pat. 2,462,125 (Feb. 22, 1949), L. F. Oakes (to International Standard Electric Corp.).
70. U.S. Pat. 2,495,630 (Jan. 24, 1950), S. O. Dorst (to Sprague Electric Co.).
71. U.S. Pat. 2,530,366 (Nov. 21, 1950), A. G. Gray (to E. I. du Pont de Nemours & Co., Inc.).
72. U.S. Pat. 2,530,546 (Nov. 21, 1950), J. M. Snyder (to Bell Labs.).
73. U.S. Pat. 2,536,734 (Jan. 2, 1951), O. Flint.
74. U.S. Pat. 2,556,257 (June 12, 1951), P. Dénes.
75. U.S. Pat. 2,576,129 (Nov. 27, 1951), I. Levin (to United States of America).
76. U.S. Pat. 2,635,995 (April 21, 1953), H. T. Swanson (to R.C.A.).
77. U.S. Pat. 2,640,024 (May 26, 1953), R. E. Palmateer (to Sylvania Electric Products Co.).
78. U.S. Pat. 2,699,426 (Jan. 11, 1955), M. C. Hoffman (to Sylvania Electric Products Co.).
79. U.S. Pat. 2,707,703 (May 3, 1955), S. O. Dorst (to Sprague Electric Co.).
80. U.S. Pat. 2,800,448 (July 23, 1957), M. N. Fredenburgh (to R.C.A.).
81. U.S. Pat. 2,826,541 (March 11, 1958), H. Barr, J. J. Shyne, and F. Fahnoe (to Vitro Corp. of America).
82. U.S. Pat. 2,826,542 (March 11, 1958), J. J. Shyne and H. G. Scheible (to Vitro Corp. of America).
83. U.S. Pat. 2,828,254 (March 25, 1958), F. Fahnoe and J. J. Shyne (to Vitro Corp. of America).
84. U.S. Pat. 2,848,391 (Aug. 19, 1958), F. Fahnoe and J. J. Shyne (to Vitro Corp. of America).
85. U.S. Pat. 2,858,256 (Oct. 28, 1958), F. Fahnoe and J. J. Shyne (to Vitro Corp. of America).
86. U.S. Pat. 2,860,098 (Nov. 11, 1958), F. Fahnoe and J. J. Shyne (to Vitro Corp. of America).
87. U.S. Pat. 2,843,541 (July 15, 1958), S. Senderoff and W. E. Reid, Jr.
88. U.S. Pat. 2,843,596 (July 15, 1958), M. C. Hoffman (to Sylvania Electric Products Co.).
89. U.S. Pat. 2,851,408 (Sept. 9, 1958), N. F. Cerulli (to Westinghouse Electric Corp.).
90. U.S. Pat. 2,872,388 (Feb. 3, 1959), F. Fahnoe and J. J. Shyne (to U.S. Atomic Energy Commission).
91. U.S. Pat. 2,894,888 (July 14, 1959), J. J. Shyne and W. D. Fletcher (to Vitro Corp. of America).
92. U.S. Pat. 2,947,677 (Aug. 2, 1960), T. W. Blickwedel (to Sylvania Electric Prods., Inc.).
93. U.S. Pat. 2,982,707 (May 2, 1961), H. G. Scheible (to Vitro Corp. of America).
94. U.S. Pat. 3,094,477 (June 18, 1963), T. Jackson and A. McPherson (to Associated Electrical Industries, Ltd., London).
95. U.S. Pat. 3,145,156 (Aug. 18, 1964), G. Oster (to The Carter's Ink Co.).
96. L. Walter, *Can. Paint & Varnish Mag.* **38**, 43, 58–59 (1964).
97. A. C. Werner (Vitro Labs., Inc., W. Orange, N.J.), "Deposition of Glaze Materials on Foam Ceramics by Electrophoresis," *Armed Services Technical Information Agency (ASTIA) Doc. 158445 (1958); 158446 (Feb. 1958).*
98. A. C. Werner and R. J. Abelson (Vitro Labs., W. Orange, N.J.), "Preparation of Protective Coatings by Electrophoretic Methods," *U.S. Dept. of Comm. Office Tech. Serv. AD Rept. 150970 (PB Rept. 131726) (Feb. 1958).*
99. B. Wolk, *J. Phys. & Colloid Chem.* **54**, 472–482 (1950).
100. *Anodic-Hydrocoating (Electrocoating)*, Ashdee Corp., Evansville, Ind., 1964.
101. A. I. Avgustinik et al., *Zh. Prik. Khim.* **36** (8), 1646–1650 (1963); *Chem. Abstr.* **60**, 1434 (1964); *Zh. Prik. Khim.* **36** (11), 2539–2540 (1963); *Chem. Abstr.* **60**, 10360 (1964).
102. C. P. Gutierrez and J. R. Mosley, "Electrophoretic Deposition," in C. A. Hampel, ed., *The Encyclopedia of Electrochemistry*, Reinhold Publishing Corp., New York, 1964, pp. 542–544.
103. H. J. McDonald, "Electrophoresis," in C. A. Hampel, ed., *The Encyclopedia of Electrochemistry*, Reinhold Publishing Corp., New York, 1964, pp. 540–542.
104. U.S. Pat. 3,157,588 (Nov. 17, 1964), E. D. Parent, Jr. (to Sylvania Electric Prods., Inc.).

105. U.S. Pat. 3,163,592 (Dec. 29, 1964), A. W. Dolan and J. Theodosopoulos (to Sylvania Electric Prods., Inc.).
106. U.S. Pat. 2,938,839 (May 31, 1960), F. Fahnoe and J. J. Shyne (to Vitro Corp. of America).
107. U.S. Pat. 2,994,654 (Aug. 1, 1961), F. Fahnoe and J. J. Shyne (to Vitro Corp. of America).

MYRON A. COLER
Markite Corporation

ELECTROPLATING

Electroplating is "the electrodeposition of an adherent metallic coating upon an electrode for the purpose of securing a surface with properties or dimensions different from those of the basis metal" (3). This definition may be broadened for purposes of the present article in two respects: The term "adherent" "excludes the increasingly important area of electroforming, which is nevertheless usually considered to be a branch of electroplating technology; and even the term "electrodeposition" itself must be stretched to include "electroless" plating and immersion processes which do not employ electric current. See also Film deposition; Metallic coatings.

As is usual, the practical and technological phases of electroplating matured much earlier than the science; electroplating with copper, silver, and gold was mentioned in the literature, and even patented (4), almost as soon as Faraday enunicated the laws of electrolysis. Until about World War I, electroplating remained essentially an art: Solution compositions were closely guarded secrets handed down from father to son, and most electroplaters made no pretense of knowing even the fundamentals of electricity or chemistry. Most early uses of electroplating were predominantly decorative, and the physical and chemical properties of the product were not as important as its appearance; there was much emphasis on such artistic effects as verde antique, ormolu, and highlighting; but the demands of World Wars I and especially II for finishes having close tolerances and rigidly specified properties forced the electroplater to become a technologist rather than a craftsman, and forced electroplating to depend heavily on basic science and engineering. This development has been forwarded by advances in metallurgy and physical and electrochemistry, by improvements in sources of direct current and in measuring instruments, and by the rise, between the wars, of the chemical industry which made available reliable sources of pure chemicals (5).

Electroplating is a surface treatment; it has for its purpose the alteration of the surface properties of the work being treated, which is made the cathode in an electroplating solution, or "bath." Such baths are almost always aqueous solutions, so that the metals which can be deposited are limited to those which are capable of being discharged from aqueous solutions of their salts; the only major exception at present is aluminum, which is being plated on a semicommercial scale from organic electrolytes and fused salts. Some of the refractory metals (eg, niobium, tantalum) can also be deposited from fused salts as coherent plates, and interesting developments in this field have been reported (6).

The thickness of deposit applied by electroplating varies with the application: from as little as 0.025μ (10^{-6} in.) for decorative gold deposits, through $25–50 \mu$ (1–2 mil) for standard nickel/chromium plate on exterior automotive hardware, to 1 mm (40 mil) or more for electroforms. Table 1 shows ASTM specifications for the more commonly applied decorative and protective coatings.

Table 1. ASTM Specifications for Plated Coatings

Basis metal	ASTM designation	Plate	Type and thickness of plate, min, μ[a]				
copper and copper-base alloys	B141-58	nickel[b]	FC 13	KC 7.6	QC 2.5		
		chromium, if required[c]	0.25	0.25	0.25		
steel	A165-55	cadmium	NS 13				
	B200-60	lead	ES 25	MS 13	OS 7.6	PS 6.4	TS 3.8
	A166-61T	copper/lead	EES 0.38/25	MMS 0.38/13	PPS 0.38/6.4		
		nickel or copper and nickel	DS 51	FS 30	KS 19	QS 10	
		nickel (if copper is used), min	25	15	10	5.1	
		chromium (if required), min	0.25	0.25	0.25	0.25	
	B375-63T	total nickel	51	38	25		
		dull or semibright nickel	41	29	19		
		bright nickel[d]					
		chromium[e]	0.25	0.25	0.25		
zinc and zinc-base alloys	A164-55	zinc	GS 25	LS 13	RS 3.8		
	B142-61	copper and nickel, min[b]	DZ 51	FZ 30	KZ 19	QZ 13	
		copper, min	5.1	5.1	5.1	5.1	
		final nickel, min	25	13	7.6	7.6	
		chromium (if required), min	0.25	0.25	0.25	0.25	
	B405-63T	copper, min	A 6.3	B 6.3	C 6.3	D 6.3	
		total nickel, min	51	38	25	13	
		semibright nickel, min	40	30	20	10	
		bright nickel, min	2.5	2.5	2.5	2.5	
		chromium, min[e]	0.25	0.25	0.25	0.25	

[a] Letter designations FC, KC, etc, are arbitrary. The second letter designates the basis metal; C = copper, S = steel, Z = zinc; Min = minimum, 25 μ = 1.0 mil = 0.001 in.

[b] Thicknesses are based on experience with buffed dull nickel; if other types are used the thickness may have to be altered.

[c] Chromium coatings of 1.3 μ or more are likely to cause cracking of the nickel deposits on brass.

[d] Remainder. The thickness of the bright nickel should not exceed 25% of the total nickel thickness for maximum durability.

[e] Chromium thickness may be increased to 0.5 μ or more with beneficial effect on protective value. If these heavier chromium deposits are used they should be either crackfree or microcracked.

The beneficial properties conferred by electroplating include improved corrosion resistance, better appearance, wear resistance and hardness, solderability, specific electrical properties, improved frictional characteristics, and many others. Heavy deposits may be used to build up the dimensions of worn or mismachined tools, and electroforming (including electrotyping) is used to manufacture articles that cannot be made as economically in any other way.

Accurate statistics on the consumption of metals in electroplating are not available for most metals. Total U.S. consumption of cadmium in 1962 was about 12 million pounds, and the most important single use was in electroplating. In the same year about 17,800 short tons of nickel was consumed in electroplating, representing about 15% of total U.S. consumption. The 5 million short tons of electrolytic tinplate produced in 1962 required 26,400 long tons of tin or about 33% of U.S. consumption. Data for the other major plating metals, copper, zinc, chromium, and silver, are too fragmentary for quotation (7).

Applications

It is usual to classify applications for plating according to the principal function of the plate: Thus, the plating may be applied mainly for (1) appearance; (2) protection; (3) special surface properties; or (4) engineering or mechanical properties. Rather obviously, these distinctions are not clear-cut: A purely "decorative" deposit must be, to some extent at least, protective as well, and other overlaps among the four named functions are common. Nevertheless the classification is convenient.

Decorative Plating. The most familiar plating applied for appearance is the so-called chromium plate (commonly but improperly referred to as "chrome"), which almost always consists of a composite coating having a very thin (0.25–1.0 μ) deposit of chromium as the final or topcoat. The undercoats, usually nickel or copper followed by nickel, have been relied upon for protective value, but it has recently been shown that the type and thickness of chromium play a very important role. Other metals having decorative applications include silver, gold, brass, bronze, nickel, copper, and rhodium; and occasionally, for special effects, lead, tin, and other metals may be used.

The list of articles plated for appearance is almost endless: automotive and aircraft parts, refrigerator hardware, electrical appliances, plumbing fixtures, office furniture, photographic equipment, golf clubs, firearms, handbag frames, pens and pencils, costume jewelry, office equipment—the list could be extended. Usually, protection of the basis metal is also involved; one example in which appearance is almost the only factor is the plating of stainless steel trim with chromium, so that the color will match that of other chromium-plated parts. (Even here some protective function is involved.)

Plating for Protection. Steel, the most common structural metal, must be protected against rusting in almost all its applications. Paints and organic coatings are, of course, widely used for this purpose, as are zinc and cadmium electroplates. Both of these deposits protect the basis steel galvanically: ie, they corrode sacrificially, thus preventing electrochemical attack on the steel even when pores or scratches permit penetration of the corrodent (see Corrosion). Although both zinc and cadmium can be plated "bright" or can be brightened after plating by simple chemical treatment, this bright appearance does not last long in use, and neither metal would usually be chosen for applications where retention of pleasing appearance is an important factor, although by the application of so-called "clear dip" conversion coatings the appearance of these two electroplates is rendered sufficiently attractive for cheap hardware and such items. Zinc can be applied to steel by methods other than electroplating, including hot galvanizing, Sherardizing, and "Peen plating" (see Metallic coatings). Judged by tonnage of product, hot galvanizing is far more important than electroplating (often called electrogalvanizing). The protective value of zinc deposits depends almost entirely upon their thickness rather than on the method of application, but electroplating has some advantages in not forming a brittle alloy layer and in the absence of dross formation.

Zinc is the most economical plate that can be applied to steel for rust prevention. Thickness for thickness it is superior to cadmium in typical industrial atmospheres; although cadmium is better in marine conditions by the thickness criterion, it is so much more expensive (about twenty times, as of 1964) that the economic advantage remains strongly in favor of zinc. Thus cadmium is used primarily in applications where two disadvantages of zinc are of importance: zinc forms bulky corrosion products that may interfere with the proper functioning of moving parts, and it is not easily soldered by usual techniques. Cadmium is superior to zinc in appearance, and the plating process has the advantage of being somewhat more easily controlled.

Industry has been plagued by recurring shortages of cadmium, which have driven the price to very high levels and at times have made it almost unobtainable. Zinc has been substituted where possible; other substitutes that have found special applications include tin–zinc alloy, bronze, and tin–lead.

The use of tin for protection of steel forms the basis of the very important tinplate and tin can industries. Tin does not protect steel galvanically under normal outdoor conditions as zinc and cadmium do, but under the special conditions obtaining inside the hermetically sealed tin can, in contact with the organic acids of foods, tin becomes sacrificially protective. An important property of tin in this use is its nontoxic nature; cadmium, by contrast, is extremely poisonous. Electroplating has almost entirely superseded the older hot-dip method of applying the tin coating for tinplate in the U.S., and is supplanting it in other countries. In 1962, in the U.S., almost 5,000,000 short tons of electrolytic tinplate was produced and only 212,500 tons of hot dip (7). The manufacture of electrolytic tinplate represents the largest single application of electroplating.

Other metals, such as copper, nickel, and chromium, are applied partly for protection and partly for appearance, and have already been mentioned under "decorative plating."

Special Surface Effects. In this category fall such uses of electroplating as tin plating for solderability, rhodium plating for reflectance, silver and rhodium plating for electrical properties, and gold plating for good electrical contact. This list is representative, not exhaustive. In addition to tin, for example, gold, cadmium, and some tin alloys such as tin–lead are used when solderability is the aim. Modern production methods in the electronic industry demand that components be practically instantaneously wetted by soft solders using only noncorrosive fluxes, and that the soldered joints be sound; further, they demand that parts remain solderable for a reasonable period after fabrication and plating in order to simplify inventory problems. Copper and brass, though easily solderable when clean, quickly tarnish and acquire films not readily wetted by solder; plating with tin or other metals mentioned largely overcomes this problem.

As industry becomes more sophisticated in its use of materials, it can be expected that there will be fewer "all-purpose" metals and more application of specific materials for specific properties. This is one reason for the expectation that alloy plating will increase in usefulness, as special alloys will be developed for special applications. This trend is already evident in the burgeoning development of magnetic alloys, which are applied not only by electroplating but also by vacuum evaporation and other techniques, for computer memories and similar devices (1,8–10).

Engineering Applications. Electroplates may be applied for their mechanical, physical, or chemical properties rather than primarily to protect or beautify the substrate. Such applications are generally termed "engineering," and usually involve the application of much heavier deposits than would be considered for the preceding three categories. Metals of most interest in this connection are nickel and chromium; iron, copper, lead, silver, gold, and tin also have engineering uses.

The mechanical properties of nickel, ie, hardness, tensile strength, and stress, can be varied by controlling the conditions of deposition. These properties, combined with the generally good resistance of nickel to many corrosive chemicals, make it useful in a host of industrial applications. Steel pipe is electroclad on the inside with heavy nickel plate (0.13–2.5 mm or 0.005–0.1 in.) (11). Tank cars are lined with nickel by the "electroless" process (12). Electrotypes are faced with nickel or chromium for longer press runs.

The hardness and favorable frictional characteristics of chromium account for its use on cutting tools, files, dies, rolls for paper-making machinery, etc. The term "hard chromium" is used in the trade for such applications, although this chromium is not necessarily any harder than that applied for decorative purposes; "heavy" or "thick" chromium would be more descriptive. Chromium can also be plated with a special surface condition known as "porous," in which form it holds oil films well and is useful as cylinder liners for internal combustion engines.

Worn or mismachined parts can be built up to proper dimensions by nickel or chromium plating; much expensive equipment is thus salvaged at a small fraction of the cost of replacing it.

Bearing properties can often be greatly improved by electroplating; porous chromium has been mentioned. In addition, aluminum alloy pistons for internal combustion engines are tin-plated to prevent scoring of the cylinder walls by the abrasive aluminum oxide during the running-in period. Lead and its alloys, silver, and indium also find use in this general area.

Electroplates are applied for temporary use in metal treatments: Steel parts are copper-plated in selected areas to prevent carburization at specific locations; tin–copper alloys are similarly used as a stop-off in the nitriding of steel.

Electroforming. This procedure is a special case of the engineering uses of electroplating. In electroforming, the electrodeposited metal is usually much thicker than for other applications, up to 0.6 cm (0.25 in.) or more. In this manufacturing technique metal is deposited upon a form or mandrel; this is later separated from the deposit which then becomes an independent entity. Although this would seem to be a very expensive method for producing articles, it has been adapted to a few high-production items. Its principal applications arise from its unique capabilities: Complicated shapes can be duplicated exactly with little or no scrap from machining; physical and mechanical properties of the electroformed metals can be closely controlled; and surface contour of the master is exactly reproduced down to the finest detail. This is illustrated by its use in the production of masters, positives, and stampers for phonograph records.

Mandrels for electroforming are of two types: temporary, which are used to produce one electroform and then removed by melting or dissolving away from the electroform; and permanent, which are removed from the electroform intact. Choice between them depends on many factors, including the shape of the electroform and the number of pieces to be produced. Temporary mandrels may be of low-melting alloys or waxes that can be melted out, metals like aluminum or zinc that can be dissolved away chemically, or plaster and similar materials that can be easily broken away. Permanent mandrels are usually of stainless steel, chromium-plated steel, nickel alloys, or aluminum.

Success in electroforming depends primarily on two factors: extreme care in the plating operation, and skill and foresight in the design of mandrels to ensure their successful removal from the form (13,14).

The Substrate in Electroplating

There is much more to electroplating than the final step of laying down a coating of the plating metal, and much more has to be considered than the properties of the plated metal. The final article will consist not of the deposit alone, but of deposit plus substrate, and it is the properties of this combination that have to be considered in choosing the right metal to plate, and often the right solution to plate it from. A few examples may be illustrative.

Many metals, corrosion-resistant themselves, may actually worsen the corrosion resistance of a composite when plated over a less noble metal. This is because of the galvanic couple set up by the contact of two dissimilar metals; it is particularly important in plating upon aluminum, which is electrochemically more active than any metal with which it can be plated. For this reason applications for plating on aluminum must be carefully chosen and plating procedures themselves must be carried out with special care.

The plating process itself may have deleterious effects upon the properties of the substrate: the best example of this is the embrittling effect of hydrogen upon the high-strength steels, particularly in zinc and cadmium plating (15–17).

Diffusional effects must also be considered (18). The possibility that the deposit may in time, or at elevated temperatures, form an alloy with the substrate must be kept in mind; such alloys may be brittle or have other undesirable properties. Where such effects must be avoided, a barrier layer of another metal, most often nickel, is interposed between the substrate and the final plate.

Where the application involves exposure to high temperatures, relative coefficients of expansion of the substrate and the plate may have to be taken into account. Even the disposal of rejects may be a factor: Some platers of zinc-base die castings will not consider tin plating, because common practice is merely to remelt rejected items, and there is a widespread suspicion of the effect of any tin at all in this alloy.

These examples could be multiplied; they suffice to show that the system substrate–electroplate must always be carefully considered.

PREPARATION OF THE SUBSTRATE

Before a useful electroplate can be deposited on a surface, the surface must be in condition to receive it. Useful usually means, among other things, adherent; in electroforming the aim is just the opposite; but in either case the surface must be so prepared as to ensure the desired bond or lack of it. Except in the special case of electroforming, it is desired that the deposit adhere firmly to the substrate, and in the discussion which follows this will be assumed. The special treatments designed to ensure easy removal of the deposit must be left for treatises on electroforming (13).

The preplating treatments necessary to prepare the surface for acceptance of an adherent deposit are generally subsumed under Cleaning, below, but there are many aspects of this problem. The ideal surface would be one consisting entirely of atoms of the metal to be plated upon, and having no foreign material at all. This is virtually impossible to attain, even in the laboratory, and then only under the most stringent conditions and for a few special surfaces. A practical definition, then, of a satisfactorily clean surface would be a surface containing no foreign material that interferes with the formation of an adherent deposit. In general this connotes the removal of gross dirt and soil, heavy oxide or tarnish films, and in some cases surface skins of damaged metal produced by prior mechanical operations.

Choice of the proper cleaning or preparative cycle depends primarily upon (1) the nature of the substrate to be prepared and (2) its prior history, which determines the nature and amount of the soils to be removed. Ferrous and nonferrous metals generally require different types of cleaners; the more active metals such as aluminum in turn require special techniques to prepare them for plating. And obviously, the more contaminated the surface the more cleaning it will require.

A typical cleaning cycle includes the following steps: (1) pickling to remove gross scale; (2) any mechanical preparation such as polishing or buffing; (3) cleaning to remove oils, greases, shop dirt, polishing and buffing compounds; (4) rinsing; (5) acid dipping to remove oxide films; and (6) rinsing.

This cycle is modified according to individual requirements. Step (1) might be omitted if the metal as received is free of scale; in fact this step is often performed before the work is received in the plating department. Step (2) will be necessary or not depending on the surface condition of the metal and the appearance requirements of the finished part. Step (3), on the other hand, can almost never be omitted but may easily consist of several separate operations.

Cleaning (19). The purpose of this step is to remove dirt, oils, greases, and other foreign material from the surface. The nature of these soils may vary widely, and the cleaning step may correspondingly be anything from a simple dip in a mild detergent to a rather severe combination of several treatments. Although largely displaced by more automated methods, even hand scrubbing of individual pieces is not unknown.

Organic solvents are used to dissolve most oils and greases, including those used to bind buffing and polishing compounds. Although they may be used merely as dips, it is more common and effective to employ "vapor degreasing," in which vapors of the solvent condense on the parts to be cleaned and run back into a pool of liquid solvent below them. The most common solvents for this purpose are perchloroethylene (tetrachloroethylene) and trichloroethylene (see Chlorocarbons). One danger in organic cleaners is that removal of oils and greases from a highly contaminated surface may merely leave the nonoily dirt dry and more firmly attached than ever.

Following organic cleaning, the next step is alkaline cleaning. Alkaline cleaners are aqueous solutions of sodium compounds such as carbonate, silicate, phosphate, or hydroxide; they usually contain in addition a surfactant (qv) and may contain chelators (see Complexing agents). The function of alkaline cleaners is to dislodge surface soil, principally by dispersing it in such form that it does not settle back on the work, and to some slight extent by saponifying the saponifiable oils and greases. (The role of actual saponification, formerly thought to be a major one, has been much belittled in more recent studies.) Alkaline cleaning may be accomplished by one of three techniques, and sometimes by a combination of them: soak, cathodic or direct, and anodic or reverse. The last two are included under the heading of electrolytic cleaning. Alkaline cleaners are invariably applied at elevated temperatures.

In soak cleaning the part is merely immersed in the cleaner, possibly with mild agitation. Better results are usually obtained by electrolytic cleaning, which adds to the detergent action of the solution the scrubbing action of gas evolution on the surface of the work. When the work is cathode (direct or cathodic cleaning), twice as much gas, in this case hydrogen, is evolved as when the work is anode (reverse or anodic cleaning), in which the gas evolved is oxygen. But there are other considerations: in cathodic cleaning one runs the risk that impurities in the cleaner may be deposited on the surface, or that the hydrogen may embrittle the basis metal. Anodic cleaning, on the other hand, may form oxides on the surface of susceptible materials. Often the two are combined: A longer cathodic period is followed by a shorter period with the work as anode.

Table 2. Cleaning Solutions[a]

	For ferrous metals[b]	For copper and brass[b]	For aluminum[c]
sodium carbonate, Na_2CO_3, g/liter	30–45	12–22	23
trisodium phosphate, $Na_3PO_4 \cdot 12H_2O$, g/liter	15–30	8–18	23
sodium hydroxide, NaOH, g/liter	7.5–15	3–12	
surfactant, g/liter		0.3–0.5	
current density, mA/cm^2	30–60	10–30	
time as cathode, min	1–2	1–3	
time as anode, sec	15–30	5–10	
soak time, min			1–3
temp, °C	at least 90	60–70	60–80

[a] Although compositions have been published for cleaning zinc-base die castings, most authorities (1,21) refer to proprietary solutions the composition of which is not disclosed.

[b] See reference 1.

[c] See reference 20.

Compositions of some typical cleaning solutions are given in Table 2. In most cases the plater will be better advised, however, to make use of one of the many proprietary formulations offered by manufacturers and distributors, unless his cleaning problem is of the simplest kind. These proprietaries can be tailored to the specific conditions, and have the further advantage of the availability of expert advice and service in the solving of problems.

The best cleaner will not do a good job if not properly maintained; it should not be, but often is, forgotten that since the function of a cleaner is to remove dirt, the cleaner itself gets dirty; thus, at intervals the cleaner must be dumped and replaced with fresh solution.

Although emphasis here has been on alkaline cleaners, other types have been developed and have their areas of usefulness. Emulsion and di-phase cleaners combine, to some extent, the functions of organic solvents and alkaline cleaners. Alkaline cleaning itself is often divided into two steps: so-called precleaning, utilizing "heavy-duty" cleaners to remove the bulk of the soil, followed by milder alkalies to finish the job. No single prescription can serve for all cases. Cleaners may be applied as jets or sprays impinging on the work, as well as by the more usual method of immersion.

Almost universally used as a test of adequate cleaning is the "water-break" test. Water-break is the gathering of a film of water into droplets or streaks, and its occurrence is a sign that the surface is not clean. Water will run off a clean surface in an unbroken sheet or film. The alkaline solution of a cleaner may mask this test, which should therefore preferably be applied after acid dipping, or it may even show up in later parts of the plating cycle. More sophisticated and delicate tests for surface contamination have been developed (22) but the water-break test remains in most general use.

The final test of good cleaning is the plating itself. It would be an exaggeration to say that most troubles in plating can be traced to improper cleaning; but it is no exaggeration to say that many of them can be, and that in troubleshooting in the plating shop, the cleaning cycle should be suspect until exonerated.

Rinsing. Adequate rinsing between all steps in cleaning and plating is of the utmost importance. Rinse waters should be clean and should not be allowed to become contaminated by drag-in of preceding solutions. Countercurrent rinsing is often employed as a means of conserving water while at the same time ensuring that the last rinse is relatively pure. Hot water is more efficient than cold for removing contaminants; on the other hand, it entails the risk that the work may dry off before entering the next operation. Quality of the available water supply is often of importance; softened or deionized water or condensate may be required for final rinses in many instances.

Acid Dipping. This is generally practiced after cleaning, and serves two purposes: It removes slight tarnish or oxide films formed in the cleaning step, and it neutralizes the alkaline film which even good rinsing cannot completely remove from the surface. It is thus particularly important when the plating solution is acid. The acid dip is usually a 10–30% by vol solution of hydrochloric or sulfuric acid, more usually the latter.

If plating is to be done in an alkaline solution, it is good practice to use an alkaline dip following the rinse after the acid dip. In general, when work is to proceed from an acid to an alkaline solution or vice versa, it is wise to insert a neutralizing dip between the two.

Drag-Out and Drag-In. Every solution in a plating cycle is contaminated, to a greater or less extent, by the solution that precedes it in the cycle. How serious this situation is depends on many factors, some controllable and some not. The shape of the parts and how they are positioned in the tank is of great importance, drain times vary, some solutions are more free-rinsing than others. Contamination caused by this drag-in may be serious or inconsequential: Thus, the introduction of a little alkali from a neutralizing dip into a cyanide plating bath is of little concern, but the introduction of chromate (from racks that have not been properly rinsed from a preceding cycle) into a nickel bath may cause havoc.

Drag-out, also, may be of great or little importance. Economic effects of the loss of a little copper sulfate solution are slight; but in gold plating every effort must be made to reclaim the metal from rinse waters. Drag-out can be positively beneficial, inasmuch as it helps to prevent the buildup of undesirable impurities in plating baths. Drag-out must also be considered in connection with the problem of waste disposal (see p. 51).

Special Preparation Cycles. For plating on the more usual substrates such as ferrous metals and copper and its alloys, the cycles briefly outlined above will usually suffice. Other substrates require more specialized treatment; they include aluminum and magnesium; zinc-base die castings; "refractory" metals like titanium, zirconium, tantalum, niobium, molybdenum, and tungsten; and nonmetallics like synthetic plastics, leather, wood, and plaster.

Aluminum and Magnesium. These metals are so active both chemically and electrochemically that ordinary preparative cycles would leave them in an entirely unsatisfactory condition for electroplating. (For analogous reasons, as already mentioned, plating on these metals may be subject to unusual corrosion hazards and such applications should be approached carefully.) The most usual methods of preparing these metals involve replacement of the naturally occurring oxide films with a thin film of zinc. This is effected simply by immersion in a solution of a zinc salt from which aluminum replaces zinc. Good results depend on proper cleaning before the zinc-immersion step as well as on the zinc-immersion film itself. After zincating, the first electroplate applied is copper, from a low pH Rochelle or pyrophosphate bath (see Table 5, p. 46); copper thickness is then built up in a "standard" copper bath, after which any desired deposits may be applied. Zinc-dip solutions are shown in Table 3.

Table 3. Zinc-Immersion Solutions for Plating on Aluminum[a]

	Regular	Modified I	Modified II	Modified III
NaOH (76% Na_2O), g/liter	525	525	50	120
ZnO (technical), g/liter	100	100	5	20
$FeCl_3.6H_2O$, g/liter		1.0	2	2
Rochelle salt,[b] g/liter		10	50	50
$NaNO_3$, g/liter			1	1
temp, °C	<27	<27	21–24	21–24
time, min	0.5–1	0.5–1	not >0.5	not >0.5

[a] See reference 20. [b] $KNaC_4H_4O_6.4H_2O$.

The "modified" zinc-immersion solutions in Table 3 have several advantages over the "standard" bath, particularly for some wrought and cast alloys. They are also recommended when the "double-immersion" treatment is used. In this modification the zinc film is dissolved off in nitric acid and the work put through the zinc-immersion cycle a second time.

Proprietary zinc-immersion processes are available. A process has been announced which uses tin rather than zinc to form the immersion film. Early results appear promising (23).

For plating on magnesium the work after cleaning is activated and zinc-immersion plated, followed by copper "striking" (electroplating a thin deposit of copper). Typical formulations are given in Table 4.

Table 4. Preparation of Magnesium for Plating

	Activating	Zinc immersion
H_3PO_4 (85%), % by vol	20	
NH_4HF_2, g/liter	100	
$Na_4P_2O_7$, g/liter		120
$ZnSO_4 \cdot H_2O$, g/liter		30
KF, g/liter		7
K_2CO_3, g/liter		5
temp, °C	28 ± 12	80–85
time, min	1–3	3–5

Zinc-Base Die Castings. Many of the problems in plating on zinc-base die castings have arisen from poor or porous castings, and as metallurgical techniques have improved these problems have disappeared or considerably decreased. After cleaning, zinc die castings are almost invariably plated with copper, first striking in a bath such as shown in Table 5. This may then be followed by any desired plate.

Table 5. Copper Strike Baths for Aluminum and Zinc-Base Die Castings

	Aluminum	Zinc-base
copper cyanide, g/liter	41	21–27
total NaCN, g/liter	49	
free NaCN, g/liter		11–17
Na_2CO_3, g/liter	30	15
NaOH, g/liter		4
Rochelle salt, g/liter	60	45
pH (electrometric)	10.2–10.5	11.5–12.2
temp, °C	38–54	50
current density, mA/cm²	25	20–25
time, min	2–5	2

Refractory Metals. The interest in plating on such metals as titanium, molybdenum, and niobium has arisen primarily from the needs of aerospace technology. Many of these metals possess desirable high-temperature properties but require protective coatings for adequate chemical resistance. For this and other reasons techniques have been worked out for electroplating on most of these metals, although some of the results still leave something to be desired. Each of the metals poses it own particular problems of surface preparation; for further details see references 1 and 24.

Nonmetallics. Plating on nonmetallics was formerly confined to the art of gilding bric-a-brac and baby shoes for sentimental or "artistic" reasons, but it has recently assumed considerable industrial importance, especially in the printed circuit field. Plastics are also being increasingly used as substrates for decorative plates for automotive hardware and similar applications (25).

The most important application for plating on nonmetallics involves plastics, and more specifically the so-called ABS (acrylonitrile–butadiene–styrene) plastics, as the substrate. The cycle includes the following steps: mechanical roughening, etching, and cleaning; sensitizing in a stannous chloride solution; nucleation or activation in a solution of palladium chloride; electroless copper plating; followed by building up of the copper thickness by standard methods and final plating in any desired bath. More recently it has been found possible to substitute for the first three steps a chemical conditioning treatment which has several advantages (25).

For other nonmetallics not adaptable to these procedures, shellac or varnish containing "bronze" powder or graphite may be painted on to provide a conducting surface, or metal spraying and sputtering can be used (1).

Engineering

The operations of electroplating, including the cleaning, rinsing, plating, and postplating treatments, can be carried on manually or with almost any desired degree of automation. Parts may be hung in the plating tank on wires or on racks; when many small parts are to be plated they may be contained in wire baskets or, more commonly, in barrels which rotate in the plating tank. Movement from one operation to another may be by hand or by machine.

The necessary dc power is derived from motor–generators or rectifiers (see Transistors and solid rectifiers); the latter are much the more popular of late, and may be of three types: selenium, germanium, or silicon. It seems likely that the last will soon dominate the field. Power is conveyed to the plating tanks by bus bars; the anodes are hung into the tank from the positive bus bar, usually along the two sides (see Fig. 1) and the work to be plated from the negative or cathode bar, usually down the center. Tank voltage is read from a voltmeter, and current from an ammeter: these two instruments should be available for each plating tank. A third instrument, an ampere-hour meter, is often helpful as a means of regulating the thickness of deposit and for general control of the operations.

Some degree of agitation of plating solutions or of the work is usually helpful, and this may be provided in many ways. The oldest and simplest consists of an operator merely swishing the work around at intervals, but automatic cathode rod agitation is preferable; in some automatic plating machines the work is moved through the solution while being plated. Provided clean air is used and the solution is not sensitive to oxygen or carbon dioxide, air agitation is convenient and efficient. Agitation may

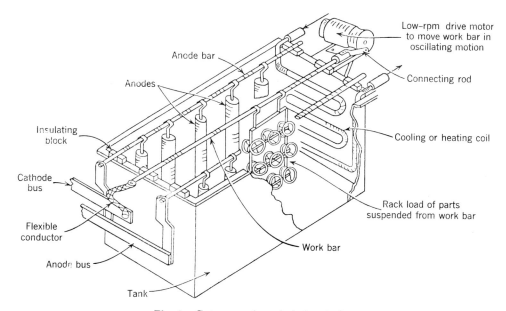

Fig 1. Cut-away view of plating tank.

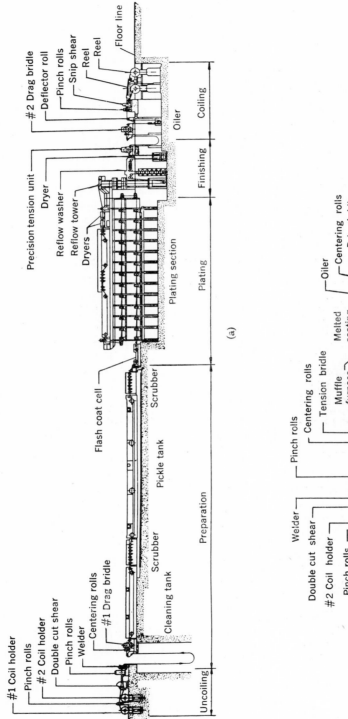

(a)

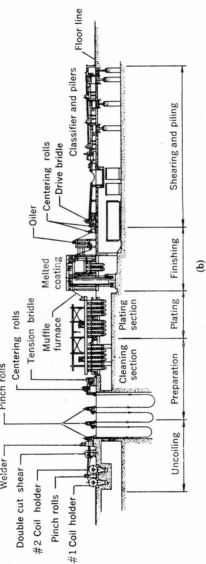

(b)

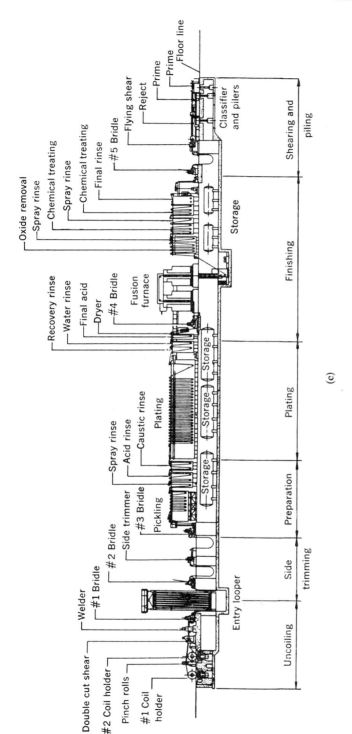

Fig. 2. Schematic diagrams of the three general types of electrolytic tinplate line. (**a**) A horizontal acid or "Halogen" line;   (**b**) a vertical acid or Ferrostan line;   and (**c**) an alkaline line. All are schematically to the same scale.   Courtesy Reinhold Publishing Corp.

be provided by stirring or pumping the solution; the latter is often necessary when heat exchangers are used for temperature control or where continuous filtration is required. In barrel plating agitation is supplied by the movement of the barrel.

Temperature control is almost always desirable in plating operations, because the characteristics of plating solutions, of the deposit, or of both usually depend to a large extent on the temperature of operation. Heating or cooling coils in the tank itself may be used, or the solution may be circulated through a heat exchanger; electric immersion heaters may be used; occasionally plating tanks are heated by open gas flames beneath the tank.

Figure 1 shows a cut-away view of a typical plating tank, but there are many variations on this basic design; instead of two anode and one cathode bars, there may be three anode and two cathode, etc. If tanks are of bare metal, they should be well insulated from the floor and other precautions should be taken against stray currents, which may be very troublesome and extremely difficult to trace.

In addition to the basic equipment—power source, plating, cleaning, and rinsing tanks, and bus bars—most plating installations require one or more of the following: filters, for either continuous or intermittent purification of solutions; drying facilities, which may range from a simple jet of compressed air to large ovens; racks of design appropriate to the part being plated, and a racking station where the work may be conveniently hung on these racks and unracked after plating; one or more stripping tanks for stripping faulty deposits so that parts can be reworked, and for stripping the plating racks themselves; reclaim tanks if the drag-out is valuable and worth reclaiming; portable pumps for transferring solutions; and at least one empty tank so that a plating tank can be emptied and worked on.

Continuous Plating. Electrolytic processes are well adapted to plating continuous coils of strip or wire, in which the substrate is uncoiled, pickled, cleaned, plated, given postplating treatments, and re-coiled in one continuous operation. The manufacture of electrolytic tinplate by the steel mills is the largest and best developed of these processes, but continuous plating of strip and wire with zinc, copper, and other metals is also extensively practiced. Equipment is highly specialized; solutions may be conventional or, as in the case of the "Halogen" process for tinplate, especially adapted to the application. It is not necessary that continuous plating be done on the enormous scale of the tinning lines of the steel mills (see Fig. 2); wire and narrow strip are economically plated for special applications on a very modest scale.

The *economics* of plating operations is a controversial and not very well investigated subject. Except where the deposited metal is very expensive, eg, gold, the actual cost of the deposited metal is generally considered to be a minor factor in the total cost of plating, and power cost is even less important. It is, of course, cheaper to plate zinc at 15¢/lb than cadmium at $3.00, but the difference is not twenty times. Overhead and labor are the major factors; thus it is more important, economically, to deposit the required plate quickly and satisfactorily—to produce the most work in the least space with the fewest rejects—than to economize on supplies or power. It must be admitted, however, that cost accounting procedures for the plating trade have not been well developed, at least in the published literature.

Safety. Hazards in plating operations arise from the nature of the materials routinely handled, many of them highly toxic. Thus, certain minimum precautions are absolutely necessary. Many of the cleaning, plating, and pickling steps evolve fumes and spray, which must be vented without being permitted to come in contact with workers. Chromic acid spray is highly irritating to nasal mucosa, as is caustic spray, fumes from vapor degreasing are toxic, and many solutions cause dermatitic reactions. Fluoborates and fluorides must not come in contact with skin; cyanide solutions, normally alkaline, should never come in contact with acids. Most of the normal hazards of a plating room can be adequately handled by a combination of proper ventilation and appropriate protective clothing. Most State Labor Departments have definite codes, which should be consulted, specifying the maximum limits of various contaminants which are permitted in the air of the work place. Because of the low voltages employed, electrical hazards in plating are not usually of concern.

Waste Disposal. Drag-out of solutions into rinse waters which finally find their way to the sewer inevitably contaminates the effluents from plating departments; and occasionally it will almost certainly be necessary to "dump" a solution which is beyond possibility of being restored to satisfactory condition. Cyanides, copper, and chromium compounds are the most troublesome contaminants to dispose of. Local regulations will govern the seriousness of the problem, but it can be said that these are, in general, becoming (justifiably) more and more stringent as time goes on. Wastes may either be diluted to a nonobjectionable concentration or chemically treated to render them harmless. Dilution is effective but wasteful of water and very expensive; the effectiveness and economics of chemical treatment vary with the contaminant and its concentration. It is obvious that the subject of waste disposal is very closely related to that of good and efficient rinsing.

Because of the imminence of tighter governmental regulation, this subject is very active in current literature, which should be checked for up-to-date information.

Materials of Construction. Plating tanks and auxiliary equipment are constructed of materials resistant to the particular solution involved; in effect this usually means plain steel for alkaline solutions and rubber- or synthetic-lined steel for acid solutions. In using steel tanks the possibility of "bipolar" effects must be kept in mind, ie, since the tank is a conductor, it may become interposed in the electrical circuit. The path anode–tank–cathode may be electrically shorter than the path anode–cathode, and this may have various unwanted side effects. In choosing linings for use with acid solutions, also, several factors must be considered: The heat resistance of the lining must be adequate for the temperature of operation of the solution; and some plating solutions, notably the bright nickels, are sensitive to the materials which may be leached out of the lining. Chromium plating solutions, because of their highly oxidizing nature, require special care in the selection of lining materials; various lead alloys and brick are also commonly used.

Some of the newer "refractory" metals are being made use of to some extent in designing plating equipment: Tantalum heating coils and titanium racks and anode baskets are examples. Advances in plastics are also having their effect, in improved lining materials having better heat resistance, plating barrels with higher mechanical strength, etc.

Plating Solutions

General Considerations. Almost without exception, plating solutions are aqueous. Aluminum is plated on a semicommercial scale from organic electrolytes and fused salts, and some of the refractory metals, tungsten, molybdenum, tantalum, and niobium, have been deposited from fused electrolytes.   Except for strictly laboratory procedures, these are the only present exceptions to the opening statement.

Every plating solution contains ingredients to perform at least the first, and usually several, of the following functions:

1. Provide a source of ions of the metal(s) to be deposited.
2. Form complexes with ions of the depositing metal.
3. Provide conductivity.
4. Stabilize the solution against hydrolysis or other forms of decomposition.
5. Stabilize (buffer) the pH of the solution.
6. Regulate the physical form of the deposit.
7. Aid in anode corrosion (see below under Anodes).
8. Modify other properties peculiar to the solution involved.

This is not to say that all plating solutions are made up of eight ingredients, because many compounds perform more than one of the stated functions.   As an example, a typical nickel-plating bath contains nickel sulfate and nickel chloride, both of which provide nickel ions and the necessary conductivity; the chloride aids in anode corrosion.   Boric acid is added to buffer the solution; and small amounts of organic addition agents regulate the physical form and properties of the deposit.

The sections that follow contain brief descriptions of the processes for plating the commercial metals.   All of the baths are characterized by certain properties about which the plater will want information for proper control of his operations.

Current Density Range.   Current density is the average current in amperes divided by the area through which that current passes; the area is usually nominal area, since the true area for any but extremely smooth electrodes is seldom known. Units used in this chapter are milliamperes per square centimeter (mA/cm^2) which is almost equal to the more common commercial unit of amperes per square foot (as for A/ft^2).   (Accurately, one $mA/cm^2 = 0.929 \ A/ft^2$.)   Current densities at the anode and cathode are both important; they may differ considerably although not by so large a factor as to make necessary very great differences between the anode area and the cathode area.   Most solutions exhibit a range of current densities within which deposits are satisfactory and outside of which they are not; for bright plating solutions this is called the "bright range."   At the anode also, too high a current density may passivate the anode, and too low a current density may cause the metal to dissolve in an unwanted valence state.   Other factors being equal, the higher the current density obtainable, the faster the plating rate and thus, in general, the more economical the operation; but this generalization is subject to many individual modifications.

Throwing Power.   Except in the special case where the anode and cathode are concentric, the current density over the electrodes will vary from point to point; in general the areas on the cathode nearest to the anode will receive a higher current density than those more remote.   Thus more metal will be plated on the projections than in the recesses.   Many plating solutions, however, have the ability to ameliorate this condition to some degree, and "throwing power" may be defined as the improvement in metal distribution over primary current distribution on a cathode.   (Primary current distribution is the distribution of current that depends only on the geometry of the cell.)   This concept is qualitative rather than quantitative, because all methods of measuring throwing power are open to various theoretical objections; in addition, throwing power is a function not only of the solution but also of many other operating variables. Nevertheless the property is real enough, and plating solutions may be categorized as having excellent, good, poor, or negative throwing power.

Acidity. Plating baths are either acid, neutral, or alkaline, and for most of them close control of the pH is essential to successful operation. Acid solutions include acid copper and tin and the various fluoborate baths; since most of these contain substantial amounts of free acid, pH control is not usually required. "Neutral" solutions (pH from about 5 to 8) include nickel and some of the pyrophosphate baths; and alkaline baths include most of the cyanide formulations as well as stannate tin. The last-named bath is controlled not by determining the pH but by titration for free alkali.

Anodes. Anodes in a plating bath perform two functions: They act as the positive electrode, introducing current into the solution, and in most cases they replenish the metal deposited at the cathode, thus maintaining the balance of the bath. Exceptions to the latter include chromium plating and some of the precious metals, where the bath must be replenished chemically.

Anodic replenishment is often the factor placing an upper limit on the usable current density, and for ultra-high speed plating some recent installations have deliberately chosen to use insoluble anodes with outside chemical replenishment (26).

Anodes may be a source of difficulty if they produce slimes and sludges as they corrode. To keep the particles thus formed from reaching the cathode, anodes are often bagged in fabric such as cotton duck or nylon. Diaphragm cells are also in use.

Temperature. Control of temperature is important in almost all plating processes; each solution is characterized by a range of temperatures within which it gives best results. Temperature affects almost all the variables of the solution: conductivity, current efficiencies, nature of the deposit, and stability.

Current Efficiency. Faraday's laws predict the amount of metal which will be deposited at the cathode or dissolved at the anode, but these amounts are not always realized; the deficiency is due to evolution of hydrogen at the cathode, oxygen at the anode, or other side reactions. In practical plating operations, current efficiency is not usually of direct concern so long as it is known, but it is often important to equalize the efficiencies at cathode and anode so that the bath remains in balance.

Purity. Plating processes differ in sensitivity to the presence of impurities in the bath. Stannate tin is extremely tolerant of most impurities; bright nickel and most zinc-plating solutions quite sensitive. Specific means are available for purifying most plating baths by chemical treatment; filtration through activated carbon is a generally useful method for removing organic contaminants. Another common technique for purifying solutions is the process known as dummying, which consists of plating for a period of time and usually at low current densities upon cathodes which are not intended for use, such as pieces of scrap sheet steel. This low-current-density electrolysis plates out metallic impurities or decomposes some organic contaminants.

A universal ingredient of all alkaline baths is carbonate, formed from decomposition of cyanides or pickup of CO_2 from the air. Since carbonate is always present in these baths it can hardly be classed as an impurity, but it may have deleterious effects in some baths if present at excessive levels. Several methods are available for removing excess carbonate; from baths formulated with sodium salts, advantage can be taken of the lowered solubility of sodium carbonate decahydrate at low temperatures, and it may be frozen out by cooling to about 0°C. This expedient is not effective with potassium baths and methods based upon the addition of lime, calcium sulfate, or barium cyanide have been used (27). With alkaline stannate baths the carbonate is of little moment and can be allowed to build up until drag-out removes it as fast as it is formed.

One possible method of purification is filtration, since solid particles may interfere with satisfactory plating by being trapped in the deposit. Depending on circumstances, baths are filtered continuously during operation, or intermittently either as need arises or on a definite schedule. Filtration is often combined with treatment with activated carbon. Some baths, particularly if used only intermittently, may be clarified by settling; care is taken not to disturb the bottom few inches in the plating tank, and occasionally the tank is emptied and the sludge shoveled out.

Bright Plating. Most deposits from simple plating solutions are matter, unless the substrate is bright and the plate very thin. If the use is purely functional this is no drawback, but for decorative purposes obviously a bright appearance is desired. This brightness was formerly obtained by mechanical treatment, buffing after plating, but today most metals can be bright as they come from the bath, and require little or no further treatment, at least as regards appearance. This bright appearance is produced by the addition to the plating bath of small amounts of one or more "addition agents" or brighteners, usually organic compounds; most such agents are covered by patents and the processes are proprietary. The most thoroughly investigated of the bright plating processes is bright nickel; the patent literature is voluminous and many processes are marketed. Copper, silver, gold, zinc, cadmium, brass, and bronze can also be plated bright; tin is usually brightened when required by "reflowing," which consists of, heating the deposit slightly above its melting point and quenching. Matte deposits may also be brightened by posttreatment in bright dips.

The mechanism by which minute amounts of specific organic compounds so markedly change the character of the deposit has not been thoroughly elucidated, in spite of a great deal of effort and a copious literature.

Maintenance of Plating Baths (28). All plating baths require more or less chemical control. They must be analyzed, often or seldom, depending on individual circumstances, and adjustments made. For some baths a determination of specific gravity suffices for routine control, whereas other baths require frequent and complete analysis (29).

A very useful tool in control is the Hull cell test. This patented cell consists of a trapezoidal box of nonconducting material with electrodes so arranged that by performing one plating experiment the operator can observe the characteristics of the deposit over a range of current densities; from his experience with the bath he can often draw accurate inferences regarding its condition, whether adjustments are needed, and if so, of what kind.

When the need for chemical additions is shown, these should usually be made gradually, with thorough stirring, and in liquid form; addition of solid materials to a bath is usually bad practice. Some automatic machines can be set up to feed needed additions continuously or intermittently on a preset schedule.

INDIVIDUAL PLATING BATHS

In addition to the bath compositions presented in the following paragraphs, most metals can be plated from proprietary solutions, the compositions of which are secret, or patented, or both. In many cases, exemplified by the bright nickel processes, the principal ingredients are well known and standard but the additives are proprietary. Use of proprietary processes has both advantages and disadvantages which must be weighed in each case; such processes cannot, for obvious reasons, be discussed here. The formulas presented should be regarded as typical, and many modifications are in satisfactory use; for the effect of changes in composition, impurities, and other details, monographs on electroplating should be consulted.

Cadmium affords good corrosion protection to steel and other substrates in marine atmospheres; it is readily solderable, and has a relatively pleasing appearance. It may be plated bright, semibright, or matte, depending on the addition agents used. Corrosion resistance may be enhanced by chromate conversion coatings. Disadvantages of cadmium include its extremely poisonous nature and its high cost; in recent years shortages have plagued the supply situation.

Cadmium is usually plated from cyanide solutions such as that shown in Table 6. Additional carbonate is formed during operation by decomposition of cyanide and absorption of CO_2 from the air. In amounts up to about 75 g/liter this is not harmful, but excessive amounts should be eliminated.

Table 6. Cadmium-Plating Bath

	Still plating	Barrel plating
CdO, g/liter	25–35	17–23
Cd metal, g/liter	20–30	15–20
NaCN, g/liter	90–120	70–90
NaOH, as formed by the reaction $CdO + 4 NaCN + H_2O \rightarrow Na_2Cd(CN)_4 + 2 NaOH$		
addition agents	qs	qs
cathode current density, mA/cm²	. . . . 5–50	
anode current density, mA/cm²	. . . . .not >20.	
temp, °C	. . . . .20–35.	
throwing power	. . . . good.	

In the plating of high-strength steels, cadmium from cyanide baths embrittles the steel, and sometimes this cannot be relieved by the usual baking treatments. Fluoborate and other solutions have been developed to overcome this defect; but except for these special cases the cyanide bath is almost universally used.

Chromium is the plate most familiar to the public, as the final finish on the great majority of plated consumer items. As "hard" chromium it also has a host of engineering uses. The chromium plating process is unique in several respects, and it vies with nickel in capturing the attention of research workers. Although chromium can be deposited from solutions of chromium(III) salts, such baths are not practical for plating purposes and solutions of chromic acid (chromium trioxide, CrO_3) are used exclusively. In order to permit the deposition of chromium, a small amount of another anion, called a catalyst (typically sulfate) is essential; the ratio CrO_3/H_2SO_4 is usually about 100:1 (by weight), although for special purposes it can be varied from 50:1 to 150:1 or more.

There have been many recent developments in chromium plating; they may be summarized as (1) improvements in the plating process itself and (2) greater knowl-

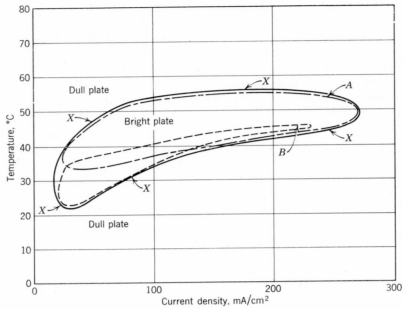

Fig. 3. Chart of bright plating conditions.

edge of the role of chromium in the nickel/chromium composite, which has led to dramatically improved performance.

(1) In addition to the "conventional" chromic acid–sulfate bath, there are now available several proprietary processes possessing such advantages as better throwing power, higher efficiency, and easier control. These advantages result at least in part from the use of catalyst anions other than sulfate, such as fluoride and fluosilicate.

(2) The final very thin chromium deposit was long thought to be merely a tarnish preventive, having little effect on the corrosion resistance of the composite. It has recently been shown, however, that the structure and thickness of the chromium have far-reaching effects. Conventionally, the thickness of chromium in the nickel/chromium composite has been specified as 0.13–0.4 μ, with an average of 0.25 μ (10 micro-inches). Dramatic improvement in performance has been gained by increasing this thickness to 0.63–1.25 μ (0.025–0.05 mil); further, the chromium may be advantageously either crackfree, or micro-cracked, or combinations of these. The nature of the underlying nickel interacts with the structure and thickness of the chromium in rather complicated ways. No final verdict has been reached as to the best combinations, but it can be said as of 1964 that the performance of present chromium plate over nickel is greatly improved as compared to that obtained as little as three years ago (30–38).

For the reasons stated, the typical bath compositions given should be considered only as guides; for maximum performance the current literature and the vendors of proprietary processes should be consulted.

	Dilute bath (no. 1)	Concentrated bath (no. 2)
chromic acid, g/liter	250	400
sulfuric acid, g/liter	2.5	4

The current density for bright plating and the temperature are interrelated. A convenient chart is shown in Figure 3. In this figure the dot-and-dash line *A* circumscribes the bright plate area for dilute solutions and the dashed line *B* circumscribes the bright plate area for concentrated solutions.

In addition to its decorative uses, chromium plating is widely used as an engineering process, for its great hardness and excellent bearing properties. This so-called "hard" chromium plating is not different in principle from decorative plating, but because of the greater thicknesses employed certain problems are magnified: The long plating times entail the danger of etching the basis metal in low-current-density areas, and the close control of the physical and mechanical properties of the deposit requires more care in the entire cycle (39).

The benefit of the hardness of chromium deposits is not obtained unless the basis metal is sufficiently hard and the coating thickness satisfactory. Even a heavy deposit of chromium may be crushed or indented if applied over a soft basis metal such as copper. Table 7 gives basis metal hardnesses and thicknesses of chromium plate suggested for different applications.

Table 7. Basis Metal Hardness and Thickness of Hard Chromium

Application	Hardness, Rockwell C	Chromium thickness, mil
drills	62–64	0.05–0.5
reamers	62–64	0.1–0.5
burnishing bars	60–62	0.5–3.0
drawing plugs or mandrels	60–62	1.5–8.0
drawing dies	62 inside, 45 outside	0.5–8.0
plastic molds	55–60	0.2–2.0
gages	48–58	0.1–1.5
pump shafts	55–62	0.5–3.0
rolls and drums		0.25–12.0
hydraulic rams		0.5–4.0
printing plates (engraved steel)		0.2–0.5

Unlike most plating baths, chromium plating does not employ anodes of the depositing metal. Anodes are usually of lead–antimony or lead–tin alloy, although many other types have been recommended. Anode area is important principally because it determines the proportion of trivalent chromium in the bath.

Current efficiency of a chromium plating solution is low: 8–12% for "conventional" baths; as high as 20% for some of the newer proprietary solutions. Efficiency tends to increase with current density, and this leads to the notoriously poor throwing power of these baths as compared with most other metals. The low efficiency also entails the copious evolution of hydrogen, causing spray which must be vented for safety of operators, although spray suppressants are now available which greatly alleviate this problem. Low efficiency and unusually small electrochemical equivalent ($52/6 = 8.7$ g/faraday) combine to require abnormally long plating times for deposits of the thicknesses used in "hard" chromium plating. Table 8 (39) indicates average plating conditions.

In spite of all the disadvantages inherent in chromium plating, it enjoys as widespread use as any plating process, proof enough of its unique properties.

Table 8. Typical Chromium-Plating Conditions

	Decorative plates	Hard chromium	
CrO_3, g/liter	250–400	250	400
H_2SO_4, g/liter	2.5–4	2.5	4
cathode current density, mA/cm^2	125–175	310	220
temp, °C	38–43	55	50
deposition rate, mil/hr	0.3–0.5	1.0	0.5

Cobalt plating is little used, since for general purposes it seems to have no advantage over nickel and is more expensive. The magnetic properties of its alloys have made them of interest in computer technology; alloys with nickel, molybdenum, phosphorus, iron, and tungsten in particular have been investigated. Typical plating baths are shown in Table 9.

Table 9. Cobalt-Plating Solutions

	Sulfate	Chloride	Ammonium sulfate
$CoSO_4.7H_2O$, g/liter	330–565		
$CoCl_2.6H_2O$, g/liter	45 (optional)	300–430	
$Co(NH_4)_2(SO_4)_2.6H_2O$, g/liter			175–200
H_3BO_3, g/liter	30–45	30–45	25–30
NaCl or KCl, g/liter	17–25 (optional)		
H_2SO_4 or HCl to pH	3.0–5.0	2.3–4.0	5.0–5.2
temp, °C	35–38	52–71	25
cathode current density, mA/cm^2	22–50	50–65	10–30

Copper, although sometimes used as a final finish, is more often applied as an undercoat for other metals. As such it has a wide variety of uses and is very extensively employed in the industry. Many different types of plating bath are available, both open and proprietary. Copper may be deposited matte, or with appropriate brightening agents either semi- or fully bright. It is easily buffed to a high luster; this property accounts for its widespread use as a coating on steel to be followed by other deposits, since by this means scratch marks and other defects in the steel are more readily covered than by working on the steel itself. It is universally used in plating on zinc-base die castings as the basis for further coatings.

The relative merits of copper/nickel/chromium vs nickel/chromium deposits on steel for automotive service are still debatable; various test programs have given somewhat inconsistent results, which appear to depend to some extent on the nature of the nickel deposits.

The areas of application of the various copper plating solutions overlap somewhat, but each has fairly well-defined areas of usefulness. The cyanide bath is used for "copper-striking" steel preparatory to further plating with acid copper, and for the initial plate on zinc-base die castings. Its plating rate is rather low, but it is fairly easily controlled in operation. The Rochelle bath is similar to the cyanide, but additions of Rochelle salt permit higher operating current densities. Still higher speeds of operation are possible in the "high-speed" baths, in which some or all of the sodium salts are replaced by potassium. Proprietary materials are available which claim advantages over Rochelle salt, and brighteners may also be used.

Current manipulation techniques such as PR (periodic reversal of the current) and current interruption are useful in improving the plating characteristics of the high-efficiency baths. Table 10 gives typical formulas.

Table 10. Cyanide Copper Plating

	Strike	Rochelle	High-efficiency
CuCN, g/liter	15	26	75
NaCN, g/liter	23	35	93
or			
KCN, g/liter			115
Na_2CO_3, g/liter	15	30	
NaOH, g/liter			30
or			
KOH, g/liter			42
Rochelle salt, g/liter		45	optional
by analysis			
Cu, g/liter	11	19	53
free cyanide, g/liter	6	6	10
pH		12.6	
temp, °C	40–60	55–70	60–80
cathode current density,			
mA/cm^2	10–30	15–65	10–110
anode current density,			
mA/cm^2	5–10	8–33	15–40
efficiency range, %			
cathode	10–60	30–70	99+
anode	95–100	50–70	99+
bath voltage, V	6	6	0.75–4
limiting thickness, mil	0.1	0.5	no limit

Pyrophosphate solutions find applications in the plating of printed circuits (40); their freedom from cyanide has made them of interest where waste disposal is a problem (see Table 11).

Although it cannot be used directly on steel, the copper sulfate bath is widely employed because it is inexpensive, plates rapidly, and is easily controlled. For building up heavy deposits the work is first "struck" in a cyanide bath and then transferred to the

Table 11. Pyrophosphate Copper Bath

$Cu_2P_2O_7$, g/liter	75
$K_4P_2O_7$, g/liter	260
KNO_3, g/liter	15
NH_3, g/liter	2
pH	8.2–8.8
ratio $P_2O_7^{4-}/Cu^{2+}$	7–8
temp, °C	50–60
cathode current density, mA/cm^2	10–80
agitation (required)	air
current efficiency, %	ca 100

sulfate. Brighteners are available for this bath also. Another acid bath, the fluoborate, has advantages in speed of deposition, in spite of its higher initial cost.

Acid copper baths are extensively used in electroforming, including electrotyping, and in wire plating and many other engineering applications. Typical formulations are shown in Table 12. Physical and mechanical properties of electroformed copper have been reported (13).

Table 12. Acid Copper Plating

	Sulfate bath	Fluoborate bath
$CuSO_4.5H_2O$, g/liter	188	
H_2SO_4, g/liter	74	
$Cu(BF_4)_2$, g/liter		220–440
HBF_4, g/liter		15–30
H_3BO_3, g/liter		15–30
temp, °C	30–45	30–45
cathode current density, mA/cm²ᵃ	10–100	10–400

ᵃ Very much higher current densities are obtainable under conditions of violent agitation.

Gold plating has emerged from the category of purely decorative use on jewelry and flatware, to become extremely important in electronics and in space-oriented applications. The number of special-purpose baths for both pure gold and numerous gold alloys has also multiplied, so that gold and its alloys can now be plated with almost any desired combination of properties such as hardness, ductility, and electrical characteristics. Almost all of these developments have been proprietary. The high cost of the metal, obviously, requires that drag-out recovery systems be employed and that other economic safeguards be instituted, including those against theft. Some typical cyanide baths are given in Table 13. Many other compositions are in use, de-

Table 13. Typical Cyanide Gold-Plating Solutions

bath no.	1	2	3	4
metallic gold, g/liter	1.0	2.0	4.0	8.0
free KCN, g/liter	0.1–15	15	30	20
K_2HPO_4, g/liter	15	15	30	20
K_2CO_3, g/liter			30	20
pH	10–11.5	11–11.5	11–11.5	11–11.5
temp, °C		55–70		
cathode current density, mA/cm²		1–10		

pending on the purpose of the deposit. Alloying elements used to control the color and physical properties of the plate include antimony, tin, nickel, copper, silver, and cobalt.

Indium is soft and tarnish resistant, and has uses in bearings, usually in combination with silver or lead. It may be plated from cyanide, sulfate, or sulfamate solutions (see Table 14). Cyanide baths are preferred in spite of the better efficiency of the sulfamate and other baths.

Iron is not used for decorative or protective purposes, but does have applications in electroforming and for other engineering uses. Many baths have been proposed for iron plating; all contain iron in the iron(II) (ferrous) oxidation state. The ferrous

Table 14. Indium-Plating Baths

	Cyanide	High-pH cyanide	Sulfamate
In metal, g/liter	30–60[a]	15–30[a]	2.0[b]
D-glucose, g/liter	15–30	20–30	
NaCN, g/liter	150		
KCN, g/liter		140–160	
KOH, g/liter		30–40	
pH (adjusted with sulfuric acid)			0.2
anodes	Pt or graphite	Fe or steel	In
cathode current density, mA/cm²	10–160	10–40	20–100
temp, °C	20–30	20–30	20–30
current efficiency, %	50	50	90

[a] As freshly precipitated hydroxide.   [b] As sulfamate.

sulfate and ferrous ammonium sulfate baths can be operated at room temperature; the hot chloride bath requires elevated temperatures but can yield more ductile deposits. Physical and mechanical properties of the deposit depend strongly on the operating conditions. Typical formulations are shown in Table 15, but many variations are possible.

Table 15. Iron-Plating Baths

	Sulfate	Hot chloride	Fluoborate	Electrotype Chloride	Electrotype Sulfate–chloride
FeSO$_4$(NH$_4$)$_2$SO$_4$.6H$_2$O, g/liter	350				
FeCl$_2$.4H$_2$O, g/liter		300		240	42
Fe(BF$_4$)$_2$, g/liter			225		
FeSO$_4$.7H$_2$O, g/liter					250
NH$_4$Cl, g/liter					20
CaCl$_2$, g/liter		335			
NaCl, g/liter			10		
KCl, g/liter				180	
temp, °C	25/60	90	55–60	25–40	40–43
pH	2.8–3.4	0.8–1.5	2.0–3.0	5.0–5.5	3.5–5.5
cathode current density, mA/cm²	20/75	65	20–100	20–50	50–100

Lead is plated from fluoborate solutions (see Table 16); fluosilicate and sulfamate solutions are also in use. It finds application in battery parts and chemical construction, particularly for its resistance to sulfuric acid. It is more corrosion resistant than would be expected from its position in the emf series, because in most atmospheres pores tend to fill with insoluble corrosion products which prevent further attack. ASTM specifications for lead on steel are shown in Table 1. More widely used than pure lead deposits are the lead–tin alloys of varying composition. They are useful in bearings, in the 90:10 lead/tin range, and for solderability in the 50:50 range. Plating baths are similar to those for lead plating, with the addition of tin(II) (stannous) fluoborate (see Table 16).

Table 16. Lead and Lead–Tin Alloy Plating

	Lead	50% tin	10% tin
lead, g/liter	120	27	90
stannous tin, g/liter		61	10
free HBF_4, g/liter	30	48	38
H_3BO_3, g/liter	13		
animal glue or gelatin, g/liter	0.2		1.0
peptone,[c] g/liter		5.1	
temp, °C	25–40	25–40	25–40
cathode current density, mA/cm²	5–50[a]	12[b]	12

[a] By doubling the concentrations of the constituents of this bath (except the glue) current densities can be raised to 70 mA/cm² for faster plating and heavier deposits.

[b] By raising the current density to 55 mA/cm² the tin content is increased to about 63%.

[c] A grade of processed albumin.

Nickel shares with chromium the distinction of having been the subject of the most intensive and extensive research efforts, on all levels from the practical to the highly theoretical, of all the plating metals. It has almost innumerable uses, it is plated in all thicknesses from a mere "flash" to many millimeters, and there are available many different plating baths, each with its own advantages and limitations.

Most nickel-plating baths of today are based on the bath originally formulated by O. P. Watts and accordingly called the Watts bath (see Table 17). Hydrogen peroxide may be added to the Watts bath to prevent hydrogen pitting; this additive cannot be used in the "bright" and "semi-bright" modifications of the Watts bath, and for these some type of surfactant such as sodium lauryl sulfate is substituted for the peroxide.

For most decorative plating, the various bright, semi-bright, and leveling solutions have almost completely superseded the plain Watts bath, which yields a matte deposit. These baths, for the most part, are Watts solutions to which organic compounds are added in relatively small amounts to produce deposits which may be sufficiently bright, as plated, to require no buffing before final chromium plating. Other additives are capable of yielding deposits that can fill in minor scratches and other imperfections in the basis metal, a property known as leveling.

The number of organic compounds which are capable of modifying the deposit in this way is legion, and the patent literature is extremely voluminous. Most of them, however, are impractical because they have concomitant disadvantages, such as instability or deleterious effects on the physical or mechanical properties of the deposit, so that the number of commercially used brighteners is small relative to the number of patents. This field is almost entirely proprietary.

For maximum resistance to corrosion, recent work has pointed up the advantages of so-called duplex nickel, which consists of a layer of semi-bright, sulfurfree leveling nickel followed by a thinner layer of fully bright sulfur-containing deposit; the sulfur originates from the brightener. Table 1 includes specifications for duplex nickel.

In a recently proposed, further modification of the Watts bath finely divided insoluble materials are suspended in the bath; these are occluded in the deposit and since they are nonconducting, the final chromium plate has a "microporous" pattern which is said to be favorable to the corrosion resistance of the composite (41).

Table 17. Nickel Baths for Heavy Plating

Type	Ingredients[a]	Concentration, g/liter	pH (electrometric)	Temperature, °C	Cathode current density,[b] mA/cm²	Hardness (Vickers)	Tensile strength, kg/cm²	Tensile strength, psi	Elongation, %	Residual stress, kg/cm²	Residual stress, psi
Watts	nickel sulfate, $NiSO_4 \cdot 7H_2O$	330	1.5–4.5	45–65	25–100	140–160	3850	55,000	30	1260	18,000
	nickel chloride, $NiCl_2 \cdot 6H_2O$	45									
	boric acid, H_3BO_3	38									
hard	nickel sulfate, $NiSO_4 \cdot 7H_2O$	180	5.6–5.9	43–60	20–100	350–500	10,500	150,000	5–8	3080	44,000
	ammonium chloride, NH_4Cl	25									
	boric acid, H_3BO_3	30									
chloride	nickel chloride, $NiCl_2 \cdot 6H_2O$	300	2.0	50–70	25–100	230–260	7000	100,000	20	2800–3500	40,000–50,000
	boric acid, H_3BO_3	38									
chloride–sulfate	nickel sulfate, $NiSO_4 \cdot 7H_2O$	200	1.5–2.0	45	25–100						
	nickel chloride, $NiCl_2 \cdot 6H_2O$	175									
	boric acid, H_3BO_3	40									
chloride–acetate	nickel chloride, $NiCl_2 \cdot 6H_2O$	135	4.5–4.9	30–50	20–100	350	14,000	200,000	10		
	nickel acetate, $Ni(C_2H_3O_2)_2 \cdot 4H_2O$	105									
nickel–cobalt	nickel sulfate, $NiSO_4 \cdot 7H_2O$	240	4.7	40	50	450–500				1050–1190	15,000–17,000
	nickel chloride, $NiCl_2 \cdot 6H_2O$	22.5									
	boric acid, H_3BO_3	30									
	ammonium sulfate, $(NH_4)_2SO_4$	1.5									
	nickel formate, $Ni(CHO_2)_2 \cdot 2H_2O$	15									
	cobalt sulfate, $CoSO_4 \cdot 7H_2O$	2.6									
fluoborate	nickel (as fluoborate)	75	2.0–3.5 (colorimetric)	40–80	40–100	183	5250	75,000	15–30	1120	16,000
	free fluoboric acid, HBF_4	3.7–37.5									
	free boric acid, H_3BO_3	30									
sulfamate	nickel sulfamate, $Ni(NH_2SO_3)_2$	450	3.0–5.0	40–60	20–300	250–350	6300	90,000	20–30	35	500
	boric acid, H_3BO_3	30									
sulfamate–chloride	nickel sulfamate, $Ni(NH_2SO_3)_2$	300	3.5–4.2	28–60	20–250	190	7560	108,000	15–20	105	1500
	nickel chloride, $NiCl_2 \cdot 6H_2O$	6									
	boric acid, H_3BO_3	30									

[a] An antipitting agent is normally used in these baths.   [b] Higher current densities can be used with increasing rate of agitation.

Nickel has a host of engineering uses, including especially electroforming (13), in which its physical and mechanical properties are of greater importance than its appearance. These properties can be varied over a fairly wide range by manipulation of the bath composition, including additives, and operating conditions. Although the Watts bath is used for these applications, many other types have advantages for specific purposes (see Table 17). In particular the sulfamate solutions are being increasingly used, and are beginning to invade the field of decorative plating as well.

Of the **platinum group** metals, the most commonly used in plating is *rhodium*. In addition to its decorative applications, rhodium has electrical and optical properties which make it useful for electrical contacts and for reflectors. Typical formulas are shown in Table 18. The metal content of these baths is derived from prepared solutions, and replenishment is also chemical. Anodes of the depositing metal are inert.

Table 18. Rhodium Sulfate Baths

	Thin plates	Heavy plates
rhodium (in prepared solution), g/liter	2	10–20
sulfuric acid, conc, ml/liter	20	20–100
temp, °C	40–45	50
current density, mA/cm²	10–100	5–20

In addition to the sulfate baths shown, baths based on phosphates and mixed sulfate–phosphate systems can be used.

In addition to rhodium, *platinum* and *palladium* have some applications in plating; ruthenium and iridium can be deposited but find little use (42). Only osmium has been entirely neglected by the electroplater.

Silver is deposited from cyanide baths exclusively; modern formulations differ only in detail from the earliest published plating bath, that of Elkington (4). In addition to its widespread use on flatware, hollow-ware, and in jewelry, silver has many applications that depend on its electrical and mechanical characteristics, being widely used in the electronics and related industries, and for bearings. Because of its nobility, silver will deposit by simple immersion on most substrates and such immersion

Table 19. Silver-Plating Baths

	KCN bath	NaCN bath	Mixed bath	High-speed bright	High-speed bearings	Strikes For steel	Strikes Second for steel[a]
silver cyanide, g/liter	28–37	28–37	18–21	35–50	40–110	1.5	3–4.5
copper cyanide, g/liter						11.5	
free KCN, g/liter	30–45			85–115	45–150		
K₂CO₃, g/liter	30–90			20–90	15–75		
KNO₃, g/liter			115–150	100			
free NaCN, g/liter		30–38	15–22				
total NaCN, g/liter						75–90	75–90
Na₂CO₃, g/liter		38–45	22				
KOH, g/liter					4–30		
current density, mA/cm²		5–15		50–100		15–25	15–25
temp, °C		20–27		38–47		20–30	20–30

[a] Or for nonferrous metals.

deposits are nonadherent and constitute a poor base for subsequent plating; consequently a two-step process is usually employed: a "strike" in a bath low in silver and high in cyanide to prevent this immersion deposit, followed by a regular silver-plating bath to build up the deposit to desired thickness. Two such strikes, the first containing copper, are recommended for plating on steel. Bath formulations are shown in Table 19.

Tin manufacture as continuous coils of tinplate in tinning "lines" of the steel mills in the U.S. has almost completely superseded the older method of sheet-by-sheet dipping in molten tin. Cold-reduced steel strip as wide as 91 cm (36 in.) is pickled, cleaned, plated, rinsed, and either sheared or re-coiled in continuous fashion in these lines at speeds up to 550 m/min (1800 ft/min). Plating baths used are of three types: acid stannous phenolsulfonate ("Ferrostan"), acid "Halogen," and alkaline stannate. Characteristics of these plating baths dictate to a great extent the design of the plating lines. Copper wire is also tin plated in continuous coils in somewhat analogous fashion.

As distinguished from the manufacture of electrolytic tinplate, tin plating baths for general plating are predominantly alkaline stannate types; the stannous sulfate and stannous fluoborate baths have some application in repetitive operations or where the high operating temperature of the stannate bath is unacceptable. All acid tin plating baths require the presence of organic or colloidal addition agents to produce acceptable deposits.

The alkaline stannate bath (Table 20) may be formulated with either sodium or potassium salts, the latter being favored for their generally superior operating charac-

Table 20. Tin-Plating Baths

	Stannate	Sulfate	Fluoborate
potassium stannate,[a] $K_2Sn(OH)_6$, g/liter	100		
potassium hydroxide,[a] KOH, g/liter	15		
stannous sulfate, $SnSO_4$, g/liter		100	
sulfuric acid, H_2SO_4, g/liter		100	
glue or gelatin, g/liter		2	
2-naphthol, g/liter		1	0.5
tin (as $Sn(F_4)_2$)			40
free HBF_4			40
gelatin			2
temp, °C	65–90	20–30	20–40
current density,[c] mA/cm²	30–60[b]	10–100	20–100

[a] Sodium salts may be substituted, at some sacrifice in cathode efficiency and current density.

[b] By increasing the concentration of the solution, much higher current densities can be obtained.

[c] Under conditions of violent agitation, as in high-speed strip and wire plating, much higher current densities are used.

teristics. The principal key to satisfactory operation of the stannate bath lies in proper control of the anode current density to ensure that the tin dissolves in the quadrivalent form as stannate; when improper conditions obtain, the anode may dissolve as tin(II), which has immediate deleterious effects on the deposit.

Tin has long resisted efforts to brighten the deposit by the use of addition agents, but some progress has been reported (43,44). Commercial experience with these developments is as yet too limited to permit evaluation of their practical utility. Almost all electrolytic tinplate and some miscellaneous tin-plated items are brightened by heat-flowing the deposit after plating, as mentioned previously.

Zinc is plated on continuous sheet and wire, on conduit, and on all types of hardware, for corrosion protection. The acid chloride, sulfate, and fluoborate baths are capable of higher plating speeds and are used in strip and wire plating, but the cyanide bath is almost exclusively used for general plating. A pyrophosphate bath, recently commercialized, has the obvious advantage of no cyanide disposal problem (45). From cyanide baths the plate may be either matte or with appropriate addition agents fully bright. Better appearance and performance can be obtained by the use of chromate post-treatments. Zinc-plating solutions are particularly sensitive to impurities, and for satisfactory results good control of the bath composition, and impurities must be maintained. Typical formulas are shown in Table 21 (46).

Table 21. Cyanide Zinc Bath

	Barrel	Still	Conduit and strip
zinc metal, g/liter	25–45	25–45	45–60
total NaCN, g/liter	70–140	62–135	90–150
total NaOH, g/liter	70–120	70–120	90–140
ratio NaCN/Zn	2.8–3.1	2.5–3.0	2.0–2.5
temp, °C	20–35	20–35	40–60
cathode current density, mA/cm^2	10	20–60	100–180

Zinc is deposited from aqueous solution only by virtue of its high hydrogen overvoltage, since hydrogen would be preferentially deposited under equilibrium conditions. On some substrates that exhibit abnormally low hydrogen overvoltage, such as cast iron (because of the graphite inclusions), it is difficult to deposit zinc, and such metals are often struck with tin or cadmium before zinc plating.

Alloy plating (10) is the simultaneous deposition of two or more metals. In general, electrodeposited alloys have the properties one would expect from a knowledge of the thermal equilibrium diagrams, but there are some notable exceptions. Although alloy plating has been a very attractive field for the research worker, relatively few processes have been commercialized. Interest in the field remains strong, and as needs increase for deposits having specific properties not attainable with single metals, it can be expected that more processes will emerge from the laboratory into production.

To the practicing plater the principal problems in alloy plating arise from the need for additional control. Since changes in the operating variables such as temperature, current density, and bath composition will probably affect the two depositing metals in different degrees, it is usually necessary to maintain these variables within somewhat narrower ranges than in plating single metals. Except in the cases, usually confined to copper alloys, where an idea of the composition of the deposit can be gained from its color, it is also generally advisable to analyze the deposit to ensure that specified results are being obtained.

Complications in practical alloy plating increase almost exponentially as the number of codepositing metals is increased; thus very little has been accomplished with ternary or higher-order alloys, and all of the practical processes, with minor proprietary exceptions, involve only two metals. Some alloys can be formed by depositing the two metals separately and subsequently interdiffusing them by the application of heat, but such processes are not alloy plating in the true sense and are not considered here. The following list of commercial alloy-plating processes is not exhaustive but is believed to cover the principal ones being carried out on a large scale.

Brass is no doubt the earliest commercially plated alloy. It is plated for decorative applications; its principal engineering use is to ensure good adhesion of rubber to steel wire in tire manufacture. All commercial baths are of the cyanide type. Table 22 shows some representative formulas, but wide variations in composition are encountered. "White brass" was extensively used as a nickel substitute when nickel

Table 22. Brass Plating

	70/30	"White"
CuCN, g/liter	53	16–20
Zn(CN)$_2$, g/liter	30	35–40
total NaCN, g/liter	90	52–60
free NaCN, g/liter	7.5	4.5–6.5
Na$_2$CO$_3$, g/liter	30	<37.5
NaOH, g/liter		30–37.5
NH$_4$OH, g/liter	5–13	
Na$_2$S, g/liter		<0.23
Rochelle salt, g/liter		1.5–2.2
pH	10.3–10.7	
temp, °C	43–56	21–29
cathode current density, mA/cm^2	5–35	45
Cu in anodes, %	70	35

was in very short supply, and some use has survived in the manufacture of inexpensive toys and tubular furniture; it is also being used by one major automotive manufacturer.

Bronze, as the term is loosely used in the industry, may cover alloys of copper with zinc, cadmium, or tin, so long as the color matches that of wrought bronze. True

Table 23. Copper–Tin Alloy Plating

	Red bronze (10% Sn)	Speculum[a]
potassium stannate, g/liter	60	100
potassium hydroxide, g/liter	7.5	10
copper cyanide, g/liter	40	12
potassium cyanide, g/liter	90	28
free KCN, g/liter	34	16–18
Rochelle salt[b]	45	
brightener	if required, 2 ml/liter	
temp, °C	60–70	63–67
cathode current density, mA/cm^2	20–100	15–25
anodes	copper	copper and tin in separate circuits

[a] Sodium salts instead of potassium.

[b] Proprietary addition agent at about 5% by vol gives improved efficiencies.

bronze, however, is a copper–tin alloy, and bronzes in the 90:10 copper/tin range are plated fairly extensively for a variety of purposes. A typical formulation is a cyanide–stannate bath shown in Table 23. Anodes may be of copper, the tin content being maintained by additions of potassium stannate. Copper–tin alloys higher in tin, up to 45%, have also been used; the 45% tin alloy is known as speculum, and had some commercial success in England but little in the U.S. When the tin content rises above about 18% the alloys are white. Proprietary processes are available.

Gold alloy plating has been mentioned under Gold.

Lead–tin alloy plating; see section on Lead.

Nickel-base alloys are of interest for their magnetic properties in computer technology.

Tin–nickel is unusual; it has the composition 65:35 tin/nickel, corresponding to the compound NiSn, which is confirmed by x-ray data. No such intermetallic compound appears on the thermal equilibrium diagram; thus it represents an exception to the statement that electrodeposited alloys correspond to thermally prepared ones. The deposit is semibright, fairly hard, but solderable, and has remarkable resistance to a long list of chemical reagents as well as to most atmospheric environments, particularly industrial. Its principal use has been in printed circuits (47) (see Table 24).

Table 24. Tin–Nickel Alloy Plating

stannous chloride, $SnCl_2$,[a] g/liter	50
nickel chloride, $NiCl_2.6H_2O$, g/liter	300
ammonium bifluoride, NH_4HF_2, g/liter	56
ammonium hydroxide, NH_4OH	to pH 2.0–2.5
temp, °C	65–70
cathode current density, mA/cm²	10–30
anodes	nickel, bagged with nylon
anode current density, mA/cm²	to 50

[a] The dihydrate, "tin crystals" $SnCl_2.2H_2O$, may be used; 20% more is required.

Tin–zinc alloy plating has been used as a substitute for cadmium, since it exhibits to a considerable degree the corrosion resistance of zinc combined with the solderability of tin. Composition is usually 80:20 tin/zinc, deposited from a stannate–cyanide bath as shown in Table 25.

Table 25. Tin–Zinc Alloy Plating

	Still	Barrel
potassium stannate, $K_2Sn(OH)_6$, g/liter	120	95
zinc cyanide, $Zn(CN)_2$, g/liter	11.3	15
potassium cyanide, KCN, g/liter	30	34
free potassium hydroxide, KOH, g/liter	7.5	11.3
temp, °C	..........65±2.........	
cathode current density, mA/cm²	..........10–80.........	
anodes	80:20 Sn/Zn; must be filmed	
anode current density, mA/cm²	..........15–25.........	

Tungsten has not been successfully plated from aqueous solutions, but its alloys with cobalt are easily deposited and have interesting properties.

Nonelectrolytic Plating Processes

There are many ways besides electroplating whereby a coating of a metal can be deposited on a substrate, including hot dipping, vacuum evaporation, chemical vapor deposition, and various aqueous processes not requiring current. These last processes are sufficiently related to electroplating to be included in a discussion of the technology. These nonelectrolytic aqueous processes include contact plating, immersion plating, and chemical, "autocatalytic," or what has come to be known as "electroless" plating.

Contact Plating. In this process the outside source of current is replaced by an internal galvanic couple, so that the plating current is in effect generated in situ. Such processes are applicable principally to tin, the internal contact metal being zinc or aluminum. Although these methods are obsolescent they are still in use here and there.

Immersion Plating. When the substrate metal is less noble than the plating metal, or can be made so by appropriate complexing agents in the solution, an immersion deposit may be formed, the prototype of which is the familiar $Fe + Cu^{2+} \rightarrow Cu + Fe^{2+}$. Many such immersion deposits are of no value because they are powdery or nonadherent, and in fact are to be avoided, as in copper on iron. On the other hand, some immersion processes have commercial utility. Tin can be deposited on copper and its alloys from solutions containing a tin salt and a complexing agent for copper such as cyanide or thiourea. Two formulas are given in Table 26, and proprietaries are available. Tin can be deposited on lead and its alloys from solutions of tin(II)

Table 26. Immersion Tin on Copper

Alkaline		Acid	
potassium stannate, g/liter	60	$SnCl_2$, g/liter	4
KCN, g/liter	120	thiourea, g/liter	50
KOH, g/liter	7.5	H_2SO_4, g/liter	20
temp, °C	30–65	temp, °C	25
time, min	2–20	time, min	5–30

chloride (48). It is deposited by immersion on aluminum alloy pistons from alkaline stannate solutions; this process is practiced on a very large scale by all the major automotive manufacturers. Copper–tin alloys are applied to steel wire ("liquor finish") as a drawing lubricant and for color in such items as paper clips and bobby pins.

Gold and some of the other precious metals are also frequently applied by immersion techniques.

In general, immersion deposits cannot be built up to thicknesses comparable to those obtainable by electrolytic methods, for as soon as the substrate is completely covered the reaction ceases. Nevertheless some such deposits have quite appreciable thickness, entirely sufficient for the intended application. Immersion processes have the advantages of practically unlimited throwing power (limited only by access and renewal of the solution to the surface) and low capital cost, since they require no source of dc power.

Electroless Plating. This term, coined by its inventor Brenner, covers processes in which a metal compound is reduced to the metallic state by means of a chemical reducing agent in the solution. The typical case is electroless nickel, in which nickel ions are reduced to the metal by the action of sodium hypophosphite. The deposition process is "catalyzed" by certain metallic surfaces, including the deposited metal itself; thus once initiated the deposition is "autocatalytic." Fortunately, under proper control the reaction takes place only at the catalytic surface and not on the walls of the containing vessel or in the bulk of the solution, although if allowed to get out of hand the last can occur, with catastrophic results.

Since its beginnings about twenty years ago, electroless nickel has been intensively investigated (49–51), and its commercial development has been brought to an advanced state. Typical formulations contain nickel chloride, sodium hypophosphite, and one or more hydroxy acids such as lactic or hydroxyacetic; operating temperatures range from 65–100°C. Several proprietary processes are available.

Electroless nickel is not pure nickel but a nickel–phosphorus alloy, containing 5–15% phosphorus. The process has several advantages over electroplating: virtually unlimited throwing power, little or no excess deposit on high points, deposits of excellent chemical and physical properties, and the ability to coat surfaces such as those on the inside of tank cars which would be difficult or impossible to do with conventional electrolytic techniques. The principal disadvantage is high cost; the reducing agent, sodium hypophosphite, is expensive and is consumed in substantial quantities, and the setup is often complicated and requires exacting control. If ordinary electrolytic techniques will do the job, they are preferred; but electroless methods enlarge the area of possibilities.

Next in commercial importance to electroless nickel is electroless copper (25,52,53). This has been particularly useful in plating on nonmetallics in printed circuitry. Electroless copper solutions typically contain a copper salt, a complexing agent, a pH buffer, and a reducing agent. One formula for plating on plastics (25) is: $Cu(NO_3)_2 \cdot 3H_2O$, 15 g/liter, $NaHCO_3$, 10 g/liter, Rochelle salt, 30 g/liter, formaldehyde (37%), 100 ml/liter. Proprietaries are available.

Other electroless processes have been reported for gold, rhodium, palladium, and cobalt (54). Electroless chromium has been reported but results have been unreproducible.

The term "electroless" plating has been carelessly applied to all processes which do not require an outside source of current, but the distinction between truly chemical reduction methods, ie, electroless plating, and electrochemical replacement such as immersion plating is a valuable one and should be maintained.

Postplating Treatments

Postplating treatments (see Metal surface treatment) include chromate conversion coatings for zinc and cadmium, phosphate treatments for zinc, and various passivating and brightening dips. In most general use are the chromate conversion coatings for zinc and cadmium, which are designed to convert the surface from the naturally occurring oxide to one containing hexavalent chromium. Such treatments enhance the corrosion-protective value of the deposit, and inhibit the formation of bulky and unsightly corrosion products; they also reduce the tendency of the surface to finger-stain on handling. Chromate conversion coatings impart various colors to the deposits, depending on specific details of the treating solutions; some of them can be dyed. Although formulas have been published, the great majority of chromate treatment is done by proprietary processes.

Phosphate conversion coatings are applied to zinc-plated surfaces as a base for subsequent painting.

Specifications and Tests

As the capabilities of electroplating have expanded, there has been a great increase in the use of specifications. Almost universally, the electroplater is instructed to apply deposits of a certain minimum thickness, and other properties of the deposit are often specified as well, for example, hardness, tensile strength, corrosion resistance, adhesion, and others. Although the requirement for a specified thickness may seem self-evident, it was not always so; deposits in former times were often applied to the least thickness that would look well. Specifications call for tests to determine compliance. Many of these tests are highly specific to particular metals or are slight modifications of standard metallurgical procedures, and will not be discussed here. Probably the three most widely useful tests are those for thickness of deposit, for corrosion resistance, and for adhesion.

Thickness. The thickness of a deposit on parts of any but the very simplest shape is not uniform (see Throwing power, above). Most specifications call for a minimum thickness on significant surfaces, these being defined either by direct reference in the specification or by the general rule that any functional or visible surface is significant. Many tests for measuring deposit thickness have been devised; none is universally applicable to all combinations of deposit and basis metal and some are highly specialized. They may be classified as destructive or nondestructive; the former may be destructive to the part itself or only to the coating, permitting the part to be salvaged and replated.

The most common destructive test, as well as the most widely applicable and possibly least subject to error, is sectioning followed by microscopic observation using standard metallographic techniques of polishing and etching. Although the principle of this method is obvious, there are many precautions to be observed and the literature should be consulted for details (55,56).

Tests that destroy the coating but permit reuse of the part for replating include the many chemical methods: jet, spot, and time-of-gassing tests, weigh-strip-weigh, and stripping followed by chemical analysis of the stripping solution. The last two yield average rather than local thickness. In the spot test and its variations (55) use is made of the fact that a given reagent penetrates a given coating metal at a definite rate that depends on the concentration and temperature of the reagent. A jet, stream, or drop of reagent acts on a small area of the test piece, and the time necessary to penetrate the coating, as evidenced by a change in the appearance of the piece, is recorded. Reference to a calibration curve for the reagent–coating combination permits determination of the thickness.

In the stripping tests, a part (or in the case of very small items many parts) of known area is stripped of the coating in a reagent that attacks the coating but not the basis metal; knowing the weight before and after stripping, the weight per unit area is calculated; the density of the deposited metal is either known or assumed to be the bulk, handbook value, enabling calculation of the average thickness. A variation is to strip the coating and determine it analytically; this is widely used for tinplate.

The anodic solution test makes use of the difference in anode potential when the nature of the anode changes suddenly. A small area of the test piece is made anode in a specific electrolyte and the time at which the potential undergoes an abrupt change is measured. This test has been embodied in an instrument which is almost automatic and reads thickness directly.

Where geometry permits and deposits are thick enough, simple measurement with a micrometer before and after plating can be used. Most nondestructive methods, however, rely on differences in physical properties between coating and substrate; these differences may be magnetic, electrical, or nuclear. For a nonmagnetic coating over a magnetic substrate, the thicker the coating the less attraction the piece will have for a magnet; by pulling a standard magnet away from the piece by means of an instrument that can measure the force necessary to do this the thickness can be determined. This principle is the basis of the most widely used thickness tests (64).

Differences in electrical properties lead to the several instruments that measure eddy currents induced in the coating, which vary as a function of its thickness.

Scattering of x rays or beta or gamma radiation by the basis metal will vary with the thickness of coating interposed between it and the source, provided the atomic numbers of coating and substrate are not too close (57). Beta-ray backscatter gages have been made available which are direct-reading in coating thickness (58,59).

Corrosion Resistance. The final criterion of corrosion resistance is actual service, but accelerated tests are needed both for predicting service life and for acceptance or rejection in production. Many such tests have been devised, but there is considerable doubt whether some of them correlate well with service. No accelerated corrosion test can exactly duplicate while merely speeding up the corrosive process that takes place during the life of the part. Correlation with service experience must be proved if the accelerated test is to have any meaning.

In spite of much evidence of its unreliability, the "salt-fog" or salt-spray test is still widely used. The parts are exposed in a closed chamber to a fog or spray of a solution of sodium chloride (5% or 20%) under specified conditions, and examined for failure after stated time periods (60). For anodic coatings like zinc and cadmium, this test measures only the thickness of the coating; for cathodic coatings it may be an indication of gross porosity (56), and as such an acceptable tool for quality control. It is of doubtful value for research and development purposes.

Variations on the salt-spray test include the acetic acid salt spray, in which the pH of the spray is reduced by additions of acetic acid (61), and the copper-accelerated acetic acid–salt spray or CaSS test (62). The latter is finding favor for testing nickel/chromium coatings, since experience is showing that it correlates fairly well with actual performance. Copper chloride is added to the sodium chloride–acetic acid solution, and thereby the corrosion is both accelerated and caused to occur in patterns more nearly resembling actual service.

Another recent test about equally favored for automotive hardware is the "Corrodkote" (63), in which a slurry of clay containing several corrosive ingredients is painted on the test pieces which are then placed in a humidity cabinet and examined after stated times of exposure.

Adhesion. Obviously a plated coating must adhere to the substrate if it is to perform its function. Tests for adhesion, once a process has been set up and found to be satisfactory, then become a quality-control function and in reality measure the degree to which proper control is being maintained. Quantitative measurement of the adhesive force is possible but is more a research tool than a routine test procedure; most shop tests are of a go-no-go type, and are crude but apparently adequate. They involve heating, bending, sawing, filing, hammering, or otherwise abusing the part and observing the nature of the break when failure occurs. Crude and unscientific as these procedures appear, they are useful in judging the quality of plated parts (56).

Physical and mechanical properties often specified, especially in engineering applications, include hardness, stress, and ductility (56). Tests for solderability, smoothness of surface, and other properties have been devised.

Bibliography

"Electroplating" in *ECT* 1st ed., Vol. 5, pp. 611–646, by C. L. Faust and W. H. Safranek, Battelle Memorial Institute.

1. F. A. Lowenheim, ed., *Modern Electroplating*, 2d ed., John Wiley & Sons, Inc., New York, 1963.
2. A. K. Graham, ed., *Electroplating Engineering Handbook*, 2d ed., Reinhold Publishing Corp., New York, 1962.
3. "Tentative Definitions of Terms Relating to Electroplating," *ASTM Designation B 374-63T*.
4. Brit. Pat. 8447 (1840), G. and H. Elkington.
5. G. B. Hogaboom, *Metal Finishing* **51** (1), 72 (1953); F. A. Lowenheim, *Metal Finishing* **51** (1), 78 (1953).
6. G. W. Mellors and S. Senderoff, *Plating* **51**, 972 (1964).
7. *Minerals Yearbook*, U.S. Bureau of Mines, 1962.
8. W. O. Freitag, J. S. Mathias, and G. DiGuilo, *J. Electrochem. Soc.* **111**, 35 (1964).
9. G. V. Elmore and P. Bakos, *J. Electrochem. Soc.* **111**, 1244 (1964).
10. A. Brenner, *Electrodeposition of Alloys*, Academic Press, Inc., New York, 1963.
11. *Corrosion Mater. Protection* **2** (9), 28 (1945).
12. "Symposium on Electroless Nickel Plating," *Am. Soc. Testing Mater. Spec. Tech. Publ.* **265** (1959).
13. "Symposium on Electroforming," *Am. Soc. Testing Mater. Spec. Tech. Publ.* **318** (1962).
14. "ASTM B-8 Sub VII," *Plating* **51**, 1075 (1964).
15. H. J. Read, ed., *Hydrogen Embrittlement in Metal Finishing*, Reinhold Publishing Corp., New York, 1961.
16. W. Dingley and J. Bednar, *Tech. Proc. Am. Electroplaters' Soc.* **50**, 71 (1963).
17. E. E. Dougherty, *Plating* **51**, 415 (1964).
18. R. S. Modjeska and S. N. Kann, *Tech. Proc. Am. Electroplaters' Soc.* **50**, 117 (1963).
19. S. Spring, *Metal Cleaning*, Reinhold Publishing Corp., New York, 1963.
20. "Recommended Practice for Preparation of and Plating on Aluminum Alloys, *ASTM Designation B 253-53; Plating* **51**, 559 (1964).
21. "Recommended Practice for Preparation of Zinc-base Die Castings for Electroplating," *ASTM Designation B 252-53*.
22. H. B. Linford and E. B. Saubestre, *Plating* **38**, 713, 847 (1951); H. B. Linford and E. B. Saubestre, *Plating* **40**, 489, 633 (1953).
23. E. J. Seyb, J. C. Jongkind, and L. P. Gowman, *Tech. Proc. Am. Electroplaters' Soc.* **51**, 133 (1964).
24. C. Marzano, *Plating* **51**, 207 (1964).
25. E. B. Saubestre, L. J. Durney, and E. B. Washburn, *Metal Finishing* **62** (11), 52 (1964).
26. G. H. Poll, Jr., *Prod. Finishing Cincinnati* **28** (11), 66 (1964).
27. J. R. Crain, *Plating* **51**, 31 (1964).
28. D. G. Foulke and F. D. Crane, *Electroplater's Process Control Handbook*, Reinhold Publishing Corp., New York, 1963.
29. K. E. Langford, *Analysis of Electroplating and Related Solutions*, 3rd ed., Robert Draper, Teddington, England, 1962.
30. E. J. Seyb, *Tech. Proc. Am. Electroplaters' Soc.* **47**, 209 (1960).
31. E. J. Seyb, *Tech. Proc. Am. Electroplaters' Soc.* **50**, 175 (1963).
32. W. H. Safranek, H. R. Miller, and C. L. Faust, *Plating* **50**, 507 (1963).
33. W. H. Safranek and H. R. Miller, *Plating* **51**, 551 (1964).
34. T. E. Such and M. Partington, *Proc. 6th Intern. Metal Finishing Conf.* 110 (1964).
35. W. H. Safranek and C. L. Faust, *Proc. 6th Intern. Metal Finishing Conf.* 217 (1964).
36. A. H. DuRose, *Proc. 6th Intern. Metal Finishing Conf.* 59 (1964).
37. H. Brown and H. Silman, *Proc. 6th Intern. Metal Finishing Conf.* 21 (1964).

38. S. E. Beacom, D. W. Hardesty, and W. R. Doty, *Proc. 6th Intern. Metal Finishing Conf.* 14 (1964).
39. "Recommended Practice for Chromium Plating on Steel for Engineering Use," *ASTM Designation B 177-55.*
40. J. W. Dini, *Plating* **51**, 119 (1964).
41. T. W. Tomaszewski, R. J. Clauss, and H. Brown, *Tech. Proc. Am. Electroplaters' Soc.* **50**, 169 (1963).
42. R. Duva, *Metal Finishing Guidebook Directory*, Metals & Plastics Publications, Inc., Westwood, N.J., 1964, p. 279ff.
43. M. Clarke and S. C. Britton, *Trans. Inst. Metal Finishing* **39**, 5 (1962).
44. A. Riesser, *Proc. 6th Intern. Metal Finishing Conf.* (1964).
45. W. H. McMullen and F. W. Eppensteiner, *Plating* **52**, 123 (1965).
46. E. L. Gabel, *Plating* **50**, 1089 (1963).
47. R. W. Couch and R. G. Bikales, *Tech. Proc. Am. Electroplaters' Soc.* **48**, 176 (1961).
48. F. A. Lowenheim, *Plating* **51**, 551 (1964).
49. K. M. Gorbunova and A. A. Nikiforova, *Physicochemical Principles of (Chemical) Nickel Plating*, Engl. transl. available from U.S. Govt. Office of Technical Services, Washington, D.C., 1963.
50. D. J. Levy, *Tech. Proc. Am. Electroplaters' Soc.* **50**, 29 (1963).
51. R. M. Lukes, *Plating* **51**, 969 (1964).
52. R. M. Lukes, *Plating* **51**, 1066 (1964).
53. W. Goldie, *Plating* **51**, 1069 (1964).
54. R. N. Rhoda, *Plating* **50**, 307 (1963).
55. "Standard Methods of Test for Local Thickness of Electrodeposited Coatings," *ASTM Designation A 219-58.*
56. "Symposium on Methods of Test," *Tech. Proc. Am. Electroplaters' Soc.* **50**, 37 (1963).
57. E. H. Babcock, W. T. Barnes, and F. T. Eddy, *Tech. Proc. Am. Electroplaters' Soc.* **50**, 78 (1963).
58. G. A. Goethner, *Plating* **51**, 429 (1964).
59. B. B. Joffe and R. S. Modjeska, *Metal Finishing* **61** (12), 44 (1963).
60. "Standard Method for Salt Spray (Fog) Testing," *ASTM Designation B 117-64.*
61. "Standard Method of Acetic Acid-Salt Spray (Fog) Testing," *ASTM Designation B 287-62.*
62. "Tentative Method of Copper-Accelerated Acetic Acid-Salt Spray (Fog) Testing (Cass Test)," *ASTM Designation B 368-62T.*
63. "Tentative Method of Corrosion Testing of Decorative Chromium Plating by the Corrodkote Procedure," *ASTM Designation B 380-61T.*
64. "Tentative Recommended Practice for Measuring Coating Thickness by Magnetic or Electromagnetic Methods," *ASTM Designation E 216-63T.*

ACKNOWLEDGMENTS.   This article has drawn heavily on references 1 and 2, and where no other citation is given it may be assumed that authority for the statements made comes from the appropriate chapter or section in one or the other.   Reference 1 in particular contains fairly complete bibliographies, so that for the most part the references below are to papers published since the appearance of these two volumes.

F. A. LOWENHEIM
M & T Chemicals, Inc.

ELECTROSTATIC PRECIPITATION

The electrostatic precipitation process can be defined as the use of electrostatic fields for removing solid or liquid particles from a gas in which the particles are carried in suspension. The equipment used to carry on this process is variously termed a Cottrell, a precipitator, or treater in the U.S. and an electrofilter in Germany.

The removal of suspended matter from gases by the aid of electrical discharges, as typified by the Cottrell electrostatic precipitation process, is by no means a new idea. As early as 1828, Hohlfeld suggested the use of electrical discharges as a means of suppressing ordinary smoke. In 1850 the principle was again discovered by Guitard. In 1886, Sir Oliver Lodge independently rediscovered the phenomenon discussed by Hohlfeld and Guitard. He attempted to apply the principles commercially to a problem at the Dee Bank Lead Works in Great Britain. The general principle of electrical precipitation of suspended matter from a moving gas stream was at that time patented by Alfred O. Walker of the Lead Company. The apparatus used apparently did not, in practice, fulfill expectations for there is nothing further on it in the literature. The most cogent weakness of the project was probably the reliance on the Wimshurst electrostatic machine, which had then just been brought out and from which far more was expected than was justified by subsequent experience.

Almost simultaneously with the work of Lodge and Walker, and apparently without any knowledge of it, Dr. Karl Moeller of Brackwede, Germany, secured a patent on electrical precipitation.

From about 1886 to 1906 there appeared to be a lull in the work on electrical precipitation and it was not until Dr. Frederick Gardiner Cottrell revived the interest that a new start was made. Dr. Cottrell, at that time at the University of California, was studying various methods for the removal of acid from mists in the contact sulfuric acid process. He had occasion to repeat the earlier experiments of Lodge and became convinced of the possibility of developing them into commercial realities. Subsequently, Dr. Cottrell followed up these experiments with further work, which essentially amounted to reducing the principles to engineering practice. The first practical demonstration of the process occurred about 1906 at the Hercules works of the E. I. du Pont de Nemours Powder Company at Pinole, California, on the contact gases from one of the Mannheim contact sulfuric acid plants. The work at Pinole attracted the attention of the Selby Smelting and Lead Company whose smelter, located at Vallejoe Junction, was at that time under injunction proceedings brought by the farmers of the surrounding country, and a second installation was made there.

The subsequent progress of the Cottrell process in the U.S. and other countries has been one of engineering development. It is altogether fitting that a process bearing as much of the personal imprint as that of Dr. Cottrell should carry his name.

Dispersoids in Gases. Dispersion systems, in which the dispersed medium is a gas or a vapor, may consist of only one component (as for example a fine mist of liquid water suspended in water vapor), or of two or more components as in metallurgical fumes. The dispersed phase may be a liquid as in clouds, mists, or sprays, or it may be a solid as in a dust cloud or metallurgical fume. Such familiar natural phenomena as dusts, fogs, clouds, mists, hazes, fumes, or smokes are essentially disperse systems in which solid or liquid substances are dispersed in a gas, in most cases the atmosphere (see also Dust).

The properties of dispersoids in gases (see Aerosols) differ in several important respects from those of disperse systems in liquids. In the first place, owing to the relatively small viscosity and specific gravity of the gases, the liquid or solid particles of the disperse phase tend to settle more readily from the system under the influence of gravity. In the second place, the molecules of a gas move with much greater freedom and have longer paths than those of liquids or solids. Consequently, the amplitude of the Brownian motion of the particles is very much greater in an aerosol than in any other disperse system. This tends to increase the rate at which the particles collide to form aggregates. Also, in a given aerosol, some particles of the disperse phase may be electrically neutral, while others may be charged either positively or negatively.

Solid and liquid suspended matter in gases may be divided into two main classes according to their method of formation: (1) mechanical dispersoids, and (2) condensed dispersoids. *Mechanical dispersoids* are formed by dispersing large masses into finer particles, as by grinding solids or spraying liquids, and these are generally called *dusts* and *sprays*, respectively. *Condensed dispersoids* are formed by the condensation of the vapor phase of the substance and these generally are termed *fumes* when solids, and *mists* when liquids.

The most important characteristic of such dispersoids affecting their removal from the gas is their particle size and this, in fact, differentiates between the two classes. While it is extremely difficult to ascribe rigid dimensions to each class, it can be assumed that the much larger portion, by weight, of dust will consist of particles of average diameter between 5–100 μ, while with fumes, the diameters may range from 0.1–5.0 μ. As an example of the particle size of each of these classes, the size analysis of a typical fly ash dust is as follows:

particle size, μ	0–5	5–10	10–20	20–30	30–50	over 50
size analysis, %	9	18	23	17	14	19

and a particle-size analysis of fume removed from steel open-hearth combustion gases showed the following size classification:

particle size, μ	below 0.15	0.15–0.5	0.5–1	1–3
size analysis, %	14.8	49.5	28.4	7.3

In general, from a gas-cleaning standpoint, the most important factor is the size distribution of the particles, for this dictates, to a large extent, the method of handling. A graphical representation of the characteristics of a number of particle dispersoids, the methods of particle size analysis usually used, and types of gas cleaning equipment that are applicable to the various particle size ranges appears under Dust (see Vol. 7, p. 429).

The second important factor is the amount of suspended matter carried by the individual gases. Typical concentrations found in industrial processes are shown in Table 1. It is customary to express gas loadings in grains per cubic foot; 7000 grains (gr) = 1 lb; 1 gr = 0.0648 g; 1 gr/ft^3 = 2.286 mg/l.

The final important property of the dispersoid is the electrical conductivity which is influenced by the chemical composition of the material, and treatment temperature.

Removal of Dispersoids from Gases. In general, the purposes of gas-cleaning installations may be classified into three categories as follows: (1) for the collection and recovery of suspended matter from gases before they are wasted to atmosphere. In this category, the removal of metallurgical fumes with their attendant values is a prime example. (2) For the elimination of a hazard or nuisance that may result from

Table 1. Concentrations of Suspended Matter in Industrial Process Gases

Suspended matter	Concentration, gr/ft³ of gas, STP
acid mist—sulfuric acid (contact plant)	
after roaster	
multiple-hearth roaster—zinc and pyrites	1.08–5.8
flash roaster—zinc blende	0.00475–0.0555
after absorbers—tail gases	0.722–2.31
acid mist—phosphoric acid—from burning phosphorus (basis 100% H_3PO_4)	48.3–66.2
assay offices and mines—ventilating gases from furnaces and assay operations	0.0028–0.0515
carbon black	
from cracking natural gas	5.1–17.0
from oil cracking	19.0–40.0
carbureted water gas	
dry-tar basis	0.765–1.59
wet-tar basis	1.08–2.26
catalytic cracking units—oil	
atmospheric-pressure units—after mechanical collector	
natural catalyst	19.45–85.6
synthetic catalyst	16.5–52.9
high-pressure units—after mechanical collector	
natural catalyst	7.19–22.75
synthetic catalyst	4.69–94.6
cement-kiln gases (wet process)—dust concentrate entering stack	
wet-gas basis	2.62–3.8
dry-gas basis	3.34–4.68
coke-fired producer gas	0.03–0.06
coke-oven gas	
ahead of exhausters, dry-tar basis	4.51–4.88
after positive displacement exhausters, wet-tar basis	3.14–4.58
after centrifugal exhauster, wet-tar basis	1.66–3.74
fly ash from boilers burning pulverized soft coal	1.0–5.0
gypsum-plant gas	
from rotary calciners, wet-gas basis	32.82–48.07
from dryers, wet-gas basis	64.52
from gypsum kettles, dry-gas basis	6.72–26.98
incinerators burning dry sewage sludge	3.17–4.35
silica-rock treatment	
oil-fired rotary dryer	6.42–23.5
preheater gases	6.65–15.8
ventilating system	9.37–26.2
tin smelting	
reverberatory furnaces	2.20–3.12
calcining tin ores—rotary kilns	1.44–4.59
zinc sintering machine—straight and chloridized roast	0.311–1.908
zinc-ore roasting	
flash roaster	3.92–45.05
multiple-hearth roaster	3.82–7.07
zinc oxide—Waelz plant	12.65–28.62

the presence of suspended matter in gases discharged to the atmosphere. In this class are the cleaning of gases from the burning of pulverized coal and the removal of burning embers from the gases resulting from the combustion of wood. (*3*) For the removal of suspended matter before the utilization of the gases for industrial purposes in which the presence of the dispersoid is objectionable. In this class are the cleaning of blast-furnace gas, coke-oven gas, and sulfur dioxide-bearing gas in the contact sulfuric acid plant.

Five separate and distinct types of gas-cleaning (qv) equipment are commercially available: (1) gravitational (settling chambers); (2) filtrational; (3) wet inertial (scrubbing); (4) dry inertial (cyclone collectors); and (5) electrostatic (precipitators).

Although no single type of dust-removal equipment embodies all virtues, the following are the most important requirements: (1) The dispersoid concentration in the clean gas stream should be below the predetermined permissible limit; (2) the equipment should retain its cleaning efficiency throughout its life; (3) the cleaning efficiency should be substantially constant throughout its daily operating cycle; (4) the cleaning efficiency should be nearly independent of the rate of gas flow and the entering dust concentration; (5) the equipment should require no shutdowns for cleaning or routine maintenance during normal working hours—the cleaning and disposal should be automatic; (6) normal maintenance and periodic disposal of collected dust should introduce no other hazard; (7) the equipment should embody the usual conditions of low cost, durability, minimum maintenance, and minimum space.

Principles of Electrostatic Precipitation

In the Cottrell electrostatic precipitator, an unsymmetrical electrode geometry results in the formation of a corona discharge and a high unidirectional difference of potential between the two electrodes. This results in a stable corona discharge at one electrode and leads to the formation of an electrically neutral plasma of positive ions and electrons. The electrons, under the influence of the electric field, pass into the regions of lower potential where they attach to gas molecules, transforming them into gas ions. The gases to be treated are passed through this electric field and profusion of unipolar ions. The ions become attached to the suspended particles via a variety of processes (field-directed charging, ion-diffusion charging, direct-electron attachment). The charged particles, under the influence of the electric field, are then separated from the gases by Coulomb forces and deposited on the surface of the electrodes. Essentially, the Cottrell process proceeds in four definite steps: (1) charging the particles by means of gaseous ions or electrons; (2) precipitating or transporting the charged particles through the gas to the collecting electrode by the force exerted on the charged particles by the electric field; (3) discharging the charged particles; and (4) removing the precipitated material from the electrode to a suitable receptacle.

The charge on a conducting spherical particle, under the usual practical conditions, where field-directed charging dominates is expressed as follows:

$$C = 3Ea^2 \frac{\pi NeKt}{1 + \pi NeKt} \tag{1}$$

where C = the number of electron charges on a particle of radius a; e = the electronic charge (4.8×10^{-10} esu); E = the electric field in the neighborhood of the particle; a = the particle radius; N = the ion density; K = the ion mobility; and t = the time the particle is in the charging zone (1). Formula 1 indicates that the saturation charge on a particle is $3Ea^2$ and is, therefore, proportional to both the electric field and the surface area. Consequently, from a theoretical viewpoint, the large dust particles receive a greater electrical charge and should, therefore, be precipitated more rapidly than the smaller particles. Practical considerations modify this situation to make the electrostatic precipitation process relatively nonselective as regards particle size.

The average migration (or precipitation) rate of dust particles through the collecting electrode, or the rate constant of the process may be expressed theoretically as

$$\omega = \frac{E_0 E_p a}{2 \pi \eta} \tag{2}$$

where ω = the average migration rate through the collecting electrode; E_0 = the charging field; E_p = the collecting field; a = the particle radius; and η = the gas viscosity.

Formula 2 can be applied to conducting spherical particles in the size range for which Stokes law is valid. For particles below about 1 μ diameter, the formula must be modified to take account of the Cunningham correction factor for Stokes' law (1) (see Dust).

Table 2. Calculated Precipitation Rate Constant ω for Representative Precipitator Conditions (1).
Courtesy Addison-Wesley Publishing Co.

Particle diameter, μ	Gas temperature, °C	Gas viscosity, P	Particle velocity, ft/sec
0.5	20	1.8×10^{-4}	0.21
1	20	1.8×10^{-4}	0.37
5	20	1.8×10^{-4}	1.60
10	20	1.8×10^{-4}	3.20
50	20	1.8×10^{-4}	16.00
0.5	350	3.0×10^{-4}	0.13
1	350	3.0×10^{-4}	0.23
5	350	3.0×10^{-4}	1.00
10	350	3.0×10^{-4}	2.00
50	350	3.0×10^{-4}	10.00

Representative values of ω calculated by the theoretical formula 2 are shown in Table 2 for purposes of orientation. These values serve as a useful guide to expected precipitator performance. However, because the theoretical rate is influenced by many practical factors such as particle re-entrainment, uneven gas distribution, etc, the values of ω are normally established empirically; the empirically determined values may deviate from theoretical values by as much as 100%, depending upon the extent to which these practical factors influence the process; the practical values are usually lower than the theoretical values, particularly in dry electrostatic precipitation.

The degree of purification (efficiency), ζ, of a precipitator may be expressed as follows:

$$\zeta = 1 - e^{-A\omega/V} \tag{3}$$

where ζ = the degree of purification; ω = the average migration rate of the dust particles; A = the effective total surface area of the collecting electrodes; V = the total volumetric flow rate.

Equipment

In general, there are two types of precipitators, depending on how the above-mentioned precipitation steps are handled. In installations operating on industrial gases, all the precipitation steps are usually handled in one piece of equipment; this is the familiar Cottrell process. Another type is that in which the charging of the particles is made a distinct step; this is generally called a precharging precipitator or a two-stage precipitator. In both types of installation the same four precipitation steps are involved, although they are handled in two different ways.

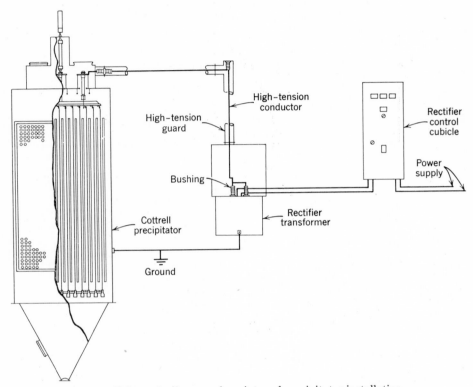

Fig. 1. Schematic diagram of nonintegral precipitator installation.

An electrostatic precipitation installation comprises two major elements: the precipitator itself and the electrical energizing equipment. Figure 1 shows a schematic diagram of the equipment normally required in a Cottrell installation in which the electrical equipment is segregated from the precipitation equipment. Figure 2 shows a Cottrell installation in which a precipitator is equipped with an integral electrical power unit. Figure 3 shows a schematic diagram of a typical two-stage air-cleaning type of precipitator.

ELECTRICAL EQUIPMENT

Ions or electrons, which are required to charge the particles, may be obtained in different ways such as from flames, radioactive disintegration, or friction, but at present the only practical source for electrostatic precipitation is the corona discharge

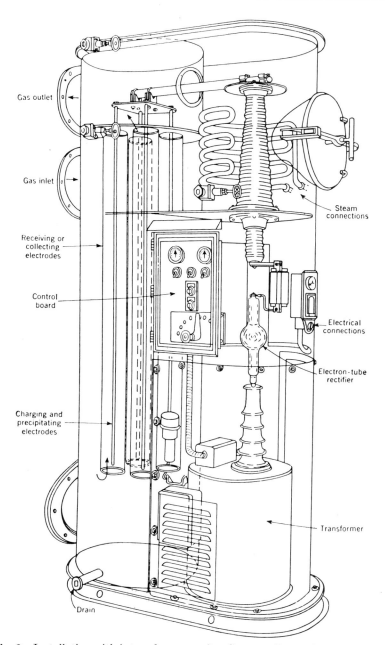

Gas outlet

Gas inlet

Receiving or
collecting
electrodes

Control
board

Charging and
precipitating
electrodes

Drain

Steam
connections

Electrical
connections

Electron-tube
rectifier

Transformer

Fig. 2. Installation with integral power unit. Courtesy Research-Cottrell, Inc.

obtained by electrical forces. Many types of electrical energization have been used to produce the corona discharge, but unidirectional voltages of either full-wave or half-wave rectification are most generally used.

The electrical equipment consists primarily of a high-voltage transformer, a rectifier for converting the high-voltage alternating current to unidirectional current, and suitable manual or automatic control equipment.

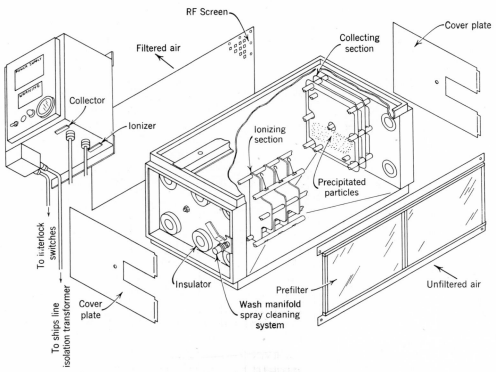

Fig. 3. Schematic diagram of two-stage air cleaner-type precipitator installation.   Courtesy Research-Cottrell, Inc.

Rectifying Equipment.   There are three types of rectifying equipment in use in the U.S.: (*1*) the mechanical rectifier, (*2*) the electron-tube rectifier, and (*3*) the semiconductor or solid-state rectifier.

The *mechanical rectifier* for full-wave rectification is in effect a synchronously driven switch, comprising rotor and stator elements.   Four metal shoes spaced 90° apart on a circle are mounted on fixed insulating arms of laminated plastic material and attached to the motor frame.   Usually, for full-wave rectification, the top shoe is connected to the precipitator, the bottom shoe is grounded, and each side shoe is connected to one secondary terminal of the transformer.   Rotating within these shoes with a clearance of $\frac{1}{8}$–$\frac{1}{4}$ in., and mounted on the motor shaft, is a rotor with four metallic tips at 90° intervals mounted on plastic arms or a plastic disc.   Two adjacent tips of the rotor are electrically connected.   The rotor advances one-half turn per complete cycle of alternating voltage, or for 60-cycle current runs at a rate of 1800 rpm.   In cases where half-wave rectification is used, a second rotor and stator mounted on the same motor shaft are provided, and act as a synchronous commutating switch in the high-tension circuit.   The motor for driving the mechanical rectifier is of the shaded-pole induction type, which starts as an induction motor but runs as a synchronous motor at full speed.   The motor in general use may be for 220 or 440 V, 2 or 3 phase, and 25–60 cycles.   The transformers for mechanical rectifiers may vary in capacity from 2.5–25 kVA, depending on the requirements of the precipitator installation.   Standard designs call for a single-phase, 25 or 60 cycle, 200, 400, or 500 V

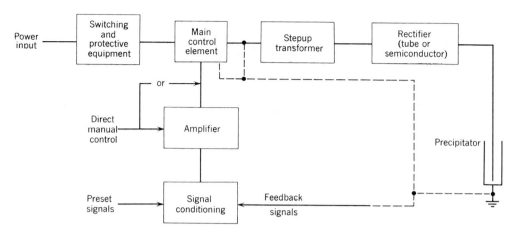

Fig. 4. Generalized block diagram—industrial precipitator control. Courtesy Air Pollution Control Association.

primary, and 35–75 kV secondary with a number of primary taps to afford a range of secondary voltages. The coils are immersed in oil or nonflammable liquids such as chlorinated diphenyls. The transformers are internally surge-protected. Radio interference coils are provided to prevent interference with radio reception.

Electron tube rectifiers are normally double half-wave, bridge circuit units utilizing four high-vacuum-tube diodes. The transformer rectifier assembly consists of the main and filament transformers in a single tank, immersed in oil or askarel (liquid dielectric), and air-cooled. On top of the tanks are mounted the receptacles for the rectifier tubes. Electron tube rectifiers are available in the range of 70–105 kV peak and 250–750 mA output.

The *semiconductor* or *solid-state rectifier* consists of double half-wave bridge rectifiers made up of silicon diodes with suitable transient shunt protection, tanked with the high voltage transformer in a single oil or askarel-filled, air-cooled tank. Solid-state rectifiers are available for output ratings in the range of 70–105 kV peak and 250 to over 1000 mA.

Electron tube and solid-state rectifiers are equipped with either manual or automatic control systems for matching the electrical outputs of the equipment to the particular load conditions of the application. Both types of rectifiers are also available in enclosures suitable for outdoor installation. (See Transistors and solid rectifiers.)

A general block diagram of control equipment is shown in Figure 4. Delivery of power to the high voltage transformer and rectifiers is modulated by a main control element introduced in series with the input to the transformer. The main control elements in present use are saturable reactors or electronic devices of suitable rating. The action of the main control element is determined by a signal furnished by the amplifier section of the control equipment. The function of this section is to modify the signals received at its input by changing their power amplitude to make them suitable for driving the main control element. Direct manual control may be accomplished by setting components of the amplifier section or by introduction of a manually controlled signal in place of the amplifier signal to the main control element. The input signal to the amplifier section is derived from a signal conditioning network.

In general this network compares signals derived from the actual operation of the precipitator against preset signals adjusted by the installer or operator, with the signal to the amplifier being the difference between these two. Since the purpose of the control system is to maximize the electrical power input into the precipitator, and since this maximum power input is usually determined by the sparking potential of the precipitator, the feedback signal is usually based upon precipitator sparking rate. The spark sensing signal is taken from measurement of primary or secondary current, or from the voltages across the transformer primary or reactor, since all of these fluctuate when sparking occurs. The response of these automatic control systems is rapid enough to accommodate extremely short time variations in process conditions which influence the precipitator sparking potential. Therefore they maintain a maximum power input under all conditions of operation both long- and short-term on any given process. Control equipment in present-day practice is universally all-electronic and is usually mounted in a single control cubicle located remotely from the transformer-rectifier itself; this latter equipment is normally located immediately adjacent to the precipitator proper.

The switchboard or control panel carries the switches, meters, and control instruments for the rectifier and the primary circuit of the transformer.

PRECIPITATORS

The equipment comprising the precipitator proper consists of a shell for containing the gases, means for uniformly distributing the gas, the collecting electrodes, the discharge electrodes, and the hoppers or conveying systems for handling the precipitated dust. In general, the precipitators are of two types: the wire-in-pipe or wire-in-duct. Wire-in-pipe installations comprise a multiplicity of parallel pipes through which the gas passes, and the energy is supplied from a discharge electrode coaxially located within each pipe. The pipes are usually round but may be square, hexagonal, or octagonal in cross section. Square or hexagonal pipes are usually nested to conserve space. Plate or duct precipitators are made up primarily of a series of parallel plates encased in a shell, thereby forming ducts or passages through which the gas passes. Discharge electrodes are centrally located within the ducts and insulated from the collecting members.

Plate-type precipitators have been made in many varieties distinguished primarily by the orientation of the gases and the type of electrodes utilized. According to the problem, collecting electrodes have been made of flat steel, corrugated steel, reinforced concrete slabs, rod curtains, hollow electrode plates with pockets, hollow electrodes of tulip-shaped cross section, expanded metal, asbestos board, or plates formed by batteries of v-shaped bent sheets. Discharge electrodes have been made of round wire, barbed wire, twisted square wire, star-shaped wire, etc. Also, precipitators have been constructed of a variety of materials to meet the particular operating situations. Electrodes of steel, nickel alloys, lead, carbon and other corrosion-resistant materials have been made. Duct-type precipitators have been utilized where gases pass either horizontally or vertically through the passages formed by the ducts. At the present time the usual configuration of the duct-type precipitator is that of a horizontal flow arrangement, consisting of ducts formed by flat smooth sheets equipped with suitable stiffeners which serve the dual function of providing structural adequacy and controlling re-entrainment of the deposited material. A typical modern duct-type precipitator used in the great majority of present-day installations is shown in Figure 5.

The choice of size of precipitator for a specific problem is determined by a number of factors including the nature of the operation, and the physical, chemical, and electrical characteristics of both the gases and the material to be removed. These factors establish the rate constant of the process which in turn establishes the physical size and the power requirement for a desired particle removal efficiency.

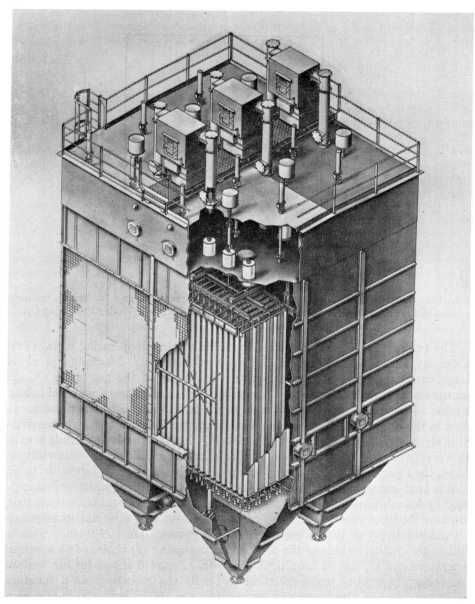

Fig. 5. Modern duct-type precipitator. Courtesy Research-Cottrell, Inc.

Precipitator Operating Characteristics

As indicated by the efficiency equation, the performance of the precipitator depends on the ratio of collecting surface area to the total volume of gas handled, and on the precipitation rate parameter ω. This parameter, in turn, depends on the charging and collecting field strength (both of which are dependent on operating voltage), the particle size, and the gas viscosity. Practical factors which influence the constant ω are primarily the resistivity of material to be collected, the gas flow distribution, and the re-entrainment of collected material back into the main gas stream.

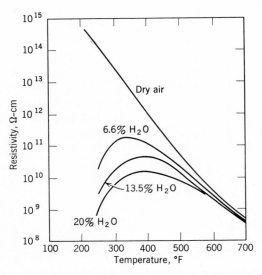

Fig. 6. Resistivity of air containing typical semiconducting material as a function of temperature and of the percentage of moisture in the air. Courtesy Addison-Wesley Publishing Co.

The two primary factors which influence the maximum operating voltage are the gas density and the resistivity of the collected material. Maximum precipitator voltage varies approximately directly with the density of the gas under conditions close to normal ambient pressures. The resistivity of the collected material influences the onset of back corona, a phenomenon which is destructive to the process. Back corona is the descriptive term for the local discharge from the normally passive collecting electrode. In a corona discharge system, when the passive electrode is covered with a poorly conducting dust or fume, under suitable conditions of corona voltage and current, the layer breaks down locally and a small hole or crater is formed from which a visible back-corona occurs. Such back-corona reduces precipitator collecting efficiency by lowering spark-over voltage and by producing ions which decrease particle charging. In large precipitators the onset of back-corona does not usually appear until the resistivity of the collected material is greater than 10^{10} Ω-cm. Two basic methods are utilized to control the onset of back-corona: (1) choice of an appropriate temperature and (2) use of conditioning agents. Figure 6 shows for air containing cement dust (a typical semiconducting material) the resistivity as a function of temperature, and of the percentage moisture in the air. These curves of a cement dust indicate the means by which resistivity may be partially or completely controlled.

The precipitator may be located in the process to treat gases at a temperature either below or above the critical region where resistivity is highest. If this is not possible, the alternate technique of use of conditioning agents is possible. Naturally, a combination of these two techniques may be utilized. Over the years, a large number of conditioning agents such as water vapor, ammonia, sulfuric acid, sodium chloride, etc, have been tried with varying degrees of success. Fortunately, in many industrial processes, conditioning agents such as water vapor and sulfur dioxide are already present in the process gases and effectively condition the material so that no external requirement exists for use of additional conditioning agents.

The interrelated factors of gas flow distribution and particle re-entrainment exert an influence on the overall performance of a precipitator which is equal to, or greater than, that of the corona and the electrostatic forces acting upon the particles. For proper function of an electrostatic precipitator, provision must be made to ensure that the gas flow quality, as measured by uniformity of flow and low degree of turbulence, is maintained. Further, the gas velocity must not exceed a certain maximum above which re-entrainment of collected material back into the gas flow abruptly increases. Good gas flow quality can be achieved in the precipitator system by the application of known principles and methods. The devices used are guide vanes and diffusers (perforated plates). With these devices the relatively abrupt flow transitions, which must be dealt with in the normal precipitator plant layout problem, are handled satisfactorily. One of the techniques used for proper establishment of guide vane and diffuser configurations has been the scale model. Similitude techniques for gas flow model studies have been developed and refined in the years since 1945 by various investigators (2), and practically all modern workers use or have used these models. They are usually constructed of transparent plastic so that the flow is actually visible. In addition, measurements of flow profiles can be made using sensitive anemometers. Gas flow model experience has added considerably to a more basic understanding of these low-speed systems so that in many cases good designs can now be established without the use of models (3). They have also been utilized successfully for the qualitative evaluation of dust dropout in the gas flow system.

Table 3. Values of Basic Design Parameters Used in Practice (1). Courtesy Addison-Wesley Publishing Co.

Basic parameter	Symbol	Normal range
precipitation rate	ω	0.05–1.0 ft/sec
collection surface	$\dfrac{A}{V}$	50–1,000 ft²/1,000 cfm
duct width	$2S$	6–15 in.
gas velocity	v	3–15 ft/sec
corona power	$\dfrac{P_c}{V}$	50–500 W/1,000 cfm
corona power density	$\dfrac{P_s}{A}$	0.3–3 W/ft²
high-tension sectionalization	$\dfrac{N}{V}$	0.5–10 sections/100,000 cfm (active sections)
number of series sections	N_s	1–5 sections (active sections)

Typical values of basic design parameters, used in practice in the design of electrostatic precipitators, are shown in Table 3.

The final essential element in the electrostatic precipitator is the system utilized for the removal of accumulated deposits from the electrodes. This is necessary not only to remove the collected material from the precipitator, but also to maintain optimum electrical conditions in the precipitation zones. The deposits are usually dislodged by mechanical jarring or vibration of the collecting electrodes, a process generally referred to as rapping. In some instances it is also necessary to dislodge material from the discharge electrodes in order to prevent choking off of the corona discharge and a reduction in precipitator efficiency. Pneumatic and mechanical rappers of various designs have been used widely and successfully over the years. Modern practice tends to favor the use of impact rappers for plates, and vibrator rappers for the discharge electrodes. Modern techniques also favor electric rappers because of their high reliability, their ease of adjustment, and their ability to maintain uniformity of operation over long periods of time without supervision. Far from being a minor adjunct in electrostatic precipitation, proper rapping equipment is of the utmost importance in determining overall performance and has been one of the difficult problems.

Two-Stage Electrostatic Treater

This type of treater consists of unit cells and a power pack, and is widely used in connection with air conditioning (see Figure 3). A unit cell consists of two distinctly separate stages, the ionizing stage and the precipitation stage (4).

Ionizing Stage. In the leading edge of the cell are alternate very fine tungsten wires and grounded rods or plates, between which about 13,000 V dc is applied; the wires are usually positively charged. As dust-laden air passes through the static field the dust particles receive a positive charge.

Precipitation Stage. The precipitation stage consists of thin, flat plates for both high voltage and ground electrodes installed in a horizontal or vertical position and spaced $\frac{1}{4}$ to $\frac{5}{16}$ in. apart. Adjacent plates are insulated from one another. A potential of 6000 V dc is applied to alternate plates. The plates are usually coated with a thin layer of oil or other similar material to aid in holding the collected dust.

The main advantage of using two stages and positive polarity on the discharge electrodes is that nitric oxide and ozone formation is reduced to a minimum. In the ionization section the gas is subject to a very short period of ionization at high voltage, the positive-ion formation causing less generation of ozone. In the collecting section the ionized gas is subject to a strong electrostatic field, but corona discharge is reduced to a minimum because both positive and negative electrodes are smooth, flat plates. The use of lower voltages and close electrode spacing permits the construction of small compact cells with relatively large collecting surfaces, and permits the energization of these cells with small compact power packs.

Normal treatment velocities are in the range of 8–10 ft/sec and efficiencies in the range of 85–90% are attained. Specially designed precipitators of the two-stage type have been utilized, however, at treatment velocities as high as 100 ft/sec and efficiencies in the 99%+ range (5).

Power packs for the two-stage type precipitator usually consist of a voltage doubler circuit with outputs of ionizer voltage in the range of 10–15 kV peak and collector voltage in the range of 5–7.5 kV peak. They are always of the electronic type with electron tube or solid-state rectifiers, and are equipped with suitable filtering circuits for minimizing output voltage ripple, and with suitable protective circuitry to accommodate ionizer sparking conditions and frequent short circuits in the collector section. The power pack and very elementary control equipment are located in a cubicle external to the precipitator element proper. The control, protecting, and indicating elements usually include an on-off switch combined with some type of overload circuit breaker, a pilot light, and a secondary voltmeter or milliammeter.

A variety of methods for removing the collected material from the collecting plates are utilized. The first method involves the use of a water soluble adhesive which is applied to the collecting surfaces at the beginning of each cycle of operation. After a period of operation, determined primarily by the amount of contaminants being removed, the unit is de-energized and automatically washed with water with a traveling manifold arrangement. The adhesive application, operation, and washing cycle is usually automatically controlled. A second system involves the use of mechanical arrangements which cause the collecting electrode surfaces to pass from the active precipitating zone through a bath of some type of solvent and then return to the precipitating zone in a continuous cycle. The third method allows accumulations of solids to build up to the point where they are re-entrained back into the air stream as large agglomerates and subsequently collected by a filter located downstream of the electrostatic precipitator.

Applications

There are, essentially, only two fundamental limitations to the applicability of the electrostatic precipitation process, and one overwhelming practical limitation. As fundamental limitations, the process must be restricted to the removal of particulate solid or liquid contaminants in gases, and system conditions must be such that corona occurs; as a practical limitation, the process must be restricted to nonexplosive mixtures of gases because of the existence of occasional sparks in the normal operation of the precipitator. Thus, electrostatic precipitators can, and have been, applied in a great number of industrial processes. In terms of operating variables, gas flows from 1 cfm to over 3,000,000 cfm have been treated and gas temperatures have varied from ambient to over 1200°F, at gas pressures from atmospheric to over 400 psi gage; particles from 0.1 μ to over 200 μ have been removed; concentrations from 0.0001 to 100 gr/ft^3 have been treated and efficiencies in the range or 80–99.9% have been obtained. In addition, these relatively high collection efficiencies have been obtained with modest corona and fan power requirements. The draft loss through an electrostatic precipitator rarely exceeds 0.5 in. water gage and the corona power requirements are normally in the range of 50–500 W/1000 cfm of gas treated. As a result, electrostatic precipitators are used extensively in a large variety of applications (1,6–8). Worldwide figures are difficult to assemble, but some indication is evident from practice in the U.S. There are today an estimated 3300 precipitators in use in the U.S. treating over 350 million cfm of various industrial gases. Of this total capacity, over 60% is in the electric power generation industry for the collection of fly ash from fossil fuel boilers. The remaining 40% is distributed approximately as follows: 10% in the steel industry; 10% in the cement industry; 7% in the paper industry; 7% in the nonferrous metallurgy and the remaining 6% in the chemical industry and in the detarring of fuel gases and production of carbon black. The principal growth areas have been in the electric power and steel industries. Cement, paper, and chemicals have shown a continuing requirement for precipitators. Detarring of fuel gases and collection of carbon black have by now become essentially obsolete applications.

Some representative industrial applications are as follows:

Collection of Fly Ash from Coal-Fired Boilers. Electrostatic precipitators have been used for the collection of fly ash which results from the combustion of coal in a variety of boiler types, such as Stoker-fired boilers, pulverized-fuel-fired boilers, and cyclone-fired boilers. Treatment temperatures range from 250–600°F and efficiencies of 85 to over 99% are achieved. Early practice was based on efficiency requirements of 90–95% but over the years a continuing demand for higher efficiencies has been evident so that today, in the large central-station pulverized-fuel installations, efficiency requirements of 99% and higher are not uncommon.

Blast Furnace Gas. The blast furnace is a large producer of by-product fuel gas, the utilization of which is an important factor in the economics of pig-iron production. In order to utilize the gas effectively it must be cleaned to less than 0.01 gr/ft³. Generally, this has been done in a three-step treatment consisting of a dry cyclonic or inertial dust catcher, a packed-tower combination washer and gas cooler, and an electrostatic precipitator or a high-energy direct-contact scrubber. Although this application was a major one for precipitators in the past years, the recent trends in blast furnace practice toward the use of higher top pressures favor the use of the high-pressure-drop wet scrubber, where energy, previously wasted across top pressure controlling valves, is now utilized for gas cleaning. In this application precipitator treatment conditions are temperature approximately 100°F; blast furnace gas saturated with water vapor; loadings approximately 0.1 gr/ft³. Outlet loadings below 0.01 are routinely obtained.

Open-Hearth Furnaces and Basic Oxygen Converters. Precipitators have been used extensively for the collection of iron oxide fume from open-hearth furnaces operating with and without the use of oxygen lancing. Gas volumes in the range of 200,000 cfm, containing approximately 6 gr/ft³ of iron oxide fume, are treated at temperatures of about 500°F after the gases have been passed through waste heat boilers. The efficiency generally ranges on the order of 99%.

Gases from the basic oxygen furnace process for the production of steel, in quantities of about 1,000,000 cfm, and containing loadings in the range of up to 3 gr/ft³, are treated at temperatures of about 500–600°F after the gases have been passed through water quenchers and heat recovery equipment. Efficiencies in the range of 99.5% are normally obtained.

Collected iron oxide from both open-hearth and basic oxygen furnace operations is returned to the process for recovery of iron by sintering the material. Gas cleaning systems on the exhaust from the sintering operation normally involve the use of a cyclone collector and an electrostatic precipitator. Gas volumes in the range of 200,000 cfm containing loadings of about 2 gr/ft³ are treated at temperatures of 250–300°F. Efficiencies of 97% are normal.

Sulfate Recovery Boiler. In the kraft process for the production of paper, lignins which result from the cooking process are burned in recovery boilers for the generation of process steam and for the recovery of pulping chemicals. A significant proportion of the recovered chemicals are in the form of solids entrained in the exhaust gases from the boiler. The gases are treated with electrostatic precipitators for the retention of these chemicals and for the elimination of air pollution. Gas volumes in the range of

200,000 cfm containing 3–6 gr/ft³ of entrained solids are treated at temperatures in the range of 300°F; efficiencies in the 98% range are typical.

Catalytic Cracking of Petroleum. In the years following World War II, precipitators were used extensively for the recovery of catalyst from fluidized-bed cracking processes for the production of high-octane gasoline. The gases leaving the catalyst regenerators were treated in precipitators after they had passed through waste heat boilers. Gas volumes in the range of 300,000 cfm containing loadings up to 50 gr/ft³ of catalyst were treated in the precipitator at 5 lb pressure and temperatures of about 500°F. Efficiencies in the range of 95% were obtained and the collected catalyst was returned to the process. In the years from about 1955–1965 the trend has been toward the elimination of the precipitator and the reliance on cyclones located in the regenerator vessel for retention of the catalyst. This trend was primarily related to the

Fig. 7. Typical commercial two-stage electrostatic air-cleaner cell of stackable type. Courtesy Research-Cottrell, Inc.

reduction in the cost of catalyst and the desire to eliminate extreme fines from the equilibrium catalyst. Present trends toward the use of more expensive synthetic catalysts, increasing entrainment rates, and the growing stringency of air pollution control increase the demand for higher gas cleaning efficiency and indicate the possibility of a return to the use of precipitators in this process.

Miscellaneous Chemical and Metallurgical Operations. Precipitators have been used extensively in the metallurgical and chemical industries for a great variety of processes where the recovery of products or by-products and the elimination of air pollution have been required. Applications for the removal of acid mists from sulfuric acid plant tail stacks, for the removal of phosphorus dust from electric furnace processes for manufacture of elemental phosphorus, and for recovery or elimination of fluorine-bearing solids from electrolytic aluminum cells have all involved the use of precipitators. These applications typically involve gas volumes in the range of 50,000–100,000 cfm, efficiencies of 99% or higher, and temperatures from 100–1000°F.

Air Cleaners. All of the foregoing industrial applications of the electrostatic precipitator utilize the single-stage type where the particle charging and particle collecting processes occur simultaneously. A general class of applications where two-stage precipitators are utilized exists in the cleaning of ambient air of entrained solids. This class of electrostatic precipitators ranges from the highly specialized design required in critical applications, such as the maintenance of the totally recirculated environment in nuclear submarines, to the appliance variety of air cleaner utilized in homes or offices for the reduction of allergens and tobacco smoke. Specially designed, two-stage electrostatic air cleaners have been used to treat ambient air at velocities up to 100 ft/sec at efficiencies up to 99.8%. Commercially available standard units are being used extensively for the cleaning of air in large commercial and industrial buildings in order to reduce maintenance costs of cleaning drapes, rugs, walls, etc, as well as for the improvement of the esthetic qualities of the environment; they are also finding extensive use in the maintenance of air cleanliness in machine rooms, and various industrial plants where a dustfree environment is required. In these applications gas volumes treated may range from as low as 500 cfm to over several hundred thousand cfm, in a large office building. Efficiencies on the order of 85–95% are normally attained and in situations where cleanliness requirements are extremely critical, such as in white room facilities in the aerospace industry, electrostatic precipitators are followed by high-performance absolute filters which result in the attainment of overall efficiencies on the order of 99.98% on materials larger than 0.3 μ. Figure 7 illustrates a typical stackable air cleaner cell of the type used in this service. And, finally, coupled with the increasing use of central air-conditioning systems, electrostatic air cleaners are beginning to find increasing use in smaller office buildings and homes.

Bibliography

"Electrostatic Precipitation" in *ECT* 1st ed., Vol. 5, pp. 646–662, by L. M. Roberts, Research Corporation.

1. H. J. White, *Industrial Electrostatic Precipitation*, Addison-Wesley Publishing Co., Reading, Mass., 1963.
2. C. L. Burton and R. E. Willison, "Application of Model Studies to Industrial Gas Flow Systems," *ASME Paper 59-A-280, Dec. 1959.*
3. V. W. Copcutt, *Combustion* **35** (6), 46–48 (1963).
4. G. W. Penney, *Electrical Engineering* **56,** 159–163 (1937).
5. H. J. White and W. H. Cole, *J. Air Pollution Control Assoc.* **10,** 239–245 (1960).
6. H. J. White, "Recent Advances in Electrostatic Precipitation in America," *Grenoble Conference on Electrostatics 1960*, Editions du Centre National de la Recherche Scientifique, Paris, France.
7. H. J. White, "Fifty Years of Electrostatic Precipitation," *Air Pollution Control Association, Paper 57-35, June 1957.*
8. H. J. Hall, "Trends in Electrostatic Precipitation and Industrial Gas Cleaning," *Chem. Eng. Progr. Monograph Ser.* **59** (3), AIChE, New York, 1963.

L. M. ROBERTS AND A. B. WALKER
Research-Cottrell, Inc.

ELEMENTS—PERIODIC SYSTEM

Before the discovery of radioactivity and nuclear transformations, a pure substance was to be regarded as an element if it could not be split up into simpler substances. An element may now be defined as a pure substance in which all the constituent atoms have the same atomic number and the same arrangement of extranuclear electrons (4). See also Atoms; Radioisotopes; Nuclear reactors; Radioactive elements, natural.

To the ancients, the physical world was composed of only four elements: *terra*, *aqua*, *aer*, and *ignis* (earth, water, air, and fire). To these Aristotle added *aether*, the substance of the sky and stars. Some of the alchemists attempted to base all matter on salt, sulfur, and mercury, and even long after the more modern denotation of the word "element" was applied by Boyle, there was still much confusion concerning which pure substances were elements and which were compounds. Only after the concept of molecules (as distinct from atoms) was introduced by Avogadro, and after many advances in thermochemical and electrochemical methods for isolating elements were made in the nineteenth century, were the chemical elements clearly established as physical entities. Thus, sodium, potassium, calcium, strontium, barium, magnesium, and chlorine were all isolated by Davy between 1807 and 1810; cesium, rubidium, thallium, and indium were all discovered within the period 1860 to 1863. By Mendeleev's time (1869) some sixty-three elements were known and there was much speculation about whether or not there was a limit to the number that might be found.

Correlation of the elements under some comprehensive system had been a subject of active discussion since 1750. There could be no basis for an orderly list, however, until quantitative methods led to Dalton's atomic theory and to his concept of atomic weights based on H = 1. After Stas had completed his accurate survey of atomic weights in the 1850s several schemes of classification appeared. Newlands first demonstrated periodicity among the elements in 1863, but there was no place in his scheme for new elements, which then were appearing frequently. Lothar Meyer expressed the periodic idea more thoroughly, but credit for an enduring scheme of chemical elements goes to Dmitri Ivanovich Mendeleev, because he first grasped the significance of the periodic relationship and extended it to fruitful predictions. His two articles in 1869 and 1872 usually are summarized in the form of a periodic law: The properties of the chemical elements and their compounds are a periodic function of their atomic weights (1).

Actually, Mendeleev proposed six revolutionary ideas:

1. The elements arranged according to the magnitudes of their atomic weights show a periodic change in properties.

2. Chemically analogous elements have atomic weights either very close together (Fe, Co, Ni) or separated by equal increments (Cl, Br, I).

3. The arrangement according to atomic weights corresponds to the so-called valency of the elements.

4. The magnitude of the atomic weight determines the properties of the element, that is, a mere increase in weight in a group (Cl, Br, I) produces striking differences as well as analogies.

5. The discovery of many new elements may be predicted.

6. Some atomic weights will experience correction (that is, they do not fit in the table under the old weights).

	IA	IIA	IIIA	IVA	VA	VIA	VIIA	VIIIA			IB	IIB	IIIB	IVB	VB	VIB	VIIB	0
1	1 H																	2 He (2)
2	3 Li	4 Be											5 B	6 C	7 N	8 O	9 F	10 Ne (2,8)
3	11 Na	12 Mg											13 Al	14 Si	15 P	16 S	17 Cl	18 A (2,8,8)
4	19 K	20 Ca	21 Sc	22 Ti	23 V	24 Cr	25 Mn	26 Fe	27 Co	28 Ni	29 Cu	30 Zn	31 Ga	32 Ge	33 As	34 Se	35 Br	36 Kr (2,8,18,8)
5	37 Rb	38 Sr	39 Y	40 Zr	41 Nb	42 Mo	43 Tc	44 Ru	45 Rh	46 Pd	47 Ag	48 Cd	49 In	50 Sn	51 Sb	52 Te	53 I	54 Xe (2,8,18,18,8)
6	55 Cs	56 Ba	57 La *	72 Hf	73 Ta	74 W	75 Re	76 Os	77 Ir	78 Pt	79 Au	80 Hg	81 Tl	82 Pb	83 Bi	84 Po	85 At	86 Rn (2,8,18,32,18,8)
7	87 Fr	88 Ra	89 Ac **															

Rare earth metals *

58 Ce	59 Pr	60 Nd	61 Pm	62 Sm	63 Eu	64 Gd	65 Tb	66 Dy	67 Ho	68 Er	69 Tm	70 Yb	71 Lu

Uranium metals **

90 Th	91 Pa	92 U	93 Np	94 Pu	95 Am	96 Cm	97 Bk	98 Cf	99 Es	100 Fm	101 Md	102 No	103 Lw

Fig. 1.   Periodic table—long form.

As a direct consequence of Mendeleev's predictions and as corroboration of his views, three new elements soon were discovered; many more followed in the next half century (5).

The principal objections to Mendeleev's first periodic table have long since been obviated. His deliberate reversal of the atomic weights of tellurium and iodine, and of cobalt and nickel (also, later, of argon and potassium) was not justified by more accurate determination of their atomic weights, but was made reasonable by Moseley's all-important concept of atomic number as a superior basis of periodicity. Moseley's experimental determination of atomic numbers also resolved the question of what to do about the rare earth elements. Until it was shown that there were only fourteen rare earths (of atomic numbers 58 through 71, fitting perfectly between lanthanum and hafnium), it was feared that any "element" in Mendeleev's table might be split into a variety of closely similar elements. However, after the discovery of the inert gases they were fitted into the original scheme in a logical manner, as has every other element discovered since Mendeleev's time. Even the transuranium elements constitute but a logical extension, being in effect a second rare earth series.

A long-period representation of the periodic table appears in Figure 1. In essence this is an expanded and modernized version of Mendeleev's first table, except that the several periods are shown horizontally instead of in vertical lists of elements. Mendeleev emphasized the periods rather than the groups because only in the periods does the progressive change in the character of the elements with gradual change of atomic weight become apparent; in terms of later knowledge the periods show the development of atomic structure with increase in atomic number. Hence, the classification of the elements has a logical and fundamental basis when considered in terms of developing periods, and only a convenient sorting or filing connotation when considered in terms of the vertical columns called groups. For this reason the long-period representation has come to be preferred by most teachers and authors of textbooks after 1940.

The short-period form of the periodic table, shown in Figure 2, enjoyed long popularity because of its compact arrangement. It first appeared in Mendeleev's writings as a further attempt at simplification; basically it is derived from the long-period form by cutting the latter almost in half and superimposing the right-hand half on the left-hand half so that copper, silver, and gold lie in the first group. There is chemical justification for this in that the ions with completed d shells (copper core, silver core, or gold core) resemble those with completed p shells (inert-gas cores). A difficulty arises, however, because a period of eighteen elements cannot be spread on a period of eight elements by doubling; the elements in the center of the longer periods (Fe–Co–Ni, Ru–Rh–Pd, Os–Ir–Pt) have to be left in an anomalous eighth group. Furthermore, some confusion has arisen in designating the subgroups, which result from the doubling process. In the convention followed in Figure 2, the elements from the left-hand part of each long period comprise the A subgroups, and those from the right-hand part the B subgroups. However, the designations A and B have sometimes been reversed for some of the later groups. Although there has been no ruling on the subject from the International Union of Pure and Applied Chemistry or the American Chemical Society, it may be pointed out that the traditional way of designating the subgroups is to use A or a for the elements on the left side of the double columns and B or b for the elements on the right side. As for which should be put on the left and which on the right, Mendeleev himself established that custom in his

Group →	0	I A	I B	II A	II B	III A	III B	IV A	IV B	V A	V B	VI A	VI B	VII A	VII B	VIII
Hydrides		RH		RH₂		RH₃		RH₄		RH₃		RH₂		RH		
Oxides		R₂O		RO		R₂O₃		RO₂		R₂O₅		RO₃		R₂O₇		
Period 1		1 H 1.008														
2	2 He 4.003	3 Li 6.94		4 Be 9.013		5 B 10.81		6 C 12.00		7 N 14.01		8 O 16.00		9 F 19.00		
3	10 Ne 20.18	11 Na 22.99		12 Mg 24.31		13 Al 26.98		14 Si 28.09		15 P 30.97		16 S 32.06		17 Cl 35.45		
4	18 A 39.95	19 K 39.10		20 Ca 40.08		21 Sc 44.96		22 Ti 47.90		23 V 50.94		24 Cr 52.00		25 Mn 54.94		26 Fe 55.85 / 27 Co 58.93 / 28 Ni 58.71
	36 Kr 83.80		29 Cu 63.54		30 Zn 65.37		31 Ga 69.72		32 Ge 72.50		33 As 74.90		34 Se 78.96		35 Br 79.91	
5	54 Xe 131.30	37 Rb 85.47		38 Sr 87.62		39 Y 88.91		40 Zr 91.22		41 Nb 92		42 Mo 95.91		43 Tc 99		44 Ru 101.07 / 45 Rh 102.91 / 46 Pd 106.4
			47 Ag 107.87		48 Cd 112.40		49 In 114.82		50 Sn 118.69		51 Sb 121.75		52 Te 127.60		53 I 126.90	
6	86 Rn 222	55 Cs 132.91		56 Ba 137.34		57 La 138.91 *		72 Hf 178.49		73 Ta 180.95		74 W 183.85		75 Re 186.2		76 Os 190.2 / 77 Ir 192.2 / 78 Pt 195.09
			79 Au 196.97		80 Hg 200.59		81 Tl 204.37		82 Pb 207.19		83 Bi 208.90		84 Po 210		85 At 211	
7		87 Fr 223		88 Ra 226		89 Ac 227 **										

* Rare earths lanthanide series (58–71)														
58 Ce 140.12	59 Pr 140.91	60 Nd 144.2	61 Pm 147	62 Sm 150.35	63 Eu 152.0	64 Gd 157.25	65 Tb 158.92	66 Dy 162.50	67 Ho 164.93	68 Er 167.26	69 Tm 168.93	70 Yb 173.04	71 Lu 174.97

** Rare earths actinide series (90–96)														
90 Th 232.04	91 Pa 231	92 U 238.03	93 Np 237	94 Pu 239	95 Am 241	96 Cm 242	97 Bk 247	98 Cf 249	99 Es 254	100 Fm 253	101 Md 256	102 No 253	103 Lw 257

Fig. 2. Periodic table—short form.

famous article in Liebig's *Annalen der Chemie und Pharmazie* in 1872 (1). There is no strong reason for changing the convention.

For certain elements, European usage for symbols and names has differed from American usage. The International Union of Pure and Applied Chemistry serves as a forum for discussion of conflicting claims to the discovery of new elements, and has as a general task the unification of all chemical terminology; its recommendations on the names and symbols of elements may therefore be expected to be those adopted by the member societies after full agreement has been reached.

The relative abundance of the chemical elements in the earth's crust (the combined lithosphere, hydrosphere, and atmosphere) is shown in Table 1. It should be noted, however, that this ignores the core of the earth, which has a density that suggests metallic iron and nickel.

Table 1. Abundance of Chemical Elements in the Crust of the Earth

Element	Crust, %	Element	Crust, %
oxygen	49.20	chlorine	0.19
silicon	25.67	phosphorus	0.11
aluminum	7.50	manganese	0.09
iron	4.71	carbon	0.08
calcium	3.39	sulfur	0.06
sodium	2.63	barium	0.04
potassium	2.40	nitrogen	0.03
magnesium	1.93	fluorine	0.03
hydrogen	0.87	strontium	0.02
titanium	0.58	all others	0.47

The concept of the *atomic number* as the net positive charge on the nucleus of an atom arose from Rutherford's experiments with alpha-particle projectiles falling on metallic foils, and was established as a fundamental and characteristic quantity for each element by Moseley's demonstration of the sequence of the elements based on the characteristic frequencies of the x-ray emission spectra. Thus, the periodic system of the elements, which began without any assumptions concerning the structure or composition of atoms, now has become a pattern which coordinates the atomic structures of the elements as well as their chemical properties.

Mendeleev required no more than the "solid, massy, hard, impenetrable, movable" atoms of Newton to make his successful predictions, for he interpolated the properties of the unknown elements from those of the known. As it became apparent through the years that some of the expected elements were not obtained despite repeated and exhaustive searches, Mendeleev's method became less and less helpful. The heaviest halogen (element 85, astatine) and the heaviest alkali metal (element 87, francium) were two that continually eluded chemists, because, although many claims were advanced for their discovery, all proved to be premature in that no visible or weighable amounts of the elements were forthcoming. The same might also be said about the long-missing elements 43 (technetium) and 61 (promethium). It became an accepted fact that these four elements, if they existed in nature at all, were in such low concentration as to defy all methods of chemical extraction. The ultimate "discovery" and isolation of these elements (and also of the transuranium elements) therefore required an entirely different mode of attack, based not on methods of chemical extraction but on actual synthesis from other elements, using known nuclear reactions. In this way, neptunium (element 93) was made by the capture of neutrons by the uranium atoms of weight 238, followed by emission of beta particles (electrons) to form neptunium 239, which in itself is radioactive. The beta decay of neptunium leads to plutonium, element 94, another isotope of which can be made from uranium-238 by an alpha-neutron reaction. Americium (element 95) was obtained in the form of the isotope 241 from the beta decay of plutonium-241. Curium (element 96) was first prepared as the isotope of weight 242 by the bombardment of plutonium-239 with alpha particles in a cyclotron; a neutron is lost from the aggregate nucleus and curium-242, an active alpha emitter, results. The same isotope results from the reaction of neutrons with americium-241, for the americium-242 formed in this way decays to curium-242 by the emission of beta particles (3). Curium itself has been obtained in gram amounts, but the elements 97 through 103 have been made only in submicroscopic amounts by cyclotron bombardments or by painstaking isolation from atomic bomb debris (2). It may become possible some day to isolate berkelium, californium, and einsteinium in visible amounts because isotopes of sufficiently long life already are known for these elements. Fermium, mendelevium, and nobelium may always remain known to us only in the form of submicroscopic amounts, due to the fact that they are intensely radioactive because of short half-lives. Lawrencium, element 103, has been made only to the extent of a few *atoms* (by bombardment of californium with boron nuclei), but such is the accuracy of prediction from alpha-emission systematics that even a few atoms of Lw could be recognized.

The chemical properties of the heaviest elements are known only from tracer experiments, but there is no doubt any longer that they correspond closely to the rare earth elements. The filling of the *5f* orbitals proceeds in large part like that of the *4f* orbitals, with curium and gadolinium representing half-filled *f* orbitals in the respective series. The oxidation state of $+3$ prevails for all the trans-curium elements, with a $+4$ state appearing only in berkelium; therefore, separation of the heaviest elements can only be achieved by methods which depend upon differences in *size* of the hydrated ions, rather than upon differences in oxidation state.

Technetium (element 43) and promethium (element 61) have been obtained by entirely different methods. The fission of uranium-235 leads to a great variety of lighter elements as fission products, ranging all the way from germanium and zinc to the rare earths, with the two maximum yields near zirconium and barium. The fact that all the known elements in this range were found in the strongly radioactive debris of fission naturally suggested that the missing elements 43 and 61 might also be found.

In 1937 technetium was identified in the cyclotron transmutation products of molybdenum, but by 1948 much more substantial amounts were available from the uranium pile at the Oak Ridge National Laboratory, Tennessee. In 1945 promethium was isolated and identified from fission products, and visible amounts are available from Oak Ridge. By such processes all of the gaps in the periodic table have been filled (see Fig. 1), including some of the elements beyond uranium. There is no reason to believe that an end has been reached to the number of possible new heavy elements that may be synthesized, but it seems highly improbable that any beyond uranium (and a trace of plutonium) will be found in natural sources.

Nuclear reactions have been applied to the synthesis of many other stable and radioactive atoms, so that in all some 700 atomic species are known. That these are grouped under 103 elements shows that in some instances there are many different kinds of atoms grouped under the name of one element. Atoms that differ in weight (mass number) but have the same nuclear charge are termed *isotopes* of the element of that atomic number; some elements (such as fluorine and aluminum) have no isotopes in their natural form whereas others (such as tin and xenon) may have nine or more stable isotopes. In addition, there are numerous pairs (and larger groups) of atoms of the same mass but different atomic number, and these are called *isobars*. There exist as well several examples of nuclear isomerism, in which two species of atoms have the same atomic number and weight but show different radioactive behavior, which can only be related to some difference in nuclear structure or condition.

The isotopes of hydrogen are separated in quantity by the purely chemical method of electrolysis, and much differential behavior of hydrogen and deuterium has been observed in chemical reactions. In addition, it appears that growing seaweed has the power of taking up more of one isotope of potassium than another, and a number of similar isotopic selection processes are reported for other living structures. Hence, it may no longer be said that an element may not be separated into two or more different substances by purely chemical means, and the only acceptable definition of an element is that based on atomic number. The convenience gained by the concept of element is lost to some extent when separate isotopes must be followed through a reaction, because a distinctive symbol and test for each are required. As the structures of nuclei become elucidated, it is probable that the ultimate particles of matter will assume the importance of elements (elementary particles), and that the aggregate bodies, which we now call chemical elements, will be considered to be diverse compounds of the true elementary particles.

Bibliography

"Elements—Periodic System" in *ECT* 1st ed., Vol. 5, pp. 668–674, by E. G. Rochow, Harvard University.

1. D. I. Mendeleev, *Ann. Chem. Pharm.* **8** Suppl., 151 (1872).
2. *Chem. Eng. News* **28,** 326 (1950).
3. G. T. Seaborg, *Am. Scientist* **36,** 361 (1948).
4. *Webster's New International Dictionary*, 2nd ed., G. & C. Merriam Co., Publishers, Springfield, Mass., 1934.
5. M. E. Weeks, *Discovery of the Elements*, 5th ed., J. Chem. Ed., Easton, Pa., 1945, Chap. 21.

E. G. Rochow
Harvard University

ELEMI. See Resins, natural.

EMBALMING FLUIDS

Embalming fluids are used for their preservative efficacy, germicidal potency, and cosmetic and restorative effects when injected into dead bodies. These preparations have long been essentially aqueous or hydroalcoholic solutions of formaldehyde in combination with a variety of other constituents, even though today many formulas specify one or more preservatives in addition to formaldehyde or in place of it. Formaldehyde coagulates and thus hardens proteins, thereby inducing resistance to autolytic and other putrefactive changes. From the point of view of the mortician embalming fluids must (*1*) ensure complete sanitation of the remains regardless of their condition; (*2*) preserve bodies against putrefactive influences over reasonably prolonged periods; (*3*) possess ability to preserve or impact lifelike consistency to tissues; and (*4*) replace as far as possible the pallor of death with every semblance of vital coloration, especially on exposed parts of the body.

A long time ago, the effectiveness of all embalming fluids was based on their content of arsenical compounds, mercuric chloride, zinc chloride or zinc sulfate, and other chemical substances of equally high toxicity. France, however, in 1846, prohibited the use of arsenic in these preparations, and in the United States the state of New York in 1906 assumed the initiative by enacting legislation to ensure the exclusion of arsenicals and equally toxic chemical substances from embalming fluids. This was done in order to avoid the possibility of medico-legal complications in all cases of suspected homicidal poisoning. In 1906, the Research Committee of the National Funeral Directors' Association of America recommended a germicidal preservative for general embalming purposes. This preparation was designated as the Approved Disinfectant indicated in regulations governing interstate transportation of the dead, and was subsequently sanctioned by the Conference of State & Provincial Boards of Health convening in Washington, D.C., in 1907.

Many state laws require the inclusion of formaldehyde in formulations of embalming fluids. Although most available embalming fluids still retain formaldehyde, their compositions vary so much that only a general idea of their constituents (1) can be given. All of these commercial fluids are available in concentrated form, ready for dilution according to directions recommended by the manufacturers.

Formaldehyde is the classical active preservative. The customary range of commercial fluids varies from 4 to 32% of formaldehyde gas, corresponding to 10 to 80% of USP formaldehyde solution. There are various state and territorial regulations (2) governing the potency of embalming fluids to ensure prophylactic and hygienic results, especially where embalmed bodies are to be objects of interstate transportation. Other active preservatives and germicides used in embalming fluids include synthetic organic germicides, such as certain quaternary ammonium compounds (3) as well as the sodium derivative of phenylphenol, *p*-chloro-*m*-cresol, tribromothymol, glyoxal (4), glutaraldehyde (5), and others.

Glycerol serves as both a diffusing medium and humectant, thereby imparting a temporary softening action upon tissues; its greatest value as a penetrating agent lies in its ability to facilitate the diffusion of embalming fluids throughout the capillary and general circulatory channels by materially reducing the surface tension of preservative solutions for injection.   In place of glycerol, now, sorbitol, glycols and their esters, colloidal modifying agents, such as gum tragacanth, gum karaya, and synthetic thickeners are frequently being used. The important role of synthetic dispersing and wetting agent ingredients should be emphasized as they serve to facilitate deep tissue penetration and increase overall preservative action to a marked degree.

The function of sodium nitrate in embalming fluids is a controversial matter. There is a difference of opinion as to whether sodium nitrate serves as a blood "solvent" or anticoagulant or whether it acts as a modifying agent, stabilizing the red color of the hemoglobin in the presence of formaldehyde. Sodium citrate, sometimes used in place of the nitrate, is definitely an anticoagulant. Some commercial embalming fluids contain organic chelating agents to sequester metallic ions in order to prevent these ions from coagulating the blood during the arterial injection of the embalming fluid. Some of these chelating agents are claimed (3) to have such an affinity for metallic ions that they denature enzymes and thereby prevent their normal catalytic action of breaking down or decomposing tissues.

Various red dyes impart a distinctive shade to embalming fluids. These cosmetic dyes, in combination with wetting, dispersing, and spreading agents (5), impart a lifelike appearance to an embalmed body by overcoming the blanching effects of formaldehyde and other ingredients upon skin tissues. The success of this phase of embalming, generally referred to as the restorative aspect, is completed by the judicious application of external cosmetics to highlight the tinctorial, lifelike flesh tones produced by the arterial embalming fluid dyes.

Perfumes have sometimes been added to embalming fluids to mask as far as possible the harsh penetrating odor of formaldehyde; for this use there are available synthetic odors in combination with sulfonated oils, ethylene glycol diethylene ether, or similar compounds that render the odorous concentrate miscible with aqueous solutions.

There are also numerous nonformaldehyde embalming preparations on the market but, because of higher costs entailed in manufacture and use, they are unlikely to find extensive application other than the preservation of anatomical specimens. Considerably more of this type of preservative would be needed to effect results comparable with those attained through the use of the usual formaldehyde fluids. Embalming solutions of the nonformaldehyde type may contain phenol or other germicides already mentioned, glycerol, alcohol, potassium nitrate, alum, salt, boric acid, salicylic acid, volatile oils (cinnamon and/or clove oil), wetting agents, etc. For this purpose, the usefulness of formaldehyde derivatives has been investigated in recent years. For example, trioxane, a cyclic ether, gradually evolves monomeric formaldehyde in a proper environment. Glycerol–formal, under optimum conditions, also decomposes slowly to yield glycerol and formaldehyde. Tris(hydroxymethyl)-nitromethane is reported to split off formaldehyde in alkaline solution.

Embalming fluids are also available in very highly concentrated forms usually called "cavity fluids"; these solutions contain considerably greater percentages of formaldehyde gas and are intended for injection into, and preservation of, the organs lying within the visceral and thoracic cavities. This special treatment is necessary to prevent the singularly rapid putrefaction that occurs in these parts of the cadaver.

"Preinjection fluids" have become useful adjuncts in modern practice. Such agents are essentially low-formaldehyde germicidal solutions for the preliminary irrigation of the circulatory channels and serve to facilitate the removal of residual blood and debris before the introduction of an arterial embalming solution.

Bibliography

"Embalming Fluids" in *ECT* 1st ed., Vol. 5, pp. 674–677, by Simon Mendelsohn, College of Pharmacy of the University of Cincinnati.

1. H. Bennett, *The Chemical Formulary*, Vols. 1–12, Chemical Publishing Co., New York, 1945–1964.
2. S. Mendelsohn, *Embalming Fluids*, Chemical Publishing Co., New York, 1939.
3. J. F. Fredrick, U.S. Pat. 2,918,402 (Dec. 22, 1959) (to The Dodge Chemical Co.).
4. H. I. Jones, U.S. Pat. 2,333,182 (Nov. 2, 1943) (to Hizone Products).
5. L. Rendon, U.S. Pat. 3,057,775 (Oct. 9, 1962) (to The Champion Co.).
6. L. McDonald, U.S. Pat. 2,318,319 (May 4, 1943) (to The Dodge Chemical Co.).
7. R. Amory and R. L. Emerson, *Poisons*, Vol. 2, 5th ed., of F. Wharton and M. Stille, eds., *Medical Jurisprudence*, Lawyers' Cooperative Publishing Co., Rochester, New York, 1905.
8. C. L. Barnes, *Art and Science of Embalming*, The Embalmers' Monthly, Chicago, 1905.
9. C. O. Dhonau, *Manual of Case Analysis*, The Embalming Book Co., Cincinnati, Ohio, 1928.
10. J. H. Eckels, *Modern Mortuary Science*, 3rd ed., Westbrook Publishing Co., 1948.
11. L. G. Frederick and C. G. Strub, *The Principles and Practice of Embalming*, Lawrence G. Frederick, Publisher, Dallas, Texas, 1959.
12. J. A. Kolmer and F. Boerner, *J. Lab. Clin. Med.* **11**, 608–614 (1926).
13. R. McFate, *Outlines of Chemistry*, 4th ed., Edwards Brothers, Inc., Ann Arbor, Mich. 1946.
14. S. Mendelsohn, *Chemist* **22**, 465 (1945).
15. S. Mendelsohn, *Embalming*, Part 4, Ciba Pharmaceutical Products, Inc., Summit, New Jersey, 1944.
16. *Proc. Ann. Conv. Natl. Funeral Directors' Assoc. Am. 27th (1908); 29th (1910); 30th (1911);* National Funeral Directors' Association of America, Milwaukee.
17. A. J. Nunnamaker and C. O. Dhonau, *Hygiene and Sanitation*, Vol. 2, The Embalming Book Co., Cincinnati, Ohio, 1930.
18. N. C. Pervier and F. L. Hansen, *Report and Review of Research in Embalming Fluids*, Minnesota State Department of Health, 1940.
19. U.S. Public Health Service, *Public Health Rept. 30* (Reprint No. 292) (1915).
20. C. O. Vermillion, *Chemical Principles of Mortuary Science*, John S. Swift, Co., Inc., St. Louis, Mo., 1946.

HAYDN JONES
Hizone Laboratories

EMBEDDING

The use of synthetic resins for embedding, potting, and encapsulating has been rapidly increasing since the early 1940s. The applications range from electrical insulation and protective packaging to mechanical and decorative utilization (see Fig. 1).

The use of embedding materials is an old-established practice. In the early days, the use of waxes and bituminous compounds was widely accepted. The major weakness of these materials lies in their temperature limitations. The development of phenolic casting materials by Baekeland in 1906 began one of the first uses of synthetic resins. The use of phenolics has not become widespread because an acidic catalyst is used in their manufacture which is detrimental to circuitry and components in electronic equipment, and because of the inherent brittleness of the resins, ie, their tendency to crack upon temperature cycling.

The real advances in embedding technology have taken place during and after World War II. The development of new synthetic polymers such as polyesters, epoxies, urethans, and silicones, has led to the present large-volume applications.

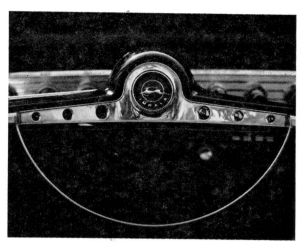

Fig. 1. An extremely common use of embedment is in automobile manufacture, where decorative medallions are frequently embedded in clear epoxy or other plastics, as in the horn button emblem above.   Courtesy General Electric Company.

The arrangement of material in this article is to some extent based, with acknowledgement, on earlier treatments by Harper and by Volk, Lefforge, and Stetson (see under Bibliography).

Although there are variations in terms, some broad definitions will be given as a guide for the reader who is not completely familiar with this technology.

The processes commonly used for packaging equipment are embedment, encapsulation, potting, and impregnation; in combination, they are rather specific to the electronic industry.   However, embedding is a fairly long established practice in both industry and the arts and sciences where specimens, decorative pieces, medallions, and other objects are embedded in plastic for a variety of purposes.   The specific definitions of all techniques are given below.

Embedment is completely surrounding or burying one or more objects or components in a medium.   This implies the complete encasement of a part, a component, or an assembly.   In decorative embedments, the item is completely isolated, while in electronic applications, it is not completely isolated, since leads or terminals must be accessible.   An embedding operation is usually performed by housing the item in a mold.   The embedment material is then poured into the mold until it completely surrounds the item.   Thus, the mold contains the embedding resin while it is converted from the liquid to the solid state.   The mold is then removed and a smooth uniform surface results, the final article having the shape of the mold.

Encapsulation is best defined as a conformal or dip-coating applied to a part or an assembly.   This usually involves dipping the part into a high-viscosity or thixotropic material to obtain a conformal coating with a thickness of approximately 5–50 mil.   The main problems in encapsulation are surface wetting, resin run-off, coating thickness control, or surface control in general (see Fig. 2).

Potting is the simplest cavity-filling process (Fig. 2).   The usual procedure is to position the component in its container, adding the potting material to fill the container, then curing to polymerize or harden the resin.   In the original applications for waxes and tars, these materials were melted and either forced or allowed to flow as

Fig. 2. Potting (left) and encapsulation (right) of electronic parts, using liquid silicone rubber. Courtesy General Electric Company.

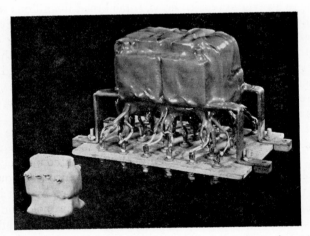

Fig. 3. Forcing the fluid polymer into the component constitutes impregnation. Electrical components (above) have been impregnated with an RTV (room-temperature-vulcanizing) liquid silicone rubber for protection.

liquids into the pots, resolidifying in final form on cooling. The use of an integral container is the main difference between potting and casting. In potting, it is usually advantageous to develop good adhesion to the parts and container, thus primers (bonding agents) are sometimes required. This is the case with silicones, which normally possess natural release characteristics when bonding agents are not used. With other resins which have inherently good adhesive properties, such as epoxies and polyurethans, no special container preparation is necessary.

Casting is very similar to potting. However, the container is removed after cure of the embedment resin. Normally, casting implies room-temperature curing with no application of pressure to effect the cure. The resin sets or hardens on standing at ambient temperature.

Molding consists of injecting or otherwise forcing the encapsulating medium into a mold, then curing under pressure. Molding thus is usually associated with heat and pressure in the curing cycle and usually with highly distinctive shapes. Molds are generally of the closed type, vented to allow for complete filling. Depending upon the material being used, both high- and low-pressure processes are employed.

Impregnation means saturation by forcing the fluid polymer of suitable viscosity into the component or assembly (see Fig. 3). The liquid is forced into all interstices of the assembly, after which the resin is cured or hardened. Impregnation differs from encapsulation in that encapsulation results in only an outer protective coating with little or no resin penetration into the assembly. Components containing coils or capacitor elements are processed by impregnation. Impregnation is sometimes accomplished by centrifugal casting and by vacuum techniques, as well as by the application of positive pressure.

Materials

The materials used for embedment and encapsulation are primarily the large class of materials known as plastics. This is due to the fact that plastics are most readily fabricated into complex structures and they provide the proper physical characteristics required of encapsulations. Plastics as a class are insulators. They therefore provide the necessary insulation required in electronic and electrical applications. Useful plastics fall into two major classes, thermoplastics and thermosets.

Thermoplastics are characterized by their ability to be made to flow upon the application of heat and substantial pressure. They become rigid again upon subsequent cooling in a reversible manner. Thermoplastics are polymers made up essentially of difunctional units. Simple chains formed of difunctional units can slip past each other to a limited extent upon heating or stressing; upon cooling or the relief of stress, the cohesive forces between molecules becomes predominant and the plastic becomes rigid again. Typical examples of thermoplastics are polyethylene and polystyrene.

The other class of plastics are known as thermosets. These polymers contain sizable portions of tri- or multifunctional units between which the cohesive forces are insufficient to prevent flow. These materials are liquids which, upon the addition of hardeners, ie, curing agents, and the application of heat cure, harden into solids. Enough crosslinks are formed so that flow is no longer possible. These changes are not reversible. Typical examples of thermosets are the phenolics and epoxies. Rubbery polymers are composed of chains which, because of the way the difunctional units are held together, tend to coil up into helixes. These helixes act as springs. This elasticity gives them the name elastomers. In this case, the crosslinking reaction is commonly known as vulcanization. All degrees of rigidity and flexibility are available, since most of the thermosetting resins can be modified or obtained in flexibilities almost equal to those of elastomeric materials, even softer than the low-melt thermoplastic materials.

THERMOPLASTICS

Waxes (qv).   Wax is probably the original encapsulating and embedding material.   It is excellent electrically and its use is extremely simple.   Most waxes are fluid at 200°F for dipping or casting.   Their low melting temperature limits their utility to approximately 125°F.   Asphalts and tars have similar properties and are even less expensive.   Cellulose esters are employed in the same way as the waxes.   Physically they are stronger but their moisture absorption is high and they are inferior to wax electrically.

Hydrocarbons.   The hydrocarbon polymers, polyethylene, polystyrene, and polybutadiene, are all outstanding in electrical properties, particularly in high-frequency applications where their low dielectric constants, 2.3–2.5, and outstanding low loss tangents, 0.0003–0.0005, make them the chosen materials.   Polystyrene resins are not widely used for embedding applications because of certain practical limitations.   They are generally useful only below 125°C.   They have a long cure cycle and have a high shrinkage upon cure, therefore a tendency to crack during the curing operation.   Their normal expansion is high and the curing reaction is air-inhibited.   The exposed surface will remain tacky.   Polybutadienes also have some usefulness as embedding materials.   They also must be cured in the absence of air to prevent surface inhibition.   The curing temperature is high.   These materials have not been widely used as yet (see Diene polymers; Olefin polymers; Styrene and Styrene polymers).

Vinyls.   Poly(vinyl chloride) and its copolymers are used in encapsulation techniques.   Conformal coatings are possible using plastisols or organosols (see Vinyl compounds and polymers).   Plastisol applications make use of a suspension of finely divided particles of polymer in a liquid plasticizer.   The component is dipped into the plastisol and the adhering layer is baked to form a solid impervious layer.

An organosol is a true solution of the plastic in solvent.   It is usually applied by brushing or spraying.   The solvent is subsequently removed in the baking operation.   Organosol coatings must be much thinner than plastisol coatings due to the danger of film rupture by solvent vaporization.

Fluorocarbons.   The extremely inert fluorocarbons have a better combination of physical and electrical properties than any other plastic.   They are very difficult to fabricate as they require heating to 650°F and, usually, substantial pressures.   Recently, moldable copolymers of tetrafluoroethylene and hexafluoropropylene have become available.   At present they are used mainly as wire insulation and molding resins.   They are not readily usable as typical encapsulation resins (see Fluorine compounds, organic).

THERMOSETS

The thermosets include the most useful embedding polymers.   As a class, they are characterized by higher safe-use temperatures.   They are more frequently formulated with fillers.

Phenolics.   Phenolic resins are not used to a large degree for embedding electrical assemblies primarily due to the corrosive effects of the acid catalyst, shrinkage, and the water given off in the curing reaction.   Unfilled phenolics are useful as coating compounds.   Phenolics are rigid, have good physical properties, tensile strength on the order of 7000 psi even at 250°F, and have excellent adhesion to most materials.   Electrically they are inferior to the hydrocarbon polymers and their moisture resistance is poor. Use of unfilled phenolics is limited due to the high shrinkage during cure. However, phenolics filled with silica, asbestos, or wood flour are used in tonnage quantities for electrical structural applications. These filled systems have excellent dimensional stability and provide superior strength properties up to 250°F.

Polyesters (qv). Polyesters were the first casting or potting resins widely used for embedment of electronic assemblies. Polyesters are formed by the reaction of polyfunctional acids and alcohols to form esters. This is a condensation polymerization and is accompanied by the formation of water. An example of this type of polyester is alkyd resins; they are used, combined with fillers, as molding compounds. These require less pressure and time than phenolics.

The most important types of polyesters useful in embedding are furnished as low-molecular-weight reactive polymers. The manufacturer reacts alcohols and polyfunctional acids containing unsaturation (or in some cases other compounds containing vinyl groups) to form small molecules containing reactive groups. The undesirable by-products of the condensation reaction, such as water, are eliminated while the resins are still liquids. Those polyesters containing vinyl groups are capable of polymerizing upon the addition of a peroxide catalyst and heat. In contrast to the alkyds, which cure by a condensation reaction, these materials cure by an addition mechanism. Everything that is added to the polymer becomes an integral part of the final solid material.

As a type of material, polyesters are easy to handle. The viscosity of the initial material is low, thus it can flow into and penetrate fine structures and can be deaerated readily. Curing is relatively simple, below 200°F, with room-temperature cure possible in some cases. The coefficient of thermal expansion of these resins is high, thus resulting in a high volumetric rate of shrinkage (6–8%) which causes many cracking problems. Methyl methacrylate and other acrylic copolymers are almost perfectly transparent and this accounts for their use in certain nonelectrical embedment applications. The high shrinkage and high exotherms of these acrylics limits their electrical applications.

Epoxy Resins (qv). Like the other thermosetting resins, epoxies are liquids available in a wide range of viscosities and even as low-melting solids. Growing rapidly in the past ten years, the epoxies are now (as of 1965) rapidly displacing the other thermoset systems, ie, phenolics and polyesters, for electronic encapsulations despite their higher cost. Their polymerization is a true addition reaction with no by-products to be removed. They have the lowest shrinkage of any of the thermosets. The bonds formed during cure are very stable. The cured polymer is tightly crosslinked, compact, and very chemically resistant. The basic epoxy resins have unlimited shelf life and by choice of the proper curing agents can be cured at room temperature or at elevated temperatures. Thus, it is possible to obtain a wide variety of pot life and curing conditions. These resins are compatible with most types of modifiers so that a considerable range of final physical properties can be achieved from typical rigid solids to soft, flexible plastics. An outstanding property of epoxy resins is their excellent adhesion to most materials.

It is very common to use reactive diluents to reduce the viscosity of the base epoxy resins so that complete penetration of the assembly is easily achieved. These reactive diluents, phenyl, butyl, and allyl glycidyl ethers contain reactive epoxy groups and become chemically, rather than physically, bound in the cured resin (see Epoxy resins).

Another major advantage of epoxy resins is the fact that a wide variety of curing conditions is possible through the use of different types of curing agents or hardeners. One type, tertiary amines, are very active curing agents and lead to room-temperature cures. Another type, typified by aliphatic primary amines, cures at room temperature or slightly elevated temperatures to cause polymerization by cross-linking with the amine nitrogen. This reaction is rapid and very exothermic, thus the pot life is very short. A third class of curing agents is the acid anhydrides which crosslink at elevated temperatures. This type causes a high degree of crosslinking and results in a solid having higher heat-distortion temperatures than the other preceding types. Acid anhydride systems have good shelf life since the curing reaction does not proceed at room temperature.

Moisture-sensitive amines such as the ketimines exhibit a very low order of reactivity with epoxy resins in the absence of moisture; however, the active polyamine is released when water is introduced into the system. Thus it is possible to formulate coatings that are stable in the can but that will give rapid room-temperature cures upon exposure to the air. Resin coatings up to thickness of 10 mil are possible using this system.

Silicones (qv). The outstanding characteristic of the silicone materials is their utility over an extremely wide temperature range. Silicones are available that are still flexible below $-150°F$ and provide stability to $500-550°F$ (most other materials become brittle at temperatures not much below $0-32°F$). Silicones also have excellent electric properties; they have a low dielectric constant, 2.7–3.0, and excellent corona and ozone resistance. They have high dielectric strength and low dielectric loss, and their electric properties do not change very much with temperature. Silicones have low water absorption. Silicone potting materials, even when saturated with moisture, still have extremely good electrical characteristics; the moisture is evidently unable to form a continuous conducting path through the silicone.

Probably the most important other characteristic of silicone materials is their convenience for the user. They are nontoxic, odorless, and very easy to handle in production.

Like the epoxies, silicones come in a variety of viscosities for ease of handling. The earliest silicone resins were high polymers supplied in solvents and cured by a condensation process with the addition of a metal soap catalyst, but several more convenient curing systems have been developed.

Room-temperature vulcanizing (RTV) silicone rubbers are furnished in a variety of viscosities and with a variety of curing agents, whereby the pot life and cure rate can be controlled. The RTV silicones cure by means of a condensation mechanism; however, the disengagement of water during cure is a problem only with extremely thick sections, and even this has been overcome by developing special catalyst systems.

One-package RTV silicone rubbers are similar to the one-package epoxies in that the moisture in the air catalyzes the condensation reaction in these materials. Thus these materials are limited to conformal coatings, encapsulating applications where the coating thickness is limited to approximately 100 mil.

RTV silicones have been developed that cure by a true addition reaction. These new materials are supplied as a two-package system. They are available in a great variety of viscosities ranging from very fluid liquids to quite viscous materials which are thixotropic and do not flow unless force is applied. The cured silicones range from nonflowing gels to tough, elastic solids. The curing rate is easily adjusted to give either room-temperature cures or cures at elevated temperatures. Thus the pot life is quite variable. Certain materials have a tendency to inhibit this curing reaction; They are, typically, sulfur-containing materials, amines, and other basic substances. This inhibition is usually a localized condition and can be eliminated by coating the offending items with a primer or one of the one-package RTV silicone rubbers.

Even though the RTV silicone compounds are the most expensive of the embedding and encapsulating materials, the great interest in military and space applications has given rise to large-volume applications. This is true because of the handling properties and the versatility of these RTV silicones as far as extremes of temperature are concerned.

Polyurethans (see Urethan polymers). Polyurethan resins can be formulated over a wide range of hardnesses and provide another material useful where resilience and resistance to shock are required. Another property of urethans that makes them useful in mechanical applications is their excellent abrasion resistance. Liquid polyurethan encapsulating compounds are generally two-component systems consisting of resin prepolymer and curing agent. The mixing ratio is generally critical and does not permit a wide variation. Because of the sensitivity of isocyanates to water and the tendency to cause bubbling, it is important to dehydrate the raw materials fully before reacting. It is necessary for the manufacturer to package and maintain the prepolymer and curing agent under dry nitrogen to prevent contact with moist air. The exotherm temperature rise for room-temperature curing liquid polyurethans is much lower than for epoxies, and this is a decided advantage in encapsulating semiconductors. The safe handling of these polyurethan systems requires good ventilation, safety goggles and protective apparel and protective hand skin creams, due to the fact that free isocyanates are hazardous when breathed. The presence of moisture and other polar compounds is detrimental to good cure of polyurethans, thus the necessity of dry and clean parts is evident. The justification for polyurethans stems more from their unique properties than their handling characteristics. As cured materials, polyurethans have high tensile strength and high elongation. Dielectric properties are good within the useful service temperature of the material, typically Class A service, 105°C. At low temperatures, polurethans do not become embrittled as rapidly as do flexible epoxy or polysulfides.

Polysulfides (see Polymers containing sulfur). Polysulfide rubbers are available as liquids for use in certain embedded electronic packaging applications. The cured polysulfide rubber product is flexible and has excellent resistance to solvents, oxidation, ozone, and weathering. Conversion of the liquid polysulfide polymer to solid rubber material is accomplished by the use of oxidizing agents such as cobalt or manganese octoate, lead octoate, p-quinonedioxime, and di- or trinitrobenzene. Conversion of these polymers from liquid to solid is exothermic and heat is not necessary. However, heat, high humidity, alkalinity, and sulfur accelerate the reaction. Acids retard the cure. Compounds based on these polysulfides are used in many applications where intermediate electrical properties are required. Fillers are required for strength and improved electrical properties. Nonblack fillers such as zinc sulfide, lithopane, silica, and titanium dioxides are recommended.

USE OF FILLERS

Fillers are generally dry, finely ground, inert materials that will not react with the basic embedding compound. Typical fillers include silica, quartz, zirconium sili-

Table 1. Filler Selector Guide

Filler	Increasing properties					Decreasing properties				
	Physical	Dielectric	Thermal conductivity	Thermal stability	Processability	Coefficient of expansion	Density	Shrinkage	Exotherms	Cost
sand			min			min		min	min	maj
silica, amorphous	min[a]		min			min		min	min	maj
silica, aerogel	min				maj			min	min	
quartz	min		min			maj		min		
microballoons, quartz and phenolic							maj			
powdered metals			maj	min		min		min		min
clays						min		min	min	min
calcium carbonate	min				min	maj		min	min	min
aluminum oxide			maj	maj					min	
iron oxide				min		min			min	min
graphite	min		min	min						
mica		min								min
asbestos	maj[b]		min	min		min		min	min	maj
silicates	min		min	min		maj		min	min	

[a] Min = minor contribution.   [b] Maj = major contribution.

Table 2. Utilization of Various Embedding Resins

Resin	Cost, $/lb	Advantages	Disadvantages
polyesters	0.40	low cost, ease of processing, wide range of viscosities, excellent electric properties, and wide choice of curing conditions	tendency to crack on heat ageing, tendency to develop severe loss of insulation resistance upon high-humidity conditions at high temperatures, high shrinkage upon cure, and air inhibition of cure
epoxy resins	0.70	wide choice of curing conditions: room-temperature cure with aliphatic amines; moderate-temperature cure with aromatic polyamines or acid anhydrides; for high-temperature applications, cycloaliphatic diepoxides, epoxy novolacs, epoxidized polyolefins, and bisphenol epoxies; for long pot life, BF_3 catalyst systems; and for one-package systems, the ketimine catalysts; also, excellent adhesion to embedded components	higher cost than polyesters, odors, toxicity, and health hazards of the curing systems, tendency to crack upon heat ageing, and high viscosity
silicones	4.00	excellent dielectric properties, room-temperature cure, resiliency, extreme low-temperature performance, low moisture absorption, repairability, wide choice of curing conditions, and excellent ozone, corona resistance	high cost, modest physical properties, primer required for adhesion with two-part materials, and limited solvent resistance
polyurethans	1.50	resiliency, vibration damping, excellent physical properties, good resistance to oils, oxidation, good ozone resistance, and repairability	reduced electrical properties at elevated temperatures, and toxicity and handling problems
hydrocarbons (polybutadiene, etc)	0.75	low dielectric constant, high heat distortion, and low electrical loss	high viscosity, handling properties, and availability
polysulfides	1.00	good solvent resistance, good adhesion, and repairability	toxicity, odor, handling problems, and reduced electrical properties at elevated temperatures

cate, calcium carbonate, powdered metals, iron oxide, aluminum oxide, mica, and glass. For low-density compounds, either organic or inorganic, light weight, hollow spheres are used. These low-density fillers range in screen mesh size from 20 through 325 and in bulk density from 3–30 lb/ft^3. Kanamite hollow glass beads, Bakelite phenolic microballoons, Colfoam urea–formaldehyde microballoons, Eccosphere hollow glass microballoons, and Eccosphere epoxy hollow spheres are examples of these low-density fillers.

Fillers may be used for some or all the following reasons: to reduce the coefficient of thermal expansion of the system; to increase the thermal conductivity of the embedding compound; to reduce the curing exotherm in epoxy and other resin systems; to improve the thermal resistance and raise the safe-use temperature; to increase the mechanical strength of the compound; to modify the flow characteristics of the system, ie, colloidal silica acts as a thixotropic filler; to improve the appearance or allow color coding of the castings; and to decrease cost. For the effects of various fillers on different properties, see Table 1.

Although the main emphasis in the foregoing has been slanted to the more stringent requirements of the electronics industry, there are several other applications that employ embedment technology ranging from decorative packaging for display to special material selection for environmental protection and/or mechanical support.

In addition, embedding materials have been extended into the medical field as, for example, the use of a clear silicone potting compound for encapsulating pathologic specimens for purposes of preservation, display, and medical studies.

A general discussion of the pros and cons of embedment is presented, as well as the selector guide in Table 2 covering the specific advantages and disadvantages of the most commonly used embedment materials.

Utilization of Embedded Packages

The design engineer must often choose whether to use embedment or encapsulation processes or whether to settle strictly on a mechanical solution to the packaging problems. There are many considerations that can be made along these lines. Some of the advantages and disadvantages of embedment are outlined below.

The advantages of embedment include the following: (1) reliability, through hermetic sealing (for protection against fungi, moisture, dirt, fumes, and other environmental conditions) and mechanical strength (for shockproofing and vibration damping); (2) design flexibility, which includes broad use of unitized construction, miniaturization, space factor, three-dimensional circuit construction, specific design requirements obtained by selection of proper resins, and better circuit characteristics; and (3) economy, through elimination of mounting hardware, elimination of environmental protection (because the resin provides this where needed), reduced cost of maintenance because of ease of replacement of embedded unit, and rapid production due to ease of assembly of embedded units.

The disadvantages include: (1) difficulty of repair, which varies from resin to resin, polyesters and epoxies being a problem and silicones and polyurethans less so; (2) heat dissipation, which can be avoided by adapting the design to (a) keep high-wattage resistors away from temperature-sensitive components, (b) space out the components as much as possible, (c) provide heat-conductive paths, and (d) deaerate all components; (3) thermal limitations, eg, the stability of the embedding resin must conform to the temperature requirements of the system, although proper design of the package can eliminate stresses that cause cracking; (4) increased weight of the embedded circuit must be considered, although low-density filled formulations or foams can reduce this problem; (5) dielectric properties of an embedded circuit must be considered in selection of resin since the resin has properties different than air; and (6) curing stresses can cause difficulties, due to the difference in coefficients of thermal expansion of the resin and metals, etc (this problem can be minimized by proper choice of resin and use of elastomeric coatings on the components).

Processing

The application techniques for any embedment material will vary according to the size and complexity of the application. Small-scale preparation and handling of material (ten grams to one or two pounds) for single projects or delicate processes can be easily performed with standard laboratory equipment. With two-package materials, scales or balances are usually necessary to provide accurate mixes. Also, spatulas, Dixie cups, or standard laboratory glassware will provide the entire equipment investment necessary. For precision work, vacuum equipment is suggested in order that material deaeration and techniques of vacuum impregnation may be possible for embedding delicate apparatus, such as for electronic uses.

When the operation is large enough to require an assembly line, or curing agent mixing in volumes of more than one gallon at a time, some degree of automation is highly desirable. In-plant automation is convenient, more economical, and provides for improved processing uniformity and cleaner housekeeping. The size and type of automatic metering, mixing, and dispensing equipment are dependent upon: (*1*) the embedment material to be used (consistency, mixing ratio, etc); (*2*) volume production requirements, ie, rate of finished items; (*3*) complexity in the process and the type of item being produced, ie, injection molding, impregnation, potting, etc; and (*4*) cost of the equipment itself.

Whether or not automation for metering and mixing is used in the material preparation, other types of dispensing techniques for high-speed production include spraying, dipping, flow coating, etc. In some cases embedment materials are now available in aerosol packages for immediate spraying, as well as being packaged in collapsible tubes, plastic cartridges, and premixed bulk containers adaptable to most dispensing equipment.

Once the materials have been prepared and applied, rate of cure or set can usually be adjusted with heating or cooling equipment. In the case of thermoset plastics, various types of heating apparatuses ranging from standard air-circulating ovens, high-temperature conveyor drying lines, or simple heat lamps, will provide for accelerated processing of the finished item.

For thermoplastics such as waxes, simple heating baths followed by ambient-temperature cooling are suitable. In high-speed production work with phenolics, etc, induction heating equipment is available.

A more detailed technical instruction on handling techniques and applicable equipment is available from any of the material suppliers. In most cases, they do provide references to manufacturing sources for such processing equipment. Also, a technical review of the materials will point out many of the optimum features as well as limitations (cure inhibitors and mixing ratios) to be considered with each product selection and its processing.

Equipment (Selection and Sources)

A fairly complete listing of suppliers for recommended equipment is covered in the Appendix of Volk, Lefforge, and Stetson (see under Bibliography). The reference

Table 3. Equipment for Automatic Dispensing of Embedment Materials

Company	Description
Bell & Gossett Company, Morton Grove, Ill.	self-contained dispenser for deaerating and mixing two-part encapsulating compounds for application by a hand gun on a 10-ft flexible hose, etc
United Process, Santa Monica, Calif., and Wayne, Pa.	a small batch mixer shot dispenser used in silicone embedding compound applications; the company has considerable liquid plastics experience
H. V. Hardman Company, Belleville, N.J.	firm has considerable experience with multiple-component liquid polymers; certain dispenser machines use catalyst piston pump and base compound gear pump, to handle two or three components
Automatic Process Control, Union, N.J.	builds machines to mix, deaerate, and dispense RTV silicone resins at a rapid rate for automatic molding
Pyles Industries, Detroit, Mich.	a large engineering staff available; has two-component pumps to mix and meter shotwise in large volume
Semco Sales and Service, Inglewood, Calif.	has gas-pressure and ratchet cartridge guns, as well as automatic equipment for handling bulk material
Gray Pump Company, Minneapolis, Minn.	air-powered positive displacement pumps and airless spray equipment; tested with most embedment materials; also involved in dispensing and metering
Diehl-Mateer, Philadelphia, Pa.	makes equipment requiring low pressure for one-component RTV silicone rubber dispensing
Hull Corporation, Hatboro, Philadelphia, Pa.	fair, small unit for meter mix and shot dispensing; reservoir is small and there is no deaeration, but it could be adapted
H. S. Bancroft, Philadelphia, Pa.	has a simple design, easy to use and maintain (ie, shot dispenser for premixed or one-component polymers); it is designed to work from a "Semco" plastic cartridge and could be used with a gravity or pressure feed larger reservoir
Alemite Company, Chicago, Ill.	a source for cartridge or small-reservoir dispensing guns
Lincoln Engineering, St. Louis, Mo.	a source for valves and parts where customer is designing his own unit
Kenics Corporation, Wakefield, Mass.	small-volume liquid polymer metering and dispensing equipment; has one-component experience
Martin Sweets Company, Louisville, Ky.	has experience dispensing liquid silicone rubbers with oil-diluted catalyst either as spray or as solid stream

list includes such items as standard laboratory apparatus, suitable mixers, grinders, scales, ovens, etc.

In addition, Table 3 covers a list of some of the manufacturers of automatic dispensing equipment.

Controls. The embedment process, like all industrial processes, requires a well-planned set of manufacturing standards. Actually, these processes require much more control than conventional mechanical operations. Frequently, the importance of the embedment process in the overall manufacturing procedure is overlooked due to the fact that the material cost of the embedding resin may be quite insignificant in relation to the cost of the expensive electronic assembly. The importance of proper controls cannot be stressed too strongly from the standpoint of higher yield, lower cost, and increased efficiency, and from the standpoint of safety. Frequently, the potential hazard of handling chemicals (embedding resins) is not nearly so well recognized in an electronics plant as it would be in a chemical plant.

Table 4. Applicable Specifications and Standards

U.S. Military Specifications
   MIL-I-27,27A
   MIL-I-16923D
   MIL-I-17023C
   MIL-T-5422, 5422B
   MIL-STD-202, 202A
   MIL-R-10509C
   MIL-E-5272A
   MIL-S-8516
U.S. Federal Specification
   FED-L-P-406b
American Society for Testing and Materials Standard Methods
   ASTM D 149, D 149-44, D 149-59
   ASTM D 150-59T
   ASTM D 257-57T
   ASTM D 648
American Institute of Electrical Engineers Standards
   AIEE no. 1
   AIEE no. 510
National Association of Electrical Manufacturers' Classification
   temperature classifications for electrical insulation

Table 5. Material Considerations

Conditions	Requirements
physical properties	application to determine materials function (hardness, color, clarity flexibility, etc)
thermal stability	dependent upon the application and material selected: for electrical application, a severe but not uncommon test consists of 50 continuous thermal cycles of 2 hr at $+120°C$ followed by 2 hr at $-55°C$; under such conditions, material shall show no evidence of softening, cracks, crazing, voids, etc
mechanical support	performance in this area is dependent on material stability under testing of shock, vibration and/or damping, abrasion, etc; degree of testing is dependent upon exact application requirements
environmental protection	the main purpose of embedding is to provide a protective coating; common environmental tests include humidity, salt spray, fungus resistance, etc

Quality control should be well planned and properly organized, and should cover the following major categories: (1) manufacturing and production control, including process specifications covering manufacturing instructions, in-process tests, safety procedures, well-organized record keeping, and any specialized manufacturing precautions; (2) final product control, including quality control tests designed to ensure that the product will meet customer requirements and good monitoring and record keeping of final product properties to eliminate many processing and product problems before they arise.

In summary the process of embedding, or even completion of the finished item desired, must include some form of quality control, both on the materials and their preparation, and finally in the evaluation of the finished assembly against given specifications. A list of several specifications and standard test methods most useful to this industry to assure material and product control are presented in Table 4.

Finally, the key to reliable embedding techniques lies in proper product selection and maintaining the material quality by extensive testing. Standard tests should be used wherever possible in all end-product testing. Applicable publications include MIL, FED, and ASTM specifications, as well as SPI (Society of the Plastics Industry), NEMA (National Electrical Manufacturers' Association), and U.S. Underwriters' Laboratories Standards. In most cases a check with material suppliers will provide a more exact definition to the quality control procedures for these materials and their applicable government and industrial specifications. Table 5 covers the more common physical conditions and requirements placed in embedment materials for all types of applications.

Bibliography

M. C. Volk, J. W. Lefforge, and R. Stetson, *Electrical Encapsulation*, Reinhold Publishing Corp. New York, 1962.
    See especially "Trade Names and Manufacturers of Encapsulating Materials," Chap. 5, p. 54.
C. A. Harper, *Electronic Packaging with Resins*, McGraw-Hill Book Co., Inc., New York, 1961.
H. Lee and K. Neville, *Epoxy Resins*, McGraw-Hill Book Co., Inc., New York, 1957.
J. R. Lawrence, *Polyester Resins*, Reinhold Publishing Corp., New York, 1960.
M. B. Horn, *Acrylic Resins*, Reinhold Publishing Corp., New York, 1960.
L. E. Nielsen, *Mechanical Properties of Polymers*, Reinhold Publishing Corp., New York, 1962.
The Encyclopedia of Plastics Equipment, Reinhold Publishing Corp., New York, 1960.
Modern Plastics Encyclopedia, Modern Plastics, New York. (Annual publication.)
J. Delmonte, *Plastics in Engineering*, 3rd ed., Penton Publishing Co., Cleveland, O., 1949.
H. R. Simonds, *Source Book of the New Plastics*, Reinhold Publishing Corp., New York. (Annual publication.)
C. A. Harper, *Plastics for Electronics*, Kiver Publications, Inc., Chicago, 1964.
C. G. Clark, "Potting, Embedment, and Encapsulation," *Space Aeronautics* (Dec. 1961).
J. Dexter, "Using Silicones to Meet Performance Demands in Electronic Equipment, "*Machine Design* (May 24, 1962).
J. W. Hawkins, "Silicones—Coatings, Encapsulants, Potting, Embedding," *Electronic Design News* (July 1962).
F. L. Koved, "Encapsulating to Military Specifications," *Electronic Industries* (July 1963).
C. V. Lundberg, "A Guide to Potting and Encapsulating Materials," *Materials in Design Engineering*, (May, June 1960).
"Properties of Encapsulating Compounds," *Electronic Products* (April 1963).
D. C. R. Miller, "High-Temperature Flexible Potting Resins Offer Unique Properties," *Electronics and Communications* (Oct. 1962).
J. M. Segarra, "A New Embedding Procedure for the Preservation of Pathologic Specimens, Using Clear Silicone Potting Compounds," *Am. J. Clinical Pathology* 40 (6), 655–658 (Dec. 1963).
H. L. Uglione, "Evaluation of Polyurethans, Polysulfides, and Epoxies, for Connector Potting and Molding Applications," *Insulation* (April 1963).

Journals

Electrical Design News (monthly); *Electronic Design* (weekly); *Electronics* (weekly); *Insulation* (monthly); *Materials in Design Engineering* (monthly); *Modern Packaging* (monthly); *Modern Plastics* (monthly); *Plastics World* (monthly); *Product Engineering* (weekly); and *SPE Journal* (monthly).

F. J. Modic and D. A. Barsness
General Electric Company

EMERY. See Abrasives.

EMULSIONS

An emulsion is a two-phase system consisting of two incompletely miscible liquids, the one being dispersed as finite globules in the other. The *dispersed, discontinuous,* or *internal phase* is the liquid that is broken up into globules. The surrounding liquid is known as the *continuous* or *external phase.*

Industry usually broadens this description to include colloidal dispersions or solubilizations as well as dispersions of solids such as wax emulsions or "emulsion" paints (with both an emulsified polymerized vehicle and a pigment system).

In addition to emulsions, there are similar systems based on other than liquid–liquid phases (see Table 1). A suspension is a two-phase system closely related to an emulsion, in which the dispersed phase is a solid. A foam is a two-phase system, similar to an emulsion, where the dispersed phase is a gas. An aerosol is the inverse of a foam, air being the continuous phase and liquid (or solid) being the dispersed phase. An emulsifying agent is a material usually added to one of the phases to promote ease of formation and stability of the dispersion.

Table 1. Disperse Systems

Type	Internal phase	External phase
emulsion	liquid	liquid
foam	gas	liquid
aerosol	liquid	gas
suspension (sol)	solid	liquid

Industry is most concerned with the emulsification of oil and water, and the designations O/W for oil in water and W/O for water in oil are widely used. Circumstances exist where the emulsion type, whether O/W or W/O, is not clearly defined; the internal and external phases, instead of being homogeneous, each contain portions of the opposite phase. Such an emulsion is said to be a dual emulsion.

Emulsions can be prepared that are free of water, under which condition the designations O/W and W/O are meaningless.

Such a vast majority of commercial emulsions employ water as one phase that little has been done and little is known concerning nonaqueous emulsions.

Formulation of nonaqueous emulsions is generally a complete trial-and-error process (58). The HLB system (see p. 131) may exhibit some effectiveness if one of the phases is strongly hydrophilic. But the basis of operation of the system (attraction to an aqueous phase) is not present, hence it is only by chance if there is correlation. In general, nonaqueous emulsions are much more difficult to form and stabilize than their aqueous counterparts.

Theory of Emulsions. The theory of emulsions will be considered broadly under two main categories: (*1*) formation, which includes a problem of emulsion type (O/W or W/O); and (*2*) stability, under its various aspects such as inversion, creaming, and demulsification. Unquestionably, emulsion formation is aided and guided by the emulsifying agent, the usual function of which is to reduce interfacial tension and allow the formation of the greatly enlarged interfacial area with a much reduced energy input via mechanical agitation. In addition, the emulsifying agent contributes to the stability of the emulsion via a variety of effects. These may include the formation of a rigid or semirigid interfacial film (the formation of which may be qualitatively understood in terms of the oriented-wedge theory), its relative partial solubility in the two phases, and its contribution to the formation of an electrical double layer of charge at the interface (which has the effect of inhibiting coagulation). Detailed discussion of these theories is beyond the scope of this article. The theoretical background for an understanding of these phenomena is given in detail in several texts and publications (1,5,14,20,25,60,66).

Value of Emulsions. The value of emulsions has long been recognized, based no doubt on the observation and use of natural emulsions. Milk is one of the most prevalent natural emulsions. Rubber latex is an example of an industrial use of a natural emulsion. Crude oil represents a somewhat different natural emulsion, in which case industry is interested in demulsification. The human body contains a myriad of emulsion systems, and bile acids are one of the most commonly recognized natural emulsifiers.

Emulsions are widely used in our present economy. Those most commonly encountered by the consumer occur in foods (mayonnaise, ice cream, cake batter, bread dough, icings, and beverage flavors, to name a few), cosmetics and pharmaceuticals (creams, lotions, soluble vitamin preparations, etc), and many household items (floor and furniture polishes, insecticides, cleaners, etc). The consumer usually does not see the many industrial applications, such as in textile finishes, paper coatings,

Table 2. Major Uses of Surfactants, 1962, in Nondetergent Applications

End use	Surfactant, millions of pounds	Application
petroleum		
automotive oils	145	additive
industrial oils	95	emulsifier
crude oil production	80	demulsifier
binders		
road	150	wetting agent
miscellaneous	30	
food		
baked goods	65	emulsifier
shortening, excluding bread	65	emulsifier
miscellaneous	10	
textile	90	finishes, emulsifiers
concrete	80	air entrainment
dispersants	50	dispersing agents
cosmetics		
shampoos	15	detergents
creams and lotions	10	emulsifiers
toothpaste	2	foaming agents
chemical intermediates	25	
agriculture	20	emulsifiers, wetting agents
flotation	12	foaming (frothing) agents
paint and latex polymers	12	emulsifiers
plastics	10	plasticizers, antistatic agents
paper	8	emulsifiers, wetting agents
leather	7	emulsifiers
pharmaceuticals	4	emulsifiers, solubilizers
dyes and pigments	3	dispersing agents
total	938	

metal working, coolants and lubricants, oil well drilling fluids, asphalt paving emulsions, leather-treating emulsions, and others.

Emulsions are used for a wide variety of reasons. In many consumer items the emulsion form provides an elegant or a practical means of dispersion of a material that could not be achieved otherwise. Industrially, emulsions often provide a safer form of dilution than by the use of a solvent, as well as being more economical. Many processes are totally dependent upon emulsifier systems.

By the same token, emulsions have disadvantages; they always incur the risk of breakdown, and even creaming is damaging in some industrial processes. Corrosion is usually greater than that exhibited by a solvent system. Freezing can occur, and evaporation may cause spurious instability. In textile applications "wicking" may cause uneven distribution. Emulsion concentrates may have improper handling during dilution, giving poor emulsions.

The benefits of emulsions usually overshadow the detriments sufficiently to provide ample incentive to overcome the latter, and industry makes wide use of emulsions.

Some idea of the extent of the use of emulsifiers may be gained from the statement that about a billion pounds of surfactants are consumed annually in the United States exclusive of detergent purposes. A breakdown of these uses is shown in Table 2.

Characteristics of Emulsions

Emulsification usually allows a formulator to produce an end product that will exhibit most, if not all, of the physical characteristics that are desired. This is one of the unique advantages of emulsions.

For example, to apply a small percent of an oil, wax, or film former to a surface, the active ingredient may be dissolved in a solvent. The resulting solution will have relatively fixed properties of appearance, viscosity, flammability, etc. On the other hand, the active ingredient may be emulsified (as is or in a small amount of solvent) and the emulsion can be formulated over a wide range of appearances, viscosity, flammability, and many other characteristics.

It is worthwhile to consider the normal characteristics of emulsions and emulsifiable concentrates, and how they may be controlled.

Table 3 presents a listing of key characteristics divided according to the method of use, for example, emulsions or emulsifiable concentrates, etc.

For emulsions, the major characteristics are generally controllable over reasonable ranges, as described in the following paragraphs.

Appearance. Emulsions may vary tremendously in appearance. They are usually thought of as being opaque or milky; however, their appearance may range through a gray translucence to sparkling clarity. The appearance is governed essentially by the particle size and by the difference in refractive index of the external and internal phases. Transparency may be gained either by having both phases of the same refractive index or by virtue of the internal phase being dispersed in such small particles that refraction does not occur because the particle size of the emulsion is several times smaller than the wavelength of light (see Table 4).

There are even observable variances in the milky-white emulsions, some of them obviously having a grayish cast while others have a bluish cast. This latter effect is noted particularly when the emulsions are in a thin film; for example, draining from a jar sidewall. Again, the appearance is related to particle size; usually the bluish cast

Table 3. Key Emulsion Characteristics

Used as Emulsifiable Concentrates (soluble oil, miscible oil, etc)
    miscibility (ease of desired emulsion formation)
    variety of emulsification procedures that may be employed
    stability to dilution contaminants (salts, acids, etc)
    viscosity
    stability (chemical breakdown or solubility, cold temperature)
    toxicology
    corrosivity
    density
    flammability (flash point, fire point)
Used as Emulsified Concentrates (paste, concentrated emulsion, etc)
    ease of dilution (generally related to apparent viscosity)
    variety of dilution procedures that may be employed
    stability to dilution contaminants (salts, acids, etc)
    apparent viscosity
    high-temperature stability
    viscosity stability
    freeze–thaw stability
    particle size
    corrosivity
Used as Emulsions (at application concentration)
    ease of preparation (if prepared on the site)
    ease of application
    viscosity
    stability-use condition (static)
    stability-use condition (dynamic)
    stability to added salts, acids, bases, etc
    particle size
    toxicology
Properties during Drying of Emulsions
    emulsion stability during drying
    properties of deposited film

Table 4. Effect on Particle Size on Appearance

Particle size	Appearance
macroglobules	two phases may be distinguished
greater than 1 micron	milky-white emulsion
1 to approx 0.1 micron	blue-white emulsion
0.1–0.05 micron	gray semitransparent (dries bright)
0.05 micron and smaller	transparent

is indicative of a smaller particle size than the dull gray cast superimposed upon the milky whiteness.

    Viscosity. Emulsions can be thin or thick fluids, pastes, or gels. Their viscosity is close to that of the external phase so long as the external phase represents more than half of the volume of the emulsion. The viscosity of the continuous phase may be increased by adding thickeners or gelling agents that are compatible with the emulsifier. Many thickeners, such as CMC (sodium carboxymethylcellulose), methylcellulose, and natural gums or clays may often be added with little or no change in the basic emulsifier. If the thickener or gelling agent is a surfactant in its own right, it is probable that the overall balance of the emulsifier will require readjustment. Emulsion viscosity can often be reduced by increasing the proportion of the continuous phase, usually water. However, the addition of polar solvents, such as alcohol or acetone, usually causes a marked reduction in emulsion stability. This is presumably because the emulsifier, being more soluble in the alcohol, is extracted from the interface and the interface is weakened. Thickening or thinning of the dispersed phase usually has little or no effect upon the viscosity of the emulsion. Fryling (31) has observed that in normally fluid O/W emulsions of polymers, manifold differences in viscosity can be achieved by influencing the nature of an adsorbed water structure around each particle by means of a variation in soap or electrolyte concentration.

Thickening agents, particularly of the surfactant type, may either have a straight thickening action or a thixotropic effect. A thixotropic product may appear to be essentially gel-like in character until it is agitated mildly, when it will become quite fluid. Upon standing quietly, it will once again become gel-like in character.

Emulsions also may be formulated that are gels or have soft-gel characteristics which, upon stirring, become liquid and do not turn again into gels. This is not thixotropy; it is merely an initial gel formation.

As the proportion of internal phase is increased beyond fifty volume percent, the viscosity of an emulsion increases to a point where the emulsion is no longer fluid. When the volume of the internal phase exceeds the volume of the external phase, the emulsion particles become crowded and the apparent viscosity is partially "structural viscosity." Under these conditions, particle size, particle charges, and similar relationships assume greater importance in determining the apparent viscosity. Theoretically, the maximum volume that can be occupied by uniform spherical particles for the dispersed phase of an emulsion is 74% of the total volume. Emulsions may be prepared that have as high as 99% internal phase. In these cases considerable distortion from the usual spherical particle shape of the dispersed phase occurs. The actual crowding and distortion that occur at high concentrations of internal phase may be seen for O/W emulsions in Figure 1 (e–h) and for W/O emulsions in Figure 3 (e–h). Simultaneous viscosity changes may be seen in corresponding Figure 1 (a–d) and Figures 2 and 3 (a–d). These pictures further illustrate that, contrary to popular belief, viscous or nonfluid emulsions are not all W/O. Equivalent apparent viscosities may be built up with either type.

Structural viscosity is also characteristic of pigment suspensions and is often materially reduced by the addition of emulsifiers. The viscosity of emulsions and suspensions often increases with aging owing, at times, to thixotropic action.

The viscosity of an emulsion may be controlled as follows: To lower viscosity, (1) increase the proportion of continuous phase; (2) decrease the viscosity of the continuous phase; and (3) for suspensions, the addition of various types of surface-active agents frequently is effective, probably because of flocculation or deflocculation action. To raise viscosity, (1) add thickeners such as soap gels, lipophilic fatty acid esters, gums, and alumina gel to the continuous phase; (2) increase the proportion of internal phase; (3) reduce the particle size of the emulsion, or reduce clumping of existing particles; and (4) incorporate finely divided air as a third phase.

The practice of emulsion viscosity control is exemplified in the preparation of cosmetic lotions. The object is to prepare a lotion that appears "heavy," that is, it must have a high apparent viscosity, although it must remain fluid on long standing. These requirements are met by a formula containing approximately 90% continuous phase (water). The desired results are obtained by a proper balance of emulsifiers and

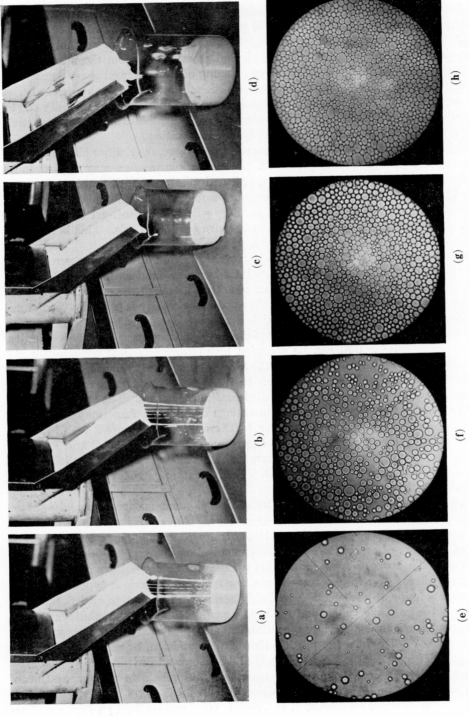

Fig. 1. O/W emulsions: (**a–d**) The increase in viscosity of an O/W emulsion with an increase in the proportion of oil (dispersed phase); (**e–h**) photomicrographs (× 250) of emulsions (**a–d**), respectively.

viscosity builders (soaps, lipophilic fatty acid esters). A major difficulty encountered in these formulations is that under varying storage conditions the gel structure changes, and frequently the product sets to a semisolid that will not pour.

Feel. The initial feel of an emulsion is usually related to the feel of the external phase; thus an oil in water emulsion will feel like water with whatever is dissolved or dispersed in the aqueous phase of the emulsion, whereas a water in oil emulsion will feel oily. This feel is, of course, modified by the viscosity of the emulsion as the greater the viscosity the greater the tendency for it to feel emollient or even oily. After an emulsion is applied as, for example, in cosmetics, the feel will change with the evaporation of water; and, depending upon the smoothness with which the emulsion inverts, it will become more or less oily. The smoothness of inversion of a cosmetic emulsion does not influence the eventual feel, but it does influence the feel at the moment of inversion during application. If the inversion is not accomplished smoothly, the emulsion may be said to "weep" or to "sweat" or more accurately to "break." As would be expected, the feel of an emulsion after inversion is largely influenced by the nature and content of the nonvolatile ingredients.

Fig. 2. Amounts of water (left) and oil (right) used in preparing W/O emulsion shown in Figure 3.

Dispersed-Phase Particle Size (Liquids). The particle size of an emulsion of one liquid in another is related to the method of preparation, the energy input, the viscosity difference between the phases, and the amount and type of surfactant used. Becher has found that within relatively narrow limits, energy input is one of the most important variables (8). Particle size generally decreases with more vigorous agitation, closer viscosity of the two phases, and the use of more of the proper surfactant. It is interesting that the coarsest and the smallest particle size emulsions may be prepared in similar fashion, in which the mechanical work input is less than all other methods, by simple stirring. In some instances, a fine particle size may be achieved by use of the inversion technique described under Manufacturing procedure.

Determination of emulsion particle size is best done, at present, by careful photomicroscopic techniques, particle size counting, and construction of a particle size distribution curve or profile. Particle size determinations have been made in several ways (12,44,68). A simplified counting tool has been described by Becher (9). This procedure must be repeated several times during the test life of the emulsion. Obviously, because of the amount of time involved, such a technique does not lend itself to a

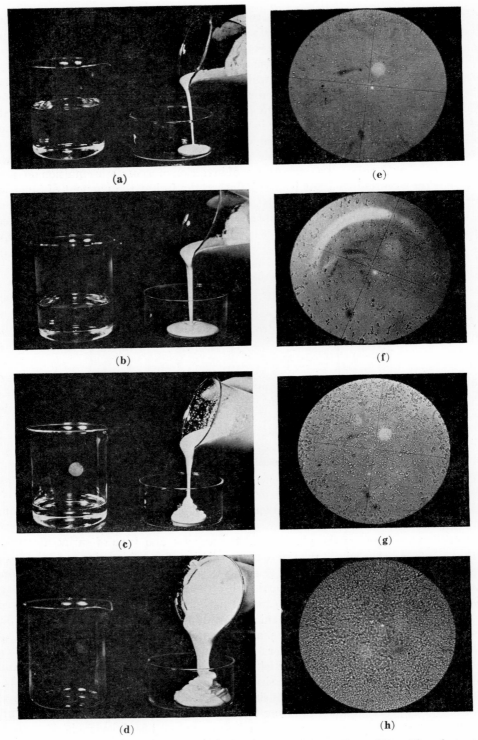

Fig. 3. W/O emulsions: (**a–d**) The increase in viscosity of a W/O emulsion with an increase in the proportion of water (dispersed phase), as shown by the amounts of water left in the beaker in each instance; (**e–h**) photomicrographs (× 250) of emulsions (**a–d**), respectively.

formulation study that requires the evaluation of many closely related formulas in an effort to choose the best.

The particle size of an emulsion may be roughly estimated by noting the appearance of a thin layer as it drains from the side wall of a jar, Table 4.

Exceptions to the appearance and color of emulsions as listed in Table 4 occur if addition of dyes and pigments is made, and if the two phases have a similar refractive index. In the latter instance, a transparent emulsion will result regardless of particle size.

In an emulsion, the larger the particle size, the greater is the tendency to coalescence and to further increase of particle size. Thus, fine particle size promotes stable emulsions. Coalescence may be retarded by use of an emulsifier or a gum having a protective-colloid action. Increasing the viscosity of the continuous phase will also retard coalescence mechanically.

The particle size of an emulsion may usually be reduced by increasing the amount of emulsifier, by improving the hydrophile–lipophile balance (HLB) of the emulsifier, by preparing the emulsion by phase inversion to provide an "extended internal phase" at the time of inversion to the final emulsion type, and by improved agitation.

Stability. Emulsion stability is usually thought of in two ways, according as the emulsion undergoes *creaming* or *phase separation*. These are two different actions and they will be treated separately.

Since the particles of an emulsion are freely suspended in a liquid, they obey Stokes' law, unless electrically charged. The settling or rising of the particles is made apparent by a difference in color shading of the layers formed; these actions are termed sedimentation or *creaming*, respectively, at times referred to as "downward" or "upward" creaming, the direction depending upon the specific gravities of the two phases. The rate of creaming depends upon the difference in specific gravities of the two phases and several other characteristics of the emulsion. The greater the difference of the specific gravities, the more rapid and more complete the separation will be. The greater the electrical charge on the particles and the higher the viscosity of the continuous phase, the slower this separation will be. The finer the particle size, the less rapid and complete the creaming will be. In most formulas, creaming is undesirable and the formula will be designed to avoid it if at all possible. A fluid emulsion that is truly stable, ie, shows no coalescence, when it has creamed, can be easily redispersed to its original form.

When an emulsion creams, globules of the internal phase become more and more crowded together and show an increased tendency to coalesce, leading to complete phase separation. Creaming may be sufficiently complete to essentially effect a separation of the bulk of the continuous phase. This is usually not considered phase separation unless the continuous phase becomes clear.

Phase separation is a result of agglomeration and coalescence of the dispersed phase. This is actual breakdown of the emulsion and, depending upon the formulation, is either reversible or irreversible. It is usually reversible if a relatively large proportion of emulsifier is employed and if the emulsifier has been chosen so as to exhibit the greatest ease of emulsification. Most emulsions that are prepared using considerable mechanical effort are not reversible. Coalescence occurs when the interfacial film ruptures at the point of juncture of two particles of the discontinuous phase or internal phase. The choice of the nature of the emulsifier (assuming that it is adjusted to the proper HLB) is of utmost importance to provide stability against coalescence. Other factors favoring this type of stability are fine particle size, properly induced particle charges, and use of compatible thickeners in the continuous phase.

Stability to freeze–thaw cycling is required for many products. It is presumed that the mechanism in this case is the avoidance of the destruction of the interface by ice crystals which form during freezing. It is likely that this is a direct physical action. Choice of emulsifier and use of an adequate amount of emulsifier can increase markedly the resistance to this form of destruction.

Stability to elevated temperature is one of the most common demands. If stability is acquired in part, at least, by physical means, or, in other words, by a higher viscosity, and this viscosity is reduced by elevated temperature, a reduction of stability is certainly to be expected. It is quite possible that this reduction in stability at elevated temperatures also occurs as a result of changes in solubility of the emulsifiers in one or the other of the phases, thus altering its distribution and affecting the interface. Sometimes this lack of stability is related to the dispersed phase in that the temperature is raised above the melting point of the dispersed phase, and this again poses a situation different from that for which the emulsion was designed.

Incorporation of air in an emulsion may result in greatly reduced stability (62). Stability actually is not sought under certain circumstances, for example, insecticide emulsions. Often it is desired that the insecticide be applied from an emulsion and that it "break" as soon as possible so that the active ingredients are deposited. Some salad dressings and hair dressings have been formulated with an oil phase in which case it was desired that the oil phase separate on a few hours' standing but that the emulsion be easily reformed with quick shaking. The purpose here was to allow the customers to see the oil content of the product.

Emulsions are evaluated for performance and stability either during formulation studies or in plant control. Formulation evaluation during laboratory formulation poses a much greater problem since the purpose is to obtain quantitative data (see Emulsion testing). Usually for plant controls an examination of the emulsion, either by particle size or by some form of accelerated testing, has been correlated with actual aging tests so that some degree of surety of its performance has been established.

Dispersibility. The dispersibility (solubility) of an emulsion is determined by the continuous phase; thus, if the continuous phase is water-soluble, the emulsion may be diluted with water; conversely, if the continuous phase is oil-soluble, the emulsion may be diluted with oil. The ease with which an emulsion may be diluted may be increased by decreasing the viscosity of the emulsion.

Electrical Conductivity. The electrical conductivity of an emulsion depends upon the conductivity of the continuous phase.

Ease of Preparation of Emulsions from Emulsion Concentrates. With a given formula, the ease of formation of an emulsion is controlled by the choice of emulsifier, the choice including optimization of both HLB and chemical types.

If formula manipulation is feasible, emulsifiability may be improved by matching the viscosity of the oil with the aqueous phase, increasing the emulsifier content, and if salts of acids are part of the formula, holding them back till a primary emulsion is formed, then adding them with part of the aqueous phase toward the end of the process.

One of the more perplexing problems in formulation of an emulsion concentrate occurs when the viscosity of the concentrate is sufficiently high that dilution with water or a solvent presents problems, chiefly because of the wide difference in viscosity. Either the use of high temperature or a compromise in which the concentrate is prediluted sufficiently with solvent to allow proper dilution is the only easy solution to this dilemma.

Point of Inversion. Yeh et al. (75) studied emulsions of two immiscible liquids, without an emulsifier. At a certain ratio of the two liquids inversion takes place, and what was previously the external phase becomes the internal phase. The phase volume ratio at the point of inversion was found to be equal to the square root of the ratio of the viscosities of the two components.

However, when an emulsifier is present, it exerts a controlling effect. Schulman and Cockbain (67) studied this phenomenon and described the mechanism of inversion. Becher (7) has also studied the effect of the emulsifier on inversion. The work indicates that the inversion phase ratio depends on the concentration of the emulsifier, its chemical nature, and its HLB. There is an HLB at which inversion occurs most easily. On changing the HLB to either higher or lower values, the stability of either O/W or W/O emulsions increases, then reaches a maximum, and then decreases. In most commercial systems the HLB of the emulsifier is chosen to be a safe distance away from the HLB at which inversion might occur easily. This usually results in a more stable system.

Properties of Emulsifiers

The term emulsifier is often misused. Emulsifiers are a subdivision of the general class of surface-active agents (see Surfactants). Other subdivisions are wetting agents, solubilizers, detergents, suspending agents, etc. These terms are frequently used indiscriminately, the only justification being their common classification as surface-active agents and the fact that the uses of many do tend to overlap in the sub-classifications.

An emulsifier is employed in an emulsion formulation to increase the ease of formation of the emulsion and/or to promote the stability of the emulsion. These actions are usually accompanied by reduction of interfacial tension between the two phases and by protective colloid behavior, respectively. Emulsifiers are usually quite complex materials. It does indeed appear that the more complex they are the more efficiently they function (53). This is recognized in formulating practice and frequently combinations of two or more emulsifiers are used.

Emulsifiers may be divided according to their behavior into ionic and nonionic. The ionic type of emulsifier is composed of an organic lipophilic group and a hydrophilic group. The ionic types may be further divided into anionic and cationic, depending upon the nature of the ion-active group. The lipophilic portion of the molecule is usually considered to be the surface-active portion. Thus, in soap the surface-active fatty acid portion of the molecule represents the anion in the molecule, and, therefore, soap is classed as an anionic emulsifier. As would be expected, anionic and cationic surface-active agents are not mutually compatible. Owing to opposing ionic charges they tend to react with each other, and their surface-active effect is nullified.

Nonionic emulsifiers are completely covalent and show no tendency to ionize. They may, therefore, be combined with other nonionic surface-active agents and with either anionic or cationic agents. The nonionic emulsifiers are likewise more immune to the action of electrolytes than the anionic surface-active agents.

Table 5. Calculated and Determined HLB Values of Surfactants (37)

Name	Manufacturer[a]	Chemical designation	Type[b]	HLB[c]
Span 85	1	sorbitan trioleate	N	1.8
Arlacel 85	1	sorbitan trioleate	N	1.8
Span 65	1	sorbitan tristearate	N	2.1
Arlacel 65	1	sorbitan tristearate	N	2.1
Atlas G-1050	1	polyoxyethylene sorbitol hexastearate	N	2.6
Atmul 200	1	lactylated mono- and diglycerides of fat-forming fatty acids	N	2.6
Emcol EO-50	2	ethylene glycol fatty acid ester	N	2.7
Emcol ES-50	2	ethylene glycol fatty acid ester	N	2.7
Atmos 300	1	mono- and diglycerides of fat-forming fatty acids	N	2.8
Atmul 84	1	mono- and diglycerides from the glycerolysis of edible fats	N	2.8
Atmos 150	1	mono- and diglycerides from the glycerolysis of edible fats	N	3.2
Emcol PO-50	2	propylene glycol fatty acid ester	N	3.4
"Pure"	6	propylene glycol monostearate	N	3.4
Emcol PS-50	2	propylene glycol fatty acid ester	N	3.4
Atmul 500	1	mono- and diglycerides from the glycerolysis of edible fats	N	3.5
Emcol EL-50	2	ethylene glycol fatty acid ester	N	3.6
Emcol PP-50	2	propylene glycol fatty acid ester	N	3.7
Arlacel C	1	sorbitan sesquioleate	N	3.7
Arlacel 83	1	sorbitan sesquioleate	N	3.7
Atlas G-2859	1	polyoxyethylene sorbitol-4,5-oleate	N	3.7
Atmul 67	1	glycerol monostearate	N	3.8
Atmul 84	1	glycerol monostearate	N	3.8
Tegin 515	5	glycerol monostearate	N	3.8
Aldo 33	4	glycerol monostearate	N	3.8
"Pure"	6	glycerol monostearate	N	3.8
Emcol PM-50	2	propylene glycol fatty acid ester	N	4.1
Span 80	1	sorbitan monooleate	N	4.3
Arlacel 80	1	sorbitan monooleate	N	4.3
Atpet 200	1	sorbitan partial fatty esters	N	4.3
Atlas G-3570	1	high-molecular-weight fatty amine blend	C	4.5
Emcol PL-50	2	propylene glycol fatty acid ester	N	4.5
Span 60	1	sorbitan monostearate	N	4.7
Arlacel 60	1	sorbitan monostearate	N	4.7
Emcol DS-50	2	diethylene glycol fatty acid ester	N	4.7
Brij 72	1	polyoxyethylene(2 mole) stearyl ether	N	4.9
Brij 92	1	polyoxyethylene(2 mole) oleyl ether	N	4.9
Atlas G-1702	1	polyoxyethylene sorbitol beeswax derivative	N	5
Emcol DP-50	2	diethylene glycol fatty acid ester	N	5.1
Tween-Mos 100	1	mono- and diglycerides from the glycerolysis of edible fats and Tween 80	N	5.2
Brij 52	1	polyoxyethylene(2 mole) cetyl ether	N	5.3
Emcol DM-50	2	diethylene glycol fatty acid ester	N	5.6
Tween-Mos 280 VS	1	mono- and diglycerides from the glycerolysis of edible fats and Tween 65	N	5.9

(continued)

Table 5 (*continued*)

Name	Man-ufac-turer[a]	Chemical designation	Type[b]	HLB[c]
Emcol DL-50	2	diethylene glycol fatty acid ester	N	6.1
Glaurin	4	diethylene glycol monolaurate (soap-free)	N	6.5
Span 40	1	sorbitan monopalmitate	N	6.7
Arlacel 40	1	sorbitan monopalmitate	N	6.7
Atcor HC	1	high-molecular-weight amine blend	C	7.5
Atlas G-2684	1	sorbitan monooleate polyoxyethylene ester mixed fatty and resin acids blend	N	7.8
Atlas G-2800	1	polyoxypropylene mannitol dioleate	N	8
Atlas G-1425	1	polyoxyethylene sorbitol lanolin derivative	N	8
Span 20	1	sorbitan monolaurate	N	8.6
Arlacel 20	1	sorbitan monolaurate	N	8.6
Atlas G-1234	1	polyoxyethylene sorbitol esters of mixed fatty and resin acids	N	8.6
Emulphor VN-430	3	polyoxyethylene fatty acid	N	9
Atlox 1087	1	polyoxyethylene sorbitol oleate	N	9.2
Tween 61	1	polyoxyethylene sorbitan monostearate	N	9.6
Atlas G-3284	1	polyoxyethylene sorbitol tallow esters	N	9.6
Atlox 1256	1	polyoxyethylene sorbitol tall oil	N	9.7
Brij 30	1	polyoxyethylene lauryl ether	N	9.7
Tween 81	1	polyoxyethylene sorbitan monooleate	N	10.0
Atlas G-1086	1	polyoxyethylene sorbitol hexaoleate	N	10.2
Tween 65	1	polyoxyethylene sorbitan tristearate	N	10.5
Tween 85	1	polyoxyethylene sorbitan trioleate	N	11.0
Arlacel 165	1	glycerol monostearate (acid stable, self-emulsifying)	N	11.0
Aldo 28	4	glycerol monostearate (self-emulsifying)	A	11
Tegin	5	glycerol monostearate (self-emulsifying)	A	11
Atlas G-1790	1	polyoxyethylene lanolin derivative	N	11
Myrj 45	1	polyoxyethylene monostearate	N	11.1
Atlas G-1096	1	polyoxyethylene sorbitol hexaoleate	N	11.4
P.E.G. 400 mono-oleate	6	polyoxyethylene monooleate	N	11.4
P.E.G. 400 mono-oleate	7	polyoxyethylene monooleate	N	11.4
Renex 36	1	polyoxyethylene(6 mole) tridecyl ether	N	11.4
Atlas G-1045	1	polyoxyethylene sorbitol laurate	N	11.5
S-541	4	polyoxyethylene monostearate	N	11.6
P.E.G. 400 mono-stearate	6	polyoxyethylene monostearate	N	11.6
P.E.G. 400 mono-stearate	7	polyoxyethylene monostearate	N	11.6
Atlas G-3300	1	alkyl aryl sulfonate	A	11.7
		triethanolamine oleate	A	12
Brij 76	1	polyoxyethylene(10 mole) stearyl ether	N	12.4
Brij 96	1	polyoxyethylene(10 mole) oleyl ether		12.4
Atlas G-2090	1	polyoxyethylene sorbitol oleate–polyoxyethylene amine blend	C	12.5
Atlas G-2127	1	polyoxyethylene monolaurate	N	12.8

(*continued*)

Table 5 (*continued*)

Name	Manufacturer[a]	Chemical designation	Type[b]	HLB[c]
Igepal CA-630	3	polyoxyethylene alkyl phenol	N	12.8
Brij 56	1	polyoxyethylene(10 mole) cetyl ether	N	12.9
Renex 690	1	polyoxyethylene alkyl aryl ether	N	13
S-307	4	polyoxyethylene monolaurate	N	13.1
P.E.G. 400 monolaurate	6	polyoxyethylene monolaurate	N	13.1
Emulphor EL-719	3	polyoxyethylene vegetable oil	N	13.3
Tween 21	1	polyoxyethylene sorbitan monolaurate	N	13.3
Renex 20	1	polyoxyethylene esters of mixed fatty and resin acids	N	13.8
Atlas G-1441	1	polyoxyethylene sorbitol lanolin derivative	N	14
Renex 30	1	polyoxyethylene(12 mole) tridecyl ether	N	14.5
Atlox 8916P	1	polyoxyethylene sorbitan esters of mixed fatty and resin acids	N	14.6
Atlas G-7596J	1	polyoxyethylene sorbitan monolaurate	N	14.9
Tween 60	1	polyoxyethylene sorbitan monostearate	N	14.9
Tween 80	1	polyoxyethylene sorbitan monooleate	N	15
Myrj 49	1	polyoxyethylene monostearate	N	15.0
Brij 78	1	polyoxyethylene(20 mole) stearyl ether	N	15.3
Brij 98	1	polyoxyethylene(20 mole) oleyl ether	N	15.3
Renex 31	1	polyoxyethylene(15 mole) tridecyl ether	N	15.4
Emulphor ON-870	3	polyoxyethylene fatty alcohol	N	15.4
Atlox 8916T	1	polyoxyethylene sorbitan esters of mixed fatty and resin acids	N	15.4
Atlas G-3780A	1	polyoxyethylene alkyl amine	C	15.5
Atlas G-2079	1	polyoxyethylene glycol monopalmitate	N	15.5
Tween 40	1	polyoxyethylene sorbitan monopalmitate	N	15.6
Brij 58	1	polyoxyethylene(20 mole) cetyl ether	N	15.7
Atlas G-2162	1	polyoxyethylene oxypropylene stearate	N	16.0
Atlas G-1471	1	polyoxyethylene sorbitol lanolin derivative	N	16
Myrj 51	1	polyoxyethylene monostearate	N	16.0
Atlas G-7596P	1	polyoxyethylene sorbitan monolaurate	N	16.3
Tween 20	1	polyoxyethylene sorbitan monolaurate	N	16.7
Brij 35	1	polyoxyethylene lauryl ether	N	16.9
Myrj 52	1	polyoxyethylene monostearate	N	16.9
Atlas G-1795	1	polyoxyethylene lanolin derivative	N	17.0
Myrj 53	1	polyoxyethylene monostearate	N	17.9
		sodium oleate	A	18
Atlas G-3634A	1	quaternary ammonium derivative	C	18.5
		potassium oleate	A	20
Atlas G-263	1	N-cetyl N-ethyl morpholinium ethosulfate	C	25–30
	1	pure sodium lauryl sulfate	A	approx 40

[a] 1 = Atlas Chemical Industries, 2 = Emulsol Corporation, 3 = General Aniline & Film Corporation, 4 = Glyco Products Company, Inc., 5 = Goldschmidt Chemical Corporation, 6 = Kessler, division Armour Chemicals, 7 = W. C. Hardesty Company, Inc.

[b] A =anionic, C = cationic, N = nonionic.

[c] HLB values, either calculated or determined, believed to be correct to ±1.

Examples of many typical emulsifiers are presented in Table 5. In this presentation a complete list of commercial emulsifiers was not included because of the large number and because of the paucity of data available on many of them. Several lists and reviews have been published and reference may be made to these (23,49,70,72).

In addition to the types of emulsifiers discussed above, mention should be made of gums and solids that are employed as protective colloids (see Hydrocolloids). Emulsion and suspension stabilizers that act as protective colloids and, in some instances, as thickeners include: acacia, tragacanth, alginates, starch and starch derivatives, casein, glue, eggs, mustard, methylcellulose, sodium carboxymethylcellulose, hydrated magnesium alumina silicate, sodium salts of condensed alkylated arenesulfonic acids, silica, bentonite, activated carbon, and alumina gel. These products show varying degrees of sensitivity to acids, alkalies, and monovalent and multivalent salts. Without exception, emulsions formed with these protective colloids require large energy input in the form of vigorous mechanical action in their production.

Hydrophile–Lipophile Balance (HLB) of Surfactants. Of the various properties of emulsifiers the hydrophile–lipophile balance is one of the most important (36). The hydrophile–lipophile balance is an expression of the relative simultaneous attraction of an emulsifier for water and for oil (or for the two phases of the emulsion system being considered). It would appear to be determined by the chemical composition and extent of ionization of a given emulsifier. For example, propylene glycol monostearate (pure) has a low HLB (strongly lipophilic); a polyoxyethylene monostearate $(H(OC_2H_4)_nOOC(CH_2)_{16}CH_3)$ having a long polyoxyethylene chain has a high HLB (hydrophilic); and sodium stearate $(CH_3(CH_2)_{16}COONa)$ has a very high HLB (strongly hydrophilic), since it ionizes and thus provides an even stronger hydrophilic tendency.

The HLB of an emulsifier determines the type of an emulsion that tends to be formed. However, it is an indication of the behavior characteristics and not an indication of emulsifier efficiency. Thus, all emulsifiers that have low HLB values will tend to make W/O emulsions. For any specific problem, however, both the best HLB and the best chemical class of emulsifiers must be found.

The HLB number, for most nonionic emulsifiers, is merely an indication of the percentage weight of the hydrophilic portion of the molecule. If a nonionic emulsifier were 100% hydrophilic (which, of course, does not exist), it would be assigned an HLB value of 20, the factor $1/5$ having been adopted because of the convenience of handling smaller numbers.

HLB values for most nonionic emulsifiers can be calculated from either theoretical composition or analytical data. The "theoretical composition" method may lead to considerable error, since many surfactants are unfortunately known by names that do not properly reflect their actual composition. Thus data obtained by actually analyzing the emulsifier are usually a better basis for determining HLB values (37) than a possibly erroneous commercial name. This is especially true among the nonionics.

Determination of HLB. For many nonionic emulsifiers, HLB values may be calculated by one of the following methods.

1. $HLB = E/5$, in which E is the wt % of hydrophilic content of the molecule (or wt % oxyethylene for ethylene oxide condensation products) (52).

For example, in a polyoxyethylene stearate, in which the oxyethylene content was determined to be 85%, $HLB = 85/5 = 17$. Likewise, in a polyoxyethylene oleyl alcohol condensation product in which the oxyethylene content was determined to be 25%, HLB = 25/5 = 5.

2. HLB = 20 $(1 - S/A)$, where S is the saponification number (84) of the emulsifier (ester type). The saponification value or number is a measure of the amount of alkali required to saponify a definite weight of fat, and it is commonly expressed as the number of milligrams of potassium hydroxide required to saponify one gram of fat. In this equation, A is the acid number (85) of the fatty acid moiety of the surfactant. The fatty acid is separated from the emulsifier by saponification with excess alkali, made acid with inorganic acid, extracted from the aqueous phase with hexane, and recovered by evaporation of the solvent. The acid number is determined on the recovered acid and is the neutralization value or equivalent expressed as the number of milligrams of potassium hydroxide required to neutralize one gram of fat.

For example, in a typical commercial-grade glycerol monostearate (mono- and diglycerides) in which the saponification number was determined to be 175 and the extracted acids had an acid number of 200, the HLB = 20 $(1 - 175/200)$ = 2.5. In the same way, a sorbitan monolaurate having a saponification number 164 and prepared from acids having an acid number of 290, has an HLB of 8.7 determined by the equation HLB = 20 $(1 - 164/290)$ = 8.7. Also, the above example may be complicated by the addition of ethylene oxide, whereupon the saponification number becomes 48.5 while the acid number of the fatty acid moiety remains 290. Under these conditions, the HLB value calculation is HLB = 20 $(1 - 48.5/290)$ = 16.7. Even with blended nonionics, for example a blend of mono- and diglycerides and a polyoxyethylene sorbitan monooleate, analysis reveals a saponification number of 150 and an acid number (of the extracted combined acids) of 203. In this instance, the calculation is HLB = 20 $(1 - 150/203)$ = 5.2.

Although the formulas given above are satisfactory for many nonionic emulsifiers, certain other nonionic types exhibit behavior which is apparently unrelated to their composition; for example, those based on propylene oxide or butylene oxide or those containing nitrogen or sulfur. Ionic types of emulsifiers do not follow this weight percentage HLB basis, because even though the hydrophilic portion of such emulsifiers is low in molecular weight, the fact that it ionizes lends extra emphasis to that portion and, therefore, makes the product more hydrophilic.

Therefore, the HLB values of these special nonionics, and of all ionics, must be estimated by experimental methods so that their HLB values are "aligned" with those of the nonionic emulsifiers. An experimentally determined HLB value for such an emulsifier will not necessarily indicate the percentage weight of its hydrophilic portion; for example, it is found experimentally that the HLB of pure sodium lauryl sulfate is about 40, which surely does not mean that it is 200% hydrophilic but merely that it shows an apparent HLB of 40 when used in combination with other emulsifiers.

The experimental method of HLB determination (36), while not precise, briefly consists of blending the unknown emulsifier in varying ratios with an emulsifier of known HLB, and using the blend to emulsify an oil of known "required HLB." The blend which performs best is assumed to have an HLB value approximately equal to the "required HLB" of the oil so that the HLB value of the unknown can be calculated. In practice, a large number of experimental emulsions must be made from which an average HLB value for the unknown is finally calculated.

Needless to say, such a procedure can be difficult and time-consuming. However, the lack of knowledge of an exact HLB number for an emulsifier is not necessarily a serious disadvantage.

Table 6. HLB by Dispersibility

Appearance	HLB range
no dispersibility in water	1–4
poor dispersion	3–6
milky dispersion after vigorous agitation	6–8
stable milky dispersion	8–10
translucent to clear dispersion	10–13
clear solution	13+

A rough estimate of HLB can be made from the water solubility of the emulsifier, and in many instances, this is adequate for screening work. Although this method is not an infallible guide, it can be used to approximate the HLB of many emulsifiers according to their solubility or dispersibility characteristics as shown in Table 6. It must be pointed out that the HLB of an emulsifier is not absolutely related to solubility, in water or in oils; thus two emulsifiers of similar HLB may exhibit differences in solubilities.

The HLB values of many surfactants have been published; some of these are presented in Table 5 along with some additional data pertinent to their use.

HLB determination has been attempted by titration (34), by comparison with chemical structures (ref. 25, pp. 372–376), by correlation with surface and interfacial tensions (10), by spreading coefficients (10), by dye solubilization (10), by dielectric constants (35), by solution, and by a modified gas–liquid chromatograph technique (6,39), but all fall short in one way or another.

Surfactant Solubility. The solubility of an emulsifier is of the greatest importance in the preparation of emulsifiable concentrates. Here it is usually desirable that the concentrate remain homogeneous for an indefinite period of time and over a wide range of temperatures. The emulsifier must remain dissolved throughout all storage conditions. It is frequently possible to enhance the solubility of one emulsifier by the use of a coemulsifier. Also, the use of various solvents as couplers or cosolvents is commonplace.

Surface-Active Properties of Emulsifiers. Emulsifiers, being surface-active agents, lower surface and interfacial tensions of most systems. By so doing, they often promote spreading and wetting. Surface tension is defined as the force that exists at the surface of a liquid set up by the attraction between its molecules, and that resists breaking of the surface. In many applications surface tension data are useful, though in emulsion formulation their application is limited. Interfacial tension is the force required to break the surface between two immiscible liquids and is of interest in emulsification because the lower the interfacial tension between the two phases of an emulsion, the greater the ease of emulsification. When the values approach zero, emulsion formation is spontaneous. Spreading coefficient (S.C.) is calculated from surface tension (S.T.) and interfacial tension (I.T.) with a given oil by the formula $S.C. = S.T._{oil} - (S.T._{soln} + I.T._{oil/soln})$. The greater the spreading coefficient (more positive), the greater the wetting and spreading power (23). For applications requiring good wetting, such as insecticide and floor-polish emulsions, a spreading coefficient greater than unity is usually required.

Zisman's concept of critical surface tension of solids is also useful in predicting wettability of surfaces by liquids (3,76).

Emulsifier Migration. In studying the phenomena of surface activity, it has been noted that surface and interfacial tension values decrease with time. This is explained by the migration of the emulsifier to the surface or interface (16). At present, surface and interfacial tension measurements are usually made and reported under static conditions, although the advisability of this practice is open to question.

Emulsifier Particle Charge. Ionic emulsifiers produce emulsions having a dispersed phase that exhibits a distinct particle charge. This may be observed and determined by electrophoresis. Generally, nonionic agents and the emulsions they produce exhibit only a slight degree of particle charge. For this reason, the nonionics are less sensitive to a wide variety of additives. For example, nonionic emulsions as a class are more stable to electrolytes and to the addition of either of the types of ionic surface-active agents than most ionic emulsifiers.

Chemical Reactivity. For most emulsion formulations an emulsifier should have a low chemical reactivity. Exceptions to this are cases in which subsequent precipitation of the emulsion is desired, as, for example, in the waterproofing of paper, where a soap emulsion is precipitated by the addition of aluminum salts.

Emulsifier Volatility. Volatility or lack of volatility is an important characteristic of emulsifiers or emulsifier ingredients. For most uses a permanent emulsifier is desired. Some formulations of dry-bright floor waxes utilize volatile amines for forming the soap emulsifier in situ. No truly volatile emulsifier is known.

Tests for Emulsifiers. Several empirical physical tests have been devised for different uses and industries (21,24,28,30,32,33,36,38,57). They indicate suspending power, wetting time, etc. These must be applied and interpreted with caution.

Formulation of Emulsions

The characteristics of the final emulsion will depend upon the external phase, the ingredients, the emulsifier, and the manufacturing procedure. None of these can actually be considered totally independent of the other.

Choice of External Phase. The properties of the external phase will generally be the properties of the bulk emulsion. If an emulsion is desired that can be diluted with water, that will dry on application, that will penetrate a cellulosic substance such as wood, paper, or a textile fiber, and that has other properties similar to water, the external phase should be water. If the opposite properties are desired, the external phase should be oil or solvent.

Generally, it is easier to prepare a long-time stable emulsion of the O/W type than of the W/O type. The increased stability is attributed to the much greater charges that are present on the particles in an O/W emulsion.

The type of emulsion, O/W or W/O, is effected by the proportion of oil to water, the ingredients in both phases, and the HLB of the emulsifier. Of the three, the last two are probably the major controlling factors (see Point of inversion, above).

Choice of Ingredients. The ingredients and their amounts are dictated by the application of the emulsion. Ingredients are usually grouped and, in fact, often physically added as combinations of hydrophilic material and lipophilic material.

Oil Phase. The oil phase contains all oils, fats, waxes, nonpolar solvents, oil-soluble materials (dyes, medicine, and pesticides, etc) and possibly the oil-soluble portion of the emulsifier. Frequently, the oil phase must be heated to liquify or effect solution of some of the ingredients. When this is done, the temperature should be high enough to assure that there is no separation or crystallization (about 5–10°C over the melting point of the highest melting point ingredient).

The choice of ingredients and the amounts used are dictated by the purpose or end use of the emulsion, coupled with the desired general characteristics. Except for specific active ingredients it is often possible to select materials that will serve a duplicate function and be more easily emulsified (and possibly yield a more stable emulsion). For example, vegetable oils are usually more difficult to emulsify than mineral oils, highly refined mineral oils more difficult than less highly refined oils, chlorinated solvents more difficult than hydrocarbon solvents, and so on. Because emulsions are more complex to manufacture (and store and ship) than solutions, it is best formulation practice to choose the more easily emulsified raw material when there is a choice possible.

Aqueous Phase. The aqueous phase contains the water, all polyols, salts, polar solvents (not recommended because of extraction of emulsifier from the interface), water-soluble materials (dyes, medicines, and pesticides, etc), and probably the water-soluble portion of the emulsifier. If the oil phase is heated, it is best practice for the aqueous phase to be at least 2–3°F over the oil phase to avoid chilling and possible crystallization. When salts or acids are included in an O/W formula, it is usually best to divide the aqueous phase into two parts, the latter and smaller one containing the salts or acids, to be added after a good primary emulsion has been formed.

Choice of Emulsifier. The objective in any emulsifier selection system is to satisfy the emulsion requirements of ease of preparation and stability with the least costly emulsifier system and at the lowest selection cost. The multiplicity of surfactants available places a heavy burden on a complete trial-and-error system even when some past experience has somewhat narrowed the range of emulsifiers to be tested (49). This is especially true because for any system most single emulsifiers are not correct and the trial of blends multiplies the number of tests required.

A partial system has been devised, based largely on empirical findings, that is called the HLB system. To a large extent the system is instinctively used by "those experienced in the art." It is a refinement of the statement that O/W emulsions are best prepared with water-soluble emulsifiers and W/O emulsions are best prepared with oil-soluble emulsifiers, there is little chance of success if a trial is made with the opposite emulsifier. Conversely, a means of selecting emulsifiers with the right solubility will eliminate a goodly part of the amount of trial. This is what has been accomplished in the HLB surfactant selection system.

HLB Surfactant Selection System. When two or more surfactants are to be blended (and, in fact, blending is usually to be preferred) the HLB of the combination is easily calculated. If x is the proportion of one surfactant having an HLB of A, and the other surfactant has an HLB of B, the HLB of the combination can be expressed for all practical purposes as $xA + (1 - x)B$. Since this is a straight-line relationship, it can be computed graphically with the greatest of ease. However, it should be noted that the straight-line relationship is not precisely true, according to work by Becher and Ohba (6,54,55).

By this procedure the many emulsifiers and blends that have HLB numbers different from the required values may be automatically eliminated and only those having the proper HLB number should be included. Trial-and-error is not eliminated, but it is reduced to a narrow band and is directed toward selection of the best chemical type surfactants. This is much more direct than the original trial-and-error in which the search was for both the right chemical type and the right HLB without realizing the difference or the correlation that existed.

The HLB of an emulsifier is related to its tendency towards solution in oil or water since emulsifiers are totally soluble in neither. Low HLB (2–8) emulsifiers tend to be oil soluble, high HLB (14–18) emulsifiers tend to be water soluble (see Table 6).

To implement the HLB system all that is needed is emulsifiers of known HLB values. Assuming that surfactants are available with known HLB values, the selection system consists of basically three steps: (1) determining the required HLB of the desired combination of ingredients in the product; (2) trying a variety of different emulsifier chemical types at the "required HLB" determined in step 1; and (3) making a final adjustment in HLB value.

Step 1; Determination of Required HLB. The first step is to determine the required HLB, the optimum HLB for the ingredients in the desired formula using the proposed method of manufacture.

To determine the required HLB, select any matched pair of emulsifiers, one lipophilic and one hydrophilic, of known HLB values (for example, Atlas Span 60, HLB = 4.71, and Tween 60, HLB = 14.9). A trial run is first made so the selection of emulsifiers at this point need not be perfect for the particular formula.

The first series can consist of seven test emulsions, using a different mixture of the above emulsifier samples in each. Use an excess of emulsifier (approximately 10–20% of the weight of the oil phase) and dissolve or intimately disperse the emulsifier into the oil phase, melting ingredients together if necessary.

While simple mixing of ingredients and emulsifiers might be sufficient at this point, it is best that for each of the seven emulsions, preparation methods be used that are as nearly identical as possible to plant methods.

Using appropriate methods for comparison and evaluation based on the product requirements, including emulsion type (O/W or W/O), one or more of the seven emulsifier combinations will fairly quickly give a better emulsion than the others, even though not necessarily a very good one. If all the emulsions seem fairly good, with not much noticeable difference, then repeat the seven tests using less emulsifier. Conversely, if all the emulsions are poor and show no great difference, repeat the tests but use a higher emulsifier content.

More often than not, the emulsions will be compared for stability (separation of ingredients), perhaps in a matter of minutes, perhaps overnight, or after heating or freeze–thaw cycles. However, it is entirely possible that the criterion for a good emulsion might be clarity or viscosity, ease of preparation, or ease of application. Whatever the index for judgement might be, these preliminary tests will enable selection of an approximate HLB range (eg, plus or minus 2) for the emulsifier system that will work best.

Suppose it is found that an HLB of approximately 12 is optimum. Further tests should be made around this value to establish the HLB value more accurately, ie, these same two emulsifiers might be blended to try making emulsions at HLB values ranging stepwise between 11 and 13.

In this preliminary test it is possible that a fairly good emulsion might be formed at HLB 4.7 as well as the one at HLB 12.0. If something like this occurs, the low HLB emulsion is probably a W/O emulsion (does not dilute readily with water and does not conduct electricity), and the high HLB emulsion is an O/W emulsion (easily water dispersible, conducts electricity). However, if as noted above, the type of emulsion, O/W or W/O, has already been selected, the wrong type is rejected. Merely by this one set of trials the field for further emulsifier trials has been narrowed. In the next step, concerned with finding the ideal chemical type, regardless of the chemical type finally chosen for the particular formula, it will fall fairly closely within the HLB limits that were found in the preliminary tests. Valuable time will be lost if emulsifiers having HLB values appreciably different from 12 are tried.

Step 2; Determination of Best Chemical Type. Right chemical type is just as important as right HLB; the two go hand in hand. Suppose that it was found that a blend of Span 60 and Tween 60 (both of which are stearates), at an HLB of 12, gave a better emulsion than any other HLB of these two emulsifiers in the above test series. That particular HLB of about 12 will be best for any chemical type. Now it must be determined whether some other blend at HLB 12 (laurates, palmitates, or oleates, for example) might not be better or more efficient than the stearates. (In any case, it will have an HLB of about 12.) By blending two emulsifiers, the exact HLB needed can be attained rather than trying a single emulsifier having an HLB that is close but not quite right. Moreover, the emulsifier chemical type can be selected to suit the oil or other active ingredients, instead of having to limit or adjust the active ingredients to suit the emulsifier.

It has been found that the most stable emulsion systems usually consist of blends of two or more emulsifiers, one portion having lipophilic tendencies, the other hydrophilic. (For example, glycerol monostearate, self-emulsifying grade, is actually a blend of lipophilic non-self-emulsifying glycerol monostearate with a hydrophilic soap or other substance to make it more water soluble.) Only in relatively rare instances is a single emulsifier suitable, even though it might have the exact HLB needed.

Of course, a chemical type is at times dictated by application requirements. For example, a paper chemical emulsion must be precipitated with alum and therefore a soap is indicated as the emulsifier; if acid stability is required, a nonionic emulsifier is suitable; food emulsions require FDA-approved emulsifiers, etc.

After making the preliminary screening based on these premises, choose a variety of low-HLB emulsifiers of different chemical types for which corresponding high-HLB emulsifiers are available. For example, low- and high-analog blends might include: (*1*) soaps; sodium stearate ranging from a medium to high pH; (*2*) stearyl alcohol and sodium stearate; (*3*) Brij 72 and Brij 79; (*4*) Span 20 and Tween 20 (and other fatty acid pairs); (*5*) lauryl alcohol and sodium lauryl sulfate; (*6*) a calcium sulfonate and a sodium sulfonate, etc. The objective is to select several pairs of emulsifiers, each pair bearing a chemical relationship, and the overall group covering a wide area of chemical nature.

A blend of each pair is then prepared in a weight ratio so that its HLB will be 12, the required HLB for the emulsion, and test emulsions are prepared. An evaluation of these will usually show wide differences for different chemical types and a selection is easily made based on the criteria for the emulsion system.

Step 3; Final Adjustment of HLB. After selecting the best chemical type, it is usually desirable to try blends of the selected emulsifier having incremental HLB values close to the indicated required HLB. In this example where the value was 12.0, tests at 11.0, 11.2, 11.4, 11.6, 11.7, 11.8, 11.9, 12.0, 12.1, 12.2, 12.3, 12.4, 12.6, 12.8, and 13.0 will confirm the exact blend with the chosen pair. This is necessary because HLB values are not precise, since they are based on approximate calculations and on empirical tests.

Manufacture of Emulsions

Formulation should, insofar as possible, take into consideration the intended manufacturing procedure. The emulsifier usually promotes ease of formation of the emulsion as well as stability. It may be stated as a general rule that the greater the mechanical energy input the less demand there is on the emulsifier. Frequently, the amount of emulsifier may be reduced with increased energy input. Two extremes may illustrate this; an emulsifiable concentrate which requires a minimum of agitation and a sizable amount of emulsifier, and the "mayonnaise" dormant spray mineral oil emulsion concentrate made with repeated homogenization where a few tenths of a percent emulsifier is sufficient.

Laboratory Preparation. The laboratory scale of operation deserves special consideration because of the need, and yet the tremendous difficulty, of duplicating plant manufacturing techniques. As an example, in preparing an emulsion of moderate viscosity in a typical laboratory beaker-motor driver propeller apparatus, the actual work input may be surprisingly high. In equipment scale-up, surface-to-volume ratios differ markedly, peripheral speeds of agitators are different, tendencies to maelstrom and suck in air or produce foam differ, rates of heating and especially rates of cooling differ, chances for local overheating are greater, and all these factors increase the complexity of the problem.

Laboratory preparations should endeavor to duplicate plant conditions and err, if possible, on the side of too little energy input. A batch kettle, either heated or unheated, is approximated by a beaker-motor propeller of appropriate size (slow motor speed is preferred and a simple baffle is usually an improvement). A plant homogenizer is approximated by a hand homogenizer or by a gear pump with a pressure relief valve. Emulsification of a concentrate is most uniformly handled by motor-timer controlled shaking (11).

A Waring blendor, when used to prepare emulsions, imparts fantastic amounts of energy and also incorporates large quantities of air. For this reason, it often gives results that are not achieved in subsequent plant scale-up.

An additional major problem in the laboratory occurs with emulsions that are prepared hot and then cooled. A laboratory beaker of emulsion will cool from 60–30°C in a few minutes. A 1000-gallon tank requires much longer, even with forced cooling. For emulsions that contain waxy components the rate of cooling through the melting range can be all important. Hence, the best procedure is to determine in the laboratory the best practical cooling schedule, then determine the deviation leeway allowable, and finally set plant conditions to satisfy those criteria.

Plant Preparation. If laboratory and pilot plant formulation is done with careful attention to the duplication of plant conditions, scale-up will have only the usual number of pitfalls. Based on the laboratory tests, it is wise to establish a specific procedure for preparing an emulsion on plant scale. Apparently small deviations in procedure may result in a totally different end product.

Addition of Ingredients. Order and rate of addition of ingredients is often of no concern, yet in many cases a given order and rate of addition results in acceptance or rejection of the product.

An apt illustration is the preparation of an O/W emulsion by the inversion technique. A generally superior procedure consists in blending oil phase and emulsifier in the tank. Water is then added to the oil phase slowly with stirring. The initially hazy oil and emulsifier blend usually clarify at first and then again become cloudy. As more water is added, the emulsion assumes a milky cast while the viscosity increases. At some point, called the inversion point, the viscosity suddenly decreases. This is significant of the fact that the emulsion has changed from W/O to O/W. Further additions of water may be made rapidly. If the oil is initially added to the water, a poor emulsion will result unless enough of the right emulsifier is employed. Commercially, it is usually economically advisable to use the inversion technique to prepare O/W emulsions in order to have a formula with less emulsifier.

Specific procedures must be worked out for each formulation. Generally, all the oils and oil-soluble ingredients are best combined as the oil phase. Generally, polyols are added with the water but salts are best added with the last half to quarter of the water after a good primary emulsion has been established.

Temperature of Ingredients. In most instances of liquid–liquid emulsification, ambient temperature is to be preferred. With some equipment, heat will be generated during the emulsification step and this must be removed.

Heating of ingredients may be necessary to effect emulsification; it may also be necessary to pasteurize or sterilize the product. In making wax emulsions, heating is necessary. The wax or the oil phase should be heated to at least 5°C over the melting point of the highest-melting wax and the aqueous phase should be heated to at least 2–3°C over the temperature of the oil phase. This procedure will avoid shocking the wax by cooling during mixing.

Rate of cooling of a wax emulsion, especially at the melting point of the wax, is critical. Each emulsion must be studied to determine if the best rate of cooling is fast or slow. Fast cooling may be done with a cooling board or by means of a heat-exchange unit.

When an emulsion system is heated, emulsifier co-solubility is altered and this may change its emulsifying properties. In addition, care must be taken to avoid unwanted chemical reaction.

Equipment for Manufacture. The choice of emulsification equipment is usually dictated by the application of the resulting emulsions; thus elaborate machinery is not available for the preparation of insecticide emulsions in the field, whereas in a plant it may be economical to install extensive equipment. The purpose of the emulsification equipment, whether simple or complex, is to break up or disperse the internal phase in the external phase, so that the particle size of the resulting emulsion is sufficiently small to retard coalescence and resulting breakdown of the emulsion in the required time of stability. The major concerns in the choice of emulsifying equipment are the apparent viscosity in all stages of manufacture, the amount of mechanical energy input required, and heat-exchange demands. Preparation of emulsions is greatly affected by the type of agitation (see also Mixing).

Hand Stirring. Hand stirring is the simplest form of agitation. Depending upon the selection of emulsifiers and the ingredients to be emulsified, either stable or semistable, large or small particle-size emulsions may be prepared. For hand stirring, a formulation having a maximum ease of dispersibility is, of course, required. Good ease of dispersibility is not related to good stability.

Slow-Speed Mechanical Stirring. For many viscous emulsions containing high solids, soap gels, resinous materials, etc, a mechanically rotated paddle or anchor-type agitator is best.

The planetary stirrer has actually been developed for one branch of this high-viscosity field, the food industry. In a planetary stirrer, the paddle rotates and at the same time the axis about which it rotates follows a circular orbit. In this way a large batch of heavy batter may be intimately mixed. These same mixers are used at higher speeds with a wire whisk for aeration and whipping of low-viscosity emulsions because of excessive aeration.

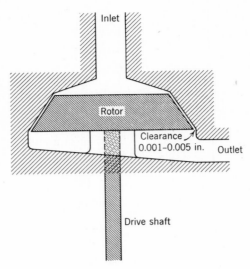

Fig. 4. A colloid mill.

Aeration. Stirring by means of bubbling air or gas through a liquid is not much more efficient than hand stirring unless extremely large volumes of gas are used. A modification of this system, consisting of the injection of live steam into a tank, is usually much more efficient because of the condensation of the steam and the resulting cavitation or "steam-hammer effect." The use of air or steam is most practical in low-viscosity systems.

Propeller Agitation. One of the most popular types of emulsification equipment is one or more propellers mounted on a common shaft in a mixing tank. Modifications of this include variation in the location of the propellers in the tank, the use of two or more propeller shafts, and the use of complex propellers. Propeller agitation is most satisfactory for low- and medium-viscosity emulsions. When properly used with adequate emulsifying agents, propeller agitation will result in finer particle size than homogenization or milling with lesser quantities of emulsifiers.

Turbine Agitation. The inclusion of fixed baffles either on the tank wall or adjacent to the propellers, as in a turbine rotor and stator, increases the efficiency of agitation considerably. The use of a turbine agitator is by far the preferred of the two methods since baffle plates in a tank frequently result in areas of little or no agitation, although the general effect is to increase the efficiency of agitation. Turbine-type agitators are available in various sizes and speeds and rotor–stator clearances, and in many modified designs. Turbine-type systems may be designed to give a very high degree of shearing action. Turbine combinations may be used with higher-viscosity fluids than propellers. At high viscosities, the gross agitation of the batch may be insufficient.

Colloid Mill. The colloid mill may actually be considered as a modification of a turbine, although in this case the clearance between the rotor and stator is of the order of a few thousandths of an inch (Fig. 4). With such small clearances, an extremely high shearing action occurs. The product from a colloid mill usually has a uniform particle size, no doubt due to the fixed clearance between the rotor and stator. Owing to the tremendous shearing forces applied to the emulsion, a significant temperature rise occurs during emulsification and in most cases external cooling must be employed. Milling may be done on fluids and pastes (with positive feed for the latter). Rate of throughput varies inversely with the viscosity.

Homogenization. In a homogenizer, emulsification is effected by forcing the two phases past one or two spring-seated valves (Fig. 5). This is usually done at relatively high pressures of 500–5000 psi. Emulsification occurs not only while the components pass under the valve seat but also when the emulsion impinges against the retaining wall that surrounds the valve. Homogenizers are also built with more than one stage of emulsification, that is, successive relief valves. This is claimed to be of value in some instances wherein the high-pressure homogenization promotes clumping of the fine particles of emulsion that it forms. The second stage of homogenization, at a lower pressure, breaks up the clumps and produces a lower-viscosity product. Using comparable ingredients, homogenizers usually give an emulsion of finer average particle

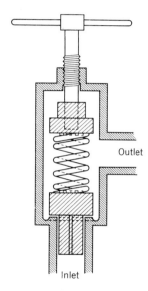

Fig. 5. A homogenizer.

size than colloid mills, although the particle size is not as uniform. A further contrast is that the temperature rise during homogenization is not very large, 10–30°F. The actual temperature rise throughout the homogenizer and pump may be only 10–30°F, or it may be as high as 50–90°F, depending upon the type of pump employed. A piston pump gives a lower temperature rise than a gear pump. Owing to clearances in the gear pump, a certain quantity of liquid continually by-passes the pump and is partially homogenized before reaching the homogenizer head. Homogenizers will handle liquids or paste and the rate of throughput is little affected by viscosity.

Ultrasonics (qv). A more recent development in the field of emulsifying equipment is the high-frequency or ultrasonic oscillator. It is possible that a portion of the mechanical action is somewhat similar to the steam ejector, that is, cavitation (4,45,69,79). The ultrasonic emulsifier is best suited for liquids of low viscosity, though it has been successful with systems having viscosities as high as salad dressings and dye-paste emulsions. A laboratory size is available for small-scale work.

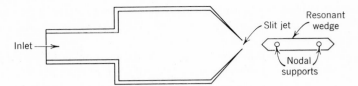

Fig. 6. Schematic diagram of a Pohlman whistle. The nodal supports of the blade are separated by a distance equal to half the wavelength of the characteristic vibration of the system.

Ultrasonic energy is developed either mechanically (Fig. 6) or electrically. In the former, a pump forces the combined phases past a tuned vane which vibrates and produces energy via cavitation. Pressures range from 150–500 psi in the chamber surrounding the tuned vane.

Electrically, an oscillator generator causes ultrasonic vibration in either a magnetostriction device or a piezoelectric crystal. Major difficulties in transfer of this energy to the liquid have retarded extensive commercial use of this form of ultrasonic energy in emulsification.

Table 7. Emulsification Equipment

Type	Agitator speed, rpm	Mechanical energy input	Usable viscosity range	Heat-exchange demand range [a]
anchor agitator	slow	low	best for high viscosity	fair
wall-scraping anchor agitator[b]	slow	low	best for medium and high viscosity	good
propellor mixer[c]	medium	low–medium	best for low–medium viscosity	fair–poor
votator	medium	low–medium	best for high viscosity	excellent
rotating cage mills[d]	high	high	best for low–medium viscosity	fair
rotating disc mills[e]	high	high	best for low–medium viscosity	fair
homogenizer	slow	high	low–moderately high	fair–poor
colloid mill	high	high	low–medium	fair–poor
mechanical ultrasonic[f]	high	low–medium	low–medium	fair–good
electric ultrasonic	not critical	low–medium	low–medium	fair

[a] Without auxiliary equipment.
[b] Usually in pairs; counter-rotating.
[c] Lightning mixer.
[d] Premier dispersator.
[e] Cowles dissolver or Hockmeyer dispersator.
[f] Rapasonic.

Other Conditions of Agitation for Emulsions. As would be expected, many combinations of the above equipment are employed and new designs are being explored (3,17, 78,80). Thus, for cosmetic cream manufacture, a motor-driven paddle in a jacketed tank is supplemented by the addition of a small high-speed turbine agitator. This is quite satisfactory for the initial emulsification of small quantities of material in the bottom of the tank and assists in emulsification, even at the completion of a batch when the tank is full. Industrial combinations of homogenizers and colloid mills are available with proportioning scales and pumps for the continuous production of emulsions. Means for calculating equipment requirements have been published (18).

Table 8. Power Requirements, in hp, for Typical Emulsion Equipment

	Propeller stirrer			Stirrer turbine	Turbine	Homogenizer				Colloid mill					
gal/hr[a]	Eastern, thin soln, slow rate	Eastern, thin soln, rapid rate	Eastern, paste, rapid rate	Nortal	Eppenbach, homo-mixer	Cherry-Burrell, model 41	Cherry-Burrell, model A	Manton-Gaulin	Marco	Eppenbach, model QV	Eppenbach, model A, B, C, D	Manton-Gaulin	Premier, liquid	Premier, paste	Sonolator
½–2	1/100	1/100	⅛		¼					¼–½	½		½		
2–5	1/100	1/30	¼							¼–¾	½–2		½		
5–8	1/100	1/20	⅓							¼–1	½–2		½–5	1½	
8–10	1/100	1/20	⅓							½–1	½–2		½–5	1½	
10–15	1/30	⅛	½	⅓						¾–1	2	1½	3–7½	1½	
15–20	1/30			⅓	½					1	2		3–7½	1½–3	
20–25	1/30	⅛	½	⅓				1½		3	2–7½	1½–5	3–7½	1½–3	
25–30	1/20	¼	¾	⅓							2–7½		3–7½	3	
30–40				½							7½		3–7½	3–5	
40–50		¼	¾	½	1					3–10	7½–15	1½–10	3–7½	3–5	
50–75		⅓	1	1		3		3		3–10	7½–15		3–7½	5–10	
75–100	1/20	⅓	1	1	2–3					10	7½–15	1½–10	3–7½	5–10	
100–125	⅛	⅓	1½			5		5			15		5–7½	5–30	1
125–150											15		5–7½	10–30	
150–200	⅛	½	1½		5	7½		7½	7½		15			10–30	
200–300	¼	¾	2		7½	10	10		7½–10	10	15	5–10		20–40	
300–500	¼	1	3			15	15	20	7½–10					25–40	3–5
500–750	⅓	1	3		10	20	20–25	25	10			10	50	40–75	
750–1000	½	1½	5		15	30–40	30–40	30–40	10–20				50	40–75	5–10
1000–1250	¾	2	7½			40	40–50		20				50–75	75	
1250–1500	¾	2	7½		20	50	50–60	50	25				50–75	75	
1500–2000	1	3	10		25	60	75	60	40				50–75	75	10
2000–2500	1½	5					75	75	40				50–75		15
2500–3000	1½	5							50				75		
3600															20

[a] Gallons per batch for batch operations. The time required to emulsify a batch depends upon the size of the equipment, but will usually be between 15 min and 2 hr.

The rated power requirements for several different types of agitation are presented in Tables 7 and 8. The general order of increase in power demand is: propeller mixing (lowest); turbine; homogenizer; and colloid mill (highest) (see Fig. 7).

Pebble and ball mills and other grinding equipment are used to make some emulsions and more extensively in pigment suspension. They represent a class of relatively slow speed equipment for emulsification.

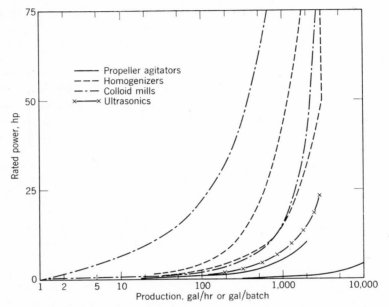

Fig. 7. Range of power requirements of emulsification equipment.

Pieces of laboratory equipment corresponding to all of these types of emulsification equipment, and others, are in common use. Small-scale laboratory and pilot-plant models of planetary mixers, motor-driven propellers, turbines, colloid mills, and homogenizers are available. In addition, use is made of motor-driven egg beaters, high-speed blender food mixers, and shaking machines. Laboratory agitation is usually much more vigorous and efficient than that in plant-scale equipment, and this variable must be considered in translating results from one to the other.

Emulsion Evaluation and Analysis

Emulsion Evaluation. In a basic sense, an emulsion is evaluated against the demands, specific to its use, for each characteristic. Fortunately, most of these are established by the choice of ingredients and formula and evaluation narrows to ease of quality of preparation and/or stability (see under Emulsion characteristics, p. 119).

Ease of Preparation. This is usually related to an emulsion concentrate from which an emulsion is prepared in the field. A typical example is agricultural chemical pesticide concentrates that are diluted by the farmer. A suitable emulsion must form with a minimum of agitation. The emulsion quality is judged by (though not truly related to) the appearance of the "bloom" when a small amount of concentrate is poured into water. Hence, this is one evaluation. A good evaluation will also include emulsion preparation with agitation estimated equal to prototype energy input. With a uniform repetitive preparation procedure, the test emulsions are examined for quality at the time of preparation.

In any study of ease of preparation, attention must be given to the aqueous phase. Possible variations in the hardness, salt content, pH, temperature, etc, of the water should be considered. It is possible that a system will operate more efficiently in water containing salt than in distilled water. Unwanted anomalies in behavior can usually be eliminated by changes in formulation.

Quality, as prepared, can usually be correlated with particle size if there is no gross instability. A rough estimate of particle size is possible by visual inspection (see p. 125).

Performance Evaluation. Performance evaluation is related to use tests which, for the most part, may be spelled out and for which there are usually direct tests. Since they vary with each type of product, no attempt will be made to consider them except to state that the evaluation should be made in a manner duplicating end-use procedures as nearly as possible.

Emulsion Stability. True emulsion stability is achieved when the particles of the dispersed phase do not agglomerate and increase in size. Many commercial emulsions have additional requirements; that the emulsion show no creaming, that it be stable to vibration or high shear, to freeze–thaw cycles, at elevated temperatures, to dilution, to salts, and to solvents, or other demands. This lack of a simple definition for emulsion stability or excellence is a serious impedance to progress in emulsion technology.

Creaming is usually undesirable in any consumer product because it then demands the label of "Shake Well Before Using." It is undesirable in commercial products for the same reason, though in a few instances it is tolerated. Accelerated creaming tests may be made by centrifuging and by dilution of the continuous phase. Centrifuging merely accentuates the effect of the difference in specific gravity of the two phases. It does not provide test conditions under which the emulsion interface is naturally aged. On the other hand, dilution of the continuous phase also changes the distribution ratio of the surfactants within the system and again changes the surfactant distribution at the interface. Even so, the appearance of emulsions on extreme dilution, for example 100:1, is often quite revealing. For example, an emulsion that dilutes uniformly and, when diluted, presents a white, milky, uniform appearance usually is a better emulsion than one which upon dilution shows appreciable flocculation.

If creaming does occur in a product, it is often quite important that the cream layer be easily redispersible and this may well be considered as part of a test procedure.

A reading of the volume of cream layers is most difficult. It is important that the containers in any comparative test have a similar diameter-to-height ratio. To facilitate this, special equipment has been designed for fluid emulsions (11). Cream layers are usually expressed as a percent of volume of the overall volume of emulsion. It must be recognized that this percentage may or may not bear a relationship to the actual volume of dispersed phase contained in the cream layer.

Almost from the definition of an emulsion there evolves the theoretical or classical definition of an emulsion stability: Emulsion stability is inversely related to the rate of change (increase) of particle size of the emulsion.

Even if the classic definition is followed, however, the measurement of the rate of change of particle size is sufficiently laborious to discourage its use much of the time.

Usually practical formulation studies are based on visual observations. Gross particle size and creaming observations when carefully made and combined with other stability studies as dictated by the requirements of the product will generally provide a satisfactory basis for formulation studies.

For wax O/W emulsions, a churning test, which is relatively easy to make, is often employed. This indicates the stability of the emulsion during shipping and during certain handling operations.

Depending upon the nature of the end product, a single "practical" stability test, or a number of them, may be employed. Two examples will illustrate the variety of choice possible. In an agricultural pesticide test the emulsion concentrate must be evaluated for long-time storage stability. An accelerated test at elevated temperatures (about 45°C) is frequently employed. This may or may not yield directly correlatible results. For such storage tests, containers must be resistant to corrosion, since breakdown products may attack metals which will in turn catalyze further breakdown. Emulsion stability tests should then be run on both fresh and aged samples. A pesticide emulsion usually is required to be stable with little agitation for a working day. Further, it is required that any separation that occurs on overnight standing be easily re-emulsifiable the next day. This constitutes a fairly well defined set of criteria for stability.

A second example, that of a pharmaceutical or cosmetic lotion, presents a totally different picture. Long emulsion shelf life is required with little or no change in viscosity of the lotion. Further, proper stability is required during application so that the lotion dries smoothly and does not roll or break. Long shelf life is a major problem because even a single test, aged for a year or two under laboratory storage conditions, does not truly represent distributor handling and store shelf treatment. What is used, with considerable reservation and question, is storage at one or two elevated temperatures from 35–50°C plus a few freeze–thaw cycles. Many manufacturers have correlations with which they are reasonably satisfied, for example, accelerated storage at 37 and 50°C in which separation and viscosity are followed. These two examples show the variability that may be anticipated.

Determination of Emulsion Type. Whether the emulsion is O/W or W/O is of primary importance. This may be detected in several ways, of which three will be outlined:

1. The simplest method is to determine electrical conductivity. Equipment for this may be easily constructed by wiring in series a 10,000-ohm, $\frac{1}{2}$-watt resistor, electric contacts for the test sample, a resistorless neon lamp ($\frac{1}{4}$ watt, 105–120 volts, General Electric type NE-57), and a push-button switch. The sample is placed across the test contacts and the circuit is closed; if the neon lamp glows the emulsion is O/W, if it does not the emulsion is W/O. There are occasions when the lamp will glow dimly or will start to glow upon continued application of the electric current. This usually indicates either a dual emulsion or a gradual inversion of the emulsion.

2. A second method of detecting the type of emulsion is to determine its dispersibility in water or oil. O/W emulsions will disperse in water, while W/O emulsions will disperse in oil.

3. A water-soluble dye will spread through an O/W emulsion and an oil-soluble dye will spread throughout a W/O emulsion. Dyes may be used in either liquid or solid form.

Emulsion Analysis. The analysis of emulsions, usually for duplication purposes, must consider the type and properties of the emulsion, the nature of the major components, and an identification of the emulsifier. A good start on the analysis would be a consideration of the advertised properties of the emulsion. In some instances, for example foods and some pharmaceuticals, this includes a list of ingredients or at least a partial list of ingredients. Emulsion type (O/W or W/O), viscosity, particle size, stability, pH, and any other pertinent characteristics should be noted.

The water content of an emulsion is of considerable importance. One of the best methods for this determination is by Karl Fischer titration (2,51). If the emulsion is alkaline, a correction may usually be made.

The separated phases of the emulsion should be examined chemically and physically to the degree necessary to allow the formulator to duplicate the ingredients to the desired degree. This type of analysis has been reported for some products (15,19, 29,56).

The pH of an emulsion is of considerable importance. Emulsions based on soaps usually have a pH of 8 or over. Emulsions having a pH greater than 9 are usually not prepared with ester-type emulsifiers because of saponification of the ester. The pH is easily determined by either the use of standard glass electrode equipment or test papers. When test papers are used, caution must be observed if any product is present that might exhibit bleaching tendencies.

An indication of the chemical type of emulsifier may usually be obtained by breaking the emulsion, if possible, by addition of salts, acids, or alkalies. There have been a number of procedures developed to try to identify in detail the nature and amount of emulsifier in a variety of products (66). These are laborious and are, in most instances, only partially successful.

Uses of Emulsions

Mention is made here of only a selected number of the uses of emulsions, classified according to market. Actual formulas are not presented.

Industrial Oil and Wax Emulsions. The scope of industrial oil and wax emulsions is tremendous, especially when textile, polymerization, paper, leather, and other related uses are included. Emulsified oils (O/W) are extensively employed in all forms of metal working including rolling, stamping, and machining. Likewise, oil and solvent emulsions are sold as cleaners and polishes for either home or commercial use. Textile finishes, leather finishes, and some paper coatings are based on oil or wax emulsions. Emulsifiers are used in such widely different applications as marine lubricants, battery electrolytes, soldering fluxes, printing inks, and embalming fluids. Emulsified paints and lacquers are available for various applications. Emulsifiers are used in the chemical industry and for the control of polymerization reactions. Emulsifiers are added to natural asphalt emulsions in order to provide proper flow and wetting characteristics. Emulsifiers and emulsions are also employed as corrosion inhibitors. The formulation of an emulsion at the surface of an oil fire aids in extinguishing the fire.

Emulsions are also used in drycleaning. Here a suitable hydrocarbon-soluble emulsifier is usually formulated with a small amount of water and hydrocarbon, to be blended with the drycleaning solvent at the time of use. The purpose of this product is to provide proper acceptance by the drycleaning solvent of moisture that is carried in with the clothing, and to permit the addition of sufficient water to the drycleaning solvent when first used, so that water-soluble or dispersible stains are at least in part removed.

The most common sanitary emulsion is pine oil emulsified with a rosin soap. This mixture will disperse easily in water for all types of applications including laundries. Hand cleaners may be formulated from emulsified solvents in addition to the usual lipuid soap. Industrial cleaners for machinery are often composed of a poorly emulsified solvent and water. When applied hot with considerable force, these cleaners are quite efficient. In certain instances, a minimum amount of emulsifier is desirable in this application so that a sufficiently unstable emulsion will result (59).

Polishes of all types, consumer and industrial (24,26), are formulated as emulsions for a variety of reasons including assistance in cleaning, nonflammability, and lack of injury to asphalt tile. Dry-bright floor polishes achieve this quality by their fine particle size (63,64).

Foods. Many of our foods are emulsions. The commonly recognized ones are milk, butter, mayonnaise, salad dressings, gravies, and ice cream. Some of the other easily recognized emulsions and foods in which emulsions are an important step in production are beverages, cakes, candy, frostings, marshmallow, condiment preparations, shortening, margarine, pickles, flavoring oils, yeasts, and eggs.

In the preparation of homogenized milk, the natural emulsifier in the milk is utilized. Milk is pasteurized and passed through high-pressure homogenizers while at pasteurizing temperature, and then quickly cooled. The fat particles are thereby reduced to such size that they do not rise to the surface, as cream does in ordinary milk. In the addition of vitamin D-containing oils to milk, the activated oil may be pre-emulsified with skim milk either mechanically or with an emulsifier and this is added to the milk before homogenization. In a somewhat different application, chocolate milk is "stabilized" by the addition of small amounts of gum, usually Irish moss. In this case the effect of the stabilizer is simply to retard the settling of the denser chocolate particles.

In most ice cream, stabilizers are also utilized. Various gums, gelatin, or carboxymethyl cellulose are added to ice cream to stabilize the foam. In addition to stabilizers, egg or emulsifiers are added to reduce the time required to achieve overrun (aeration) and to stabilize the product against formation of ice crystals and heat shock shrinkage (82). Foam-promoting agents are also utilized in whipping cream. A dual requirement is imposed on emulsifiers in preparation of filled cream (high-fat-content cream for whipping in which a portion of the fat is hydrogenated shortening), and in the manufacture of sterilized whipping cream. Here the emulsifier must produce an initial emulsion that behaves like heavy cream and must subsequently provide the proper whipping action. Another instance where heavy demands are made on the emulsifier is in mellorine (a nondairy fat, ice cream-type dessert).

The batter of a cake is improved by the addition of a suitable emulsifier (42). Here the action is not as well known, but it apparently provides better emulsification of the oil, liquid, and solid ingredients of the cake batter. A smoother batter and a more uniformly textured cake is the result. Both the bakers' cake and cake mixes place special, heavy demands upon the emulsifier. Often these products will contain blends of two, three, four, or even more emulsifiers to achieve better smoothness density, cake volume, cell structure, symmetry, and other characteristics that are desired.

A better-known application of emulsifiers is in salad dressings. This type of food is an emulsion that is frequently of uncertain stability. Emulsifiers may be added to increase shelf life and resistance to freezing. A side effect sometimes observed in this and other foods is the blending, or at times accenting, of certain flavor constituents in the formula. Thus, when an emulsifier is added to an established formula, a flavor may be altered unpredictably. This change in flavor level is at times most desirable, for example, in the processing of pickles. Here, emulsification or solubilization of the flavor oil with proper surface-active agents frequently renders the oil much more potent, and lower quantities may be used in pickling operations.

It is often advantageous to utilize the dispersing power of emulsifiers for flavor oils to replace the alcohol in the extract of the flavor oil. Flavor and essential oil extracts usually contain 70–85% alcohol to assure solubility of the oil. Even at these concentrations, the extracts must be aged and filtered to attain clarity, and, as a result, a portion of the oil is lost. Certain moderately hydrophilic emulsifiers may be used to prepare either clear (hydrotropic or solubilized) or cloudy (milky) emulsions of essential flavor or oils. To have clarity in water, several parts of emulsifier are used for one part of oil. Cloudy dispersions require less emulsifier. The action of the emulsifier and the solubility induced by alcohol are complementary, so that low concentrations of alcohol may be used with reduced amounts of emulsifier. The need for aging and filtration is usually eliminated by using emulsifiers.

Both clear (solubilized) and cloudy (emulsified) types of flavor dispersions are used in the soft drink industry, in which both clear and cloudy final beverages are required; for example, root beer, cola, cream soda, grape, and ginger ale are clear, whereas orange is cloudy. Nonalcoholic flavor dispersions are particularly adapted for application of flavor by spraying because less essential oil is lost than with alcoholic extracts.

Convenience foods lean heavily on emulsifiers. Synthetic coffee whiteners, of both the powdered and liquid types, contain critically balanced emulsifiers to provide rapid opaque "bloom" from the formulated fat. Pressure-packed and prepared frostings and cake decorating icings utilize emulsifiers to maintain stability. The number of frozen foods containing emulsifiers to increase stability and to promote good mouth feel and texture is increasing rapidly.

An interesting step toward synthetic meat has been taken in the pet food market where simulated ground meat has been prepared by careful formulation. Emulsifiers are required to produce an emulsion that will give the desired texture, both during processing and in the final product.

Pharmaceuticals and Cosmetics. Many pharmaceuticals and cosmetics are based on ointments, creams, or lotions. In these, emulsifiers are most important. Absence of toxicity and chemical reactivity are, of course, prime requirements for emulsifiers used in such applications. Both O/W and W/O types of emulsions are used for external and internal applications. In addition, emulsifiers have been found to be of value in emulsifying and solubilizing vitamins (83) and hormones. The resulting medicaments are assimilated better than those without the emulsifier. It has been demonstrated that feeding of certain emulsifiers can increase the fat assimilation of the human body (43), and, in fact, that medicaments absorption may be enhanced (74).

Cosmetic emulsions cover a wide variety of formula types. O/W formulas are typified by facial creams, hand creams, vanishing creams, and shaving creams and lotions. Many of the more emollient creams, such as cold creams, dry-skin creams, hair dressings, suntan oils, insect-repellent lotions, and antiperspirant creams may be formulated as O/W or W/O. Solubilization is utilized in perfume oil dispersions in making clear and also cream colognes, hair tonics, and similar preparations.

Agricultural Products. Agricultural formulations are concerned with insecticides, herbicides, and fungicides. One of the major types of insecticide emulsion formulations comprises solvent–toxicant emulsifiable concentrates. In these, a chemical toxicant such as DDT or an analog, chlordane, toxaphene, benzene hexachloride, or an organic phosphate is dissolved in a suitable low-cost solvent and a soluble emulsifier is added in sufficient quantity to provide good ease of dispersibility in water of any type with moderate agitation.

Somewhat removed from emulsification is the action required when a surface-active agent is applied to dusts, which usually consist of the toxicant and an inert filler such as talc, pyrophyllite, and clay. Here the agent is used to provide an initial wetting of the powder and toxicant with water, and, in some instances, to provide a suspending action. With both active toxicant sprays and dusts the action of an emulsifier is only partly completed when the spray is prepared. The agent must not only provide proper wetting of the spray ingredients, but also proper spreading on the foliage to which the spray is applied to insure good coverage; yet, it must not wet so thoroughly that a complete film is formed, resulting in run off and loss of spray.

Hydrocarbon oil sprays are used for some insecticide and fungicide applications. These are provided either as an emulsifiable concentrate or as a concentrated "mayonnaise" (O/W) type of emulsion (see p. 138). Organic fungicides are often applied with added surface-active agents.

Herbicides such as oil-soluble esters of 2,4-D (2,4-dichlorophenoxyacetic acid) and pentachlorophenol are dissolved in a hydrocarbon solvent and are mixed with oil-soluble emulsifiers to make them dispersible in water. The surface-active agent frequently behaves not only as an emulsifier, but also affects the activity of the weed killer (40).

Recent work has indicated a synergistic effect between some of the active ingredients and emulsifiers when they are properly selected and formulated (41). This allows the use of less of the active ingredient coupled with an FDA-accepted emulsifier, a combination that leads to greater overall safety.

Related Problems and Applications

Solubilization or Hydrotropy. In the discussion of particle size, it was indicated that the size can be reduced sufficiently so that the resulting emulsion will be transparent and clear to the eye (83), even though it exhibits a Tyndall cone. Several recent studies have considered this field (46–48,50,73).

The successful preparation of this type of transparent emulsion seems to depend upon the following requirements: (*1*) that the dispersed phase be soluble in the emulsifier; (*2*) that the emulsifier be soluble or form a clear dispersion in the continuous phase (water, in most instances); and (*3*) that the hydrophile–lipophile balance of the emulsifier be moderately hydrophile (for use with water as the continuous phase).

Relatively large proportions of emulsifier are required, normally ranging from 100–1000% of the product to be solubilized. The best method for aqueous dispersions has been to dissolve the oil thoroughly in the emulsifier and then add this mixture to water. Under proper conditions clear aqueous dilutions of many oils (mineral oils, flavors, perfumes, glycerides, etc) may be prepared.

Recent work (71) has shown that emulsifier efficiency in solubilization may be greatly enhanced by extra critical selection of emulsifier with special attention being paid to the proper HLB (checked to within 0.1 unit).

Foams and Aerosols (see also Foams). The requirements for a surface-active agent to produce a stable aqueous foam have been investigated (27,65). Foaming is desirable especially in one major industrial use, household cleaning. The desirability of suds has been impressed upon the housewife, and a cleaner that has no foaming action is received with considerable resistance.

Foaming may be desirable or undesirable in emulsions. Since foam introduces a third phase, and depletes the emulsifier in the other phases, it is usually undesirable (62). In many foods (ice cream, whipped cream, marshmallow, etc) foam is desired. Egg, gums, and synthetic emulsifiers provide the desired action. An instance, in the food industry, in which foam is undesirable is in beverage manufacture. Emulsifiers may be used to "carry" the flavoring oil for a soft-drink beverage; however, the emulsifier must not promote foam because it will interfere with bottling.

Industry, in general, is interested in agents that will serve as antifoams. The choice of these is made even more by trial-and-error than in the case of emulsifiers. The action of an antifoaming agent appears to be quite specific (13,61). The usual requirements would appear to be that the material be insoluble in the product that is foaming. Commonly used antifoams in foods consists of lipophilic fatty acid esters, both partial and complete. Some of the most generally efficient antifoaming agents are based on silicones.

Aerosols or mists are usually formed mechanically, either by actual spraying or by evaporation of a carrier liquid such as a chlorofluoromethane (Freon). Surface-active agents are sometimes added to these materials, but usually not for emulsification purposes. They alter the wetting and at times the insecticidal properties of the aerosol. Emulsifiers or surface-active agents added to aerosol formulations generally do not affect the particle size of the aerosol droplet. This appears to be due to the fact that they do not migrate to the newly formed surface with sufficient rapidity to influence the surface properties of the particles.

The newer foamed plastics, for example rigid polyurethan foams, require a special type of surfactant to produce the desired bubble type and size.

Demulsification

Demulsification is agglomeration and coalescence of globules of the dispersed phase, proceeding further and further, and eventually resulting in a breakdown of the emulsion into two separate phases. This, of course, relates to a liquid. Waxy solids on agitation can also exhibit a churning effect in which the waxy particles will gradually flocculate, agglomerate, and separate out as chunks. If the dispersed phase is a paraffin wax, the churning effect may be reduced or eliminated by adding small amounts of free fatty acid and a sorbitol borate (22).

The logical approach to demulsification is to establish the properties of the emulsion to be treated and to add an antagonistic ion or emulsifier. The properties of interest are the type of emulsion (O/W or W/O), the constituents, and the sensitivity of the emulsifier or emulsifiers. Based on these findings, additions are made to the emulsion to destroy or "neutralize" the emulsifier, if necessary, and available mechanical means are employed to complete the separation.

Mechanical means of demulsification such as settling boxes and centrifuges usually depend upon the difference in specific gravity of the two phases. Alone, they are satisfactory for relatively poor emulsions. They are used in conjunction with chemical and surface-active agents for breaking good emulsions. Frequently, the specific gravity of the aqueous phase can be increased by the addition of a cheap salt such as sodium sulfate. Likewise, the specific gravity of the oil phase may be altered by the addition of a solvent.

Some industrial emulsions are purposely prepared with ionic emulsifiers that may be destroyed, so that demulsification occurs at a desired point in a manufacturing procedure. An example is a wax–rosin emulsion used in paper sizing; the emulsion, made with soap, is precipitated with alum.

Demulsification is also used in industry to recover the raw materials of unsatisfactory production batches of emulsions. In such instances, the emulsifier is known and its neutralization or destruction is usually feasible.

Many natural emulsions contain electrolytes, such as seawater, and are quite difficult to break. In the petroleum field, this has been given considerable study. Usually the demulsification must be carried out at a minimum of expense.

The stability of some emulsions is enhanced by the viscosity of the emulsion. The addition of water or a solvent may alter the viscosity or the required emulsifier balance, so that demulsification will occur.

It will be seen that a list of demulsification agents may include water, solvents, electrolytes, and antagonistic emulsifiers, in addition to surface-active products developed particularly for the purpose (77,81).

Possible Lines of Advancement

Even though emulsions are widely used, formulation techniques leave much to be desired. The most critical need in emulsion technology is a method of selecting a suitable emulsifier. The problem of devising such a system has been complicated by the complexity of emulsifier behavior and the lack of a suitable method for determining emulsifier stability. Specific items that need to be solved are (1) a good experimental means for determining HLB value; and (2) a method of correlation of emulsifier chemical type with emulsion requirements.

Bibliography

"Emulsions" in *ECT* 1st ed., Vol. 5, pp. 692–718, by W. C. Griffin, Atlas Powder Company.

1. N. K. Adam, *The Physics and Chemistry of Surfaces*, Oxford University Press, London, 1941, pp. 10–12, 336–338, 363–389, 424.
2. E. G. Almy, W. C. Griffin, and C. S. Wilcox, *Ind. Eng. Chem., Anal. Ed.* **12**, 392 (1940).
3. F. Appell, *Chim. Ind.* (*Paris*) **57**, 241–249, 341–346 (1946).
4. R. Auerbach, *Chem. Tech.* (*Berlin*) **15**, 107–109 (1942).
5. P. Becher, *Emulsions: Theory and Practice*, Reinhold Publishing Corp., New York, 1957.
6. P. Becher and R. Berkmeier, "The Determination of Hydrophile–Lipophile Balance by GLC," *J. Am. Oil Chemists' Soc.* **41**, 169–172 (1964).
7. P. Becher, "The Effect of the Nature of the Emulsifying Agent on Emulsion Inversion," *J. Soc. Cosmetic Chemists* **9**, 141–148 (1958).
8. P. Becher, *Particle Size*, to be presented, Am. Chem. Soc. Symp., Pittsburgh.
9. P. Becher, "A Particle Size Analyzer for Emulsion Photomicrographs," *J. Colloid Sci.* **19**, 468–472 (1964).

10. P. Becher, E. S. Chen, H. J. Ranauto, and S. Ross, "Spreading Coefficients and Hydrophile–Lipophile Balance of Aqueous Solutions of Emulsifying Agents," *J. Phys. Chem.* **63**, 1681–1683 (1959).

11. R. W. Behrens and W. C. Griffin, "The Evaluation of Agricultural Emulsions," *Anal. Chem.* **24** (6), 1076 (June 1952); R. W. Behrens, *J. Agr. Food Chem.* **6** (1), 20 (Jan. 1958).

12. S. Berkman, *J. Phys. Chem.* **39**, 527 (1935).

13. S. Berkman and G. Egloff, *Emulsions and Foams*, Reinhold Publishing Corp., New York, 1941.

14. J. J. Bickerman, *Surface Chemistry*, Academic Press, Inc., New York, 1947, pp. 142–153.

15. F. M. Biffen and F. D. Snell, *Ind. Eng. Chem., Anal. Ed.* **15**, 517–519 (1943).

16. A. Boutaric and P. Berthier, *J. Chem. Phys.* **42**, 117–122 (1945).

17. A. V. Brancker, *Petroleum (London)* **8**, 88–89 (1945).

18. A. Brothman, *Chem. Met. Eng.* **46**, 263–265 (1939).

19. C. F. Bruening, *J. Assoc. Offic. Agr. Chemists* **25**, 903–909 (1942).

20. W. C. Clayton, *Theory of Emulsions*, 3rd ed., The Blakiston Co., Inc., Philadelphia, 1935.

21. L. H. Cohen and H. Hackerman, *Ind. Eng. Chem., Anal. Ed.* **12**, 210–213 (1940).

22. U.S. Pat. 2,684,948 (1954), S. T. Cross.

23. H. L. Cupples, *U.S. Dept. Agr., Bur. Entomol. Plant Quarantine E-504*, 1940.

24. F. K. Daniel, *India Rubber World* **101** (3), 50–52 (1939).

25. J. T. Davies and E. K. Rideal, *Interfacial Phenomena*, Academic Press, Inc., New York, 1961.

26. A. Davidsohn and J. Davidsohn, *Shoe Creams and Polishing Waxes*, Leonard Hill, London, 1938.

27. D. Dervichian and F. Lachampt, *Bull. Soc. Chim. Belges* **55**, 486–491 (1946).

28. F. R. Eastwood, N. Banks, and E. Webster, *Textile J. Australia* **20**, 344–347 (1945).

29. S. R. Epton, *Nature* **160**, 795 (1947).

30. E. K. Fischer, *Soap* **20** (1), 28–31, 67–69 (1944).

31. C. F. Fryling, "The Viscosity of Small Particle, Electrolyte- and Soap-Deficient Synthetic Latex Gels," *J. Colloid Sci.* **18** (8), 713–732 (1963).

32. F. H. Garner, *Congr. Mondial Petrole, 2ᵉ* **4**, Sect. 5, 307–313 (1937).

33. E. Götte, *Chemiker-Ztg.* **68**, 86–87 (1944).

34. G. L. Brown, M. N. Fineman, and H. L. Greenwald, "Determination of the Hydrophile–Lipophile Character of Surface Active Agents and Oils by a Water-Titration," *Anal. Chem.* **28**, 1693–1697 (1956).

35. W. G. Gorman and G. D. Hall, "Use of Dielectric Constants in the Classification of Surfactants," *J. Pharm. Sci.* **52**, 442 (1963).

36. W. C. Griffin, *Proc. Sci. Sect. Toilet Goods Assoc.* **6** (6), 43–50 (1946).

37. W. C. Griffin, "Calculation of HLB Values of Nonionic Surfactants," *J. Soc. Cosmetic Chemists* **5**, 249–255 (1954).

38. R. Harsch and E. N. Spotswood, *Proc. Assoc. Asphalt Paving Technologists* **12**, 184–205 (1940).

39. O. Harva, Airi Keltakallio, and P. Kivalo, "Determination of the Hydrophile–Lipophile Character of Polyhydric Alcohol Esters by Gas Chromatography," *Suomen Kemistilehti B* **32**, 52–54 (1959).

40. A. E. Hitchock and P. W. Zimmerman, *Contrib. Boyce Thompson Inst.* **15**, 173–193 (1948).

41. L. L. Jansen, "Emulsifier–Herbicide Synergism," *J. Weed Soc. Am.* **12** (4), 251–255 (1964).

42. N. F. Johnston and H. H. Favor, *Food Ind.* **19**, 1196–1197 (1947).

43. C. M. Jones, P. J. Culver, A. E. Ryan, and G. D. Drummey, *Ann. Internal Med.* **29** (1), 1–10 (1948).

44. A. King and L. N. Mukherjee, *J. Soc. Chem. Ind.* **58**, 243 (1939).

45. A. Kufferath, *Zellwolle, Kunstseide, Seide* **47**, 428–429 (1942).

46. W. F. Busse and J. M. Lambert, *J. Chem. Phys.* **16**, 847–848 (1948).

47. J. W. McBain and P. H. Richards, *Ind. Eng. Chem.* **38**, 642 (1946).

48. K. E. Johnson and J. W. McBain, *J. Am. Chem. Soc.* **66**, 9 (1944).

49. J. W. McCutcheon, *Chemical Industries* **61** (5), 811–824 (1947).

50. R. H. McKee, *Ind. Eng. Chem.* **38**, 382 (1946).

51. J. Mitchell, Jr. and D. M. Smith, *Aquametry*, Interscience Publishers, Inc., New York, 1948.

52. P. W. Morgan, "Determination of Ethers and Esters of Ethylene Glycol," *Ind. Eng. Chem., Anal. Ed.* **18**, 500 (1946).

53. H. A. Neville, *Am. Dyestuff Reptr.* **34**, 534–536 (1945).
54. N. Ohba, "Hydrophile–Lipophile Balance Values of Nonionic Surfactants Determined by Emulsification," *Bull. Chem. Soc. Japan* **35**, 1016 (1962).
55. N. Ohba, "Required Hydrophile–Lipophile Balance Values of the Oil Mixture," *Bull. Chem. Soc. Japan* **35**, 1021 (1962).
56. A. Parisot, *Corps Gras, Savons* **1**, 11–14 (1943).
57. B. Persoz, *Chim. Ind. Paris* **52**, 88–90 (1944).
58. R. D. Hamill, J. D. McMahon, and R. V. Petersen, "Emulsifying Effects of Some Nonionic Surfactants on a Nonaqueous Immiscible System," *J. Pharm. Sci.* **53**, 651–655 (1964); **52**, 1163 (1963).
59. I. Reich and F. D. Snell, *Ind. Eng Chem.* **40**, 2333–2337 (1948).
60. E. K. Rideal, *An Introduction to Surface Chemistry*, 2nd ed., Cambridge University Press, London, 1930.
61. J. V. Robinson and W. W. Woods, "A General Method of Selecting Foam Inhibitors," *Natl. Advisory Comm. for Aeronautics Tech. Note 1205 Washington, D.C.* (1946).
62. H. Schmalfuss, *Fette u. Seifen* **47**, 526–530 (1940).
63. E. J. Schniedera, W. F. Gross, and C. M. Blau, Jr., *Soap Sanit. Chemicals* **24** (6), 145 (1948).
64. D. Schoenholz and C. S. Kimball, *Soap Sanit. Chemicals* **23** (8), 131–135 (1947).
65. L. Schedlovsky, *Ann. N.Y. Acad. Sci.* **46**, 427–450 (1946).
66. A. M. Schwartz, J. W. Perry, and J. Berch, *Surface Active Agents and Detergents*, Vols. I and II, Interscience Publishers, Inc., New York, 1949.
67. E. G. Cockbain and J. H. Schulman, *Trans. Faraday Soc.* **36**, 661 (1940).
68. J. O. Sibree, *Trans. Faraday Soc.* **27**, 161 (1931).
69. H. M. Beal and R. E. Singiser, "Emulsification With Ultrasonic Waves II," *J. Am. Pharm. Assoc. Sci. Ed.* **49** (7), (July 1960).
70. J. B. Speakman, *Chem. Ind.* **34**, 456–460 (1948).
71. S. J. Strianse and M. Lanzet, "Application of the HLB System to the Solubilization of Essential Oils," *Toilet Goods Assoc. Sci. Sect.* **34** (Dec. 1960).
72. G. Sutheim, *Introduction to Emulsions*, Chemical Publishing Co., New York, 1946.
73. P. A. Winsor, *Trans. Faraday Soc.* **44**, 376–451 (1948).
74. M. N. Khawam and R. T. Yousef, "HLB System—Diffusion of Chloramphenicol from an Ointment Base," *Sci. Pharm.* **32** (1), 1–6 (1946).
75. F. H. Haynie, Jr., R. A. Moses, and G. C. Yeh, "Phase-Volume Relationship at the Point of Phase Inversion in Liquid Dispersions," *Am. Inst. Chem. Engrs. J.* **10** (2), 260–265 (March 1964).
76. W. A. Zisman, *U.S. Naval Res. Lab. NRL Rept. 5699* (Nov. 29, 1961); *Ind. Eng. Chem.* **55** (10), 19–38 (1963).
77. Brit. Pat. 493,221 (Oct. 5, 1938), I. G. Farbenindustrie, A.G.
78. Brit. Pat. 568,742 (April 18, 1945), Ernest R. Hatt and Clive W. Norton (to Dussex Bitumen and Taroleum Ltd.).
79. Ger. Pat. 716,231 (Dec. 18, 1941), G. Hertz and R. Wiesner (to Siemeno and Halske).
80. Russ. Pat. 66,882 (Aug. 31, 1946), G. P. Indrikson.
81. U.S. Pat. 2,175,699 (Oct. 10, 1939), M. Powell.
82. U.S. Pat. 2,398,950 (April 23, 1946), H. E. Moore.
83. U.S. Pat. 2,417,299 (Aug. 6, 1943), L. Freedman and E. Green (to U.S. Vitamin Corp.).
84. AOCS Cd 3-25, American Oil Chemists' Society.
85. AOCS Cd 6-38 and AOCS L3a-57, American Oil Chemists' Society.

W. C. GRIFFIN
Atlas Chemical Industries, Inc.

ENAMELS (PAINT).   See Coatings, industrial.

ENAMELS, PORCELAIN OR VITREOUS

The word "enamel" has historically been used to describe decorative and protective glassy coatings on metal. This term has also been used for glassy, decorative coatings on glass, whereas the term "glaze" has been most commonly employed for glassy coatings on ceramic bodies. ("Enamel" has also been used to mean certain organic coatings, such as paints or lacquers. These are not discussed here. See Coatings, industrial.)

In the United States, the term *porcelain enamel* has been adopted as the designation of the glassy coating on metal. In some other countries, the term *vitreous enamel* rather than porcelain enamel is more common. The American Society for Testing and Materials defines porcelain enamel as "a substantially vitreous or glassy, inorganic coating bonded to metal by fusion at a temperature above 800°F" (1).

"Ceramic coatings" is another term used for coatings on metal that connote special emphasis to the protective feature of the coating for the metal. Ceramic coatings are often formulated and designed to contain mainly crystalline rather than glassy material. See also Colors for ceramics; Glass.

Although processes for making glass were discovered about 2500–3000 BC, it is not clear just when porcelain enamel originated. It is likely that metalsmiths explored the decorative technique of enameling using colored glass inlays or fabricating patterns of glass pieces on gold, silver, or copper articles. Porcelain-enameled metal art objects have been identified with early civilizations in the Middle East, specifically in the Mediterranean area and the Orient. It is believed that the knowledge of techniques for creating decorative porcelain-enameled objects was passed from one Mediterranean group to another. The Egyptians, Greeks, Romans, Spaniards, and Arabs practiced this art. Enameling is believed to have been introduced to Great Britain by the Romans. In Byzantium (Istanbul) porcelain enameling art has been traced from the fourth to the eleventh centuries, having later been introduced into Italy and parts of Western Europe.

The ancient and even more recent enameled art objects demonstrate generally four types of art enameling techniques. These four varieties are named (*1*) cloisonné, (*2*) champlevé, (*3*) basse taille, and (*4*) painting. *Cloisonné* enameling involves the technique of preparing a design of small wires or partitions ("cloisons"). The wire pattern is soldered or fused onto the metal surface. Segments of the design are filled with different colors of powdered glass and the entire ensemble is heated to fuse the enamels within the partitions and onto the metal substrate. This decorated surface, after grinding and polishing, displays a colored enameled design outlined by thin wires. *Champlevé* enameling is the art technique of carving or gouging the design into the surface of a thick metal-base material, such as copper, bronze, gold, or silver. Gouged-out areas of the design are filled with colored glass. After firing, the polished surface appears to consist of a design of enamel inlays in the metal surface. *Basse taille* is the technique of designing the metal surface in low relief and then covering the entire surface with a transparent porcelain enamel. *Painting* involves the enameling of the entire metal surface with a dark enamel layer. Lighter-colored enamels are then used to paint the designs on the first enameled layer.

Metal art objects in the early periods were made from gold, silver, copper, or bronze. It was not until the early 1800s that porcelain enameling on cast iron was developed and practiced in Central Europe. Later, as the sheet-steel manufacturing process developed about 1850, porcelain enameling of sheet steel naturally followed, first in Germany and Austria. About 1857, porcelain enameling was initiated in the United States by the Grosjean Company of New York City and the Vollrath Company of Sheboygan, Wisconsin, manufacturers of porcelain-enameled kitchenware.

Porcelain enamel, as a coating on metal, performs many important functions. It protects metal against corrosion, decorates the metal, and resists the attack of alkalies, acids, and other chemicals. This material is a sanitary coating imparting no odors or tastes. Because of its sanitary aspects, its protective and strengthening function to the metal, and its decorative character, porcelain enamel has been generally adopted as the most suitable material for bathtubs, laundry appliances, ranges, sinks, and refrigerator liners. The decorative and corrosion-resistant aspects of this coating have led to its many uses in architectural applications. Porcelain enamel, because of its extremely low porosity and resistance to chemical attack, has found widespread use in the dairy, pharmaceutical, brewing, and chemical industries. Porcelain-enameled tanks and vessels made of heavy-gage sheet steel or cast iron are commonly used in these industrial fields. Porcelain enamel on steel, cast iron, or aluminum is a most desirable composite system of materials. Sinks, stoves, ranges, refrigerators, clothes washers, dishwashers, and dryers represent a major use of this material in the home-appliance industry. Cooking utensils, architectural panels, signs, silos, bathtubs, lavatories, brewing vessels, chemical storage tanks, gasoline service stations, roofing tile, guard rails, chalkboards, and many other articles of commerce indicate the broad spectrum of home and industrial products finished with porcelain enamels.

Porcelain enamels can be classified in a number of ways. Several common classifications are as follows:

I. Function
    A. ground coats
       1. single frit
       2. multiple frit
    B. cover coat
       1. porcelain enamel applied directly to metal
       2. applied to ground-coated metal

II. Service
    A. acid resistant
    B. alkali resistant
    C. hot-water resistant
    D. chemical resistant
    E. abrasion resistant
    F. electrically resistant
    G. thermal-shock resistant

III. Composition
    A. alkali borosilicate
    B. titania
    C. lead-bearing
    D. leadless enamels
    E. phosphate

IV. Type of metal being coated
    A. sheet steel
       1. very low carbon
       2. enameling iron
       3. enameling steel
    B. cast iron
    C. aluminum
    D. copper, gold, silver
    E. stainless steel

V. Decorative character
    A. clear
    B. colored
    C. white
    D. stippled
    E. matte
    F. glossy
    G. semi-matte
    H. beading

VI. Opacifying material
    A. titania
    B. zirconia
    C. antimony oxide
    D. molybdenum oxide

VII. Method of application
    A. wet process
    B. dry process

VIII. Type of product
    A. appliances
    B. cooking utensils
    C. sanitary ware
    D. chemical equipment
    E. jewelry
    F. architectural panels

    G. signs
    H. hot-water tanks

IX. Firing temperature
    A. 1000°F (540°C)
    B. low temperature, 1100–1400°F (ca 595–760°C)
    C. normal, 1450–1600°F (ca 790–870°C)
    D. high temperature, 1600°F (ca 870°C) and above

The Enameling Process

The porcelain enameling process involves the re-fusing of powdered glass on the metal surface. The powdered glass is prepared by ball-milling a property-designed porcelain enamel glass. First, the glass is smelted from raw batch materials, such as listed for enamel glass compositions in Table 1. The enamel smelter is usually a box-shaped tank furnace. Continuous smelters, wherein the thoroughly mixed raw batch is fed in at one end and molten glass is flowing out at the other end, are common in commercial operations. Decomposition, gas evolution, and solution occur during smelting. After the molten glass has been smelted to a uniform and homogeneous liquid, it is quenched by pouring a thin stream of the molten liquid into water or onto cooled metal rollers. This quenched glass, termed "frit," is a friable material easily reduced to small particles by a ball-milling operation. The breaking up of the glass frit into small-sized particles is carried out either wet or dry. Dry powders are used for the dry-process cast-iron enameling. Dry powders are also prepared and marketed for the subsequent preparation of slurries and slips used in the wet-process application techniques.

Process flow diagrams for sheet-steel and cast-iron enameling are shown in Figures 1 and 2.

The frit-making process takes into account all technology from the proper selection of raw materials through thorough mixing and smelting, to the uniform production of quenched-glass frit. For smaller production requirements or for research and development purposes, batch-type smelters, such as crucible furnaces, rotary smelters, or box-shaped smelters are used.

For sheet-steel enameling, the porcelain enamel frit is ball-milled with clay, certain electrolytes, and water to form a stable suspension. This clay-supported slurry of small frit particles is called the slip, and has a consistency similar to that of a thick coffee cream. The ingredients comprising the mill batch are carefully controlled. The amount and purity of all materials in the mill, including the clay and water, affect the rheological character of the slip as well as a number of properties of the fired enamel, such as acid resistance (increasing clay content means lower acid resistance), reflectance, and gloss.

Ball-mill grinding is accomplished with porcelain or high-alumina balls, 0.5–2 in. in diameter. Ball size, mill speed, mill charge, and ball charge are important parameters in determining the optimum milling time required for optimum size distribution in prepared slip. Ground-coat enamels are ball-milled to a fineness of 95%

Table 1. Composition of Porcelain Enamel Frits (3)

	Sheet-steel ground coat	Titania cover enamel	Cast iron, high lead	Cast iron, low lead	Cast-iron ground coat	Cast-iron cover coat
Oxide composition						
KNaO	19.7	(14.0)	(9.4)	(18.9)	(11.4)	(20.8)
K_2O		3.5	2.3	4.6	7.1	4.4
Na_2O		10.5	7.1	14.3	4.3	16.4
B_2O_3	14.6	14.0	8.7	12.0	6.9	2.6
Al_2O_3	7.2		4.6	6.5	11.3	6.0
SiO_2	50.5	45.0	24.6	44.7	51.8	48.9
CaF_2	5.1					3.2
F_2		5.0	6.5	6.3		
CoO	0.6					
MnO	1.9					
NiO	0.2					
TiO_2		20.0				
P_2O_5		2.0				
PbO			33.6		18.4	
CaO			7.1	4.0		
ZnO			5.4			
BaO				4.0		
Sb_2O_5				3.8		8.7
AlF_3						5.0
NaF						7.5
Batch						
feldspar	30.3		17.3	22.4	35.0	22.6
borax (hydrous)	31.6		18.3	26.9	23.0	16.7
borax (anhydrous)		19.1				
quartz	20.0	42.0	10.6	22.3	15.0	26.0
soda ash	6.7			4.3		3.0
soda niter	3.8	7.8	4.8	6.7	4.0	4.5
fluorspar	4.6		8.7	4.6		2.3
cobalt oxide	0.5					
manganese oxide	1.5					
nickel oxide	0.2					
monosodium phosphate		3.2				
zinc oxide			4.8			
red lead			30.7		23.0	
cryolite			2.9	5.5		10.7
boric acid			1.9			
titania		20.2				
Na_2SiF_6		1.2				
K_2SiF_6		7.8				
Sb_2O_5				3.1		
$BaCO_3$				4.2		
$NaSbO_3$						11.4
clay						2.4

of solids smaller than 74 μ (200 mesh). Cover coats are ground finer, to 98% of solids finer than 44 μ (325 mesh).

Ground coats are applied to metal by spraying, dipping, or draining. Large articles may be coated only by spraying or flow-draining the slip, whereas small

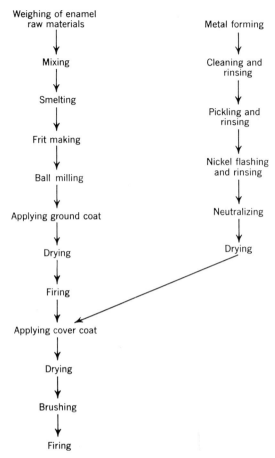

Fig. 1. Flow diagram of sheet-steel enameling.

articles may be dipped into a tank of ground-coat slip. Cover coats may also be applied by similar methods.

Dry-process cast-iron enameling involves the application of the cover coat by dusting or dredging of the dry glass powder (using a long-handled vibrating sifter) onto the heated cast-iron article. The cast iron previously ground-coated is removed from the furnace (1600°F and higher) for the dusting operation, then returned to the furnace. Several dusting and heating cycles are required for the development of a uniform coating.

Preparation of Metals. Sheet-metal parts are formed by the well-known processes of stamping, bending, and shearing. Many parts require welding, and it is important that this be carried out in such a manner that the welded joint can be enameled without defect. Cast-iron parts are formed by the usual cast-iron foundry methods with additional care given to prevent contamination of the surface, because contamination causes defects in the enamel, particularly "blisters" or bubbles.

Enameling cannot be successful unless the metal is thoroughly cleaned and kept clean until the final coat is fired. Even touching of the surface by hand may cause

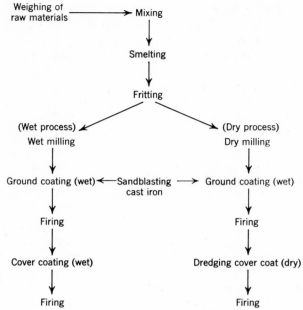

Weighing of raw materials ———→ Mixing

↓

Smelting

↓

Fritting

(Wet process)   (Dry process)
Wet milling   Dry milling

↓   ↓

Ground coating (wet) ←—— Sandblasting ——→ Ground coating (wet)
cast iron

↓   ↓

Firing   Firing

↓   ↓

Cover coating (wet)   Dredging cover coat (dry)

↓   ↓

Firing   Firing

Fig. 2. Flow diagram of cast-iron enameling.

defects. Cast-iron and thick steel parts are sandblasted without danger of excessive loss of metal and excessive warping. Sand, silicon carbide, and steel grit are satisfactory abrasives. Products made from thin sheet materials are most satisfactorily and most economically cleaned by chemical methods which require alkali and soap solutions for removing grease and dirt and acid solutions for removing oxidized metal.

The commercial chemical treatment in the metal preparation process may be carried out with continuous cleaning and pickling equipment. The fabricated sheet-metal articles are supported on a special continuously moving rack which passes first through the cleaning stage. The ware subsequently experiences pickling acids, nickel flashing, and neutralizing treatments. Metal articles are also cleaned and pickled in a batch process whereby baskets of metal articles are immersed in large tanks of various solutions and water rinses. The batch process is described to indicate some details of each step in this metal preenameling treatment.

The composition of the cleaning solution depends upon the type of oil, grease, and solid material to be removed, including the type and amount of drawing compounds used in the metal forming operations. Vegetable oils may be saponified and removed by alkalies alone, but mineral oils require soap for their removal. A well-balanced cleaning compound contains an alkali, an alkali salt as a buffer material to maintain the pH approximately constant, and a soap. Proprietary products especially adapted to the cleaning process are available and are usually employed at a strength of about 6 oz/gal of water at boiling temperatures.

After being cleaned, the ware is immersed successively in one or more tanks of water at 180–200°F and then transferred to the acid pickling solution. The pickling solution of 6–8% sulfuric acid is contained in lead-lined wooden tanks and maintained at a temperature of 140–150°F. The ware is allowed to remain in the acid solution as long as is necessary to remove all oxide scale from the metal. Pickling inhibitors are rarely used as they have a tendency to cause enameling defects, and also because some etching of the steel is desirable. Rinsing water for removing acid is maintained at a temperature of 180–190°F, with rinsing time on the order of 3 min.

To retard oxidation and enhance enamel bond, it has been found desirable to plate, or "flash," a thin film of nickel on the iron at this point. The ware is immersed in a solution containing 1 oz/gal of nickel salts, such as nickel sulfate, $NiSO_4.6H_2O$, or the equivalent. The pH is carefully controlled between 3.0 and 3.6 and the temperature between 160 and 170°F. The average time of immersion is 4–6 min and the deposit is usually 0.04–0.12 g/ft². A wooden tank normally is employed as a container.

After being removed from the nickel bath, the ware is dipped into a hot or cold water rinse, quickly removed, and transferred to a neutralizing bath to remove the last traces of acid. Neutralizing with solutions of sodium carbonate and borax is common.

After being removed from the neutralizing solution, the ware is transferred to a dryer maintained at a temperature of about 235–250°F and provided with good air circulation to insure quick and complete drying without rusting of the metal. The sheet-steel ware is now ready for the application of the enamel; after the application of the coating, the ware is ready for the firing operation.

Firing. Firing may be carried out in intermittent box-type furnaces or continuous furnaces. The drier and the furnace may form one continuous unit or separate units in the continuous firing process. In a continuous tunnel-type furnace, each coated item progresses through the furnace supported on firing racks especially designed to withstand long service at the repeated cycles of heating and cooling. Gradual heating and cooling of the ware occur more with continuous firing than with intermittent methods. In this latter process, a batch of ware loaded on a large rack of special support tools is introduced into the box furnace.

Furnace temperature in the hot zone of continuous furnaces and box furnaces is established to mature the coating in a matter of minutes. Ground-coats firing in a box furnace would be on the order of 3–6 min at 1550–1600°F. Cover-coat firing is generally carried out at shorter times and slightly lower temperatures.

Enamel-firing temperature is, of course, related to the coating composition, the metal thickness, and the type of metal. Enamels for aluminum are fired at 950–1000°F, whereas coatings for high-temperature alloys may be fired at 1700°F.

Composition

Since porcelain enamels are substantially glassy coatings, the composition of this partner in the enamel–metal materials system is based on glass-forming ingredients. The principal glass formers are B_2O_3, SiO_2, and P_2O_5. Other glass formers, such as GeO_2, BeF_2, and As_2O_3, are rarely used to comprise the base for the glass, because they are not economical and do not impart unusual properties for enamel glasses. Phosphate glasses, although low-melting and commercially economical, are in general not sufficiently resistant to alkali attack.

Table 1 (see p. 158) lists the compositions in terms of moles of the oxide components. Raw materials for the glass batch include minerals from the earth, such as the feldspars and quartz, since these are inexpensive sources of SiO_2 and Al_2O_3. The batch composition especially designed for cover coats is mainly comprised of manufactured chemicals of controlled and known levels of purity.

Although it may not be readily evident from Table 1, the composition of porcelain enamel glasses is essentially based on the alkali borosilicate glasses. Both B_2O_3 and SiO_2, the glass formers, are also called network formers, whereas the remainder of the ingredients are called network modifiers. It is considered that BO_3^{3-}, BO_4^{5-}, and SiO_4^{4-} structural units exist in the glass structure, and glass as a rigid supercooled liquid has the short-range order of BO_3^{3-} triangles or BO_4^{5-} and SiO_4^{4-} tetrahedra, but long-range order of the units does not occur. These triangles and tetrahedra are joined at corners, that is, oxygen ions at corners are joining two silicon or boron atoms and the continuous three-dimensional network of the glass structure is assured by this arrangement.

In the absence of network modifier atoms that do not contribute to the continuity of the three-dimensional network of SiO_2 or B_2O_3 glass, these oxide glasses have a very high viscosity at their liquidus (melting temperatures). The viscosity at the liquidus temperature of glasses is in the range of 10^1–10^4 P, whereas water nearing its freezing point has a viscosity of about 0.01 P. This high viscosity attests to the strong interconnecting bonds of the network and to the high degree of association in the liquid glass. Modifier atoms, such as the alkalies, alkaline earths, or halides cause the number of interconnecting bonds to decrease. Broken bonds resulting from a sodium atom attaching itself to an oxygen atom (Na–O–Si–O–Na instead of –Si–O–Si–O–Si–) or a fluoride atom bonded to a silicon atom (F–Si–O–Si–F instead of –O–Si–O–Si–O–) are associated with lower viscosity and lower firing temperatures of these modified glasses. Lead oxide as an ingredient in glass plays a role as both network former and network modifier. Lead oxide-bearing glasses have been widely used for cast-iron enamels.

While it is difficult to describe the specific action of each ingredient in the porcelain enamel composition, some generalities can be expressed as follows: (a) An increase in SiO_2 content increases firing temperature and acid resistance, and lowers the expansion coefficient; (b) an increase in alkali content decreases firing temperature and acid resistance, and raises the expansion coefficient; and (c) an increase in the Al_2O_3 and ZrO_2 content increases alkali resistance.

Each porcelain enamel composition is designed so that certain fundamental performances of the enamel are realized, such as (a) good adherence to the substrate; (b) thermal expansion fit to the metal; (c) desired chemical properties, such as acid resistance, hot-water resistance, or alkali resistance; and (d) desired physical properties, such as abrasion resistance, thermal-shock resistance, high gloss, high reflectance, and desirable color.

Enameling Metals

The most common metals for porcelain enameling are listed below. Other metals, such as titanium and the refractory metals, are coated with porcelain enamel and ceramic coatings.

1. Enameling iron. A very low carbon and low metalloid content, in a variety of cold-rolled sheet steel especially produced for porcelain enameling. Carbon content is about 0.06% or less.

2. Enameling steel. A higher carbon content in a cold-rolled rimmed steel. Carbon content about 0.06–0.10%.

3. Extra-low-carbon enameling steel. A cold-rolled decarburized steel especially produced for one-coat white enameling. Carbon content at 0.003% or less.

4. Mild steel. Types of steel such as 1010 or 1020 (0.10 or 0.20% carbon) have been used for enameling.

5. Cast iron.

6. Aluminum and aluminum alloys.

7. Copper and copper alloys for small commercial parts and jewelry enameling

8. Gold, silver, platinum. For jewelry enameling.

9. Stainless steels.

Fundamental Considerations in Porcelain Enamels

Adherence of Porcelain Metals. Since the beginning of commercial porcelain enameling, it has been known that cobalt-bearing materials incorporated in the frit composition would enhance the adherence of the enamel to sheet steel. The actual mechanism by which glass adheres to metal is still not completely clear and the role of cobalt in promoting adherence is still a fundamental research subject. It is known that adherence and wetting are associated. Under oxidizing conditions the enamel glass wets the metal, and the oxide on the metal surface tends to dissolve into the enamel layer. Under reducing or neutral conditions for enamel firing, the oxide originally on the metal surface becomes completely dissolved and the glass then fails to wet the metal surface. There are additives or ingredients of the frit other than cobalt which seem to aid adherence. The compounds of molybdenum incorporated in the enamel are considered adherence promoters.

The mechanism of adherence can be considered to fall into two main types. One is physical adherence, involving the physical gripping of the glass by a rough metal surface, roughened mechanically prior to enameling or roughened during enameling by the corrosive attack of glass on the metal and by dendritic attachments to metal forming during the enamel-firing treatment. The other adherence mechanism involves the chemical bond of the metal, metal oxide, and enamel glass.

Adherence in porcelain enamel terminology generally refers to the amount of glass remaining in an impacted, fractured area of the porcelain enamel system. If, after impact, the enamel surface is fractured to such an extent that it is stripped clean of the coating, it is said to have poor adherence. However, the enamel surface has excellent adherence if, after impact, it contains a large amount of fractured glass remaining on the impacted surface. Using an adherence test apparatus to measure the amount of glass remaining on the base metal, a standard test has been devised (ASTM test C313-59) (1).

With respect to sheet-steel enamels, approx 0.25% of cobalt oxide is used to promote adherence of the ground coat to sheet steel. In the case of cast-iron enameling, no special adherence additives are needed; this indicates that oxidation of the metal has been properly assured in this process.

The amount of force required to remove the enamel glass from the metal is not usually measured nor is the strength of the glass–metal bond generally evaluated in the porcelain enamel system.

Thermal Fit and Residual Stresses. Thermal expansion measurements, as determined by the interferometer or dilatometer method of test (ASTM C327-56 or ASTM C337-57), show typical curves as shown in Figure 3. The interferometer used for the determination of thermal expansion consists of fused-silica interferometer plates separated by three fragments of the specimen material. These plates in an

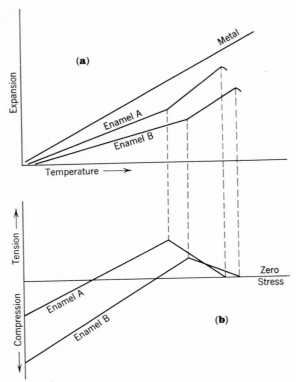

Fig. 3. (a) Relative thermal expansion of porcelain enamel and sheet steel.   (b) Stress development in enamel layer.

electric furnace are arranged in such a manner that monochromatic light is reflected from the bottom and top plates, and interference fringes appear in the interferometer eyepiece.   The increase in the distance of separation of these fused-silica plates is related to the movement of interference fringes across the field of view in the eyepiece. The interferometer softening point refers to the temperature at which the glass specimens can no longer support the load of the top fused-silica interferometer plate as noted by the reversal in the direction of fringe movement in the interferometer eyepiece.

The expansion coefficient for the metal is constant over the entire temperature range, whereas the linear expansion of the enamel glass shows a change to a greater slope as temperature is increased.   The expansion coefficient of the glass shows an apparent reversal at high temperatures above the interferometer softening point.

During firing, a porcelain enamel glass becomes less viscous as temperature is increased.   At the elevated temperatures, the enamel is relatively fluid and it conforms to the configuration of the metal surface.

As the porcelain enamel coating is cooled from the high temperatures of firing (1380–1470°F, or 750–800°C) to the interferometer softening point, the fluid glass does not maintain a stress for any measurable length of time.   As cooling proceeds, the coefficient of expansion (or contraction) of the coating exceeds that of the steel, and tensile stresses begin to develop in the coating, as shown in Figure 3.   The tensile stress continues to increase on cooling until the expansion coefficient of the glass equals that of the metal. As cooling continues further, and the coefficient of the glass becomes less than that of the metal, the tensile stress in the coating decreases and compressive stress develops.

Thermal-expansion comparisons of coatings and metals have often been used in the determination of residual stresses in the coatings. Residual-stress analysis in this qualitative picture of Figure 3 shows how enamel A would develop high tensile stress and low residual compressive stress. Enamel B with its higher softening point and lower expansion coefficient results in less tensile stress and a much greater residual compressive stress in the porcelain enamel.

Residual-stress analysis must take into account the cooling rates, the viscosity characteristics of the glass, the relative thickness of metal and coating, and the modulus of elasticity of coating and metal throughout the temperature range in which stress is developed. At high temperatures the glass behaves essentially as a viscous material, changing to viscous-elastic to principally elastic as the temperature decreases.

Thermal expansion values can be calculated from measurements of thermal deflection of enamel–metal composites. Thermal expansion coefficients in the temperature range of 0–300°C (32–572°F) can also be calculated, using the additive formula

$$P = AX_A + BX_B + CX_C + \text{etc}$$

where P is the property, such as linear expansion coefficient

A, B, C are the property factors for each ingredient in the composition

X_A, X_B, X_C are the weight percentages of each ingredient in the composition

Factors for calculating thermal expansion have been determined and are listed in Table 2 (3). Glass compositions high in SiO_2 content have low coefficients of thermal expansion, whereas alkalies and alkaline earth materials raise the expansion of the glass. These factors, given in Table 2, multiplied by the weight percentages, yield a calculated cubical coefficient expansion of the glass.

Table 2. Coefficient of Expansion Factors[a] (3). Courtesy Garrard Press.

Oxide	Factor	Oxide	Factor	Oxide	Factor	Oxide	Factor
SiO_2	0.8	CaO	5.0	SnO_2	2.0	Cr_2O_3	5.1
Al_2O_3	5.0	MgO	0.1	TiO_2	4.1	CoO	4.4
B_2O_3	0.1	BaO	3.0	ZrO_2	2.1	CuO	2.2
Na_2O	10.0	As_2O_5	2.0	Na_3AlF_6	7.4	Fe_2O_3	4.0
K_2O	8.5	P_2O_5	2.0	AlF_3	4.4	NiO	4.0
PbO	4.2	Sb_2O_3	3.6	CaF_2	2.5	MnO	2.2
ZnO	2.1			NaF	7.4		

[a] Summation of (factors × weight percentages) × 10^{-7} = cubical expansion coefficient in in.^{3}/(in.^{3}) (°C). (See ref. 4.)

Residual compression in the coating is desired since glass as well as other ceramic materials is much stronger in compression (about 300,000 psi) than in tension (about 10,000 psi). If residual compression in the enamel layer is too great, the coating may tend to fracture in the areas where the radius of curvature of the article is small. Since failure of the coating occurs because the tensile-stress limit has been exceeded, high residual compressive stresses in the coating require that any tensile load must first act to overcome this residual compressive stress before the coating is placed in tension. If the tensile stress developed during the cooling or reheating of the enamel is too high, the coating may fracture. "Crazing" results when the damage occurs during cooling; a fine crack pattern called "hairlining" may be produced during reheating.

The linear expansion coefficient for common materials in the porcelain enamel system is as follows:

steel	11.7×10^{-6}
ground coat	$10–11 \times 10^{-6}$
cover coat	$8–10 \times 10^{-6}$
aluminum	23.5×10^{-6}
cast iron	10.5×10^{-6}

Composite Modulus of Elasticity. The modulus of elasticity of the composite system of enamel glass and steel has been shown to lie between the modulus of the glass and that of the metal (5). The composite modulus can be calculated by the following expression:

$$E_c = (E_m - E_e) \, Q^3 + E_e$$

where

E_c = modulus of elasticity of the composite
E_m = modulus of elasticity of the metal
E_e = modulus of elasticity of the enamel
Q = thickness of the metal/total thickness of composite

Residual Compressive Stress. Residual compressive stress in commercial ground-coat enamels varies with enamel thickness as indicated below (6):

Ratio of enamel thickness to metal thickness	Compressive stress, psi
0.8	10,000
0.6	16,000
0.4	20,000
0.2	32,000

Thinner coatings will, other factors remaining equal, yield higher compressive stresses.

Higher residual compressive stress in the coating can be achieved by using (a) enamel glass with a lower expansion coefficient, or (b) a metal with higher expansion coefficient and higher modulus of elasticity.

Maximum Strain. Strain in enamels that leads to failure is on the order of 0.002–0.003 in./in. Thinner enamels with their high residual compressing stresses

Table 3. Some Physical Properties of Enamel Glass

density, g/ml	2.5–3.5
hardness (Mohs scale)	5–6
tensile strength, psi	$5–15 \times 10^3$
compressive strength, psi	$2–4 \times 10^5$
modulus of elasticity, psi	$8–12 \times 10^6$
dielectric constant	5–10

are more flexible or can be strained to a greater degree.   Some other physical properties of enamel glass are given in Table 3.

Appearance.   Porcelain enamels as decorative, highly durable coatings have involved the multiple-coat system, wherein the dark cobalt-bearing ground coat is covered with the decorative, property-designed second coating.

The most common cover enamel has been the white cover coat.   Whiteness or high diffuse reflectance has been called opacity in porcelain enamel terminology. The white, high-opacity cover enamel depends on certain opacifying crystals which either remain well-dispersed in the glass during smelting and subsequent firing or are recrystallized from the enamel glass during the firing process.

Prior to 1940, the most common opacifying compounds for the white-cover-coat porcelain enamel were antimony oxide and zirconium oxide.   The opacifying pigments are those crystals whose index of refraction is much different from that of the glass in which it is embedded.   The index of refraction of glass is in the range of 1.50–1.55, and the most effective opacifiers are given in Table 4 (7).

Table 4. Most Effective Opacifiers in Porcelain Enamels

Opacifier	Index of refraction
NaF	1.336
CaF$_2$	1.434
Sb$_2$O$_3$	2.087–2.35
SnO$_2$	1.997–2.093
ZrO$_2$	2.13–2.20
TiO$_2$ (anatase)	2.493–2.554
TiO$_2$ (rutile)	2.616–2.903

Commercial use of titanium dioxide as an opacifier for enamels did not begin until 1946.   As a result of extensive research and development, the recrystallizing white titania enamel is used today in practically all sheet-steel enameling involving white cover enamels.   Two opacifying crystals, the two polymorphic forms of titania anatase and rutile, are involved in the recrystallizing titania enamel.   Anatase, rather than rutile, is the desired crystalline form to recrystallize in the enamel since anatase crystals are the optimum size (0.1–0.2 μ) for maximum reflectance, as well as for the most desirable bluish-white color.   Pigment particles smaller than the optimum size

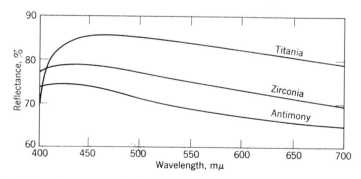

Fig. 4. Spectrophotometer curves of titania, zirconia, and antimony enamels (3a).   Courtesy *Industrial and Engineering Chemistry.*

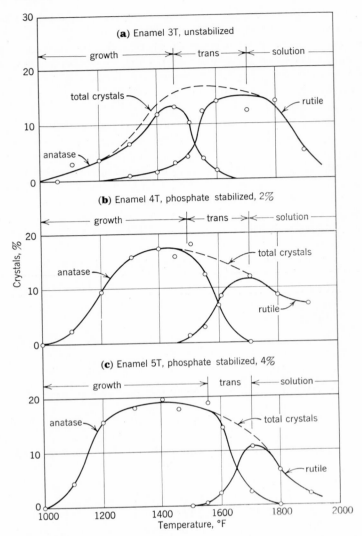

Fig. 5. Crystallization of TiO_2 (**a**) in unstabilized enamel, (**b**) in phosphate-stabilized (2% P_2O_5) enamel, and (**c**) in phosphate-stabilized (4% P_2O_5) enamel (7). Courtesy University of Illinois.

provide too much scattering of light, thereby giving a more undesirable bluish color, particles larger than optimum pigment size yield a more cream-white color. Anatase does not grow or change size with changes in firing temperature, whereas rutile crystals grow as temperature is increased.

Spectrophotometer curves for cover enamels opacified with oxides of antimony, zirconium, or titanium are shown in Figure 4. The spectrophotometer curves for these three enamels indicate the characteristics of a bluish-white color. The titania enamel shows a characteristic absorption at the violet end of the spectrum.

Color stability of titania enamels can be obtained by adjusting the chemical makeup of the glass so that anatase recrystallizes predominantly over a wide temperature range. Figure 5 shows the effect of P_2O_5 content in the glass on the relative amounts of anatase and rutile recrystallizing from a titania enamel (7).

The color of cover-coat porcelain enamels can be produced in almost any hue, saturation, and brightness by using clear glass frits milled with color oxide pigments. A typical mill batch for colored cover coats is as follows:

100	parts	frit (clear alkali borosilicate-type glass)
4	parts	clay (for producing stable suspension)
$\frac{1}{4}$	part	bentonite (for supporting suspension)
$\frac{1}{4}$	part	sodium nitrite (to disperse floccules)
3	parts	color oxide pigment
45	parts	water

Colored enamels may also be prepared by tinting the titania enamels during the smelting operation by the addition of color oxides to the smelter batch.

Decorative one-coat finishes are also prepared by milling some cover-coat frit with ground-coat frit. This produces a fine speckled coating. Single-coat finishes of ground coat stippled with a white enamel prior to firing are also common.

Titania white enamels for sheet steel and antimony oxide-opacified enamels for cast iron exhibit diffuse reflectance values of 75% or higher. Although cast-iron ground coats are not colored, as are the sheet-steel ground coats which have dark cobalt-blue color, the thickness of cast-iron enamels is much greater than that of sheet-steel enamel coats. Dry-process cast iron requires several coating cycles to build a smooth and uniform coating and to achieve high reflectance.

Titania enamels have excellent hiding power. One thin coating of 0.002 or 0.003 in. will completely mask the dark-colored ground coat and produce a white glossy coating with diffuse reflectance (green filter) of 80% or higher.

Decorating

In commercial porcelain enameling, decorating and painting are processes that involve coatings of various colors and textures. Common techniques for decorating include the following:

a. Stencil method of spraying an enamel on a stencil-covered surface.

b. Brushing the dried, unfired coating using a stencil or similar design.

c. Silk screen process.

d. Stamp design using a rubber stamp with ceramic colors as inks, or dusting of a color pigment onto the area stamped with a gum or varnish.

e. Decalcomania using ceramic decals.

f. Graining, marbleizing, and other transfer processes whereby the designs impressed on an inked rubber cylinder from one flat designed plate are transferred by rolling the cylinder on the enameled surface. Cylinders with the designed patterns are also used, first being inked with ceramic colors on a flat plate then rolled onto the surface to be decorated.

g. Stippling or splattering droplets of the slip of a different colored enamel.

h. Mottling to produce granite ware by adding cobalt or nickel sulfates to the ground coat slip. These additions cause selective rusting and a mottled pattern in the fired finish.

Microstructure and Thickness

Sheet-steel enamels consisting of a ground coat and cover enamels have many bubbles of gas entrapped in the glass. Figure 6 is a cross-section micrograph of the enamel layer on sheet steel. The grains of ferrite in the cold-rolled steel are in evidence in this acid-etched cross section. The ground coat contains more bubbles than the cover coat for three main reasons, namely (a) the dissolved mixture in the ground coat glass reacts with the metal at the firing temperature to produce hydrogen gas. Some of this gas dissolves in the steel, while some may produce bubbles in the molten glass, (b) carbon from the steel forms carbon oxide gases, and (c) there are more gas-producing, decomposable materials in the ground-coat mill batch, such as carbonates and clay.

Fig. 6. Cross-section photomicrograph of porcelain-enameled sheet steel. Titania cover coat over cobalt ground coat (150×).

Total thickness of sheet-steel enamels involving a ground coat and a titania cover enamel would be in the range of 5–8 mils (0.005–0.008 in.). Cast-iron enamel coatings are much thicker, in the range of 20 mils or greater for dry-process coatings.

One-coat titania enamels directly on steel are successful with certain steels, such as special titanium-killed steels and special extra-low-carbon steels. The thicknesses of such direct-on-white enamels range from 3 to 5 mils. Carbon or carbides at the surface of the metal form CO or CO_2 gases that produce a gas defect (called primary boiling with ground-coat processing). For direct white enameling, the carbon or carbides in these special steels must be eliminated or inactivated.

Tests on Enamels

Abrasion Resistance. Porcelain enamel is considered the most scratch-resistant and hardest of coatings. This property is one important way of distinguishing between porcelain enamel and organic-type coatings. In surface abrasion, the rate of abrasive wear increases with time, and in subsurface abrasion, which follows, the constant higher rate of wear continues. Abrasion resistance can be evaluated by the loss of gloss or loss of weight. (ASTM Standard ASTM C448-61 Abrasion Resistance of Porcelain Enamels, Porcelain Enamel Institute Test T-2, Resistance of Porcelain Enamels to Abrasion.)

Impact Resistance. Tests for impact resistance of porcelain enamels include falling weight tests such as a free-falling ball or a pendulum striking a rigidly held specimen. In such tests successively higher heights of fall are used until a failure, visibly noticeable, occurs. Factors affecting the impact resistance of porcelain enamels include the following:

1. Modulus of elasticity of metal. Lower modulus contributes to higher impact resistance.

2. Radius of curvature of article. The larger the radius, the greater the impact resistance.

3. Thickness of metal and enamel. The thicker the material, the greater the resistance to impact. For equal increases in thickness, the enamel (with its lower modulus of elasticity, 10×10^6 psi) increases the impact resistance more than steel.

4. Physical structure of enamel. Excessive bubble content, large crystalline inclusions, and other discontinuities often contribute to lower impact resistance. Weak bond of the enamel to the metal also contributes to lower impact resistance.

The size of the fracture after impact failure has occurred is generally independent of the impact resistance. The size of the fracture is larger with (a) a larger radius of curvature, (b) greater enamel thickness, and a (c) poorer bond of enamel and metal.

Thermal Shock Resistance. Resistance of porcelain enamels to failure by thermal shock was developed for enamels for cooking utensils and other items subjected to high temperatures in service. Thermal shock is experienced by a heated utensil on quenching with cold water. Thermal-shock tests involve repeated cycles of heating and quenching with water (heating for each successive cycle is carried out at progressively higher temperatures). A visible fracturing, as evidenced by spalling, constitutes a failure.

Water is an especially severe quenchant. Thermal-shock failures with water result from the water vapor entering the enamel layer through the small, submicroscopic thermal cracks formed in the enamel layer at the instant of shock. This water vapor condenses in the crack and in the bubbles of the enamel near the cracks. On subsequent heating, the entrapped water expands to cause spalling to the enamel layer. Other liquids, such as toluene, oils, and other organic liquids also bring about the series of fine, almost invisible cracks in the enamel, but visible thermal-shock failures with these liquid quenchants do not result on subsequent heating (ASTM test C385-58).

Thermal-shock resistance is a direct function of enamel thickness. The greater the residual compressive stress in the porcelain enamel, the greater is the resistance to thermal-shock failures. Thin coatings (with their greater residual compressive stress), such as one-coat enamels or the two-coat enamels with a low-expansion titania cover coat, provide excellent thermal-shock resistance.

Resistance to Chemical Attack. The resistance to alkali and acid attack is evaluated on the basis of (a) loss in weight, (b) loss in gloss, or (c) cleanability of the surface.

A citric acid spot test (10%) is used as a room-temperature test for acid resistance of glossy light-colored enamels. In the spot test, loss of gloss and cleanability are determined in a qualitative manner. Resistance to boiling acid (6% citric acid) is determined by the loss in weight (ASTM Tests C283-54 and ASTM C282-61T). Lower alkali content of the glass yields higher acid resistance. Acid-resistant enamels for chemical service are compositions very high in SiO_2 and TiO_2 content. Alkali resistance is improved with increasing Al_2O_3 and ZrO_2 content. Resistance of enamels to water attack is also developed in coatings for domestic water heaters.

Other Properties and Tests. Physical and chemical properties of porcelain enamels can be evaluated with reference to tests adapted by the Porcelain Enamel Institute, Washington, D.C., as well as by the American Society for Testing and Materials (1).

Standard tests and specifications adapted by the Porcelain Enamel Institute are as follows:

a. T-17   Test for adherence of porcelain enamel to sheet metal.
b. T-18   Gloss test for porcelain enamels.
c. T-7A   Test for weather resistance of architectural porcelain enamels.
d. T-13   Reflectance test for opaque white porcelain enamels.
e. T-2   Test for resistance of porcelain enamels to abrasion.
f. T-5   Torsion test for porcelain enameled iron and steel.
g. T-21   Test for acid resistance of porcelain enamels.
h. T-22   Cupric sulfate test for color retention.
i. AL-1a Recommended test methods for evaluation and control of quality of porcelain enamel and aluminum.

Standard Tests adapted by the American Society for Testing and Materials relative to properties of porcelain enamels are as follows:

a. C448-61   Abrasion resistance of porcelain enamels.
b. C282-61T Acid resistance of porcelain enamels.
c. C313-59   Adherence of porcelain enamel and ceramic coatings to sheet metal.
d. C283-54   Boiling acid resistance.
e. C314-62   Flatness of porcelain enamel flatware.
f. C346-59   45 degree specular gloss of porcelain enamels.
g. C347-57   Reflectivity and coefficient of scatter of white porcelain enamels.
h. C385-58   Thermal shock resistance of porcelain enamel utensils.
i. C409-60   Torsion resistance of laboratory specimens of porcelain enameled iron and steel.
j. C486-61T Spalling resistance of porcelain.

Enamel Defects. Deviations from perfect continuity in porcelain enamel coatings and unusual departures from smoothness are given in certain descriptive terms that developed with the porcelain enamel technology. For example, roughness is called "orange peel," a severe case is called "alligator hide." Blisters, pinholes, black specks, dimples, tool marks, and chipping are well-understood terms. Copperheads are defects of iron rust spots in the fired ground coat. Hairlines are defects of a strain pattern born in the first part of the cover-coat fire and healed in the latter stages of firing. Defects may result from accidents occurring at almost every stage of the enameling process. Porcelain enamel terminology is defined in "Standard Definitions of Terms Relating to Porcelain Enamel," ASTM C386-63 (1).

Bibliography

"Enamels, Porcelain or Vitreous" in *ECT* 1st ed., Vol. 5, pp. 718–735, by R. M. King, The Ohio State University.

1. *1964 Book of ASTM Standards*, Part 13, Refractories; Glass; Ceramic Materials, American Society for Testing and Materials, 1964, p. 498.
2. E. E. Bryant, *Porcelain Enameling Operations*, Enamelist Publishing Co., Cleveland, Ohio, 1964, p. 112.
3. A. I. Andrews, *Porcelain Enamels*, 2nd ed., Garrard Press, Champaign, Illinois, 1961, p. 633.
3a. P. Strong and S. Strong, *Ind. Eng. Chem.* **42** (2), 253–256 (1950).
4. M. Mayer and B. Havas, *Sprechsaal* **42**, 497 (1909); **44**, 188, 207, 220 (1911).
5. P. S. Wolford and G. E. Selby, "Stiffening Effect of Porcelain Enamel on Sheet Iron I-II," *J. Am. Ceram. Soc.* **29** (6), 162–175 (1946).
6. R. A. Jones and A. I. Andrews, "Residual Compressive Stresses in Enameled Sheet Iron Specimens," *J. Am. Ceram. Soc.* **31** (10), 274–279 (1948).
7. R. D. Shannon and A. L. Friedberg, "*Titania Opacified Porcelain Enamels,*" *University of Illinois Bull. Eng. Exp. Sta. Bull. No. 456* **57** (44), (Feb. 1960), 49 pp.

A. L. FRIEDBERG
University of Illinois

ENCAPSULATION. See Embedding; Microencapsulation.

ENZYMES, INDUSTRIAL

History. The use of enzymes goes back to the earliest written or pictured documents of human activities. Thus even in pre-Biblical times, housewives used leaven for making bread, just as today's homemakers employ cake or dry yeast. Even without any knowledge of enzymes they knew the source of their active ingredient and the optimum conditions required.

The master shepherd in ancient civilizations would curdle milk to make cheese by using the (probably dried) stomach of slain lambs and calves. He also took advantage of conditions favorable to the ripening of cheese, very much as does today's farm manager, who employs industrial enzymes.

Similar parallels may be drawn for the fermentation of wine and, later, beer, as well as for other areas of food preparation, for medical purposes, leather tanning, and other fields of enzyme utilization.

During the past fifty years the field of enzyme utilization has broadened. In addition to food and beverage preparation, and primitive pharmaceutical application, enzymes are used today in the textile industries, in the manufacture of paper and adhesives, in sewage disposal, garment cleaning, animal feeding, in chemical and diagnostic analysis, in biochemical research, and miscellaneous other fields. Also, in addition to the originally applied enzyme types, amylases, proteases, lipases, and the enzymes that take part in the naturally occurring fermentation processes, a few more were developed in recent times such as pectic enzymes, glucose oxidases, catalases, cellulases, etc. Also enzyme mixtures are formulated to satisfy diverse purposes.

Due to advances in enzyme chemistry and microbiology, more progress has been made in enzyme production and application in the past hundred years than in the previous 5000 years. The conscious knowledge and the knowhow of controlling not only the enzymic processes, but also the large scale production of enzymes, created a long line of products which we call "industrial enzymes."

The first pioneers who, with their patented processes, laid the foundations for the production of industrial enzymes in the United States around the turning of this century, were Takamine (53), Rohm (54), and Wallerstein (55).

The purpose of this article is to present a condensed picture of the industrial enzymes made in the United States, of their chemical nature, utilization, production methods, and standardization, and of the analytical methods used in the demonstration and measurement of their activities.

Definition, Specificity, and Occurrence. Enzymes are organic substances produced by living cells, that possess the ability to catalyze specific chemical reactions. Enzymes synthesize or break down chemical compounds, or transform them from one type to another type, according to the ability built in them individually. Most enzymes are highly specific; they catalyze only one specific reaction or act upon only one isomer of a particular compound. Some enzymes are less specific and are able to catalyze several, usually related, reactions. Also, the same reaction may be catalyzed by a large number of enzymes, different in their specific characteristics, and produced by different types of cells. The transformation of a compound expressed by a simple chemical equation, requires quite frequently the cooperation of a number of enzymes. This explains the presence of hundreds of different enzymes in a single cell. The number of known individual enzymes is around 750, of which about 100 have been isolated in crystalline form.

According to the purpose of the particular cell, some cells produce more and others produce fewer different individual enzymes. While most enzymes are produced in the quantities needed, some are produced in extreme excess. The enzyme formation inside the cells is controlled by the dominant genes. Certain types of cells stand out in the excess production of one or a few specific enzymes. Cells of animal glands and mucous membranes, cells in certain plant tissues of seeds, fruits, and leaves, and the cells of specific microorganisms biosynthesize one or a few enzymes in great abundance. Those are the cells utilized in the production of industrial enzymes.

Pure enzymes form the following four major groups with regard to the degree of specificity (38):

1. Absolute enzymes, catalyze the reaction of only one substrate. Example: Urease breaks down urea into CO_2 and ammonia; it will not attack any other substrate.

2. Stereospecific enzymes, catalyze reactions with one type of optical isomer, but may react on a series of related compounds of the same configuration. Example: Many proteolytic enzymes will hydrolyze only peptide bonds linking L-amino acids (natural amino acids).

3. General hydrolyzing enzymes, will react on a specific type of chemical linkage mostly respective of the associated groups. Examples: Most lipases hydrolyze a wide range of organic esters, and many phosphatases break down phosphate esters into phosphoric acid and alcohol.

4. Enzymes that attack certain specific points of a molecule. Examples: Some proteolytic enzymes act on points where the adjacent amino acid contains a benzene

ring. Some hydrolytic enzymes attack at the center of the molecule and others at the ends: α-Amylase attacks the center of the starch molecule and of the long glucose chains deriving from starch, while β-amylase attacks the ends, splits off two glucose units, and thus forms maltose; amyloglucosidase attacks the nonreducing ends of starch or its hydrolytic products, and splits off single glucose units.

Composition and Chemical Nature of the Enzymes. All enzymes are proteins, metaloproteins, or conjugated proteins. The activity of pure protein enzymes is attributed to the reactive groups of the amino acids they contain. Many enzymes are proteins with traces of certain metals (Zn, Co, Ca) which stay with the protein even in crystalline form; these are metaloproteins. The complex enzymes are conjugated proteins which contain an organic nonprotein and non-amino-acid portion, somewhat loosely attached to the protein part. If the nonprotein portion, the prostatic group, is separated from the protein portion by dialysis, the enzyme becomes inactive. The activity is reestablished, however, if the two portions are united. The dialyzable, relatively small molecular weight nonprotein, prostatic group, is the *coenzyme*. In older literature the complete enzyme is frequently called "holoenzyme," the protein portion "apoenzyme," and the dialyzable part "coenzyme."

The molecular weight of enzymes varies from 12,700–1,000,000 (ribonuclease 12,700, lactate dehydrogenase 100,000, urease 480,000, and L-glutamate dehydrogenase 1,000,000). The molecular weight of coenzymes is relatively small.

Coenzymes and Vitamins. The more general term, cofactor, includes the metallic portions of metaloprotein enzymes, and the coenzyme portions of holoenzymes. In many enzymes, the coenzyme portion is the reactive part. Most coenzymes contain a nucleotide, a vitamin, a five-carbon sugar, and possibly other compounds tied together. The vitamins in coenzymes are almost exclusively members of the vitamin B group.

Thiamine (vitamin B_1) is part of the thiamine pyrophosphate coenzyme, active in decarboxylation of α-keto acids and in certain reactions of keto sugars; riboflavin (vitamin B_2) is part of the flavin mononucleotide and of the flavin adenine dinucleotide coenzymes, which take part in several oxidation-reduction reactions; pyridoxine (vitamin B_6) is part of the coenzyme pyridoxal phosphate, active in amino acid decarboxylation, transamination, and other reactions; niacin, part of the coenzymes diphosphopyridine nucleotide (DPN) and triphosphopyridine nucleotide (TPN), catalyzes many oxidation-reduction reactions; pantothenic acid, part of coenzyme A, participates in catalyzing reactions of fatty acids, principally the transfer of acetyl groups; biotin, part of the biotin coenzyme, catalyzes some carbon dioxide-fixation reactions; folic acid, part of tetrahydrofolic acid, catalyzes reactions of single-carbon compounds; cyanocobalamin (vitamin B_{12}) is part of the cobalamide coenzymes.

Enzyme Action. The most general belief is that the enzyme takes part in the chemical reaction in the following way:

$$\text{enzyme} + \text{substrate} = \text{enzyme-substrate (ES)}$$

$$\text{ES} + H_2O = \text{enzyme} + \text{product A} + \text{product B}$$

The free enzyme then combines in rapid succession with new substrate molecules. Depending on the number of its active groups, one enzyme molecule may react simultaneously with several molecules of the substrate.

Table 1. Classification of Enzymes

Type of enzyme	Examples	Remarks
Hydrolyzing		
proteases, peptidases	pepsin, rennin, trypsin, bromelin, papain, ficin, etc	hydrolyze —CO—NH— links in proteins, peptides, etc
carbohydrases	α- and β-amylases, amyloglucosidase, oligoglucosidase, invertase, maltase, cellulase etc	hydrolyze glycosidic links
esterases	lipases, cholinesterases, pectinesterases, phytase, phosphatases, tannase, etc	hydrolyze ester links in fats, alcohol esters phosphoric esters, sulfuric esters, thioesters and phenolic esters
other	arginase, urease, deaminase, etc	
Adding		
add or remove water	aconitase, enolase, fumarase, glyoxalase, serine diaminase, etc	
add or remove CO_2	amino acid decarboxylase, carboxylase (in yeast), malic decarboxylase, oxaloacetic decarboxylase, pyruvic oxidase, etc	
other	aldolase, aspartase, etc	
Transferring		
oxidoreductases	D- and L-amino acid oxidases, 1-amino acid dehydrogenase, L-glutamate dehydrogenases, proline oxidase, Co II cytochrome reductase, alcohol dehydrogenase, glycerol dehydrogenase, glucose oxidase, aldehyde dehydrogenase, aldehyde oxidase, succinate dehydrogenase, cystine reductase, oxalate oxidase, cytochrome oxidases, peroxidases, catalases, etc	transfer hydrogen
transfer nitrogenous groups	transaminases, glutamate transaminase, glycine transamidinase, γ-glutamyl transpeptidase, γ-glutamyl transferase, etc	
transfer phosphate groups	hexokinase, glucokinase, ketohexokinase, fructokinase, ribokinase, thiamine pyrophosphokinase, phosphoglucomutase (intramolecular transfer) etc	
transacylases	amino acid transacetylase, glucosamine transacetylase, choline transacylase, glyoxylate transacetase, etc	transfer acyl groups
transglycosylases	dextrin transglucosylase, maltose transglucosylase, sucrose transglucosylase, hyaluronidase (animal) etc	transfer glycosyl groups
transfer coenzyme A	CoA transferase	
transmethylases	nicotinamide transmethylase, guanidinoacetate transmethylase, betaine-methionine transmethylase, etc	transfer methyl groups
other	transaldolase, transketolase, thiaminase, transoximase, etc	
Isomerizing		
isomerases (stereoisomerases)	alanine racemase, glutamate racemase, lactate racemase, mutarotase, etc	
Miscellaneous		
synthetases	glutamine synthetase, asparagine synthetase, tryptophan hydroxamate synthetase, etc	catalyze synthetic reactions
add groups to double bonds	fumarase, aconitase, D- and L-serine dehydrase, dihydroxy acid dehydrase, phosphopyruvate carboxylase, aldolase, citrase, isocitrase, etc	

Classification. Depending on the nature of the chemical reactions they catalyze, enzymes may be grouped in several ways. The simplest classification places them into "assimilating" (catabolizing) and "dissimilating" (anabolizing) enzymes. In another classification all enzymes may be considered as translocating or coupling enzymes; those which transplant a certain group (free or part of a compound), from a location to another, are the transferring enzymes; enzymes that build up large polymer molecules are the polymerizing or coupling enzymes; and enzymes that break down large molecules are the depolymerizing, digesting, or hydrolyzing enzymes. Enzymes that occur within the walls of the cell are called endoenzymes, and those that are secreted outside the cell wall into the surrounding medium are called exoenzymes.

In another type of classification devised by Webb (38), the approx 750 known enzymes fall in the following groups:

1. *Hydrolyzing coenzymes (200)*: proteinases, peptidases, amino acid hydrolyzing enzymes, glucosidases, polysaccharidases (amylases), saccharases, esterases, lipases, phosphorases, phenolesterases, pectinesterases, polygalacturonases, etc.

2. *Transferring enzymes (370)*: one-half of them transfer oxygen and hydrogen, and one-half transfer phosphate, amino, acyl, and glycosyl radicals.

3. *Addition and subtraction enzymes (70)*: add or remove CO_2, water, aldehydes, and ammonia.

4. *Isomerases (25)*: rearrange configuration.

5. *Synthesizing enzymes (25)*: synthesize proteins, carbohydrates, and other compounds.

6. *Miscellaneous enzymes (60)*: act on nucleic acids.

A simplified version of grouping or classifying enzymes is given in Table 1.

Nomenclature. There is no general rule for naming enzymes. The discoverer of a new enzyme, depending on the trend of his time, follows one of three customs. The most general way is to add the suffix "-ase" to the name or to the abbreviated name of the substance on which the enzyme works. "Amylase" hydrolyzes "amylum" (starch), "esterase" hydrolyzes "esters," "maltase" hydrolyzes "maltose," "sucrase" hydrolyzes "sucrose," "urease" acts on "urea," etc. In such manner, collective names are also formed for groups of enzymes which catalyze reactions on related compounds. "Carbohydrase" is a collective name for many specific enzymes which act on carbohydrates. "Amylase," a carbohydrase acting on starch, is again a collective name for a number of specific enzymes such as "α-amylase," β-amylase," and "amyloglucosidase," etc. Also the name "esterase" includes many enzymes: one group hydrolyzes carboxylic esters, another group hydrolyzes phosphoric esters, and another group hydrolyzes sulfuric esters, thioesters, phenolic esters, etc. Each of these sub-groups contains a number of specific enzymes.

Another way of naming enzymes is to add the suffix "-in" to the name or to the abbreviated name of the source from where it is produced: "Papain" is produced from the plant papaya, "ficin" is produced from a plant ficus, "pancreatin" is made of pancreas, etc.

The third manner of naming enzymes is to add the suffix "-ase" to the reaction the enzyme catalyzes. For example: "L-Glutamic dehydrogenase" catalyzes the removal of hydrogen involving L-glutamic acid, "glucose oxidase" oxidizes glucose into gluconic acid, or "invertase" inverts sucrose to glucose and fructose.

There are also names which were given without following any rules.

A number of enzymes or groups of enzymes may have more than one name. The following are typical examples for such synonyms: amylase = diastase, invertase = sucrase, etc.

Reversibility. Some enzymic reactions are demonstrated to be reversible, and the reaction comes to an equilibrium. Other enzymic reactions seem to proceed only in one direction. Unless the enzyme specificity dictates only one direction, it is assumed that most enzymic reactions are reversible. Equilibrium is reached at one side of the equation, depending upon the experimental conditions. In nature different enzymes frequently act upon the synthesis of a compound rather than on its degradation.

Reaction Speed and Factors Influencing It (9,11,18,36,38). Next to the nature of the changes, the most important general characteristic of all chemical reactions is the speed by which they proceed and the equilibrium (ratio of substrate to products) at which the speed of the reaction becomes zero. The equilibrium may be reached after the reaction is quantitatively (100%) completed, or after a certain percent of the possible change is accomplished.

The valuable function of enzymes is their influence on the reaction speed. Reactions, which proceed with almost infinitely low speed in the absence of the enzyme, may be complete within seconds or minutes in the presence of the proper enzyme.

The speed during the initial phase of the reaction depends on the amount of enzyme present, as long as the amount of the substrate is in excess and all conditions are constant. Under such conditions, the reaction speed increases in linear proportion with the amount of enzyme: in presence of a double amount of enzyme the same change requires one-half the reaction time.

If the amount of enzyme in the system is kept constant, the reaction time is influenced by a number of other factors, namely, concentration of the substrate, concentration of the product, presence of activators or inhibitors, temperature, and pH value.

An optimum temperature and an optimum pH are characteristic to every enzyme (see Table 3), and so are the minimum and maximum values of pH and temperature at which the enzyme is active.

Each enzyme has an optimum pH at which its activity is highest, all conditions being equal. The optimum for practical purposes may cover one or several units of the pH scale. The activity begins to decrease rapidly on both sides of the optimum range until the enzyme is completely inactivated. Change of the pH toward the optimum will reactivate the enzyme, and change of pH above or below the levels of temporary inactivation may gradually damage the enzyme to permanent inactivity. The optimum of the same enzyme may vary with the substrate on which it acts. Also, if the reaction is reversible, a specific pH will promote the reaction in one direction and another specific pH will promote it in the opposite direction.

The minimum temperature slows the reaction speed to zero, but does not damage the enzyme, which will exert its full activity as the temperature is elevated to the optimum. However, the maximum temperature at which the enzyme action comes to zero, inactivates the enzyme permanently; it deneutralizes the proteins, and destroys the enzyme.

The optimum pH of the various enzymes may range on a wide scale: pepsin exhibits highest activity on egg albumin at a pH of 1.5, and alkaline phosphatase exhibits highest activity on β-glycerophosphate at a pH of 9.5.

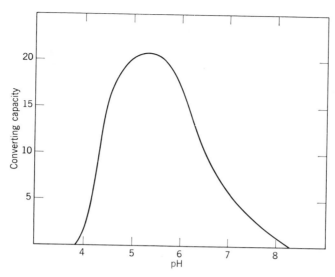

Fig. 1. The effect of pH on the activity of malt amylase expressed in units of converting capacity.

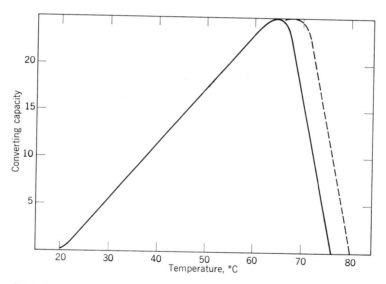

Fig. 2. The effect of temperature on the activity of malt amylase expressed in units of converting capacity.

There is also a pH range for enzyme stability (shelf life). This is usually within several degrees, up and down, from the optimum pH.

The effect of temperature for most enzymes, roughly follows the rule that every 10°C increase in temperature about doubles the activity, as long as the temperature does not damage the enzyme. In other words, one gram enzyme preparation will catalyze in one hour at 30°C the transformation of twice as much substrate as in one hour at 20°C. The effect of pH on the activity of malt amylase as measured by the

Lasché test, is illustrated in Fig. 1, the effect of temperature is illustrated in Fig. 2. Converting capacity, C, is defined by the equation

$$C = 100S/Lt$$

where S is the amount of converted starch in grams, L is the amount of enzyme solution in ml (or enzyme preparation in grams) and t is the conversion time in minutes (84). In Fig. 2 the solid line indicates the converting capacity measured under S/L conditions resulting in 30 min or longer conversion time t, when the effect of thermal inactivation became prominent; the dotted line indicates the converting capacity measured under S/L conditions and at a value of t low enough for the effect of thermal inactivation to be equal to the thermal activation up to about 72.5°C.

Characterization and Use of Industrial Enzymes

General Characteristics (3,6,8,9,13,15,18,20,22,24,34,35,39,40). Industrial enzymes may be defined as enzyme preparations manufactured industrially either for use as direct household commodities, or for use in the production of a manufactured commodity.

"The value of industrial enzymes produced in the U.S. in 1960 was estimated at 26.5 million dollars (70). In 1964 the value of marketed enzymes was estimated at $29.4 million with the following breakdown: food, $16.7 million; agricultural, $5.5 million; industrial, $4.4 million and pharmaceutical, $2.8 million. The enzymes used by the food industry were estimated at $5.7 million for amyloglucosidase, $4 million for papain, $3.5 million for rennin, and $3.5 million for others.

"These estimations do not include malt, malt products, compressed yeast, or dried yeast preparations."

Industrial enzyme preparations include pure crystalline enzymes separated from all inert material, partially purified enzyme concentrates free from cell residue and most inert material, or cells rich in certain enzymes. The cells may include plant or animal tissues, or cells of microorganisms. Example for plant tissue is barley malt, for animal tissue, dried pancreas gland. The cells of microorganisms may be used directly as crude enzyme preparations, or they may be used as a source of self-reproducing enzyme supply. Example for the first type is dried bakers' yeast which does not reproduce, or seldom reproduces during its utilization in household. Example for the second type is every microbial inoculum used in a microbial process involving cell reproduction. Although self-reproducing industrial enzyme concentrates in the form of microorganisms fit into the definition of industrial enzyme preparations, they will be considered here only in general. For a more detailed discussion of concentrates see Fermentation.

Most industrial enzyme preparations are dry, some are liquids, others are syrups. The dry products are usually pulverized (consistency of flour or bran); the malts maintain the original appearance of the barley grain. The activity of the majority of preparations is set by the manufacturer to a predetermined level, by the commingling of inactive substances, which will not interfere with the reaction or the product. In many instances the manufacturer markets the same enzyme preparation at 2–4 different strengths of activity, for different purposes. Usually, the higher the activity per unit of weight in the product, the higher is the cost per unit of activity.

Most enzyme preparations excel in one principal enzyme, and contain other enzymes in considerable quantities or just in traces; usually all derive from the common source. If the use so requires, the product is made to contain one single enzyme; the usual accompanying enzymes are eliminated, and this is so stated on the labels and in the specifications. For special purposes the manufacturer will market mixtures of enzymes, so-called "formula enzymes." These are carefully blended to correspond to the purpose for which they will be used.

Industrial enzyme preparations are widely used, almost in every field where organic products of plant and animal origin are processed into consumer goods. The fields of utilization cover three main groups: production of foods and food ingredients (95,121), production of beverages, and production of miscellaneous goods. Food and food ingredients include bread (78,79) and other bakery goods, cereals, confections, sugars, syrups, meat, fish, vegetables (66), milk (130,138), cheese, eggs, chocolate, cocoa, coffee (60), food flavors, and others. The beverages include fruit juices, fruit drinks, carbonated beverages, beer, wine, and distilled beverages. The miscellanoeus group includes pharmaceuticals, tobacco (96), adhesives, paper, textiles (138), cleaning compositions, feedstuffs, clinical and analytical reagents, etc.

Table 2. Major Producers of Industrial Enzymes in the U.S.

Producer	Code used in Table 3
Armour Pharmaceutical Co. (Reheis Chemical Co.), Chicago, Ill.	A
Cudahy Packing Co., Omaha, Neb.	Cud
Dairyland Food Laboratories, Inc., Waukesha, Wisc.	D
Fermo Laboratories, Inc. (subsidiary of Harshaw Chemical Co.), Chicago, Ill.	F
Meer Corporation, New York, N.Y.	Mr
Miles Chemical Co., Elkhart, Ind.	M
Paul-Lewis Laboratories Division (Chas. Pfizer & Co. Inc.), Milwaukee, Wisc.	PL
S. B. Penick & Co., New York, N.Y.	Pen
Premier Malt Products, Inc., Milwaukee, Wisc.	PMP
Rohm & Haas Co., Philadelphia, Pa.	R&H
J. E. Siebel Sons Co., Chicago, Ill.	Sie
Standard Brands Sales Co., New York, N.Y.	Std.
R. T. Vanderbilt Co. Inc., New York, N.Y.	Van
Wallerstein Co., Staten Island, N.Y.	Wal
Wilson Laboratories, Chicago, Ill.	Wil

Table 2 lists the leading manufacturers of industrial enzymes in the United States, and Table 3 lists the best-known industrial enzymes offered on the U.S. market, and some of their principal characteristics and utilizations.

The active ingredients in the enzyme preparations fall into six main groups: carbohydrases, proteases, lipases, pectic enzymes, glucose oxidases, and miscellaneous enzymes. Table 4 correlates the various enzymes and the fields in which they are utilized.

The number of useful enzymes as well as the number of enzyme preparations is ever increasing. The largest fields of enzyme utilization are the food and beverage industries, and the bulk of industrially used enzymes belong to the group of carbohydrases.

Specific Characteristics. Users of industrial enzymes are usually well informed in the general enzymology of their particular field. Their interest, concerning the products offered on the market is well satisfied by a few specific data, usually listed

Table 3. Most Important Industrial Enzymes Marketed in the U.S.

No.	Trade name, source	Producer's code name[a]	Principal and additional enzymes	Primary action on substrate	Utilization	Recommended values	
						For pH	For temperature, °C
1	Amyliq, bacterial	Wal	α-amylase	liquefies starch	adhesives, sizings, paper coatings	6.5–7.5	72–80
2	Amizyme R, *Bacillus subtilis*	[a]	α-amylase	liquefies starch	paper coating and wrap sizing, adhesives, conveyor belt cleaning	6.5–7.0	67–80
3	Animal Diastase, hog pancreas glands	Cud[b]	α-amylase. protease, lipase	liquefies starch	desizing agent in textile industry, sewage disposal	6.8–7.0	38–40
4	Biobate	Wal	tanners' bate	hydrolyzes proteins	bating hides		
5	Bromelain, pineapple plant	M	protease, phosphatase, peroxidase	hydrolyzes proteins	meat, baking, pharmaceuticals	4.0–9.0	30–60
6	Capalase, calf oral glands	D	lipase	hydrolyzes milk fat	cheese making		37
7	Catlase, liver, blood	Cud	catalase	decomposes H_2O_2	food, brewing, textile, fur, rubber, leather, cosmetics, cheese, analytical	4.0–8.6	10–40
8	Catalase B, microbial	M	catalase	decomposes H_2O_2	cheese, foam rubber, bleaching	6.0–9.0	0–50
9	Catalase L, microbial	M	catalase	decomposes H_2O_2	cheese, cold sterilization of milk	6.0–8.0	20–50
10	Cellase 1000, *Aspergillus niger*	Wal	cellulase	hydrolyzes cellulose and cellulose deviations	pharmaceuticals	5.0	37
11	Cellulase 36, microbial	R&H	cellulase, pectic enzymes, glucosidases	hydrolyzes cellulose, cellulose derivatives, and related compounds	digestive aids, feeds, reduction of the viscosity of cellulose suspensions	4.5	40–50
12	Cellulase, microbial	M	cellulase	hydrolyzes cellulose	citrus, essential oils and spices, beer, pomace, pharmaceuticals	4.5	40–50
13	Cellulase 36, microbial	R&H	cellulase	hydrolyzes cellulose, hemicellulose gums	feed supplementation, pharmaceuticals, vanilla extract		
14	Clarase, fungal	M	α-amylase protease, phosphatase, maltase	hydrolyzes starch	fruit juices, chocolate syrup, brewing	3.0–7.0	20–45
15	Compound C, KSTUV. bacterial culture	M	mixture of various enzymes and bacteria	decomposes sewage	digests waste in septic tanks and drain lines		
16	DeeO, microbial	M	glucose oxidase, catalase	oxidizes glucose to gluconic acid	eggs, beverages, salad dressing, sensitive foods, analytical	3.5–8.0	20–55

No.	Preparation, source	Supplier	Enzyme composition	Action	Application	pH	Temp
17	Dextrinase, fungal	M	β-amylase, protease, amyloglucosidase	converts dextrins to maltose and dextrose	cereal syrups—higher DE	4.5–5.5	40–55
18	Diastase 50, pork pancreas	Wil	α-amylase, amylopsin, animal diastase	hydrolyzes starch	digestive aid, pharmaceuticals	6.0–7.0	37
19	Diastase 73, microbial	R&H	amyloglucosidase, β-amplase	saccharification of starch	production of dextrose and dextrose syrups from starch	4.5–5.0	50–55
20	Diazyme, microbial	M	amyloglucosidase	hydrolyzes starch to glucose	dextrose manufacture, sweetener, fermentation, pharmaceuticals		
21	Diastatic Malt Syrup, malt	Std	amylases	hydrolyzes starch	baking industry	4.5–5.5	60
22	Disposzyme, microbial	Wal	protease, amylase, cellase	mixture of enzymes obtained from selected microorganisms grown on bran and a special strain of bacteria, to aid the clearing of household drain lines	cleaning drain lines, grease traps, sewage treatment	6.0–7.2	50–55
23	Drain cleaner, formulation	M	amylase, protease, lipase, and anaerobic bacteria	liquefies sewage			
24	Enzar 80, pancreas	A	protease, amylase, lipase	hydrolyzes foods	chewable tablets, dairy		
25	Enzygans, pancreas		amylase, lipase	hydrolyzes starch, fat	food products		
26	Enzyme 4511-3, bacterial	Wal	amylase, protease	hydrolyzes starch and proteins	crackers	5.0–7.0	75–80
27	Enzyme W-3-F, bacterial	Wal	α-amylase, (heat resistant)	hydrolyzes starch	starch, syrups with low sugar content	5.0–7.0	75–80
28	Enzyme TS-3, microbial	Wal	mixture of enzymes and bacteria	hydrolyzes various substrates	drain cleaning, sewage treatment		
29	Exsize	PMP	α-amylase, protease	hydrolyzes starch	desizing of textiles		
30	Fermcozyme CB-B, liquid	F	glucose oxidase, traces of cellulase, maltase invertase, amylase	removes sugar, oxygen	prevents off flavor in orange drinks, prevents iron pickup in canned beer, prevents rancidity of mayonnaise, prevents enzymatic browning of frozen fruits, co-stabilization of ascorbic acid and vitamin B_{12}	6.5–7.0	160
31	Fermcozyme 1307, liquid, microbial	F	glucose oxidase, low in trace enzymes	removes oxygen	prevents off flavor in orange drinks		
32	Fermcozyme M, liquid, microbial	F	glucose oxidase, for use at low pH	removes oxygen	salad dressings		

(continued)

Table 3 (*continued*)

No.	Trade name, source	Producer's code name[a]	Principal and additional enzymes	Primary action on substrate	Utilization	Recommended values,	
						For pH	For temperature, °C
33	Fermcozyme 653-AM. Liquid, microbial	F	glucose oxidase, low in catalase	oxidizes glucose	glucose text reagent	5.1–5.3	
34	Fermcozyme 952-DM, microbial	F	glycose oxidase, catalase	oxidizes glucose	oxidase peroxidase reagent		
35	Fermex, *Aspergillus oryzae*	Wal[b]	amylase, protease	hydrolyzes starch	bakery, wafers	4.0–7.0	40–50
36	Ficin, tropical fig tree	M	protease, phosphatase, peroxidase	hydrolyzes proteins	meat, brewing, photography, pharmaceuticals	5.5–7.5	30–50
37	Fungal Amylase, *Aspergillus oryzae*	M	α-amylase, protease	hydrolyzes starch to dextrins	baking	4.5–5.5	33–45
38	Fungal Protease, *Aspergillus oryzae*	M	protease, α-amylase	hydrolyzes proteins, starch	baking, meat tenderizing	4.0–7.5	30–50
39	Gelatinase, formulation	M	gelatinase, α-amylase, protease	solubilizes gelatin	photography	6.0–8.0	30–60
40	Glucose Oxidase, microbial	F	glucose oxidase	removes oxygen and glucose	fruit juice, food industry	4.0–6.5	60
41	Gumase	R & H	polysaccharidases	hydrolyzes vegetable gums, mucilages	baking, sizing textiles, corn degermination, oil-well-drilling fluids	4.0–6.0	40–50
42	Hemicellulase Ce-100, microbial	M	hemicellulase, cellulase	hydrolyzes hemicellulases and gums	coffee, gums	4.5–6.0	30–60
43	HT-44 and HT-440, bacterial	M	α-amylase, protease	liquefies starch	textiles, adhesives, paper, brewing, grain alcohol	5.5–7.5	20–75
44	HT-2000, bacterial	M	α-amylase, β-amylase, protease	liquefies and saccharifies starch	pharmaceuticals	5.5–7.5	20–75
45	HT proteolytic, bacterial	M	protease, α-amylase, phosphatase	hydrolyzes proteins	baking, leather	6.0–8.5	30–35
46	Hyaluronidase, beef testicles	Cud	hyaluronidase	hydrolyzes mucopolysaccharide, hyaluronic acid	clinical, local anasthesis, insulin shock	5.3	37
47	High Purity Glucose Oxidase	M	glucose oxidase	oxidizes glucose	analytical, research, pharmaceuticals		

No.	Name	Producer	Enzyme	Action	Application	pH	Temp
48	Italase, kid-goat glands	D	lipase	hydrolyzes milk fat	cheese making	3.3–5.2	37
49	Klerzyme, microbial	Wal[b]	pectinase	hydrolyzes pectins	fruit juices, wines	7.0–8.0	0–62
50	Lipase 2000 and 3000, pork pancreas	Wil	lipase	hydrolyzes fats	pharmaceuticals, digestive aids		37
51	Lipase, hog glands	Cud	lipase, amylase tripsin	splits fat	pharmaceuticals, digestives aids, animal feeds, sewage disposal research, in preparation of ribonucleotides	7.0–8.8	37
52	Lysodeicticus cells		polynucleotide, phosphorilase		research, pharmaceuticals		
53	Lysozyme	Wil	lysozyme	hydrolyzes microorganisms	research, pharmaceuticals		
54	Malt	malting companies	α-amylase, β-amylase	converts starch to maltose	brewery, distillery, bakery	4.5–5.5	60
55	Malt Syrup, Diastic	several malting companies	α-amylase, β-amylase	hydrolyzes starch	baking	4.5–5.5	60
56	Mylase SA (Allase SA), fungal	Wal	α-amylase, limit dextrinase, other carbohydrases	hydrolyzes starch and its degradation products	hydrolyzes converted starch syrups to dextrose syrups	5.2	49
57	Mylase SC (Allase SC), (a special form of Mylase SA)	Wal	α-amylase limit dextrinase, other carbohydrases with added buffer salts	hydrolyzes starch and its degradation products	hydrolyzes converted starch syrups to dextrose syrups	5.2	49
58	Mylase 100, *Aspergillus oryzae*	Wal[b]	α-amylase	liquefies starch	pharmaceuticals, digestive aids	5.2	49
59	Milezyme A	M	α-amylase	hydrolyzes starch	feedstuffs for poultry, beef cattle, swine		37
60	Milezyme P	M	protease	hydrolyzes proteins	feedstuffs for poultry, beef cattle, swine		37
61	NF VIII Papain, papaya plant, (potency adjusted to NF VIII)	Pen	protease	hydrolyzes proteins	softening woolen fabrics, tooth paste	5.0–6.0 (4.0–11.0)	
62	OH-T Papain, (Hi Test Conc.) papaya plant	Pen	protease	hydrolyzes proteins	beer chillproofing, meat tenderizing, pharmaceuticals	5.0–6.0 (4.0–11.0)	
63	Ovazyme, liquid, fungal	F	glucose oxidase, catalase	removes sugar	eggs prior to drying		
64	Oxygen Scavenger, Packets, fungal	M	glucose oxidase, catalase	removed oxygen from sealed containers	food packaging		

(continued)

Table 3 (*continued*)

No.	Trade name, source	Producer's code name[a]	Principal and additional enzymes	Primary action on substrate	Utilization	Recommended values For pH	For temperature, °C
65	Pancreatin 6XNF	A	α-amylase, protease, lipase	digests food	pharmaceuticals, digestive aids		37
66	Pancreatin, pancreas glands	M	α-amylase, protease, lipase	liquefies starch, proteins, fat	leather, pharmaceuticals, textile desizing	6.0–8.0	20–50
67	Pancreatic lipase, hog pancreas	M	lipase	hydrolyzes fats to glycerin and fatty acids	pharmaceuticals, digestive aids, improves whipping of egg whites		37
68	Pancreatin, animals: hog, ox	Cud	amylase, protease, lipase	hydrolyzes starch, (also proteins, fat)		7.4–8.2	40
69	Pancreatin NF, defatted port pancreas	Wil[b]	protease, diastase, lipase	hydrolyzes proteins, starch, fat	digestive aid	7.0	37
70	Papain, papaya plant	M	protease, phosphatase, peroxidase	hydrolyzes proteins	brewing, meat, pharmaceuticals	6.0–8.0	30–75
71	Pectinol 5-B, fungal	R&H	pectic enzymes	hydrolyzes pectins	production of wines, production of concentrates, clarification of fruit juices	3.0–5.5	50
72	Penicillinase, bacterial	M	penicillinase	hydrolyzes penicillin	pharmaceuticals, research, analytical	7.0	40
73	Pepsin, hog stomach mucosa	M	protease	hydrolyzes proteins	animal feed, cereals, pharmaceuticals	1.5–3.0	30–50
74	Pepsin NF, glandular portion of hog stomach	Wil[b]	protease, cathepsin	hydrolyzes proteins, also milk curdling activity	digestive aid, pharmaceuticals	1.5–3.0	37
75	Pepsin, 1:3000, hog stomach	Cud[b]	protease	hydrolyzes proteins	digestive aids, formulations, pharmaceuticals	1.8–2.2	40
76	P/L Ficin, tropical fig tree	PL	protease	hydrolyzes proteins	chillproofing beer, tenderizing meat, dehairing hides	4.0–8.0 (optimal 5.0)	up to 50
77	P/L Liquid Cerevase	PL	protease	hydrolyzes proteins	chillproofing beer	4.0–4.5	
78	P/L Papain, papaya plant	PL	protease	hydrolyzes proteins	chillproofing beer, tenderizing meat, dehairing hides	4.0–8.5	70
79	P/L Rennet Ext, Liquid, P/L Rennet Powder, stomach of calves, lambs	PL[b]	protease	milk clotting	cheese manufacturing		37

	Name, source	Supplier	Enzyme	Action	Application	pH	Temperature
80	P/L 219 Urease, jack bean, *Canavalia ensiformis*	PL	urease	decomposes urea	research, clinical tests in measuring urea in blood		
81	Prolase 300, papaya plant	Wal	protease	hydrolyzes proteins	pharmaceuticals	4.0–8.0	70
82	Protease, sheep pancreas	M	protease	hydrolyzes proteins	pharmaceuticals, protein hydrolysates	6.0–8.5	30–50
83	Protease 30	R&H	protease, amylase	hydrolyzes proteins and starch	processing acidulated fish press water	6.0–9.0	50
84	Purified Papain, Type A-300, papaya plant	Mr[b]	papain, chymopapain, amylase, lipase, pectase	hydrolyzes proteins	meat tenderizing, clarifying beer and malt beverages		
85	Rapidase, bacterial	Wal	amylase	hydrolyzes starch	desizing		
86	Rapidase, S-400, bacterial	Wal	protease	hydrolyzes proteins, gelatin	desizing, degumming of silk		
87	Rhozyme A-4, *Aspergillus oryzae*	R&H[b]	protease, amylase	hydrolyzes proteins, starch	baking, meat processing	6.0–9.0	50
88	Rhozyme PF	R&H[b]	protease, amylase	hydrolyzes proteins, starch	textile, paper, photographic products, laundry, brewing, dairy, fish press water	5.0–8.5	60
89	Rhozyme CL	R&H	lipase, protease	hydrolyzes fats	digestive aids, formulation		
90	Rhozyme S, *Aspergillus oryzae*	R&H[b]	α-amylase, β-amylase, amyloglucosidase	hydrolyzes starch	syrup production	4.5–6.0	50–55
91	Rhoxyme T-22, *Aspergillus oryzae*	R&H[b]	α-amylase, β-amylase, amyloglucosidase	hydrolyzes starch, dextrins	syrup production from acid hydrolyzed starch	5.0–6.0	50–55
92	Rhozyme 33, *Aspergillus oryzae*	R&H	amylase (high), low protease	liquefies and saccharifies starch	baking	3.0–5.0	
93	Rhozyme H-39, bacterial	M[b]	α-amylase, heat stable pentosanase	liquefies starch and substituted starches, pentosans	baking, brewing, cereals, cocoa and candy, distilling and fermentation, laundry, paper, starches and syrups, textiles, miscellaneous	4.0–10.0 (optimal 6.1)	60–80
94	Siebel Papain, papaya	Sie	protease	hydrolyzes proteins	beer chillproofing, meat tenderizing	5.0–6.0	
95	Siebel Ficin, fig tree	Sie	protease	hydrolyzes proteins	beer chillproofing, meat tenderizing, pharmaceuticals	5.5–7.5	30–50
96	Special Diastase, formulation	M	α-amylase, β-amylase	liquefies and saccharifies starch	baby foods, pharmaceuticals, sugar, syrups, brewing	6.0–8.0	20–50

(continued)

Table 3 (*continued*)

No.	Trade name, source	Producer's code name[a]	Principal and additional enzymes	Primary action on substrate	Utilization	Recommended values, For pH	For temperature, °C
97	SL Papain, (standardized with lactose) papaya	Pen	protease	hydrolyzes proteins	softening woolen fabrics, tooth paste	5.0-6.0 (4.0-11.0)	
98	Takabate, formulation	M	protease, bating formula	hydrolyzes proteins	leather	7.0-9.0	29-35
99	Takamine Pectinase, microbial	M	pectic, cellulase	hydrolyzes and depolymerizes pectins	grape juice and wine, apple juice, jellies, fruits	3.2-5.5	20-65
100	Talase, formulation	M	amylase, protease	hydrolyzes starch, gum and gelatin	textiles	6.0-8.0	20-50
101	Trypsin, crystalline, and Chymotrypsin beef pancreas	M	protease	hydrolyzes proteins	medical treatments		37
102	Texzyme (Liquid or L-253 Powder)	PMP	protease	hydrolyzes proteins	desizing textiles (silk and rayon fabrics)	6.5-7.0	38-44
103	RSR, formulation	Wal	protease	hydrolyzes proteins	garment cleaning	4.5-7.5	40-60
104	Tendrin, formulation	M	protease	hydrolyzes proteins	meat tenderizing	7.4-8.2	38-40
105	Trypsin, hog pancreas	Cud[b]	protease, amylase, lipase	hydrolyzes proteins	digestive aid, meat tenderizing		
106	Trypsin, high test, crystallized	Wil	protease	hydrolyzes proteins	meat tenderizing, pharmaceuticals, research		
107	Tona	Wal	protease	hydrolyzes proteins	meat tenderizer		
108	Wilzyme 400, beef pancreas	Wil[b]	amylase, protease, lipase	hydrolyzes proteins, starch, and fat, microorganisms	all purpose digestive enzyme, pharmaceuticals, research	5.0-8.0	37
109	Zymo-Best, formulation	PMP	protease, amylase, gumase	hydrolyzes proteins, starch	feed ingredients for beef and dairy cattle, sheep, swine, poultry, chickens, turkeys		37
110	Zypanar, pancreas	A	protease, amylase, lipase	hydrolyzes starch, proteins, fat	digestive aid		
111	Vanzyme and Vanzyme L	V	protease, amylase, α-amylase	liquefies starch	food ingredients, adhesives, starch, syrups		
112	Lipase B, fungal	R&H	lipase protease, amylase, pectinase	hydrolyzes fats and fatty acid esters, cellulose	foods, pharmaceuticals	5.0-7.0	45-50

[a] For explanation of the code used, see Table 2.

[b] Products are available in several preparations of various enzymic strengths.

in the manufacturer's descriptive literature and sales bulletins. They include all or most of the following data:

1. Trade name.

2. Name of principal enzyme and of additional enzymes, if present.

3. Principal reaction and possible side reactions catalyzed.

4. Physical appearance (powder, liquid, syrup) and color; size and types of containers.

5. Solubility of the active component in water and occasionally in other liquids, the amount and nature of the inactive soluble components, and the amount and nature of the inactive insoluble components.

6. General field and specific purpose of utilization, and the processing step, or steps, for which the preparation is recommended.

7. The optimum pH, the practical working pH range, the minimum and the maximum pH which will temporarily inactivate the enzyme, and the minimum and maximum pH which will permanently inactivate (destroy) the enzyme.

8. The optimum temperature, and the temperature of thermal destruction of the enzyme. (Occasionally the time needed to destroy 50 and 100% of the activity at the optimum pH, at the given temperature, is also presented.)

9. The activity given in defined units, if available, or the recommended enzyme/substrate ratio.

10. Nature and amount of activators to be added, if needed.

11. Nature of possible inactivators to be avoided.

12. Conditions of stable storage.

13. FDA regulations concerning the preparation, if the enzyme is recommended in connection with food, beverages, and pharmaceutical products.

14. Cost per pound.

Grouping of Industrial Enzymes. The following is an abbreviated account of the industrial enzymes, their actions on the substrates, and their utilizations.

Industrial enzyme preparations are conveniently discussed in groups according to the principal reactions they catalyze. In each group some of the following are considered: (*1*) chemistry of the substrate; (*2*) the principal reaction catalyzed; (*3*) the chemistry of the reaction; (*4*) names and specific activity of the individual enzymes; (*5*) general field and examples of utilization; (*6*) examples of commercial products; (*7*) optimum and practical pH and temperature values, and pH and temperature values that cause temporary and permanent inactivation; (*8*) recommended enzyme/substrate ratios; and (*9*) source of the enzyme.

For convenience the preparations are classified as (a) carbohydrases; (b) proteases; (c) lipases; (d) pectic enzymes; (e) glucose oxidases; and (f) miscellaneous enzymes.

CARBOHYDRASES (1,2,20)

Carbohydrates (qv) constitute the largest group of naturally occurring organic materials. More than 50% of the dry substance of all plant material is made up of carbohydrates, which include cellulose, hemicellulose, starches, glycogens, complex and simple sugars. The simple sugars are termed *monosaccharides;* carbohydrates composed of two simple sugar molecules are called *disaccharides;* combinations containing up to ten monosaccharides are termed *oligosaccharides* (di-, tri-, tetra-, penta-, hexa-, hepta-, octa-, nona-, and decasaccharides); *polysaccharides* are composed of

Table 4.   The Active Components and the

	Food and foodstuffs							
	Cereals, bakery goods	Confectionery, syrups, sugars	Meat, fish, proteins	Sensitive foodstuffs, salad dressing, mayonnaise	Milk, cheese	Eggs	Chocolate, cocoa	Coffee
carbohydrases								
α-amylase	X	X			X		X	
β-amylase	X	X			X		X	
amyloglucosidase		X						
amylo-1,6-α-glucosidase		X						
oligo-1,6-α-glucosidase		X						
invertase (saccharase)		X						
maltase		X						
cellulase-hemicellulase								
proteases								
pepsin, trypsin	X						X	
papain, chemopapain	X		X					
rennin					X			
ficin	X		X		X			
bromelain	X		X					
fungal proteases	X		X		X			
bacterial proteases	X				X	X		
lipases								
pectic enzymes								
pectin-methylesterase								X
pectin-polygalacturonase								X
depolymerase								
protopectinase								
glucose oxidase		X	X		X	X		
miscellaneous enzymes								
urease								
penicillinase								X
cellulase								
lysozyme								
catalase				X	X	X		
hyaluronidase								
naringinase								
yeasts	X							
bacterial culture								X
hemicellulase								

many large aggregates of monosaccharide units, and are substances of appreciable molecular weight. Among monosaccharides, glucose and invert sugar (fructose and glucose), and among disaccharides sucrose, maltose, and lactose are the most significant; among oligosaccharides the low-molecular-weight dextrins, and among polysaccharides the starches are of industrial importance.

Invert sugar (from sucrose) and dextrins, maltose, and glucose (from starch) are produced by the action of the industrial enzymes belonging to the group of carbohydrases.

Disaccharides, oligosaccharides, and polysaccharides consist of monosaccharides combined with each other, most frequently in $(1 \rightarrow 4)$-D-glycosidic linkage or less frequently in $(1 \rightarrow 6)$-D-glycosidic linkage. The various carbohydrases hydrolyze the glycosidic linkage and introduce a H^+ and OH^- into the hydrolytic products at the point of cleavage.

Invertase (28,86). Also called sucrase, or saccharase, or "β-fructofuranosidase," one of the simplest carbohydrases commercially used, catalyzes the hydrolysis of the β-D-fructofuranosyl linkage in sucrose, raffinose, gentianose, methyl- and β-fructofuranoside. Invertase produces invert sugar by hydrolyzing sucrose into glucose and fructose. Invert sugar is widely used in confectioneries, candies, syrups, cordials, ice cream, etc, for two reasons: invert or partially invert sugar is sweeter than sucrose

Utilization of Industrial Enzyme Preparations

Beverages					Miscellaneous						
Fruit juices, fruit drinks, flavors	Carbonated beverages	Beer	Distilled beverages	Wine	Pharmaceuticals	Adhesives	Paper	Textiles	Cleaning, sewage treatment	Feeds	Analytical
		X	X			X	X	X	X	X	
X		X	X		X				X	X	
X		X	X		X						X
			X								
		X	X								
					X				X	X	
		X			X				X	X	
					X			X		X	
		X			X					X	
		X			X					X	
		X			X		X	X	X	X	
					X			X			
					X				X	X	
X				X							
X				X							
X				X							
X				X							
X	X	X									X
					X						X
											X
X	X	X			X			X			X
					X						X
		X	X	X					X		
									X		

and it begins to crystallize (harden) at much higher concentrations than glucose or sucrose syrups.

Amylases (18,30,38,78,79,90,148). The most important carbohydrases, produced in far larger quantities than any other enzymes, belong to the group of amylase or diastase enzymes, which hydrolyze starch and its hydrolytic degradation products. Although all amylases hydrolyze the D-glycosidic linkage, they are different in many respects. Most of them hydrolyze only linkages between the carbons 1 and 4; others, in addition to the $(1 \rightarrow 4)$ linkage hydrolyze also bonds between the carbons 1 and 6.

One enzyme is more active in hydrolyzing larger molecules, cleaving them at random, close to the middle of a long glucose chain; another enzyme splits off maltose molecules at the nonreducing end of a chain; and another enzyme splits off single glucose units, attacking at the nonreducing ends of both long and short chains, and cleaves both $(1 \rightarrow 4)$ and $(1 \rightarrow 6)$ linkages. The various amylases differ also in their thermal-deactivation temperature, pH optimum, and other characteristics. The individual amylases alone, or in certain combinations, are used for different specific purposes.

The number of specific amylolytic enzymes is contested by various researchers. The following are the best known members: α-amylase, β-amylase, glucoamylase or amyloglucosidase, amylo-1,6-α-glucosidase, oligo-1,6-α-glucosidase, or limit dextrinase.

α-*Amylase*, present in pancreas, saliva, plants, molds, bacteria, hydrolyzes starch, glycogen, and dextrins. It is also called the "liquefying" enzyme because by cleaving at random the large starch molecules and the long chains of dextrins formed by the primary and secondary cleavages, it rapidly liquefies the thick, starchy paste. Although very slowly, it also produces some maltose and possibly glucose. α-Amylases vary in some characteristics depending on their origin. Some α-amylases of microbial origin are still active at 90°C, while the malt α-amylase is rapidly deactivated (destroyed) above 63°C.

The importance of α-amylase among the other amylases is twofold. If the purpose of the starch conversion is to liquefy the starch only with the production of dextrins, like in the manufacture of glue, starchy syrups, or other food ingredients, the α-amylase will do the job alone. Consequently, for such purposes industrial enzymes containing principally α-amylase, with no or little content of other amylases, are manufactured.

α-Amylase accelerates the action of other amylases. If the purpose of the starch conversion is to produce maltose, a sugar fermentable by yeast, β-amylase alone would do the job very slowly and incompletely by splitting one maltose molecule at a time from the nonreducing ends of the long chains of the starch molecule. The added β-amylase would not mix with the thick starch paste without the liquefying action of α-amylase.

The complete starch molecule has only a few chain ends, and the action of β-amlyase stops at the points of branching of the chains, the enzyme being incapable of splitting $(1 \rightarrow 6)$ linkages occurring at the branchings. α-Amylase, by rapidly liquefying the starch paste, will not only accelerate the physical mixing of the saccharifying β-amylase with the substrate, but will produce many short chains, with many ends, where the saccharifying enzyme can act quickly. α-Amylase will break the chains also between the branches, making those portions of the main chains available for the action of the saccharifying enzyme. Therefore, the presence of a small amount of α-amylase will accelerate the saccharification of starch by other amylases.

Conversion of the starch content of the grain into dextrins and maltose is the purpose of the mashing (brewing) step in the production of beer, ale, and malt champagne (59). The possible complete conversion of starch to maltose is the main purpose in preparing the distillers' grain mash for the production of grain neutral spirits and whiskies (14,16,37).

In both processes malt provides the needed enzyme mixture. Brewers' malt is produced and used for beer, distillers' malt for whiskey, and gibberellin-treated malt for grain neutral spirits. The principal difference between these malts is in the α-amylase content, which is the lowest in brewers' malt (25–30 units) at 20°C, about twice as high in standard distillers' malt (50–60 units), and the highest in gibberellin-treated malt (80–100 units).

In 1964 about 95 million bushels (one bu = 34 lb) of malt were produced in the United States, representing 175 million dollars. Of the 95 million bushels, 5.6 million were used by the distilling industry, 2.6 million by the food industry, and 86.8 million by the brewing industry.

The saccharifying enzyme, β-amylase, usually increases with the α-amylase content in the malt. In brewing malts the saccharifying enzyme is always measured.

In distillers' malt, only the α-amylase is determined, because usually this is in the relative minimum.

In preparing starch glue or brewers' mash, the conversion of the starch is usually interrupted by destroying the enzyme at a predetermined point, by heating the substrate to the temperature of thermal destruction of the enzyme.

In distillery practice, care is exercised to protect the enzyme for continued activity during the fermentation process. With a relatively quick conversion, the enzymes are exposed only for a period of ten minutes or less, to a 60°C temperature. During this period a sufficient amount of maltose is formed to promote the development of the yeast and a strong fermentation. As the fermentation progresses the maltose–dextrin equilibrium changes, and, if sufficient enzyme remains, the conversion progresses to completion. The successive decrease in pH slows down this secondary conversion during fermentation. The conversion is inactivated at a pH of 4 and below.

The active substance of the malt is water-soluble, and the bulk of the enzymes may be obtained in a cold aqueous solution containing about 25% of the barley malt. Concentrates may be prepared from malt by evaporating such extracts. High-diastatic malt extracts, with considerable maltose content are marketed for many purposes such as brewery and bakery adjuncts.

Commercial α-amylase preparations of microbial origin (*A. niger* and *B. subtilis*), practically free from other amylases, are offered for the production of adhesives from starch, and for the liquefaction of grain mashes in distillery practice. They are employed in the production of dextrose from starch together with another enzyme preparation containing principally amyloglucosidase. α-Amylase splits the large molecules of starch and of dextrins, and the amyloglucosidase splits off single glucose molecules from the nonreducing ends of the chains.

β-Amylase, widely distributed in microorganisms, in animal glands, and in plants, principally in germinating seeds (malt), produces maltose from starch, glycogen, and dextrins by successively removing maltose units, at the nonreducing chain terminations. It is in great abundance in brewers', distillers', and gibberellin-treated malts, and is the principal saccharifying enzyme in barley malt. Most commercial amylases and many protease products contain some β-amylase. Pure β-amylase (a Wallerstein product), is used as an analytical reagent for measuring α-amylase activity in various enzyme sources, principally in malt.

Glucoamylase or *amyloglucosidase* produces glucose by removing glucose molecules in succession from the nonreducing chain terminations from starch, glycogen, dextrins, and maltose molecules. It also catalyzes transglycosylation. It is present in blood, molds, and bacteria. Barley malt is low in amyloglucosidase. Commercial amyloglucosidase preparations are produced from molds (56,58).

Glucoamylase is used by several distillers in conjunction with gibberellin-treated malt in the conversion of grain starch to fermentable sugars. Its main application is in the production of glucose syrup, glucose paste, and crystalline glucose (cerelose) from starch in the dual-enzyme-conversion process.

In the manufacture of dextrose by the dual-enzyme process, a 30–35% starch–water suspension is prepared, the pH is adjusted to 5.5, and α-amylase dissolved in water is added in proportion of 0.045 lb per 100 lb starch. The mixture is heated under agitation to 85°C (185°F), and is kept at that temperature for 40 min. The starchy paste is well liquefied. The mixture is then cooled to 60°C (140°F), the pH is adjusted to 4.5 with hydrochloric acid, and amyloglucosidase is added in form of an aqueous suspension or solution at the rate of 0.55 lb dry preparation (or 1.3 pint liquid) for every 100 lb of starch. The starch–enzyme mixture is kept at 60°C (140°F) for 72–96 hr. The dextrin equivalent (DE) is about 98 (this means that 98 of the total solids is reducing sugar calculated as dextrose).

This process is more economical and results in a better product than either the acid conversion, or the acid-enzyme dual conversion.

In the conversion of any starchy product to dextrose, the starch content of grains and by-products derived from processing grains may be converted to glucose by the dual-enzyme process. Such products may be utilized by the feed industry or in various fermentation industries, which use glucose as a substrate or as an energy source.

Amylo-1,6-α-glucosidase (debranching enzyme) hydrolyzes $(1 \rightarrow 6)$-α-linkages, the branching-off linkage in starch, glycogen and dextrins; it is present in animal tissues, plants, yeast, and other microorganisms. The enzyme is used in two distilleries to convert the starch content of the mashed grains.

Oligo-1,6-α-glucosidase, or *limit dextrinase*, present in intestines, molds, and in limited quantities in malt, hydrolyzes $(1 \rightarrow 6)$-α-linkages in isomaltose, panose (maltotriose), and limit dextrins.

Isomaltase and *maltotriase* hydrolyze isomaltose and maltotriase, respectively.

Maltase, and α-*glucosidase*, hydrolyze maltose into two molecules of glucose.

Some authors deny the existence of the last five enzymes listed, as well as the existence of "transglucosidase," and contribute the enzymic activity ascribed to them to the enzyme glucoamylase (amyloglucosidase). The most obvious assumption, however, is that the amylase complex contains even more than the eight above-listed individual enzymes. The production of glucose may be explained without the existence of the last three enzymes by the action of glucoamylase. Glucoamylase, however, catalyzes transglycosylation reactions with the formation of $(1 \rightarrow 6)$ linkages. On the other hand, there are industrial enzymes that produce glucose almost free from transglycosidase activity. Also there are microorganisms which can assimilate and ferment maltose, but cannot ferment maltotriose, dextrines, or starch.

Because of the convenient and relatively cheap production of glucose, the cheapest sugar made from starch, the demand for the production of industrial amylase preparations is in constant increase. The value of amylase preparations exceeds the value of all other enzyme preparations produced in the United States.

Amylases are applied in considerable quantities in feed formulations and in limited quantities in pharmaceuticals as dietary aids (77,80,116,117,133).

Other enzymes that hydrolyze glucosidic linkages in substrates other than starch or its degradation products are *cellulase* (127), *lichenase, inulase, xylanase, cyclohexagluconase, cycloheptagluconase, chitinase, polygalacturonase, lysozyme, α-1,3-glucosidase, α- and β-glucosidases, trehalase, α- and β-galactosidases, α- and β-mannoglucosidases,* and *nucleosidases.* Other enzymes may be present in considerable or in trace quantities in commercial amylase preparations.

Lactase, a β-galactosidase, which hydrolyzes lactose into glucose and galactose. is present in bakers' yeast, in many *Aspergilli*, and in the digestive secretions of mammalians. Lactase is utilized in the manufacture of ice cream.

PROTEASES

Proteases degrade proteins and their degradation products, polypeptides, peptides, and other substances, by hydrolyzing —CO—NH— linkages. Proteins (protamins, histones, globulins, albumins, gluteins, scleroproteins, phosphoproteins, and conjugated proteins, etc) are organic compounds composed of a large number of amino acids (about 20 different types), connected by the —CO—NH— peptide linkage. Molecular weights of various proteins range from 16,000 to 17,000,000.

Although there are many specific enzymes involved, the proteolytic enzymes are of two major types: (*1*) endopeptidases (proteinases, pepsin, trypsin, chymotrypsin), that are able to act on the protein along the chain and do not usually attack terminal units; they produce peptides and eventually amino acids; (*2*) exopeptidases (peptidases such as carboxy-, amino-, and dipeptidases) that split the peptide linkages which join terminal amino acid residues to the main chain, and thus produce amino acids. An analogy exists between proteolytic enzymes and α- and β-amylase.

A large number of commercial preparations of plant, animal, and microbial origin, with ability of hydrolyzing the —CO—NH— linkages in proteins, polypeptides, peptides, and other substances, is offered on the market. Collectively called proteases, proteinases, or proteolytic enzymes, they may range from very specific to fairly general in their actions, and are prominent in digesting proteins and proteinaceous substances as substrate. Consequently, they may be very specific or quite general in their application. The commercial products include a number of specific enzymes such as *pepsin, rennin, trypsin, chymotrypsins, pankrin, enterokinase, papain, chymopapain, ficin, bromelin, B. subtilis proteinase, insulinase, Aspergillus proteinase, carboxypeptidase, protaminase, asparaginase, penicillin amidase* (molds), *penicillinase* (bacteria), etc (46,50,68,70,105,145).

The individual enzymes vary widely in their specific activities, in their optimum pH and pH range, and in heat sensitivity.

The recommended optimum for both temperature and pH for proteases covers a wide range, depending on the origin of the enzyme and on the purpose of its use, as recorded in Table 3.

The commerical preparations, which usually contain a number of individual proteolytic enzymes, are recommended for specific purposes on the basis of practical experiments carried out by the producers, who select the proper type (origin) of enzyme for every purpose, and set the activity to fit best the users need. The practical utilizations include cheese making (150,158), meat tenderizing (115,149,160), bread baking (155), haze elimination from beer (and other beverages), preparation of digestive aids, cleaning of food spots from garments, preparation of pharmaceuticals, surgical applications in wound cleaning, etc (71,77,105,107,118).

Digestive Aids. Enzyme preparations made from defatted pork pancreas are used in the preparation of all-purpose digestive aids. Preparations are available, of which 1 g is able to digest, within 1 hr, 25 g of proteins and 100 g of starch, in addition to considerable amounts of fat. Concentrates with up to four times this activity are also available. A typical food intake per meal may contain 35 g proteins and 100 g starch per person. For such preparations the pH optimum is 7–8 and the optimum temperature is 37°C.

Pepsin-type proteolytic enzyme preparations are made from the glandular parts of the stomach of hogs. A 1-g preparation will digest 34 g of proteins (coagulated egg albumen, dry basis) in 1 hr at a pH of 1.5–3 and at 37°C. Concentrates are made with five times higher activity. The milk-curdling activity of such preparations increases their potential use as digestive aids for infants and small children. Because of the very low pH optimum, they can be used without coatings.

Chillproofing of Beers (159).   The highly valued brilliant clarity of beers is obscured by a haze of fine protein precipitate when the beer is chilled.   A number of industrial enzyme preparations, containing proteases, will dissolve the proteins and restore the brilliance of the beer.

LIPASES

Lipases or lypolytic enzymes catalyze the hydrolysis of fats and fatty acid esters according to the following schemes:

$$\text{fat} \xrightarrow[\text{H}_2\text{O}]{\text{lipase}} \text{mono- and diglycerides} \xrightarrow[\text{H}_2\text{O}]{\text{lipase}} \text{glycerol} + \text{fatty acids}$$

$$\text{fatty acid esters} \xrightarrow[\text{H}_2\text{O}]{\text{lipase}} \text{alcohol} + \text{fatty acid}$$

Commercial lipase preparations derive from animal sources (pancreas of healthy hogs), and from fungi.   Depending on the origin, the pH optimum and the temperature of thermal inactivation may differ.

The optimum temperature for lipase of fungal origin is 40–50°C.   At 75°C and at the optimum pH lipase is inactivated in 15 min.   Depending on the substrate, the pH varies from 5–7.   The working range is as wide as 2–9.

Lipase from pancreas has an optimum pH of 7–8.8, and the enzyme is inactivated at a pH of 3 or below or of 10 or above; the temperature optimum is 37°C.   The enzyme will be denatured at 65°C.   It is recommended to store lipase preparations at 30°C or below.

Lipase preparations are used in chocolate hydrolysis, in cheese production, in feed supplementation for mink, poultry, and swine feeds, in laundering cotton and linen, in digestive aids, and in septic tank and grease-trap digestion (87,89,93).   To impart special flavors to cheese, lipase preparations are prepared from kid, goat, and lamb glands, and from oral glands of calves.   Lipase preparations containing some amylases and proteases are also used as cleaning agents to remove food spots from garments.   Due to its strong emulsifying power under certain conditions, lipase is frequently incorporated in mixtures used for cleaning drains.   In combination with protease and amylase, lipase preparations are offered for the production of human digestive aids.   For example, one commercial product is standardized to digest in one hour 150 g of casein, 600 g of potato starch, and 68 g of olive oil, at a pH of 7.0 and at a temperature of 37°C.   The same conditions prevail in the upper intestine during digestion.

GLUCOSE OXIDASE

Glucose oxidase or β-D-glucopyranose acrodehydrogenase, a typical aerobic dehydrogenase enzyme produced by *Aspergillus niger*, *A. oryzae*, and *Penicillium notatum*, oxidizes glucose to gluconic acid in the presence of molecular oxygen.   A quantitative amount of hydrogen peroxide is formed during this process.   The prostatic group of the enzyme is "alloxazine-adenine dinucleotide," or "flavin-adenine dinucleotide" (FAD).   It is a dehydrogenase (uses oxygen as hydrogen acceptor) rather than an oxidase enzyme.

First marketed as a commercial enzyme in 1952, glucose oxidase was obtained from the cells of *Aspergillus niger* cultivated in submerged culture.

The reaction the enzyme catalyzes is as follows:

$$\text{glucose} + \text{O}_2 + \text{H}_2\text{O} \xrightarrow{\text{glucose oxidase}} \text{gluconic acid} + \text{H}_2\text{O}_2$$

The hydrogen peroxide formed is decomposed by the enzyme catalase, which is either produced by the same organism, or is added to the commercial glucose-oxidase preparation.

$$2\ H_2O_2 \xrightarrow{\text{catalase}} 2\ H_2O + O_2$$

The enzyme is near specific for glucose; it oxidizes glucose 400 times faster than other sugars. It has an antibacterial property which is attributed to the H_2O_2 formation. In the presence of catalase, which decomposes the H_2O_2, there is no antibacterial action.

At room temperature the optimum pH is 5.5, with an active range of pH 3–8.5. Ninety percent of the enzyme is destroyed within 2 min at 80°C, within 23 min at 70°C, and in 100 min at 65°C.

The practical application of glucose-oxidase preparations is based on the removal of oxygen from beverages or from the air space in a closed food container, or on the removal of glucose from a food ingredient or food product.

The presence of oxygen may change the flavor and/or color of a product and may hasten the corrosion of cans containing carbonated beverages, etc. Presence of glucose may cause darkening in some foods when drying. Glucose oxidase is used when the removal of either oxygen or glucose is desirable. Examples of uses are as follows:

1. In the production of dried egg powder the small amount of glucose will react with the egg proteins causing the "maillard darkening" of the product, and some loss in flavor. Oxidation of the glucose with glucose oxidase before drying of the egg, will preserve the flavor and will prevent darkening of the product. Glucose oxidase together with some hydrogen peroxide and catalase is added to the egg that has been liquefied by proteolytic enzymes. Oxygen is supplied to the reaction as liberated from H_2O_2 by the catalase. The use of 50 g glucose oxidase preparation per 100 lb of egg white, (or 150 g per 1000 lb whole eggs) at 32°C, with the frequent addition of calculated amounts of 35% H_2O_2 and catalase (57,64), is recommended.

2. Glucose oxidase with low cellulase content, added to orange soft drinks, preserves the freshness of flavor and prevents the change of color and flavor. The oxygen is removed by the enzyme from the head space, as well as from the liquid dissolved in bottled drinks. Five units of enzyme per 12-oz bottle is added.

3. Added to canned beverages, glucose-oxidase preparations impede fading of sensitive colors, and retard iron pickup (65,123).

4. Oxidative deterioration of dry, dehydrated foods such as milk powder, cake mixes, etc is prevented, and the shelf life of the products is extended by the use of enzyme–glucose packets. The enzyme, glucose, buffer filler, and liquid are placed in a water-impermeable but oxygen-permeable polyethylene packet and sealed hermetically in the container with the dried food product. The packet will rapidly use up the oxygen from the atmosphere in the sealed container, and thus will prevent the oxidation of the fatty constituents of the dried food product (67).

5. Rancidity of salad dressings and mayonnaise is well prevented by the application of glucose-oxidase preparations.

6. Wrappers for cheese are coated on the inside with glucose oxidase and glucose to prevent growth of aerobic organisms on the surface of the cheese.

7. Glucose oxidase is used as an analytical tool in clinical diagnosis in determining the sugar content in blood and in urine (61,87,106).

PECTIC ENZYMES

Pectic enzymes are the enzymes which take part in the hydrolytic degradation of pectic substances.

Pectic substances universally present in plant tissues, principally in fruits, are carbohydrate derivatives. The term includes a multitude of compounds whose main characteristic is that they contain polygalacturonic acids and their derivatives as the main constituent. Galacturonic acid is formed by the oxidation of the sixth carbon of galactose; dehydration of many galacturonic acid molecules leads to the formation of polygalacturonic acid. The principal structure of pectic substances is composed of straight chains of anhydrogalacturonic acid residues, predominantly connected by $(1 \rightarrow 4)$-glycosidic linkages. Most of the carboxylic groups are esterified, mainly with methyl alcohol. The chains vary in size, and the molecular weight of purified pectins may range from 30,000 to 300,000, depending on the source and the method of purification. Crude pectin preparations include a number of related compounds, with properties similar to pectins. On hydrolysis arabinose, sorbose, rhamnose, and acetyl groups are frequently found besides galactose.

Because of the more than 100 terms used to name the various substances belonging to the group collectively called pectins, a "Revised Nomenclature of the Pectic Substances" was prepared and reported by Kertesz et al. in 1943. The nomenclature was adopted as official by the American Chemical Society in April 1944. Following are definitions of the most important terms defining the major groups of substances of this territory (25,101):

"*Pectic substances* is a group designation for those complex, colloidal carbohydrate derivatives which occur in, or are prepared from plants and contain a large proportion of anhydrogalacturonic acid units which are thought to exist in a chainlike combination. The carboxyl groups of polygalacturonic acids may be partly esterified by methyl groups, and partly or completely neutralized by one or more bases. . . .

"This expression is again advocated for a general designation of substances of this type in preference to the term 'pectin.' The word 'colloidal' has been added, implying that pectic substances decomposed or degenerated to the extent that they do not possess colloidal properties are outside of the scope of this definition. The expression 'they contain a large proportion of anhydrogalacturonic acid units' makes allowance for the presence of various hemicelluloses as galactans or arabans, which usually accompany the pectic substances. These materials, however, are not regarded as pectic substances. The term 'anhydrogalacturonic acid units' is used in preference to the 'galacturonic acid' used previously. The expression 'which are thought to exist in a chainlike combination' is emphasizing the present conception of the linear character of polygalacturonic acid. . . .

"The term *protopectin* is applied to the water-insoluble parent pectic substance which occurs in plants and which, upon restricted hydrolysis, yields pectinic acids. . . .

"The term *pectinic acids* is used for colloidal polygalacturonic acids containing more than a negligible proportion of methyl ester groups. Pectinic acids, under suitable conditions, are capable of forming gels with sugar and acid or, if suitably low in methoxyl content, with certain metallic ions. The salts of pectinic acids are either normal or acid pectinates. . . .

"The general term *pectin* (or pectins) designates those water-soluble pectinic acids of varying methyl ester content and degree of neutralization which are capable of forming gels with sugar and acid under suitable conditions. . . .

"The term *pectic acid* is applied to pectic substances mostly composed of colloidal polygalacturonic acids and essentially free from methyl ester groups. The salts of pectic acids are either normal or acid pectates."

The characteristic by which pectins and pectic substances became important is that, in a strict sense, they are not soluble in water but, by their highly hydrophilic colloidal nature, they disperse in water, readily forming a very viscous liquid. Also, they form a semi-solid "jelly" with sugars and acids, and a semi-solid "gel" with small amounts of bivalent ions.

The high viscosity of the fruit juices, is due to the presence of pectic substances, which prevent the quick sedimentation of the dispersed particles. This is highly desirable in some instances, like in apricot, tomato, and orange juices, but is objectionable in many instances like in apple juice, grape juice, and others.

Two major and two less important enzymes take part in the hydrolysis of pectic substances. The principal enzymes are pectin methylesterase and pectin polygalacturonase. The secondary enzymes are depolymerase and protopectinase (25,49).

Pectin methylesterase (PME), or *pectin esterase* (PE), or *pectase* (62,90), catalyzes the hydrolysis of the methyl ester groups in pectic substances with the formation of methyl alcohol and polygalacturonic acid. The enzyme is common in roots, stems, leaves, and fruits of many plants, and is produced by many microorganisms. The pH optimum is 4.5–5.5. The enzyme is sensitive below pH 3 and above pH 8. The temperature optimum is 55°C. Above 60°C the enzyme is gradually inactivated and is destroyed at 80°C. Variations exist between preparations, according to their origin.

Polygalacturonase (PG), or *pectinase*, or *pectolase*, (62,90,112,132) degrades pectic or pectinic acids by hydrolysis of the $(1 \rightarrow 4)$-glycosidic linkage of polygalacturonic acid and its derivatives, into polygalacturonic acids of smaller molecular weight, and eventually into galacturonic acid. By this, it converts the pectic substances into water-soluble compounds and reduces the viscosity of the solutions.

The optimum pH for the enzyme of fungal origin is around 3.5–4, with some variation depending on the substrate used; for polygalacturonase of bacterial origin the optimum pH is around 7–8. The temperature optimum is around 50°C. While the dry product is fairly stable up to 80°C, the aqueous solution loses activity rapidly at a temperature of 55°C. The enzyme is common in higher plants and is produced by many microorganisms.

Depolymerase, the enzyme which hydrolyzes polygalacturonic acid is different from pectin polygalacturonase in two main points. It has a very sharp pH optimum at 4.5, activated by sodium chloride; and it is almost inactive on pectinic acids, but very active on pectic acids. For its action it requires the presence of the deesterifying enzyme PE.

Protopectinase (formerly *pectosinase*) dissolves by hydrolysis the protopectin, the substance which holds the joining cells together. The process is usually called maceration. Many researchers believe that protopectinase and pectin polygalacturonase are the same enzyme.

Fruits usually contain pectin esterase, and fungi produce predominantly polygalacturonase. Industrial preparations may contain a mixture of the two enzymes or may be predominant in one type of enzyme, depending on the purpose for which they are to be used.

Small amounts of NaCl and $CaCl_2$ activate fungal pectinase at the optimum pH of 5.5. The presence of amounts up to $0.2M$ NaCl or $0.02M$ $CaCl_2$, increase the activity; amounts of NaCl higher than $0.2M$ will slowly, and amounts of $CaCl_2$ higher than $0.02M$ will rapidly decrease the activity.

Increase of temperature increases the reaction rate during the first 40% of the hydrolysis. Thermal inactivation begins at 50°C (pH 3.5) and is complete at 60°C in 30-min reaction time. A 50% inactivation is reached at 58.5°C. Tomato pectase is more sensitive than tomato pectinase. The activity of a filtered fungal-pectase solution did not change at 23°C during two weeks at pH 6.25.

A fungal pectase, essentially free from pectinase, used in the preparation of fruit gels is available commercially.

Pectic enzyme preparations may contain depolymerase, protopectinase, and additional enzymes, such as cellulase, pentosanase, arabinase, xylanase, proteases, and gumase.

The principal fields for the use of pectic enzymes are: (1) production of fruit juices and fruit-juice products; (2) production of wines; (3) fermentation of coffee and cocoa beans; (4) rehydration of dehydrated foods; (5) production of galacturonic acid and low-methoxyl pectin; and (6) recovery and stabilization of citrus oil.

Production of Fruit Juice and Fruit-Juice Products (100,102,113,131). Freshly pressed fruit juices contain colloidal material that keeps dispersed solids in suspension; most of this colloidal material is pectin. In citrus and tomato juices, where the high viscosity is a required advantage, the pectic enzymes of the juice are destroyed by pasteurization, in order to maintain the high viscosity. In other fruit juices, such as apple and grape juices, a clear flowing liquid is required, where the suspended material settles quickly. For such juices, a balanced mixture of the pectic enzymes is added. The enzyme mixture is usually added to the fruit during or after crushing; this will also increase the yield of the juice.

If the hydrolysis of the pectins goes too far, the viscosity drops and many solids may precipitate and settle with the original sediment leaving the juice too flat and watery.

For making low-sugar juices or jellies for diabetics, the pectin is hydrolyzed only by pectin esterase. The resultant low-ester pectin gels in the presence of Ca ions. In place of sugars, sorbitol is added as preservative and non-assimilable sugar substitute.

One of the major fields for the use of pectic enzymes is the preparation of brilliant clear apple cider, and other fruit juices. By adding pectic-enzyme preparations to the crushed fruit, a higher yield of the juice is obtained; by reducing the viscosity of the juice, a rapid filtration can be achieved with the production of a crystal clear brilliant juice. The pasteurized product is free from the boiled taste characteristic to the untreated pasteurized juices; and the pasteurized juice can be marketed the year round. The vinegar and the jelly produced from pectic-enzyme-treated juice are superior in brilliance, color, and aroma.

Jelly manufacturers destroy the native pectic substances in order to obtain a clear juice, and make the jelly by the addition of commercial pectins, acids, and sugar. In the production of jellies, polygalacturonic acid and Ca ions are added to the clarified juice. High concentrates can be made from prune juices with reduced viscosity.

Production of Wine. In making wine (5,80,81,103,128,134,161,163) the pectic-enzyme preparations present a number of processing advantages at different stages of the operations. When the enzyme is added to the crushed grapes, it will increase the volume of the free-flowing juice, will reduce the pressing time, and will increase the final yield of the juice; the addition of the enzymes will increase the extraction of color when the grapes are heat-extracted or fermented on the skins. Pectic enzymes may be added to the must before fermentation, to settle much of the suspended particles including part of the unwanted microorganisms, or the enzyme preparation may be added during fermentation. In either case the yeast sediment (lee) will be firmer, more compact (less voluminous) at the time of the first filling, and the wine will be clearer. Finally, the enzyme may be added to the fermented wine to increase the filtration rate and to produce a clearer wine. A good clarification eliminates the floating microorganisms and much of the precipitated proteins. The reduction of protein will improve the stability of the wine.

The processing phase at which the enzyme should be added depends on the quality of the grapes used and on many other local conditions. The winemaker can decide which treatment will solve his problem best. He must be sure that the taste of his product will not be changed for sake of clarity. Depending on the brand of enzyme preparation, the recommended quantities may vary. The commonly used ratios are 0.1–0.2 lb enzyme preparation per ton of grapes or 0.4–0.9 lb per thousand gallons of must or wine.

It is claimed that enzyme treatment does not change the characteristic bouquet of wines, but helps to develop a more mature flavor in a shorter time, and that the flavor of treated wines being superior to the flavor of untreated wines. Port wines made from enzyme-treated must fermented on skins contain a greater amount of color. It is further claimed that fruit wines made of enzyme-treated blackberries, currants, loganberries, and other berries, peaches, apples, and other fruits are superior to wines made of untreated fruit juices.

Pectic enzyme preparations are active at temperatures ranging from 32 to 150°F. The enzyme is destroyed in 40 min at 160°F, in 5 min at 180°F, and in 2 sec at 210°F.

The use of pectic enzymes in wine making is justified by the following advantages: (1) The yield of juice per ton of grapes is increased; (2) the rate of pressing the crushed grapes is faster; (3) the sediment of first racking is more compact, and better wine yield per unit of juice is obtained; (4) less bentonite is required to the wine; (5) color and heat extraction from crushed grapes at 140° F is highly improved; (6) ageing of wine is much faster; (7) color of the wine is superior; and (8) wine filtration is easier (40).

An added effect, although a disadvantage, is the increase of the methanol content. The methanol content of wines made of enzyme-treated juices is higher than of wines made from untreated juices; however, it is still well below the permissible level. For instance, an untreated red wine contained 0.019%, and an enzyme-treated wine contained 0.023% methanol.

MISCELLANEOUS ENZYMES

There are several enzymes available in the form of commercial enzyme preparations, which conveniently form a separate group, although some of them may fit into the previously discussed groups. They are lysozyme, hyaluronidase, catalase, anthocyanase, naringinase, and penicillinase.

Lysozyme, a mucopolysaccharidase, is a globulin protein, consisting of a single polypeptide chain of 129 amino acid residues crosslinked by four or five disulfate bridges. The enzyme is stable between pH 2.8 and 11.8, and is most soluble at pH

4.5. With its low molecular weight, 14,400, it diffuses through a cellophane membrane, but is retained on colloidal membranes.

The enzyme, found in egg whites, animal bodies, and plant tissues, is present in high concentration in tear fluid, mucus, heart, spleen, and liver. Besides its ability to dissolve bacterial cells, it is active in precipitating insulin, acting on nucleic acids, mucus, etc. Trypsin, chymotrypsin, and papain have no effect on lysozyme activity.

The enzyme produced from special animal tissues, is commercially available in the form of the chloride salt for greater solubility; it is principally applied in scientific research and clinical practice. It is being used, or suggested to be used in the treatment of cancer, virus diseases, eye infections, blood diseases, infectious post-operative complications, hemorrhagic conditions, varicose ulcers, multiple sclerosis, etc (74,83, 88,99,125,126,136,152).

It is recommended to protect the preparation from excessive moisture and from heat of above 25°C.

Hyaluronidase, a transglucosidase, which also hydrolyzes the mucopolysaccharide, hyaluronic acid, is present in snake venom, leaches, in some pathogenic bacteria, and in the testicles of mammals. Commercial hyaluronidase preparations are made from beef testicles. Hyaluronic acid in intestinal tissues, acts as a barrier to the diffusion of foreign substances. Hyaluronidase reduces the viscosity of hyaluronic acid, and thus facilitates the diffusion and absorption of subcutaneous injections. The optimum pH is 5.3, and the optimum temperature is 37°C. The enzyme is destroyed at a pH below 3.3 and above 7.0 and also at a temperature of 60°C.

Hyaluronidase is used together with local anesthetic agents in surgery and dentistry, in insulin-shock therapy, and with injections of antibiotics, adrenaline, and heparin (75,92,94,98,111,119,120,137,140,141,147,153).

Catalase, the enzyme which catalyzes the decomposition of H_2O_2 to water and oxygen, is a conjugated protein, found in most living cells. It has been prepared in crystalline form. Catalase is active in the pH range of 4–8.6 with an optimum at 7. The optimum temperature range is 10–40°C. The enzyme is destroyed at 65°C.

Commercially produced from the livers of slaughtered animals, catalase is marketed in dry form (1200 Keil units/g) and in sterile-filtered liquid form (100 Keil units/ml).

Besides its use in conjunction with glucose oxidase and other applications, it is used in the cold sterilization of milk. By the flash method, milk is sterilized by the addition of 0.02% H_2O_2 (229 ml of 37% H_2O_2) per 1000 lb milk, and heating by HTST (high-temperature short-time) plate pasteurizer to 120–130°F for 25–30 sec (63,69, 142–144).

Thirty minutes after its addition to the milk, the hydrogen peroxide is decomposed by the addition of catalase. The use of 5 ml liquid catalase preparation per pound of 35% H_2O_2 is recommended. The complete decomposition of the H_2O_2 is determined by suitable tests, before the milk is used for making washed curd, swiss, cheddar, colby, granular, and other cheeses.

Anthocyanase, an enzyme of fungal origin, is capable of destroying (decolorizing) the pigment that gives the color to berries like blackberries and red grapes. The anthocyan pigment is present in blackberries in such an excess that, jams and jellies made from it are dark to the extent of being unattractive. Also, the excess pigment in blackberry wines frequently precipitates on the neck and bottom of the bottles, making the otherwise good product unsalable. The excess of anthocyanin may be removed and attractive jellies, jams, and wine may be produced by treating the blackberries with anthocyanase (0.1 g enzyme preparation per 100 g juice for 8 hr or less at 80°F).

In order to produce white wines or light-red wines from red grapes, the red color may be partially or completely removed by this enzyme (97,162).

Naringinase hydrolyzes naringin, a glucoside, in two steps: first it splits off rhamnose, resulting in another glucoside prunin, then it splits off glucose resulting in naringenin.

Naringin, the 7-rhamnosido-β-glucoside of 4′,5,7-trihydroxyflavanone ($C_{27}H_{32}O_{14} \cdot 2H_2O$), present mainly in the albedo and membranous tissues of grapefruit, is responsible for the bitter taste of grapefruit juice. Its presence in 0.07% quantities is objectionable, while 0.05% is acceptable. The hydrolytic products, prunin and naringenin, are not bitter.

A naringinase preparation in 0.01% quantities will debitter grapefruit pulp and juice to acceptable levels in 1–4 hr at 50°C and at a pH of 3.1 (91,151).

Naringinase, present in several plants, is produced commercially by microbial action. Its pH optimum is 3.5–5.0, and the temperature range is 25–50°C.

ENZYMES FOR MEDICINAL USE

Since the human body produces and uses enzymes for every activity, it is logical that enzyme preparations lend themselves readily to uses where the body's enzyme supply is not sufficient to meet the specific need. Enzymes can be administered either orally, or topically, or in the form of injections. Enzymes also proved to be useful tools in medical diagnostic tests. Medicinal enzymes are used in the following fields:

1. Digestive aids aim to supplement the digestive enzymes the body is deficient in; lack of these enzymes can cause gastrointestinal disturbances such as indigestion, upset stomach, hyperacidity, gas, cramps, etc.

The principal enzymes, involved singly or formulated jointly, are amylases, proteases, lipases, and cellulases. The first three may originate from animal, plant, and fungal sources; cellulase is of fungal origin. Fungal amylase, lipases, and cellulase (to digest cabbage and salads) derive from *Aspergillus* and *Penicillium;* bacterial amylase and protease are produced by *Bacillus subtilis;* animal diastase and pancreatin, containing trypsin and pancreatic lipase, are made of hog pancreas; the powerful proteases bromelin, ficin, and papain, are made of plants.

2. Properly selected and administered, proteolytic enzymes selectively digest dead skin, necrotic tissues, and debris on wounds, without harming healthy tissues or active blood vessels which feed the wound. They are also useful in treating burns.

3. A group of enzymes used as anti-inflammatory agents include streptokinase and streptodornase (produced by *Streptococcus*), papain, bacterial amylases, and proteases.

4. Streptokinase and associated enzymes are used to dissolve blood clots (thrombosis) and to reduce the clot-forming tendency of blood.

5. Purulent exudates in wounds contain much DNA and are highly viscous. Streptodornase reduces the viscosity effectively by depolymerizing DNA, and thus facilitates the cleaning of wounds.

6. Hyaluronidase accelerates the diffusion and action of locally administered anesthetics used by dentists and surgeons in minor surgery, by partial hydrolysis of hyaluronic tissues.

7. Proteolytic enzymes with mucolytic properties, reduce the viscosity of secretions in various mucous membranes, and thus facilitate the elimination of such excretions.

8. Penicillin may cause acute reactions, usually skin rashes, in individuals allergic to this antibiotic. The enzyme penicillinase administered to the patient will destroy the penicillin in his body, and will remove the cause of the allergy.

9. Glucose oxidase is extensively used in medical diagnostics for determining the sugar content of blood and urine; urease is used to determine the content of urea in urine specimens.

10. Lysozyme preparations are recommended for the treatment of nervous ulcers, multiple sclerosis, leg ulcers, measles, varicose ulcers, nose, throat, and blood diseases, eye infections, hemorrhagic conditions, post-operative conditions, virus infections, skin diseases, and for many other purposes. Lysozyme chloride is well tolerated by the body. Quantities of 5–10 mg per kg weight caused no ill effects in rats. The enzyme preparation may be administered orally, topically, or by injection.

Production of Industrial Enzymes

The production of industrial enzymes may involve the following steps:

1. Selection of cells actually or potentially rich in the desired enzyme or enzymes.

2. Enrichment of the desired enzyme or enzymes in a carefully selected group of cells.

3. Extraction of the enzymes from the cells.

4. Concentration of the enzyme by elimination of part or all the inert substances contained in the extract (purification).

5. Stabilization of the enzymes: prevention of loss of potency.

6. Standardization of the enzyme activity in the commercial product (formulation).

In actual production the steps may or may not follow the above order; also, one or more steps may be omitted (18,31–33,37,38,42,43,45,47–49,51,52).

SELECTION OF CELLS RICH OR POTENTIALLY RICH IN THE DESIRED ENZYMES (10)

All forms of life live by enzymes and produce enzymes. Cells of animal and plant tissues and cells of microorganisms have been used as sources of active materials, to bring forth desired changes in substrates, since the beginning of time. The backbone of industrial enzyme production of present times is still based on the same cell types. During the last eighty years the field of enzyme utilization and of enzyme-rich sources has broadened, and is steadily increasing every year.

In the selection of the enzyme source there are two major governing factors: supply and cost; in reality they are in equilibrium.

Cells of Animal Origin. Cells of animal sources are obtained exclusively from healthy animals, killed for food.

In the animal body, the highest accumulation of enzymes is in the glands. Pancreas, spleen, stomach, and stomach mucus are rich in several important enzymes. For particular enzymes such as rennin, which is in great abundance in the stomach of sucklings, the age of the animal is essential. The principal source of rennin is the stomach mucus of young calves and lambs.

Since animals are raised and slaughtered for nutritional purposes, animal enzymes, or at least the selected tissues, the glands, are by-products of the slaughter houses. For this reason, the supply depends entirely on the activity of the slaughter houses. The enzyme-rich tissues are quickly removed and the deterioration of the enzyme activity is usually prevented by immediate drying or freezing of the glands used for further processing (23).

Cells of Plant Origin. If the requirement is estimated well ahead of time, plants to be used as sources of enzymes may be grown in any desired quantity. With the exception of a few special cases, however, the same plant is generally utilized for other purposes, and the supply as enzyme source becomes dependent on the primary purpose.

Three prominent intracellular proteolytic enzymes, bromelin, papain, and ficin are made of plant sources.

Bromelin (bromelain) is well distributed all over in the pineapple plant. Since the fruit is the more valuable part of the plant, the enzyme is produced from the parts of the plant unusable for food, and the enzyme is a by-product. The waste parts, leaves, core, and the skin of the fruit are chopped, the juice is pressed out and the enzyme is recovered from the juice.

Papain (50), the potent protease, is contained in the juice of the plant *Carica papaya* L., a very fast-growing, short-lived, fruit-bearing plant belonging to a family of the tropical palms. The tree that may grow to twenty-five feet, contains under the epidermis of the trunk, in the leaves, and in the fruit large latex vessels containing the enzyme. The fruit grows in clusters below the crown of the tree. For commercial enzyme production the full grown but still green, unripe fruits are used while on the tree. Shallow longitudinal scratches are made on the skin of the melon like fruit in the early morning. The drippings are caught in containers and the incisions are repeated every 3–5 days. The clear juice turns into a milky latex in the air, and the coagulated latex stops the dripping. The latex is dried on trays in the sun or in air-circulated driers at 50–55°C to a moisture content of 5–8%. If not dried rapidly the juice may become fermented. The dried latex is scraped also from the skin of the fruit. The ripe fruit will yield little or no latex.

The fruit with the scratched skin cannot be sold as fresh fruit, but can be used in preserves, or for making papaya juice. Extraction of enzyme from the leaves or bark of the papaya plant is not practical; the roots contain no enzyme. The yield of coagulated latex is about 0.1% of the weight of the fresh fruit. One tree may yield about one pound of dried latex per year. The dried latex is sold as crude papain, from which concentrates, standardized products, and formula enzyme preparations are made.

Ficin (46), also a plant protease, present in figs, is obtained by extraction from the fruit of a tropical fig tree.

The production of *malt* is the oldest example for both: selection of cells as potential enzyme source, and enrichment of their enzyme content. Seeds in germination digest their reserve substrates by the enzymes produced in great abundance during germination. Lipases are formed in oily seeds, amylases in starchy seeds, and proteases, lipases, and amylases in seeds such as soybeans which contain all three reserve substances.

Barley and its cells are used today as the most convenient potential source of enzymes that convert starch to sugar. One pound of malt may convert, under proper conditions, the starch content of 30 lb of unmalted barley. Although selected for this purpose many thousands of years ago, barley is still under close investigation. By hybridization and special selection, new varieties are being produced even in recent years for making malts with improved qualities.

At the present time about four principal varieties of barley are used in the U.S. for making malt. Their order of preference is as follows: Trophy, Larker, Kindred, and Parkland. Trophy and Larker make up 80% of the total barley used; Kindred and Parkland about 12% while the miscellaneous types make up the remaining 8%. The selection of the types is based on availability, price, processing qualities, yield, etc. Processing qualities are determined by malting tests performed on laboratory and pilot-plant scale.

Before the malting, the manufacturers separate the smaller barley kernels (5–10% of the total) from the larger ones. The small kernels, which are lower in starch and higher in protein content, yield more amylase than the starch-rich grains. The small kernels are used in the production of distillers' malt, the large ones are used for brewers' malt.

Microbial Cells as Source of Commercial Enzymes. Cells of microorganisms, available in an unlimited supply, also offer the greatest variety of enzymes, frequently in high concentrations. Within a few days from starting out with one pound of cell material, billions of tons may be produced on industrial scale, if needed. Certain species produce one or more enzymes in a far greater abundance then possibly needed by the organisms.

The enzyme activity of many organisms is well described in the literature, frequently in quantitative terms. For the production of a particular enzyme, the manufacturer will select a species described in the literature. But he will also screen all other microorganisms which he can think of, and will test their ability to produce the desired enzyme. The screening on laboratory scale may involve many hundreds of different strains of a few scores of species.

Once the most outstanding strain from production point of view has been selected (highest enzyme activity, good cell yield, inexpensive nutrient requirement, easy propagation conditions, not sensitive to infection, etc), and its characteristics well established, the manufacturer will still look for further improvements in the selection of proper cells. Usually by artificial mutation and by hybridization (analogous to cereals), if the organism is capable of sexual reproduction, many new strains are produced and screened for their enzyme-producing ability. It is not unusual that one of the newly produced strains will exhibit an ability to produce twice or several times the amount of enzyme per cell weight, as did the parent culture.

Smiley et al. (146) reported in 1964 that a newly tested culture of NRRL No. 3112 of the *Aspergillus niger* series (but not an *A. niger* in strict sense), produced three to four times the amount of amyloglucosidase enzyme than did the culture of *A. niger* NRRL No. 337 under identical conditions. The amyloglucosidase yield obtained from the culture No. 337 was considered fairly typical until that date.

The master cultures, with their original characteristics well preserved by freeze-drying or other techniques, represent the cells selected for the actual production of the enzymes.

Regardless of the method by which it is done, the selection of new strains by screening procedures is the most rewarding work in microbial research.

For the production of industrial enzymes, cells (cultures) are selected from the groups of molds, bacteria, or yeasts. Among molds, strains of *Aspergillus niger* are selected for the production of amylases, amyloglucosidase, glucose oxidase, catalase; strains of *A. oryzae* (*A. flavus*) are selected for the production of proteases, amyloglucosidase, and other amylases. From bacteria, strains of *Bacillus subtilis* are selected for the production of proteases, heat-stable α-amylase, and penicillinase; strains of *Streptococcus haemolyticus* are selected to produce streptokinase, etc. Among yeasts, *Saccharmoyces cerevisiae* is the most potent and versatile enzyme producer. Besides the many commercial and household applications as fermenting agent, it is the source of invertase. *S. fragilis* produces lactase.

Microorganisms used in the production of industrial enzymes must have good biological stability. Most organisms used for this purpose are obligate aerobes. Some organisms, under different conditions, will produce enzymes in different proportions: *B. subtilis* is used under different conditions to produce primarily either amylolytic or proteolytic enzymes.

The following organisms are known to be used in making industrial enzymes:

amylases: *Aspergillus oryzae, A. flavus oryzae, A. niger, Penicillium roqueforti, Rhizopus* sp, *Bacillus subtilis, Clostridium acetobutylicum*
proteases: *B. subtilis, Pseudomonas putida, Clostridium* sp
invertase: *Saccharomyces carlsbergiensis, Aspergillus oryzae*
pectin esterase: species of *Aspergillus, Botrytis, Penicillium*
hemolytic enzymes: *Streptococcus haemolyticus*
penicillinase: *Bacillus cereus, B. subtilis*

The microorganism employed in the production of commercially available enzymes is, in many cases, common knowledge. The industry is rather reluctant to publicize the source of the newer enzymes and keeps confidential the identity of the organisms actually used for the production of newly developed enzymes.

In several reviews the microorganisms actually used for the production of industrial enzymes, or known for their ability to produce specific enzymes and being potential sources of future industrial utilization, are discussed in detail. Beckhorn, Labbee, and Underkofler (42), list the enzymes produced by three most prominent organisms, their utilization in various industries, the maximum level of the enzymes in food, and the year of common utilization of the enzyme preparations as follows:

Bacillus subtilis, used since 1929, produces carbohydrases used by at least three industries, and proteases used by at least four industries.

Aspergillus oryzae is used in the production of carbohydrases by at least six industries, and in the production of proteases in at least one industry.

Aspergillus niger is used on industrial scale in the production of carbohydrases, cellulases, glucose oxidase, pectic enzymes, and lipase.

Davies (43), in his extensive review on microbial extracellular enzymes, presents a very comprehensive chart listing the names of the organisms, the enzymes they produce, the specific properties of the enzymes, the substrates, the enzyme activators, the purity of the enzyme preparations, and the references of his data. Some of these organisms are the source of the presently marketed industrial enzymes; many of them are potential sources of future products. Table 5 presents a highly simplified and abbreviated version of the Davies list.

CONTROLLED ENRICHMENT OF THE DESIRED ENZYMES IN CAREFULLY SELECTED CELLS

The classical example for enzyme enrichment in cells is the preparation of brewers' and distillers' malt, the principal source of amylolytic enzymes. These enzymes convert the starch content of grains into sugars that are fermentable by yeasts on industrial scale. Although it contains some β-amylase, for practical purposes, barley is free of enzymes. The enrichment is a controlled germinating process, and it includes the following phases: (1) steeping of the barley; (2) aeration and agitation of the steeped grains under controlled temperature and humidity conditions; the enrichment, the formation of the enzyme, takes place during this step; and (3) preservation of the enzymes through reduction of the excess humidity by drying the germinated barley grains. Malting simulates the natural process of seed germination under the optimum conditions for formation of the enzymes in the tissues of barley.

The possibilities of enzyme enrichment in barley cells are not exhausted by the controlled germination process. If 1–3 mg gibberellic acid is added per kg of barley (1–3 ppm) during the early stages of germination, the formation of natural enzymes in the cells is highly increased, in addition to the increase of other biological activities. α- and β-amylase, protease, cellulase, catalase, and other enzymes are produced in much greater quantities than in the standard malting process. About 80% more amylase is formed in the cells of the gibberellin-treated barley grains than in the untreated grains. Gibberellic acid, a hormone present in plants, is produced on industrial scale by the use of several molds, principally *Gibberella fujikuroi*. Stimulation by gibberellic acid is not limited to the embryo alone. Due to the effect of gibberellins, enzymes are produced in the cells of endosperm, even if separated from the embryo (44).

Seeds other than barley, such as wheat and beans, are also enhanced in their enzyme production if treated with gibberellins during germination. This example opens the gate to unforeseen developments in the enzyme enrichment in potential cells.

Cells of microorganisms are not stimulated by gibberellins, but using specific substrates in their nutrient, the production of certain enzymes can be increased. Yeast cells treated with sucrose solution will be enriched in invertase, and when treated with lactose solution will be enriched in lactase. Similarly, starch in the nutrient will stimulate the production of amylase in *Aspergilli* and *B. subtilis*.

The greatest field of enzyme enrichment is in the production of microbial enzymes. Three distinct courses of the enrichment can be distinguished: (1) propagation of the microbial cells, where under identical conditions the amount of enzyme will increase in straight proportion with the mass of newly formed cells; (2) exposition of the mass of produced cells to specific media will increase, possibly double, the production of enzymes without any significant cell reproduction; and (3) the combination of the two former methods: namely, a process of limited cell reproduction in a special medium, formulated to stimulate enzyme production. In the first method the main purpose is a high yield in microbial cells from a given amount of raw material; the result is high cell yield with normal enzyme content. In the other two methods the purpose is to obtain a high enzyme activity per weight of cells, at the expense of moderate cell yield.

PROPAGATION OF MICROBIAL CELLS (26,31–33,37,38,45,47,52,70)

All propagation methods include four major steps: (1) maintenance of the master culture; (2) preparation of the inoculum; (3) final propagation; and (4) termination of the propagation and harvesting of the organisms.

Master Culture.   The purpose of maintaining the master culture is to keep the culture alive, ready for serving as a starter for the preparation of inoculum for an industrial batch.

The master culture (or cultures) is kept alive in form of a pure culture, in a way which prevents any possible change in its propagating and enzyme-producing ability. This is done either in lyophylized state, or as a soil culture, or as an agar culture under oil, or as an agar-slant culture kept in the refrigerator and transferred at regular intervals. The agar-slant culture or its subcultures are also called "working cultures," because they may be transferred at any time, at a minute's notice. The working culture is frequently inspected under the microscope, to detect any possible infection or morphological change. It is also customary to go back to a single cell or single spore culture at predetermined intervals. The purity, stability, and enzyme-producing activity of the working cultures are constantly checked on laboratory or small-pilot-plant scale. The same principles apply for mold, yeast, or bacterial cultures.

Preparation of Plant-Scale Inoculum.   The purpose of the plant-scale inoculum is to supply a sufficient amount of cells to serve as a starter for a final batch on production-scale propagation. The amount of the inoculum depends on the size of the propagation facilities for the final batch, and is usually expressed as the percent of the final batch. It may vary from 1/1000th to several 1/100th of the final batch, expressed either in number of cells (number of initial cells vs final cells), or in weight of cell mass, or just in volume of the batch. The amount of inoculum is selected by practical experience, so that it is not much more, or not much less, than is actually needed to give a speedy start, to insure culture purity, and to result in the best yield under the processing conditions.

The manufacturer aims to keep the amount of inoculum low. The production of inoculum per volume or weight unit, is usually more expensive than the production of the final batch, because it is handmade by highly paid competent microbiologists, and it is closely checked by a team of laboratory personnel. Also, the cost of nutrients and the equipment per unit are more costly for the inoculum than for the final batch. On the other hand, the inoculum must be large enough to prevent possible contamination or degeneration of the culture. The cost of an inoculum amounting to 1/1000 or less of the final batch is not too critical. Still, the success of the enzyme enrichment depends principally on the quality of the inoculum. The number of cells per volume and the vitality and stability of the cells is generally higher in inoculums than in the final batches. The yield of cells in the inoculum per unit of nutrient does not influence the final cost significantly. Therefore all cost, knowledge, effort, and supervision are condensed into its preparation.

Corresponding to the nature of the final batch and to the characteristics of the culture used, the inoculums are of two principal types. They may contain vegetative cells, or may contain principally spores: either sexual spores (*Bacillus subtilis*) or condidospores (*Aspergillus niger*, *Aspergillus flavus-oryzae*, and species of other molds). Also, they may be liquid or semi-solid cultures. In either case the inoculum must be a pure culture.

The inoculum might be prepared in liquid, or on semi-solid medium. The liquid inoculum usually used for bacteria and yeasts, is prepared from an agar slant in one, two, or possibly more steps, depending on the size needed. A test tube full of culture is usually seeded into 0.25–0.5 gal sterile medium, and the culture grown there in about a day is used as seed for the 5–20 gal culture of the next step. The culture medium for

Table 5. List of Enzymes and of Microorganisms Known to Produce Them

Enzyme	Produced by
α-amylase	*B. subtilis, B. mesentericus, B. amyloliquefaciens, B. coagulans, B. stearothermophilus, Thermophilic bacterium, Pseudomonas saccharophila[a], Streptococcus bovis[a], Streptococci* Group A, *Clostridium acetobutylicum[a], Aspergillus awamori, A. candidus* var. *amylolyticus, A. niger* (semi[a]), *A. oryzae[a], Rhizopus delemar,* and *Endomycopsis fibuliger*
α-glucosidase	*Clostridium acetobutylicum[a],* and *Aspergillus oryzae[a]*
glucoamylase	*Aspergillus niger* (semi[a]), *A. oryzae, Rhizopus delemar,* and *Endomycopsis fibuliger*
cyclohexaglucanase	*Aspergillus oryzae*
cycloheptaglucanase	*Aspergillus oryzae*
dextranase	*Bacteroides* spp, *Cellvibrio fulva, Lactobacillus bifidus[a], Aspergillus* sp, *Penicillium funiculosum[a], P. lilacinum[a], P. purpurogenum, P. verruculosum, Spicaria violacea,* and *Bacteroides* FA-1A
limit dextrinase	*Aspergillus oryzae* and *A. awamori* var. *fumeus*
cellulases	*Aspergillus niger, Myrothecium verrucaria[a] Stachybotrys atra[a], Trichoderma koningi[a], T. viride, Fusarium roseum[b], Poria vaillantii, Penicillium pusillum[a], Pestalotiopsis westerdijkii[a], Basidiomycete* QM 806[a], *Sporotrichium pruinosium[a], Streptomycete[a], Cellvibrio gilvus,* and *Irpex lacteus*
β-glucosidases active on cellobiose	*Aspergillus niger, Irpex lacteus, Myrothecium verrucaria[a],* and *Poria vaillantii*
β-glucosidases inactive on cellobiose	*Stachybotrys atra[b],* and *Myrothecium verrucaria*
β-1,4-glucan hydrolase	*Bacillus subtilis* and *B. subtilis[b]*
laminarinase	*Aspergillus niger, Rhizopus arrhizus[b], Basidiomycete* QM 806[b], *Sporotrichium purinosum[a], Myrothecium verucaria[a], Penicillium pusillum[b], Pestalotiopsis westerdijkii[b], Trichoderma viride[b],* and *Streptomyces* sp[b]
β-1,2-glucan hydrolase	*Penicillium funiculosum,* series[b], *Aspergillus fumigatus,* series[a], and *P. javanicum,* series[a] (some)
β-1,6-glucan hydrolase	present in 100 of 150 fungal cultures examined, especially *Penicillium brefeldianum*
inulase and levan polyase	*Pseudomonas* spp[a], *Bacillus* sp[a], *B. polymyxa[a], Arthrobacter* spp[a] *Azotobacter* sp[a], and *Penicillium funiculosum*
invertase	*Bacillus subtilis* var. *saccharolyticus nov.* var., *Alternaria tenuis, Aspergillus niger, A. sydowi, A. wentii, Cunninghamella echinulata, Penicillium achro-chloron, P. brefeldianum, P. melinii, P. nigricans, P. parvum, P. quadrilineatum, P. queenslandicum, P. verruculosum, Pestalotiopsis westerdijkii,* and *Candida utilis* B 1487 and B 1505
mannanase	*Bacterium* sp
galactomannanase	*Anaerobic rumen bacteria[a]* and *Ruminococcus* sp[a]
mannosidostreptomycinase	*Streptomyces griseus*
agarase	*Vibrio liquefaciens* and *Bacterium* sp[a]
carrageeninase	*Bacterium* sp[a]
β-1,4-xylanase and pentosanases	*Bacillus firmus, Bacillus* sp., *Aspergillus batatae, A. oryzae, A. niger* (E. 19), *Fusarium roseum, Pericularia oryzae[a],* and *Trichoderma koningi[b]*
β-1,3-xylanase	*Chaetomium globosum*
β-glucuronidase	*Escherichia coli,* some strains[a]
alginase	*Pseudomonas alginoliquefaciens[a]* and *Cloaca cloacae[b]*

Table 5 (*continued*)

Enzyme	Produced by
neuraminidase	*Clostridium perfringens*, Type A, *Cl. tertium* (Iseki)[a], *Spirillum cholerae* (*Vibrio comma*)[a]
sialic acid aldolase (*N*-acetylneuraminate lyase)	*Spirillum cholerae* (*Vibrio comma*)
β-thioglucosidase	*Aspergillus sydowi*[a] and *A. versicolor*[a]
chitinase	*Streptomyces griseus*[a], *Streptomyces A1*[a], and *Streptomyces* spp. (mostly[a])
chitobiase	*Streptomyces griseus*
enzymes hydrolyzing bacterial cell wall components	*Bacillus cereus*, *B. terminalis*, *B. polymyxa*, *B. subtilis* R[b], *Flavobacterium* sp., *Staphylococcus aureus* 524SC[b], *Streptomyces albus*, *Streptomyces albus* G, and *Streptomyces* L₃
hyaluronidase	*Bacillus subtilis*, *Clostridium perfringens*[a], *Streptococci*[a], all Group B and some of Groups A and C, and *Staphylococcus aureus*
chondroitinase	*Diphtheroid bacilli*
pectin esterase	*Bacillus polymyxa*, *Pseudomonas prunicola*[a], *Byssochlamys fulva*, *Fusarium oxysporum* var. *lycopersici*[a], and *Sclerotinia libertiana*
pectin transeliminase	*Bacillus polymyxa*[a], *Erwinia carotovora*, and *Aspergillus* sp
endopolymethylgalacturonase II	*Erwinia aroideae*[b], *Flavobacterium pectinovorum*[a]
endopolymethylgalacturonase I	*Aspergillus foetiuds*, *A. niger*, and *Clostridium felsineum* var. *sikokianum*[a]
exopolymethylgalacturonase	*Klebsiella aerogenes* and *Fusarium moniliforme*
endopolygalacturonase	*Clostridium felsineum* var. *sikokianum*[b], *Erwinia aroideae*, *E. atroseptica*, *E. carotovora*, and *Saccharomyces fragilis* 351[b], *Aspergillus niger* CH[b] and *A. niger* S3
exopolygalacturonase	*Aspergillus foetidus*, *A. niger* S3[a], and *Clostridium felsineum* var. *sikokianum*[b]
bacterial proteolytic enzymes	
a. not inhibited by chelating agents	*Bacillus subtilis* strains, *B. cereus* F9d, *Micrococcus freudenreichii*, *Proteus vulgaris*, and *Pseudomonas pseudomallei*
b. inhibited by chelating agents or activated by metal ions	*Bacillus amyloliquefaciens* (*B. subtilis*), *B. cereus*, *B. stearothermophilus*, *Bacterium* sp from *Limnoria*, *Clostridium botulinum*, Type B, *Cl. histolyticum*, *Pseudomonas myxogenes*, *Streptomyces griseus*, *Streptomyces proteolyticus*
c. collagenase	*Clostridium capitovale*, *Cl. histolyticum*[b], and *Cl. perfringens*, Types A, C, E and some D
d. keratinase	*Streptomyces fradiae*
e. metal-activated peptidases	*Bacillus licheniformis* and *Clostridium histolyticum*
f. no information on metal requirements or on effect of chelating agents	*Bacillus megaterium* 3E, *B. mycoides*, *B. mesentericus* (*B. subtilis*), *B. natto* (*B. subtilis*), *B. licheniformis*, *B. vulgatus*, *Clostridium acetobutylicum*, *Cl. histolyticum*, *Cl. parabotulinum*, *Cl. perfringens*, *Pseudomonas fluorescens*, *Ps. putrefaciens*, *Serratia marcescens*[a], and *Streptococci* Group A
g. elastase	Bacillus of *subtilis-mesentericus* group and *Flavobacterium elastolyticum*
h. streptokinase	*Streptococci*
i. staphylokinase	*Staphylococcus aureus*, some strains[b]
j. staphylocoagulase	*Staphylococcus aureus*, some strains[b]
fungal proteolytic enzymes	
a. acid type	*Aspergillus oryzae*, *A. saitoi*, *A. shirousamii*, and *Penicillium janthinellum*
b. neutral type	*Aspergillus ochraceus*, *A. oryzae*

(*continued*)

Table 5 (*continued*)

Enzyme	Produced by
c. alkaline type	*Aspergillus oryzae*[b], *A. sojae*, *Penicillium cyaneo-fulvum*, *Entomophthorales*[b], and *Mortierella renispora*
d. unclassified	*Aspergillus flavus*, *A. niger*, and *Scopulariopsis brevicaulis*
protozoal proteinase	*Tetrahymena pyriformis*
α-*N*-acylamino acid hydrolases	*Aspergillus flavus*, *A. oryzae*, *A. tamarii*, *Penicillium oxalicum* var. *pectinoporum*, *P. vinacious*, *P. viridicatum*, *Aspergillus oryzae*, and *Penicillium vinacious*
ε-*N*-acyl lysine hydrolase	*Aspergillus oryzae*[a]
lipases	*Clostridium oedematiens*, *Pseudomonas fragi*, *Staphylococcus* spp., *Aspergillus swamori*, *A. flavus*, *A. melleus*, *A. oryzae*, *Penicillium chrysogenum*, and *Rhizopus nigricans*
aryl esterase	*Streptococci*, Group A
phospholipase B	*Vibrio* El Tor
phospholipase C	*Clostridium perfringens*, Type A
penicillinase	*Bacillus cereus*[a] and [b], *B. subtilis*[a], *B. megaterium*[a], and *Staphylococcus aureus*[a]
deoxyribonucleases	*Staphylococcus aureus* (all coagulase-positive strains), *Streptococci* (all Group A, some Groups B, F, G, and L, and most Group C strains), and *Penicillium citrinum*
ribonucleases	*Bacillus subtilis* H, *Streptomyces erythreus*, *Aspergillus oryzae*, and *Penicillium citrinum*
dextran sucrase	*Betacoccus arabinosaceous* (*Leuconostoc mesenteroides*), *L. mesenteroides* strains B and B-512[a], *Streptococcus bovis* (semi[a]), and *Streptococcus* sp NRRL B-1351
dextran branching enzyme	*Betacoccus arabinosaceous*
α-glucosyl transferases	*Aspergillus niger*, *A. niger* NRRL 337, *A. niger* (Takamine Diazyme) *A. oryzae*, and *A. usamii*
β-glucosyl transferases	*Aspergillus aureus*, *A. flavus*, *A. niger*, *Myrothecium verrucaria*
dextran dextrinase	*Acetobacter capsulatum*
bacillus macerans amylase	*Bacillus macerans*[a]
levan sucrase	*Bacillus subtilis*
glucose oxidase	*Aspergillus niger* and *Penicillium amagasakiense*
thioloxidase	*Pericularia oryzae* and *Polyporus versicolor*
m-polyhydroxyphenol oxidase	*Pericularia oryzae*[b] and *Polyporus versicolor*[b]
aldose mutarotase	*Penicillium notatum* FD-446
lactate racemase	*Clostridium acetobutylicum*[a]

[a] Indicates enzyme is inducible.

[b] Indicates enzyme is constitutive.

the inoculum generally contains the same ingredients as the final broth, usually in slightly higher concentrations.   During the test-tube stage and the first liquid stage, the nutrient may contain some of the more expensive nutritional ingredients such as peptone, yeast extract, etc.

The inoculated broth is then aerated at the optimum temperature for the particular organism (usually somewhere between 20–40°C), until the cell number reaches 75–80% of the maximum potential cell population in that medium.   This is reached in 12–20 hr.   Pyrex glassware is used for propagating containers, and stainless-steel propagators are used for the last stage.   The agitation and aeration (up to sizes of several gallons of liquid) may be provided by shaking the containers in shaking machines. The larger propagating vessels are provided with aerating, agitating, and cooling systems similar to those applied in the final propagating vessels.   Complete propagating systems, standard or custom-made models, for preparing inoculums with all possible comfort and with semi- or fully automatic controls, made of stainless steel or stainless steel and glass, are commercially available.

For the production of mold spores (condidospores) as inoculum, sterile moistened wheat bran, with or without other nutrients, is generally used. Humid sterile air is blown through the agitated mass of bran; agitation is provided by keeping the containers in constant rotation. Five- to ten-gallon Pyrex flasks or stainless-steel vessels are used as containers. When the nutrients are nearly exhausted, the spore formation can be hastened with proper control of the temperature and the humidity. Spores for small-size batches may be produced on agar surface in Fernbach flasks, or in large 10-gal Pyrex flasks, that have the nutrient agar solidified over the inner surface of the bottle.

In each step, but at least in the first two steps, more batches of inocula are prepared than needed. They are carefully checked for proper morphology, purity, and enzyme activity. Only the best flasks are used. It is more economical to prepare excess inoculum, than to lose one commercial batch because of a defective starter. The mold spores are usually suspended in a saline solution or in nutrient; they are also frequently pregerminated before seeding them into the final batch.

Final Batch. The carefully compounded *liquid nutrient medium* is introduced into properly cleaned and presterilized propagating tanks, shortly called fermentors. The nutrient broth might pass a continuous sterilizer-cooler system before entering the sterile fermentor, or might be sterilized in the fermentor by heating. The fermentors, made of stainless steel, are tall, cylindrical vessels provided with aerating and agitating facilities, and both heating and cooling systems. Heating is performed either by direct steam, or by steam jacket and/or heating coils. Cooling is performed through the jacket and coils. Continuous-defoaming and pH-adjusting arrangements, and aseptic inoculation and sampling devices are standard accessories on each fermentor.

After the sterile nutrient medium is cooled to the propagation temperature, and its pH is adjusted to the optimum, the inoculum is introduced under aseptic conditions, and the reproduction of the cells is accelerated by agitation and aeration, according to the general rules of standard aerobic-microbiological processes. The fermentors, constantly kept under positive air pressure, are checked for sterility before inoculation, and after that, at standard intervals, for cell population or cell-substance determination, purity, and morphological observations and, during the latter phase of the propagation, for enzyme activity. The changes in the broth composition and pH, are constantly checked and corrected if needed. According to the culture medium, and the type of enzyme produced the propagation time may take 1 to 5 days.

The liquid nutrient medium is made up of six or more components, and the formulations developed by the individual manufacturers are kept confidential. Beckhorn, Labbee, and Underkofler (42) list the following ingredients as possible components in the formulation of various liquid nutrients: cereal starch or starch hydrolyzate, milled cereal products such as grits, meal, flour, corn-steep liquor, soybean meal, distillers' solubles, yeast or yeast extract, casein, gelatin, peptone, lactose, dextrose, tannic acid, ammonium phosphate, calcium carbonate, sodium chloride, magnesium sulfate, manganous chloride, dipotassium phosphate, monopotassium phosphate, disodium salt of ethylene (dinitrilo) tetraacetic acid, ammonium hydroxide, sodium hydroxide, alkyl aryl polyether alcohol (antifoam), iron, ammonium citrate, beet pulp, citrus pulp, apple pomace, and tannic acid.

Continuous-propagation processes, although possible, are not popular. Because of the conveniences offered by the batch method, and because of the great losses in time, work, and raw material in case of infection in a continuous process, the batch method is preferred.

In the use of semi-solid cultures (154), the semi-solid medium is prepared from wheat bran and from a number of other ingredients, listed by Beckhorn, Labbee, and Underkofler (42) as follows: wheat bran, milled cereal products such as middlings, second clears, flour, soybean meal, corn-steep liquor, yeast extract, peptone, distillers' solubles, ammonium hydroxide, ammonium phosphate, dipotassium phosphate, mono-potassium phosphate, lactic or hydrochloric acid, beet pulp, citrus pulp, apple pomace, and urea. The ingredients selected from the above list are properly mixed with water according to specific formulations, to a consistency free of running liquid, where the bran adsorbs all the moisture. The mixture is sterilized at 30 psi for 2 hr, usually in the propagating equipment.

Two types of propagating systems are commonly used for semi-solid media. In one, perforated trays closed in a chamber contain the wet-supplemented bran in rela-tively thin layers. After using special techniques for nutrient sterilization, cooling, spreading out on the trays, and inoculation, humidified, sterile air is passed through the chambers which contain the carts with the trays in many layers, on racks. The tem-perature in the chambers is kept at optimum by cooling the chamber with cold air and built-in heat-cooling systems. The air is recirculated in the chambers, and part of it is constantly replaced with fresh humidified sterile air. The time needed for cell propaga-tion and enzyme formation may vary from 1 to 7 days.

Rotating drums are the other type of propagators for semi-solid medium. They are long horizontal drums, several feet in diameter, constantly rotated by a mechanism. They are filled to $1/2$–$2/3$ with the semi-solid medium which is constantly agitated by the rotating action. The medium, after being sterilized in the drums by heat under pressure, is cooled by a cold-water spray outside the drums, and by sterile cold air blown through the medium inside the drums. After inoculation through special devices, the sterile air is constantly blown through the rotating cylinder, in order to supply air to the growing organism and carry away the carbon dioxide. The heat generated by the oxidation of the carbohydrates is carried away by the water spray outside the cylinder. The propagation and the enzyme formation may take 1–7 days.

Samples taken through special devices at certain intervals from the growing cul-ture on the trays or in the drums, are carefully inspected, tested, and evaluated as in the case of liquid cultures. The propagation of the cultures and the development of the enzymes are terminated when the tests indicate the expected maximum enzyme activity.

Both liquid and semi-solid cultivations are applicable to the most frequently used cultures of *B. subtilis*, *A. flavus-oryzae*, and *A. niger*.

Extraction. In many cases, the enzyme is extracted with water from crude sources such as macerates of animal or plant tissues. Frequently the pH is set for best extraction and best stability of the enzyme by using buffered solutions.

Animal and plant tissues are minced, and possibly further homogenized in a Waring blender, by grinding with sand, by treating with ultrasonic or sonic oscillation by freezing and thawing of the cells, or by lysis with other enzymes.

When extracellular enzymes are produced in liquid medium, no separate extraction step is needed, because the enzyme is already dissolved in the liquid medium. The solution is separated from the undissolved portion by centrifugation, filtration, or a combination of the two clarification processes. To obtain a clear solution, filter aids, fractionate filtrations, or super centrifuges may be applied after a preliminary filtration. The insoluble, inert portion is discarded.

The intercellular enzymes are retained by the cells. In this case the mass of organism is separated from the exhausted nutrient broth by centrifugal separators and/or filters, and the liquid is discarded. The cells are then disrupted by mechanical means, or by autolysis. For cell autolysis, usually, chemicals are mixed with the cell mass; they are so selected as to yield a pH with a maximum stability for the desired enzyme, and the temperature is raised to speed the autolysis. The chemicals that condition the autolysis may include one or several of the following: salts ($CaCl_2$, NaCl), sugars, glycerol, acids (lactic, phosphoric, hydrochloric, sulfuric), or alkali (NaOH, KOH, NH_4OH). The cell juice is then separated from the insoluble residue by filtration or centrifugation. The residue is washed with properly-buffered water.

When semi-solid bran medium is used, the enzymes may be extracted in counter-current-extraction systems with water-containing preservatives; a relatively clear solution results.

Occasionally, the ripe semi-solid mass of exhausted bran and cell substance may be dried at low temperature, without extraction, using a proper pH. The dry substance may then be used as a crude commercial enzyme preparation, or it may be stored until the enzyme is brought into solution at a later date by extraction with buffered aqueous salt solutions.

The clear enzyme solutions obtained by either method, are usually high in enzyme content based on the solid content, but are highly diluted by water. The bulk of the water is eliminated as quickly as possible by low-temperature vacuum evaporation. During the vacuum concentration the enzyme is protected by maintaining the pH at the optimum for stability, and frequently by adding stabilizers to the solution. Gelatin or protein hydrolyzates are often used. For papain, H_2S or cysteine are added as stabilizers; for amylase obtained from *B. subtilis*, calcium ions are used.

The concentration of the enzyme solution is terminated before precipitation of the solids would occur, or before the viscosity of the concentrate would become too high for convenient handling. This semipurified syrup serves as basis for many enzyme preparations. The syrup may be diluted to standard strength, supplemented with stabilizers and packaged in this form for marketing. The majority of the semi-crude enzyme preparations are in powder form. They are shaped by spray drying or by drying on trays or belt driers, after being mixed with inert substances in a ratio suitable to give to the finished product the predetermined enzyme activity per weight unit.

Final Purification. For scientific, analytical, pharmaceutical, and special industrial purposes it is often desirable to prepare the enzyme in highly purified, or if possible, even in crystalline state. The starting material for purification usually is the freshly prepared, concentrated clear aqueous cell extract. The purpose is to separate the specific enzyme protein from the nonenzyme protein and from the nonenzyme components present in the solution. All techniques customary in protein isolations may be useful, but no general method can be applied for all enzymes. Practically each enzyme requires a specific purification technique of its own. The most useful methods include precipitation, adsorption, and crystallization.

Precipitation. When water-soluble organic solvents such as methanol, ethanol, acetone, or dioxane, or, highly water-soluble inorganic salts such as ammonium sulfate, magnesium sulfate, or other salts are added to the clear enzyme solution whose pH is set close to the isoelectric point, the enzyme will precipitate. The precipitate is then separated from the liquid by filtration or centrifugation. The organic solvent content of the precipitate evaporates during low-temperature drying. The inorganic salts may be separated from the enzyme by dialysis.

Occasionally coprecipitants are used which remain in the final enzyme preparation and act as stabilizers or as standardizing diluents.

Adsorption. At the proper pH the enzyme is adsorbed by suitable materials such as tricalcium phosphate, kaolin, aluminum hydroxide, colloidal iron, ionexchange resins, etc. The adsorbent–enzyme complex settles and after decanting the supernatant liquid, the enzyme is eluted from the adsorbent by mixing it with a slightly alkaline buffer, which will replace the enzyme. Then the enzyme solution is separated from the inert adsorbent by centrifugation, and the buffer is eliminated from the solution by dialysis. The highly purified clear enzyme solution is ready for final drying or for crystallization.

Adsorption on chromatographic column is a highly effective method for the separation of the individual enzymes from mixtures. After adsorption, the column is lifted out of the tube and is cut into sections; each section may then be eluted individually. The enzyme purity and concentration can be evaluated by determining the solid contents and the activities of the individual fractions.

Crystallization. From a relatively pure enzyme solution of high concentration the crystallization is initiated by cooling of the solution and by slow addition of highly soluble salts such as ammonium sulfate. The salt having a high affinity to water will take water away from the protein causing its crystallization. The first crystals obtained in a small batch may be used as seeds to accelerate crystallization in a larger batch. The process is concluded with the separation of the crystals by centrifugation or filtration, with the washing and drying of the crystals, or with repeated crystallization. In all these operations specific pH levels, not harmful to the enzyme, are used. Low temperature and speedy operation are essential. Ultracentrifuge and electrophoresis are also employed in the final purification of enzymes.

All previously described manipulations, which follow the termination of the microbial cell reproduction, or the obtaining of the by-products of animal or plant origin, are performed in the shortest time possible. This helps to prevent the loss of activity due to chemical or microbial actions, while maintaining the optimum pH and the safe temperature for enzyme stability. Still, to prevent possible microbial spoilage, occasionally as dictated by experience, small amounts of the following preservatives are added to the active substance: toluene, organic acids or their salts, phenolic compounds, and sodium fluoride. Their amount is so selected as not to exceed 10 ppm in the final enzyme preparation, or 0.05 ppm in the food, if the enzyme is involved in food preparation.

Measurement of Enzyme Activity

Industrial materials are evaluated according to their specific characteristics and their purity. They are purchased and sold by weight, and by the proportion of the desired component or components. The assay measures the percentage or the activity of the wanted component. Only a few enzymes are marketed in pure or near pure form, for research or analytical purposes. The pure enzyme content of industrial enzyme preparations varies on a very large scale, and its numerical value is not known in most products. The enzyme content of a material is assayed and expressed entirely in terms of activity. The activity being the basis of evaluation, the knowledge of its value is essential to both the producers and users.

Through assay procedures, the manufacturer checks the enzyme activity of his raw materials and of his intermediate products during the enrichment, purification, and standardization procedures; he sets the price of the final product according to the assayed activity. The user pays for the product on the same basis, and defines the amount of preparation to be used in his process according to the activity. The activity is expressed in units.

The consumer knows how much activity to expect for his money. Once his confidence for a product is built up by checking the manufacturers figures occasionally, he does not have to assay every batch he purchases, but he will formulate the use based on the manufacturer's specification.

Units and methods for the measurement of their values have been developed by individual researchers, have been standardized and accepted by interested groups, scientific societies, or government agencies, and have been published in periodicals, reviews, and reference books.

Numerous efforts have been made to establish uniform systems for "enzyme units," which would indicate the amount of chemical change they catalyze, and to establish "enzyme values," which would give the number of enzyme units contained in a definite amount of enzyme preparation. For example, a proposed "lipase unit" would be the quantity of the enzyme which would hydrolyze 24% of a 2.5% olive-oil emulsion in 1 ml in 1 hr. The "lipase value" would be the number of "lipase units" present in one weight unit (1 cg) of enzyme preparation. The "amylase unit" would be 100 times the amount of enzyme for which the velocity constant k equals 0.01, and the "amylase value" would equal the number of "amylase units" present in one weight unit (1 cg) of preparation, etc.

For several reasons, however, there is no generally followed pattern in establishing and using "enzyme units." Frequently a score of units have been proposed for the same enzyme, and usually several units are in use for each enzyme. Practically every researcher spending some time with enzyme work, develops one or more assay methods, and proposes a new unit or a new modification. Usually, units which have practical merits will survive.

Several units are specified in official publications. For example, enzyme units concerning pharmaceutical enzymes are interchangeably published in the *U.S. Pharmacopeia* (29), the *National Formulary* (NF) (27), and the *United States Dispensatory* (17). Concerning several enzymes utilized in the preparation of food and beverages, "enzyme units" are established by the AOAC (Association of Official Agricultural Chemists) (7), by the CCA (Cereal Chemists Association) (12) and by the ASBC (American Society of Brewing Chemists) (4). For enzymes used by the paper industry, units are established by TAPPI (Technical Association of the Pulp and Paper Industry).

The *National Formulary* even established a few enzyme standards and reagent standards used in the assay methods.

There are also units established by the individual enzyme manufacturers, usually acceptable to their customers. Also, one manufacturer may use two or more units to express the activity of a preparation, depending on the purpose for which the preparation will be used.

Many assay methods do not specify units as such. The method results, in some numerical value which may be converted into units, frequently defined by the individual who wants to use them.

The results of enzyme assays are expressed in many different ways. On final analysis they define one of the following data: (1) the amount of change that has taken place at the action of a specified amount of enzyme preparation, under specific conditions of pH, temperature, time, substrate concentration, and enzyme/substrate ratio; (2) the amount of time needed for a given amount of enzyme preparation to accomplish a certain amount of chemical change under closely specified conditions; (3) the initial reaction-velocity constant measured, under closely specified conditions, where the reaction speed is a linear function of the enzyme concentration, usually in low-enzyme high-substrate systems. If the activity (expressed in units) of the enzyme preparation is known, the user can estimate the time required by a given amount of enzyme under specified circumstances to complete the reaction. On final analysis, the enzyme unit is the basis for selling, buying, and using industrial enzymes.

Eventually, all types of units establish a workable relation between the enzyme activity and the practical utilization of the enzyme preparation, regardless which factor is determined as a variable in the assay. In most cases the relation of the main factors is expressed by the following equation:

$$A = S/Et$$

where A is the activity, S the amount of substrate in grams, E the weight of enzyme preparation in grams, and t the reaction time in minutes. The equation is valid within certain limits of time, of enzyme/substrate ratio, and of substrate concentration in the digest.

In cases where a first-order constant may be determined without much effort, an enzyme unit can be established to equal the amount which, under specified conditions, will cause the first-order constant to have an arbitrarily selected numerical value. The more general practice is to determine the initial rate of the reaction in terms of grams of substrate converted by grams of preparation per minute.

Most units are arbitrary and intend to express some convenient value for its use. For this reason, wherever possible, it is expedient to select the assay conditions with regard to temperature, pH, substrate concentration, and enzyme/substrate ratio to be similar to the conditions of the practical utilization. The assay method should also be specific for the action for which the enzyme is intended to be used.

It is expected that a good assay method should yield results with high precision (± 2–5%), within a relatively short period of time, and with a limited amount of human work.

In all enzyme assays, an exact amount of enzyme preparation (or its aqueous solution) is permitted to act upon an exact amount of a well-defined (often standardized) substrate. The assay is run in an aqueous solution or emulsion at a specified concentration, at a specific temperature and pH (mostly buffered), for a definite time, or until a definite amount of change has been accomplished. Then the action of the enzyme is measured by determining one of the following factors: (1) The amount of unchanged substrate. The difference $S_0 - S_t$ indicates the change during the period t. (2) The amount of product. The difference $P_0 - P_t$ is the amount of change during the period t. (3) The time necessary to degrade a substrate to an easily measurable fixed point such as the time necessary for a 50% conversion of the substrate; or, if the progress of the reaction may be followed by a color reaction, the time until a certain color is reached; or, if acids are produced, the time until a certain amount of neutralizing chemical is used up; or, if gas is produced, the time until a predetermined amount of gas is produced; or, if change in rotation is one of the consequences of the enzyme action, the time to reach a certain point of optical rotation, etc.

Following are examples for the measurement of enzyme activity:

The amount of unchanged substrate is measured in catalase assays, where the quantity of unchanged peroxide is determined after a certain reaction time. Similar principle is applied in some penicillinase assays.

A physical property of the unchanged substrate and product mixture is measured by viscosity measurements in the assay of α-amylase preparations made for the liquefaction of starch (114). The viscosity is the result of the partially-digested substrate–product mixture. Similarly, in invertase assays, the optical rotation of the sucrose–invert sugar mixture is measured; in this case, the change in rotation is one of the results of the enzyme action.

In the assay of saccharifying activity of various amylases, the amount of product formed is measured by determining the reducing power of the digested substrate. The results are calculated as maltose (ME) or dextrose equivalents (DE), depending on the type of enzyme activity. The reducing sugars are determined by the ferricyanide or the Fehling procedure. In some assays the maltose and glucose content of the digest is determined individually.

In assaying proteolytic activities, the amount of newly formed free amino acids may be measured by the Sorensen-Van Slyke method, or the change in soluble-nitrogen content of the digested substrate can be determined by the Kjeldahl method.

The progress of lipolysis is followed by determining the free acids formed from glycerides. Pectin methylesterase activity can be measured by determining the change in methanol content of the digested substrate; methanol may be determined by the gas chromatographic method.

In addition to standard chemical methods, visible and ultraviolet spectrophotometric, polarographic, photometric, polaroscopic, manometric, pressuremetric, and other techniques are frequently applied in assay methods.

Continuous automatic micro-sample spectrophotometers, with recording systems especially suited for enzyme assay, are available on the market. Levy constructed an automatic-recording polarimeter, and Levy and Cook applied it to enzyme-kinetic studies (108,109).

In the α-amylase method, in the Lasché test, in the test for rennin, and in a number of other assay methods, the time necessary to bring about a definite amount of change in a substrate under specified conditions is measured.

ENZYME UNITS

The following examples illustrate the characteristics of various enzyme units, and the methods used to determine their values:

Invertase Unit (saccharase, sucrose, or β-fructofuronidase unit). A 50-mg preparation has "one unit of invertase" if it converts to a 0° rotation 20 ml of a 20% sucrose solution at 20°C in 1 hr. At 0° rotation, 75.93% of the sucrose is hydrolyzed (21,124).

α-Amylase Unit (4). This unit is defined as the quantity of α-amylase, which will dextrinize soluble starch in the presence of an excess of β-amylase at the rate of 1 g/hr at 20°C.

The assay method is described in detail (4,7,19). An infusion is prepared at 20°C from 25 g of enzyme preparation (malt) and 500 ml of a 0.5% sodium chloride solution. A portion of the infusion is further diluted five times with 0.5% salt solution. 5 ml of this dilute enzyme solution is added to 20 ml of a 2% special starch solution which has been predigested with excess β-amylase for 18–72 hr. The mixture of the enzyme-limit-dextrin solution is then digested at 20°C. Definite portions of the digest are withdrawn in specified time intervals, and are mixed with definite amounts of iodine solution. The color formed by the digest and iodine is compared in a Heilige comparator with a special α-amylase color disc. The time necessary to produce a digest, which after mixing with the iodine will form a color matching the color disc, is used in the formula below to calculate the dextrinizing or α-amylase unit:

$$\text{(as is) } DU = 24/Wt$$

$$\text{(dry basis) } DU = DU \text{ (as is)} \times 100/(100 - M)$$

where DU is the dextrinizing unit, W is the malt weight (or other enzyme preparation) equivalent, t is the dextrinizing time in minutes and M is the percentage of moisture in malt.

Starch Dextrinization "SKB" Unit. The method developed by Sandstedt, Kneen, and Blish (139) is defined as the number of grams of β-amylase-treated soluble starch dextrinized by 1 g of enzyme in 1 hr at 30°C and at pH 4.85. This is the original unit on which the α-amylase unit is based. The method is based on the original Wohlgemuth method. The difference between the SKB and the Wohlgemuth method is that in the SKB method the malt infusion is prepared with water and the limit dextrin is digested at 30°C.

Starch-Liquefying Unit (72). An enzyme with 1000 liquefying units per gram will reduce by 90% the viscosity of 300 times its weight of potato starch, or of 560 times its weight of tapioca starch, in 10 minutes at 70°C and at pH 6.7.

Diastatic Power or Saccharifying Power (4). ("degree of diastatic power," formerly "degrees Lintner" or "Lintner units, LU.")

A malt or another enzyme preparation has a diastatic power of 100 LU if 0.1 ml of a clear 5% infusion of the malt acting on 100 ml of a 2% starch solution at 20°C for 1 hr, produces sufficient sugar to reduce completely 5 ml of Fehling solution.

The revised method uses 0.5% sodium chloride for extraction of diastase; the word "Lintner" was dropped, and "diastatic power" is used as designation for the units. The principles of the method described at length (4,7) are as follows:

An infusion is prepared in 2.5 hr using 25 g of enzyme preparation (malt) and 500 ml of 0.5% sodium chloride solution at 20°C. A filtered portion is then diluted five times with 0.5% sodium chloride solution. Ten ml of this dilute infusion is used to the "diastasis" (digestion) of 200 ml buffered starch solution containing 4 g soluble starch. The mixture is digested at 20°C for exactly 30 min, after which the enzyme is inactivated by the addition of 20 ml 0.5N sodium hydroxide solution. The digest is then diluted to 250 ml. The reducing power of 5 ml of the digest (converted starch) is determined either by the ferricyanide procedure, or by the Fehling's (Soxhlet) solution procedure. The degree (unit) of diastatic power is calculated by the following formulas:

1. *For ferricyanide procedure:*

$$\text{(as is) } DP° = (B - A) \times 23$$

$$\text{(dry basis) } DP° = DP° \text{ (as is)} \times 100/(100 - M)$$

where A is the number of ml of sodium thiosulfate used in the direct titration, B is the number of ml of sodium thiosulfate used in the blank correction titration, and M is the percent moisture in malt.

2. *For Fehling's procedure:*

$$\text{(as is) } DP^\circ = 500/A \times B/A$$

$$\text{(dry basis) } DP^\circ = DP^\circ \text{ (as is) } \times 100/(100 - M)$$

where A is the number of ml of digested starch solution used in direct titration, B is the number of ml of digested starch solution used in the blank correction titration, and M is the percent moisture in malt.

Lasché Time or Lasché Units (85).   This method gives the time, in minutes, required by the infusion of 0.55 g malt to convert to the achromic point 5 g of soluble starch in 100 ml aqueous solution at 62.5°C.

In the revised Lasché test (standardized by the chemists of Schenley Distillers, Inc.), at the present time 4.4 g soluble starch is used (according to Lintner) instead of 5 g (19).

According to this test, distillers' malts are designated as 4-minute, 5-minute, or X-minute malts.   The smaller the minutes (units), the higher the amylase content. One gram of 4-minute malt contains twice as much diastase enzyme as an 8-minute malt.

The method for determining the Lasché time (19,84,85) is as follows: 4.4 g soluble starch is digested in 100 ml volume by 2.2 ml of enzyme infusion corresponding to 0.55 g preparation (malt) at 62.5°C and at pH 4.9–5.1. Beginning after 3–4 min of digestion, small portions of the digest are withdrawn every 30 sec (and around the achromic point every 15 sec) to a white porcelain spotplate and are tested with a few drops of $0.001N$ iodine solution.   The exact time, expressed in minutes and quarter-minutes, that is needed to reach the achromic point is the Lasché time.   The results can be reproduced to an accuracy of 15 seconds.   An operator may assay twenty-five samples per day.

Converting Capacity. Using the modified Lasché test for assay method, de Becze et al. (84) defined the units of converting capacity to measure the joint activities of malt amylases to convert soluble starch to the achromic point.   Converting capacities (values from 0.02 to 200) can be calculated from the equation

$$C = 100 \, S/Lt$$

where C is the converting capacity; S the g of starch converted to the achromic point; L the ml of enzyme solution (or g of malt represented by the enzyme solution); and t the time in minutes, required to convert S to the achromic point.

The converting capacity of a 5-min malt measured by the modified Lasché test is calculated as shown:

$$C = (100 \times 4.4)/(0.55 \times 5) = 160$$

This means that 1 g enzyme preparation (malt) converts 100 g of starch to the achromic point in 100 min. At the achromic point about 70% of the starch is converted to reducing sugars calculated as maltose (85).

In calculating the converting capacity, the conversion time is determined by the Lasché test. The test is modified to the extent that the substrate/enzyme ratio and concentration may be changed within certain limits in order to facilitate the measurement of converting capacities at a wide range of 0.02–200.

Both the Lasché units and the converting capacity units are determined under conditions close to the practical utilization of the enzyme preparation, by using high conversion temperature. At such temperatures amylase components with low thermal tolerance are eliminated and the effects of thermal destruction during prolonged digestion periods are indicated in the results.

Limit Dextrinase (100). The units are expressed as the milligrams of fermentable sugar produced from standard limit-dextrin solution by 1 g of enzyme preparation in 1 hr at 30°C (determined according to the specified method).

Diastatic Activity of Flour (7). This is expressed in units equaling the mg of maltose produced by 10 g of flour in 1 hr at 30°C under specified conditions. The value seldom, if ever, exceeds 350 units.

In the assay method 5 g of flour mixed with a teaspoonful of ignited quartz sand and 46 ml acetate buffer solution is digested at 30°C for 1 hr. The enzyme is inactivated by 2 ml in H_2SO_4 (1 + 9 soln) and is clarified with 12% $Na_2WO_4.2H_2O$ solution, then filtered. The maltose content is calculated from the reducing power determined by the ferricyanide method.

Dextrin Saccharifying Unit (**DSU**) (72). This unit is a measure of the ability of an enzyme to hydrolyze corn-white dextrin. An amount of enzyme containing 0.025 DSU will affect 35% hydrolysis of 30 mg of corn-white dextrin in a total volume of 30 ml in 1 hr at 40°C.

Pancreatin. An enzyme preparation made from the pancreas of hog or ox and containing pancreatic amylase, trypsin, and pancreatic lipase, should convert not less than 25 times its weight of NF potato starch reference standard (17,29,27).

Pepsin. A substance containing proteolytic enzyme obtained from the glandular layer of hog stomach, should digest not less than 3000 and not more than 3500 times its weight of coagulated egg albumin (17,27).

Pepsin is assayed by digesting 10 g of freshly prepared coagulated, minced egg albumen (boiled egg whites) at 52°C with 5 ml of a solution of 0.1 g pepsin in 150 ml diluted hydrochloric acid (35 ml N acid + 385 ml distilled water) in 40 ml dilute HCl solution for 2.5 hr, under frequent agitation. Under identical conditions, egg albumen is digested with 4.7 ml NF standard pepsin solution, and in a third test with 5.0 ml NF standard pepsin solution. The volume of the undissolved albumen is estimated in NF-specified volumetric flasks. The amount of the undissolved albumen in the two tests of the unknown should not be less than in the test of NF standard.

Pepsin and Rennin Elixir. The elixirs should possess in 100 ml a proteolytic activity of not less than 2.25 g reference pepsin NF (17). The elixir is assayed in tests similar to the tests used for pepsin.

Rennin. The milk-curdling enzyme obtained from the glandular layer of the stomach of calves, should possess a coagulating activity of no less than 90%, and no more than 110% of the reference rennin, NF (27).

In the assay 100 mg rennin preparation is extracted with 50 ml water for 15 min; a similar extract is prepared from NF reference standard. In two flasks (about 12 cm high and 4.5 cm in diameter) 50 ml cows milk is brought to 43°C, and is kept at that temperature in a water bath. One ml of the reference standard extract is added to one flask, and 1 ml of the rennin preparation extract is added to the other flask. The time needed to thicken the milk in each flask is noted. The curdling is indicated by a distinct convex surface, when the vessel is tipped to an angle of 45°.

The milk exposed to the solution of the unknown sample should coagulate in no less than 90%, and no more than 110% of the time required by the reference rennin.

Hemoglobin Units (HU) (157). A proteolytic enzyme has an activity of 1000 hemoglobin units per gram if 11.18 mg of it produces a 5.00 mg increase in soluble nitrogen from 0.417 g of hemoglobin, in 5 hr, at 40°C, and at pH 4.7. This is equivalent to solubilizing approximately three times its weight of hemoglobin under these specified conditions.

Proteolytic activity of flour and malted wheat flour (7) is expressed in hemoglobin units (HU) per gram enzyme preparation. In the assay method (7) 2.5 g bacto-hemoglobin as substrate is digested in 50 ml acetate-buffer solution (pH 4.7) by an exact weight of the enzyme source (from slightly active material such as flour, up to 10 g is used, from active preparations, first an extract is prepared and an aliquot portion of the extract is used) at 40°C for $5\frac{1}{4}$ hr. The digestion is terminated by the addition of trichloroacetic acid solution. A control is digested for 15 min. The samples are clarified by centrifugation and filtration if necessary and the soluble-nitrogen content in an aliquot portion is determined by the Kjeldahl method. The difference in the nitrogen content between the sample digested for $5\frac{1}{4}$ hr and the control, is the product hydrolyzed by the enzyme. The HU is calculated from this value.

Casein Solubilization Unit (commercial definition). An enzyme with an activity of 1000 casein solubilization units per gram will solubilize nine times its weight of casein in 1 hr at 40°C, and at pH of about 8.0.

Proteinase Unit. In papain (7) the proteinase unit is the quantity of enzyme that produces (in the casein test) a titration difference of 1 ml 0.1N KOH. The value of the preparation is expressed as units/mg or as mg papain preparation necessary to make one unit.

In the assay procedure, (7), 10 ml of a 6% specially prepared soluble casein is digested with the activated extract of 10 mg enzyme preparation at pH 5 and 40°C for 20 min. The enzyme is activated by a half saturated H_2S–H_2O solution for 1 hour at 40°C.

The formed acids are titrated in the digested solution with 0.1N KOH in the presence of thymolphthalein indicator. The titration is executed in small portions, under specific conditions, in an alcoholic medium to a final pale-blue color. A similar titration is performed in a blank using inactivated enzyme, and allowing no time for digestion.

Northrop Units (NU) (122,156). Northrop units are used for the measurement of protease activity in bacterial protease, papain and other proteolytic enzymes. The NU is defined as the amount of enzyme which produces 40% hydrolysis in 60 min at pH 8 and at 40°C.

Triacetin Unit (TAU). The lipolytic activity of a preparation is standardized on the ability to hydrolyze the water-soluble lipid triacetin (glyceryl triacetate) under standard conditions. The TAU activity of an enzyme is defined as the ml of 0.1N acetic acid produced by 1 g of enzyme from 1 ml of triacetin in 25 ml of water at 50°C and at pH 5.5, in 1 hr. (This unit is specified by a manufacturer.)

Pectin Methylesterase (Pectase) Units (25). The three different units used are as follows:

1.   One of the useful units, PMU, equals the mg of methoxyl split off by 1 g or 1 ml of the enzyme at pH 6.0 and at 30°C, in 30 min.

2.   Another is the PEU unit which is the quantity of enzyme which at 30°C and at the optimum pH, will catalyze the hydrolysis of pectic acid at an initial rate of one milliequivalent of ester bonds per minute, in the presence of 0.15M sodium chloride. A 0.5% solution of citrus pectin containing 9–11% methoxyl should be used as substrate.   One PMU equals 930 PEU (PEU units express activities in whole numbers).

3.   A third unit defines the amount of enzyme which will liberate in 1 min at pH 8.0, and at 20°C, 32 mg of methanol from pectic acid dissolved in 0.1M phosphate-buffer solution.

Pectin Galacturonase Units (25).   The generally used pectolytic unit equals the amount of enzyme capable of hydrolyzing 1 mg of pectic polygalacturonide at 40°C in 1 hr.

Pectin galacturonase unit equals the reducing power (expressed in terms of galacturonic acid) in milliequivalents of reducing groups liberated from pectic acid, per minute, per unit of enzyme, ie, "PGU, cc," "PGU, mg," or "PGU, mg PN" (milligram of protein nitrogen basis); the activity is measured under specific conditions. These three units did not become popular.

A revised "pectin galacturonase unit" is defined as the enzyme activity which results in the production of 1 mg of reducing-power increase (expressed as galacturonic acid) in 30 min at pH 3.5 and at 30°C, when 1 g of dry enzyme material is used.   Pectic acid is to be used as a substrate.

Levy Unit.   Penicillinase activity (73,110) is most frequently expressed in Levy units.   One Levy unit of penicillinase inactivates 59.3 units (35.6 mcg, or 10^{-7} moles) of penicillin G in 1 hr, when the substrate is in sufficient concentration to maintain a zero-order reaction.   The Bowman test (73) is suited for assaying penicillinase activities of solutions containing 4000–40,000 Levy units/ml.   The solubilization time at such levels is a linear function of the dose.

Katalase Fahrigkeit Unit.   Catalase (7) activity of a sample is expressed in terms of Kf = Katalase Fahrigkeit units, as $Kf = k/n$.   In this expression k is the first-order reaction constant (log base 10) determined at 0°C, and n = g sample/50 ml reaction mixture.

Pure catalase has Kf of 40,000–60,000, depending on source.   The principle of the assay method is the determination of the undecomposed portion of hydrogen peroxide digested by known amounts of enzyme extract for 5 and 10 min, respectively, at 0°C, and at pH between 6.5–7.5.   The H_2O_2 content of the blank and of the two digested (5-min and 10-min) samples, a and b, is determined by sodium thiosulfate–iodine titration.   The Kf is calculated from the following formula (where t_a is titer at 5 min, t_b is titer at 10 min, and t_{bl} is blank titer):

$$Kf = \frac{1/(t_b - t_a) \log \left[(t_{bl} - t_a)/(t_{bl} - t_b) \right]}{\text{g sample/50 ml reaction mixture}}$$

Future

The intensive trend toward the discovery of new enzymes and the development of new techniques for their production started about two decades ago, and is ever increasing.   Four main avenues project promises for further development: the use of microorganisms, the use of tissue cultures, the application of hormones, and the periodical or continuous harvesting of exoenzymes from the same cells without destroying them.

The modern technique of producing cells of microorganisms in almost unlimited quantities, in a very short period of time, in a relatively small space, and the inexhaustible ability of microbial cells to manufacture an almost unlimited number of different enzymes, perpetuates their rank as the main source for the production of industrial enzymes.

It is also conceivable that, in the future, cells of animal or plant origin will be propagated, with not much difficulty, on, large scale, just as cells of microorganisms are propagated today. The supply of cells from specially selected tissues of plant or animal origin may then become independent from the meat production.

The example of enhancing enzyme production in plant cells by the effect of gibberellins points the way to future possibilities, to find additional biochemical agents which will stimulate enzyme production by cells.

Another possibility for future utilization is to maintain live cells under such conditions that they will continuously produce and excrete enzymes, which may be harvested without destroying the cells.

A program, oriented to coordinate possibilities of enzyme application in new fields, development work for new production techniques, as well as the standardization of assay methods, would speed up what is yet to be done in the fields of industrial enzymes.

Bibliography

"Enzymes and Enzymology" in *ECT* 1st ed., Vol. 5, pp. 735–762, by A. K. Balls, Agricultural Research Administration, U.S. Department of Agriculture; "Enzymes, Industrial," Suppl. 1, pp. 294–312, by Gerald Reed, Red Star Yeast and Products Company.

Reference Books, Textbooks

1. W. W. Pigman, ed., *Advances in Carbohydrate Chemistry*, Vol. 17, Academic Press, Inc., New York, 1962.
2. W. W. Pigman, ed., *Advances in Carbohydrate Chemistry*, Vol. 18, Academic Press, Inc., New York, 1963.
3. R. F. Nord, ed., *Advances in Enzymology*, Vol. 25, Interscience Publishers, a division of John Wiley & Sons, Inc., New York, 1963.
4. *Methods of Analysis*, 6th ed., American Society of Brewing Chemists, 1958.
5. M. A. Amerine and M. A. Joslyn, *Table Wines*, University of California Press, Berkeley, Calif., 1951.
6. J. M. Luck, ed., *Annual Review of Biochemistry*, Vol. 27, Annual Reviews, Inc., Palo Alto, Calif., 1958.
7. *Official and Tentative Methods of Analysis*, Association of Official Agricultural Chemists, Washington, D.C., 1965.
8. E. Baldwin, *Dynamic Aspects of Biochemistry*, 3rd ed., Cambridge University Press, London, 1959.
9. P. D. Boyer, H. Lardy, and K. Myrbäck, eds., *The Enzymes*, Vols. 1–8, Academic Press, Inc., New York, 1959–1963.
10. J. Brachet and A. E. Mirsky, *The Cell*, Vols. 1–6, Academic Press, Inc., New York, 1960–1964.
11. H. G. Bray and K. White, *Kinetics and Thermodynamics in Biochemistry*, J. & A. Churchill Ltd., London, 1957.
12. *Cereal Laboratory Methods*, 7th ed., American Society of Cereal Chemists, 1962.
13. S. P. Colowick and N. O. Kaplan, eds., *Methods in Enzymology*, Vols. 1–7, Academic Press, Inc., New York, 1955–1964.

14. A. H. Cook, ed., *Barley and Malt, Biology, Biochemistry and Technology*, Academic Press, Inc., New York, 1962.

15. R. W. Cowgil and A. B. Pardee, *Biochemical Research Techniques*, John Wiley & Sons, Inc., New York, 1957.

16. J. De Clerck, *Textbook of Brewing*, 2 vols., Chapman and Hall, Ltd., London, 1957.

17. *The Dispensatory of the United States of America*, J. B. Lippincott Co., Philadelphia, Pa., 1950.

18. M. Dixon and E. C. Webb, *Enzymes*, Academic Press, Inc., New York, 1958.

19. F. D. Snell and C. L. Hilton, eds., *Encyclopedia of Industrial Methods of Analysis*, Vol. 1, Interscience Publishers, a division of John Wiley & Sons, Inc., New York, 1965.

20. J. L. Fairley and G. L. Kilgour, *Essentials of Biological Chemistry*, Reinhold Publishing Corp., New York, 1963.

21. K. G. Falk, *The Chemistry of Enzyme Actions*, The Chemical Catalog Co., Inc., New York, 1924.

22. J. S. Fruton and S. Simmonds, *General Biochemistry*, John Wiley & Sons, Inc., New York, 1958.

23. R. J. C. Harris, ed., *Biological Applications of Freezing and Drying*, Academic Press, Inc., New York, 1954.

24. Z. I. Kertesz, in J. B. Sumner and K. Myrbäck eds., *The Enzymes*, Academic Press, Inc., New York, 1954.

25. Z. I. Kertesz, *The Pectic Substances*, Interscience Publishers, Inc., New York, 1951.

26. E. M. Linday, *Handbook of Microbiology for Engineers*, Spon, London, 1962.

27. *The National Formulary*, 10th ed., J. B. Lippincott Co., Philadelphia, Pa., 1955.

28. C. Neuberg and I. S. Roberts, *Invertase Monograph*, Sugar Research Foundation, New York, 1946.

29. *The Pharmacopeia of the United States of America*, U S P XVI, Mack Publishing Co., Easton, Pa., 1960.

30. W. Pigman, ed., *The Carbohydrates, Chemistry, Biochemistry, Physiology*, Academic Press, Inc., New York, 1957.

31. S. C. Prescott and C. G. Dunn, *Industrial Microbiology*, 2nd ed., McGraw-Hill Book Co. Inc., New York, 1949.

32. C. Rainbow and A. H. Rose, eds., *Biochemistry of Industrial Microorganisms*, Academic Press, Inc., New York, 1963.

33. A. H. Rose, *Industrial Microbiology*, Butterworths & Co. Ltd., London, 1961.

34. H. W. Schultz, ed., *Food Enzymes*, Avi Publishing Co., Westport, Conn., 1960.

35. H. Tauber, *The Chemistry and Technology of Enzymes*, John Wiley & Sons, Inc., New York, 1949.

36. M. V. Tracey, *Principles of Biochemistry*, Pitman, London, 1954.

37. L. A. Underkofler and R. J. Hickey, eds., *Industrial Fermentations*, 2 vols., Chemical Publishing Co., Inc., New York, 1954–1955.

38. F. C. Webb, *Biochemical Engineering*, D. Van Nostrand Co., Inc., Princeton, N.J., 1964.

39. G. Zemplén, *Az Enzimek és Gyakorlati Alkalmazásuk*, Kir. Magy. Természettudományi Társulat Kiadása, Budapest, 1915.

Reviews

40. R. R. Barton and C. E. Land, Jr., "How Latest Enzymes Sharpen Your Process Control," Miles Chemical Co., Elkhart, Ind.

41. E. J. Beckhorn, "Application of Enzymes," *Drug Cosmetic Ind.* **90** (6) (June 1962).

42. E. J. Beckhorn, M. D. Labbee, and L. A. Underkofler, "Production and Use of Microbial Enzymes for Food Processing," *J. Agr. Food Chem.* **13**, 30–34 (1965).

43. R. Davies, "Microbial Extracellular Enzymes, their Uses and Some Factors Affecting their Formation," in C. Rainbow and A. H. Rose, eds., *Biochemistry of Industrial Microorganisms*, Academic Press, Inc., New York, 1963, pp. 68–150.

44. R. V. Dahlstrom and M. Sfat, "Relationship of Gibberellic Acid to Enzyme Development," in *Gibberellins*, No. 28 of *Advancement in Chemistry*, Series V. 28, Am. Chem. Soc., Washington, D.C., 1961, pp. 59–70.

45. J. C. Hoogenheide, "Microbial Enzymes Other Than Fungal Amylases," in L. A. Underkofler and R. J. Hickey, eds., *Industrial Fermentations*, Vol. 2, Chemical Publishing Co., Inc., New York, 1954.

46. *Ficin*, Merck & Co., Inc., Chemical Division, Rahway, N.J. 1955.

47. B. M. Miller, ed., *Development in Industrial Microbiology*, Plenum Press, New York, 1960.

48. *Production and Application of Enzyme Preparations in Food Manufacture*, Monograph No. 11, Soc. Chem. Ind., London, 1961.

49. G. Reed, "A Review of the Action of Pectic Enzymes and a Discussion of their Commercial Production," *Proc. Am. Soc. Enologists* **2**, 54–58 (1951).

50. M. C. Tainter et al., "Papain," *Ann. N.Y. Acad. Sci.* **54**, 147 (1951).

51. L. A. Underkofler and W. J. Perracone, "Commercial Enzymes—Potent Catalyzers that Promote Quality," *Food Eng.* (April 1957).

52. L. A. Underkofler, R. R. Barton, and S. S. Rennert, "Microbiological Process Report. Production of Microbial Enzymes and Their Application," *Applied Microbiol.* **6** (3), 212–221 (1958).

Patents

53. U.S. Pats. 525,830 and 525,823 (1894), J. Takamine.

54. U.S. Pat. 886,411 (1908), O. Rohm.

55. U.S. Pats. 995,820 and 995,823–6 (1911), L. Wallerstein.

56. U.S. Pat. 2,893,921 (July 7, 1959), D. P. Langlois and W. Turner.

57. Can. Pat. 593,575 (March 1, 1960), J. F. Murphy and E. H. Rhing.

58. U.S. Pat. 3,067,066 (Dec. 4, 1962), I. Ehrenthal and G. J. Block (to Anheuser-Busch Inc.).

59. U.S. Pat. 3,081,172 (March 12, 1963), G. E. Dennis and R. C. Quittenton (to John Labatt Ltd.).

60. U.S. Pat. 2,526,873 (1950), W. R. Johnston and G. W. Kirby.

Papers

61. E. C. Adams, C. E. Burkhart, and A. H. Free, "Specificity of a Glucose Oxidase Test for Urine Glucose," *Science* **125**, 1082–1083 (1957).

62. H. Altermatt and H. Deuel, "Enzymatic Hydrolysis of Pectic Acid on the Isolation of Oligogalacturonic Acids," *Helv. Chim. Acta* **35**, 1422 (1952).

63. Anon., "Approved Peroxide-Catalase Use of Cheesemaking," *Milk Prod. J.* **53**, 9 (1962).

64. R. R. Baldwin, H. A. Campbell, R. Thiessen, and G. J. Lorant, "The Use of Glucose Oxidase in Processing of Foods with Special Emphasis on Desugaring of Egg White," *Food Technol.* **7**, 275–82 (1953).

65. R. R. Barton, S. S. Rennert, and L. A. Underkofler, "Enzyme Protects Canned Drinks," *Food Eng.* **27**, 79, 198 (1955).

66. R. R. Barton, "The Action of an Enzyme for Flavor Enhancement of Legumes, *Food Technol.* **14** (4), 25 (1960), Abstract 51.

67. R. R. Barton, S. S. Rennert, and L. A. Underkofler, "Glucose Oxidase in the Protection of Foods and Beverages," *Food Technol.* **11** (12), 683–686 (1957).

68. V. Bavisotto, C. Miller, and R. Dewane, "Compatability of Plant, Animal and Microbiological Proteases," *Food Res.* **25** (1), 58–63 (1960).

69. F. E. Baum, "The Use of Hyaluronidase in Pudenal Block," *Am. J. Obstet. Gynecol.* **60**, 1356 (1950).

70. E. J. Beckhorn, "Production of Industrial Enzymes," *Wallerstein Lab. Commun.* **23** (82), (1960).

71. H. E. Bode, "Enzyme Acts as Tenderizer," *Food Eng.* **26**, 94 (1954).

72. H. C. Borghetty and J. T. Taylor, "Desizing Procedures in Relation to Enzyme Evaluation," *Am. Dyestuff Reptr.* **44** (8), 256 (1955).

73. F. W. Bowman, "Rapid Visual Assay for Penicillinase Concentrates," *J. Pharm. Sci.* **51**, 706 (1962).

74. G. Brunelli and A. E. Poggi, "Lysozyme Used by the Intraarticular Route in Chronic Arthosynovitis. Clinical Observations," *Minerva Med.* **54**, 1016–21 (1963).

75. L. C. Burket and P. Gyorgy, "Clinical Observations on the Use of Hyaluronidase," *J. Pediat.* **3**, 56–63 (1949).

76. E. J. Calesnick, C. H. Hills, and J. J. Willaman, "Properties of a Commercial Fungal Pectase Preparation," *Arch. Biochem. Biophys.* **28**, 433 (1950).

77. J. W. Carr, T. C. Loughheed, and B. E. Baker, "Studies on Protein Hydrolysis. IV. Further Observations on the Taste of Enzymic Protein Hydrolysates," *J. Sci. Food Agr.* **7** (10), 627–629 (1956).

78. L. P. Carroll, B. S. Miller, and J. A. Johnson, "The Application of Enzymes in Pre-Ferment Processes for Bread Production," *Cereal Chem.* **33** (5), 303 (1956).

79. J. F. Conn, J. A. Johnson, and B. S. Miller, "An Investigation of Commercial Fungal and Bacterial Alpha-Amylase Preparations in Baking," *Cereal Chem.* **27** (3), 191 (1950).

80. W. V. Cruess and J. Besone, "Observations on the Use of Pectic Enzymes in Wine Making," *Fruit Prod. J.* **20** (12), 365–7 (1941).

81. W. V. Cruess and J. H. Kilbuck, "Pectic Enzymes in Wine Making," *Wines & Vines* **28**, 23–24 (1947).

82. M. L. Cushing and C. W. Turner, "Enzyme Converted Starches as Coating Adhesives," *Tappi* **41**, 345 (1958).

83. N. Cusma and V. Mastandrea, "Research on the Antibacterial Activity of Lysozyme," *Voll. Soc. Ital. Biol. Sper.* **39**, 572–6 (1963).

84. G. I. de Becze, J. W. Votaw, Jr., and R. H. Nanz, Jr., "Evaluation of Diastatic Activity of Malt-Containing Liquids by a Modified Lasché Test," *Cereal Chem.* **25** (2), 148 (1949).

85. G. I. de Becze, "Qualifications of Malt," *Am. Wine & Liquor J.* (Feb. 1941).

86. R. G. Dworschach and L. J. Wickerham, "Invertase from Yeasts," *Appl. Microbiol.* **9**, 291 (1961).

87. Anon., "Enzyme Forms Blue Cheese Flavors," *Chem. Eng. News* **38**, 124 (Dec. 5, 1960).

88. Z. V. Ermol'eva, et al., "Experimental Study and Clinical Applications of Lysozyme," *Antibiotiki* **8** (1), 39 (1963).

89. M. G. Farnham, J. H. Nelson, and A. R. Kemp, "A Study of the Lipolysis Induced in Various Milks by Pregastric Esterases Obtained from Suckling Mammals," *J. Dairy Sci.* **39**, 928 (1956) (Abstract).

90. R. L. Gates and R. M. Sandstedt, "A Method of Determining Enzymatic Digestion of Raw Starch," *Cereal Chem.* **3**, 413 (1953).

91. F. P. Griffiths and B. J. Lime, "Debittering of Grapefruit Products with Naringinase," *Food Technol.* **13**, 430 (1959).

92. W. M. Gysin and J. L. Wilson, "Hyaluronidase in Insulin Coma Therapy," *Diseases Nervous System* **15** (5), 1–4 (1954).

93. W. J. Harper, "Lipase Systems Used in the Manufacture of Italian Cheese. II. Selective Hydrolysis," *J. Dairy Sci.* **40**, 556 (1957).

94. D. Herbert and J. Pinsent, "Crystalline Bacterial Catalase," *Biochem. J.* **43**, 193–202 (1948).

95. E. J. Jewett, D. A. M. Mackay, K. S. Koningsbacher, and T. Hasselstrom, "The Role of Enzymes in Food Flavors," *Food Technol.* **10** (10), 387–489 (1956).

96. M. Holden, "A Study of Enzymes that can Break Down Tobacco Leaf Components. V. Unfractionated Fungal Enzymes," *Biochem. J.* **47**, 426 (1950).

97. H. T. Huang, "Decolorization of Anthocyanins by Fungal Enzymes," *J. Agr. Food Chem.* **3** (2), 141 (1955).

98. A. A. Jaworski and J. E. Farley, "Hyaluronidase in Administration of Fluids," *Am. J. Diseases Children* **79**, 59 (1950).

99. K. Kovacs, "Lysozyme in Bronchopulmonology," *Tuberkulozis* **14**, 75–7 (1961).

100. Z. I. Kertesz, "A New Method for the Enzymic Clarification of Apple Juice," *N.Y. State Agr. Exp. Sta. Bull.* **589** (1930).

101. Z. I. Kertesz, G. L. Baker, G. H. Joseph, H. H. Mottern, and A. G. Olsen, "Report of the Committee for the Revision of the Nomenclature of Pectic Substances," *Chem. Eng. News* **22** (2), 105 (Jan. 25, 1944).

102. J. H. Kilbuck, F. Nussenbaum, and W. V. Cruess, "The Effect of Pectic Enzymes Used in the Clarification of Apple Juice," *Food Res.* **18**, 511 (1953).

103. J. H. Kilbuck, F. Nussenbaum, and W. V. Cruess, "Pectic Enzymes. Investigations on Their Use in Making Wines," *Wines & Vines* **30** (Aug. 1949).

104. T. Kitamikado and N. Toyama, "An Assay Method for Cellulase Based on the Breakdown of Filter Paper," *J. Ferment. Technol.* (Japan) **40** (2), 85 (1962).

105. R. B. Koch and C. G. Ferrari, "Investigation of Proteolytic Enzymes by a Gelatin Viscosity Technic," *Cereal Chem.* **32**, 254–269 (1955).

106. F. V. Kosikowski and R. A. Ledford, "Anaerobiosis Produced by Glucose Oxidase to Control Growth of Test Bacteria in Antibiotic Assays," *J. Dairy Sci.* **47** (7), 758–760 (1964).

107. M. A. Krishnaswamy, D. S. Johar, V. Subramanyan, and S. P. Thomas, "Cheese Making, Using Vegetable Proteases," *Food Technol.* **15**, 482 (1961).

108. G. B. Levy, "Automatic Measurement of Optical Rotation," *Anal. Chem.* **23**, 1089 (1951).

109. G. B. Levy and E. S. Cook, "A Rotographic Study of Mutarotase," *Biochem. J.* **57** (1), 50 (1954).

110. G. B. Levy, "A Unit for Penicillinase," *Nature* **166**, 740 (1950).

111. L. Lofgren, "Local Changes in Experimental Arthritis and the Effect on Them of Hyaluronidase," *Ann. Med. Exptl. Biol. Fenniae* (*Helsinki*) **37**, 276 (1959).

112. R. M. McCready and E. A. McComb, "Course of Action of Polygalacturonase on Polygalacturonic Acids," *Agr. Food Chem.* **1**, 1165 (1953).

113. R. E. Marshall, "Prevention of Sedimentation in Apple Juice Clarified by the Enzymic Method, *Food Packer* **27** (Aug. 1946).

114. M. J. Mason and R. J. Horst, "Use of the Corn Industry Viscometer for the Evaluation of Starches and Enzymes," *Tappi* **35**, 25 (1952).

115. G. Mier, V. J. Rhodes, L. G. Mahrag, N. S. Webb, et al., "Beef Tenderization with Proteolytic Enzymes," *Food Technol.* **16**, 111 (1962).

116. B. S. Miller and J. A. Johnson, "Fungal Enzymes in Baking," *Baker's Dig.* **29**, 95, 166 (1955).

117. B. S. Miller, J. A. Johnson, and D. L. Palmer, "A Comparison of Cereal, Fungal, and Bacterial Alpha-Amylase as Supplements for Breadmaking," *Food Technol.* **7**, 38–42 (1953).

118. D. S. Miyada, and A. L. Tappel, "The Hydrolysis of Beef Proteins by Various Proteolytic Enzymes," *Food Res.* **21** (2), 217 (1956).

119. D. C. Moore, "An Evaluation of Hyaluronidase in Local and Nerve Block Anesthesia: A Review of 519 Cases," *Anesthesiology* **11**, 470 (1950).

120. V. Moseley and B. M. Montgomery, "Subacute Bacterial Endocarditis: The Use of Hyaluronidase as a Supplement to Penicillin Treatment in Bacterial Endocarditis," *J. S. Carolina Med. Assoc.* **46**, 244 (1950).

121. G. Reed, "Industrial Enzymes," *Food Eng.*, pp. 9–12 (May 1952).

122. J. H. Northrop, *J. Gen. Physiol.* **9**, 767 (1926).

123. Donald W. Ohlmeyer, "Use of Glucose Oxidase to Stabilize Beer," *Food Technol.* **11** (10), 503–507 (1957).

124. W. J. Olson, R. Evans, and A. D. Dickson, *Cereal Chem.* **21**, 533 (1944).

125. A. Perlazzo and G. Lombard, "Fleming's Enzyme (Lysozyme) and its Importance for Infant Nutrition," *Ann. Paediat.* (*Basel*) **200**, 305–18 (1963).

126. J. L. Parrot and G. Nicot, "Antihistaminic Action of Lysozyme," *Nature* **197**, 496 (1963).

127. J. C. Pew, "Properties of Powdered Wood and Isolation of Lignin by Cellulytic Enzymes," *Tappi* **40** (7), 553 (1957).

128. E. M. Popova and M. G. Puchkova, "Significance of the Enzyme Complex of the Preparation from *B. cineria* for Grape Wort (Must)," *Biokhim. Vinodeliya* **1**, 71 (1947).

129. F. E. Potter, "A Colorimetric Method for the Quantitative Determination of the Degree of Lactose Hydrolysis," *J. Dairy Sci.* **33**, 803–808 (1950).

130. F. E. Potter and B. H. Webb, "The Enzymatic Hydrolysis of Lactose in Skimmilk and Whey," *The Butter, Cheese & Milk Products Journal* (Nov. 1951).

131. D. E. Pratt and J. J. Powers, "The Thermal Destruction of Pectic Enzymes in Grapefruit Juice," *Food Res.* **18**, 152 (1953).

132. B. Rahman and M. A. Joslyn, "The Hydrolysis of Pectic Acid by Purified Fungal Polygalacturonase," *Food Res.* **18**, 308 (1953).

133. G. Reed, "Fungal Enzymes in Bread Baking," *Food Technol.* **6**, 339–341 (1952).

134. G. Reed, "Recent Investigations of Pectic Enzymes and Their Application in Wine Making," *Am. J. of Enol.* **6**, 17–24 (1955).

135. I. Regan, "Enzymes and their Application in Textile Processing, Especially Desizing," *J. Soc. Dyers Colourists,* **78** (11), 533–542 (1962).

136. V. Ricci, "The Therapeutic Action, in Various Diseases of the Nose and Sinuses, of Lysozyme in Combination with Antihistaminics and Synthetic Capillary Protective Agents," *Omnia Therap.* **12**, 379–96 (1961).
137. L. P. Ruiz, "Therapeutic Applications of Hyaluronidase," *Rev. Clin. Espan.* **56**, 343 (1955).
138. J. J. Sampey and C. E. Neubeck, "Low-Lactose Concentrate makes Better Ice Cream," *Food Eng.* **17**, 68 (1955).
139. R. M. Sandstedt, E. Kneen, and M. J. Blish, "A Standardized Wohlgemuth Procedure for alpha-Amylase Activity," *Cereal Chem.* **16**, 712–723 (1939).
140. J. Schwartzman, "Use of Hyaluronidase in General Practice," *Clin. Med.* **61**, 469 (1954).
141. J. Schwartzman and M. Levbarg, "Hyaluronidase: Further Evaluation in Pediatrics," *J. Pediat.* **36**, 79 (1950).
142. D. Scott, "Kinetics of Action of *Aspergillus* Catalase." *Enzymologia* **22**, 223–228 (1960).
143. D. Scott and F. E. Hammer, "Properties of *Aspergillus* Catalase." *Enzymologia* **22**, 229–237 (1960).
144. D. Scott and F. E. Hammer, "Assay of Catalase for Commercial Use," *Enzymologia* **22**, 194–200 (1960).
145. R. A. Srinivasan, M. K. K. Lyengar, I. J. Babbar, S. C. Chakravorty, A. T. Dudandi, and K. K. Iya, "Milk-Clotting Enzymes from Microorganisms." *Appl. Microbiol.* **12** (6), 475 (1964).
146. K. L. Smiley, M. C. Cadmus, D. E. Hensley, and A. A. Lagoda, "High-Potency Amyloglucosidase-Producing Mold of the *Aspergillus niger* Group," *Appl. Microbiol.* **12** (5), 455 (1964).
147. Szendroi, et al., "Influencing the Urinary Bladder Wall by Hyaluronidase," *Z. Urol.* **51**, 99 (1958).
148. J. Takamine, "Enzymes of *Aspergillus oryzae* and the Application of its Amyloclastic Enzyme to the Fermentation Industry," *Ind. Eng. Chem.* **6**, 824 828 (1914).
149. A. L. Tappel et al., "Application of Meat Tenderizer," *Calif. Agr.* **10**, 10 (1956).
150. L. J. Tepley, P. H. Derse, and W. V. Price, "Composition and Nutritive Value of Cheese Produced from Milk Treated with Hydrogen Peroxide and Catalase," *J. Dairy Sci.* **41**, 593–605 (1958).
151. D. W. Thomas, C. V. Smythe, and M. D. Labbee, "Enzymatic Hydrolysis of Naringin, the Bitter Principle of Grapefruit," *Food Res.* **23**, 1 (1958).
152. G. C. Tinozzi and L. Bruni, "On the Possible Therapeutic Utility of the Association of Lysozyme and Corticoids in Dermatology," *Minerva Dermatol.* **38**, 34–7 (1963).
153. M. S. Tuchman and S. E. Moolten, "The Use of Hyaluronidase in Preventing the Pain of Subcutaneous Heparin Injection," *Am. J. Med. Sci.* **219**, 147 (1950).
154. L. A. Underkofler, G. M. Severson, K. J. Goering, and L. M. Christensen, "Commercial Production and Use of Mold Bran," *Cereal Chem.* **24**, 1–22 (1947).
155. L. A. Underkofler, "Enzyme Supplementation in Baking," *Baker's Dig.* **34** (Oct. 1961).
156. L. A. Underkofler, R. R. Barton, and F. L. Aldrich, "Methods of Assay for Microbial Enzymes," *Develop. Ind. Microbiol.* **2**, 171 (1960).
157. L. A. Underkofler, "Proteolytic Activity of Patent Flour and Malted Wheat Flour," *J. Assoc. Offic. Agr. Chemists* **44** (2), 344 (1961).
158. H. A. Veringa, "Rennet Substitutes," *Dairy Sci. Abstr.* **23**, 197 (1961).
159. L. Wallerstein, "Chillproofing and Stabilization of Beer," *Wallerstein Lab. Commun.* **19**, 95–107 (1956).
160. H. Wang and N. Maynard, "Studies on Enzymatic Tenderization of Meat. I. Basic Technique and Histological Observation of Enzymatic Action," *Food Res.* **20** (6), 587 (1955).
161. H. Y. Yang, G. E. Thomas, and E. H. Wiegand, "The Application of Pectic Enzymes to Berry and Concord Wines," *Wines & Vines* **31** (4), 77–79 (1950).
162. H. Y. Yang, and W. F. Steele, "Removal of Excessive Anthocyanin Pigment by Enzyme," *Food Technol.* **12** (10), 517 (1958).
163. H. Y. Yang, and E. H. Wiegand, "Production of Fruit Wines in the Pacific Northwest," *Fruit Prod. J.* **29**, 8 (1949).

GEORGE I. DE BECZE
Schenley Distillers, Inc.

EPINEPHRINE

Epinephrine, USP XVII (adrenaline, BP), is the principal pressor hormone of the medulla of the adrenal (suprarenal) gland (see also Hormones). It was the first hormone to be obtained in crystalline form, and is a colorless, odorless, bitter-tasting substance, which on exposure to air gradually assumes a tan or light-brown color. Epinephrine (**1**) is an amino alcohol, 1-(3,4-dihydroxyphenyl)-2-methylaminoethanol (CA, 3,4-dihydroxy-α-(methylaminomethyl)benzyl alcohol), $(OH)_2C_6H_3CHOHCH_2$-$NHCH_3$. It may exist in two optically active forms; the more physiologically active one, occurring in the adrenal gland, is the levo isomer. Epinephrine possesses powerful physiological activity; in common with a group of related amines, its action mimics the effects of stimulating the sympathetic nerves and for that reason it is called a "sympathomimetic" amine (see also Vol. 4, p. 517). The name epinephrine (from the Greek *epi*, on, and *nephros*, kidney) was proposed in 1897 by Abel (2), who isolated the product in the form of the monobenzoyl derivative (1). The name Adrenalin, which has been kept as a trademarked name in the United States (by Parke, Davis & Co.) was given the product by Takamine, who isolated the crystalline base in 1900 (33). Other trademarked names are Suprarenin (the name first proposed by von Fürth), Sterling Drug Inc.; Suprarenalin, Armour & Co.; Supranephrin, William H. Rorer, Inc.; and Adnephrine, Frederick Stearns & Co. In the older literature, epinephrine is generally designated chemically either as a derivative of β-phenylethylamine (phenethylamine), $C_6H_4CH_2CH_2NH_2$, or of protocatechuyl alcohol $(OH)_2C_6H_3CH_2OH$.

epinephrine (**1**)   norepinephrine (**2**)

Goldenberg and his associates showed that norepinephrine (noradrenaline), (**2**), which differs from epinephrine only by the absence of the *N*-methyl group, occurs together with epinephrine in the adrenal medulla (14), and has been a constituent of epinephrine prepared from natural sources. The co-occurrence of these compounds in varying proportions has also been demonstrated in blood (30) and other tissues (23).

Physical and Chemical Properties

Epinephrine, mp 211–212°C (215°C, when heated rapidly), crystallizes from aqueous solutions in plates, prisms, or needles, depending upon the conditions of precipitation. Crystallographic constants have not been reported. Optical rotation in aqueous solution as the hydrochloride is −50 to −53°. Epinephrine, in powder form, is quite stable over a period of months, and a dark-brown sample may still retain 90% of its physiological activity. However, the *U.S. Pharmacopeia* requires packaging in airtight, light-resistant containers, and warns against using epinephrine in water solution (prepared with the aid of hydrochloric acid) if the solution has turned brown or contains a precipitate. The solubility of epinephrine in water is approx 1 part in 3000 at 20°C and, in absolute ethyl alcohol, 1 part in 2000 at 25°C; epinephrine is insoluble in ether and in chloroform.

Epinephrine is amphoteric and, because of its basic amino group, is readily extracted with the aid of dilute acids; but, because of its acidic (phenolic) groups, epinephrine fails to precipitate when an excess of strong alkali is added. Moreover, since it is a polyhydroxyphenol, it is readily oxidized yielding highly colored solutions, especially in the presence of alkali, a reaction in which iron is a catalyst. Epinephrine is oxidized with hydrogen peroxide or potassium permanganate to form oxalic acid. Epinephrine boiled with hydrogen iodide yields methylamine; fusion with an alkali yields protocatechuic acid and pyrocatechol.

Isolation

The observation that extracts of the adrenal gland contain an active principle that constricts the blood vessels and thereby raises the blood pressure was reported in 1894–1895 by the English physicians Oliver and Schäfer. Within a year, this pressor principle was identified with the reducing agent, a chromogenic substance, that had been found in the adrenal gland by Vulpian as early as 1856. Soon after Oliver and Schäfer's announcement, the work of isolation and chemical identification was undertaken independently by Moore in England, Fränkel and von Fürth in Austria, and Abel, Aldrich (3), and Takamine in the United States, among others. One month after Takamine isolated the hormone in crystalline form, Aldrich also completed his isolation, and, in 1901, announced the correct empirical formula, $C_9H_{13}NO_3$. He also pointed out that Abel's epinephrine differed from the pure principle in possessing a benzoyl radical, a fact which was recognized independently by Abel. Although the relationship to pyrocatechol was suspected by some of the early workers and structural formulas for epinephrine were soon proposed, the final proof of structure awaited synthesis.

The method of isolation as disclosed in Takamine's patents is surprisingly simple and still remains a satisfactory laboratory procedure (33): Finely chopped adrenal glands (separation of cortex and medulla is unnecessary) are extracted with hot water (the glands contain sufficient lactic acid), the solution is concentrated in vacuum, alcohol is added to precipitate proteins and inorganic salts, the alcohol is removed by distillation, and the principle is precipitated by addition of sodium hydroxide followed by excess carbon dioxide, or by ammonia. For purification, the product is dissolved in the minimum amount of acid, excess alcohol is added, the precipitate is removed by filtration, and the crystalline principle is precipitated by the addition of ammonia, the process being repeated if necessary to obtain a product free of ash and of maximum melting point. Other methods, such as Fränkel's procedure and von Fürth's lead acetate precipitation method (tried out by Abel), also possessed merit.

Epinephrine is present in the adrenal gland in a relatively high concentration (0.2% on the basis of fresh gland tissue, which corresponds to 1% on the dry basis). Since only 25% of gland tissue is water-soluble, the investigators had available crude extracts containing the relatively enormous concentration of 4% of active principle on the basis of solid content. A mere 25-fold concentration was necessary to isolate the hormone, which crystallized without difficulty from deproteinized solutions. Extracts of adrenal glands of cattle were found by Goldenberg to contain 82–88% of epinephrine and 12–18% of norepinephrine (14). Separation of the two hormones may be effected by repeated precipitations, but better still by crystallization of the tartrates.

Biogenesis and Metabolism

By the use of radioactive-tracer techniques, Udenfriend (28) has demonstrated that the main pathway of synthesis in the mammalian body is from phenylalanine (**3**), to tyrosine (**4**), to 3,4-dihydroxyphenylalanine (DOPA) (**5**), and via 3,4-dihydroxyphenethylamine to (adrenal) norepinephrine (**2**) and epinephrine (**1**). The tracers

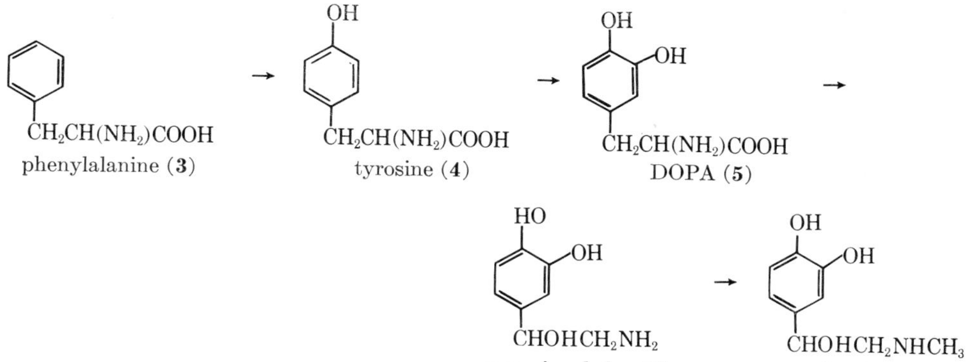

OH

CH₂CH(NH₂)COOH
phenylalanine (**3**)

CH₂CH(NH₂)COOH
tyrosine (**4**)

CH₂CH(NH₂)COOH
DOPA (**5**)

CHOHCH₂NH₂
norepinephrine (**2**)

CHOHCH₂NHCH₃
epinephrine (**1**)

which proved to serve as precursors in this experiment were DL-phenylalanine-3-^{14}C, DL-tyrosine-2-^{14}C, and DOPA-3-^{14}C; the highest labeling was achieved with DOPA.

The methyl group for the final conversion from norepinephrine to epinephrine is supplied by methionine (see Amino acids). This latter step may well be an equilibrium since Yagi and Nagatsu (31) have shown that rat liver mitochondria will demethylate epinephrine to norepinephrine.

Shaw, McMillan, and Armstrong (26) showed that dihydroxyphenylalanine (**5**) was metabolized to homovanillic (**6**) and homopyrocatechuic (**7**) acids.

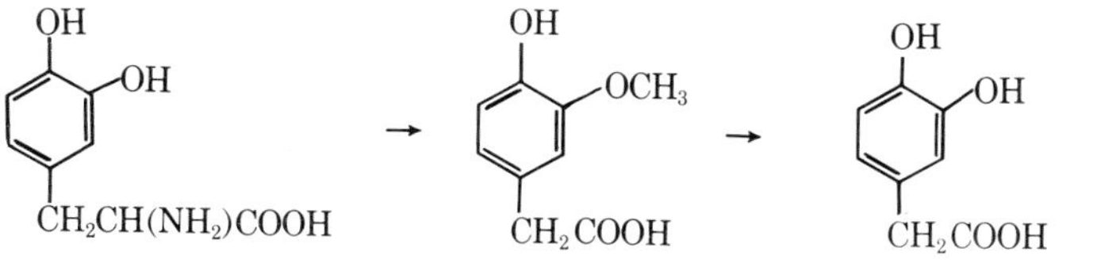

CH₂CH(NH₂)COOH
DOPA (**5**)

CH₂COOH
homovanillic
acid (**6**)

CH₂COOH
homopyrocatechuic
acid (**7**)

Axelrod (21), using tritiated epinephrine, demonstrated that in man the major metabolites found in the urine are free and conjugated metanephrine (epinephrine 3-methyl ether) (**8**) (54%) and 3-methoxy-4-hydroxymandelic acid (**9**) (36%), which are biologically inert. Labeled metanephrine gave essentially the same recovery and proportion of product.

CHOHCH₂NHCH₃
metanephrine (**8**)

CHOH COOH
3-methoxy-4-hydroxy-
mandelic acid (**9**)

Synthesis

Epinephrine has been synthesized by several methods. The first synthesis, by Stolz in 1904, involved the following steps:

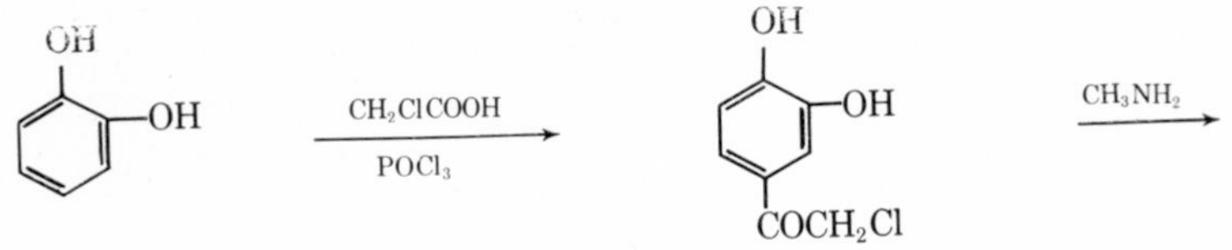

pyrocatechol (**10**)

3,4-dihydroxy-α-chloroacetophenone (**11**)

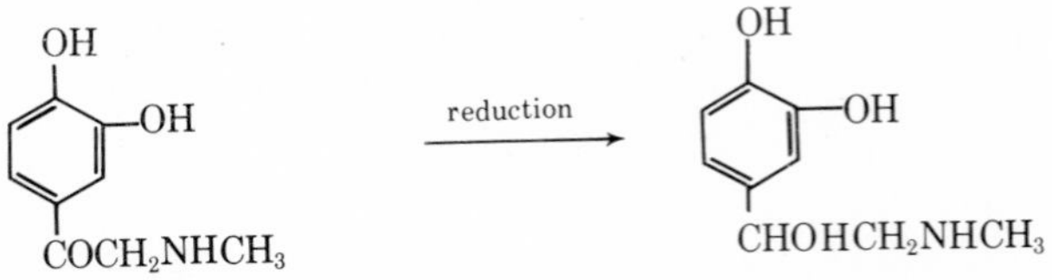

adrenalone (**12**)

epinephrine (**1**)

Some of the other published methods involve modifications of this procedure or of its individual steps. A distinctly new and unusually simple method was described by Nagai (32):

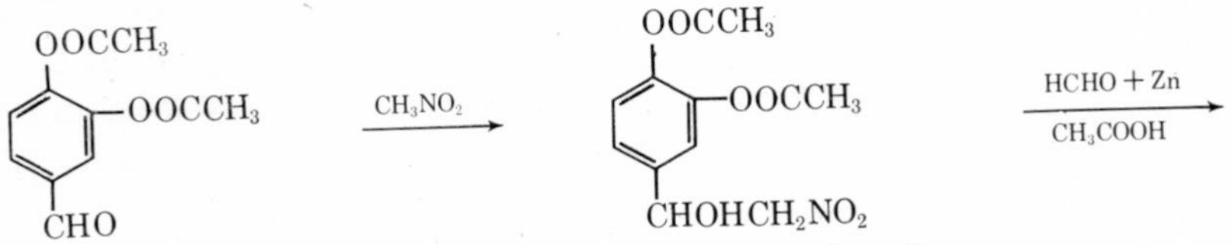

protocatechu-aldehyde diacetate (**13**)

1-(3,4-diacetoxyphenyl)-2-nitroethanol (**14**)

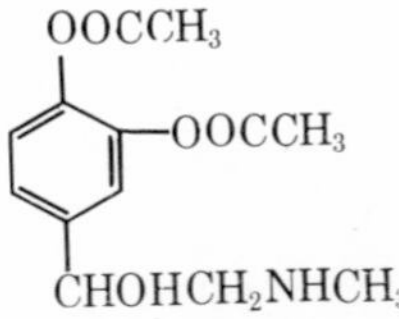

1-(3,4-diacetoxy-phenyl)-2-methyl-aminoethanol (**15**)

By removal of the acetyl groups, epinephrine was obtained. Synthesis of compounds closely related to epinephrine by Dakin (10) and Friedmann (13) also contributed to the proof of structure.

The synthetic epinephrine is, of course, the *dl* form, which is about one-half as active as the natural product. The *dl* isomer is resolved into the optically active forms with *d*-tartaric acid. Synthetic *l*-epinephrine has captured the major share of the pharmaceutical market.

Analysis and Testing

Epinephrine yields colored solutions with ferric chloride, iodine, and several other oxidizing agents, and quantitative assay methods can be based on such reactions, which however, fail to differentiate between the two optical isomers. The USP assay method is based upon the blood-pressure effect when dilute solutions (usually 1 part in 100,000) are administered intravenously. The method is essentially the same as the one described by Houghton (20).

Sensitive fluorimetric methods of assay have been developed from the observations of Ehrlén (11) on the fluorescence of trihydroxyindole (**17**) and have been critically compared by Udenfriend (29). By combining chromatographic techniques with the reaction of ethylenediamine and the catecholamine oxidation products, Weil-Malherbe and Bone (30) developed a fluorescent method sensitive to a level of 1 μg/liter whereby epinephrine and norepinephrine can be determined simultaneously in tissues. The fluorophor structure is probably (**19**). This may be, and is, used as a diagnostic method, for example, in pheochromocytoma (tumor of the adrenal gland), where the ratio of norepinephrine to epinephrine is greatly increased.

Pharmacological Action

Epinephrine performs several physiological functions by stimulating the effector cells innervated by the sympathetic (autonomic) nervous system, which, as differentiated from the central or cerebrospinal nervous system, governs involuntary functions of the various organs (see Psychopharmacological agents). Each tissue that is controlled by the sympathetic system gets its stimulus from two kinds of nerve fibers, the sympathetic (adrenergic) and parasympathetic (cholinergic), which convey opposing impulses to the effector cells through the release of specific chemical substances. In the simplest terms, sympathetic nerve impulses release norepinephrine and parasympathetic nerve impulses release acetylcholine (16) (see Vol. 5, p. 409).

The most striking effect of intravenous administration of small amounts of epinephrine is the increase in blood pressure. This effect is brought about by direct action on the smooth muscle of the heart, increasing of cardiac output, and constriction of the arterioles (see Vol. 5, pp. 510, 517). In its effect on blood pressure, l-epinephrine was reported by Cushny to be 15 times as potent as the dextro isomer (9). Later work showed the levo form to be 18.5 times as potent as the dextro isomer (27).

Epinephrine is a metabolic stimulant, increasing oxygen consumption and promoting the combustion of carbohydrate. It mobilizes sugar from the liver and thus elevates the blood-sugar level. Another important result is its relaxing effect on the bronchial muscles, which is the basis of its usefulness in the treatment of asthma. Epinephrine also relaxes the musculature of the gastrointestinal tract, but contracts the spleen; the latter action accounts for an increase in the number of red cells released into the blood stream following the injection of epinephrine.

Few compounds have been used so extensively in physiological experiments in the laboratory and in clinical applications as has epinephrine. This is due partly to its early discovery, but also to the multiplicity of its physiological reactions. And yet few, if any, of the uses of epinephrine relate to substitution therapy, that is, its use to overcome an adrenal deficiency. Such applications are of little importance; the adrenal medulla, in contrast to the adrenal cortex, is not essential to life.

Goldenberg et al. claim that l-epinephrine acts as an overall vasodilator (15), in extremely dilute physiological concentrations only. In higher concentrations, however, l-epinephrine acts as a vasoconstrictor and, in this capacity, is used clinically (usually in the form of its hydrochloride) in hemorrhages of the skin and mucous membranes and in catarrhal and congestive conditions, in the treatment of asthma.

and in order to prolong the effects of local anesthetics. Where a slower but more lasting action is desired, epinephrine may be injected as a sterile suspension of the base in vegetable oil. An ointment containing the bitartrate salt is useful, topically, for reducing intraocular tension in chronic simple glaucoma. The usual dose of epinephrine hydrochloride is 0.06–1.00 mg in 1:1000 solution.

Epinephrine is contraindicated in case of shock, hyperthyroidism, arteriosclerosis, and angina pectoris. Doses larger than 1 mg may cause mild restlessness, anxiety, headache, tremor, weakness, dizziness, and palpitations.

Pharmacologists have noted no difference between natural and synthetic *l*-epinephrine in regard to their localizing action on local anesthetics. Norepinephrine, on the other hand, differs from epinephrine by acting as an overall vasoconstrictor. It also differs by causing no change or only a slight decrease in cardiac output.

More extensive treatment of the pharmacological and clinical aspects of epinephrine and norepinephrine may be found in Barcroft (4), Manger (22), and especially the Ciba Foundation Symposium on adrenergic mechanisms (8).

Relation of Structure to Physiological Activity. The classical publication of Barger and Dale in 1909 constitutes the first pretentious inquiry concerning the relationship of structure to physiological activity (5). Even in 1905, Dakin had directed an inquiry into this field (10). Pyrocatechol was found to have an appreciable effect on blood pressure whereas the compound corresponding to the side chain of epinephrine possess no such activity. Publications of Barger, Dale, and Pyman indicate the following conclusions (summarized by Hartung) (19): (*1*) Methylamine causes a drop in blood pressure. With increase in molecular weight in the homologous series of aliphatic amines, pressor activity is observed and reaches a maximum in *n*-hexylamine. (*2*) In the aromatic series, pressor activity is at a maximum in compounds possessing a β-amino group in the side chain. Shift of the amino group either to the α or γ position in the side chain decreases activity. (*3*) An additional alkyl (usually methyl) in the side chain may confer oral activity on the compound. (*4*) Substitution on the amino group usually decreases activity. (*5*) Introduction of a phenolic hydroxyl group in 1-phenyl-2-aminoethanol, $C_6H_5CHOHCH_2NH_2$, increases pressor activity. Phenolic groups in both the 3 and 4 positions produce a maximum effect. (*6*) The alcoholic hydroxyl group in the α-position enhances the pressor effect. (*7*) Activity resides almost entirely in the levo isomers, as has already been discussed. A more detailed discussion of structure–activity relationships is given by Goodman and Gilman (16).

The relative approximate pressor effects of the following compounds support these generalizations: 1-phenyl-2-methylaminoethanol, 0.002; 1-(4-hydroxyphenyl)-2-methylaminoethanol (Synephrine), 0.01; 1-(3-hydroxyphenyl)-2-methylaminoethanol (Neo-Synephrine), 0.1; 1-(3,4-dihydroxyphenyl)-2-methylaminoethanol (epinephrine), 1.0; and 1-(3,4-dihydroxyphenyl)-2-aminoethanol (norepinephrine), 1.6.

Derivatives and Related Compounds

Numerous derivatives of epinephrine have been synthesized and a number of them have been introduced into medicine and have found limited applications. Other compounds related to epinephrine are found in nature also, the best known being the ephedra alkaloids (see Vol. 1, pp. 769, 788).

The first synthetic substitute for epinephrine to be marketed was Epinine, Burroughs-Wellcome & Co. Inc., $(OH)_2C_6H_3CH_2CH_2NHCH_3$. Others include

Synephrine, Frederick Stearns & Co., $4\text{-}HOC_6H_4CHOHCH_2NHCH_3$; Neo-Synephrine, Sterling Drug Inc., $3\text{-}HOC_6H_4CHOHCH_2NHCH_3$; Corbasil, I. G. Farbenind., A.G., $(OH)_2C_6H_3CHOHCH(CH_3)NH_2$; Butanephrine, Winthrop-Stearns, $(OH)_2C_6H_3CHOHCH(C_2H_5)NH_2$; and Aludrine, C. H. Boehringer, Sohn, $(OH)_2C_6H_3CHOHCH_2NHCH(CH_3)_2$, which was developed in Germany during World War II, and recently received extensive clinical evaluation in the U.S. (17). Norepinephrine, the racemic form of which was marketed in 1907 under the name of arterenol, although once abandoned clinically, has been extensively studied in recent years, particularly in the laboratory, because of the primary role of the levo isomer in the function of the sympathetic nervous system. Resolution of the synthetic product into its optical isomers has shown that, just as in the case of epinephrine, physiological activity resides chiefly in the levo isomer (6,12,14).

Oxidation products of epinephrine are illustrated by formulas (16) to (19). Adrenochrome (18) and some of its derivatives have been considered as possible therapeutic agents in hypertension (24,25). In Germany during World War II it was tried in diabetes mellitus but without success.

      (16)   **(17)**   **(18)**   **(19)**

The extent of the literature on derivatives of epinephrine is presented impressively in Bovet's monograph on the subject (7). A three-volume annotated bibliography on epinephrine itself has been published by Griffith (18).

Bibliography

"Epinephrine" in *ECT* 1st ed., Vol. 5, pp. 763–768, by Oliver Kamm, Parke, Davis & Company.

1. J. J. Abel, *Am. J. Pharm.* **75**, 301 (1903).
2. J. J. Abel, *Z. Physiol. Chem.* **28**, 320 (1899).
3. T. B. Aldrich, *Am. J. Physiol.* **5**, 457 (1901); *J. Am. Chem. Soc.* **27**, 1074 (1905).
4. H. Barcroft, *Sympathetic Control of Human Blood Vessels*, Edward Arnold and Co., London, and The Williams & Wilkins Co., Baltimore, Md., 1953.
5. G. Barger and H. H. Dale, *J. Physiol.* (*London*) **41**, 19 (1910).
6. S. Bergstrom, U. S. von Euler, and U. Hamberg, *Acta Chem. Scand.* **3**, 305 (1949).
7. H. D. Bovet and F. Bovet-Nitti, *Médicaments du Système Nerveux Végétatif*, Verlag S. Karger, A.G., Basel, 1948.
8. J. R. Vane, ed., *Ciba Foundation Symp. Adrenergic Mechanisms* (1960).
9. A. R. Cushny, *J. Physiol.* (*London*) **37**, 130 (1908); **38**, 259 (1909).
10. H. D. Dakin, *Proc. Roy. Soc.* (*London*) **B76**, 491, 498 (1905).
11. I. Ehrlén, *Farm. Revy* **47**, 242 (1948).
12. U. S. von Euler and U. Hamberg, *Nature* **163**, 642 (1949).
13. E. Friedmann, *Beitr. Chem. Physiol. Path.* **6**, 92 (1905); **8**, 95 (1906).
14. M. Goldenberg, M. Faber, E. J. Alston, and E. C. Chargaff, *Science* **109**, 534 (1949).
15. M. Goldenberg, K. L. Pines, E. F. Baldwin, D. G. Greene, and C. E. Roh, *Am. J. Med.* **5**, 792 (1948).
16. L. Goodman and A. Gilman, *The Pharmacological Basis of Therapeutics*, 2nd ed., The Macmillan Co., New York, 1955, pp. 476–502.
17. L. N. Gray and J. W. Long, *J. Am. Med. Assoc.* **139**, 452 (1949).
18. F. R. Griffith, *Adrenaline*, Buffalo, 1956. (Annotated bibliography.)

19. W. H. Hartung, *Chem. Revs.* **9**, 389–465 (1931).
20. E. M. Houghton, *Am. J. Pharm.* **73**, 531 (1901).
21. E. H. LaBrosse, J. Axelrod, and S. S. Kety, *Science* **128**, 593 (1958).
22. W. M. Manger, *Chemical Quantitation of Epinephrine and Norepinephrine in Plasma, in Hypertension, Shock and Mental Disease*, Charles C Thomas, Springfield, Ill., 1959.
23. K. A. Montagu, *Biochem. J.* **63**, 559 (1956).
24. K. Oster, *Nature* **150**, 289 (1942).
25. K. Oster and H. Sobotka, *J. Pharmacol. Exptl. Therap.* **78**, 100 (1943).
26. K. N. F. Shaw, A. McMillan, and M. D. Armstrong, *J. Biol. Chem.* **226**, 255 (1957); M. D. Armstrong and A. McMillan, *Fed. Proc.* **16**, 146 (1957).
27. E. E. Swanson, C. C. Scott, H. M. Lee, and K. K. Chen, *J. Pharmacol. Exptl. Therap.* **78**, 100 (1943).
28. S. Udenfriend and J. B. Wynegarden, *Biochem. Biophys. Acta* **20**, 48 (1956).
29. S. Udenfriend, *Fluorescence Assay in Biology and Medicine*, Academic Press, Inc., New York and London, 1962, pp. 139–157.
30. H. Weil-Malherbe and A. D. Bone, *Biochem. J.* **51**, 311 (1952); *Lancet* **1**, 974 (1953); *Biochem. J.* **58**, 132 (1954).
31. K. Yagi and T. Nagatsu, *Nature* **184**, 1316 (1959).
32. Brit. Pat. 118,298 (July 13, 1917), N. Nagai.
33. U.S. Pats. 730,175; 730,176; 730,196; 730,197 (June 22, 1903), J. Takamine.

H. M. CROOKS, JR.
Parke, Davis & Company

EPOXIDATION

Epoxidation may be defined as the reaction in which olefinic unsaturation is converted to a cyclic three-membered ether by active oxygen agents, as in equation 1.

$$-\overset{|}{C}=\overset{|}{C}- \quad \rightarrow \quad -\overset{|}{C}\underset{\diagdown O\diagup}{\quad}\overset{|}{C}- \tag{1}$$

The products of epoxidation are 1,2-epoxides (α-epoxides); they may also be designated as *oxirane compounds*. See also Epoxides; Epoxy resins.

Epoxides are extremely valuable commercially because of the many reactions which they undergo. Most noteworthy of these is the addition of such active hydrogen compounds as ammonia, organic acids, alcohols, and water. Their ability to donate electrons to hydrogen atoms in hydrogen bonding is important in such diverse applications as ulcer therapy and the stabilization of poly(vinyl chloride) resins. The fact that epoxides polymerize under thermal, ionic, and free radical catalysis has encouraged considerable research on epoxy homopolymers and copolymers for industrial applications. The epoxides of long-chain α-olefins are potentially useful as detergent precursors. These samples show the commercial usefulness of epoxides, particularly as chemical intermediates.

In 1963, the volume of epoxides produced in the United States by the epoxidation reaction probably amounted to more than 60 million lb (17). These materials included the epoxy plasticizer–stabilizers (41), the epoxy insecticides (60), and certain epoxy intermediates which were converted further to various end products consumed in the drug (63), coating (3), and cosmetics (71) fields. The manufacturers of these materials used hydrogen peroxide or peroxyacetic acid (peracetic acid) derived from acetaldehyde as convenient vehicles for epoxidation.

Hydrogen peroxide (52) and peroxyacetic acid prepared by the oxidation of acetaldehyde (23) are also used in Europe to manufacture epoxidized ester plasticizers, but no information is available on the quantities produced.

The years 1948–1950 mark the period in which the epoxidation reaction began to achieve commercial importance. The first epoxidation, however, was carried out by Prileschajew (31) at the Polytechnic Institute in Warsaw in 1909 when he used peroxybenzoic acid to convert such olefins as diisobutylene to the corresponding epoxide. In the forty years which elapsed between Prileschajew's discovery and industrial utilization, the epoxidation reaction was used primarily in the laboratory as a preparative method or as an analytical tool for the estimation of isolated ethylenic unsaturation. Research work during 1944–1948 by Dr. Daniel Swern and co-workers (19) of the U.S. Department of Agriculture probably has done most to focus attention on the commercial possibilities for the epoxidation reaction. Following Swern's work, the Rohm & Haas Company, Philadelphia, Pa., developed and installed the first commercial process for the production of epoxy soybean oil plasticizer–stabilizers (56).

Epoxidizing Agents

Hydrogen Peroxide. The principal chemical sold for use in commercial epoxidations has been hydrogen peroxide (qv). Hydrogen peroxide, however, is a mild oxidizing agent and must usually be transformed to a more active form for effective use in organic reactions. Convenient systems for activation of hydrogen peroxide in epoxidation include the organic peroxy acids (39), metal-activated hydrogen peroxide, and alkaline hydrogen peroxide. Peroxy acid systems involving hydrogen peroxide used commercially as epoxidizing agents may be classified as (a) preformed peroxyacetic acid, (b) peroxyacetic acid formed in situ, and (c) peroxyformic acid formed in situ. (By the in situ formation of peroxy acid is meant a one-step reaction in which peroxy acid is formed and used in the presence of the material to be epoxidized.) In 1958, the Union Carbide Corporation announced plans to construct a plant at Institute, West Virginia, to produce epoxides using peroxyacetic acid prepared by the autoxidation of acetaldehyde. This announcement marked the introduction of an important commercial epoxidizing agent not derived from hydrogen peroxide. The Institute plant is now in operation and produces epoxidized ester plasticizers and other epoxides in significant quantities. Other firms have also developed peroxyacetic acid systems based on acetaldehyde, including Celanese Corporation of America's vapor-phase oxidation (50) and Shawinigan Products Corporation's liquid-phase reaction (49). The Celanese and Shawinigan processes, however, have not been commercialized to date.

Preformed Peroxyacetic Acid. Peroxyacetic acid is prepared commercially by mixing hydrogen peroxide and glacial acetic acid as illustrated by the following equilibrium reaction (eq. 2) (14):

$$H_2O_2 + CH_3CO_2H \overset{H^+}{\rightleftharpoons} CH_3CO_3H + H_2O \qquad (2)$$

Mixtures of hydrogen peroxide and acetic acid, however, attain equilibrium at an impractically slow rate unless a strong acid catalyst is present. Therefore, 1–2% sulfuric acid is commonly used as a catalyst to hasten the formation of peroxyacetic acid. Thus, the time required for attainment of equilibrium is reduced from about 7 days in the absence of a catalyst to a period of about 4–16 hr in the presence of sulfuric acid, depending upon reaction conditions.

Many epoxides, however, are subject to ring opening in the presence of strong acids to produce hydroxyacyloxy derivatives (37). These derivatives are valuable as sources of glycols but are undesirable if epoxides are required (see eq. 3).

$$-\overset{|}{\underset{|}{C}}\underset{\diagdown \diagup}{\overset{|}{\underset{O}{C}}}- + CH_3CO_2H \xrightarrow{H^+} -\overset{|}{\underset{|}{C}}\underset{OH}{}-\overset{|}{\underset{OCOCH_3}{C}}- \xrightarrow{OH^-} -\overset{|}{\underset{OH}{C}}-\overset{|}{\underset{OH}{C}}- \qquad (3)$$

Thus, peroxyacetic acid solutions obtained under catalysis by sulfuric acid cannot be used to prepare epoxides which are sensitive to sulfuric acid. In such cases, the sulfuric acid catalyst is neutralized by sodium acetate prior to use of the peroxyacetic acid solution in epoxidation (51).

In 1953 and 1954, E. I. du Pont de Nemours & Co., Inc., introduced the concept of using poly(styrenesulfonic acid) resins as catalysts for the preformation of peroxyacetic acid and for in situ epoxidation (32). These cation exchange resins are solids, and this minimizes the problem of separating the catalysts and the peroxy acid solutions. Such catalysts may be confined in stationary columns through which the hydrogen peroxide–acetic acid mixtures flow, emerging in the effluent as peroxyacetic acid solutions free of strong acid catalysts.

Preforming peroxyacetic acid, whether under resin or sulfuric acid catalysis, requires that high-strength peroxide be used or that water be removed to obtain concentrated solutions of peroxy acid. For example, obtaining a 40% peroxyacetic acid solution in the equilibrium reaction of hydrogen peroxide and acetic acid dictates that 90% hydrogen peroxide be used. Such high-strength solutions as 70 and 90% material are available from the manufacturers of hydrogen peroxide, but use of high-strength material requires special care and handling to avoid hazards.

Distillation techniques may be employed to preform peroxyacetic acid solutions with the special characteristics often desired in epoxidation. Waterfree solutions in inert media of negli0ible acidity may be prepared by the azeotropic distillation of hydrogen peroxide, acetic acid, and catalyst in such solutions as ethyl, isopropyl, and n-propyl acetates (30). If water is required as a reaction medium, aqueous peroxyacetic acid solutions approximating a homogeneous azeotrope may be generated by flash-distilling a 1:1 molar solution of 50% hydrogen peroxide and acetic acid from a still pot containing a relatively large quantity of sulfuric acid (11,52). The reaction is conducted by continuously feeding acetic acid and hydrogen peroxide to the still pot, which is maintained at a pressure of about 50 mm Hg and a temperature of less than 50°C. Peroxyacetic acid concentrations of 45–60% in water may be obtained by this method.

Peroxyacetic Acid Formed in Situ. Where possible, hydrogen peroxide is used in epoxidation under conditions for the in situ formation of peroxyacetic acid. In in situ systems, hydrogen peroxide is charged to the reactor containing the epoxidizable substance, the catalyst, and a minimum of glacial acetic acid. Within limitations, the catalysts may be poly(styrenesulfonic acid) exchange resins (51) or sulfuric acid (67, 69). In most cases in which acid catalysts may be used, solid cation exchange resins are desirable because the surface effects of these materials operate to minimize epoxy-ring opening. Sulfuric acid tends to promote by-product formation. Undesirable by-product formation (see Fig. 1) may occur even under resin catalysis, however, if reaction time is overextended, if reaction temperature is excessive, or if excess acetic acid is used.

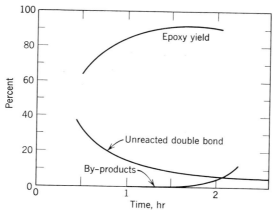

Fig. 1. Rate of product formation in the epoxidation of methyl oleate by the resin technique.

Preformed Peroxyformic Acid. Like peroxyacetic acid, peroxyformic acid may be prepared by mixing concentrated formic acid and hydrogen peroxide as in equation 4 (15).

$$HCO_2H + H_2O_2 \rightleftharpoons HCO_3H + H_2O \tag{4}$$

Mixtures of formic acid and hydrogen peroxide attain equilibrium much more rapidly than mixtures involving acetic acid so that the use of strong acid catalysts is not necessary. Formic acid, however, is approximately 12 times stronger than acetic acid and tends to induce epoxy-ring opening. For this reason, preformed peroxyformic acid is more suitable for hydroxylation reactions and is not used commercially for epoxidation.

Peroxyformic Acid Formed in Situ. Peroxyformic acid oxidation of unsaturated materials has led to good yields of hydroxyformoxy derivatives and glycols, but not epoxides. The Rohm & Haas Company in 1949, however, disclosed the first successful use of peroxyformic acid, prepared and utilized in situ, in epoxidation reactions (56). The tendency of formic acid to open the epoxy ring has been diminished in the Rohm & Haas system by use of only 0.25–0.5 mole of formic acid per mole of unsaturation. Combining the use of a minimum of formic acid and low reaction temperatures has produced an epoxidation system which is equivalent to the in situ peroxyacetic acid systems in many respects, but which precludes the necessity for a catalyst.

Peroxyacetic Acid from Acetaldehyde. The autoxidation of acetaldehyde at low temperatures in the presence of ozone or other catalysts leads to the formation of acetaldehyde hemiperoxyacetate, also called acetaldehyde monoperoxyacetate or AMP (see eq. 5) (68).

$$2\ CH_3CHO + O_2 \rightarrow CH_3\underset{OH}{CHOOCOCH_3} \tag{5}$$

Epoxides may be produced by decomposing the hemiperoxyacetate in the presence of an epoxidizable olefin while distilling off acetaldehyde liberated in the reaction (47). Presumably peroxyacetic acid is formed as an intermediate during epoxidation.

Peroxyacetic acid can be obtained from acetaldehyde hemiperoxyacetate by vapor-phase pyrolysis, followed by rapid fractional distillation to remove liberated acetaldehyde. An inert solvent such as acetone or ethyl acetate is employed to avoid the hazards of high peroxide concentrations and to increase the efficiency of the process. The resulting product is a solution of peroxyacetic acid in the inert solvent containing a small amount of by-product acetic acid. In the presence of buffering agents, such solutions constitute effective epoxidizing agents for olefins which form epoxides sensitive to ring opening by acetic acid. The acetaldehyde oxidation route forms the basis for the operation of peroxyacetic acid and epoxidation plants by the Union Carbide Corporation.

In the Celanese version (23,50) of peroxy acid formation, excess acetaldehyde and oxygen are fed to a reactor maintained at a temperature of about 120°C. Vapors containing the reaction products then flow into a distillation column into which acetone or ethyl acetate also is fed simultaneously. Peroxyacetic acid, and not acetaldehyde hemiperoxyacetate, is obtained at the base of the column in the solvent employed while unreacted acetaldehyde and solvent are recycled to the reactor.

The Shawinigan process (49), like that of Union Carbide, involves a liquid-phase oxidation of acetaldehyde. It differs, however, in the use of catalysts such as cobaltous chloride dissolved with acetaldehyde in ethyl acetate solvent. The Shawinigan process also employs temperatures ranging up to 35-55°C to preclude the formation of acetaldehyde hemiperoxyacetate.

The various acetaldehyde oxidation processes probably do not differ substantially in the economics of producing peroxyacetic acid for epoxidation. Investment and costs exclusive of raw materials may be comparable regardless of whether one elects to undertake the investment required by refrigeration or that inherent in the use of special aluminum alloys and high acetaldehyde recycles. Each of the processes probably requires the use of barricades, more or less elaborate depending upon reaction conditions, to ensure the safety of operating personnel. A large factor influencing costs may well be the relative values of acetaldehyde and acetic acid to the epoxidizer at the point of use.

Epoxidizing systems based on hydrogen peroxide for the formation of peroxy acids are probably safer, particularly for in situ systems, and more convenient to use than peroxyacetic acid processes involving acetaldehyde. The epoxidizer also has the option of purchasing hydrogen peroxide whereas he is required to develop or license an acetaldehyde oxidation process. Acetaldehyde processes for peroxyacetic acid epoxidation basically show high investment and low raw materials costs. Raw material costs in epoxidation with hydrogen peroxide are somewhat higher, but the investment required is judged to be less by about 50%. Hydrogen peroxide systems also offer other advantages. These include single-stage operation, minimum refrigeration, possible elimination of solvents, and continuous processing.

Alkaline Hydrogen Peroxide. Peroxy acids are often not satisfactory for the epoxidation of such materials as α,β-unsaturated carbonyl compounds and nitriles. Alkaline hydrogen peroxide, however, effectively converts this type of ethylenic bond to the epoxide although nitrile and aldehyde functions in such molecules may be hydrolyzed or oxidized further to amides and acids during epoxidation.

Alkaline peroxide systems for epoxidation were first used by Weitz and Scheffer (44) in 1921 for the epoxidation of mesityl oxide and benzal ketones, as shown in equation 6.

$$\underset{CH_3}{\overset{CH_3}{>}}C=CHCOCH_3 \xrightarrow[OH^-]{H_2O_2} \underset{CH_3}{\overset{CH_3}{>}}C\underset{\diagdown\diagup}{\underset{O}{\text{——}}}CHCOCH_3 \qquad (6)$$

The reactions of hydrogen peroxide in alkaline mediums are apparently those of the hydroperoxide anion, also known as the perhydroxyl ion, as shown below.

$$H_2O_2 + OH^- \rightleftharpoons OOH^- + H_2O \tag{7}$$

The action of the perhydroxyl ion makes the reactions of alkaline peroxide different from peroxy acid reactions. This difference is demonstrated by the fact that α,β-unsaturated ketones are usually converted by peroxy acids to esters instead of epoxides.

The alkaline peroxide systems for epoxidation developed by Weitz and Scheffer required the use of alcoholic solvents. The use of aqueous alkaline mediums was shown later to eliminate the need for reaction and extraction solvents and, in many instances, increased the yields of epoxides (53). However, alkaline hydrogen peroxide solutions in methanol, ethanol, pyridine, and dioxane have been proved satisfactory for epoxidation. Alkaline peroxide systems are now used occasionally in the drug industry for epoxidation of unsaturated linkages located in α,β positions to keto groups of steroid molecules.

Metal-Activated Hydrogen Peroxide. The mild oxidizing action of hydrogen peroxide is increased considerably by use of certain metallic catalysts. For example, such catalysts as osmic acid (OsO_4) and tungstic acid (WO_3) have been used in conjunction with hydrogen peroxide in inert solvents to form intermediate inorganic peroxy acids (26). Such peroxy acids are unstable, but are effective in converting ethylenic unsaturation to vicinal diols. They are, therefore, excellent hydroxylating agents.

Work by Shell Development Company, however, has indicated that systems involving metal-catalyzed hydrogen peroxide can be used for epoxidation (66). The system is operated by dissolving the epoxidizable substance in *tert*-butyl alcohol–water mixtures to which is added a small quantity of tungstic or molybdic acid catalyst. Excess hydrogen peroxide is then charged to the mixture held at 70–80°C until the reaction is complete. Hydrogen peroxide used in this manner has transformed the insecticide aldrin to the epoxy insecticide dieldrin in 95% yields. As yet, metal-catalyzed hydrogen peroxide systems have not found wide usage in industry but offer considerable promise.

Miscellaneous Organic Peroxy Acids. Such organic peroxy acids as peroxybenzoic acid (36) and monoperoxyphthalic acid (9) are efficient epoxidizing agents for isolated double bonds. These oxidizing agents can be used advantageously over peroxyacetic or peroxyformic acid in cases in which the epoxides formed are sensitive to ring opening by inorganic, acetic, or formic acids. Reactions employing these peroxy acids are generally conducted in nonreactive solvents like chloroform, ether, or benzene, and invariably result in high yields of epoxides.

Emmons and co-workers (18) have investigated the use of peroxytrifluoroacetic acid as an epoxidizing agent. This peroxy acid is made by reacting trifluoroacetic acid, or trifluoroacetic anhydride, and hydrogen peroxide in methylene chloride. In epoxidation, the peroxy acid solution obtained in this fashion is added to a methylene chloride solution containing the epoxidizable substance and a buffering agent like disodium hydrogen phosphate. Like peroxybenzoic and monoperoxyphthalic acids, buffered peroxytrifluoroacetic acid is an excellent reagent for the preparation of epoxides with ring-opening tendencies.

Peroxymaleic acid (45) may be used to effect epoxidation of terminal double bonds and conjugated olefins. Peroxymaleic acid is not as strong an epoxidizing agent as trifluoroperoxyacetic acid; but it is considerably less expensive, a stronger oxidizing agent than most peroxy acids, and may be used in nonbuffered systems. Peroxy-maleic acid is easily prepared by adding maleic anhydride to an ice-cold solution of high-strength hydrogen peroxide in methylene chloride.

Peroxybenzoic, monoperoxyphthalic, and peroxytrifluoroacetic acids are higher-cost materials than peroxyacetic or peroxyformic acid. Therefore, their commercial use is limited. Monoperoxyphthalic acid is prepared conveniently by dissolving phthalic anhydride in 35% hydrogen peroxide and cooling the reaction mixture to effect crystallization. Peroxybenzoic acid can be made by hydrolysis of dibenzoyl peroxide with sodium methoxide in chloroform–methanol solution. The reaction is highly exothermic. It can also be prepared by the air oxidation of benzaldehyde or by treating benzoyl chloride with alkaline hydrogen peroxide. In the latter case, however, the reaction must be controlled to preclude the formation or benzoyl peroxide. Aromatic peroxy acids—such as peroxybenzoic, m-chloroperoxybenzoic, or p-nitroperoxybenzoic acids—and long-chain aliphatic peroxy acids can only be prepared from the corresponding organic acid by reaction with hydrogen peroxide in strong sulfuric or methane-sulfonic acid media (34).

Hydrogen peroxide and such nitriles as benzonitrile react in methanol at pH 8 to give a peroxy acid believed to be peroxybenzimidic acid (see eq. 8) (29).

$$\text{C}_6\text{H}_5\text{CN} + \text{H}_2\text{O}_2 \longrightarrow \text{C}_6\text{H}_5\overset{\overset{\displaystyle \text{OOH}}{|}}{\text{C}}=\text{NH} \qquad (8)$$

Peroxycarboximidic acids, in general, exhibit the reactions of the conventional peroxy acids if prepared in the presence of epoxidizable substrates. These peroxy acids are too reactive to be isolated and tend to decompose in the absence of oxidizable materials yielding amides and oxygen gas. Peroxybenzimidic acid appears to be more reactive than peroxyacetic acid and has the added advantage of permitting reaction under mildly alkaline conditions (pH 7–8) in aqueous or alcoholic media. As a result of its lack of acidity, peroxybenzimidic acid converts 2-allyl cyclohexanone to the corresponding epoxide as the only product. Conventional peroxy acids usually transform such unsaturated ketones to esters or lactones in the well-known Baeyer–Villiger reaction (2,22). Peroxycarboximidic acids may also participate in intramolecular epoxidation if unsaturation is available in the molecule. Thus, acrylonitrile may be converted

$$\text{CH}_2\!\!=\!\!\text{CHCN} + \text{H}_2\text{O}_2 \rightarrow \text{CH}_2\!\!=\!\!\text{CHC}(\!=\!\text{NH})\text{OOH} \rightarrow \underset{\text{O}}{\text{CH}_2\!\!-\!\!\text{CHCONH}_2} \qquad (9)$$

to glycidamide in the presence of hydrogen peroxide, as in equation 9. Peroxycarboximidic acid also offers improved efficiency in preparing spiro epoxides from alicyclic methylene compounds (29).

Epoxides by Other Routes

Although epoxides are the products of oxidation of ethylenic unsaturation by active oxygen agents, they may also be obtained by reactions not involving epoxidation. Methods which do not depend upon active oxygen compounds include the hypohalogenation and dehydrohalogenation sequence (24), autoxidation of olefins (25), and the Darzens glycidic ester condensation (27). The first two procedures are related to epoxidation in that the starting materials are olefins and the end products are epoxides. The Darzens condensation, however, does not utilize ethylenic unsaturation but involves the condensation of an aldehyde or ketone with an α-halo ester to produce an α,β-epoxy ester. Those epoxides not produced commercially by epoxidation are usually made by hypohalogenation and dehydrohalogenation or by autoxidation of olefins.

Hypohalogenation and Dehydrohalogenation. The manufacture of glycerol (qv), ethylene glycol, and propylene glycol demonstrates the use of hypohalous acids to make intermediate epoxides. Methods which have been used commerically involve the addition of hypohalous acid to double bonds to produce halohydrins which are subsequently dehalogenated. The first step in the addition of hypohalous acid appears to involve the attack of a positive halogen atom, as follows:

$$CH_2\!\!=\!\!CH_2 + HOCl \rightarrow \underset{\underset{+}{Cl}}{CH_2\!\!-\!\!CH_2} + OH^- \tag{10}$$

$$\underset{\underset{+}{Cl}}{CH_2\!\!-\!\!CH_2} + H_2O \rightarrow \underset{OH \quad Cl}{CH_2\!\!-\!\!CH_2} + H^+ \tag{11}$$

Dehydrohalogenation is carried out by distilling the chlorohydrin from alkaline agents to form the epoxide, as shown in equation 12. Hypochlorous acid may be obtained by passing chlorine into water under controlled conditions or by use of such hypohalites as calcium hypochlorite.

$$\underset{Cl \quad OH}{CH_2\!\!-\!\!CH_2} \xrightarrow{\text{NaOH}} \underset{O}{CH_2\!\!-\!\!CH_2} + NaCl + H_2O \tag{12}$$

The addition of hypochlorous acid to a double bond to form a chlorohydrin is generally considered to involve Walden inversion (46). Subsequent dehydrochlorination of the chlorohydrin may also involve a second case of inversion. Thus, cis-2-butene is converted to cis-2,3-epoxybutane by the hypohalogenation and dehydrohalogenation sequence. The two inversions which occur produce the effect of no inversion.

The epoxidation of cis-2-butene with peroxy acids should also result in the formation of cis-2,3-epoxybutane. In this case, no inversions are believed to occur although a transformation identical to that occurring with the hypochlorous acid route has been made. These factors are important in considering the mechanism of epoxidation.

Autoxidation of Olefins. Ethylene oxide may be made (25) by passing ethylene and air over a silver catalyst at 300°C. Considerable carbon dioxide and water, however, are formed as by-products to impair the efficiency of this reaction. Despite its shortcomings, the reaction is an example of a direct attack by oxygen on a double bond to form an epoxide. It introduces the possibility of developing the use of oxygen as a general epoxidizing agent.

Except for ethylene oxide, however, few epoxides have been prepared in acceptable yields by the autoxidation of olefins. The chief obstacle to the formation of epoxides by air oxidation is that oxygen tends to attack reactive centers other than the double bond. The favored point of attack appears to be the carbon atom adjacent to the double bond, as shown in equations 13–15, so that hydroperoxides (13) rather than epoxides are formed.

$$-CH_2CH=CHCH_2- \quad \rightarrow \quad -CHCH=CHCH_2- \tag{13}$$
$$\text{(A)}$$

$$-\dot{C}HCH=CHCH_2- \quad \longleftrightarrow \quad -CH_2CH=CH\dot{C}H- \tag{14}$$
$$\text{(A)} \qquad\qquad\qquad\qquad \text{(B)}$$

$$-CH_2CH=CH\dot{C}H- \xrightarrow{O_2} -CH_2CH=CHCH- \rightarrow -CH_2CH=CHCH- \tag{15}$$
$$\underset{\text{OO·}}{|} \qquad\qquad \underset{\text{OOH}}{|}$$

The attack by oxygen is favored at the α-carbon atom by formation of allylic free radicals which are resonance stabilized. Since allylic structures (A) and (B) are stabilized by resonance, their tendency to form is high. Thus, when hydrogen atoms are present on carbon atoms adjacent to ethylenic unsaturation, the formation of epoxides by autoxidation of the double bond becomes difficult. If epoxides are formed in such cases, it is possible that the hydroperoxides formed as primary products subsequently react with the double bonds to form epoxides. Hydroperoxides, however, are low-order epoxidizing agents so that yields are low.

Reaction Mechanism

A reasonable interpretation of the mechanism of epoxidation may be postulated if existing data obtained experimentally on there actions of organic peroxy acids and olefinic double bonds are considered (40). These data indicate that the attacking agent in epoxidation is undissociated and electrophilic in nature.

Specific reaction rates obtained experimentally in epoxidation clearly show that peroxy acids function as electrophilic agents and are not nucleophilic or radical entities. The specific reaction rates for a variety of olefins prove that an increase in the electron releasing effect of substituents at the double bond increases the rate of epoxidation. Conversely, the presence of aldehyde, ketone, carboxyl, or other electron-withdrawing groups at the double bond reduces the reaction rate greatly. Terminal double bonds are also less readily epoxidized than internal bonds, presumably because fewer structures of equivalent energy contributing to the resonance of the transition state are available. These facts indicate that as ethylenic linkages become more nucleophilic, they react more rapidly with peroxy acids.

The stereospecificity of epoxidation militates against the postulation that ions are the attacking agents in this reaction. Two oppositely charged ions which may be visualized as emanating from peroxyacetic acid are the peroxyacetate anion (CH_3COO^-) and the hydroxyl cation (OH^+). The peroxyacetate ion is unlikely as the attacking moiety because it is formed under basic conditions and possesses nucleophilic properties. When formed in the absence of an oxidizable substrate, it is unstable and decomposes rapidly with evolution of oxygen. The hydroxyl cation is a more likely candidate as the attacking agent. It has electrophilic tendencies, and its postulation is compatible with existing theories on the addition of reagents to olefinic systems. However, epoxidation has been shown by unequivocal evidence to involve cis addition to the double bond. Thus the cis olefins, oleic acid and oleyl alcohol, form the corresponding cis epoxides on treatment with peroxyacetic or peroxybenzoic acid. The hydrolysis of such epoxides in preparing α-glycols results in inversion in neutral, acid, and alkaline mediums. If the attacking agent is an ion like the hydroxyl cation, epoxidation of such olefins as oleic acid or elaidic acid should also be accompanied by inversion.

Epoxidation may, therefore, proceed by interaction of undissociated peroxyacetic acid and ethylenic linkages to form (eq. 16) an activated or transition state (**1**).

$$
\text{(1)} \qquad\qquad\qquad\qquad\qquad\qquad\qquad\qquad\qquad\qquad\qquad \text{(16)}
$$

The structure (**1**) represents the maximum energy stage of the system. It depicts peroxyacetic acid as a quasi-5-membered ring in a position favorable to the formation of the new oxirane bonds. Giguère and Olmos (20) have assigned a 5-membered ring structure to peroxyacetic acid on the basis of infrared absorption studies which showed hydroxyl stretching and hydrogen bonding. The postulate of undissociated peroxy acid accounts for the ease with which epoxidation reactions are performed in nonionizing solvents and in heterogeneous systems.

The resonance hybrid (**1**) may be identified (7) as an indefinite intermediate complex of the π-electron type postulated by Dewar (16). Its involvement in epoxidation, has not been proved beyond the scope of the evidence indicated above. However, although direct measurements have not yet been made there is reason to believe that entropies of activation for epoxidation are negative and relatively large. The number of degrees of freedom in an activated complex of the type visualized for epoxidation is less than in the initial state because the motions of atoms in a quasi ring are restricted. Hence, negative and large values for entropies of activation, if obtained, should provide additional evidence in favor of the π-electron complex in epoxidation.

Reactions

Prileschajew (31) used peroxybenzoic acid in inert solvents for epoxidation with great success. With this reagent he prepared such epoxides as octylene oxide, decylene oxide, allyl alcohol oxide, limonene oxide and dioxide, and pinene oxide in virtually quantitative yields. Prileschajew showed that practically any olefin could be epoxidized with peroxybenzoic acid with the exception of α,β-unsaturated carbonyl compounds and conjugated olefins. Smit (35) later found that conjugated olefins could be epoxidized to the extent of 50%. The α,β-unsaturated carbonyl compounds apparently involve 1,4-unsaturation and are unlike 1,2-unsaturated compounds which respond to peroxy acids. In 1921, Weitz and Scheffer (44) showed that alkaline hydrogen peroxide is effective in epoxidizing α,β-unsaturated carbonyl compounds.

$$
\text{RCH=CH-CR} \xrightarrow{\text{HOO}^-} \text{RCH-CH=C-R} \xrightarrow{-\text{OH}^-} \text{RCHCHCOR} \qquad \text{(17)}
$$

In 1937, Böhme (6) found that monoperoxyphthalic acid reacts with ethylenes, but it remained for Chakravorty and Levin in 1942 (9) to isolate epoxides of cholesterol derivatives prepared with this reagent. Emmons and co-workers (18) subsequently demonstrated that peroxytrifluoroacetic acid is much like peroxybenzoic and monoperoxyphthalic acids in epoxidizing such olefins as 1-dodecene and 1-hexene. This reagent, however, is more effective than peroxybenzoic acid in epoxidizing double bonds located near negative groups.

Early work indicated that peroxyacetic acid could not be used for epoxidation of olefinic compounds since the products isolated were hydroxyacetates or glycol. Arbuzow and Michailow (1) in 1930, however, found that the oxidation of α-pinene with peroxyacetic acid could be effected to produce an 89% yield of epoxide if an inert solvent like diethyl ether were employed. Peroxyacetic acid in acetic acid solution gave only the hydroxyacetate. In 1945, Findley, Swern, and co-workers (19) found that the epoxides of fatty oils and esters could be obtained with peroxyacetic acid in acetic acid by using relatively short reaction periods and low temperatures. Later, Terry and Wheeler (55) discovered that the epoxidation of fatty materials did not require their dissolution in excess acetic acid. The reaction could be carried out in a two-phase system containing the fatty oil and aqueous peroxyacetic acid.

Oxidation of unsaturated materials with peroxyformic acid ordinarily leads to good yields of glycol or hydroxyformate (58). Peroxyformic acid, prepared and utilized in situ, however, has also been used successfully for the epoxidation of fatty oils and esters (56). This has been accomplished by using a minimum of formic acid. Other in situ systems for epoxidation of fatty materials have been developed which employ a minimum of acetic acid and sulfuric acid as catalyst (67,69).

An important contribution to epoxidation techniques employing peroxyacetic acid formed and utilized in situ has been the Du Pont development of using poly(styrene-sulfonic acid) exchange resins as catalysts (51). This method eliminates the need for separate reactions, minimizes acetic acid requirements, reduces by-products, and allows operation at higher temperatures. The surface effects (adsorption) of the resin catalyst in this technique are important in obtaining good epoxy yields (8,43). If the nature of the resin bead or the epoxidizable material is such as to allow absorption (volume effect) by the resin, by-products may result. The method is generally applicable to the epoxidation of such large molecules as alkyd resins, butadiene–styrene polymers, polybutadiene, glycerides, linoleate esters, tall oil acid esters, and undecylenic esters. It can also be used to epoxidize smaller molecules which are not absorbed by the resin. Tetrahydrophthalic anhydride and derivatives, for example, have been epoxidized in yields as high as 90% by use of the resin technique.

It is not surprising that earlier workers obtained little epoxidation with systems employing acetic or formic acid. Certain epoxy compounds, when dissolved in glacial acetic acid, are converted completely to hydroxyacetates in 1 hr at 100°C and in 4 hr at 25°C (19). Since commercial peroxyacetic acid solutions contain both glacial acetic acid and sulfuric acid, they must be treated to remove sulfuric acid prior to use in epoxidation. Even under mild conditions, sulfuric acid catalyzes the ring opening of epoxides by acetic acid. Cyclooctene, however, produced a 69% yield of the epoxide in the presence of sulfuric acid catalyst (59). Furan derivatives treated with peroxyacetic acid in acetic acid containing traces of mineral acid generally formed polymerized, isomerized, or cleavage products (5).

Ease of epoxidation depends considerably upon the nature of the unsaturated substance. Expoxidation of isolated double bonds, such as are present in most fatty acids and oils, occurs easily in 2–4 hr as compared with 28 hr under the same conditions for terminally unsaturated compounds such as 1-octadecene and 1-tetradecene (54). A study of the reaction rates of peroxy acids on olefins showed that substitution of alkyl groups for the hydrogen atoms attached to the double bond increased the rate (38).

Also, in compounds like isoprene, the more substituted double bond was attacked first, in spite of the greater steric hindrance. The rate was decreased when such electron attracting groups as carbonyl or carboxyl groups were attached to, or were in close proximity to, the double bond (4).

Peroxyacetic acid in an inert solvent free of acetic acid has been used to prepare styrene oxide in good yields. Commercial diisobutylene, consisting of an 80:20 mixture of the α- and β-isomers, $CH_2:C(CH_3)CH_2C(CH_3)_3$ and $(CH_3)_2C:CHC(CH_3)_3$, respectively, has also been epoxidized effectively with this reagent. Epoxidation of the diisobutylene mixture produced two epoxides boiling far enough apart to allow their separation by distillation. Other epoxides which have been prepared by use of peroxyacetic acid in an inert solvent include vinylcyclohexene monoxide and dioxide, triisobutylene oxide, glycidic esters of α,β-unsaturated acids, and the epoxides of various unsaturated nitriles, alcohols, amides ethers, and imides (65). Butadiene dioxide has been made by ep-

$$\underset{O}{CH_2\!-\!CH}\!-\!\underset{O}{CH\!-\!CH_2},$$

oxidation of 1,4-dichloro-2-butene, followed by hydrolysis of the epoxide and treatment of the intermediate 1,4-dichloro-2,3-dihydroxybutane with alkali.

Peroxyacetic acid in acetic acid has been used to epoxidize 4-vinylcyclohexene, forming the dioxide in about 70% yield (62). Cyclohexene has been epoxidized by peroxypropionic acid in chloroform. Peroxyacetic acid in acetic acid has been extremely satisfactory in epoxidizing the Diels-Alder product (aldrin) of hexachlorocyclopentadiene (see Cyclopentadiene and dicyclopentadiene) and bicyclo[2.2.1]-2,5-heptadiene (60,61).

$$(18)$$

The epoxidized products are known commercially as dieldrin (endo-exo isomer) and endrin (endo-endo isomer). Aldrin, dieldrin, and endrin are general insecticides. The epoxide, dieldrin, has also been prepared by reacting aldrin with hydrogen peroxide in the presence of tungsten trioxide in *tert*-butyl alcohol–water mixtures (66). The combination of tungstic acid and hydrogen peroxide has also been used to epoxidize monoethylenic alcohols of various molecular-weight ranges (70).

Many epoxides of the steroid series have been prepared with peroxyacetic acid, peroxybenzoic acid, and alkaline hydrogen peroxide. Examples include the 5,6,16,17-diepoxy derivative of the pregnane series produced with peroxyacetic acid in chloroform (63), the 16,17-oxidoallopregnan-20-one derivative made with alkaline hydrogen peroxide in methanol (64) and 9,11-oxido steroids synthesized with peroxybenzoic or monoperoxyphthalic acid.

Such α-olefin epoxides as octene-1 oxide have been prepared in yields of 80% and higher by reacting octene-1 in methylene chloride at 0°C and a peroxyacid solution prepared from 90% hydrogen peroxide and maleic anhydride in methylene chloride (45). Peroxyacetic acid–water azeotrope, generated by feeding 50% hydrogen peroxide and acetic acid to a still pot containing 10–20% sulfuric acid with concomitant vacuum distillation, has also been employed to prepare α-olefin epoxides and some of the epoxides (12) which are otherwise difficult to synthesize.

Manufacture

The use of the epoxidation reaction in manufacture has involved hydrogen peroxide as the principal source of epoxidizing agents. Peroxyacetic acid derived from acetaldehyde has become increasingly important in epoxidation. To date, however, this material has not appeared as a merchant commodity, and no plans for shipment to prospective users have been announced. Chances are, therefore, that hydrogen peroxide will remain the principal agent commercially available for epoxidation. However, the manufacturer of epoxides with facilities available for oxidation of acetaldehyde may wish to make use of peroxyacetic acid in an inert solvent in cases in which epoxides are sensitive to ring opening or are difficult to form.

For the purchaser of active oxygen, the essential details of manufacture to be considered involve the conversion of hydrogen peroxide to an effective agent for epoxidation. Other pertinent details are those of arranging proper storage for hydrogen peroxide near the site of operations and installing equipment constructed of materials suitable for epoxidation reactions. The manufacture of epoxides most likely will involve either (a) preformation of peroxyacetic acid with its subsequent use in epoxidation or (b) use of hydrogen peroxide in epoxidation under conditions for the in situ formation of peroxy acid.

MANUFACTURE OF PEROXYACETIC ACID

Sulfuric Acid Catalyst. Merchant peroxyacetic acid is produced from hydrogen peroxide via sulfuric acid catalysis and is marketed by the FMC Corporation (21). Peroxyacetic acid (40%) may be prepared at the site of epoxidation, however, by

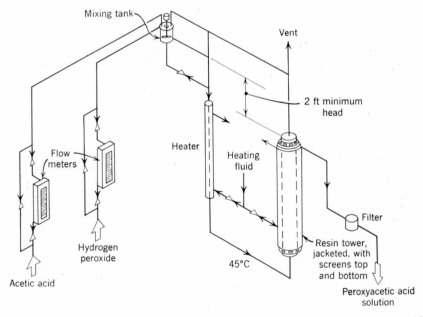

Fig. 2. Schematic flow diagram for the continuous preparation of peroxyacetic acid.

mixing 1.6 moles of glacial acetic acid with 1 mole of 90% hydrogen peroxide in the presence of about 2–3% sulfuric acid.   The mixture attains equilibrium if allowed to stand overnight.

Acetic anhydride may also be added to displace equilibrium by removing water (57).   The use of acetic anhydride adds to the hazards of the reaction, however, by making it possible to obtain explosive diacetyl peroxide as a by-product.   Peroxyacetic acid solutions prepared by mixing acetic anhydride and 35% hydrogen peroxide at 40°C have been found by the author to contain about 8% diacetyl peroxide.   Such mixtures have exploded.

Cation Exchange Resin Catalyst.   Information on the use of cation exchange resins to prepare peroxyacetic acid solutions free of traces of mineral acid has been disclosed by Du Pont.   This method can be operated continuously or batchwise and is a convenient procedure for the manufacture of equilibrium peroxyacetic acid at the site of operations (48).

The Du Pont method consists of passing a mixture of glacial acetic acid and hydrogen peroxide through a cation exchange resin bed confined in a column (see Fig. 2). The column contains poly(styrenesulfonic acid) resin in the acid form which has been treated with acetic acid to remove excess water.   The flow of peroxyacetic acid solution from the column as effluent is adjusted to give the peroxide–acetic mixture the proper contact time with the resin bed.   For the preparation of 40% peroxyacetic acid solutions, 90% hydrogen peroxide is required (see Figs. 3 and 4).   A 15% peroxyacetic acid solution may be prepared, however, at the rate of about 265 lb/hr by feeding a mixture containing a ratio of 6.33 gal of glacial acetic acid to 1 gal of 50% hydrogen peroxide to the resin tower.   Proper contact times are maintained by charging 17–18 lb of such cation exchange resins as Amberlite IR-120 (a registered trademark of Rohm & Haas Company) or Dowex 50-X-8 (registered trademark of The Dow Chemical Company) to the tower for each gallon per hour of 50% hydrogen peroxide that is introduced.

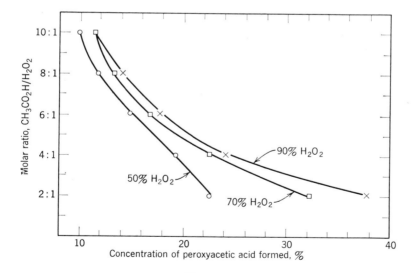

Figure 3.

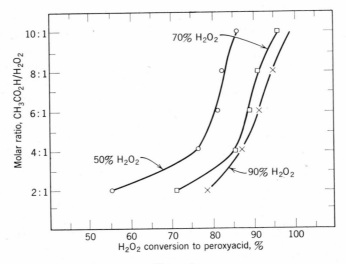

Figure 4.

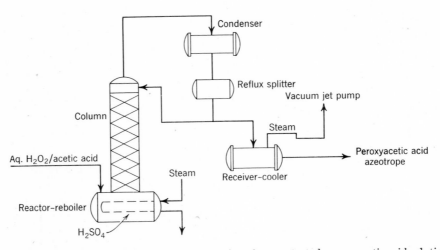

Fig. 5. Vacuum-distillation process for preparation of concentrated peroxyacetic acid solutions.

Generator or Azeotropic Peroxyacetic Acid. Concentrated peroxyacetic acid solutions in water may be prepared by vacuum distillation of a mixture of hydrogen peroxide, acetic acid, and sulfuric acid. The process (see Fig. 5) is operated by continuously feeding 0.5:1 to 2:1 molar ratios of acetic acid to hydrogen peroxide (as a 50% aqueous solution) to a reactor–reboiler (generator) containing 10–20% sulfuric acid catalyst. The reaction products are distilled off concomitantly at reduced pressures of 40–60 mm Hg.

The reactor boiler is maintained at a temperature of about 45–50°C during reaction and distillation. Aqueous peroxyacetic acid solutions drawn off overhead vary in concentration between 50 and 60% depending upon the ratios of hydrogen peroxide to acetic acid employed. Higher ratios of peroxide to acetic acid lead to higher concentrations of peroxyacetic acid while acetic acid content is decreased. Based on hydrogen

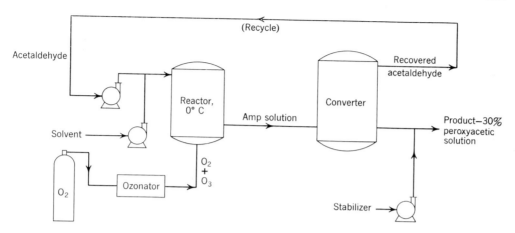

Fig. 6. Acetaldehyde oxidation process for manufacture of 30% peroxyacetic acid.

peroxide, yields of peroxyacetic acid are practically quantitative at 97–98%. The aqueous peroxyacetic acid solutions obtained approximate an azeotropic mixture reported (30) to constitute 56.5% peroxy acetic acid and 43.5% water.

Certain safety precautions are required in the manufacture of peroxy acids and in their use in epoxidation. Safety factors are discussed at the end of this article and should be considered by those interested in epoxidation.

Acetaldehyde Oxidation. The Union Carbide plant, the first of its kind, for production of 30% peroxyacetic acid in ethyl acetate is based on the research efforts of Phillips, Frostick, and Starcher (see Fig. 6) (68).

In the process, acetaldehyde and solvent are fed in one stream to an oxidizer maintained at 0°C by a refrigeration unit, probably backed by a standby unit for safety. Oxygen, containing perhaps 2% ozone, is obtained as effluent from a small ozone plant and enters the reactor in a separate stream. Acetaldehyde is converted to acetaldehyde monoperoxyacetate, $CH_3CH(OH)OOCOCH_3$, in the oxidizer under ozone catalysis and then decomposed in the converter into peroxyacetic acid and acetaldehyde. These products are separated rapidly, as formed, to avoid interaction producing two moles of acetic acid. However, if acetaldehyde is taken off immediately and recycled as released in the decomposition of acetaldehyde monoperoxyacetate, a 30% peroxyacetic acid solution in acetone or ethyl acetate results.

MANUFACTURE OF EPOXY OILS AND ESTERS

The epoxidation of fatty oils and esters for commercial manufacture involves making a choice of proper raw materials, choosing a process to meet established product standards, and installing equipment which will insure safe and efficient operations. To the manufacturer depending upon merchant active oxygen to generate the epoxidizing agent, these tasks are made relatively simple by the use of hydrogen peroxide. To date, hydrogen peroxide processes for the production of epoxy oils and esters have been based on in situ processes including the formic acid process (56), the resin-catalyzed processes (48,51), and the sulfuric acid–acetic acid process (67,69). In in situ systems, such as the hydrogen peroxide–resin procedure for epoxidation, the peroxyacetic acid as formed is utilized by the oxidizable matter. Thus, the removal of peroxyacetic acid from the system causes a shift of the equilibrium to the right resulting in the complete conversion of hydrogen peroxide to peroxy acid. Increased conversion of hydrogen peroxide to peroxy acid results in increased efficiency for such systems.

Sulfuric Acid Processes. In situ processes for the epoxidation of soybean oil based on the use of acetic acid with sulfuric acid as a catalyst have been developed by such firms as the Archer-Daniels-Midland Company and the FMC Corporation. In the Archer-Daniels-Midland process, the sulfuric acid catalyst is added last admixed with 0.5 moles of glacial acetic acid (69). Epoxy ring opening by sulfuric acid is minimized because the system is heterogeneous and involves an interaction of an oil phase and an aqueous phase containing hydrogen peroxide and acetic acid. The process is operated by first adding 20% of the total requirement of hydrogen peroxide (50%) to soybean oil and warming the mixture to about 50°C. A solution of acetic acid containing catalytic amounts of sulfuric acid is then added to the charge over a period of 4 hr with separate and simultaneous addition of the remainder of the hydrogen peroxide. The batch is held between 50 and 60°C for about 13 hr when the agitation is halted and the aqueous and oil layers are separated. The oil layer, which contains the epoxy soybean oil product, is refined and dried. The aqueous layer, containing about 5–6% unused active oxygen, 25–30% acetic acid, and 1–2% sulfuric acid, is not discarded, however, but used to partially epoxidize fresh soybean oil. Utilization of the spent aqueous layer in this fashion is a useful innovation contributing to reaction efficiency and good economics. The aqueous layer is then separated from the partially epoxidized oil, treated with a peroxide decomposition agent, and stripped of acetic acid. The partially epoxidized oil, containing about 18% of its eventual epoxy oxygen content, is reacted with fresh hydrogen peroxide and acetic acid, in the manner outlined above, to complete its epoxidation.

A second process based on the use of sulfuric acid for the epoxidation of soybean oil has been disclosed by the FMC Corporation (67). In its usual modification, the process employs an inert solvent, like benzene or hexane, to reduce the effect of sulfuric acid in catalyzing epoxy ring opening. In a typical run (10), 2000 lb of soybean oil is charged to a 600-gal stainless-steel reactor (jacketed) fitted with agitator, cooling coils, reflux condenser, vent, rupture disc, sample line, direct and recording thermometers, feed lines, and manhole. The reactor is also equipped with an automatic system for flooding the reaction with water in emergencies. The oil is heated gently by applying steam (to the jacket) and 400 lb of hexane solvent is added. To the solution of soybean oil in hexane 320 lb of glacial acetic acid is then added followed by 796 lb of 50% sulfuric acid. When the temperature reaches 50°C, the steam is shut off, cooling water is circulated through the coils, and the controlled addition of hydrogen peroxide is begun. About 765 lb of 50% hydrogen peroxide is added over a period of 2 hr with the temperature maintained between 50–60°C. When peroxide addition has been completed, the temperature is allowed to rise to 60–65°C and is maintained in this range until the hydrogen peroxide has been consumed. When the reaction is complete, the organic layer is washed with water and pumped to a vacuum stripping column where water and solvent are removed.

Repeated Resin Process. The first successful trials on the resin-catalyzed epoxidation of soybean oil and methyl oleate were conducted in 1953 in the Du Pont Laboratories, Niagara Falls, N.Y. (51). These trials led to the development of the repeated resin process for epoxidation. Of the processes now available for the epoxidation of fatty oils and esters, the repeated resin process probably eliminates unsaturation most efficiently and produces the highest epoxy oxygen values. The process is so

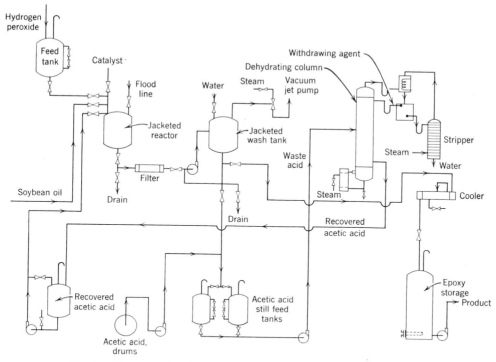

Fig. 7. Schematic flow diagram for epoxidation of fatty oils and esters.

named because a relatively large amount of poly(styrenesulfonic acid) resin is used as the catalyst, requiring its reuse in succeeding epoxidation batches for good economics. The general practice is to use 10–15% (dry weight) of the poly(styrenesulfonic acid) based on the weight of the fatty oil or ester to be epoxidized. Advantages which may be listed for this process include high epoxy yields, little by-product formation, nearly complete elimination of unsaturation, low reaction temperatures (60°C), and short reaction periods.

Operating the resin process simply involves mixing the fatty oil or ester containing 1.0 mole of unsaturation, 0.55 moles of glacial acetic acid, and 12% dry resin based on the weight of epoxidizable material. Hydrogen peroxide (1.1 moles) is added slowly so that a reaction temperature of 60°C is not exceeded. The reaction medium is maintained at 60°C for about 4 hr and then separated from the resin catalyst by decantation or filtration. The resin catalyst remains in the reactor for succeeding runs.

The average poly(styrenesulfonic acid) catalyst available commercially can be reused in approximately 6–8 runs at a 10–12% catalyst level. Factors which contribute to degradation of these catalysts and militate against their indefinite use include (a) the presence of heavy-metal contaminants which induce rapid attack on the resin by hydrogen peroxide, (b) the slow degradation of resin crosslinkage by peroxy acid, and (c) the physical breakdown of the catalyst beads by mechanical attrition. The life of the resin catalyst is tripled by use of commercial resins with low metals contents.

Although use of the repeated resin technique produces excellent epoxy products, the procedure is characterized by one difficulty. Degradation of the catalyst produces fine particles which introduce problems in filtration. Therefore, if products with maximum epoxy oxygen values are not required, it is common practice to use much less resin. A smaller amount of resin can be economically discarded after each run. This procedure is termed the *minimal resin technique*.

Minimal Resin Process. The minimal resin process for epoxidation requires the use of about 2% resin (dry weight) based on the weight of the material to be epoxidized (8). Since the quantity of catalyst in the minimal technique is much less than that used in the repeated resin process, adjustments in the reaction variables of epoxidation must be made to account for the loss in catalyst surface area. This is partially accomplished by increasing reaction temperature (to 75–80°C) and time (to 7–8 hr). Despite these changes, however, the minimal resin process is 12–15% less effective in producing epoxy oxygen. In this respect, it is approximately equivalent to the sulfuric acid process.

Figure 7 represents a flowsheet for the epoxidation of fatty oils and esters by the minimal resin process. Although the flowsheet is based on extensive laboratory data, it may not be an accurate duplication of a large-scale process. The flowsheet is intended for the guidance of those interested in epoxidation.

The operations of the minimal technique are essentially those indicated for the repeated resin and sulfuric acid processes with adjustment of the reaction variables indicated above. After reaction is complete, the resin catalyst is filtered from the reaction mixture and discarded. The reaction mixture is then pumped to a steam-jacketed wash tank equipped with a vacuum jet pump. The oil and aqueous layers are allowed to settle, and a separation of phases is effected. The lower aqueous layer is dropped to the acetic acid still feed tanks and later recovered by azeotropic dehydration using the Othmer method (28). The crude epoxidized product in the wash tank is washed successively with water or treated with alkaline agents and then washed with water to remove residual acid. Vacuum is applied to the tank containing the washed crude and traces of water are removed at 60–75°C (12–15 mm). If a wash tank equipped with vacuum is not available, the washed crude may be pumped to a flash tank or to a vacuum stripping column for drying. The finished product is filtered, if required, and piped to storage.

Continuous Processes. A continuous process for the epoxidation of fatty oils and esters has yet to be installed commercially. Considerable work on continuous processing has been completed, however, and offers promise for the future if the annual consumption of epoxidized oils and monoesters increases at the rate expected. Epoxidation processes dependent upon acetaldehyde-derived peroxyacetic acid, aqueous peroxyacetic acid azeotrope, or in situ hydrogen peroxide systems are all amenable to continuous operation.

Materials

Among the products made by epoxidation of fatty oils and esters are epoxidized soybean oil and such epoxidized monoesters as those of *n*-butyl tallate, 2-ethylhexyl tallate, *n*-butyl oleate, and 2-ethylhexyl oleate. These materials are used as stabilizers and plasticizers for poly(vinyl chloride) resins. The quality of the raw materials used in the manufacture of these epoxy products may have considerable effect upon the yields of epoxy oxygen obtained, the ease of elimination or residual unsaturation, and upon color. Oftentimes the quality of the raw materials may influence the properties of the final products as plasticizers. See Fats and fatty oils; Fatty acids.

Soybean Oil. Epoxy soybean oil products usually are prepared from alkali-refined soybean oil grades. Cheaper grades of soybean oil may contain phosphatide fractions and other impurities which are undesirable. Use of alkali-refined soya oil, which may vary in ethylenic unsaturation from 125 to 135 as measured by iodine absorption numbers (IV), permits the manufacture of epoxy products having average epoxy oxygen values of 6.4–7.1% and residual unsaturation indicated by iodine values of about 2.0 or less. In plasticizer applications, low iodine values of 2.0 or less combined with good epoxy values apparently contribute greatly to the compatibility of these materials in poly(vinyl chloride) resin formulations. Starting from alkali-refined soya oil also helps to obtain epoxy products which are low in color. In general, epoxy soybean oil plasticizers indicate Gardner color values of about 1–2 units.

The metal contents of soya oils to be epoxidized are kept at a minimum level. A good indicator of whether or not these oils are low in metals may be given by analysis for iron. A value of about 5 ppm for iron is probably rated as good, although soybean oil with as much as 35 ppm of iron has performed well in epoxidation trials. A minimum of iron and other heavy metals, however, helps in the efficient utilization of hydrogen peroxide. The absence of heavy metals also contributes to good color in epoxy oils and helps to minimize degradation of the catalysts used in resin catalyzed epoxidation processes.

Tall Oil Acid. See Fatty acids. Certain requirements must also be met by tall oil acid grades which are to be esterified for eventual use in epoxidation. Tall oil acids suitable for epoxidation should have low rosin acid and unsaponifiable matter contents. These impurities may contribute to undesirable color in epoxy tallate products and consume hydrogen peroxide unnecessarily affecting reaction efficiency. Tall oil acids used to produce esters for epoxidation generally contain 1% or less rosin acids and less than 2% unsaponifiable materials.

Tall oil esters prior to use in epoxidation possess unsaturation averaging between 95 and 105 IV. Such unsaturation consists essentially of oleic and linoleic acid esters. Saturated acid and conjugated linoleic acid components are preferably at a minimum. Upon analysis, finished epoxy tallate products may indicate epoxy oxygen values between 3 and 5% and residual iodine numbers of about 4. At present, color values in epoxy tallates may be slightly higher than those found in epoxy soybean oil products, averaging between Gardner 2 and 6.

Oleic Acid. The specifications for raw materials used in the production of epoxy oleates are similar to those given for tall oil acids. For example, saturated and conjugated unsaturated components should be low for products intended for plasticizer end use. Commercial oleic acids are derived from animal fats and therefore do not contain the traces of rosin found in tall oil acids. Tall oil acids are derived from the southern pine tree as products of the kraft wood pulp process.

Hydrogen Peroxide. Hydrogen peroxide presents the manufacturer of fatty epoxides with few of the problems associated with the use of other raw materials. Commercial solutions of hydrogen peroxide are probably among the purest of chemical commodities. They consist essentially of mixtures of hydrogen peroxide and deionized water to which stabilizing components, measured in parts per million, have been added.

Materials of Construction. Such common (18–8) stainless steels as types 304 and 316 are satisfactory for use in both peroxyacetic acid formation and epoxidation reactions. Type 316 stainless is preferred. Mild steel (1020) coupons have been exposed to peroxy acid formation in laboratory tests, but the coupons are attacked severely in a short time and cause exothermic decomposition of hydrogen peroxide and peroxyacetic acid.   Aluminum 1100 coupons have shown considerable etching and staining.   The surfaces of the stainless-steel coupons have shown no visible change.

Welds in reactors or tanks are avoided as much as possible.   Welds cause some decomposition of active oxygen and may become corroded in time.   Corrosion of 18–8 stainless steels near welded joints is probably related to the precipitation of carbide when the steels are heated in the welding process.   If welds are required, the use of low carbon steels and electrodes should help reduce carbide precipitation at the grain boundaries.   Examples of such materials are SS 316 ELC (extra low carbon) and SS 304 ELC.   SS 347 contains columbium which helps to reduce carbide precipitation.

Storage tanks and other equipment intended for long-term contact with hydrogen peroxide are constructed of high-purity (99.6%) aluminum.   Aluminum, however, is not a satisfactory material for use with peroxy acids.   Stainless steels (18–8) are resistant to corrosion by concentrated hydrogen peroxide but mildly catalyze the decomposition of peroxide.   Tanks constructed of stainless steels are therefore not used for long-term storage of hydrogen peroxide.

Equipment intended for use in epoxidation should be thoroughly cleaned and passivated.   Metal surfaces and parts should be examined to make certain they contain no imbedded foreign materials to catalyze decomposition of active oxygen. Surfaces to be cleaned should be treated with detergent solution or degreased with trichloroethylene.   Passivation of surfaces is effected with nitric acid.   Stainless-steel surfaces may also be passivated with glacial acetic acid containing small amounts of hydrogen peroxide.   Continued use of equipment with hydrogen peroxide in epoxidation tends to improve the passive condition of its surfaces.

Commercial Aspects

Cost of Manufacture.   In 1963, epoxy oils and esters sold in bulk quantities in the price range of about 29 to 28¢/lb.   Epoxy soybean oil products, as a rule, were less expensive than the epoxy monoesters.   Price differentials also existed among product types, depending upon the degree of epoxidation and the amount of residual unsaturation characterizing each product.   Of the epoxidized monoester, the epoxy tallates tended to be less expensive than equivalent epoxy oleate products.

Table 1 summarizes the materials costs involved in epoxidizing soybean oil with an iodine value of 130.   The cost for hydrogen peroxide is based on use of an 8% molar excess, the minimal quantity required to produce a premium epoxy product.

A factory cost for epoxy soybean oil may be estimated by adding a figure for processing costs to the materials costs.   Factors which influence the magnitude of the processing costs include labor, salaries, overhead, benefits, maintenance, depreciation, taxes, and insurance.   These costs may vary considerably depending upon locale,

Table 1.   Materials Costs in the Manufacture of Epoxy Soybean Oil

Materials	Amount used/100 lb finished product	Unit cost,[a] $	$/100 lb produced
soya oil	93.5	0.1375	12.85
hydrogen peroxide (70%)	25.2	0.32	8.05
acetic acid	9.47	0.10	0.95
resin catalyst	1.0	0.74	0.74
total			22.59[b]

[a] Prices as of November 1964.   [b] Materials, cost/lb, 22.6¢.

method of operation, and investment required to begin manufacture. For example, for a plant capacity of about 2 million lb/year of epoxy soybean oil, the processing costs may approximate roughly 10–15% of the materials costs listed above.

Epoxy Plasticizers. Epoxy oils and esters are used chiefly as plasticizer–stabilizers (41) for poly(vinyl chloride) resins. The incorporation of these materials into resin compositions helps to impart flexibility, elasticity, and toughness to the brittle vinyl resins. To be effective plasticizers, the epoxy materials must possess, above all, the properties of permanence and compatibility. Such properties are donated to the otherwise incompatible soybean oil and unsaturated fatty esters by the epoxide linkage.

The epoxy plasticizers are also effective stabilizers for poly(vinyl chlorides). They apparently act as acid acceptors to prevent degradation by small amount of hydrochloric acid released in the polymer. The mechanism by which stabilization occurs is open to question but appears to involve the epoxy group. It is generally believed that the epoxy ring is opened by hydrochloric acid to form the chlorohydrin, thus removing the harmful acid. An alternate mechanism, which may be in operation at the same time, is one in which the acid forms a hydrogen bond with epoxy oxygen but does not necessarily open the ring. The epoxy plasticizer, possessing a degree of mobility, migrates in the resin to release the acid to an auxiliary stabilizer such as barium or lead stearate.

The epoxy monoester and epoxy soybean oil products display somewhat different plasticizing properties. Epoxy soybean oil appears to be used in instances requiring low volatility and low extraction by solvents. The epoxy monoesters have better low-temperature properties and may provide improved compatibility.

The volume of epoxy plasticizers sold in 1963 has been reported to be 58.8 million lb (17). Epoxy soybean oil products accounted for 68% of this market with the remainder supplied essentially by octyl epoxy tallates (27%).

Among the commercial articles containing epoxy plasticizers are vinyl-coated wiring, vinyl furniture and automobile upholstery, rain gear, shower curtains, toys, floor covering, and insulating sheeting.

Coatings and Other Applications. The epoxy oils and esters have an excellent opportunity to expand into areas of use unrelated to the vinyl plasticizer field. An area of promise is that of using epoxidized fatty materials in the manufacture of coatings and polymers in general (72,73).

Uses for cycloaliphatic (42), linear aliphatic, and other epoxides are now indicated in coating, adhesive, and electrical applications. These uses involve markets now supplied predominantly by epoxy resins. Unlike the epoxy resins, which are based on the reactions of bisphenol and epichlorohydrin, the newer epoxides are prepared via the epoxidation reaction. In 1963, markets for the epoxy resins amounted to about 88 million lb going into such end uses as coatings (55%), construction (14%), and those pertaining to the electrical–electronic fields (10%). The cycloaliphatic epoxides, made by epoxibation of cyclic olefins, are intended to contribute improved properties in these end uses by incorporating the epoxycyclohexyl (**2**), epoxycyclopentyl (**3**), and epoxydicyclopentyl (**4**) in various molecules:

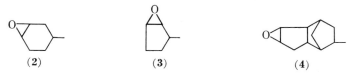

     (**2**)   (**3**)   (**4**)

The cycloaliphatic products are under development by Ciba Products Company, Div. of Ciba Corp., Union Carbide Corp., and to some extent by FMC Corporation. Epoxidized polybutadiene, an aliphatic epoxide made via hydrogen peroxide, has been offered by FMC Corporation for encapsulating, laminating, and adhesive uses. The peroxide-derived epoxides are not expected to supplant epoxy resins, but serve rather as useful adjuncts to these materials.

The bis-epoxydicyclopentyl ether of ethylene glycol is a new epoxide marketed by Rohm & Haas Company. Reacting with polyhydroxy compounds, this material leads to polyethers which range in form from viscous liquids to hard resins. The diepoxide also reacts with polybasic acids to produce thermosetting resins useful in epoxy resin outlets.

Recent announcements (1965) by such firms as General Tire & Rubber Company and Goodyear Tire & Rubber Company in the United States and Dunlop Tire & Rubber Corp. in Canada indicate development of a new sulfur-curable elastomer involving the copolymerization of the epoxy linkages in propylene oxide and unsaturated epoxides. The unsaturated epoxide (exemplified by butadiene monoxide, allyl glycidyl ether, or vinylcyclohexene monoxide) is used as a minor component in the polymer to supply unsaturated sites for reaction with sulfur. The new elastomers are thus essentially propylene oxide rubbers and exhibit such desirable properties as low-temperature flexibility, ozone resistance, and heat resistance.

The foregoing discussion on epoxide applications by no means delineates the extent of work under way in epoxidation. Other opportunities, such as that afforded by the development of low-cost α-olefins from petroleum sources, are continually explored in epoxidation. E. I. du Pont de Nemours & Co., Inc., a prime producer of hydrogen peroxide, has been concerned with development of techniques for preparation of α-olefin and other epoxides. Petroleum-derived olefin epoxides and glycols of suitable chain length are of particular interest as surfactant intermediates.

Safety Factors

Hydrogen peroxide requires careful handling. Its use, however, does not demand precautions which are burdensome or unduly exacting. Even the high concentrations are shipped and stored in large quantities with little difficulty (17). This is accomplished by preventing contact between hydrogen peroxide and substances which are combustible or cause its decomposition.

Many common substances decompose hydrogen peroxide. These materials include dirt, alkali, heavy-metal particles, organic matter, and many other substances found universally. Contamination by such materials causes hydrogen peroxide to decompose rapidly, releasing much heat and evolving considerable oxygen. The decomposition of hydrogen peroxide in confined spaces or closed systems may result in explosions. Such explosions properly qualify as pressure ruptures, but can cause great damage. The contamination of highly concentrated hydrogen peroxide vapor, however, may result in propagating detonations. These hazards are easily avoided by the use of proper equipment and the application of good standards of cleanliness.

Like other strong oxidizing agents, hydrogen peroxide may cause fires when in contact with combustible materials. The possibility of such fires is easily eliminated by preventing the storage of wood, paper, organic matter, and other combustible materials near equipment or lines handling hydrogen peroxide.

Such high concentrations of hydrogen peroxide as 90% solutions have not been detonated by shock or heat. Hydrogen peroxide vapor containing a 26 mole % concentration of H_2O_2, however, can be exploded by a hot spark or by the introduction of a contaminant. Mixtures of high-strength hydrogen peroxide and organic materials, however, may be extremely hazardous from the standpoint of explosions. In general, mixtures with alcohols, ketones, and sugars are highly explosible. Ternary diagrams of systems containing hydrogen peroxide, organic materials, and water show the explosive nature of these systems (33). A study of these diagrams allows the formulation of a useful rule-of-thumb; ie, that a 10-ml solution of an organic compound containing 3 ml of 90% hydrogen peroxide represents the lower explosive limit for many organic systems. The possibility of approaching such explosive limits is decreased considerably by use of lower strength material. For this reason, a 50% concentration of hydrogen peroxide is generally recommended for epoxidation.

If proper procedures are followed, the possibility of explosions in the epoxidation of fatty oils and esters is remote. These molecules are large and, though combined with peroxide, present an oxygen balance unfavorable to explosions. Safety is further enhanced by conducting the epoxidation process so that the concentration of active oxygen in the reactor is prevented. This is accomplished by arranging the reaction to utilize the peroxy acid as formed or to consume hydrogen peroxide as added. An additional safety measure requires that residual peroxides be decomposed prior to recovering acetic or formic acid used in epoxidation.

Epoxidation reactions are exothermic and therefore present the possibility of runaway reactions. In the Du Pont laboratories, a value of 50.8 kcal/mole has been measured for the heat of epoxidation of methyl oleate. An approximate value of 63.6 kcal/mole has been calculated by adding bond energy values for each bond formed in the product and subtracting those for each bond broken in the reactants. These values indicate that every precaution should be taken to ensure effective control of the heat evolved in epoxidation.

As the above discussion indicates, hydrogen peroxide and the organic peroxy acids are not ordinary chemicals. However, they are easily handled if their inherent hazards are recognized. In doubtful cases, the scale of reaction involving these materials in preliminary work should be limited to the smallest practicable quantity. The producers of hydrogen peroxide may be consulted to obtain information on hazards.

Bibliography

"Epoxidation" in *ECT*, 1st ed., Suppl. 2, pp. 325–346, by J. G. Wallace, E. I. du Pont de Nemours & Co., Inc.

1. Arbuzow, B. A., and Michailow, B. M., *J. Prakt. Chem.* **127**, 1 (1930).
2. Baeyer, A., and Villiger, V., *Ber.* **32**, 3625 (1899).
3. Batzer, H., *Chem. & Ind.* (*London*) **1964**, 179.
4. Boeseken, J., *Rec. Trav. Chim.* **45**, 838 (1926).
5. Boeseken, J., Vermij, C. O. J., Bunge, H., and van Meeuwen, C., *Rec. Trav. Chim.* **50**, 1023 (1931).
6. Böhme, H., *Ber.* **70B**, 379 (1937).
7. Carlin, R. B., Wallace, J. G., and Fisher, E. E., *J. Am. Chem. Soc.* **74**, 992 (1952).
8. Chadwick, A. F., Barlow, D. O., D'Addieco, A. A., and Wallace, J. G., *J. Am. Oil Chemists' Soc.* **35**, 355 (1958).
9. Chakravorty, P. N., and Levin, R. H., *J. Am. Chem. Soc.* **64**, 2317 (1942).
10. *Chem. Week* **75** (26), 32 (Dec. 25, 1954).

11. *Chem. Week* **91** (4), 64 (July 28, 1962).
12. *Chem. Week* **92** (14), 55 (April 6, 1963).
13. Criegee, R., Pilz, H., and Flygare, H., *Ber.* **72B,** 1799 (1939).
14. D'Ans, J., and Frey, W., *Ber.* **45,** 1845 (1912).
15. D'Ans, J., and Frey, W., *Z. Anorg. Chem.* **84,** 145 (1914).
16. Dewar, M. J. S., *Nature* **176,** 784 (1945); *J. Chem. Soc.* **1946,** 406, 777; *The Electronic Theory of Organic Chemistry,* Oxford University Press, London, 1949.
17. Eihausen, J. W., and Wilde, E. C., *Mod. Plastics* **42,** 120 (1964).
18. Emmons, W. D., and Pagano, A. S., *J. Am. Chem. Soc.* **77,** 89 (1955).
19. Findley, J. W., Swern, D., and Scanlan, J. T., *J. Am. Chem. Soc.* **67,** 412 (1945).
20. Giguère, P. A., and Olmos, A. W., *Can. J. Chem.* **30,** 821 (1952).
21. Greenspan, F. P., *Ind. Eng. Chem.* **39,** 847 (1947).
22. Hassal, C. H., *Organic Reactions,* Vol. IX, John Wiley & Sons, Inc., New York, 1957, p. 73.
23. John, J. A., and Weymouth, F. J., *Chem. Ind.* **1962,** 62.
24. McCaslin, Jr., L. S., *Oil Gas J.* **47,** 88, 128 (1948).
25. McClure, H. B., and Bateman, R. L., *Chem. Eng. News* **25,** 3286 (1947).
26. Milas, N. A., and Sussman, S., *J. Am. Chem. Soc.* **58,** 1302 (1936).
27. Newman, M. S., and Magerlein, B. J., *Organic Reactions,* Vol. V, John Wiley & Sons, Inc., New York, 1949, p. 413.
28. Othmer, D. F., *Chem. Met. Eng.* **40,** 631 (1933); **47,** 349 (1940).
29. Payne, G. B., *Tetrahedron* **18,** 763 (1962).
30. Phillips, B., Starcher, P. S., and Ash, B. D., *J. Org. Chem.* **23,** 1823 (1959).
31. Prileschajew, N., *Ber.* **42,** 4811 (1909).
32. Schmitz, W. R., and Wallace, J. G., *J. Am. Oil Chemists' Soc.* **31,** 363 (1954).
33. Shanley, E. S., and Perrin, J. R., *Jet Propulsion* **28,** 382 (1958).
34. Silbert, L. S., Siegel, E., and Swern, D., *J. Org. Chem.* **27,** 1336 (1962).
35. Smit, W. C., *Rec. Trav. Chim.* **49,** 675 (1930).
36. Swern, D., Findley, T. W., and Scanlan, J. T., *J. Am. Chem. Soc.* **66,** 1925 (1944).
37. Swern, D., Billen, G. N., and Scanlan, J. T., *J. Am. Chem. Soc.* **68,** 1504 (1946).
38. Swern, D., *J. Am. Chem. Soc.* **69,** 1962 (1947).
39. Swern, D., *Chem. Rev.* **45,** 1 (1949).
40. Swern, D., *Organic Reactions,* Vol. VII, John Wiley & Sons, Inc., New York, 1953, p. 378.
41. Swern, D., *Paint Varnish Prod.* **46,** 35 (1956).
42. Van Cleve, R., and Mullins, D. H., *Ind. Eng. Chem.* **50,** 873 (1958).
43. Wallace, J. G., Peterson, W. R., Chadwick, A. F., and Barlow, D. O., *J. Am. Oil Chemists, Soc.* **35,** 205 (1958).
44. Weitz, E., and Scheffer, A., *Ber.* **54,** 2327 (1921).
45. White, R. W., and Emmons, W. D., *Tetrahedron* **17,** 31 (1962).
46. Wilson, C. E., and Lucas, H. J., *J. Am. Chem. Soc.* **58,** 2396 (1936).
47. Brit. Pat. 735,974 (Aug. 31, 1955), B. Phillips and P. S. Starcher (to Union Carbide Corp.).
48. Brit. Pat. 776,758 (June 12, 1957), A. T. Hawkinson and W. R. Schmitz (to E. I. du Pont de Nemours & Co., Inc.).
49. Brit. Pat. 815,353 (1959) (to Shawinigan Products Corp.).
50. Brit. Pat. 892,631 (1962) (to Celanese Corp. of America).
51. Can. Pat. 531,112 (Oct. 2, 1956), A. A. D'Addieco (to E. I. du Pont de Nemours & Co., Inc.).
52. Fr. Pat. 1,297,057 (1962) (to Degussa Industrieofenbau).
53. U.S. Pat. 2,431,718 (Dec. 2, 1947), R. S. Wilder and A. A. Dolnick (to Publicker Industries Inc.).
54. U.S. Pat. 2,457,328 (Dec. 28, 1948), D. Swern and G. N. Billen (to U.S. Dept. of Agriculture).
55. U.S. Pat. 2,458,484 (Jan. 4, 1949), D. E. Terry and D. H. Wheeler (to General Mills, Inc.).
56. U.S. Pat. 2,485,160 (Oct. 18, 1949), W. D. Niederhauser and J. E. Koroly (to Rohm & Haas Company).
57. U.S. Pat. 2,490,800 (Dec. 13, 1949), F. P. Greenspan (to FMC Corp.).
58. U.S. Pat. 2,492,201 (Dec. 27, 1949), D. Swern, J. T. Scanlan, and T. W. Findley (to U.S. Dept. of Agriculture).
59. U.S. Pat. 2,571,208 (Oct. 16, 1951), L. E. Craig (to General Aniline & Film Corp.).
60. U.S. Pat. 2,655,514 (Oct. 13, 1953), M. Kleiman (to Velsicol Chemical Corp.).
61. U.S. Pat. 2,676,132 (Apr. 20, 1954), H. Bluestone (to Shell Development Co.).

62. U.S. Pat. 2,687,406 (Aug. 24, 1954), R. E. Foster (to E. I. du Pont de Nemours & Co., Inc.).
63. U.S. Pat. 2,751,381 (June 19, 1956), G. Slomp, Jr. (to The Upjohn Co.).
64. U.S. Pat. 2,773,887 (Dec. 11, 1956), G. Rosenkranz and C. Djerassi (to Syntex S. A.).
65. U.S. Pat. 2,785,185 (Mar. 12, 1957), B. Phillips and P. S. Starcher (to Union Carbide Corp.).
66. U.S. Pat. 2,786,854 (Mar. 26, 1957), C. W. Smith and G. B. Payne (to Shell Development Co.).
67. U.S. Pat. 2,801,253 (July 30, 1957), F. P. Greenspan and R. J. Gall (to FMC Corp.).
68. U.S. Pat. 2,804,473 (Aug. 27, 1957), B. Phillips, F. C. Frostick, and P. S. Starcher (to Union Carbide Corp.).
69. U.S. Pat. 2,813,878 (Nov. 19, 1957), A. W. Wahlroos (to Archer-Daniels-Midland Co.).
70. U.S. Pat. 2,833,788 (May 6, 1958), J. R. Skinner, C. H. Wilcoxen, Jr., and G. J. Carlson (to Shell Development Co.).
71. U.S. Pat. 2,866,826 (Dec. 30, 1958), H. E. McLaughlin, J. H. Stump, Jr., and M. C. Cleere (to Heyden Newport Chemical Corp.).
72. U.S. Pat. 2,993,920 (July 25, 1961), W. M. Budde, Jr., and G. W. Maxson (to Archer-Daniels-Midland Co.).
73. U.S. Pat. 3,050,480 (Aug. 21, 1962), W. M. Budde, Jr. (to Archer-Daniels-Midland Co.).

JOHN G. WALLACE
E. I. du Pont de Nemours & Co., Inc.

EPOXIDES

The epoxides are compounds incorporating the *oxirane* structure, a three-membered ring containing one oxygen atom and two carbon atoms, ie,

$$\text{C} \underset{\text{O}}{\overset{\diagup \quad \diagdown}{\text{——}}} \text{C}$$

The simplest member of the series is ethylene oxide, CH_2CH_2O. This and propylene oxide constitute the two most important commercial epoxides. Epoxides have a great affinity for labile hydrogen, a fact which permits them to enter into a remarkable variety of useful reactions. The open-chain ether analogs, ROR, are characterized by inertness to most reagents; the epoxides, on the other hand, are susceptible to attack by almost all known nucleophilic reagents.

Ethylene oxide (qv) is discussed separately. This article discusses epoxides in general, then propylene oxide (p. 275), butylene oxide (p. 288), and styrene oxide (p. 289). See also Epoxidation; Epoxy resins.

Physical Properties

The epoxides are generally liquids with an etherlike odor. The oxide ring raises the boiling point relative to the hydrocarbon or ether analog; the effect is most

Table 1. Boiling Point Comparison of Epoxides with Hydrocarbons and Ethers

Epoxide, $RCHCH_2O$			Hydrocarbon, RH			Ether, ROR'		
R	Mol wt	Bp, °C	R	Mol wt	Bp, °C	R, R'	Mol wt	Bp, °C
H	44	11	C_3H_7	44	−45	CH_3, CH_3	46	−25
CH_3	58	34	C_4H_9	58	−1	CH_3, C_2H_5	60	7
C_2H_5	72	59	C_5H_{11}	72	36	CH_3, C_3H_7	74	39
C_3H_7	86	88	C_6H_{13}	86	69	CH_3, C_4H_9	88	71

Table 2. Properties of Some 1,2-Epoxides, $R_1R_2C\overset{\overset{\displaystyle\ulcorner O \urcorner}{}}{\text{—}}CR_3R_4$

$R_1{}^a$	$R_2{}^a$	$R_3{}^a$	$R_4{}^a$	Bp, °C[b]	n_D	Sp gr	Infrared absorptions, μ
H	H	H	H	10.5	1.3597[7]	0.8694[20]	7.9, 11.4
CH$_3$	H	H	H	34	1.3657[20]	0.8287[20]	7.9, 10.5, 12.1
C$_2$H$_5$	H	H	H	59	1.3855[17]		11.1, 12.6
CH$_2$=CH	H	H	H	66.5[735]	1.4093[21]	0.8712[21]	8.0, 12.2
C$_3$H$_7$	H	H	H	88	1.4195[25]		
(CH$_3$)$_2$CH	H	H	H	82			
C$_5$H$_{11}$	H	H	H	145	1.4164[13.5]	0.8385[13.5]	
C$_6$H$_{13}$	H	H	H	61[115]	1.4199[20]	0.839[20]	
(CH$_3$)$_2$CH(CH$_2$)$_3$	H	H	H	156			
C$_8$H$_{17}$	H	H	H	89[10]	1.4288		10.9, 12.0
C$_{16}$H$_{33}$	H	H	H	137[0.5]			
C$_{18}$H$_{37}$	H	H	H	96[0.4]	1.4405[20]	0.845[20]	
C$_6$H$_5$	H	H	H	192	1.5331[25]		8.0, 11.4, 12.3
C$_6$H$_5$CH$_2$	H	H	H	100[17]		1.0059[20]	
C$_6$H$_5$(CH$_2$)$_2$	H	H	H	109[14]	1.684[18]	1.0259[0]	
C$_6$H$_5$(CH$_2$)$_3$	H	H	H	122[16]	1.517[18]	1.0477[0]	
C$_6$H$_5$(CH$_2$)$_4$	H	H	H	139[15]		1.013[0]	
CH$_2$OH	H	H	H	66[2.5]	1.4302[25]		11.1, 11.8, 12.0
CH$_3$OCH$_2$	H	H	H	54[85]	1.4012[25]		
C$_2$H$_5$OCH$_2$	H	H	H	126	1.4046[25]	0.94[25]	
C$_3$H$_7$CHOH	H	H	H	90[25]			
C$_6$H$_5$OCH$_2$	H	H	H	244	1.5307[21]	1.1109[21]	
CH$_3$CO$_2$CH$_2$	H	H	H	169		1.124	
CH$_2$=CHCO$_2$CH$_2$	H	H	H	115[78]	1.4472[20]	1.0993[20]	
CH$_2$=C(CH$_3$)-CO$_2$CH$_2$	H	H	H	65[5]	1.4506[20]	1.0760[20]	
CH$_3$CH=CH-CO$_2$CH$_2$	H	H	H	104[18]	1.4568[25]		
Br	H	H	H	92			
CH$_2$F	H	H	H	86			
CH$_2$Cl	H	H	H	115	1.4359[20]	1.181[20]	7.9, 10.8, 11.8
CH$_2$Br	H	H	H	136		1.615[14]	
CH$_2$I	H	H	H	64[24]		1.984[24]	
CF$_3$	H	H	H	39[748]	1.2997[20]	1.3068[20]	
CCl$_3$	H	H	H	149[750]		1.4962[19]	
(C$_2$H$_5$)$_2$NCH$_2$	H	H	H	65[20]			
C$_2$H$_5$	H	C$_2$H$_5$	H	106	1.5012[20]	0.862[20]	
C$_2$H$_5$	H	CF$_3$	H	79[745]	1.3340[20]	1.146[20]	
C$_2$H$_5$	H	C$_3$F$_7$	H	111[749]	1.3218[20]	1.358[20]	
C$_4$H$_9$	H	CH$_2$Br	H	205[11]	1.4676[13]	1.2468[17]	
C$_5$H$_{11}$	H	Cl	H	95[50]	1.4370	0.9874[16]	
C$_6$H$_5$	H	CH$_3$	H	90[13]	1.521[16]	1.029[0]	
C$_6$H$_5$	H	C$_2$H$_5$	H	111[21]	1.5152[16]	0.9987[0]	
C$_6$H$_5$	H	C$_3$H$_7$	H	115[15]	1.5088[18]	0.9798[0]	
C$_6$H$_5$	H	C$_3$H$_7$ (iso)	H	110[17]	1.5672[18]	0.9882[0]	
C$_6$H$_5$	H	C$_6$H$_5$CH$_2$	H	165[6]	1.575[18]	1.0826[0]	
CF$_3$	H	F	H	37			

Table 2 (*continued*)

$R_1{}^a$	$R_2{}^a$	$R_3{}^a$	$R_4{}^a$	Bp, °C[b]	n_D	Sp gr	Infrared absorptions, μ
CH₃	CH₃	CH₃	H	78	1.3896[18]	0.8277[20]	
CH₃	C₂H₅	CH₃	H	108		0.831⁰	
CH₃	CH₃	C₃F₇	H	103[747]	1.3187[20]	1.351[20]	
CH₃	CH₃	CO₂C₂H₅	H	183	1.4202[18]		
CH₃	CF₃	Cl	H	66	1.3428[20]	1.322[25]	
C₂H₅	C₂H₅	CH₃	H	130		0.820⁰	
CH₃	CH₃	CH₃	CH₃	91[753]	1.3984[16]	0.8156[16]	
CH₃	CH₃	H	H	51	1.3745[20]	0.8117[20]	
CH₃	CF₃	H	H	55	1.3128[20]	1.191[25]	
CH₃	C₂H₅	H	H	83		0.843	
CH₃	C₃F₇	H	H	93	1.3107[20]	1.391[20]	
C₂H₅	CH₂Br	H	H	166[768]	1.4725	1.4096[15.5]	
C₆H₅	CH₃	H	H	75[11]			
C₆H₅(CH₂)₃	CH₃	H	H	116[4]			
C₆H₅	OH	H	H	115[5]	1.5441[26]		
Cl	Cl	H	H	170			
CH₃	H	CH₃(cis)	H	63	1.3825[20]	0.8301[20]	7.8, 11.3, 12.9
CH₃	H	H	CH₃(trans)	57	1.3739[20]	0.8025[20]	7.8, 11.3, 12.3
CH₃	H	C₂H₅(cis)	H	85[748]	1.3941[20]	0.8195[25]	
CH₃	H	H	C₂H₅(trans)	80[748]	1.3867[20]	0.8031[20]	
CH₃	H	C₃H₇	H	110		0.8236[14]	
CH₃	H	C₃H₇(iso)	H	100			
CH₃	H	CF₃	H	59[747]	1.3167[20]	1.207[20]	
CH₃	H	CH₂Br	H	144	1.4685[18]	1.468[18]	
CH₃	H	C₃F₇	H	94[748]	1.3091[20]	1.424[20]	8.0, 11.3, 12.6
CH₃	H	CO₂H	H	mp 88.5			

Other epoxides

		Bp, °C	n_D	Sp gr	IR, μ
1,2-cyclopentene oxide,	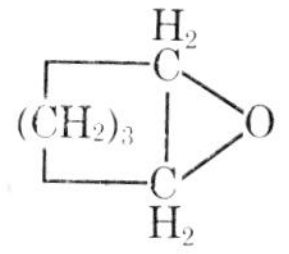	102	1.4330[23]		11.9
1,2-cyclohexene oxide,	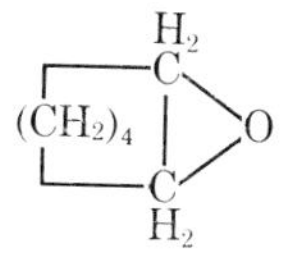	131	1.4519[20]	0.9663[20]	7.9, 11.2, 12.3
1,2,3,4-diepoxybutane,	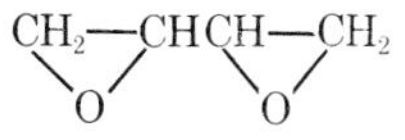	138	1.4272[30]	0.962[25]	8.0, 10.9, 12.3
vinylcyclohexene dioxide,	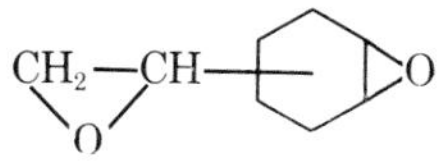	227	1.4787[20]	1.0986[20]	

[a] In a radical of the form C_nH_{2n+1}, the normal isomer is intended; thus, C_3H_7 means $CH_3CH_2CH_2$.

[b] Unless specified, the boiling point is listed at 760 mm Hg.

marked for the early members, as shown in Table 1. Epoxides are more soluble in water and polar solvents than are the corresponding hydrocarbons or ethers. The properties of a variety of epoxides are listed in Table 2.

Ethylene oxide has a dipole moment of 1.8–1.9 D and propylene oxide of 1.9–2.0 D (104); the increase is due to the electron-repelling methyl group. Dipole moments in epoxides are the result of a nonuniform electron distribution in σ-bonds caused by an electronegative atom in the ring. A group moment of 1.3 D was used for an epoxide function in order to calculate the expected dipole moments of halogen-substituted epoxides (161).

Nuclear magnetic resonance spectroscopy of epoxides indicates that epoxide protons will generally be found in the region extending from 7.0–8.0 τ (162).

Preparation and Chemical Properties

Epoxides are prepared by a variety of methods including oxidation of olefins with peroxy acids, oxygen, and hydrogen peroxide; cyclodehydrohalogenations; cyclizations involving a leaving group other than halogen; and numerous miscellaneous syntheses. These methods have been reviewed in some detail (1,2).

Oxidation of Olefins. The most direct method for the synthesis of epoxides is the oxidation of the corresponding olefin.

$$\text{C=C} \xrightarrow{\text{(O)}} \underset{\text{O}}{\text{C—C}}$$

Direct Oxidation. A method of considerable industrial importance for ethylene oxide manufacture is the direct oxidation of ethylene at elevated temperatures over a suitably prepared metallic silver catalyst:

$$CH_2{=}CH_2 + O_2 \xrightarrow{\text{Ag}} CH_2CH_2O$$

Unfortunately, other olefins, such as propylene and isobutylene, give only low yields of epoxide by this route, so that the parent substance, ethylene oxide, has been the only representative accessible by this method.

Peroxy Acid Oxidation. The procedure of great importance and most frequently encountered for general usefulness in all areas of organic chemistry is peroxy acid oxidation of a suitable olefin (3):

$$\text{C=C} + RCO_3H \rightarrow \underset{\text{O}}{\text{C—C}}$$

Included among the peroxy acids used for the conversion of olefins into epoxides are peroxyformic, peroxyacetic, peroxybenzoic, monoperoxyphthalic, and trifluoroperoxyacetic acids. It is important to note that peroxyformic and peroxyacetic acids are generally not satisfactory for epoxidation unless addition is conducted in a buffered medium to prevent rupture of the oxide ring by excess acid.

In general almost all classes of olefins can be satisfactorily converted into epoxides with one or more peroxy acids (1): (1) aliphatic olefins, —C=C—, C=C(CH$_2$)$_n$;

(2) olefins carrying at least one olefinic, acetylenic, or aromatic substituent, —C=C-C=C—, —C=CC≡C—, C$_6$H$_5$C=C—; (3) olefins having at least one carbon atom

singly or doubly bonded to a polar atom, —C=CCOH, —C=CCCl, —C=CC(OR)$_2$, —C=CC(O$_2$CR)$_2$, —C=CCO$_2$H; (4) olefins attached directly to polar atoms, —C=CCl, —C=CO—.

The rate of epoxidation is quite sensitive to the kind of substituents on the ethylenic carbon atoms. Simple alkyl-substituted olefins gave relative rate sequences with peroxyacetic acid as follows (3): R$_2$C=CR$_2$ > R$_2$C=CHR, 6500 > R$_2$C=CH$_2$, 500 = RCH=CHR, 500 > RCH=CH$_2$, 24 > CH$_2$=CH$_2$, 1.

The cyclic olefins have rates comparable to the open-chain analogs. When the ethylenic linkage is conjugated with a carboxyl, carboalkoxy, or carbonyl group, the reaction with a peroxy acid is quite slow or fails completely (166). In general, α-aryl substituents are rate-enhancing. 1-Phenyl-1-propene, C$_6$H$_5$CH=CHCH$_3$, reacts 23 times faster than 3-phenyl-1-propene, C$_6$H$_5$CH$_2$CH=CH$_2$.

Alkaline Hydrogen Peroxide Oxidation. A large number of epoxidations have been conducted with alkaline hydrogen peroxide:

$$CH_2{=}CHCHO \xrightarrow[pH\,=\,8]{H_2O_2/OH^-} CH_2{-}CHCHO$$
$$\diagdown\!O\!\diagup$$

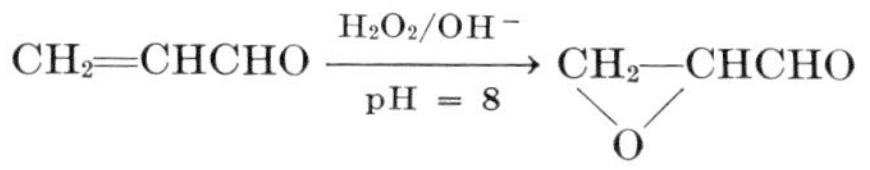

Although used predominantly with α,β-unsaturated ketones, the reagent has also been used with α,β-unsaturated nitriles, aldehydes, and esters. A notable feature of alkaline hydrogen peroxide is its ability to epoxidize heavily substituted and sterically inaccessible double bonds when they are linked to a carbonyl group (4).

Cyclodehydrohalogenation. A β-halo alcohol or halohydrin (see Chlorohydrins) is cyclized in alkali to produce an epoxide. The halohydrins may be isolable, or they may be transient, unstable species that undergo spontaneous ring closure under the conditions used to generate them. Schematically the course of such reactions would be as follows, with X as a halogen and B as a base:

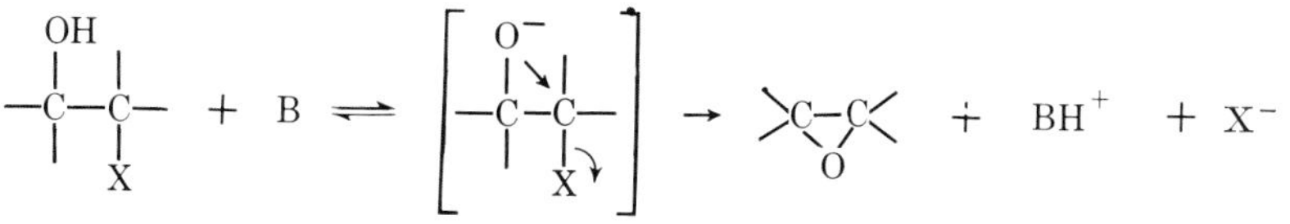

The most common of these methods is the dehydrohalogenation of a halohydrin with alkali, the halohydrin being generated by the addition of a hypohalous acid across the double bond. The addition of hypochlorous acid to propylene followed by cyclization in alkali is the present commercial method for propylene oxide manufacture. A description of the manufacturing process is given in a later section. The hypochlorous acid is generated from the reaction of chlorine with water, establishing the following equilibrium:

$$Cl_2 + H_2O \leftrightharpoons HOX + H^+ + X^-$$

In the presence of an extremely reactive olefin, the hypochlorous acid, although present in relatively low concentration, will be sufficient to initiate addition. The equilibrium will be continually reestablished to compensate for HOCl depletion, provided the external chlorine supply is maintained.

The addition of hypochlorous acid to olefinic double bonds is generally regarded as a typical electrophilic substitution reaction. The mechanism is believed to be one in which an intermediate halonium ion is formed, $\overset{\diagdown}{\underset{\diagup}{C}}\text{-----}\overset{\diagup}{\underset{\diagdown}{C}},$ and subsequent at-

$\overset{}{X^+}$

tack by a nucleophile (HOH) occurs at the site of greatest incipient carbonium ion stabilization. The kinetics of hypochlorous acid addition are extremely complicated (163). The attack is probably led by a protonated species H_2OCl^+ since the reaction is acid-catalyzed.

Treatment of isobutylene with aqueous hypohalous acids yields predominantly 1-halo-2-methyl-2-propanol (5):

$$\underset{CH_3}{\overset{CH_3}{\diagdown}}C\text{=}CH_2 \xrightarrow{HOX} \underset{CH_3}{\overset{CH_3}{\diagdown}}COHCH_2X \xrightarrow{base} \underset{CH_3}{\overset{CH_3}{\diagdown}}\underset{O}{C\text{----}CH_2}$$

The halonium ion presumably adds to the least hindered site of a double bond and subsequent ring closure will lead to products in which oxygen is on the opposite or more hindered side. This is in contrast with the action of peroxy acids, which effectively function by cis-addition and afford products in which oxygen assumes the less hindered position. This difference acquires particular significance in the steroid field.

The rate-determining step for epoxide formation is the conversion of the halo-

hydrin to the anion $\overset{O^-}{\underset{\diagup}{\overset{\diagdown}{C}}}\text{--}\overset{|}{\underset{|}{C}}X$ (6). The effect of alkyl substitution on the rate of oxide formation can be seen from the rate sequence (7).

Halohydrin	*Relative reaction rate*
$(CH_3)_2C\text{---}CHCH_3$ $\quad\quad\underset{OH}{\mid}\ \underset{Cl}{\mid}$	424
$(CH_3)_2C\text{---}CH_2$ $\quad\quad\underset{OH}{\mid}\ \underset{Cl}{\mid}$	78
$CH_3CH\text{---}CH_2$ $\quad\ \underset{OH}{\mid}\ \ \underset{Cl}{\mid}$	6.5
$CH_2\text{---}CHCH_3$ $\underset{OH}{\mid}\ \ \ \underset{Cl}{\mid}$	1.7
$CH_2\text{---}CH_2$ $\underset{OH}{\mid}\ \ \ \underset{Cl}{\mid}$	0.31

The 1-chloropropylene chlorohydrin (1-chloro-2-propanol), which is the major isomer formed on addition of hypochlorous acid to propylene, is almost 4 times as reactive as the 2-isomer. Both are more reactive than ethylene chlorohydrin.

Rosowsky (1) in his excellent article has extensive discussions on epoxide preparative methods. Several of the more important miscellaneous methods are given below.

Darzens Condensation (8).   The Darzens condensation for the synthesis of an α,β-epoxy ester (glycidic ester) can be formulated:

$$\overset{\text{O}}{\overset{\|}{\text{R}'\text{CR}''}} + \text{XCHRCO}_2\text{Et} + \text{B}^- \rightarrow \text{R}'\text{R}''\text{C}\underset{\diagdown_{\text{O}}\diagup}{\text{---}}\text{CRCO}_2\text{Et} + \text{X}^- + \text{HB}$$

Most aldehydes and ketones can be used.   The halogen-containing substance must have an activated hydrogen on the halogen-bearing carbon, as in ethyl α-chloroacetate.

The glycidic esters are of interest primarily because they can be converted into aldehydes and ketones having a higher carbon content than the original aldehydes or ketones.   This transformation occurs after hydrolysis to and decarboxylation of the epoxy acids, and is accompanied by rearrangement when an aldehyde is formed.

$$\text{R}'\text{R}''\text{C}\underset{\diagdown_{\text{O}}\diagup}{\text{---}}\text{CRCO}_2\text{H} \xrightarrow[-\text{CO}_2]{\Delta} \text{R}'\text{R}''\text{CHCOR} \quad \text{or} \quad \text{RR}'\text{R}''\text{CHO}$$

Cyclization of 1,2-Diol Monosulfonates.   A cyclization of considerable synthetic importance involves the hydrolysis of the monoester of a 1,2-diol with an alkane- or arenesulfonic acid.

$$\overset{\text{OH}}{\underset{\text{OSO}_2\text{R}}{\overset{|}{-}\text{C}-\overset{|}{\text{C}}-}} \xrightarrow{\text{base}} \diagdown\text{C}\underset{\diagup_{\text{O}}\diagdown}{\text{---}}\text{C}\diagup + {}^-\text{OSO}_2\text{R}$$

Addition of Diazomethane to Carbonyl Compounds.   Epoxides have been prepared from a wide variety of carbonyl compounds by diazomethane addition (9).   Yields range from a few percent to nearly quantitative.

$$\text{R}_2\text{CO} + \text{CH}_2\text{N}_2 \rightarrow \text{R}_2\text{C}\underset{\diagdown_{\text{O}}\diagup}{\text{---}}\text{CH}_2 + \text{N}_2$$

Reactions.   Epoxides react with a variety of reagents, due to their great affinity for labile hydrogen, to produce chemicals of broad interest.   To illustrate their potential as reactive intermediates, a table of typical reactions, Table 3, is presented.   However, not every organic oxide will undergo all the reactions shown.   The course of any individual reaction depends upon the structure of the epoxide, the solvent and catalyst used, and the nature of the other reactants.   The more reactive epoxides such as ethylene or propylene oxide would be expected to undergo all of the reactions listed.   In general, whenever the reaction has been described in the literature with propylene oxide as the reactant, that example has been used.

The ring-opening reactions of epoxides take place by ionic mechanisms (15).   (A possible exception is catalytic hydrogenation.)   The bond which breaks is the highly polar carbon–oxygen bond, and the reactions are generally conducted in polar solvents.   In fact, the reaction between ethylene oxide and diethylamine in methanol does not occur in the absence of the solvent (169).

When the epoxide ring is opened, three kinds of rate-determining steps become

Table 3. The Reactions of Epoxides

Reactant		Epoxide[a]	Product		Reference
Type	Example		Type	Example	
acetals	$CH_2(OCH_3)_2$	EO	mixed acetals	$CH_3OCH_2OCH_2CH_2OCH_3$	10
acetoacetates	$CH_3COCH_2CO_2Et$	PO	lactone	[β-lactone ring structure with CH_3, $=O$, $COCH_3$]	11
acetylenes	$HC{\equiv}CR$	PO	hydroxy substituted acetylenes	$RC{\equiv}CCH_2CH(OH)CH_3$	12
acids, carboxylic	$RCOOH$	PO	hydroxy substituted ester	$RCOOCH_2CHOHCH_3$	13
acids, mineral	$HX: HF, HCl, HBr, HI$	PO	chlorohydrin	$XCH_2CHOHCH_3$	14,15
acyl halides	CH_3COCl	EO	β-chloroester	$ClCH_2CH_2O_2CCH_3$	16
alcohols	CH_3OH, H^+	PO	primary + secondary alcohol	$HOCH_2CH(OCH_3)CH_3 +$ $CH_3CH(OH)CH_2OCH_3$	17
	CH_3OH, OH^-	PO	secondary alcohol	$CH_3OCH_2CHOHCH_3$	17
aldehydes	CH_3CHO	PO	cyclic acetal	CH_3CHO [1,3-dioxolane ring, CH_2O, $CHCH_3$]	18
alkyl halides	C_2H_5Br	CyO	β-halo ether	[cyclohexane ring with OC_2H_5 and Br]	19
amides, primary; amides, secondary	$RCONH_2,$ $RCONHR'$	EO	hydroxy substituted amides	$RCONHCH_2CH_2OH,$ $RCON(CH_2CH_2OH)_2,$ $RCONR'CH_2CH_2OH$	20
amines, primary	RNH_2	PO	hydroxy substituted amines	$R_2NCH_2CH(OH)CH_3$	21
amines, secondary	R_2NH				
amines, tertiary	R_3N	Epi	quaternary salt	$R_3\overset{+}{N}CH_2CH(OH)CH_2NR\ Cl_2$	168
ammonia	NH_3	PO	alkanolamines	$CH_3CHOHCH_2NH_2$	22
anhydrides	$(CH_3CO)_2O$	Epi	diesters of 1,2 diols	$ClCH_2CHCH_2O_2CCH_3$ (O_2CCH_3)	23
antimony halides	$SbCl_3$	EO	antimonates	$(ClCH_2CH_2O)_n(SbCl_{3-n})$	24
	$SbCl_{5-}{\cdot}(Et)_2O$	EO		$Cl_4SbOCH_2CH_2OEt$	25
aromatics	C_6H_6	PO	hydroxyalkyl aromatic	$C_6H_5CH(CH_3)CH_2OH$	26

Reagent	Formula	PO/EO	Product	Product structure	Ref.
azide ion	N_3^-	PO	organic azide	$CH_3CHOHCH_2N_3$	27
beryllium halides	$BeCl_2$	PO	β-chloroalkoxy ester	$(ClCH_2CH(CH_3)O)_n(BeCl_{2-n})$	25
bisulfite salt	$NaHSO_3$	PO	bisulfite	$CH_3CHOHCH_2SO_3Na$	28
borane	B_2H_6	EO	bis(β-hydroxy alkyl) borane + polymer	$HB(CH_2CH_2OH)_2$	29
boron halides	BCl_3	PO	boron ester	$CH_3CHClCH_2Cl + CH_3CHClCH_2OBCl_2$ / $OBCl_2$	30
carbanions	$NaHC(CO_2Et)_2$	PO	butyrolactone	[cyclic structure with CO_2Et, CH_3]	31
carbon dioxide	CO_2	PO	carbonate	$CH_3CH{-}CH_2$ [cyclic carbonate]	32
carbon disulfide	CS_2	EO	cyclic trithiocarbonate	$SCH_2CH_2SC(S)$	33
carbon oxysulfide	COS	PO	episulfide	CH_3CHCH_2S	34
chlorocarbonates	$CH_3OCO_2CH_2Cl$	PO	β-chloroalkyl carbonate	$CH_3CHOCO_2CH_3$ / CH_2Cl	35
chloroformamide	NH_2COCl	EO	urethan	$NH_2CO_2CH_2CH_2Cl$	36
cyanate ion	$NaOCN$	EO	oxazolidone	$H_2C{-}NH$ / $H_2C{-}O$ $C{=}O$	37
dinitrogen tetroxide	N_2O_4	PO	β-nitroalkyl nitrites	$CH_3CH(ONO)CH_2ONO_2$	38
dithiophosphates	$(RO)_2PSSH$	EO	thiophosphite	$HOCH_2CH_2SP(OR)_2$	39
epoxides	CH_2CH_2O	EO	1,4-dioxane	[dioxane ring structure]	40
	CH_3CHCH_2O	PO	2,5-dimethyldioxane + 2-ethyl-4-methyldioxolane	[ring structures]	41

(continued)

Table 3 (*continued*)

Reactant		Epoxide[a]	Product		Reference
Type	Example		Type	Example	
Friedel-Crafts halides, metallic			see aromatics		
halogens	Cl_2	PO	see under specific element chlorinated products	$ClCH_2CHOHCH_2Cl$, $ClCH_2COCH_3$, + mixture of products	42
halohydrins	CH_2ClCH_2OH	Epi	epoxide	CH_2CH_2O	43
hydrazine	N_2H_4	EO	alkyl hydrazine	$NH_2NHCH_2CH_2OH$	44
hydrogen	H_2/Ni	PO	secondary alcohol	$CH_3CH(OH)CH_3$	45
hydrogen cyanide hydrogen halides	HCN HX: HF, HCl, HBr, HI	PO	β-hydroxynitrile, see acids, mineral	$CH_3CHOHCH_2CN$	
hydrogen sulfide	H_2S	PO	β-hydroxysulfide	$(CH_3CH(OH)CH_2)_2S$	46
hydroperoxides	$RCOOOH$	PO	peroxide	$RCOOOCH_2CHOHCH_3$	47
hydroselenide	H_2Se	$CH_3C\equiv C-\overset{O}{C(CH_3)-CH(CH_3)}$	selenophene	(ring: CH_3, CH_3, Se)	48
hydroxylamine	NH_2OH	EO	N-substituted hydroxylamine	$(HOCH_2CH_2)_2NOH$	49
imines	CH_3CH_2NH	EO	β-hydroxyimine	$HOCH_2CH_2NCH_2CH_2$	50
isocyanates	C_6H_5NCO	EO	oxazolidone	$H_2C-N-C_6H_5$ / H_2C-O with $C=O$	51
isomerization	CH_3CHCH_2O	PO PO	olefin aldehyde	$CH_2=CHCH_2OH$ CH_3CH_2CHO	52 53
isothiocyanate salts	$KCNS$, OH^- $KCNS$, H^+	PO PO	ethylene sulfides β-thiocyanate alcohol	CH_3CHCH_2S $CH_3CH(OH)CH_2SCN$	54 54
ketene	$CH_2=C=O$	PO	γ-lactone	CH_3CH / CH_2CH_2 with $O-C=O$	55
ketones	CH_3COCH_3	PO	cyclic ketal	$(CH_3)_2C$ with $O-CH_2$ / $O-CHCH_3$	56

lithium aluminum hydride	$LiAlH_4$	PO	secondary alcohol	$CH_3CH(OH)CH_3$	57
malonates			see carbanions		
mercaptans	C_2H_5SH	EO	sulfide	$C_2H_5SCH_2CH_2OH$	58
nitriles	CH_3CN	CyO	nitrile	(cyclohexane ring with OH and CH_2CN)	59
nitric acid	HNO_3	PO	isomeric nitrato alcohols	$CH_3CH(OH)CH_2ONO_2 +$ $CH_3CH(ONO_2)CH_2OH$	59
nitrosyl halides	$NOCl$	PO	β-chloroalkyl nitrites	$CH_3CH(ONO)CH_2Cl$	60
organometallics	$Mg(Et)_2$	PO	alcohol	$CH_3CH(OH)CH_2Et$	61
	$NaC{\equiv}CEt$	EO	alcohol	$EtC{\equiv}CCH_2CH_2OH$	62
	LiC_6H_5	PO	alcohol	$CH_3CH(OH)CH_2C_6H_5$	63
oxidation	conc HNO_3	Epi	α-hydroxy acid	$ClCH_2CH(OH)CO_2H$	64
peroxides	H_2O_2	MSO	ketone	$C_6H_5COCH_3$	65
phenols	C_6H_5OH	PO	1,2-diol monaryl ethers	$C_6H_5OCH_2CH(OH)CH_3 +$ $C_6H_5CH(CH_3)CH_2OH$	66
phosgene	$COCl_2$	PO	β-chloroacetyl chloroformate and carbonate	$CH_3CH(CH_2Cl)CO_2Cl +$ $(CH_3CH(CH_2Cl)O)_2CO_3$	67
phosphines	RPH_2	EO	phosphine	$HOCH_2CH_2PHR$	68
phosphines, alkyl-dichloro	CH_3PCl_2	PO	alkanechlorophosphimite	$CH_3P(Cl)OCH(CH_3)CH_2Cl$	69
phosphines, dialkoxy-chloro	$(C_2H_5O)_2PCl$	EO	trialkyl phosphite	$ClCH_2CH_2OP(OC_2H_5)_2$	70
phosphites, dialkyl	$(C_2H_5O)_2P(O)H$	PO	trialkyl phosphite	$CH_3CH(OH)CH_2OP(OC_2H_5)_2$	71
phosphoric acid	H_3PO_4	EO	phosphate ester	$PO(OCH_2CH_2O{\rightarrow})_{3n}H$	72
phosphorous acid	H_3PO_3	EO	dialkyl phosphite	$HP(O)(CH_2CH_2O{\rightarrow})_{2n}H$	72
phosphorus halides	PCl_3	PO	β-chloroalkoxy phosphites	$(ClCH_2CH(CH_3)O{\rightarrow})_n(PCl_{3-n})$	73
	$POCl_3$	EO	β-chloroalkoxy phosphates	$(ClCH_2CH_2O)POCl_2$	74
	$POCl_3$ + dimethylformamide	EO	β-chloroalkyl formate esters	$HCOOCH_2CH_2Cl$	75
	PBr_5	SO	vic-dihalide	$C_6H_5CHBrCH_2Br$	76
polymerization	CH_3CHCH_2O	PO	polyalkylene oxides	$({-}OCH_2CH{-})_x$ with CH_3	77
reduction	see hydrogen; lithium aluminum hydride				

(continued)

Table 3 (*continued*)

Reactant		Epoxide[a]	Product		Reference
Type	Example		Type	Example	
silicon tetrahalide	$SiCl_4$	PO	β-chloroalkoxyl silicon esters	$(ClCH_2CH(CH_3)O)_n(SiCl_{4-n})$	78
sulfenyl halides	Cl_3CSCl	PO	sulfenic ester	$CH_3CH(CH_2Cl)OSCCl_3$	79
sulfites	Na_2SO_3	see bisulfite			
sulfonic acids	CH_3SO_3H	CyO	sulfonate	(cyclohexane ring with $-OH$ and $-O_3SCH_3$)	80
sulfoxides	$(CH_3)_2SO \cdot BF_3$	SO	α-hydroxyketone	$C_6H_5C(O)CH_2OH$	81
sulfur dioxide	SO_2	PO	cyclic sulfite	CH_3CHCH_2 (cyclic O–S(=O)–O)	82
sulfur trioxide	SO_3	EO	cyclic sulfate	CH_2-CH_2 (cyclic O–SO$_2$–O)	83
sulfuryl halides	SO_2Cl_2	EO	chlorosulfonate	$ClCH_2CH_2OSO_2Cl$	84
thiolcarboxylic acids	CH_3COSH	PO	thiol ester	$CH_3CH(OH)CH_2SC(O)CH_3$	85
thiocyanic acid	$KSCN,\ H^+$	EO	2-imidazolidinethione	(ring: NH, C=S, N–CH_2CH_2OH)	86
thionyl chloride	$SOCl_2$	EO	sulfite	$(ClCH_2CH_2O)_2SO$	87
thiosulfates	$K_2S_2O_3$	EO	sulfinic acid	$HOCH_2CH_2SO_2H$	88
thiourea	$NH_2C(S)NH_2$	PO	β-mercapto alcohol	$CH_3CH(OH)CH_2SH$	89
titanium halides	$TiCl_4$	PO	β-chloroalkoxy titanates	$(ClCH_2CH(CH_3)O)_n(TiCl_{4-n})$	90
trityl halides	$(C_6H_5)_3CBr$	PO	trityl ether	$(C_6H_5)_3COCH(CH_3)CH_2Br$	91
water	$H_2O,\ H^+$	PO (+)	(+) glycol	$CH_3CH(OH)CH_2OH$	92
water	$H_2O,\ OH^-$	PO (+)	(−) glycol	$CH_3CH(OH)CH_2OH$	
xanthamides	NH_2CSSH	Epi	cyclic sulfide	$ClCH_2CHCH_2S$	93

[a] EO, ethylene oxide; PO, propylene oxide; SO, styrene oxide; Epi, epichlorohydrin; CyO, cyclohexene oxide; MSO, α-methylstyrene oxide.

possible. These are symbolized below for the reaction with a reagent such as an alcohol under neutral, acid-catalyzed, and base-catalyzed conditions. Since the ring-opening

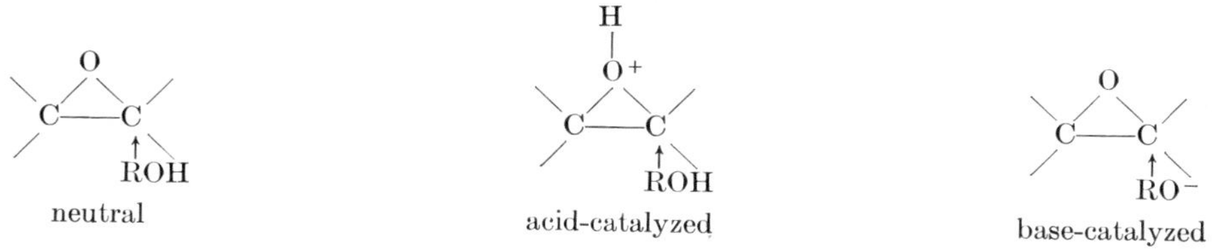

neutral	acid-catalyzed	base-catalyzed

reactions are nucleophilic displacements on carbon, inversion of configuration is generally observed; the opening is trans.

Propylene Oxide

Propylene oxide (1,2-epoxypropane), CH_3CHCH_2O, is a colorless, low-boiling, flammable liquid, partially soluble in water, and miscible with most organic solvents. The derivatives of propylene oxide are generally less water and more oil soluble than the corresponding ethylene oxide derivatives.

Propylene oxide is primarily a chemical intermediate for the manufacture of propylene glycol and polypropylene glycols. It is also used as an effective stabilizer in acid-releasing systems, as an excellent solvent for a variety of applications, and for the synthesis of a variety of different products.

Structure and Physical Properties. Propylene oxide is the first homolog of ethylene oxide. One of its unique features is its ability to exist in two isomeric forms since carbon atom 2 is asymmetric, $CH_3C^*H \text{—} CH_2$.

Utilizing the parameters obtained for ethylene oxide from its microwave spectra (94), the structure of propylene oxide was determined by Swaler and Herschbach (95). A representation of these values is shown below. In this diagram, $\alpha = 61° 24'$, $\beta = 116° 15'$, $\gamma = 59° 18'$, and $\delta = 120° 57'$.

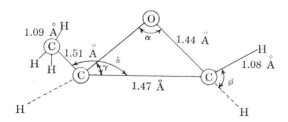

The large strain energy of this small ring endows it with a reactivity which is not present in alkyl ethers (96). Propylene oxide has a lower basicity than the larger-ring oxygen heterocyclics but does form compounds with strong acids such as boron trichloride and boron trifluoride (97).

The low electron donor ability of propylene oxide has been determined by measuring its heat of mixing with chloroform (98). At 3°C the heat of mixing is 570 cal/mole for propylene oxide, 365 cal/mole for ethylene oxide, and 650 cal/mole for diethyl ether. The basicity or electron donor ability of propylene oxide is thus higher than ethylene oxide but considerably lower than normal ethers.

Table 4. Physical Properties of Propylene Oxide

		Reference
boiling point, °C,		
760 mm	34.0	99
50 mm	−26	99
10 mm	−52	99
vapor pressure, 20°C, mm	449	99
density, °C	0.8598	100
20°C	0.8287	100
melting point, °C	−111.8	101
refractive index, n_D^5	1.3712	100
n_D^{20}	1.3667	100
critical temperature, °C	215.3	99
viscosity, cP, 0°C	0.410	100
20°C	0.327	100
coefficient of expansion per °C, cubical, liquid	0.00213	100
heat of vaporization, 25°C, kcal/mole	6.3	102
specific heat, 15°C, cal/(g)(°C)	0.465	99
heat of combustion, kcal/mole	450.6	103
heat of melting, cal/mole	1561.4	101
entropy, absolute, 298.15°K	46.91	101
dipole moment, D	1.98	104
electric moment, esu	1.88×10^{18}	105
magnetic susceptibility, $-\xi \times 10^6$	42.5	106
explosive limits in air, 760 mm		
(upper), % by vol	21.5	99
(lower), % by vol	2.1	
flash point, Cleveland open cup, °F	−350	99
solubility in water, 20°C, wt of soln	40.5	99
solubility of water in compound, 20°C, wt of soln	12.8	99

The physical properties of propylene oxide are listed in Table 4.

The vapor pressure over the range −30 to +33.4°C has been described by the equation $\log p = 1722.7/T + 8.49$ (107).

A plot of vapor pressure versus temperature over the range −12 to +215°C is reproduced in Figure 1 from reference (108).

Propylene oxide does not form an azeotrope with water at atmospheric pressure (109), but azeotropes do form at higher pressures (99). At 30 psig, the azeotrope (bp 69°C) contains 99.9% by wt propylene oxide and 0.1% water. At 60 psig (bp 86.5°C) the composition is 99.8% propylene oxide and 0.2% water.

Propylene oxide has been reported to undergo compound formation with water to yield a hydrate, $C_3H_6O \cdot 16H_2O$, which melts at −3°C (110).

Raman (111) and infrared (112) spectra of propylene oxide have been reported and an infrared assignment to the epoxy ring made. Two characteristic bands were observed, the first at 11 μ and the second at 12 μ. These are apparently characteristic of terminal alkyl epoxides.

Optically Active Propylene Oxide. The separation of d- and l-propylene oxides has been conducted by the sequence of reactions shown below (113):

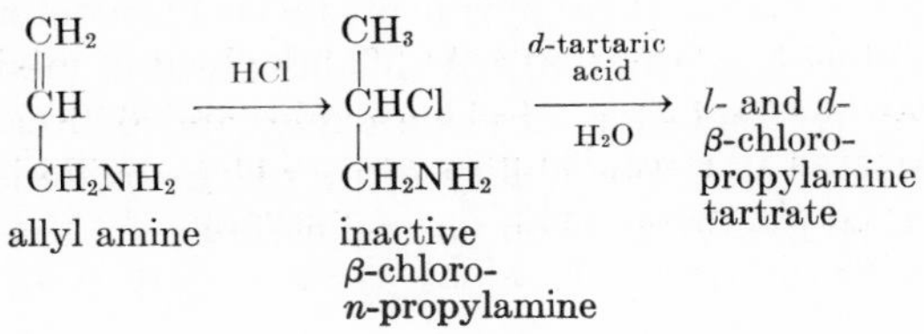

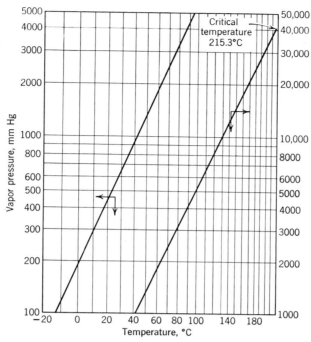

Fig. 1. Vapor pressure of propylene oxide.

The *d*-tartrate of the *d*-isomer precipitates from solution first and on treatment with base releases *d*-β-chloropropylamine. The amine hydrochloride is then used in the preparation of the alcohol and, subsequently, the epoxide. The *l*-propylene oxide, $[\alpha]_D^{18} = -8.26°$, is prepared similarly from the tartrate remaining in solution.

$$
\begin{array}{ccccc}
\text{CH}_3 & & \text{CH}_3 & & \text{CH}_3 \\
| & \xrightarrow{\text{NaNO}_2} & | & \xrightarrow{\text{KOH}} & | \\
\text{CHCl} & & \text{CHCl} & & \text{HC} \\
| & & | & & \diagdown \!\!\!\! \text{O} \\
\text{CH}_2\text{NH}_2\cdot\text{HCl} & & \text{CH}_2\text{OH} & & \text{H}_2\text{C} \diagup \\
{}[\alpha]_D^{18} = 34.8° & & [\alpha]_D^{18} = 9.26° & & [\alpha]_D^{18} = 12.72°
\end{array}
$$

Levene and Walti (114) prepared *d*-propylene oxide from active propylene glycol prepared enzymically, and Price and Osgan (115) used this same procedure.

Russian workers (116) have reported partial resolution of *dl*-propylene oxide by contacting it with optically active quartz (*l*) which had been coated with silver, copper, or platinum.

The *d*-isomer more readily isomerizes to acetone and propionaldehyde on the (*l*-) quartz, producing an increase in the *l*-propylene oxide isomer relative to the *d*-isomer in the unreacted gas stream.

REACTIONS

A great many reactions of propylene oxide are known, and most involve the opening of the three-membered oxirane ring. The high chemical reactivity is ascribed to the strain in the three-membered ring resulting from the deviation in the bond angles from those normally found in aliphatic compounds. Generally, the ring-opening reactions involve an ionic mechanism in which the highly polar carbon–oxygen bond is broken.

A tabular summary of the reactions of epoxides has been presented in the first section. Reactions of particular commercial interest are now described in more detail.

Isomerization. High yields of either allyl alcohol or propionaldehyde can be obtained by the high-temperature isomerization of propylene oxide over various catalysts. If propylene oxide is passed over pumice at 500°C, rearrangement occurs to give propionaldehyde and acetone in a ratio of 2:1 (117):

$$CH_3\overset{\cdot}{C}HCH_2 \rightarrow CH_3CH_2CHO + CH_3COCH_3$$
$$\diagdown\!\!\diagup$$
$$O$$

At 280°C in the vapor phase over potash alum, an 80% yield of propionaldehyde was obtained, along with 2% allyl alcohol, 15% unchanged oxide, and some highly condensed products (53). With a different catalyst, the course of the isomerization was completely altered, and high yields of allyl alcohol were obtained using lithium phosphate (56):

$$CH_3CHCH_2 \rightarrow CH_2\!=\!CHCH_2OH$$
$$\diagdown\!\!\diagup$$
$$O$$

This process, using an improved catalyst system (119), has been employed for the production of allyl alcohol on a large scale by Olin Mathieson Chemical Corporation.

Polymerization. Two basic types of polymers are prepared from propylene oxide: (1) those initiated by the reaction of the epoxide with compounds having a labile hydrogen atom; and (2) those resulting from catalyzed polymerization of the epoxide.

The first type of reaction occurs with water, alcohols, phenols, ammonia, amines, amides, acids, etc, to yield oxyalkylated derivatives which can contain anywhere from two to a hundred units of propylene oxide. The second type of reaction occurs with various Lewis acids and bases, as well as with numerous salts and complex catalysts, to yield polyalkylene oxides, which range from liquids and greases to waxy solids with molecular weights up to 100,000, and resinous plastics, with molecular weights up to several million (see Glycols; Polyethers).

Unlike polyethylene oxide, whose structure can have only one particular form, polypropylene oxide can possess several types of monomer arrangements in the molecule, all of which have an effect on the properties of the polymer.

Among the possible arrangements are the following:

A. Head-to-tail structure.

$$\sim\!\!\sim\!\!CCOCCO\!\!\sim\!\!\sim$$
$$\quad|\quad\;|$$
$$\quad C\quad C$$

B. Repeating head-to-head and tail-to-tail structure.

$$\sim\!\!\sim\!\!OCCOCCOCCOCCO\!\!\sim\!\!\sim$$
$$\quad|\;\;|\quad\;|\;\;|$$
$$\quad C\;C\quad C\;C$$

C. Random structure.

$$\sim\!\!\sim\!\!CCOCCOCCOCCO\!\!\sim\!\!\sim$$
$$\quad|\quad\;|\;\;|\quad\;\;|$$
$$\quad C\quad C\;C\quad\;\;C$$

D. Isotactic structure.

$$d\;\sim\!\!\sim\!\!CCOCCOCCO\!\!\sim\!\!\sim \qquad l\;\sim\!\!\sim\!\!CCOCCOCCO\!\!\sim\!\!\sim$$
$$\quad|\quad\;|\quad\;| \qquad\qquad\quad\;|\quad\;|\quad\;|$$
$$\quad C\quad C\quad C \qquad\qquad\quad C\quad C\quad C$$

E. Isotactic structure, optically active;—exclusively d or l.

From the frequent observations that have been made showing that neither homogeneous acid- nor base-catalyzed polymerization occurs with 100% stereospecificity, it is most likely that commercial polymers have a type C structure. With base catalysis, most of the polymerization would occur by a head-to-tail addition, while acid catalysis, although involving a different mechanism, yields a polymer indistinguishable from the former.

Condensation with Compounds with Active Hydrogen. The addition of propylene oxide to a compound with an active hydrogen atom to yield a hydroxy alkyl derivative is the first step in the polymerization reaction, wherein the newly formed intermediate can react with another molecule of propylene oxide. This process is then repeated to build long polyoxyalkylene chains which can contain as many as one hundred oxyalkylene units.

$$\underset{\overset{|}{CH_3}}{RCH_2CHOH} \xrightarrow{nCH_3CHCH_2O} \underset{\overset{|}{CH_3}\quad\overset{|}{CH_3}}{RCH_2CHO(CH_2CHO)_n H}$$

These alkylene oxide derivatives are not single compounds but complex mixtures where the number of polyoxyalkylene units attached to the initiation species, ie, the distribution of oxyalkylene groups among the individual molecules, closely follows Poisson's distribution formula.

The majority of oxyalkylation reactions are carried out at 100–200°C in the presence of alkaline catalysts. Many types of compounds containing active hydrogen atoms serve as the initiator for oxyalkylation.

Self-Polymerization. This field had developed at a moderate pace until 1955, when the optically active polymers of Price and Osgan (115) and the very high-molecular-weight polymers of the Dow Chemical Company research team were reported (77,120). Levene and Walti (92) in 1927 were the first to report the polymerization of propylene oxide by heating the oxide with 50% potassium hydroxide at 117°C for 12 days. The dimer, trimer, and tetramer of polypropylene glycol were obtained. Prior to the work of Pruitt and Baggett (120) in 1955, all polymers reported were liquids or heavy oils. They succeeded in obtaining polymers of average molecular weights in excess of 100,000. A number of different iron III compounds were excellent catalysts. Inert hydrocarbons and ethers were used as solvents for the polymerization. A wide variety of other catalysts, usually materials capable of acting as Lewis acids, have also been shown to be active (121). A recent study on the mechanism of the solid potassium hydroxide-catalyzed reaction indicates it is essentially the same as the homogeneous base-catalyzed condensation reaction (171).

The polymer obtained from the heterogeneous, potassium hydroxide-catalyzed polymerization may be composed exclusively of head-to-tail addition products. The high optical activity of the polymer prepared by this method (115) is suggestive of this degree of specificity. Thus, using dl-monomer, type A polymer is obtained with KOH while the use of d- or l-monomer exclusively would yield type E polymer. The crystalline polymer prepared by Price and Osgan by the Pruitt-Baggett technique from l-monomer can also be considered to be of type E.

The crystalline polymers obtained by Pruitt and Baggett (77) are probably type D.

The possibility of a syndiotactic polymer, type B, cannot be excluded but is a more complex rational for the observed results.

The terminal monomer units in polypropylene oxide can both be primary hydroxyl groups, a primary and a secondary hydroxyl group, both secondary hydroxyl groups, or may include a hydroxyl group and either an allyl or propenyl group.

Reaction with Water. The reaction of propylene oxide with water yields propylene glycol (see Glycols). The rate of reaction is slow at room temperature and is catalyzed by acids and bases. Robeson and Webb (122) report that the hydrolysis can best be accomplished at a pH of 4.5–6.5. The ratio of water to propylene oxide should be kept at 3:1 or 5:1 to reduce the amount of dipropylene glycol formed. At a pH of 6.2, a temperature of 150°C, and a pressure of 170 psi, the yield of propylene glycol was 92%.

Reaction with Ammonia and Amines. Krasuskii (22) studied the reaction of aqueous ammonia with propylene oxide and obtained 1-amino-2-propanol, along with varying amounts of the di- and trisubstituted amines. Higher ratios of ammonia to propylene oxide served to increase the yields of 1-amino-2-propanol at the expense of the secondary and tertiary amines. Industrially, the isopropanolamines are prepared by diffusing propylene oxide into an aqueous solution of ammonia at a temperature below 55°C (123) (see Alkanolamines).

Krasuskii (124) also conducted reactions of ethylamine and propylene oxide and obtained both 1-ethylamino-2-propanol and 1-ethylaminodi(2-propanol). The same investigator (125) in 1930 reacted propylene oxide with diethylamine, obtaining a 65% yield of diethylamino-2-propanol. Reaction rates and energies of activation for propylene oxide addition to a number of amines (mono-, di-, and trimethylamines, and similar ethyl-substituted amines) were determined by Hansson (21).

Reaction with Alcohols. When propylene oxide is reacted with alcohols in the presence of alkali, the product is exclusively the secondary alcohol resulting from attack on the terminal epoxide carbon atom (126):

$$CH_3CHCH_2 + RONa \rightarrow CH_3\overset{\underset{\textstyle |}{OH}}{C}HCH_2OR$$
$$\underset{O}{\diagdown\diagup}$$

Heating propylene oxide with alcohols in the absence of added base (127) or in the presence of an acid catalyst such as sulfuric acid yields a mixture of primary and secondary alcohols:

$$CH_3CHCH_2 + ROH \overset{H^+}{\rightarrow} CH_3CH(OH)CH_2OR + CH_3(OR)CH_2OH$$
$$\underset{O}{\diagdown\diagup}$$

MANUFACTURE

Chlorohydrin Process. Present production of propylene oxide is based on the classical route via propylene chlorohydrin. The analogous method in ethylene oxide production is rapidly declining in importance as direct oxidation of ethylene proves itself economically preferable in most situations. The chlorohydrin units formerly used for ethylene oxide are readily converted to propylene oxide production, requiring only 24–36 hr to accomplish (128).

The chlorohydrin process is essentially a two-stage process in which propylene is chlorohydrinated and then cyclized with calcium hydroxide:

$$CH_3CH{=}CH_2 + HOCl \rightarrow CH_3CHOHCH_2Cl$$
$$2\ CH_3CHOHCH_2Cl + Ca(OH)_2 \rightarrow 2\ CH_3CHCH_2O + CaCl_2 + 2\ H_2O$$

The oxide is recovered by steam stripping and purified by fractionation, which leaves the chlorinated by-products, 1,2-dichloropropane and 2,2'-dichloroisopropyl ether, as the predominant residue components.

Chlorohydrination of Propylene. The first step of the process is the reaction of chlorine, water, and propylene, to produce an aqueous solution of propylene chlorohydrin in the chlorohydrin tower (see Fig. 2). Most favorable results are obtained when the propylene chlorohydrin concentration is kept low (4 % by wt).

The major reactions occurring at this stage are the following:

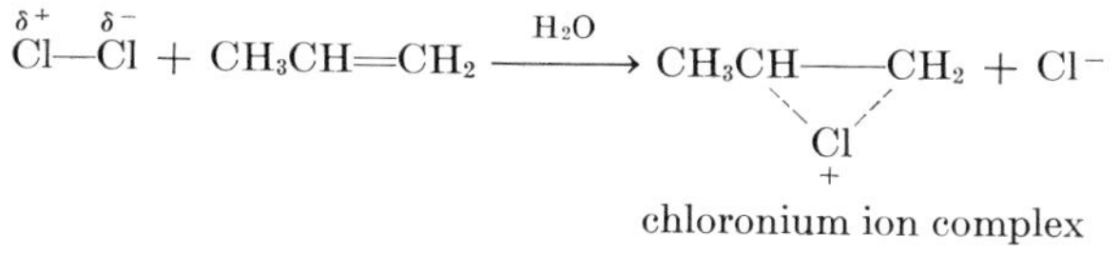

$$\overset{\delta^+}{Cl}-\overset{\delta^-}{Cl} + CH_3CH{=}CH_2 \xrightarrow{H_2O} CH_3CH\text{——}CH_2 + Cl^- \tag{1}$$

chloronium ion complex

$$CH_3CH\text{——}CH_2 + HOH \longrightarrow \begin{cases} CH_3CH\text{——}CH_2 + HCl \\ \quad\;\; OH \quad\;\; Cl \\ \alpha\text{-chlorohydrin } (75\%) \\ \\ CH_3\text{—}CH\text{—}CH_2 + HCl \\ \quad\quad\;\; Cl \quad OH \\ \beta\text{-chlorohydrin } (25\%) \end{cases} \tag{2}$$

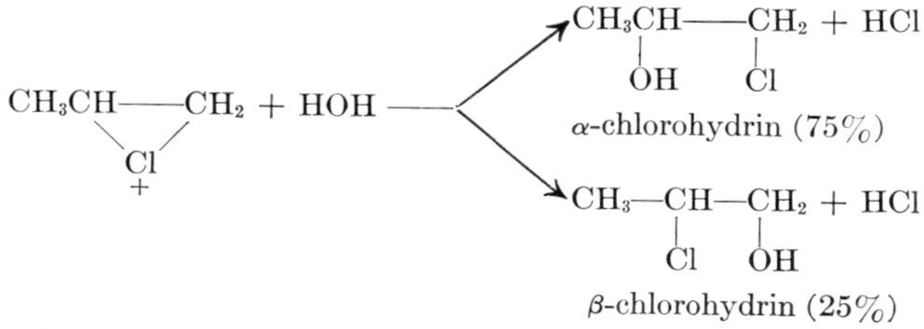

Attack by the water molecule occurs mainly at the secondary carbon atom (most stable carbonium ion) to give the isomers in a 3:1 ratio (129). Smith (130) reports the ratio of isomers to be 90% α and 10% β.

Side reactions occur, producing mainly propylene dichloride along with chloro ethers (largely bis(chloroisopropyl) ether):

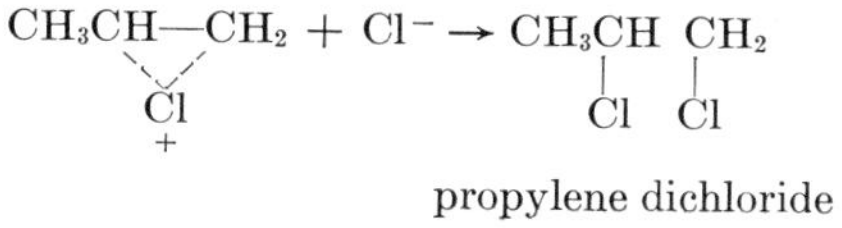

$$CH_3CH\text{—}CH_2 + Cl^- \rightarrow CH_3CH\;CH_2 \tag{3}$$
$$\qquad\qquad Cl \qquad\qquad\qquad Cl \quad Cl$$

propylene dichloride

$$CH_3CH\text{—}CH_2 + HOCH \rightarrow CH\text{—}O\text{—}CH + HCl \tag{4}$$

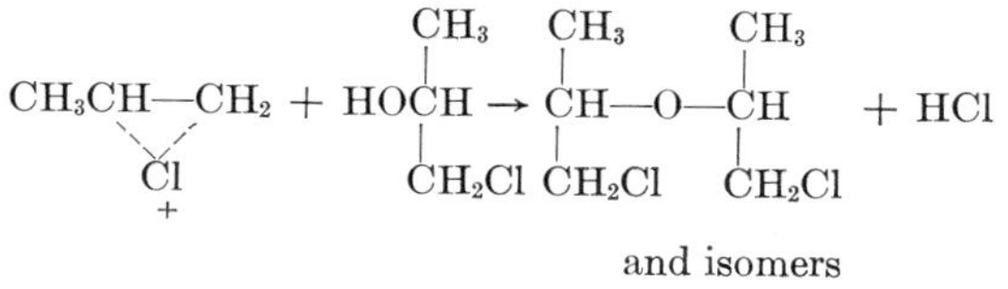

and isomers

Although propylene and chlorine react rapidly in the gas phase to form propylene dichloride, there is no evidence of such a reaction occurring during hypochlorination. Propylene dichloride formation is favored by high chloride ion concentration (eq. 3), while chloroether formation is favored by high chlorohydrin concentration (eq. 4).

Oxidation of the chlorohydrin by chlorine produces small amounts of carbonyl with chloroacetone as the main product.

$$CH_3CHOHCH_2Cl + Cl_2 \rightarrow CH_3COCH_2Cl + 2\ HCl$$

The main by-product is propylene dichloride which dissolves only to a small extent in water, as shown below.

Temperature, °C	Propylene dichloride, wt %
20	0.26
30	0.29
40	0.32

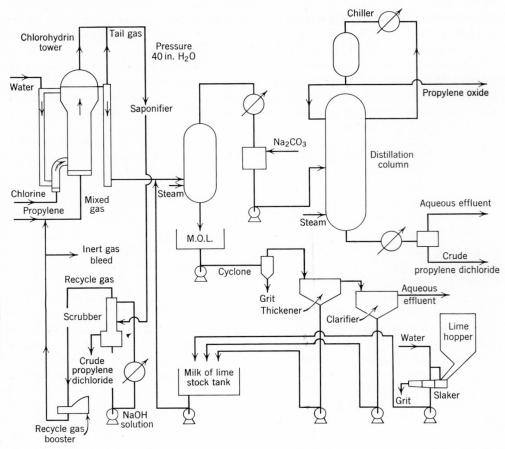

Fig. 2. Diagram of a typical chlorohydrin reactor for manufacture of propylene oxide.   Courtesy *Chemistry and Industry.*

If the solubility level is exceeded so that a propylene dichloride second phase forms, propylene and chlorine dissolve in it and react to form propylene dichloride. Therefore, it is essential that the concentration of propylene dichloride is kept below the solubility limit.   Conditions favoring the formation of propylene chlorohydrin include: (*1*) using an excess of propylene or propane to evaporate the propylene dichloride; (*2*) maintaining a low concentration of propylene chlorohydrin so that dichloride concentration is below the solubility limit plus the amount which can be removed by evaporation; and (*3*) rapid solution of propylene.   Yields on hypochlorination are in the neighborhood of 90% (164,165).   Yields can be improved by reducing the chlorohydrin concentration to less than 4% and lowering the reaction temperature. As the temperature is reduced, however, the solubility of propylene dichloride is less in the aqueous reaction mixture, and the separation of an organic phase can occur at a lower propylene dichloride concentration.

The flowsheet for a typical chlorohydrin reactor is shown in Figure 2 (131). Water and chlorine are added to the chlorination tower and the propylene chlorohydrin produced in solution overflows to the hydrolyzer.   Unreacted gases are washed in a chilled caustic soda scrubbing tower to remove traces of chlorine, hydrogen chloride, and propylene dichloride, while inert gas, equal in quantity to that fed, is eliminated in a bleed system.

Fresh propylene is added to the scrubbed gas stream and the mixture is recycled. A temperature of 35°C resulting from the heat of reaction gives good yields. Although the solubility of propylene in chlorohydrin solution is greater at lower temperatures, as illustrated below, the rate of solution of propylene is found to be more important than the limiting solubility for maximum reaction rate.

Temperature, °C	Soly in water, mmole/liter	Soly in chlorohydrin liquid, mmole/liter
21	6.2	6.6
30	4.7	5.0
40	3.6	3.8

It is important that the chlorine concentration of the solution is maintained at such a level that it does not appear to a significant extent in the effluent gas since in addition to the loss of chlorine, explosions can occur due to the reaction between hydrocarbon and chlorine.

Process equipment for ethylene oxide manufacture by the chlorohydrin route (132) is also used for propylene oxide. The chlorohydrin towers are acidproof brick and rubber-lined steel vessels. A typical tower measures 4 ft in diameter, is 50 ft high, and is packed with 2-in. Raschig rings. The separator leg of each chlorohydrin tower is constructed of corrosion-resistant material such as Haveg (phenol–formaldehyde resin on asbestos fiber) and stoneware. The top of each leg is fitted with two connections to the reaction tower. The solution flowing into the separator leg through the lower connection releases gas to the upper connection. The product may be sent directly to the hydrolyzer or collected in a corrosion-resistant holding tank. The holding tank pumps, which transport the acid liquor to the hydrolyzer, are constructed of stoneware.

Hydrolysis of Propylene Chlorohydrin. Epoxide formation from the reaction of a halohydrin with alkali is rapid and quantitative at room temperature (160). The cyclization of propylene chlorohydrin is approximately 20 times as rapid as ethylene chlorohydrin (167). The two propylene chlorohydrin isomers react at different rates (170), the isomer in excess (1-chloro-2-propanol) being more reactive. Plant yields are high on hydrolysis, and losses due to separation and purification of propylene oxide are less than 5%.

The formation of propylene oxide from propylene chlorohydrin by the action of aqueous base is conducted in mild steel equipment after the point of mixing of the chlorohydrin solution with the base. The hydrolyzer may be a plug-flow pipe reactor followed by a stripping column or just the column. The primary function of the stripper is to rapidly recover the propylene oxide in the overhead for further purification. They can be horizontal, cylindrical, flat-ended vessels with reflux condensers mounted on each. The lime and chlorohydrin streams enter through a pipe at one end and pass back and forth between baffles about 10 in. apart. The effluent stream leaves the hydrolyzer through a variable overflow tank.

The base is a 10 % by wt lime-water slurry and a 10% excess of lime is used. This is added to the chlorohydrin solution and heated with direct steam. It is important to complete the hydrolysis rapidly since propylene chlorohydrin is itself volatile (bp of water azeotrope, 96°C), and if unconverted is liable to be found in the propylene oxide concentrate. The propylene oxide so formed is rapidly hydrated to propylene glycol by the alkaline conditions in the reactor and it is important that the oxide be stripped from the solution as quickly as possible after formation:

$$CH_3CHCH_2 + OH^- \rightarrow CH_3CHCH_2 \rightarrow CH_3CHCH_2 + OH^-$$

The distillate obtained under reduced pressure contains water, propylene oxide, propylene dichloride, some propionaldehyde, bp 49°C (formed by isomerization of propylene oxide in the basic reaction media), and small amounts of miscellaneous products.

The separation of propylene oxide from water and chloro and carbonyl compounds can be effected in a one-step distillation. Chloro compounds may be separated from the two-phase column bottom product by settling. Lower pressures in distillation are favored to avoid the formation of water-containing azeotropes.

Distillation towers as high as 130 ft and having as many as 60 trays may be needed to obtain propylene oxide with water and carbonyl impurities within specifications (0.05 % by wt).

The liquid residue contains excess lime which is recovered by means of a Dorr thickener and clarifier. The final aqueous effluent can present a major disposal problem. For every ton of oxide produced, about 40 tons of an aqueous effluent arise; a typical analysis is as follows (131): $CaCl_2$, 5–6 % by wt; $Ca(OH)_2$, 0.1 % by wt; propylene glycol, 0.05–0.1 % by wt.

Plant location and local ordinance restrictions determine the method of disposal. Whenever local conditions permit, the effluent is simply discharged into a sufficiently large body of water flowing to the sea. In some cases the effluent is treated by a sewerage works before it is directed to a water tributary.

Direct Oxidation Processes for Propylene Oxide. Direct oxidation of ethylene has proved itself economically preferable in most situations. Much research has, therefore, been devoted to the exploration of lower cost direct oxidation processes of propylene.

The main possibilities for the direct oxidation of propylene are summarized below.

Homogeneous Gas-Phase Oxidation. There has been no practical success in attempts to produce propylene oxide by one of the silver-catalyzed vapor-phase oxidation techniques which are today the basis for most of the ethylene oxide manufacture. In fact, it has been concluded that catalytic oxidation of propylene over silver will not proceed via propylene oxide formation because propylene is absorbed on the surface of silver and is followed by abstraction of a hydrogen atom from the methyl group (133), leading to carbon dioxide and water.

$$HCH_2CH{=}CH_2 + O_2 + Ag_2 \rightarrow \underset{\overset{|}{Ag}}{OH} \ \underset{\overset{|}{Ag}}{OCH_2CH{=}CH_2} \xrightarrow{O_2} CO_2 + H_2O$$

Uncatalyzed direct partial oxidation of propylene yields mainly carbon monoxide, formaldehyde, acetaldehyde, some propylene oxide (about 30% of converted propylene), as well as carbon dioxide, peroxides, acids, and other oxygenated compounds (134, 135). Separation of such mixtures would usually not be economical.

Noncatalytic vapor-phase oxidation of propane in the presence of propylene is reported (172) to give under optimized conditions yields of 44.8 lb of oxide per 100 lb of C_3 hydrocarbon consumed (33% yield). Imperial Chemical Industries, Ltd. (173) have also reported that they are oxidizing propylene directly to the oxide in a pilot plant.

Liquid-Phase Oxidation. This area appears to be most promising. Propylene has been oxidized in 38 mole % yield to propylene oxide by molecular oxygen in water-immiscible liquid hydrocarbon solvents (136, 137). Yields of 87 mole % are claimed from the reaction using dibutyl phthalate in the presence of a supported silver or other catalyst (138).

Peroxacetic acid has been used on a pilot-plant scale (139) for the production of propylene oxide. The use of hydroperoxide, such as *t*-butyl hydroperoxide, in the presence of catalysts such as molybdenum naphthenate is reported to give high yields of propylene oxide (140). The oxidation of propylene by molecular oxygen in a liquid phase containing acetone or an ester formed from acetic, boric, carbonic, or benzoic acid is reported to produce high yields of propylene oxide (141). The oxidation does not require catalysts or other additives.

A recent study on the effect of various parameters on a noncatalyzed liquid-phase oxidation was reported (142). Under the most favorable conditions at 150°C, for each 1 kg of propylene consumed, 366 g of propylene oxide and 346 g of propylene glycol were formed. Major by-products were acetic and formic acids.

It is expected that within the next several years a direct oxidation process for propylene oxide will be used commercially. One of the most important factors which limits such development at the present time is the extreme flexibility in propylene oxide capacity. Realistically, the total capacity of the ethylene as well as the propylene chlorohydrin-type units must be considered since conversion is so simple from one olefin to the other. Therefore, as new propylene oxide capacity is needed, the older chlorohydrin units are diverted from ethylene service and new oxidation units are built to oxidize ethylene. In fact, it is more economical to oxidize propylene than ethylene via the chlorohydrin route.

ECONOMIC ASPECTS

Propylene oxide requirements for 1963 were about 497 million pounds in the United States. The estimated level for 1964 is 537 million pounds and 790 million pounds is predicted for 1970 (143). There is at present sufficient propylene oxide capacity to absorb any requirements for the next several years. A list of producers and their plant capacities is given below. Most capacities are extremely flexible.

Producer	Plant location	Capacity, million lb/yr
Celanese Corp. of America	Bishop, Tex.	10
Dow Chemical Co.	Freeport, Tex.	125
Dow Chemical Co.	Midland, Mich.	25
Dow Chemical Co.	Plaquemine, La.	50
Jefferson Chemical Co.	Port Neches, Tex.	140
Olin Mathieson Chemical Corp.	Brandenburg, Ky.	50
Union Carbide Corp.	S. Charleston, W. Va.	200
Wyandotte Chemical Corp.	Wyandotte, Mich.	140
	Total	740

The growth in propylene oxide demand over the 1959–1963 period has been at 12.8 %/yr. Further growth is estimated to be 8%/yr through 1969 (143). The price of propylene oxide has fluctuated in the period of 1952–1964 from a high of 17.5 ¢/lb, tank cars, to a low of 14.5 ¢/lb. The price of propylene oxide in April, 1965, was 14.5 ¢/lb in tank car lots, delivered east.

Propylene oxide is riding high due to the increasing demand for polyether polyols for urethan foams. Furthermore, propylene glycol consumption (from hydrolysis of the oxide), after remaining constant in 1960–1961, rose 7.5% in 1963 and may have risen another 10.5% in 1964 (143).

SPECIFICATIONS AND SAFETY

Specific gravity, 20/20°C; 0.829–0.831; distillation range, IBP, °C, min, 33.0; dry point, °C, max, 37.0; acidity as acetic acid, % by wt, max, 0.005; nonvolatile, % by wt, max, 0.002; aldehydes, as propionaldehyde, % by wt, max, 0.05; water, % by wt, max, 0.05; color, APHA, max, 10; odor, nonresidual; and suspended matter, substantially free. Test methods of these specifications are described in reference 99.

Propylene oxide is an extremely flammable and highly volatile liquid that must be handled with all the care generally observed for flammable liquids. Precautions must be taken to prevent contact with electric sparks, static electricity, excess heat, open flames, or any other source of ignition. Rapid polymerization and/or decomposition of propylene oxide due to high temperatures, or contact with catalysts such as acids, bases, and certain salts, may develop into an explosive condition.

Propylene oxide should be stored under inert nitrogen-gas pressure in a steel or stainless-steel tank that is adequately cooled and located in a well-ventilated area.

Propylene oxide is considered to be moderately toxic both by inhalation and by ingestion but it is slightly less toxic than ethylene oxide. Propylene oxide is a severe irritant of the eyes and mucous membranes but it does not penetrate the skin in harmful amounts, nor is it irritating to the skin, except for possible burns due to rapid evaporation. Hazards are minimized by maintaining adequate ventilation in areas where propylene oxide is being handled and by providing suitable protective equipment and instruction for personnel.

The American Conference of Governmental and Industrial Hygienists has accepted as safe a level of 100 ppm in air (240 mg/m³ of air). Although care should be exercised in handling and breathing propylene oxide, it is much less harmful than other irritating gases, such as hydrogen chloride or sulfur dioxide. It is much less dangerous than epichlorohydrin which is classified as a poison. In single oral doses to rats the

Table 5. Toxicity of Epoxides

	Ethylene oxide	Propylene oxide	Epichloro-hydrin	1,2-Butylene oxide
single oral LD₅₀ dose, rats, g/kg	0.33	1.14	0.09	1.41
single skin absorption LD₅₀ dose, rabbits, ml/kg		1.50	1.3	2.10
inhalation, rats	4,000 ppm for 4 hr killed none of 6	4,000 ppm for 8 hr killed 4 of 6	250 ppm for 8 hr killed 4 of 6	8,000 ppm for 4 hr killed 6 of 6
eye injury, rabbits	severe	severe	moderate	moderate

LD_{50} is 1.14 g/kg, and to guinea pigs 0.70 g/kg. Skin absorption is poor, the LD_{50} for a 4-day poultice application to guinea pigs being 8.64 ml/kg. The inhalation of 400 ppm vapors for 2 hr killed none of six guinea pigs while 4 hr inhalation killed all from lung and kidney injury (144).

The vapors are somewhat less toxic to guinea pigs than those of ethylene oxide, and oral toxicity is one-fifth that of ethylene oxide dissolved in water.

A summary of some additional toxicological studies with several epoxides is given in Table 5 (99).

ANALYSIS

The most frequently reported, and, in general, the most specific and practical methods for determination of α-epoxides are those based upon the addition of hydrogen chloride to the α epoxy group, forming the corresponding chlorohydrin:

$$-\overset{|}{C}\overset{|}{\underset{O}{\diagup\diagdown}}\overset{|}{C}- + H^+ + Cl^- \rightarrow -\overset{|}{\underset{OH}{C}}\overset{Cl}{\underset{|}{\overset{|}{C}}}-$$

The difference between the amount of acid added and the amount unconsumed, determined by titration with standard base, is a measure of the α epoxide. Various solvents have been employed for carrying out the reaction: water, alcohol, ethylene glycol monoethyl ether, ethyl ether, dioxane, pyridine, and pyridine–chloroform. Two excellent reviews have been written (145, 146) which discuss in detail the various hydrochlorination procedures, the applicability to various epoxides, and the precision and accuracy of the methods. Most methods give satisfactory results with propylene oxide.

A fairly sensitive test for the detection of propylene oxide has been reported by Gunther et al. (147). The amine, lepidine, gives an intense color with various epoxides under the reaction conditions employed.

USES

Propylene oxide is primarily a chemical intermediate for the manufacture of propylene glycol and polyether polyols for urethan foams.

The end-use pattern for propylene oxide in the year 1963 is given below (148).

Outlet	Estimated consumption, million lb, 1963 (% total)
propylene glycol	160 (37)
polyethers for urethans	145 (35)
dipropylene glycol	20 (5)
fluid lubricant	25 (6)
surfactants	20 (5)
crude-oil demulsifiers	10 (2)
miscellaneous	40 (10)
Total	420 (100)

Chemical Intermediates. Propylene oxide is used principally as an intermediate in the manufacture of propylene glycol and polypropylene glycols of various molecular weights (149) (see Glycols). It is highly reactive, combining exothermically with compounds having a replaceable hydrogen atom. The reactions of propylene oxide are closely similar to those of ethylene oxide, but at room temperature liquid propylene oxide can be handled more easily than gaseous ethylene oxide. Propylene oxide derivatives have been useful in a wide variety of applications in many industries including textiles, cosmetics, pharmaceuticals, agricultural chemicals, petroleum, plastics, rubber, and paints.

Urethan Chemicals (150). The year 1957 can be considered the first year of large-scale use of polyether polyols. Polyether triols were specifically developed for urethan applications. The products generally consist of propylene oxide adducts of polyhydric alcohols such as glycerol, 1,2,6-hexanetriol, and "trimethylolpropane" (1,1,1-trihydroxymethylpropane) and are used in urethan elastomers, coatings, and flexible foams. Similar adducts of alcohols of higher functionality, such as sucrose, sorbitol, methyl glucoside, and pentaerythritol, have also been developed for rigid urethan foams (see Alcohols, polyhydric).

Surfactants (qv). Many nonionic surface-active agents are made by ethoxylating polypropylene glycols of various molecular weights. Others are made by the reaction of propylene oxide with polyhydric alcohols, fatty acids, sugars, and various phenols, to form materials which, upon further condensation with ethylene oxide, produce nonionic surfactants. The properties of these products can be modified by adjusting the oxypropylene-to-oxyethylene ratio. The great variety of surfactants made from propylene oxide have found wide industrial application as wetting agents, detergents, emulsifiers, and de-emulsifiers (149,151).

Solvents (qv). Propylene oxide is a powerful, low-boiling solvent for hydrocarbons, cellulose derivatives such as cellulose nitrate and cellulose acetate (152), vinyl acetate, and vinyl chloride. It has good solvency for shellac, gums, linseed oil, unvulcanized rubber, and many adhesives.

Resins. Propylene oxide is used as a stabilizer for unsaturated hydrocarbon solvents and vinyl chloride resins, and reduces deterioration during storage (153,154). It is an acid scavenger and small amounts will help prevent discoloration of nitrocellulose lacquers. As an intermediate it forms water-soluble resins with ethylenediamine and urea.

Petroleum. A major application of propylene oxide is as an intermediate in the preparation of emulsion breakers for crude oil–water emulsions. These de-emulsifiers have low water solubility and prevent re-emulsification (155). Lube oil sludge inhibitors and pour point depressants have been prepared from propylene oxide.

Textiles, Leather, and Paper. Derivatives of propylene oxide are effective wetting, emulsifying, leveling, and softening agents for textiles, leather, and paper. Propylene oxide is an intermediate in the synthesis of antistatic agents, dyes and dye assistants, textile lubricants, and sizes for both textiles and paper. Propylene oxide derivatives are aids in leather tanning, and propylene oxide is an excellent solvent for cellulose nitrate shoe cements.

Butylene Oxide

Butylene oxide (99) (1,2-epoxybutane), $CH_3CH_2CHCH_2O$, has the following properties: specific gravity, 20/20°C, 0.8312; boiling point, °C, 63.2 at 760 mm, −0.9 at 50 mm; vapor pressure, 20°C, 141 mm; freezing point, −150°C; absolute viscosity,

20°C, 0.41 cP; refractive index, n_D^{20}, 1.3840; heat of vaporization, 181 Btu/lb; heat of combustion, 14.665 Btu/lb; solubility, % by wt of soln, 20° C, 5.91% in water, 2.65% water in butylene oxide.

Butylene oxide is a colorless, mobile, low-boiling liquid of limited water solubility, but miscible in most common organic solvents. It is commercially available from The Dow Chemical Company and Union Carbide Chemical Company, and is most probably prepared by epoxidation of 1-butene with peroxyacetic acid. It undergoes the usual reactions of epoxides with compounds having labile hydrogen atoms such as water, alcohols, polyols, phenols, thiols, ammonia, amines, and acids. It can be polymerized or copolymerized with other alkylene oxides to yield polyethers. Its polymers are less water soluble than ethylene oxide or propylene oxide polymers of equivalent chain length.

A major use of butylene oxide is as an acid scavenger for chlorine-containing materials such as trichloroethylene. Inclusion of about 1/4 to 1/2 of 1% of butylene oxide, based on the solvent weight, during preparation of vinyl chloride and copolymer resin solutions serves to minimize both container corrosion and metal pickup, which may be detrimental to resin color and properties.

Butylene oxide has been suggested as an intermediate for nonionic emulsifiers and detergents, petroleum demulsifiers, oil additives, lubricants, textile chemicals, and similar products.

Styrene Oxide

Styrene oxide (156) (1,2-epoxyethylbenzene, phenyloxirane), $C_6H_5CHCH_2O$, has the following properties: specific gravity, 20/20°C, 1.0540; boiling point, 194.1°C; vapor pressure, 20°C, 0.3 mm Hg; freezing point, − 36.8°C; viscosity, 20°C, 1.99 cP; refractive index, n_D^{20}, 1.5339; solubility, 20°C, by wt of soln, in water, 0.30%, water in styrene oxide, 0.50%; it is completely soluble in acetone, benzene, carbon tetrachloride, ethyl ether, heptane, and methanol.

Styrene oxide is commercially available from Union Carbide Chemical Company. It is most probably prepared via the chlorohydrin route but can also be conveniently prepared by epoxidation with peroxyacetic acid.

The reactions of styrene oxide are similar to those of the aliphatic epoxides described earlier. Thus, alcohols add to styrene oxide in the presence of acid or basic catalysts to form monoethers of phenylethylene glycol. Methanol reacts to give a 90% yield of 2-methoxy-2-phenylethanol (157), $C_6H_5CH(OCH_3)CH_2OH$, when catalyzed by acid. The secondary alcohol is obtained using sodium methoxide as a catalyst (158).

The base-catalyzed condensation of phenol with styrene oxide gives a mixture of 2-phenoxy-2-phenylethanol, $C_6H_5CH(OC_6H_5)CH_2OH$ (I), and 2-phenoxy-1-phenylethanol, $C_6H_5CH(OH)CH_2OC_6H_5$ (II). When the reaction is conducted in aqueous base or in nonaqueous solvents, compound I is the major product. When excess phenol is used as the solvent, compound II predominates (159). When styrene oxide is reacted with phenol at elevated temperatures, resinous condensation products form which have been used for the manufacture of varnishes with excellent water resistance (160).

Bibliography

1. A. Rosowsky in A. Weissberger, ed., *Heterocyclic Compounds With Three- and Four-Membered Rings*, Part I, Interscience Publishers, a division of John Wiley & Sons, Inc., New York, 1964, pp. 1–523.
2. S. Winstein and R. B. Henderson in R. C. Elderfield, ed., *Heterocyclic Compounds*, Vol. I, John Wiley & Sons, Inc., New York, 1950, pp. 1–60.
3. D. Swern, *Organic Reactions*, Vol. VII, Chap. 7, John Wiley & Sons, Inc., New York, 1953.
4. R. C. Fuson, D. J. Byers, C. A. Sperati, R. E. Foster, and P. F. Warfield, *J. Org. Chem.* **10**, 69 (1945).
5. P. B. D. de la Mare and A. Salama, *J. Chem. Soc.* **1956**, 3337.
6. S. Winstein and H. J. Lucas, *J. Am. Chem. Soc.* **61**, 1576 (1939).
7. H. Nilsson and L. Smith, *Z. Physik. Chem.* **166A**, 136 (1933).
8. M. S. Newman and B. J. Magerlein, *Organic Reactions*, Vol. V, John Wiley & Sons, Inc., New York, 1949, p. 413.
9. C. D. Gutsche, *Organic Reactions*, Vol. VIII, John Wiley & Sons, Inc., New York, 1954, p. 364.
10. O. C. Dermer and A. M. Durr, *J. Am. Chem. Soc.* **76**, 912 (1954).
11. R. M. Adams and C. A. Vander Werf, *J. Am. Chem. Soc.* **72**, 4368 (1950).
12. L. J. Haynes and E. R. H. Jones, *J. Chem. Soc.* **1946**, 954.
13. H. Fraenkel-Conrat and H. S. Olcott, *J. Am. Chem. Soc.* **66**, 1420 (1944).
14. C. A. Stewart and C. A. VanderWerf, *J. Am. Chem. Soc.* **76**, 1259 (1954).
15. R. E. Parker and N. S. Isaacs, *Chem. Rev.* **59**, 737 (1959).
16. E. L. Gustus and P. G. Stevens, *J. Am. Chem. Soc.* **55**, 378 (1933).
17. H. C. Chitwood and B. T. Freure, *J. Am. Chem. Soc.* **68**, 680 (1946).
18. F. G. Ponomarev, *Dokl. Akad. Nauk SSSR* **108**, 648 (1956); *Chem. Abstr.* **51**, 3565 (1957).
19. P. Bedos, *Compt. Rend.* **183**, 562 (1926).
20. U.S. Pat. 2,520,381 (1950), J. J. Carnes (to American Cyanamid Co.).
21. J. Hansson, *Svensk Kem. Tidskr.* **60**, 183 (1948); *Chem. Abstr.* **43**, 926 (1949).
22. K. A. Krasuskii, *J. Gen. Chem. USSR* **6**, 460 (1936).
23. G. Stadnikov, *J. Russ. Phys. Chem. Soc.* **36**, 485 (1904); *Brit. Abstr.* **Ai** 665 (1904).
24. M. S. Malinovskii and M. K. Romantsevich, *Chem. Abstr.* **43**, 6155 (1949).
25. H. Meerwein, E. Battenberg, H. Gold, E. Pfeil, and G. Willfang, *J. Prakt. Chem.* **154**, 83 (1939).
26. J. Colonge and P. Rochas, *Compt. Rend.* **223**, 403 (1946).
27. J. D. Ingham, W. L. Petty, and P. L. Nichols, Jr., *J. Org. Chem.* **21**, 373 (1956).
28. J. D. Swan, *Anal. Chem.* **26**, 878 (1954).
29. F. G. A. Stone and H. J. Emeleus, *J. Chem. Soc.* **1950**, 2755.
30. J. D. Edwards, W. Gerrard, and M. F. Lappert, *J. Chem. Soc.* **1955**, 1470.
31. A. R. Graham, A. F. Millidge, and D. P. Young, *J. Chem. Soc.* **1954**, 2180.
32. U.S. Pat. 2,667,497 (1954), W. K. Clive (to Olin Mathieson Chemical Corp.).
33. J. C. C. Culvenor, W. Davis, and N. S. Heath, *J. Chem. Soc.* **1949**, 278.
34. J. A. Durden, H. A. Stanburg, and W. H. Cattette, *J. Org. Chem.* **26**, 836 (1961).
35. U.S. Pat. 2,518,058 (1950), A. Pechukas (to Pittsburgh Plate Glass Co.).
36. F. Boberg and G. R. Schultze, *Ber.* **88**, 275 (1955).
37. E. Paterno et al., *Gazz. Chim. Ital.* 38(1), 243 (1908).
38. G. Rossmy, *Ber.* **88**, 1969 (1955).
39. M. I. Kabachnik, T. A. Mastryukova, and V. N. Odnorolova, *Zh. Obshch. Khim.* **25**, 2274 (1955); *Chem. Abstr.* **50**, 9281 (1956).
40. M. Schmeisser and H. Jenkner, *Z. Naturforsch.* **7b**, 583 (1952).
41. A. Noshay and C. C. Price, *J. Org. Chem.* **23**, 647 (1958).
42. A. F. Dobryanskii, M. I. Davydova, and Z. T. Papkina, *Zh. Obshch. Khim.* **7**, 291 (1937); *Chem. Abstr.* **31**, 4645 (1937).
43. W. Bradley, J. Forrest, and O. Stephenson, *J. Chem. Soc.* **1951**, 1589.
44. U.S. Pat. 2,660,607 (1953), G. Gever and C. J. O'Keefe (to Easton Laboratories, Inc.).
45. U.S. Pat. 2,653,162 (1953), L. S. Luskin (to Rohm & Haas Co.).
46. C. S. Marvel and E. D. Weil, *J. Am. Chem. Soc.* **76**, 61 (1954).
47. U.S. Pat. 2,605,291 (1952), M. R. Barusch and J. Q. Payne (to California Research Corp.).

48. F. Ya. Perveev, N. I. Kudryashova, and D. N. Glebovskii, *Zh. Obshch. Khim.* **26**, 3331 (1956); *Chem. Abstr.* **51**, 9569 (1957).
49. L. W. Jones and G. R. Burns, *J. Am. Chem. Soc.* **47**, 2970 (1925)
50. A. Funke and G. Benoit, *Bull. Soc. Chim. France* **1953**, 1021.
51. G. P. Speranza and W. J. Peppel, *J. Org. Chem.* **23**, 1922 (1958).
52. U.S. Pat. 3,090,815 (1964), W. I. Denton (to Olin Mathieson Chemical Corp.).
53. U.S. Pat. 2,159,507 (1939), G. H. Law and R. W. McNamee (to Carbide and Carbon Corp.).
54. C. C. Price and P. F. Kirk, *J. Am. Chem. Soc.* **75**, 2396 (1953).
55. R. Oda, S. Muneimiya, and M. Okano, *J. Org. Chem.* **26**, 1341 (1961).
56. F. G. Ponomarev, *Dokl. Akad. Nauk SSSR* **108**, 648 (1956); *Chem. Abstr.* **51**, 3565 (1957).
57. W. G. Brown in *Organic Reactions*, Vol. VI, John Wiley & Sons, Inc., New York, 1951, p. 469.
58. J. P. Danehy and C. J. Noel, *J. Am. Chem. Soc.* **82**, 2511 (1960).
59. M. Mousseron and M. Canet, *Compt. Rend.* **232**, 637 (1951).
60. M. S. Malinovskii and N. M. Medyantseva, *Zh. Obshch. Khim.* **23**, 84 (1953); *Chem. Abstr.* **48**, 2580 (1954).
61. F. Evans and R. C. Huston, *J. Org. Chem.* **24**, 1178 (1959).
62. F. Sondheimer, *J. Chem. Soc.* **1950**, 877.
63. S. J. Cristol, J. R. Douglass, and J. S. Meek, *J. Am. Chem. Soc.* **73**, 816 (1951).
64. E. Abderhalden and E. Eichwald, *Ber.* **48**, 113 (1915).
65. J. Hoffman, *J. Am. Chem. Soc.* **79**, 504 (1957).
66. A. R. Sexton and E. C. Britton, *J. Am. Chem. Soc.* **70**, 3606 (1948).
67. J. I. Jones, *J. Chem. Soc.* **1957**, 2735.
68. I. L. Knunyants and R. N. Sterlin, *Dokl. Akad. Nauk SSSR* **56**, 49 (1947); *Chem. Abstr.* **42**, 519 (1948).
69. S. Z. Ivin and K. V. Karavanor, *Zhur. Obshch. Khim.* **29**, 3419 (1959).
70. A. N. Pudovik and B. A. Ivanor, *Izv. Akad. Nauk SSSR* 947 (1952); *Chem. Abstr.* **47**, 10464 (1953).
71. N. Kreutzkamp, *Naturwiss.* **43**, 81 (1956).
72. U.S. Pat. 2,372,244 (1945), C. E. Adams and B. H. Shoemaker (to Standard Oil Co. of Indiana).
73. N. I. Shuikin and I. F. Balskii, *Zhur. Obshch. Khim.* **29**, 2973 (1959).
74. M. Tachimori and T. Matsushima, *J. Soc. Chem. Ind. Japan* **46**, 1270 (1943); *Chem. Abstr.* **42**, 6319 (1948).
75. W. Ziegenbein and W. Franke, *Ber.* **93**, 1681 (1960).
76. M. Tiffenean and A. Fourneau, *Compt. Rend.* **146**, 697 (1908).
77. U.S. Pat. 2,706,181 (1955), M. E. Pruitt and J. M. Baggett (to Dow Chemical Co.).
78. U.S. Pat. 2,381,137 (1945), W. I. Patnode and R. O. Sauer (to General Electric Co.).
79. R. B. Langford and N. Kharash, *J. Org. Chem.* **23**, 1694 (1958).
80. M. F. Clarke and L. N. Owen, *J. Am. Chem. Soc.* **71**, 315 (1949).
81. T. Cohen and T. Tsuji, *J. Org. Chem.* **26**, 1681 (1961).
82. G. A. Razuvaev, V. S. Etlis, and L. N. Grobov, *Zhur. Obshch. Khim.* **31**, 1328 (1961).
83. G. E. Ham, *J. Org. Chem.* **25**, 864 (1960).
84. M. S. Malinovski, *J. Gen. Chem. USSR* **17**, 1559 (1947); *Chem. Abstr.* **42**, 2229 (1948).
85. B. Sjoberg, *Ber.* **75**, 13 (1942).
86. P. G. Sergeev and B. S. Kolychev, *J. Gen. Chem. USSR* **7**, 1390 (1937); *Chem. Abstr.* **32**, 2534 (1938).
87. U.S. Pat. 2,576,138 (1951), A. Pechukas (to Pittsburgh Plate Glass Co.).
88. W. C. J. Ross, *J. Chem. Soc.* **1950**, 2257.
89. F. G. Bordwell and H. M. Anderson, *J. Am. Chem. Soc.* **75**, 4959 (1953).
90. N. I. Shuikin and I. F. Balskii, *Zhur. Obshch. Khim.* **29**, 2973 (1959).
91. F. R. Jensen and R. L. Bedard, *Abstr. 136th Am. Chem. Soc. Meet.* **26P**, (1959).
92. P. A. Levene and A. Walti, *J. Biol. Chem.* **73**, 263 (1927).
93. C. C. J. Culvenor, W. Davis, and N. S. Heath, *J. Chem. Soc.* **1949**, 278.
94. G. L. Cunningham, A. Boyd, R. J. Meyers, W. D. Gwinn, and W. I. LeVan, *J. Chem. Phys.* **17**, 211 (1949); **19**, 676 (1951).
95. J. D. Swalen and D. R. Herschbach, *J. Chem. Phys.* **27**, 100 (1957).
96. R. A. Nelson and R. S. Jessup, *J. Res. Natl. Bur. Std.* **48**, 206 (1952).

97. J. Grimley and A. K. Holliday, *J. Chem. Soc.* **1954**, 1212, 1215.
98. S. Searles and M. Tamres, *J. Am. Chem. Soc.* **73**, 3704 (1951).
99. *Alkylene Oxides*, Union Carbide Chemical Co. Technical Bulletin, New York, 1961.
100. P. V. Zimakov and V. A. Sokolova, *Zh. Fiz. Khim.* **27**, 1079 (1953); *Chem. Abstr.* **49**, 3597 (1955).
101. F. L. Oetting, *J. Chem. Phys.* **41**, 149 (1964).
102. F. R. Bichowsky and F. D. Rossini, *The Thermochemistry of the Chemical Substances*, Reinhold Publishing Corp., New York, 1936, pp. 46–47.
103. R. W. Zubow and W. Swientoslawski, *Bull. Soc. Chim. France* **37**, 271 (1925).
104. M. T. Rogers, *J. Am. Chem. Soc.* **69**, 2544 (1947).
105. H. Hibbert and J. S. Allen, *J. Am. Chem. Soc.* **54**, 4115 (1932).
106. J. R. Lacher, J. W. Pollock, and J. D. Park, *J. Chem. Phys.* **20**, 1047 (1952).
107. V. A. Kireev and A. A. Popov, *J. Gen. Chem. USSR* **5**, 1399 (1935).
108. G. O. Curme, Jr. and F. Johnston, eds., *Glycols*, Reinhold Publishing Corp., New York, 1952, p. 252.
109. J. N. Wickert, W. S. Tamplin, and R. L. Shank, *Paper presented before the American Institute of Chemical Engineers, Houston, Texas, February, 1950.*
110. P. V. Zimakov and V. A. Sokolova, *Zhur. Fiz. Khim.* **27**, 1079 (1953); *Chem. Abstr.* **49**, 3597 (1955).
111. O. Ballaus and J. Wagner, *Z. Physik. Chem.* **B45**, 272 (1939).
112. O. D. Shreve, M. R. Heether, H. B. Knight, and D. Swern, *Anal. Chem.* **23**, 277 (1951).
113. E. Abderhalden and E. Eichwald, *Ber.* **51**, 1312 (1918).
114. P. A. Levene and A. Walti, *J. Biol. Chem.* **68**, 415 (1926).
115. C. C. Price and M. Osgan, *J. Am. Chem. Soc.* **78**, 4787 (1956).
116. A. P. Terent'ev, E. I. Klanbunovskii, and V. V. Patrikeev, *Dokl. Akad. Nauk SSSR* **74**, 947 (1950); *Chem. Abstr.* **45**, 3798 (1951).
117. W. Ipatiew and W. Leontowitsch, *Ber.* **36**, 2017 (1903).
118. U.S. Pat. 2,426,264 (1947), G. W. Fowler and J. T. Fitzpatrick (to Carbide and Carbon Corp.).
119. U.S. Pat. 3,090,816 (1964), W. I. Denton (to Olin Mathieson Chemical Corp.).
120. U.S. Pat. 2,706,189 (1955), M. E. Pruitt and J. M. Baggett (to Dow Chemical Co.).
121. L. E. St. Pierre in N. C. Gaylord, ed., *Polyethers*, Part I, Chap. III, Interscience Publishers, a division of John Wiley & Sons, Inc., New York, 1963.
122. U.S. Pat. 2,623,909 (1952), M. O. Robeson and T. P. Webb (to Celanese Corp.).
123. U.S. Pat. 1,988,225 (1935), J. N. Wickert (to Carbide and Carbon Chemical Corp.).
124. K. A. Krasuskii, *J. Chim. Ukraine* **1**, 398 (1925).
125. K. A, Krasuskii and G. T. Pilyugin, *J. Chim. Ukraine* **5**, 135 (1930).
126. H. C. Chitwood and B. T. Freure, *J. Am. Chem. Soc.* **68**, 680 (1946).
127. A. C. Cope, G. A. Berchtold, P. E. Peterson, and S. H. Sharman, *J. Am. Chem. Soc.* **82**, 6366 (1960).
128. *Chem. Eng. News* **43** (Jan. 4, 1965).
129. J. A. Wojtowicz, Unpublished data, Olin Mathieson Chemical Corp.
130. L. Smith, *Z. Physik. Chem.* **93**, 59 (1918); *Chem. Abstr.* **13**, 1461 (1919).
131. A. C. Fyvie, *Chem. Ind.* 384 (1964).
132. R. M. Goepp, D. L. Fuller, W. E. Vaughan, and J. D. Brandner, *FIAT Final Report 874* (1947).
133. L. Ya. Margolis in *Advances in Catalysis*, Vol. 14, Academic Press, Inc., New York, 1963, p. 458.
134. Belg. Pat. 623,552 (1963), C Wegner, H Haberland, H Heinz, D. Hellstrung, K. Sigwart, and R. Haupt (to Farbenfabriken Bayer A.G.).
135. Union Carbide Chemical Corp., South African Application 612,234.
136. Brit. Pat. 917,926 (1963), (to Escambia Chem. Corp.).
137. Brit. Pat. 959,218 (1964), (to Distillers Corp.).
138. U.S. Pat. 2,985,668 (1961), H. Shinger.
139. R. Landau and R. N. Simon, *Chem. Ind.* **10** (1962).
140. Belg. Pat. 641,452 (1964), Halcon International, Inc.
141. Fr. Pat. 1,367,762 (1964), Monsanto Chemical Co.
142. F. Lanos, G. M. Clement, and F. Pouliguen, *Chim. Ind.* **91**, 47–55 (1964).

143. *Chemical Profiles, Propylene Oxide,* Schnell Publishing Co., New York, 1964.
144. H. F. Smyth, Jr., J. Seaton, and L. Fischer, *J. Ind. Hyg. Toxicol.* **23**, 259 (1941).
145. S. Siggia, *Quantitative Organic Analysis Via Functional Groups,* 3rd ed., Chap. 5, 1964, John Wiley & Sons, Inc., New York, pp. 238–254.
146. J. L. Jungnickel, E. O. Peters, A. Polgar, and F. T. Weiss in *Organic Analysis,* Vol. I, Interscience Publishers, Inc., New York, 1953, pp. 127–154.
147. F. A. Gunther, et al., *Anal. Chem.* **23**, 1835 (1951).
148. *Chem. Eng. News,* 101 (May 13, 1963).
149. A. S. Kastens in N. G. Gaylord, ed., *Polyethers,* Part I, Chap. IV, Interscience Publishers, a division of John Wiley & Sons, Inc., 1963.
150. H. Saunders and K. C. Frisch, *Polyurethanes, Chemistry and Technology,* Part I, Interscience Publishers, a division of John Wiley & Sons, Inc., New York, 1962, p. 32.
151. U.S. Pat. 2,478,859 (1949), Carnes and Warner (to American Cyanamid Co.).
152. Ger. Pat. 605,725, Boston Blacking and Chemical Co.
153. U.S. Pat. 2,371,645 (1945), A. G. Atchison and W. H. Petering (to Westvaco Chlorine Products Corp.).
154. U.S. Pat. 2,364,587 (1944), R. C. Morris and E. C. Shokal (to Shell Develop. Co.).
155. U.S. Pat. 2,278,838 (1942), M. DeGroote and B. Keiser (to Petrolite Corp.).
156. *Peracetic Acid and Derivatives,* Technical Bulletin, Union Carbide Chemical Corp., 1957.
157. W. Reeve and I. J. Christoffel, *J. Am. Chem. Soc.* **72**, 1480 (1958).
158. A. Kaelin, *Helv. Chim. Acta* **30**, 2132 (1947).
159. C. O. Guss and H. R. Williams, *J. Org. Chem.* **16**, 1809 (1951).
160. U.S. Pat. 2,422,637 (1937), E. C. Thomas (to Monsanto Chemical Co.).
161. W. D. Kumler, A. C. Huitric, and H. K. Hall, Jr., *J. Am. Chem. Soc.* **78**, 4345 (1956).
162. Ref. 1, p. 20.
163. K. D. Reve and G. C. Israel, *J. Chem. Soc.* **1952**, 2327.
164. Fr. Pat. 982,969 (1951).
165. P. Ferrero, L. R. Flamme, and M. Fourez, *Ind. Chim. Belge* **19**, 113 (1954).
166. Ref. 2, p. 6.
167. D. Porret, *Helv. Chim. Acta* **30**, 701 (1947).
168. E. A. Schmidt (with H. Hartman), *Ann.* **337**, 116 (1904); *J. Chem. Soc.* **1904**, AI, 23–28.
169. W. H. Horne and R. L. Shriner, *J. Am. Chem. Soc.* **54**, 2925 (1932).
170. G. Forsberg, *Acta Chem. Scand.* **8**, 135 (1954).
171. E. C. Steiner, R. R. Pelletier, and R. O. Trucks, *J. Am. Chem. Soc.* **86**, 4678 (1964).
172. U.S. Pat. 3,132,156 (1964), R. C. Lemon, P. C. Johnson, and J. M. Berty (to Union Carbide Chemical Co.).
173. *Chem. Eng. News,* 25 (March 22, 1965).

General References

A. Rosowsky in A. Weissberger, ed., *Heterocyclic Compounds With Three- and Four-Membered Rings,* Part I, Interscience Publishers, a division of John Wiley & Sons, Inc., New York, 1964, pp. 1–523.
G. O. Curme, Jr., and F. Johnston, eds., *Glycols,* Reinhold Publishing Corp., New York, 1952.
L. E. St. Pierre in N. C. Gaylord, ed., *Polyethers,* Part I, Chap. III, Interscience Publishers, a division of John Wiley & Sons, Inc., New York, 1963.
J. Furukawa and T. Saegusa, *Polymerization of Aldehydes and Oxides,* Chap. III, Interscience Publishers, a division of John Wiley & Sons, Inc., New York, 1963.

M. Lapkin
Olin Mathieson Chemical Corporation

EPOXY RESINS

Epoxy resins are characterized by the presence of the epoxy group,

$$-C-C-$$
$$\diagdown O \diagup$$

In some respects the term "epoxy resins" is somewhat misleading because, although these materials may be resinous in nature, they are more properly defined as intermediates. In general, the epoxy resin is never used by itself but requires the addition of a curing agent or hardener to convert it to a thermoset material. Epoxy resins have gained wide acceptance in structural applications and in protective coatings because of their excellent toughness, adhesion, chemical resistance, and electrical properties. The combination of these properties is generally not found in any other single plastic material.

The most widely used epoxy resins are made by reacting epichlorohydrin (**1**) (see Chlorohydrins) with bisphenol A (**2**) (4,4′-isopropylidenediphenol, see Vol. 1, p.

$$CH_2 \underset{\diagdown O \diagup}{} CHCH_2Cl \qquad\qquad HO \underset{}{\longleftarrow} \bigcirc \underset{\underset{CH_3}{|}}{\overset{\overset{CH_3}{|}}{C}} \bigcirc \longrightarrow OH$$

epichlorohydrin (**1**)   bisphenol A (**2**)

912). However, other polyols, such as aliphatic glycols and novolac resins, can be used in place of the bisphenol.

In addition there is a new type of epoxy resin, obtained by the epoxidation, with peroxy compounds, of double bonds in certain Diels-Alder adducts. These resins were introduced in the early 1960s by some of the major epoxy resin suppliers in the U.S. The chief interest in these new resins appears to be in the field of electrical applications, particularly where good high-temperature properties and exterior durability are required.

Epoxy resins were first introduced commercially in the United States in about 1950, and their use has grown rapidly. The sales of epoxy resins increased from less than 1 million lb in 1950 to about 75 million lb in 1963. It is estimated that the worldwide usage of epoxy resins in 1963 was approx 120 million lb. Although the growth of epoxy resin sales has never reached the optimistic estimates which were given in the late 1950s, epoxy resins have still grown steadily, at a rate of about 10–20% per year for the past few years. The domestic production capacity for epoxy resins is being increased at the present time (1964), and the total capacity in the U.S. will be about 140 million lb by the end of 1964.

Table 1. Epoxy Resin Producers and Trade Names Used

Company	Trade name
Ciba Products Company	Araldite
Dow Chemical Company	D. E. R.
Jones-Dabney Company	Epi-Rez
Reichhold Chemicals, Inc.	Epotuf
Shell Chemical Corporation	Epon
Union Carbide Plastics Company	Bakelite

Epoxies are somewhat higher in price than other thermosetting resins, such as polyesters, because they are based on comparatively costly materials. The low-molecular-weight, liquid epoxy resins are sold in the $0.60/lb range, while the higher-molecular-weight, solid epoxy resins are sold in the $0.55–0.60/lb range. Table 1 lists the basic producers of epoxy resins in the U.S.

During the early stages of development of the epoxy market, coatings were the biggest single outlet for these resins. Although their use in coatings still accounts for a considerable portion of the market, some of the other applications, such as electrical and reinforced plastics, have shown a very significant growth. Table 2 illustrates the usage of epoxy resins in 1963 by application.

Table 2. Use Pattern of Epoxy Resins, 1963

Application	Industry distribution, %
bonding and adhesives	16
protective coatings	43
reinforced plastics	14
other uses	27

History. The synthesis of a polyglycidyl ether was first described by Schlack in 1934 (1). He did not, however, claim any rights to the epoxy compounds themselves, but only to their use as intermediates in the conversion to high-molecular-weight polyamines. These were to be used primarily for textile treatment.

The Swiss chemist Castan was the first to realize that epoxy resins were suited to applications in the field of plastics. In 1938 he claimed several rights with regard to plastic materials which cured without evolution of volatile matter and with low shrinkage, and possessed outstanding mechanical properties (2). These were epoxy resins cured with acid anhydrides. A second patent followed in 1943, this time covering the use of basic materials as curing agents. Castan limited the application of the new resin compositions to the field of dentistry, but Ciba, as a licensee, started research work on the introduction of these resins into the plastics industry. In July of 1945 the first patent application in the field of epoxy adhesives was filed, and early in 1946 the first epoxy adhesive was offered at the Swiss Industries Fair. In the field of surface coatings, the first patent in Europe was taken out in August of 1946.

At about the same time, the development of epoxy resins in the United States took place independently of the work carried out in Switzerland. The work was aimed in a somewhat different direction. The first patent application was that of Greenlee (Devoe & Raynolds Co.), filed in the early 1940s (3). Not long after this, Shell also started to work in the field of epoxy resins.

Resin Manufacture

Glycidyl Ether Resins. These are reaction products of epichlorohydrin with polyhydric materials. In the reaction, the epichlorohydrin is combined with a polyol at temperatures up to about 150°C in the presence of alkaline or other-type catalysts. The conversion to epoxy resin proceeds with high yields under relatively mild conditions. The method appears to be generally applicable to materials containing several alcoholic or hydroxyl groups. Various polyols can be used in the reaction, but the commercial types of epoxy resins are principally based upon bisphenol A, which is a condensation product of acetone and phenol. When epichlorohydrin and bisphenol A are reacted in the presence of an alkaline catalyst, the simplest epoxy resin or monomer produced is the *diglycidyl ether of bisphenol A*.

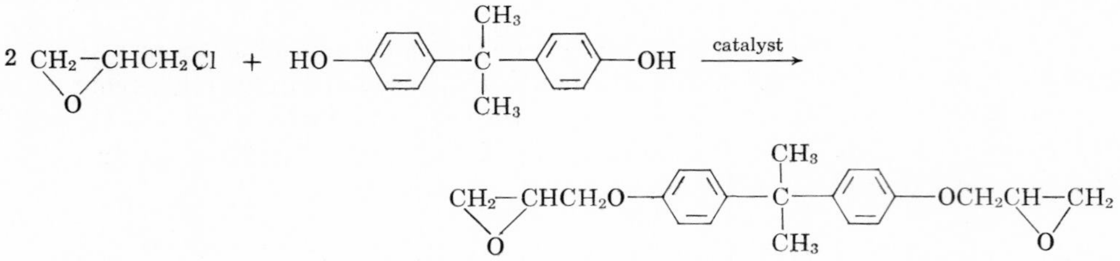

$$2\ CH_2-CHCH_2Cl\ +\ HO-\underset{O}{\underbrace{\quad}}-\underset{CH_3}{\overset{CH_3}{C}}-\underset{\quad}{\underbrace{\quad}}-OH\ \xrightarrow{\text{catalyst}}$$

$$CH_2-CHCH_2O-\underset{O}{\underbrace{\quad}}-\underset{CH_3}{\overset{CH_3}{C}}-\underset{\quad}{\underbrace{\quad}}-OCH_2CH-CH_2$$

By varying the operating conditions and the ratio of epichlorohydrin and bisphenol A, resins of low, intermediate, or high molecular weight can be prepared. The general structure for an epoxy resin is shown below.

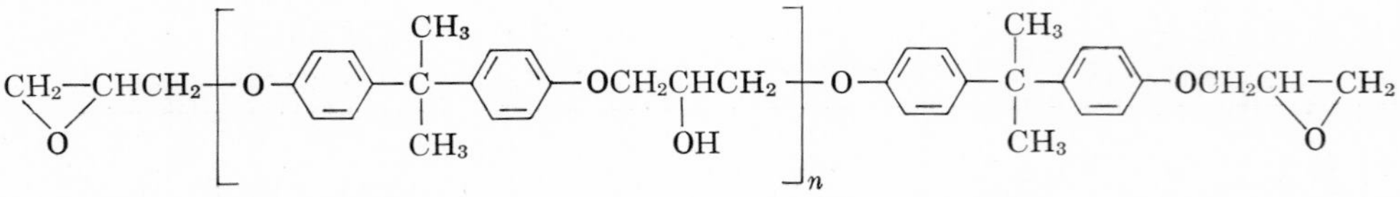

$$CH_2-CHCH_2\left[O-\underset{CH_3}{\overset{CH_3}{C}}-OCH_2CHCHCH_2\right]_n O-\underset{CH_3}{\overset{CH_3}{C}}-OCH_2CH-CH_2$$

For the liquid epoxy resins n is generally less than 1, while for the solid types n is generally 2 or greater, although in either case the product is a mixture of various molecular weight resins. An examination of the structure of an epoxy resin points out the following characteristics:

a. The epoxy and hydroxyl groups are the centers for reaction with curing agents such as amines, acids, anhydrides, aldehyde resins, and other materials.

b. Other than carbon-to-carbon bonds, ether linkages are the only type present.

c. Three kinds of polar groups are present, epoxy, hydroxyl, and ether. These groups increase the adhesion of the resin.

The reaction between epichlorohydrin and the bisphenol is believed to take place in two steps, according to the equations

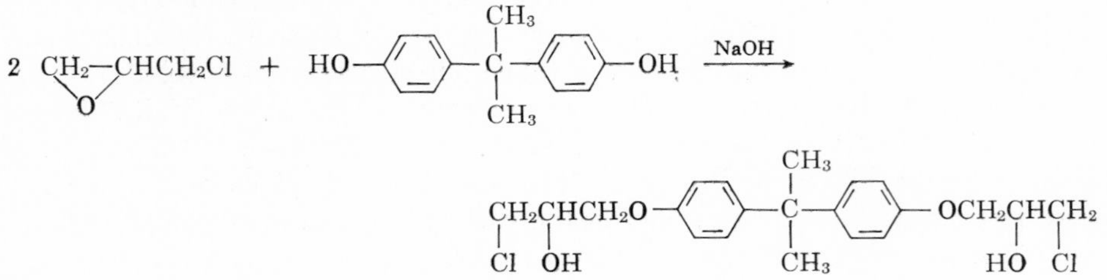

$$2\ CH_2-CHCH_2Cl\ +\ HO-\underset{CH_3}{\overset{CH_3}{C}}-OH\ \xrightarrow{\text{NaOH}}$$

$$CH_2CHCH_2O-\underset{CH_3}{\overset{CH_3}{C}}-OCH_2CHCH_2 \quad (1)$$

$$CH_2CHCH_2O-\underset{CH_3}{\overset{CH_3}{C}}-OCH_2CHCH_2 \xrightarrow{\text{NaOH}}$$

$$CH_2-CHCH_2O-\underset{CH_3}{\overset{CH_3}{C}}-OCH_2CH-CH_2\ +\ NaCl\ +\ H_2O \quad (2)$$

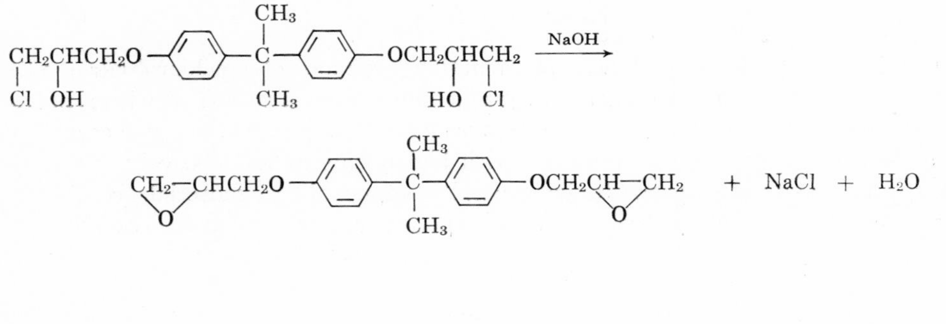

In manufacture by the *one-stage* process, epichlorohydrin is reacted with bisphenol A in the presence of sodium or potassium hydroxide. Both of the above reactions take place. Certain side reactions also take place. In the presence of the alkali catalyst, epichlorohydrin will react with the chlorohydrin hydroxyl group to form a product with the following structure:

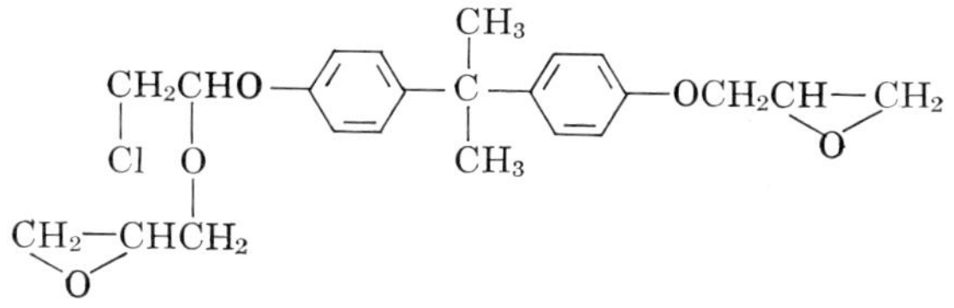

In order to avoid this reaction, temperatures are maintained as low as possible, since elevated temperatures promote the reaction of epichlorohydrin and alcoholic hydroxyl groups.

To produce the *lower-molecular-weight* epoxy resins, large excesses of epichlorohydrin are used, since this will favor the formation of $n = 0$ type of resins. However, this method is not completely effective, and all liquid resins that are not subjected to molecular distillation contain a small percentage of high-molecular-weight resin.

The solid or *higher-molecular-weight* epoxy resins are prepared in the same general manner, except that less than 2 moles of epichlorohydrin per mole of bisphenol A are used. The product often becomes extremely viscous, and the operation is sometimes referred to as the "taffy" process.

Two major side reactions take place in this preparation of solid resins, and both contribute to the variable reactivity of conventional epoxies. These reactions are branch chain formation and phenol termination.

1. Branch chain formation results from the reaction of an epoxy group of one molecule and the hydroxyl group of an adjacent molecule. In this reaction one epoxy group is eliminated, and the same number of hydroxyl groups is maintained. This reaction is illustrated as follows:

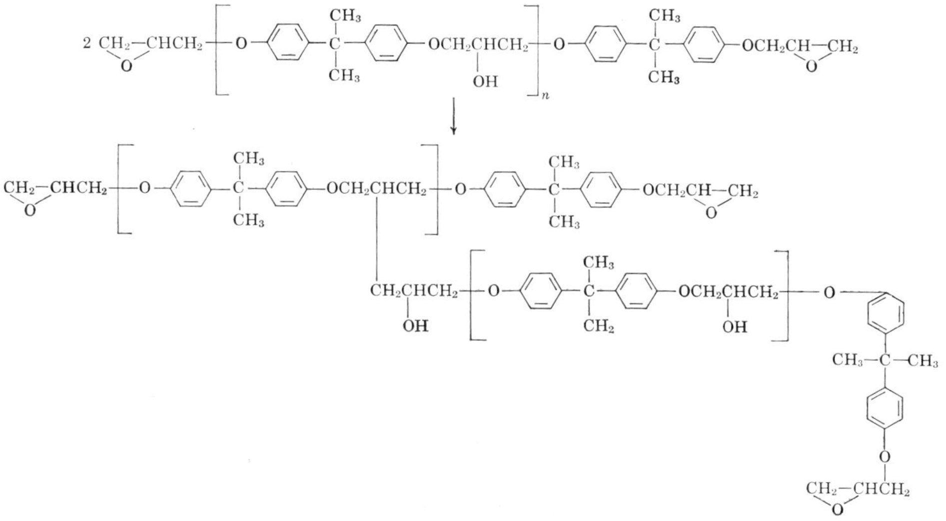

Branch chain formation increases surface tension and melting point, reduces solubility, and contributes to gel formation.

2. Phenol termination results in the following structure:

$$\text{HO}\!-\!\langle\bigcirc\rangle\!-\!\underset{\text{CH}_3}{\overset{\text{CH}_3}{\text{C}}}\!-\!\langle\bigcirc\rangle\!-\!\text{OCH}_2\underset{\text{OH}}{\text{CHCH}_2}\!\left[\!\text{O}\!-\!\langle\bigcirc\rangle\!-\!\underset{\text{CH}_3}{\overset{\text{CH}_3}{\text{C}}}\!-\!\langle\bigcirc\rangle\!-\!\text{OCH}_2\underset{\text{OH}}{\text{CHCH}_2}\!\right]_n\!\!\text{O}\!-\!\langle\bigcirc\rangle\!-\!\underset{\text{CH}_3}{\overset{\text{CH}_3}{\text{C}}}\!-\!\langle\bigcirc\rangle\!-\!\text{OCH}_2\underset{\text{O}}{\text{CH}\!-\!\text{CH}_2}$$

Although this product is not present to a large extent, it does reduce reactivity and contributes to poor color retention.

To overcome some of these deficiencies due to side reactions in the "taffy" process, new methods of manufacture have been developed, primarily through modification of the catalyst. It has been well illustrated that sodium and potassium hydroxide are not preferential catalysts and promote reaction between epichlorohydrin and phenolic hydroxyl groups as well as between epichlorohydrin and alcoholic hydroxyl groups. New catalysts have been developed that are specifically effective in promoting the reaction of epichlorohydrin and phenolic hydroxyl groups. Thus branch chain formation is avoided.

These new catalysts can also be used to effect the condensation of bisphenol A with low-molecular-weight resins to form a polymer essentially linear in nature. The resulting resins exhibit molecular weights approximately the same as the theoretical molecular weight calculated from the proportions of reactants used. The general equation for this advancement reaction may be represented as follows:

$$(n+1)\ \text{CH}_2\!-\!\text{CHCH}_2\text{O}\!-\!\langle\bigcirc\rangle\!-\!\underset{\text{CH}_3}{\overset{\text{CH}_3}{\text{C}}}\!-\!\langle\bigcirc\rangle\!-\!\text{OCH}_2\text{CH}\!-\!\text{CH}_2\ +\ (n)\ \text{HO}\!-\!\langle\bigcirc\rangle\!-\!\underset{\text{CH}_3}{\overset{\text{CH}_3}{\text{C}}}\!-\!\langle\bigcirc\rangle\!-\!\text{OH}\ \rightarrow$$

$$\text{CH}_2\!-\!\text{CHCH}_2\!\left[\!\text{O}\!-\!\langle\bigcirc\rangle\!-\!\underset{\text{CH}_3}{\overset{\text{CH}_3}{\text{C}}}\!-\!\langle\bigcirc\rangle\!-\!\text{OCH}_2\underset{\text{OH}}{\text{CHCH}_2}\!\right]_{2n}\!\!\text{O}\!-\!\langle\bigcirc\rangle\!-\!\underset{\text{CH}_3}{\overset{\text{CH}_3}{\text{C}}}\!-\!\langle\bigcirc\rangle\!-\!\text{OCH}_2\text{CH}\!-\!\text{CH}_2$$

As can be seen from this equation, all mole ratios used are based on the amount of bisphenol employed, which dictates the degree of condensation; under these conditions bisphenol termination is avoided. In addition, the catalyst used is selective to phenolic hydroxyl groups and almost completely ineffective with alcoholic hydroxyls. Hence, branch chain formation is prevented.

In the *two-stage* method for preparing epoxy resins, materials such as stannic chloride, aluminum chloride, and BF_3 complexes have been utilized to effect the condensation of bisphenol A with epichlorohydrin. The reaction that takes place under the influence of these catalysts is represented by equation 1. This stage is then followed by dehydrohalogenation with caustic. It has been found that although these catalysts will promote the reaction of epichlorohydrin with bisphenol A, once an alcoholic hydroxyl group is formed, the reaction of additional epichlorohydrin with the alcoholic hydroxyl group will be the favored reaction. Use of excesses of epichlorohydrin only increases this reaction, and the final product contains a high percentage of bound chlorine. Thus, this type of catalyst system tends to produce poor yields.

However, these catalysts, because of their tendency to favor the alcoholic hydroxyl condensations with epichlorohydrin, are very useful in the preparation of aliphatic epoxies such as illustrated by the following equation:

$$C_4H_9OH + CH_2\!\!-\!\!CHCH_2Cl \xrightarrow{SnCl_4} C_4H_9OCH_2CHCH_2Cl \xrightarrow{NaOH}$$

$$C_4H_9OCH_2CH\!\!-\!\!CH_2 + NaCl + H_2O$$

Most epoxy resins are produced by a *batch* process (regardless of whether a one-stage or a two-stage process is used). After the condensation reaction has taken place, the crude resin is stripped of residual epichlorohydrin, washed with water to remove salt and soluble by-products, dried, and packaged. Liquid resins are packaged in drums, whereas the solid resins are sold in bags or fiber containers either in flaked or in crushed form. The solid resins are also available dissolved in solvents for use in coating applications.

Resins Prepared by Epoxidation of Double Bonds. These resins are prepared from an intermediate formed by the Diels-Alder condensation of butadiene and acrolein or of butadiene and crotonaldehyde. The reaction is shown in the following equation:

    1,3-butadiene   acrolein   tetrahydrobenzaldehyde

Starting out with tetrahydrobenzaldehyde, the condensation product of butadiene and acrolein, there are several possible reactions which can yield resins with varying structures (4). This can be illustrated by the following series of reactions:

In addition to cycloaliphatic epoxy resins of the above type, butadiene polymers have also been epoxidized to give resins with the following generalized structure:

$$\left[\begin{array}{c}\text{CH}_2\text{CHCHCH}_2\text{CH}_2\text{CH}\!-\!\text{CHCH}_2\text{CH}_2\text{CH}\!=\!\text{CHCH}_2\text{CH}_2\text{CHCH}_2\text{CH}\\ \underset{\underset{\text{CH}_3}{\overset{|}{\text{CH}}}}{\overset{|}{\underset{\text{CO}}{\overset{|}{\text{HO}}}}}\quad \text{O}\qquad\qquad \text{O}\qquad\qquad\qquad \text{O}\text{CH}\quad \text{CH}\\ \qquad\qquad\qquad\qquad\qquad\qquad\qquad \text{CH}_2\quad \text{CH}_2\end{array}\right]_x$$

Resin Properties and Analysis

Table 3 indicates the approximate molecular weight, melting point, epoxy equivalent, and average "n" value for the commercially available epoxy resins of the epichlorohydrin/bisphenol A type.

Table 3.   Typical Properties of Commercial Epoxy Resins

Approximate molecular weight	Melting point, °C	Average epoxy value, equiv/100 g	Average n value/molecule
360–380	liquid	0.54	0.10
370–400	liquid	0.52	0.15
380–420	liquid	0.50	0.21
390–450	liquid	0.47	0.30
460–560	liquid	0.39	0.60
770–1,000	60–75	0.23	1.80
850–1,100	65–75	0.21	2.20
1,750–2,050	95–105	0.10	5.50
4,000–5,000	125–135	0.05	14.40
5,000–8,000	145–155	0.03	16.00

Examination of Table 3 shows that as the molecular weight of the epoxy resin increases, a transition from a relatively low viscosity liquid to a high-viscosity liquid and finally to a solid material occurs. Together with this increase in molecular weight, the number of hydroxyl groups per molecule and the equivalent weight for esterification increase also. However, the epoxy value decreases because the distance between terminal epoxy groups becomes greater. Convenient approximations have been used to provide reasonable values for the molecular weight and for the average n number per resin molecule in Table 3. In general, these values have been derived from data obtained by the most widely used chemical test for characterizing epoxy resins, the epoxy-content test.

For example, the molecular-weight values listed in Table 3, and used throughout this article, are those obtained by doubling the weight per epoxy group (WPE, or grams containing one gram-equivalent of epoxide), assuming the linear structure with terminal epoxy groups. To illustrate, if the pure diglycidyl ether of bisphenol A could be prepared, chemical tests of the resin would give a WPE value of 170, indicating the molecular weight of 340. Direct physical methods of molecular-weight determination, such as ebullioscopic procedures and those involving light scattering, are less satisfactory standards, particularly for the higher-molecular-weight resins, because they give divergent values which are highly dependent on the molecular-weight distribution of the diepoxides present. This distribution, in turn, may vary somewhat from manufacturer to manufacturer for the same resin type, because of minor differences in the production processes.

The common procedure for determining the epoxy value (often expressed as WPE) involves titrating the epoxy resin in solution with a standard solution of hydrogen bromide in glacial acetic acid (12). The hydrogen bromide reacts with the epoxy group to form bromohydrins; therefore, the quantity of acid consumed is a measure of the epoxy content.

In addition to the epoxy value, a number of other tests are run to characterize epoxy resins. Some of these tests are color, viscosity, % hydrolyzable chlorine, % volatile, and esterification equivalent.

The esterification equivalent of an epoxy resin is a value used frequently in calculating the charge for an epoxy ester preparation. The value is based on esterification of the epoxy groups and of the hydroxyl groups. The esterification equivalent weight is usually determined directly by esterification of a resin sample with excess acetic acid, followed by titration of the excess acid.

In the polymerization reaction leading to epoxy resins, close control of the operating variables is necessary. Even with the best control, resin properties may vary somewhat from lot to lot, making control tests of performance a part of standard evaluation procedures for the finished resin. For each lot of resin produced of the various molecular weight types, it is common practice to evaluate a coating or a casting made from the new resin. For example, evaluation of the rate of the curing reaction with amines and determination of the hardness or strength of a standard casting would give useful information on a lot of a liquid epoxy resin in the molecular-weight range of 350–450. For the solid resins, control testing might involve the cooking of a standard ester-type coating vehicle, or conversion of the resin with a urea–formaldehyde resin to a baked-type coating which could be evaluated.

Solubility and Compatibility. Epoxy resins are soluble in oxygenated solvents, such as ketones, esters, and ether alcohols, and in some chlorinated solvents. The solubility of the resins depends on their molecular weight, and decreases as the molecular weight increases. The solid epoxy resins are not soluble in alcohols, aliphatic hydrocarbons and aromatic hydrocarbons. The liquid resins, however, are soluble in aromatics, but, in general, are not soluble in alcohols. Although alcohols and aromatic hydrocarbons are not active solvents for the solid epoxy resins used in protective coatings, they do exhibit latent solvency characteristics when used in combination with active solvents. In practice, mixed solvents, such as toluene or xylene with oxygenated materials (mainly ketones), are used in compositions for protective coatings.

Common ketone and ester solvents give relatively low viscosity solutions, whereas ether alcohols, higher-molecular-weight ketones, and chlorinated solvents give relatively high viscosity solutions with solid epoxy resins.

In general, the higher-molecular-weight epoxy resins are not compatible with vegetable oils, alkyd resins, cellulose derivatives, melamine–formaldehyde resins, methacrylate resins, silicones, or hydrocarbon resins applied in protective coatings. Poor compatibility is also shown with natural and synthetic rubbers, and with many vinyl resins. However, the surface-coating types of epoxy resins are compatible with certain alkyd resins, pure phenolic resins, polyvinyl formal and polyvinyl acetal resins, and urea resins.

Curing

Epoxy resins require the addition of a curing agent or hardener in order to convert them to thermoset materials. A great variety of chemical reagents can be used as hardeners or curing agents. In the curing process both the epoxy and the hydroxyl groups of the resin may be involved, and curing can take place either at room temperature or upon heating. Curing may take place either by a coupling or addition process, or by a catalytic polymerization.

The curing agents or hardeners most commonly used with epoxy resins can be divided into the following general groups:

1. Amine type: aliphatic and aromatic amines, polyamides, tertiary amines, and amine adducts.

2. Acidic type: acid anhydrides, acids.

3. Aldehyde condensation products: phenol–, urea–, and melamine–formaldehyde resins.

4. Lewis acid type of catalyst: boron trifluoride complexes, etc.

Coupling Processes. The curing of epoxy resins with amine type, acidic type, and aldehyde condensation products is an addition or coupling type of reaction. The curing mechanisms for some of these agents have been investigated extensively (5–8).

Aliphatic polyamines cure at room temperature and crosslinking occurs through the epoxy groups and the active hydrogens attached to the amino nitrogen of the polyamine (8). This is illustrated by the following equation:

$$H_2N—R—NH_2 + CH_2—CH——CH—CH_2 \rightarrow H_2N—R—NHCH_2—CH——CH—CH_2$$

The epoxy ring opens, forming a hydroxyl group and a carbon to nitrogen linkage. The amine is now a secondary amine and the remaining hydrogen can also react with an epoxy group. Since polyamines containing two or more amino groups are normally employed, a highly crosslinked structure is possible.

The reaction of the amino group with the epoxy group is the principal reaction. Any reaction of epoxy and hydroxyl groups is negligible.

Polyamides react with the epoxy resin in the same manner as aliphatic polyamines. The polyamides are essentially condensation products of dimerized fatty acids and aliphatic polyamines having free amino groups.

Aromatic amines react much slower than aliphatic amines, and require heat for complete curing. Their reaction with epoxy resins proceeds in the same manner as in the case of polyamines and polyamides.

Aldehyde condensation products, such as urea–, melamine–, or phenol–formaldehyde resins, are used as curing agents for baked epoxy finishes.

Butylated urea– or melamine–formaldehyde resins react with the epoxy resin by means of transetherification, and to a limited extent through the active hydrogen of the amine and through the hydroxyl of the methylol groups. The reaction of a butylated urea–formaldehyde resin and an epoxy is as follows:

The prime reaction is through the hydroxyl groups of the epoxy and the butyl group of the urea resin. The reaction between the epoxy group and the amino hydrogen is much slower.

The principal reactions which could occur between an epoxy resin and a phenol-formaldehyde resin are (a) reaction of the methylol hydroxyl of the phenolic resin with the hydroxyl groups in the epoxy resin, (b) reaction of the epoxy groups with the methylol hydroxyl, and (c) reaction of the epoxy groups with the phenolic hydroxyl. It is believed that the first reaction is the chief reaction that occurs.

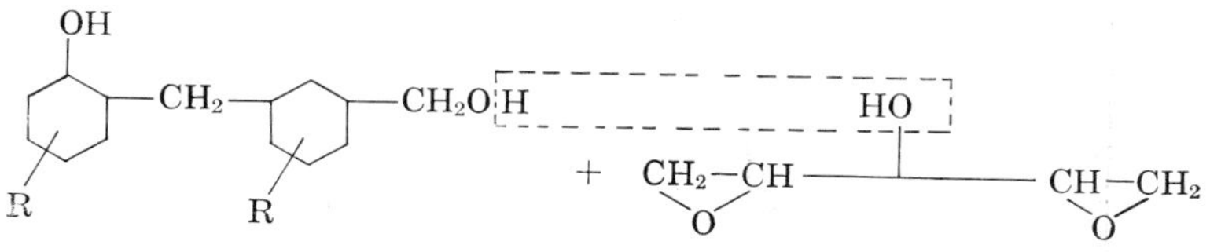

Since the aldehyde resin–epoxy reaction takes place chiefly with the hydroxyl groups of the epoxy, higher-molecular-weight resins (such as the "7" type which contain a high concentration of hydroxyl groups) are used with urea–, melamine–, or phenol–formaldehyde cured systems.

Acid Anhydrides. The first epoxy resins that were introduced were cured with polycarboxylic anhydrides. These crosslinking agents require higher curing temperatures, but compared with amines they are characterized by low exotherm. They can lead to structures such as are shown below.

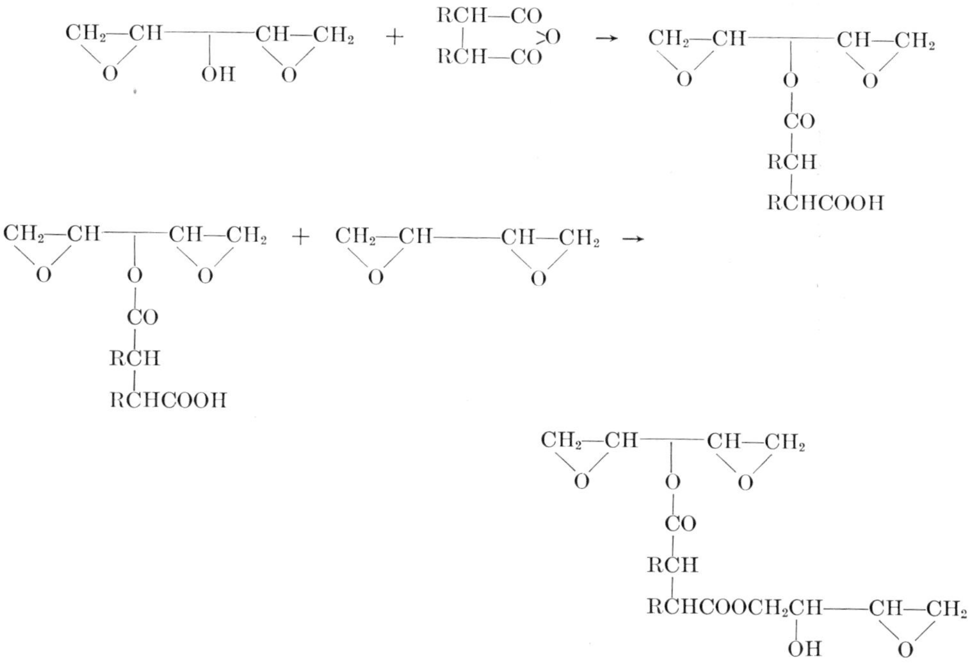

The first step in the reaction is between the anhydride and the hydroxyl group in the epoxy resin, to form a monoester. The newly formed carboxyl group then reacts with an epoxy group to give a diester and a new hydroxyl group which can then react with the anhydride.

Analytical studies of this mechanism have confirmed the sequence of reactions and, in addition, showed that the number of epoxy groups decreased much faster than the number of diester groups increased. Thus, the epoxy group must take part in further reactions apart from its reaction with the half-ester. It was established that etherification takes place between the epoxy group and the hydroxyl group of the epoxy. This reaction is slow if the resin alone is held at elevated temperatures, but proceeds readily under the catalytic presence of anhydride or carboxyl groups.

Catalytic Polymerization. Epoxy groups may be polymerized by catalysts which may be Lewis acids or tertiary amines. The terminal epoxy groups are opened and homopolymerization occurs. A possible mechanism for this reaction is shown in the following equation:

$$R_3N + CH_2\text{---}CH\text{------} \quad \rightarrow \quad R_3\overset{+}{N}CH_2CH\text{------}$$

$$R_3\overset{+}{N}CH_2CH\text{------} + CH_2\text{---}CH\text{------} \quad \rightarrow \quad CH_2CH\text{------}$$

Catalytic polymerization is less important as a curing method than the addition or coupling process, but during any treatment to which the epoxy resin may be subjected, catalytic polymerization might occur.

Epoxy Esters. Epoxy resins are polyols, and are widely used as such by the coatings industry for the manufacture of fatty acid resin and other acid esters. Epoxy resin esters are simple esterification products of the epoxy resin with a fatty acid, rosin acid, or tall oil acid, or mixtures of these acids. Limited amounts of polybasic acids, anhydrides, and other materials may also be used.

When used for esterification, both the epoxide and the hydroxyl groups enter into the reaction. Each epoxy group is the equivalent of two hydroxyl groups and can react with two molecules of fatty acid; the hydroxyl groups in the chain also enter into the reaction. The general equation for the preparation of an epoxy ester is shown in the following equation:

$$\overset{O}{\underset{\|}{\text{------C---OH}}} + CH_2\text{---}CHCH_2\text{------} \quad \rightarrow \quad \overset{O}{\underset{\|}{\text{------C---OCH}_2CHCH_2\text{------}}}$$

The first reaction is the opening of the epoxy ring with the formation of an ester and a hydroxyl group. This hydroxyl group, as well as other hydroxyl groups in the chain, can be esterified further, depending on the degree of esterification desired.

Epoxy esters may be made in long, medium, and short oil lengths with nondrying, semidrying, or drying characteristics. The effect of the type and amount of fatty acids used is similar to that in alkyd resins (qv).

Epoxy resin esters may be used in air-dry and baking applications, as well as in clear and pigmented finishes (3,9). They can be combined with either melamine or urea resins as baking finishes, or can be used with metallic driers in either air-dry or baking systems.

In addition to varying the type of acid and the extent of acid modification, the base resin used for preparing epoxy esters may also be varied. An epoxy resin with a molecular weight of 1700–2000 is used. However, where low viscosity or greater compatibility is desired, resins with a molecular weight of about 1000 can be employed. Where faster drying characteristics and improved alkali resistance are required, an epoxy with a molecular weight in the 4000–5000 range may be employed.

Besides the conventional method for preparing epoxy esters, which uses solid epoxy resins and selected fatty acids, another method may be followed using liquid resins to produce a wide range of epoxy esters (10). Reaction of a low-molecular-weight resin with bisphenol A and selected fatty acids yields an intermediate diester. This intermediate is further esterified to the desired degree. The simplified reaction scheme for the preparation of epoxy esters by this method is shown in the following equations:

1. Monoester formation.

2. Chain lengthening or polymerization step.

3. Polymerized fatty acid diester formation.

4. Full esterification.

polymerized fatty acid diester + fatty acid →

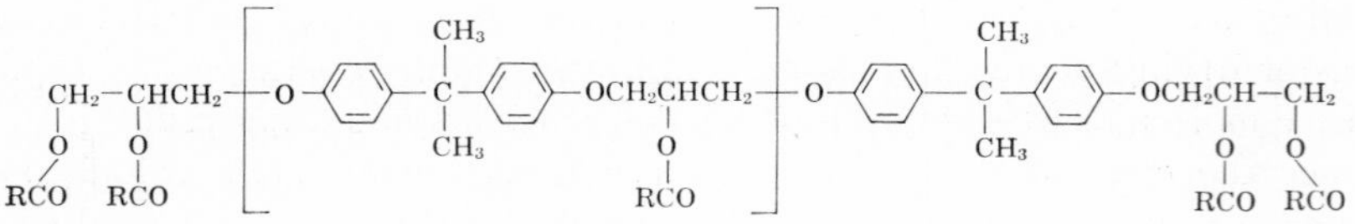

fully esterified polymer

In actual practice, steps 1, 2, and 3 of this reaction are made to occur simultaneously. The following facts are important in the chemistry of this preparation:

1. In the presence of a selected alkaline catalyst, epoxy groups react first with carboxyl groups, then with phenolic hydroxyl groups, and lastly with aliphatic hydroxyl groups.

2. Low-molecular-weight liquid resins will react with bisphenol A to produce higher-molecular-weight resins.

Consequently, it is logical to assume that the proper proportions of liquid epoxy resin, bisphenol A, and fatty acid can be reacted to obtain the desired chain length, terminated by fatty acid groups.

Through use of a special esterification technique, epoxy resins may also be incorporated into alkyd resins (11). Epoxy resins cannot be utilized directly as polyols in the normal procedures for preparing alkyds, because of premature gelation. However, when the epoxy resin is first "defunctionalized" (by heating with fatty acid) to give a resinous material having an average of three hydroxyl groups per molecule, phthalic anhydride, glycerol, and other materials can then be incorporated to yield an alkyd of excellent properties. All types of phthalic alkyd resins can be prepared by using this technique. The resulting products show properties in protective coatings somewhat between pure alkyd resins and epoxy resin esters so far as chemical resistance, adhesion, color, and hardness are concerned.

Uses

Protective Coatings. Since their introduction in the U.S. in the early 1950s, epoxy resins have been used extensively in protective coatings, and have also become accepted in many coating uses previously restricted to alkyds and phenolic resins.

Epoxy resin coatings possess certain inherent properties such as adhesion, toughness, and chemical resistance. Epoxy-coating systems are being used in automotive and appliance primers, can coatings, marine finishes, masonry and equipment finishes, industrial maintenance coatings, and other specialty finishes.

For the sake of simplicity, epoxy coating systems may be divided into two broad classes:

1. Solvent-based systems.
    a. Room-temperature curing. This group includes solid or liquid resins which are cured by polyamines, polyamides, etc. Air-dry esters are also included in this category.
    b. Heat-curing (baking) finishes. This group includes solutions of solid resins, liquid resins, or epoxy esters cured by urea–, melamine–, or phenol–formaldehyde resins.

2. Solventless (100% solid) systems. These are coatings based on liquid resins which are either room-temperature cured or heat-cured, depending on the choice of hardener.

Amine-Cured Coatings. One of the most common types of solvent-based epoxy coatings are those based on the lower-molecular-weight, solid epoxy resins, cured with aliphatic polyamines or polyamides. Systems of this type offer chemical and solvent resistance normally associated with competitive-type, heat-cured systems.

Since the curing reaction takes place at ambient temperatures, systems of this type are necessarily two-component systems. After addition of the hardener, the working life (pot life) varies from 8 to 24 hr, depending upon the formulation.

Epoxy/polyamine systems are excellent over ferrous and nonferrous metals, concrete, and wood. Typical applications are around oil refineries, petrochemical plants, and marine installations. Normally the coatings are applied by conventional means (spray or brush) in multicoats consisting of primers and top coats. Polyamide-cured epoxy systems are widely used where conditions of water immersion are encountered, particularly in marine applications. Both the amine-cured and polyamide-cured epoxy systems exhibit excellent chemical resistance, and find wide use in maintenance applications where resistance to corrosion or chemical attack must be considered.

Ester-Type Coatings. Because they are less expensive than the amine or polyamide-cured epoxy resin paints, epoxy resin esters are used widely. Epoxy ester coatings are produced in formulations paralleling alkyd coatings. Epoxy esters are available in short, medium, and long oil lengths. The long oil length epoxy esters have limited chemical resistance, whereas the short oil length esters exhibit good chemical resistance.

Epoxy esters, like drying oils, promote surface wetting, and are often used where optimum surface preparation is not possible. Because of their limited chemical resistance, epoxy esters find their greatest use in mild chemically corrosive areas and in marine environments too severe for the use of alkyd-type coatings.

Heat-Curing (Baking) Finishes. Heat-curing finishes are one of the most sizable markets for epoxy resins in combination with other resins. Generally, these systems include the higher-molecular-weight epoxy resins cured with aldehyde condensation products such as urea–, melamine–, and phenol–formaldehyde resins. In addition, short oil length epoxy esters reacted with urea or melamine resins fall into this category.

Epoxy–phenolic systems offer the optimum in chemical and solvent resistance, along with excellent mechanical properties. Depending on the choice of epoxy resin and phenolic resin, individual properties, such as hardness, ductility, and chemical resistance, can be influenced considerably.

Resins of the 4000–5000 molecular-weight range are used primarily for this type of coating. The phenolic resin is generally one of a low degree of condensation, and part of the methylol groups may be etherified with butanol. Generally the ratio of epoxy–phenolic ranges from 70:30 to 80:20, depending on the properties desired.

Acid catalysts, such as phosphoric acid or the morpholine salt of *p*-toluene sulfonic acid, may be added to accelerate the cure.

Epoxy–phenolic systems are used for coatings on process equipment, tank and drum linings, can coatings, pipe linings, and similar applications where excellent chemical resistance is required.

Epoxy–amino resin combinations have slightly less chemical resistance than epoxy–phenolic systems, but exhibit better initial color and color retention.   There are almost limitless possibilities in variation of the epoxy resin with urea, melamine, and benzoguanamine resins; the proportions in the epoxy–amino resin can vary from 90:10 to 60:40.

Systems of this type are used in appliance finishes and primers, protective coatings for the food industry, can and drum coatings.

Again, resins of the 4000–5000 molecular-weight range are generally used for this type of coating, although blends with other resins may also be used for specific requirements.   Normally the following epoxy/amino resin ratios are used:

epoxy/urea	70:30
epoxy/benzoguanamine	70:30
epoxy/melamine	80:20 or 90:10

By increasing the amount of epoxy, the following trends are observed: (a) flexibility, toughness, adhesion, and gloss improve; (b) gloss retention, solvent resistance, and hardness are reduced; (c) often more severe baking schedules are required.   To reduce bake schedules, accelerators are sometimes used with epoxy–amino resin coatings.

Solventless Coatings.   Since about 1960, paint manufacturers have been showing increased interest in solventfree or high-solids epoxy coatings.   The fact that these systems make possible the application of hard, highly resistant films in one coat has stimulated their use in a growing number of applications.

Advantages of the solventless coatings are (*1*) high buildup in a single application; (*2*) minimization of pin holes and other surface defects due to the absence of solvents; (*3*) excellent heat and chemical resistance; and (*4*) lower application cost per mil of coating applied.

Disadvantages of the solventless coatings are (*1*) poor impact resistance and flexibility; (*2*) short pot life; and (*3*) increased sensitivity to relative humidity.   Impact resistance and flexibility can be improved by the use of modifiers, but only at the expense of reduced chemical resistance.

The problem of short pot life has been attacked from two different approaches.   One approach has been the development of proper equipment, such as catalyst guns, in which the components are mixed in the correct proportion in the nozzle or by making use of a double head through which exterior mixing takes place in a converging spray.

The other approach has been in the development of complex curing agents which give fairly long pot life in the resin compared to conventional hardeners, but cure in a short time when applied in films.   *Ketimines* are examples of this type of curing agent.   Ketimines are prepared by reacting a ketone with a diamine and removing the water formed.

$$2\ R'\!-\!\overset{\overset{\displaystyle O}{\|}}{C}\!-\!R'' + H_2N\!-\!R\!-\!NH_2 \rightleftharpoons \overset{\displaystyle R'}{\underset{\displaystyle R''}{C}}\!=\!N\!-\!R\!-\!N\!=\!\overset{\displaystyle R'}{\underset{\displaystyle R''}{C}} + 2\ H_2O$$

The reaction is reversible, and the curing action of these ketimine-type materials is dependent upon liberation of the amine by moisture or water.   Since the moisture is generally picked up from the atmosphere, the curing rate depends on humidity and film thickness at which the coating is applied, and also on the method of application.   In addition, water (to promote the right-to-left reaction) and aliphatic polyamines may be added as accelerators. Phenol may also be used as a catalyst to promote the curing. Ketimines with phenol as the accelerator develop sufficient hardness for handling after drying overnight and are completely cured within one week.

Ketimine curing agents are very useful in the formulation of solventless coating systems. It may be argued that since a ketone is liberated as a by-product of the curing agent, this not a truly solventless coating system. However, the release of the ketone is so slow that it does not build up to a high concentration, and only moderate ventilation is required to keep the atmosphere below the maximum safe level.

Structural Plastics. Of all thermosetting resins, the epoxies are probably more widely used in different application areas than any others. There are resin/hardener systems which cure at room temperature, and there are systems which require extreme heat cures to develop optimum properties. The selection of various hardeners, modifiers, and fillers gives the desired properties. Formulations can be flexible, rigid, tough, soft, or hard, or can have any required properties. Formulations based on epoxy resins can be made to be heat conductive, or can serve as excellent thermal and electrical insulators. Because of the wide versatility of these materials, their use in structural plastics is most easily described by giving specific data for each of the various application areas.

Casting and Plastic Tooling. Epoxy resins are the most widely used materials for plastic tooling. Liquid epoxy resins are easily combined with room-temperature curing hardeners such as aliphatic polyamines. With the addition of inert fillers and a variety of modifiers, these resins find wide use in the aircraft and automotive tooling industries. Epoxies are also used as a printing plate material to replace metals in press molds for short runs. The resins cure without evolution of volatile matter and in many cases without pressure. They are specifically noted for their negligible shrinkage and long-term dimensional stability. Tooling, jig and fixtures, and prototypes made from epoxy resins are resistant to most environments and this contributes strongly to their stability over long periods of time. High mechanical strength

Table 4. Hardeners for Liquid Epoxy Resins

Hardener	Form	Recommended concn, phr[a]	Useful pot life[b] at 25°C	Typical cure schedule	ASTM deflection temp, °C
triethylenetetramine	low-viscosity liquid	10–13	30 min	7 days at 25°C or 2 hr at 100°C	115–120
liquid polyamide	high-viscosity liquid	40	75–120 min	2–8 hr at 75–150°C	110
modified polyamines, safety hardeners	low-viscosity liquids	20–30	30–45 min	7 days at 25°C or 2 hr at 100°C	80–120
borontrifluoride monoethylamine	solid	3–5	1–3 mo	1 hr at 150°C or 30 min at 175°C	150–170
m-phenylenediamine	solid	13–15	3 hr	3 hr at 150°C	165
methylendomethylene-tetrahydrophthalic anhydride	low-viscosity liquid	80–90	24 hr	2 hr at 140°C + 2 or more hr at 180–200°C	150–170

[a] Parts per 100 parts resin (by wt).   [b] One-lb mass.

is also characteristic of these resins and gives an added factor to their usefulness. Table 4 contains examples of some of the more widely used curing-agent combinations.

Aliphatic polyamines combined with epoxy resins result in exothermic reactions, the degree of which is dependent on the choice of hardeners and on the mass of reactants. Inert fillers extend the working life, substantially reduce costs, dissipate exotherm, and reduce shrinkage. Commonly used fillers include silica, calcium carbonate, and metal powders.

Casting compositions based on epoxy resins are also used widely in potting and encapsulating of electrical components (see Embedding). Electrical-casting compositions based on epoxy resins are characterized by high volume resistivity, low dielectric constant, and excellent dielectric strength. In addition, the characteristic high mechanical strength makes these materials a natural choice for electrical insulation for certain purposes. Cast materials are widely used in the manufacture of coils, transformers, motors, and other heavy electrical parts.

In addition to casting formulations, these materials are also widely used as sealing compounds and electrical impregnating varnishes.

Laminating Applications. Laminating covers wet lay-up as well as dry lay-up or "prepreg" uses. The prepreg method is most popular where it is advantageous to apply the resin to the reinforcing material for later use. Wet lay-up is used for on-the-job applications. Epoxy resins have long been used in the preparation of printed circuit boards. When compared to other thermosetting resins, epoxies are particularly noted for their interlaminar adhesion and low shrinkage. Various military specifications cover the types and grades which are made. (See Laminated and reinforced plastics.)

In laminating applications other than electrical printed circuit boards, epoxy resins are used for specific structural applications where maximum advantage can be taken of their properties. In general, reinforced plastic epoxy resins have only specialized uses since they have limited decorative appeal and cannot compare in price with polyester resin formulations in the production of small boats and building panels. Some properties of epoxy resin–glass cloth laminates are listed in Table 5.

During the last three years, there has been a growing interest in the field of filament winding. This new method of producing reinforced plastic lends itself for the first time to automation in the manufacture of certain products such as reinforced pipe and tank. Epoxy resins have proved to be the preferred material for these applications because of their unique ability to bond with a reinforcing material which in this case is primarily glass filament.

The rapid growth of filament winding as a method of producing reinforced

Table 5. Properties of Epoxy Resin–Glass Cloth Laminates

Mol wt of resin used	Curing agent	Phr[a]	Resin content, %	Time, min	Cure temp, °F	Flexural strength Ultimate psi	Flexural strength Modulus, psi $\times 10^6$
350–420	diethylenetriamine	8	34	30	240	74,000	1.9
350–420	3-diethylamino-1-propyl-amine	3	33	30	240	83,000	3.6
350–420	m-phenylenediamine	14	30	60	212	89,000	3.7
900–1,050	dicyandiamide	4	28	30	345	84,000	3.7

[a] Parts per 100.

plastics was primarily due to military interest in producing lightweight, high-strength missile cases, but filament winding for commercial end uses already represents an extremely large and attractive market. For the majority of applications, the wet lay-up process shows definite economic advantages. For this process, liquid resins are generally used either with liquid aromatic amines or with liquid acid anhydride curing agents. For the dry lay-up or prepreg process, generally solid resins are used, usually with an aromatic amine curing agent that will form a suitable "B" stage with the resin so that the preimpregnated glass roving has some storage stability. Although the major market in nonmilitary areas for filament wound articles is pipe and chemical storage tanks, there are a number of new interesting end uses, eg, in the electrical industries for such items as electrical conduit, transformer bobbins, and electrical high-tension insulators; sporting goods such as shotgun barrels, golf club shafts, and fishing rods are another growing end use.

Adhesives. Epoxy resins possess a number of unusual properties which make them versatile in the formulation of epoxy adhesives. Some of their more important properties are the following:

1. A wide variety of curing agents are available, and epoxy resins are compatible with a wide range of modifiers; hence, the properties of an adhesive formulation can be engineered to widely diversed specifications.

2. Epoxy resin adhesives are 100% reactive, and no volatiles are produced during the cure, as is the case with phenolic adhesives.

3. Cured epoxy resins have approximately seven times greater strength than phenolic resins.

4. Epoxy resins have very good flow characteristics; the adhesives require only slight pressure to force them into place. For these reasons only contact pressure is required during metal-to-metal bonding with epoxy adhesives.

Epoxy resin adhesives can be used for a variety of applications, including metal-to-metal, glass-to-glass, and wood-to-wood bonding, printed circuits, and body solders.

Heat resistance can be built into an epoxy adhesive formulation by use of aromatic amine hardeners such as m-phenylenediamine, methylenedianiline, diaminodiphenyl sulfone, or liquid eutectic mixtures of these hardeners (13). In addition, it has been found that certain anhydrides such as HET anhydride (the anhydride of HET-Diol, see Vol. 5, p. 241) will impart high tensile shear strengths at elevated temperatures to an epoxy adhesive formulation.

In addition to the conventional bisphenol A/epichlorohydrin epoxy resins, novolac epoxy resins can also be used in adhesive formulations. They are generally employed both for film-supported and liquid adhesive systems. Generally, the novolac-based adhesives give better resistance to high temperatures than the conventional bisphenol A/epichlorohydrin type. Excellent retention of physical properties at temperatures as high as 260°C have been noted with novolac epoxy-based adhesive systems.

Blends of nylon and epoxy resin systems have been developed for bonding metal skins to honeycomb core and also for metal-to-metal bonding. These adhesives can be applied either as a dry film or as solvent solutions. The dry films form excellent fillets between the honeycomb core and the metal skin during the cure cycle. Adhesives of this type retain their strength in environments ranging from −400°F to +200°F (14). The flexibility of the nylon imparts greater shear strength to the epoxy system and produces a system with unusual low-temperature properties (15).

In the formulation of an epoxy resin adhesive, the choice of curing agent and modifiers is very important, but it is equally important for the substance to be bonded to have the proper type of surface treatment. This could mean the difference between success and failure of any epoxy system (16).

Bibliography

"Epoxy Resins" in *ECT* 1st ed., Suppl. 1, pp. 312–329, by R. A. Coderre, Shell Chemical Corporation.

1. Ger. Pat. 676,117; U.S. Pat. 2,136,928 (Nov. 15, 1938), P. Schlack (to I. G. Farben).
2. Ger. Pat. 749,912; U.S. Pat. 2,324,483 (July 20, 1943), P. Castan (to Ciba).
3. U.S. Pat. 2,456,408 (Dec. 14, 1948), S. O. Greenlee (to Devoe & Raynolds).
4. H. Batzer and E. Nikles, *Chimia (Aarau)* **16**, 57 (1962).
5. H. Dannenberg and W. R. Harp, *Anal. Chem.* **28**, 86 (1956).
6. W. Fisch and W. Hofmann, *J. Polymer Sci.* **16**, 201 (1955).
7. L. Schecter and J. Wynstra, *Ind. Eng. Chem.* **48**, 86 (1956).
8. L. Schecter, J. Wynstra, and R. Kurkjy, *Ind. Eng. Chem.* **48**, 94 (1956).
9. Technical Service Note No. 503, Ciba Products Company.
10. Technical Service Note No. 505, Ciba Products Company.
11. G. Somerville and D. Herr, *Ind. Eng. Chem.* **49**, 1080 (1957).
12. "Determination of the Epoxy Content of Epoxy Resins," *ASTM Method D 1652–62T*.
13. I. Skeist, *Handbook of Adhesives*, Reinhold Publishing Corp., New York, 1962.
14. H. Burgman, *Machine Design*, Nov. 1963.
15. R. Kausen, *Seventh National SAMPE Symposium, Los Angeles, Calif., May 1964*.
16. Technical Service Note No. 92, Ciba Products Company.

JOSEPH R. WESCHLER
Ciba Products Company

ERBIUM. See Rare earth metals.

ERYTHRITOL, $(CH_2OHCHOH)_2$. See Alcohols, higher, polyhydric.

ERYTHRITOL TETRANITRATE, $(CH_2NO_3CHNO_3)_2$. See Explosives.

ESSENTIAL OILS. See Flavors; Oils, essential; Perfumes.

ESTER GUMS. See Rosin and rosin derivatives.

ESTERIFICATION

This article describes methods for the production of carboxylic esters, compounds of the type RCOOR′. For the properties of these compounds see Esters, organic. For esters of inorganic acids see such articles as Phosphoric acids; Sulfuric acid.

The most usual method for the preparation of esters is the reaction of a carboxylic acid and an alcohol with elimination of water. Esters are also formed by a number of other reactions, including the use of acid anhydrides, acid chlorides, amides, nitriles, unsaturated hydrocarbons, ethers, aldehydes and ketones, and by dehydration of alcohols. For ester preparation by alcoholysis and acidolysis see Ester interchange.

Reviews of esterification are given in references 1–3, in which more detailed discussions can be found of the work described here.

Commercial Importance of Esters

A survey of 1964 chemical buyer guides and manufacturers' literature indicates that more than 80 chemical companies supply over 400 esters of carboxylic acids of definite chemical compositions for resale in the industry. Table 1 lists some of the more important commercially available esters arranged by acids and alcohols.

The phthalates are the most important esters from a volume standpoint. The 1962 preliminary tariff production figures indicated 385,000,000 pounds of phthalate plasticizers were produced; of this total, di-2-ethylhexyl phthalate accounted for 44% and diisodecyl and diisooctyl phthalates each for about 16%. More than 40 different phthalates are commercially available, including mixed esters such as amyl decyl phthalate, butyl benzyl phthalate, ethyl phthalyl ethyl glycolate, etc. The longer aliphatic chain phthalates are primarily used as flexibilizing plasticizers for poly(vinyl chloride) plastics. The intermediate-chain-length esters from dibutyl phthalate through butyl octyl phthalate and dicyclohexyl phthalate are used as plasticizers in poly(vinyl acetate) emulsion systems. The lower aliphatic alcohol esters (methyl, ethyl, and butyl) and the glycolate–phthalate esters are used for plasticizing cellulose esters. Diallyl phthalate is the monomer used for manufacture of the allyl thermosetting resins; it is cured by the addition of peroxide catalysts to form highly cross-linked heat-resistant and chemically resistant resins of exceptional electrical properties and dimensional stability.

The acetates of most alcohols are also commercially available and have diverse uses. Because of their high solvent powers, ethyl, isopropyl, butyl, isobutyl, amyl, and isoamyl acetates are used in cellulose nitrate and other lacquer-type coatings; butyl and hexyl acetates are excellent solvents for polyurethan coating systems. Ethyl, isobutyl, amyl, and isoamyl acetates are frequently used as components in flavorings, while isopropyl, benzyl, octyl, geranyl, linalyl, and menthyl acetates are important additives in perfumes.

Of the formates, methyl and ethyl formates are used as fumigants and larvicides. Ethyl, isobutyl, and isoamyl formates find use in flavorings.

The acrylates are primarily used as monomers for the production of polymeric latexes; frequently, blends may be made by copolymerization of methyl acrylate, ethyl acrylate, and vinyl acetate, to give terpolymer latexes. Physical blends of polymer latexes may also be made. To provide flexibility, small amounts of higher acrylates may be incorporated; copolymerization of methacrylates with acrylates improves the

Table 1. Commercially Available Esters

	methyl	vinyl	ethyl	allyl	propyl	isopropyl	butyl	isobutyl	amyl	isoamyl	phenyl	hexyl	cyclohexyl	benzyl	phenylethyl	octyl	isooctyl	2-ethylhexyl	cinnamyl	nonyl	geranyl	linalyl	menthyl	decyl	isodecyl	cetyl
Monoesters																										
formate	×	×	×					×		×				×	×	×			×		×	×				
acetate	×	×	×		×	×	×	×	×	×	×	×	×	×	×	×		×	×	×	×	×	×			
acrylate	×		×	×	×		×	×	×				×			×		×						×		
propionate	×	×	×				×	×						×	×	×			×		×	×				
lactate	×		×				×																			
crotonate	×	×	×	×																						
methacrylate	×		×	×			×	×				×	×													
butyrate	×	×	×				×	×	×	×				×		×		×	×		×					
isobutyrate			×					×								×						×				
caproate	×		×	×				×	×																	
caprylate	×		×	×																						
benzoate	×		×				×	×		×				×												
p-aminobenzoate	×		×		×		×	×																		
p-hydroxybenzoate					×		×																			
salicylate	×						×	×	×	×	×	×		×				×					×			
cinnamate	×		×				×							×												
laurate	×		×				×		×							×										
myristate	×		×			×	×		×																	×
palmitate	×		×			×											×									×
oleate	×		×		×	×	×																			
ricinoleate	×						×						×													
stearate	×	×	×			×	×	×	×							×										×
Diesters																										
oxalate			×	×			×																			
succinate			×	×	×		×							×		×	×	×								
fumarate			×	×			×										×	×								
maleate			×	×			×										×	×								
adipate	×		×	×			×	×		×		×				×	×	×		×				×	×	
phthalate	×		×	×			×	×			×	×	×			×	×	×		×				×	×	
azelate								×				×				×	×	×								
sebacate	×		×	×			×	×		×	×	×		×		×	×	×		×				×		

hardness of the copolymer. Methyl methacrylate is used as the monomer to produce Plexiglass and Lucite clear acrylic plastics.

The butyrates, isobutyrates, isovalerates, caproates, and caprylates are primarily used in flavorings. Ethyl, amyl, and geranyl butyrates are also used in perfumes. Isoamyl and menthyl valerates and stearates, p-aminobenzoates, p-hydroxybenzoates, and salicylates are widely used in cosmetics and pharmaceutics. The benzoates, cinnamates, and lower salicylates are also used in flavorings and perfumes.

Reaction Between Organic Acids and Alcohols

In the esterification of organic acids with alcohols, it has been shown that the union is between acyl and alkoxy groups, that is, between $RC(=O)-$ and $-OR'$ rather than between $RC(=O)O-$ and $-R'$. Reid demonstrated this in 1910 by comparison of the reaction of thiobenzoic acid with ethyl alcohol with that of benzoic acid and ethanethiol (ethyl mercaptan).

$$C_6H_5C(=O)SH + C_2H_5OH \rightarrow C_6H_5C(=O)OC_2H_5 + H_2S$$
$$C_6H_5C(=O)OH + C_2H_5SH \rightleftharpoons C_6H_5C(=O)SC_2H_5 + H_2O$$

By esterifying benzoic acid with methanol containing heavy oxygen, Roberts and Urey in 1938 obtained water of ordinary isotopic composition, showing that the oxygen in the water formed in the reaction results entirely from the organic acid.

Effect of Structure on Esterification. The rate at which different alcohols and acids are esterified, as well as the extent of the reaction, is dependent upon the structure of the molecules and types of radicals present. Specific data on rates of reaction and mechanisms are discussed under Kinetic considerations, while data on extent of reaction are presented under Equilibrium constants.

Over the period 1879–1883, Menschutkin studied the general effects of structure on the esterification of a number of acids and alcohols. With acetic acid at 155°C, the primary alcohols were found to esterify most rapidly and completely, with methanol giving the highest yield and the most rapid reaction. Ethyl, n-propyl, and n-butyl alcohols reacted with about equal velocities and limits. Under the same conditions, the secondary alcohols were much slower reacting and had lower limits of esterification; however, wide variations were noted among the different members of this series. The tertiary alcohols were very slow in reacting and the limits were generally low (1–10% conversion at equilibrium). Tests with isobutyl alcohol at 155°C and various acids showed that those acids containing a straight chain (acetic, propionic, and butyric) and phenylacetic and β-phenylpropionic acids were esterified readily. Formic acid had the fastest initial rate of reaction, but the esterification limits of the acids were noted to increase with increasing molecular weight of the acid. The introduction of a branched chain in the acid decreased the rate of esterification, and two branches caused a still greater retarding effect. Double bonds also had a retarding influence. However, the limits of esterification of these substituted acids were higher than for the normal straight-chain acids. Aromatic acids (benzoic and p-toluic) also were slow-reacting but had high limits.

More recent determinations have shown some deviations from these early studies. Micheal and Wolgast, in 1909, studied esterifications with trichloroacetic acid and showed that for the normal aliphatic alcohols the speed of esterification was increased with increasing length of the carbon chain of the alcohol; thus n-octyl and cetyl alcohols reacted with this acid at two to four times the speed of ethyl alcohol at 25 and

50°C. *tert*-Butyl and *tert*-amyl alcohols reacted faster with trichloroacetic acid than secondary alcohols such as isopropyl, *sec*-butyl, *sec*-amyl, and *sec*-octyl alcohols. Tests with related alcohols and different acids in benzene solution at 100°C gave the velocity constants shown in Table 2(4). It is evident that under certain conditions the secondary and tertiary alcohols may be very reactive. The comparative behavior is not determined by a single component but rather by all of the components in the system: the alcohol, the acid, the solvent, and sometimes the catalyst.

Table 2. Velocity Constants of Reactions of Acids with Alcohols in Benzene Solution at 100°C

Alcohol	Velocity constant		
	Acetic acid	Trichloroacetic acid	Hydrochloric acid
ethyl alcohol	0.00417	0.02550	0.0348
isopropyl alcohol	0.00237	0.00644	0.0477
tert-butyl alcohol	0.00212	0.00692	0.2670
benzyl alcohol	0.00244	0.00815	0.0372
benzohydrol (diphenylmethanol)	0.00141	0.00127	0.6060
triphenylmethanol	0.00040	0.00197	2.8480

Cauquil studied the esterification of cyclohexanol and various methyl- and ethyl-substituted derivatives with acetic acid at 95°C (5). The initial velocity of the reaction was practically the same in each system, but the completeness of the esterification was influenced by the position of the substituent group and was less than with the corresponding open-chain secondary alcohols.

Sudborough and co-workers in the period 1909–1912 studied the influence of substituents on the rate of esterification of aliphatic acids. The nitrile group has a pronounced inhibiting effect. With the chloroacetic acids, the velocity decreases with increased substitution. From tests on twenty-five substituted acrylic acids, Sudborough and Gittens concluded that an α,β-unsaturated acid is esterified much less easily than its saturated analog. A triple bond in the α,β position has about the same effect as a double bond. A β,γ double bond has less of a retarding action. If the double bond is sufficiently removed (as in erucic and brassidic acids) no effect is noted. Conjugated double bonds, when one is in the α,β position, have a great inhibiting effect. Cis-substituted acids esterify more slowly than the trans isomers.

On the basis of studies on the esterification of forty-six organic acids with anhydrous ethyl alcohol and hydrogen chloride catalyst, in 1925, Bhide and Sudborough made the following observations: The rate of esterification of the straight-chain fatty acids from propionic through stearic is substantially constant. Branching of the chain causes retardation, especially with acids below valeric. In the saturated dibasic acids, the rate of esterification increases to a maximum with glutaric acid, and then falls. The ease of esterification of the cycloparaffin monocarboxylic acids increases in the order C_3, C_7, C_6, C_5, and C_4 rings; with the exception of cyclopropanecarboxylic acid, these are esterified more rapidly than the corresponding open-chain acids. Structural effects were also studied in the cyclohexane- and cyclohexenecarboxylic acid series.

Smith has investigated the effect of branching on the rate of esterification of aliphatic acids (6). Ordinarily, substitutions must take place in the α or β position to affect the reaction velocity. The greater the number of alkyl substituents, the greater is the effect on the retardation of the rate of reaction and the greater is the increase in the activation energy for the reaction. If considerable substitution in the α and β positions has already been made, substitution in the γ position may have some effect on the esterification rate. Smith concludes that acids with more than four substituents should be practically unesterifiable under ordinary conditions.

The effect of substitutions in the benzene ring on the rate of esterification of aromatic acids has been studied by Hartman and co-workers. Substitutions that displace electrons toward the carboxyl group diminish the rate of reaction (7). The substitution of fluoro, methoxy, or ethoxy groups in the o-position has an accelerating action, whereas iodo, bromo, nitro, or methyl groups produce retardation. The influence of groups in the m- and p-positions is not nearly so marked. Disubstituted benzoic acids are readily esterified, except those with 2,6 substitutions (8).

Kinetic Considerations. The kinetics of the acid-catalyzed reaction between organic acids and alcohols has been best explained on the basis of the Goldschmidt equation, which was developed by Goldschmidt and numerous co-workers over the period 1895–1929 and has been further studied by Smith (6). Equations were developed based on the assumption that the hydrogen atoms from the catalyst first react with the alcoholic hydroxyl to form a complex ROH_2^+ and the latter then reacts with the organic acid:

$$R'COOH + ROH_2^+ \rightarrow R'COOR + H_3O^+$$

The rate of esterification is proportional to the product of the concentrations of the organic acid and the activated alcohol complex:

$$d[R'COOR]/dt = k[R'COOH][ROH_2^+]$$

Since water is formed in the reaction, it will slow up the rate of esterification by reducing the number of available hydrogen ions according to the equilibrium between the alcohol and water complexes.

$$ROH_2^+ + H_2O \rightleftharpoons H_3O^+ + ROH$$

The equilibrium constant for this reaction is

$$K = [H_3O^+][ROH]/[ROH_2^+][H_2O]$$

If the concentration of alcohol may be considered constant, a factor r may be defined as

$$r = [ROH]/K = [ROH_2^+][H_2O]/[H_3O^+]$$

Assuming that all the hydrogen ions will be bound either as alcohol or as water complexes, the above equation for r may be expressed as

$$r = [ROH_2^+][H_2O]/([total\ H^+] - [ROH_2^+])$$

Solving for the concentration of alcohol complex,

$$[ROH_2^+] = r[total\ H^+]/(r + [H_2O])$$

Substituting this value in the rate equation gives

$$d[R'COOR]/dt = k[R'COOH]\,r\,[total\ H^+]/(r + [H_2O])$$

If the original concentration of the organic acid is taken as a, and x is the concentration of ester formed at time t and no water is present at the start, this relation reduces to

$$dx/dt = k(a - x)r(catalyst)/(r + x)$$

Integrating the above equation and setting $x = 0$ when $t = 0$, and solving for k, gives

$$k = ((r + a)\ln[a/(a - x)] - x)/((catalyst)\,rt)$$

The value of r must be determined empirically by substituting two values of t with the corresponding x values, setting these two equations equal to each other, and solving for r. The value of r is independent of the acid and concentration of acid, but will vary with different alcohols and with temperature. Data for r for methanol are shown below (9).

Temperature, °C	r, mole/liter
0	0.11
20	0.20
30	0.25
40	0.32
50	0.42

Values of k obtained from this equation are generally constant up to 80–90% completion of the esterification (based on organic acid, as the alcohol is taken in large excess); due to the reverse hydrolysis reaction, the values of k drop off at higher extent of reaction. Several other investigators in addition to Goldschmidt have tested this equation on a large number of esterifications at 25°C. Smith and Reichardt have applied it at temperatures of 20–50°C, and over this range found that a plot of the logarithm of the rate constant versus the reciprocal of the absolute temperature is a straight line with an activation energy of 10,000 cal/mole for acids from formic through caproic ($C_5H_{11}COOH$) and pelargonic ($C_8H_{17}COOH$) with methanol and hydrogen chloride as catalyst (9). Concentrations of 0.1–0.5 mole/liter of the organic acid were used.

The Goldschmidt equation, however, does not completely describe the effect of catalyst concentration on the rate constant. Smith and Reichardt cite the following trend noted with $0.1N$ acetic acid in dry methanol at 30°C:

Concentration HCl, N	k, liter/(mole)(sec)
0.1	0.0704
0.0075	0.0856
0.0050	0.0902
0.0025	0.0941

Unfortunately, the Goldschmidt equation cannot be applied to technical esterification reactions, as most of the kinetic studies were carried out with very large excess of the alcohol (generally about fifty moles of alcohol per mole of organic acid), at relatively low temperatures, and with relatively low catalyst concentrations compared with commercial processes. An application of kinetic principles to industrial reactions will often prove very useful. General statements have been made that the rate of esterification with acid catalysts is proportional to the acid or hydrogen-ion concentrations, as well as the concentration of the alcohol and organic acid. The effect of temperature on the reaction rate is given by the well-known Arrhenius equation. As will be shown, these various factors are interrelated and may be used to predict optimum operational conditions for the production of a given ester if the necessary data are available. The following conditions must be known: (1) the order of the reaction under the conditions to be used; (2) a mathematical relation involving the yield of ester with time; and (3) an empirical equation relating the reaction-rate constant with temperature, catalyst concentration, and proportions of reactants.

It should be pointed out that all esterification reactions do not necessarily permit mathematical treatment. Thus Shlechter, Othmer, and Marshak, in studying the esterification of 2,3-butanediol and acetic acid with sulfuric acid catalyst, found that the reaction occurs through two pairs of consecutive, reversible reactions of approximately equal speeds. However, these reactions do not conform to any simple first-, second-, or third-order equation, even in the early stages (10).

Leyes and Othmer have studied the kinetics of the reaction of n-butyl alcohol with acetic acid over the range of 0–120°C using sulfuric acid as catalyst, with molar ratio of n-butyl alcohol to acetic acid varied from 3–19.6 and catalyst concentration from 0–0.14% by weight (11). The order of this reaction is influenced by temperature and catalyst concentration. Thus, at 100°C with 5 moles of alcohol per mole of acid and no catalyst, straight-line plots were obtained for first-, second- and third-order reactions over an 8-hr reaction period (32% conversion of acid to ester). At 100°C and low catalyst concentration (0.0147%), a second- or third-order reaction is indicated, but above 0.015% catalyst well-defined straight-line plots were obtained for a second-order reaction up to 70–80% conversion of the acetic acid. With 0.03% catalyst and 5 moles of alcohol per mole of acid, the order of the reaction is not ascertainable at 0 and 30°C, but at 100°C or higher the esterification is bimolecular (second order) up to 80–85% completion.

The rate equation, $dX/dt = k(A - X)^2$, where dX/dt = velocity of reaction, X = amount of acetic acid transformed (in moles), A = amount of acetic acid present at start (in moles), and k = reaction-rate constant, fitted the experimental data for all runs up to about 75–85% conversion. Thus, in the initial stages of the reaction, the rate of the esterification is proportional to the square of the acetic acid concentration. It is interesting to note that only at conversions above 75–85% does the general reversible reaction, generally given for the esterification of an alcohol with an acid, $dX/dt = k_1(A - X)(B - X) - k_2X(W + X)$, (where k_1 = esterification reaction-rate constant, k_2 = hydrolysis-rate constant, and W = water present at start, in moles) describe the course of the reaction.

Plots of the rate constant for various runs against the percent of sulfuric acid catalyst at constant molar proportions of reactants at 100°C and of the ratio of the rate constant to the catalyst concentration versus the proportions of the reactants at 100°C both gave linear relations. A plot of the logarithm of the rate constant versus the reciprocal of the absolute temperature at constant catalyst concentration and proportions of reactants gave a straight line over the range 100–120°C, but at lower temperatures (0 and 30°C) deviations were noted. Based on the experimental data, an empirical equation was obtained, which permits estimation of the value of the rate constant with an average deviation of 15.3% from the molar ratio of reactants, catalyst concentration, and temperature.

Berman, Melnychuk, and Othmer have carried out similar studies on the formation of n-butyl phthalate over the temperature range 80–150°C with sulfuric acid catalyst (12). The reaction of phthalic anhydride to monobutyl phthalate is complete in 10 min at 100°C with 1% of catalyst by weight, and hence is no factor in technical esterifications. The rate of reaction of the monobutyl phthalate with excess butyl alcohol to form the diester was determined to be of the second order. The rate of reaction was proportional to the square of the monoester concentration up to 85% completion: $dX/dt = k(M - X)^2$, where M = concentration of monobutyl phthalate at start (in moles), which integrates into $kt = X/[M(M - X)]$.

Similar relations were found between the rate constant, catalyst concentration, proportions of reactants, and temperature, as were found with the esterification to *n*-butyl acetate. The rate constant was related to the catalyst concentration, proportions of reactants, and temperature, by an empirical equation, which fitted the experimental data within an accuracy of 8% over the range 80–150°C with 3–30 moles of butyl alcohol per mole of monobutyl phthalate and 0.0–3.6% catalyst by weight.

The kinetic data for the reaction of methanol with 85% and 44% (technical grade) lactic acid were determined by Troupe and Kobe with sulfuric acid as catalyst using molar ratios between 1 and 4 of methanol to lactic acid (13). To express the effect of reaction variables on the rate constant, k, two empirical equations were developed, one for catalyst concentrations below 0.417% and the other for concentrations between 0.417 and 1%, because of reactions of the sulfuric acid with the technical lactic acid. High ratios of methanol to lactic acid and short contact times at high reaction temperatures favored high yields of ester and minimum decomposition. Troupe and DiMilla carried out similar kinetic studies with ethyl alcohol–lactic acid systems (14).

Othmer and Rao investigated the kinetics of the esterification of *n*-butyl alcohol and oleic acid with sulfuric acid catalyst and found the reaction to be second order up to 92–97% esterification (15). The reaction rate is proportional to the catalyst concentration, to the molar ratio of reactants, and to the negative reciprocal of the temperature from 100–150°C. An empirical equation predicting the rate constant within a 4% error for molar ratios of butyl alcohol to oleic acid up to 10:1, sulfuric acid concentrations of 0.5–1.2%, and for temperatures from 100–150°C was developed. Ling and Geankoplis carried out studies on the isobutyl alcohol–oleic acid system. With no catalyst present, *n*-butyl alcohol gave an initial reaction rate about 80% greater than isobutyl alcohol. The rate of reaction was second order and proportional to the square of the oleic acid concentration (16).

In the studies on butyl acetate and dibutyl phthalate, the mechanisms of the reactions are explained on the basis of a series of reactions involving the formation of butyl hydrogen sulfate, which ionizes to produce hydrogen ions, which react with excess alcohol molecules to form a complex as in the Goldschmidt equation mechanism. However, since monocarboxylic acids are known to exist as dimers in liquid and solid states, two molecules of the acid will be involved per mole of the activated alcohol complex. This explains the reason for the reaction rate being proportional to the square of the acetic acid or monobutyl phthalate concentrations.

Equilibrium Constants. The reaction between an organic acid and an alcohol to produce an ester and water according to the equation

$$R'COOH + ROH \rightleftharpoons R'COOR + H_2O$$

is a classical example of a reversible equilibrium. This was first demonstrated in 1862 by Berthelot and Péan de St. Gilles, who found that when equimolar quantities of ethyl alcohol and acetic acid were heated together the esterification stopped when about two-thirds of the acid had reacted. Similarly, when equimolar proportions of ethyl acetate and water were heated together, hydrolysis of the ester stopped when approximately one-third of the ester was hydrolyzed. By varying the molar ratios of alcohol to acid, yields of ester above 66% were obtained by displacement of the equilibrium. The results of these tests were reported to be in accordance with the mass-action law

$$K = [\text{ester}] \, [\text{water}]/[\text{acid}] \, [\text{alcohol}]$$

which states that the ratio of the concentrations of the products divided by the concentrations of the reactants is a constant, known as the equilibrium constant.

Poznanski, however, has questioned the accuracy of these early studies, pointing out that in 1883, Schwab found that the equilibrium "constant" for the reaction of ethyl alcohol and acetic acid varied from 1.0 to 6.8 (17). Swietoslawski used an ebullioscopic method to study this reaction and confirmed the effect of proportions of reactants on the equilibrium constant for the system (18). Their results for selected molar ratios of ethyl alcohol to acetic acid were as follows:

Alcohol-to-acid ratio	K (Poznanski)	K (Swietoslawski)
3:1	2.45	2.47
1:1	3.79	3.82
1:3	4.73	4.74

Coria has also studied this reaction and obtained the relation $K = 1.31 + 4.86C$, where C is the ratio of the number of moles of acetic acid to the total moles of acid and ethyl alcohol in the starting mixture (19).

Similar variations in the calculated equilibrium constant with proportions of reactants have been reported by Leyes and Othmer with n-butyl alcohol and acetic acid (11) and by Berman, Melnychuk, and Othmer with n-butyl alcohol and mono-n-butyl phthalate (12). Freas and Reid, in 1918, also had noted a slight gradual drop in the value of the equilibrium limits with increase in the ratio of the alcohol to acid in the esterification of benzoic and toluic acids with the lower aliphatic alcohols.

The catalyst may also affect the value of the equilibrium constant. With hydrogen chloride, Durruty found, the equilibrium constant for the esterification of ethyl alcohol and acetic acid increases in an approximately linear manner with increase in the initial catalyst concentration (20). Using perchloric acid as a catalyst for this reaction, Trimble and Richardson also reported a linear relation between the equilibrium constant and the mole percent of catalyst (21). Temperature and the presence of salts may also have an influence on the equilibrium constant.

Poznanski has also studied the effect of water on the equilibrium constant for the reaction of 1 mole ethyl alcohol, 1 mole acetic acid, and 23 moles water; he obtained a value of 3.56 for this mixture compared with 3.79 for the reaction with anhydrous materials (17).

The numerical value of the equilibrium constant is dependent upon the particular acid and alcohol involved in the esterification, and must be determined experimentally. Using the esterification data obtained by Menschutkin for acetic acid and various alcohols at 155°C, values for the respective equilibrium constants have been calculated, and vary between 5.24 for methyl acetate and 1.0 for 3-butenyl acetate for various primary and secondary alcohols (3). With tertiary alcohols, the equilibrium constants are much lower and range from 0.0192 for thymyl acetate to 0.000070 for 2-methyl-2-pentanol acetate. Similar studies by Menschutkin using isobutyl alcohol and various acids at 155°C gave equilibrium constants varying from 3.22 for isobutyl formate to 8.63 for isobutyl cinnamate, the general increase being parallel to the increase in molecular weight of the acid. With aromatic acids, equilibrium constants of 7.0 and 10.62 were calculated for isobutyl benzoate and p-toluate, respectively.

The importance of the numerical value of the equilibrium constant must not be overlooked in a technical process, as this determines the yield of ester attainable at equilibrium and also indicates what effect increasing the molar ratio of reactants

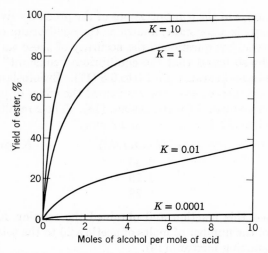

Fig. 1. Theoretical yields of ester obtainable with varying proportions of reactants for different values of equilibrium constant.

will have on the yield. Assuming the general esterification equation given above and that the value of the equilibrium constant does not vary with the molar proportions of reactants and temperature, a general equation may be written relating the yield and equilibrium constant. With no water or ester present at the start, for every mole of these products formed, one mole of acid and one mole of alcohol must have reacted. In the general case, with n moles of alcohol per mole of acid (or vice versa) these concentration terms may be substituted in the following equation for the equilibrium constant:

$$K = (X)(X)/(n - X)(1 - X) = X^2/(n - (n + 1)X + X^2)$$

where X = moles of water or ester formed at equilibrium and n = number of moles of alcohol per mole of acid at start. The theoretical yields of ester obtainable with varying proportions of reactants calculated from this equation are shown in Figure 1 for four values of the equilibrium constant. Thus, when $K = 10$ (esters of p-toluic acid with primary alcohols), with equivalent amounts of acid and alcohol, a yield of about 76% may be expected. Increasing the molar proportions of alcohol to acid (or vice versa) to 5:1 would give a 98% yield of ester; there is no advantage in increasing the ratio higher as the curve approaches the 100% yield as an asymptote. With an ester having a K value of unity (1-allyl-3-butenyl acetate) the optimum yield is obtained with about 3:1 molar ratio of reactants. Above this ratio, the yield of ester increases with increasing proportions, but the gain is too small to be economical in general. Esters with values of about 0.01 (phenyl acetate, thymyl acetate) show an increasing yield with increase in molar proportions of reactants, but with 10 moles of alcohol per mole of acid only 40% conversion to ester is attainable. With certain esters of tertiary alcohols (1,1-dimethyl-1-butanol acetate) having K values of 0.0001 or less, even with 10 moles of alcohol per mole of acid, a yield of only 3% ester is possible.

In these theoretical calculations, the acid or alcohol may be taken in excess with no difference in the yield of ester. However, from the data obtained by Poznanski, there is a distinct advantage in employing an excess of the acid rather than of the alcohol, as the numerical value of the equilibrium constant is increased by using an excess of acid and decreased with an excess of alcohol. Thus for ethyl acetate, with 3 moles of alcohol per mole of acetic acid, the equilibrium constant is 2.45, which is equivalent to 86% yield of ester. With 3 moles of acetic acid per mole of alcohol, the equilibrium constant is 4.73 and the corresponding yield of ester is 92%. Industrially, the relative costs of the reactants and ease of recovery are factors that must be considered along with the equilibrium constant in determining which reactant should be used in excess.

In general, esters having equilibrium constants below unity are not prepared by direct interaction of alcohol and acid; in these cases the acid anhydrides or acid chlorides are used. Reactions with the latter agents do not involve reversible equilibriums and hence will give high yields of esters.

Another important use of the equilibrium constant is to determine, in a given mixture of alcohol, ester, acid, and water, the course of the reaction. At equilibrium the rates of esterification and hydrolysis are equal and opposite. When the value calculated for an apparent equilibrium constant for a given four-component system is numerically less than the value for the true equilibrium constant, esterification is still possible and is occurring at a more rapid rate than hydrolysis. If the numerical value is greater than the actual value of the equilibrium constant, then hydrolysis must predominate.

Completing Esterification. Because the esterification of an alcohol and an organic acid involves a reversible equilibrium, these reactions will not go to completion. In the preceding section it was shown that yields in the order of 98% may be obtained from some systems with a large excess of one reactant. However, for industrial purposes conversions approaching 100% are desirable and can often be achieved by the simple method of upsetting the equilibrium by removing one of the products formed, either the ester or the water.

However, it must be understood that there is no universal manner in which all esterification reactions can be forced to completion; due consideration must be given to the particular system involved. In general, esterifications can be divided into three broad classes, depending upon the volatility of the esters.

Class 1. With esters of high volatility, such as methyl formate, methyl acetate, and ethyl formate, the boiling point of the ester is lower than that of the corresponding alcohol, and therefore the ester can be readily removed from the reaction mixture. The production of methyl acetate by the Backhaus distillation method is an example of this. Methanol and acetic acid are fed to a distilling column and the ester is removed as a vapor mixed with methanol from the top of the column. The water accumulates in the base of the column and is discharged. The ester and alcohol are separated by distillation in a second column.

Class 2. Esters of medium volatility are capable of removing the water formed by distillation. Examples of this type are propyl, butyl, and amyl formates, ethyl, propyl, butyl, and amyl acetates, and the methyl and ethyl esters of propionic, butyric, and valeric acids. In some cases, ternary mixtures of alcohol, ester, and water are formed. This group is capable of further subdivision: With ethyl acetate, all of the ester is removed as a vapor mixture with alcohol and part of the water, while the balance of the water accumulates in the system. With butyl acetate, on the other hand, all of the water formed is removed overhead with part of the ester and alcohol, and the balance of the ester accumulates in the system.

Class 3.   With esters of low volatility several possibilities exist.   In the case of esters of butyl and amyl alcohols, the water is removed as a binary mixture with the alcohol; the production of dibutyl phthalate is an illustration of this type.   To produce esters of the lower alcohols (methyl, ethyl, and propyl) it may be necessary to add a hydrocarbon such as benzene or toluene to increase the amount of water distilled over. With certain high-boiling alcohols (benzyl, furfuryl, and β-phenylethyl) an accessory liquid is always required to eliminate the water by distillation.

Use of Azeotropes (see Azeotropy).   With the aliphatic alcohols and esters of medium volatility, a variety of azeotropes are encountered on distillation.   Binary azeotropes may be formed between the alcohol and water, the alcohol and ester, and the ester and water.   Ternary azeotropes involving the alcohol, ester, and water are also possible.   In general, the ternary azeotropes have the lowest boiling points but the differences between the boiling points of the various combinations in some instances are very small.   Data are given in Table 3 for azeotropes encountered in the systems with ethyl acetate, *n*-butyl acetate, and isobutyl acetate (22).   It will be noted that the ester–water binaries have boiling points very close to those of the ternary mixtures; an extremely efficient fractionating column is required to obtain pure ternary azeotrope.

Table 3.   Compositions and Boiling Points of Azeotropic Mixtures Involving Esters, Alcohols, and Water (22)

Components	Boiling point, °C	Composition, wt %		
		Alcohol	Ester	Water
System: ethyl acetate–ethyl alcohol–water				
alcohol–water	78.15	95.57		4.43
ester–water	70.4		91.8	8.2
alcohol–ester	71.8	30.8	69.2	
alcohol–ester–water	70.3	9.0	83.2	7.8
System: *n*-butyl acetate–butyl alcohol–water				
alcohol–water	92.4	62.0		38.0
ester–water	90.2		73.3	26.7
alcohol–ester	117.2	47.0	53.0	
alcohol–ester–water	89.4	27.4	35.3	27.4
System: isobutyl acetate–isobutyl alcohol–water				
alcohol–water	89.92	66.7		33.3
ester–water	87.45		80.5	19.5
alcohol–ester	107.6	95	5	
alcohol–ester–water	86.8	23.1	46.5	30.4

With the higher-boiling, nonvolatile esters, binary azeotropes of the alcohol and water may be utilized for completion of the reaction.   All of the alcohols except methanol form binary azeotropes with water; data on some of these mixtures are given in Table 4.   The azeotropes formed by water with ethyl, *n*-propyl, isopropyl, allyl, and *tert*-butyl alcohols are single-phase; that is, on condensation of the vapor the components are completely miscible.   It is necessary to resort to other means to eliminate the water, for example, extraction with a water-insoluble solvent such as benzene or carbon tetrachloride, drying with potassium carbonate, or salting out.   The higher alcohols form azeotropes, which on condensation separate into two liquid phases; in such a case the alcohol-rich phase may be separated by further distillation into azeotrope and pure alcohol and the water-rich phase into azeotrope and water.

Table 4. Compositions and Boiling Points of Binary Azeotropes of Lower Alcohols with Water (22)

Alcohol	Boiling point, °C		Water, wt %
	Alcohol	Azeotrope	
methanol	64.7	none	
ethyl alcohol	78.3	78.15	4.43
allyl alcohol	96.9	88.89	27.7
n-propyl alcohol	97.2	87.72	28.31
isopropyl alcohol	82.44	80.38	12.10
n-butyl alcohol	117.75	92.4	38.0
isobutyl alcohol	108.0	89.92	33.3
sec-butyl alcohol	99.6	88.5	32.0
tert-butyl alcohol	82.55	79.91	11.76
2-ethoxyethanol (Cellosolve)	133	92.2	60
n-amyl alcohol	137.8	95.95	54.0
isoamyl alcohol	132.06	95.15	49.6
sec-amyl alcohol (2-pentanol)	119.3	92.5	38.5
tert-amyl alcohol (2-methyl-2-butanol)	102.25	87.35	27.5
1-ethyl-1-propanol (3-pentanol)	115.4	91.7	36.0
3-methyl-2-butanol	112.9	91.0	33
n-hexyl alcohol	157.85	97.8	75
2-ethyl-1-butanol	148.9	96.7	58

With the lower alcohols, an inert material, such as benzene, toluene, hexane, cyclohexane, or a chlorinated solvent is often added to form a mixture that will separate into two phases on condensation. These agents are also used with the nonvolatile alcohols to facilitate removal of water from the esterification mixture. Data on the binary azeotropes of some of these with water are given in Table 5. Some of these agents (benzene, toluene, and hexane) form ternary azeotropes with the alcohols, as is the case with ethyl and n-propyl alcohols.

Table 5. Azeotropic Data for Accessory Liquids Used in Esterifications (22)

Component	Nonaqueous component bp, °C	Azeotrope	
		Bp, °C	Water, wt %
benzene	80.2	69.25	8.83
toluene	110.7	84.1	19.6
hexane	68.95	61.55	
cyclohexane	80.75	68.95	9.0
carbon tetrachloride	76.75	66.0	4.1
chloroform	61.2	56.1	2.5

The use of steam, inert gas, or sulfur dioxide to promote agitation and to carry off the water formed in the esterification of fatty acids with polyhydric alcohols at temperatures of 450°F has also been suggested for completing esterification in systems of high-boiling reactants (23).

Removal of Water by Desiccants and Chemical Means. At times it may be necessary to utilize special means to remove the water of esterification for completion of the reaction. This is encountered in the production of acid-sensitive esters, where the use of a strong mineral acid is undesirable, or prolonged heating may contribute to the complete destruction of the ester or the formation of undesirable by-products or poor color. The chemical removal of the water has been suggested by Thielpape, who used calcium carbide supported in a thimble of a continuous extractor through which the condensed vapor from the esterification mixture was percolated (24).

Gordon and Aronowitz have obtained excellent yields of esters from 2-ethyl-1-hexanol (octyl alcohol) and polybasic acids using a column of activated bauxite (Florite) mounted over the reaction vessel to remove the water of reaction from the vapor by adsorption (25). With a 10% excess of alcohol and no catalyst, the following yields were reported:

Ester	Heating time, hr	Esterification, %
trioctyl aconitate	2	97.1
dioctyl maleate	3	96.9
dioctyl phthalate	4	90.4
didecyl maleate	2	98.8

Comparisons were made with esterifications using 1% sulfuric acid; in every case, the noncatalytic method gave better yields and lighter-colored products. Di-*n*-butyl phthalate could not be prepared in this manner, probably because of adsorption of the *n*-butyl alcohol by the desiccant (activated bauxite, activated alumina, and anhydrous calcium sulfate were tried). Aluminum oxide was also used as a desiccant with trioctyl aconitate but required the use of reduced pressures.

Catalysts. The choice of the proper catalyst for an esterification reaction is dependent upon several factors and will vary with the system under consideration. The most common catalysts used are strong mineral acids, but other agents, such as salts, silica gel, and cation-exchange resins are employed on occasion.

Considering first the mineral acids, hydrogen chloride is the most widely used in laboratory studies, but is not generally favored for plant operations because of its corrosiveness and process requirements. Anhydrous hydrogen chloride or commercial aqueous hydrochloric acid may be used. Side reactions involving the formation of alkyl chlorides are encountered when reaction times are prolonged. Tertiary alcohols react with hydrogen chloride to form alkyl chlorides rapidly.

Sulfuric acid is favored for most plant operations. However, in the case of some secondary alcohols such as cyclohexanol, as well as with tertiary alcohols, dehydration to the corresponding olefins, isomerization, or polymerization may result. In general, with aromatic acids, larger quantities of sulfuric acid are required than with the aliphatic acids. Benzenesulfonic acid and *p*-toluenesulfonic acid are frequently used as catalysts for esterifying long-chain fatty acids and aromatic acids.

Phosphoric acid is sometimes employed as a catalyst but is rather slow. Perchloric acid, hydrobromic acid, hydrofluoric acid, ethanesulfonic acid, chlorosulfonic acid, thionyl chloride, boron trifluoride, dihydroxyfluoboric acid, and silicon tetrafluoride have been used as esterification catalysts. Salts such as calcium perchlorate and magnesium, aluminum, ferric, zinc, cupric, and stannic chlorides, often exert a promoting effect on esterifications. Organotitanium and organozirconium compounds and salts of mercury, silver, cobalt, nickel, and cerium, are stated to be effective catalysts in the absence of mineral acids.

Acid-Regenerated Cation Exchangers. The use of acid-regenerated cation exchangers (see Ion exchange) as catalysts for effecting esterifications offers distinct advantages over conventional methods. During World War II, German chemists developed the use of agents of this type and were apparently on the verge of large-scale production (26).

The nature of the cation exchanger is of relatively minor importance as long as it contains strongly acidic groups. Wofatit resin was used in Germany; Amberlite IR-120, Dowex 30, and Zeo-Karb 225 have all been used in this country. Sussman found Zeo-Karb H, a sulfonated-coal type of cation exchanger superior to phenol–formaldehyde resins containing sulfonic acid groups (27).

Despite the higher cost compared with the ordinary catalysts, such as sulfuric or hydrochloric acid, the cation exchangers present several features that make their use economical. These materials are granular, insoluble masses that are readily separated from the reaction mixture by filtration and generally may be reused without regeneration or further treatment. The esters produced by these contact agents do not require neutralization, as is the case with inorganic acid catalysts. The esters generally are lighter in color than when sulfuric acid is used as catalyst. Amino acids and acid-sensitive materials that would be resinified by strong mineral acids may be prepared by this method. The ability to use these agents in fixed-bed operations makes them attractive for continuous processes.

Levesque and Craig have studied the kinetics of the esterification of n-butyl alcohol and oleic acid with a phenol–formaldehydesulfonic acid resin (similar to Amberlite IR-100) (26). The reaction is essentially second order after an initial slow period. The velocity constant is directly proportional to the surface area of the catalyst per unit weight of reactants.

The cation exchangers are used in the hydrogen condition; this is obtained by treatment with sulfuric acid in the usual manner. After the acid treatment, the exchanger is rinsed with demineralized water until the effluent rinse has a pH of between 6 and 7. Samples prepared in this manner contain very little free soluble acid; one gram of air-dried cation exchanger placed in distilled water at room temperature for 24 hr or

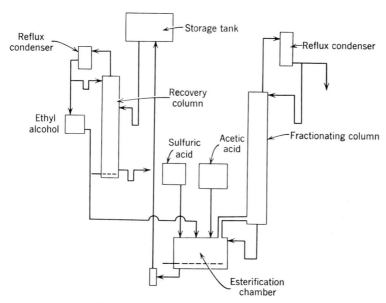

Fig. 2. Batch ethyl acetate process (2).

at 75°C for 4 hr, gave a solution containing less than 1 ppm acidity to methyl orange. The moisture content of the air-dried material was 15–30%.

Sussman has demonstrated the feasibility of re-use of the catalyst, obtaining yields of 95.8–99.5% n-butyl oleate in repeated operations (27). Others have also reported no decrease in catalytic activity observed after 20 uses.

Zeo-Karb H has been used for esterifying furfuryl alcohol and acetic acid. No evidence of resinification was noted but the yield of furfuryl acetate was only 21% after 24 hr of refluxing with benzene as entrainer. Triacetin (glyceryl triacetate) in 75% yield and glyceryl diacetate in 48% yield were also prepared with this catalyst (27).

A series of tests using Amberlite IR-120 (sulfonated polystyrene resin) to esterify diethylene glycol using toluene as the entrainer for removal of water gave the following results (28):

Acid	Diethylene glycol, mole/mole acid	Amberlite, g/100 g acid	Temperature, °C	Reaction time, hr	% mono-ester	% di-ester
lauric	1	7.5	140	18	24	71
lauric	4	15.5	130	10	71	21
lauric	6	7.5	140	18	86	11
lauric	12	15	132	18	100	
oleic	12	10.6	140	18	100	
stearic	12	8.9	150	18	100	
benzoic	2	24.6	140	4	75	

Batch Esterification. On a commercial basis, the production of esters may be carried out by batch or by continuous processing. In general, large-volume production favors continuous esterification methods. However, the older batch processing, based on the use of a still-pot reactor and an ordinary fractionating column (bubblecap or packed type), is still very extensively used.

Ethyl Acetate. Keyes has described the production of ethyl acetate, as shown in Figure 2. The esterification chamber is a cylindrical tank, or still pot, heated by a closed-coil steam pipe. The acetic acid, alcohol, and catalyst are fed into the still pot from storage tanks. The reaction charge consists of 10 parts of 8% acetic acid (obtained from fermentation), 10 parts of 95% alcohol, and 0.33 parts of 50–66°Bé sulfuric acid. The vapor from this mixture is fed into the base of a fractionating tower. The temperature at the top of this column is maintained at approximately 70°C, giving the ternary azeotropic mixture of about 83% ethyl acetate, 9% alcohol, and 8% water. The vapor is condensed, part of it is returned to the top plate of the column as reflux, and the remainder is drawn off to storage. The ternary azeotrope is satisfactory for many commercial purposes, but for those requiring an alcoholfree and waterfree ester, further purification is needed.

The reaction is carried out in the still pot until all of the acetic acid has reacted. The alcohol, sulfuric acid, and water mixture remaining in the still pot is pumped to a storage tank, from which it is fed into a second distilling column. This unit is heated by live steam introduced at the base and is used to recover the alcohol as the alcohol–water binary azeotrope. The vapor from the top plate is condensed, part is returned as reflux to the top of the column, and the balance is sent to the alcohol storage tank for

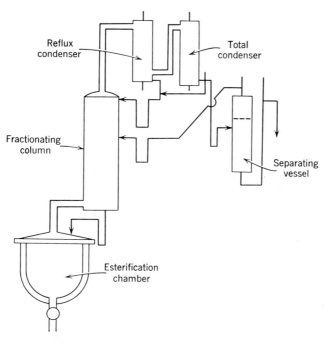

Fig. 3. Batch *n*-butyl acetate process (2).

reuse in esterification. Water and sulfuric acid are withdrawn from the bottom of the column and discharged to the sewer.

n-Butyl Acetate. Equipment used for the batch esterification to give butyl acetate is shown in Figure 3. Glacial acetic acid is mixed with an excess of butyl alcohol and a small amount of 66°Bé sulfuric acid in the still pot. The mixture is heated for several hours by means of a steam jacket to give esterification equilibrium. Any vapor from the reaction passes up through the column and is condensed and returned to the still pot. After the preliminary heating, slow rectification is permitted to remove the water already formed and thus increase the yield. Upon condensation of the vapor from the top of the column, two layers are formed; these are separated in a decanter. The upper layer consists of butyl acetate and butyl alcohol with a small amount of water and is continuously returned to the column as reflux. The lower layer consists of water with small amounts of ester and alcohol and is generally redistilled for recovery of these materials.

The esterification is continued until no more water separates. At this point, the temperature at the top of the column rises and the percentage of acetic acid in the distillate increases. In order to obtain a satisfactory product, it is necessary to neutralize the small amount of acid remaining in the still pot before further distillation. A solution of sodium hydroxide is added to the still pot and the mixture is allowed to stand to form a water layer, which is removed. The upper or ester layer is then washed with water and distilled to obtain a butyl acetate of 75–85% purity, the remainder being butyl alcohol. To obtain an ester of higher strength, Keyes recommends using acetic acid in a more dilute form than glacial acid and also taking the acid in slight excess rather than taking an excess of alcohol.

n-Butyl Tartrate. The production of butyl tartrate by batch method also may be accomplished with the same equipment used for *n*-butyl acetate (2). In this case, the reaction mixture should contain an excess of butyl alcohol and a small percentage of sulfuric acid. The mixture is heated for 24 hr, under total reflux. At the end of this time, rectification is started and the binary azeotrope of butyl alcohol and water is withdrawn from the top of the column. This mixture separates into two layers on condensation. The upper, or alcohol-rich, phase is returned to the column and the lower, or water-rich, phase is removed, and the butyl alcohol is recovered in subsequent operations.

When the reaction is completed, as shown by the lack of further water separation and by the increase in column temperature, the excess of alcohol is removed, generally by vacuum distillation. The impure ester is washed, rectified, and dried. The butyl tartrate obtained by this method will have a purity of 97–98%.

Continuous Esterification. Three major factors, namely, the law of mass action, the laws of kinetics, and the laws of distillation, all operate simultaneously in a process of this type. Esterification can occur only when the concentrations of the components give calculated values of the apparent equilibrium constant which are less than the value of the true equilibrium constant; otherwise hydrolysis must occur. The mathematical equations governing the rate of the reaction and the variation of the rate constant (as a function of such variables as temperature, catalyst strength, and proportions of reactants) control the kinetics of the liquid-phase reaction. The usual distillation laws must be modified, since most esterifications are exothermic and moles of reactants disappear while moles of products appear on each plate. Since these kinetic considerations are superimposed on distillation operations, each plate must be treated separately by successive calculations after the extent of conversion has been determined.

Leyes and Othmer have studied the continuous esterification of acetic acid in an excess of *n*-butyl alcohol with sulfuric acid catalyst using a four-plate single bubblecap column with reboiler (29). Tests were carried out over an 11-hr period using a feed of approximately 5 moles of butyl alcohol per mole of acetic acid and 0.03–0.13% sulfuric acid catalyst. After steady state was attained, samples were taken and the composition of the vapor and liquid leaving each plate, the liquid on each plate, the overhead, the feed, and the product, was determined. Radiation, heat, weight, and component balances were made. The rate constant and the theoretical extent of reaction were calculated for each plate, based on plate composition and on the total incoming material to the plate, both of which gave good agreement with the analytical data.

With 0.06% catalyst the total amount of reaction was distributed as follows: preheater, 7%; plate 1, 30%; plate 2, 20%; plate 3, 12%; plate 4, 6%; and reboiler, 25%. The large extent of reaction in the reboiler is due to its large hold-up volume (twice that of the plates); in some runs as little as 12% of the total reaction occurred on this plate. Contact time was varied from 25–47 min by varying the hold-up volume of the plates by over 300% and the feed rate by 250%, but this caused only minor changes in the extent of the reaction. However, varying the catalyst concentration from 0.03–0.13% caused the yield to be increased from 77.9 to 98.9% with 33–35 min contact time. Using experimental vapor–liquid equilibrium data in conjunction with kinetic data, plate-to-plate calculations were made (11). These indicated slightly over 6 plates required for 99% reaction compared with the 5 plates actually used.

Berman, Isbenjian, Sedoff, and Othmer extended the above studies to the continuous production of di-*n*-butyl phthalate using monobutyl phthalate and excess butyl alcohol with sulfuric acid catalyst (30). Feed compositions of 3–9 moles of butyl alcohol per mole of monoester were used with 0.5–2.0% sulfuric acid. By increasing the plate hold-up volume to 300%, the total time of contact was varied from 53–71.6 min, but this had relatively little effect on the yield of diester. Decreasing the ratio of alcohol to monoester in the feed gave an improvement in yield, but again the effect of catalyst concentration is demonstrated as being far more important. With contact times of 62–67 min, the yield of dibutyl phthalate was 54.8% with 0.5% catalyst, but 88.6% with 2% catalyst, which was the maximum effective limit, as above this value the corrosive effect of the acid on equipment and the cost or nuisance of its subsequent removal from the product are serious. Plate-to-plate calculations were made on this system using experimental vapor–liquid data and kinetic data of Berman, Melnychuk, and Othmer (12); these calculations indicated that only 4 theoretical plates were required for a 99% conversion to diester under the assumed conditions. Theoretical calculations show optimum conversion in this system to be favored by low molar ratios of butyl alcohol to monobutyl phthalate. Low reflux ratios are also to be preferred.

Schniepp, Dunning, and Lathrop have developed a continuous process for the acetylation of 2,3-butanediol (2,3-butylene glycol) (31). In these tests, a 12-plate glass reaction column maintained at 140–150°C was used; the butanediol was fed in at the top with a catalytic amount of sulfuric acid, while a continuous stream of glacial acetic acid was introduced at the base of the column. The overhead distillate from the esterification column consisted of 68% acetic acid, 27% water, 2% methyl ethyl ketone, and 3% butylene glycol diacetate. This mixture was fed to a second column for dehydration and the acetic acid recovered. The bottoms from the esterification column consisted of 75% butylene glycol diacetate, 23% acetic acid, 1% butylene glycol monoacetate, and 1% sulfuric acid esters of butylene glycol. This mixture was fractionated and the acetic acid and sulfuric acid esters were recycled. With a contact time of 2 hr in the esterification section, 97% conversion of the 2,3-butanediol to pure diacetate was obtained, with 3% of methyl ethyl ketone as by-product.

Grubb, O'Hara, and Atwood have investigated a continuous distillation process for the production of high-boiling esters from intermediate-boiling polyhydric alcohols and low-boiling monocarboxylic aliphatic or aromatic acids (32). In this method, the alcohol and catalyst are fed in at the top of a reaction zone and maintained at 140–150°C, while a 100% excess of the organic acid is introduced as a superheated vapor into the bottom of the reaction zone at 160–170°C. A rectifying section is placed over the esterification zone and the organic acid is also introduced to the top plate as reflux. The water of reaction and some of the organic acid are continuously removed overhead while pure ester and the balance of the organic acid are continuously removed from the base of the column. In the production of butylene glycol diacetate, a ratio of 4 moles of acetic acid per mole of 2,3-butanediol is used with 0.3 moles of catalyst. The reaction zone is maintained at 140–145°C at the top and 160–170°C at the bottom and requires 21 plates with a total reaction time of 105–120 min. For the stripping section, 5–9 plates are required. Other materials that may be treated in a similar manner include ethylene glycol, 1,2-propanediol, and glycerol, with formic, acetic, propionic, butyric, isobutyric, benzoic, *o*-toluic, and *p*-toluic acids.

Ethyl Acetate. The production of ethyl acetate by continuous esterification based on the Backhaus process is an excellent example of the use of azeotropic principles to obtain a high yield of ester. Originally this process was developed to utilize 8% acetic

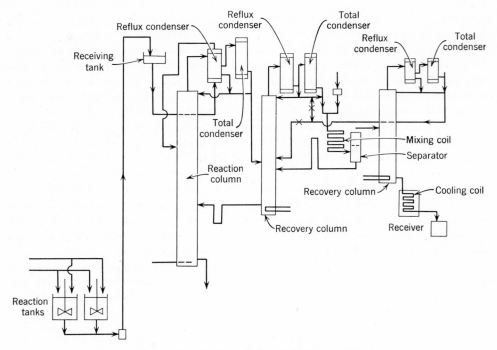

Fig. 4. Continuous ethyl acetate process (2).

acid, as obtained in fermentation, but glacial acid may also be used (2).   The acetic acid, 50 or 66°Bé sulfuric acid, and an excess of 95% ethyl alcohol are mixed in reaction tanks provided with agitators.   After esterification, equilibrium is reached in the mixture; it is then pumped into a receiving tank, and through a preheater into the upper section of a bubblecap plate column (see Figure 4).   The temperature at the top of this column is maintained at about 80°C by introduction of live steam at the base of the column.   The excess water and the sulfuric acid pass out of the column continuously from the bottom.   The acetic acid is completely consumed because of the excess of alcohol present in the reaction zone.   The vapor from this column (alcohol with the ester formed and about 10% water) is passed through the preheater and then to a condenser.   The condensate is split, part going back to the esterification column as reflux on the top plate of the column and the balance fed to a second, or separating column.   This column is operated with a top temperature of 70°C, using closed steam for heating, and it produces the ternary azeotrope of 83% ester, 9% alcohol, and 8% water.   The water and alcohol in excess of that needed for the ternary is drawn off at the base of the column and is returned to the lower section of the esterification column, where it serves to maintain a high alcohol concentration to eliminate acetic acid.   Part of the ternary mixture is returned to the top plate as reflux; if, for any reason, the ester content is less than 80%, it is fed back to the separating column at approximately the same point as the feed.   The balance of the ternary mixture is fed to a mixing coil where water is added in order to form two layers, and allowed to separate in a decanter.   The upper layer contains approximately 93% ethyl acetate, 5% water, and 2% alcohol. The lower, aqueous layer contains a small percent of ethyl alcohol and ester, and is fed back to the separating column for recovery.   The upper, or oil layer is sent to a second separating or ester-drying column, which is also heated by closed steam. The overhead from this column is the ternary mixture, which is sent back to the mixing coil. The bottoms from this column is 95–100% ethyl acetate, which is sent to a cooler and then to a storage tank. This process also applies to methyl acetate and methyl butyrate.

Vapor-Phase Esterification. The catalytic esterification of alcohols and acids in the vapor phase has received considerable attention because the conversions obtained are generally higher than in the corresponding liquid-phase reactions. No commercial applications of vapor-phase methods have been reported in the literature to date.

Physicochemical Considerations. The determination of the equilibrium constant, K_G for the reaction $C_2H_5OH + CH_3COOH \rightleftharpoons C_2H_5OOCCH_3 + H_2O$ has been the subject of a number of investigations, as summarized in Table 6. Over the temperature range of 40–300°C, the values of the equilibrium constant range from 6–559, with 71–95% ester as the equilibrium concentration from an equimolar mixture of ethyl alcohol and acetic acid, depending upon the technique used. A study of the reaction mechanism indicates that adsorption of acetic acid is the rate-controlling step; the molecularly adsorbed acetic acid then reacts with alcohol in the vapor phase. Adsorbed water molecules also act as additional centers for acetic acid adsorption (33).

Tidwell and Reid have pointed out that adsorption of materials on the catalyst may be responsible for some of the discrepancies noted in these tests; with fresh silica

Table 6. Determination of the Equilibrium Constant for the Vapor-Phase Reaction

$$C_2H_5OH + CH_3COOH \rightleftharpoons C_2H_5OOCCH_3 + H_2O$$

Year	K_G	Temperature, °C	Conversion, %	Catalyst or method	Investigators
1921	6.0	280–290		zirconium dioxide	Maihle and de Godon
1924	79.3	150	89.9	silica gel	Milligan, Chappell, and Reid
1924	347–559	72.6–77.6	95	distillation	Edgar and Schuyler
1928	59	75–76	88.5	ebullioscope	Swietoslawski and Poznanski
1930	49	280	87.5	zirconium dioxide ⎫	Frolich, Carpenter, and
1930	63	300	88.8	zirconium dioxide ⎬	Knox
1931	30.9	150	84.7	silica gel ⎫	
1931	24.9	200	83.3	silica gel ⎪	
1931	12.7	250	78.1	silica gel ⎬	Tidwell and Reid
1931	8.9	300	74.9	silica gel ⎭	
1932	33.62	150		silica gel ⎫	
1932	26.38	165		silica gel ⎬	Essex and Clark
1932	16.07	200		silica gel ⎭	
1934	39	73.7		ebullioscope ⎫	Swietoslawski and Salcewicz
1934	41	75.9		ebullioscope ⎭	
1937	10.7	230		silica gel ⎫	Jatkar and Gajendragad
1937	9.0	260		silica gel ⎭	
1942	122	40		air saturation	Halford and Brundage
1943	19.8	200	81.38	zirconium dioxide ⎫	
1943	33.3	150	84.51	zirconium dioxide ⎬	Knox and Burbridge
1943	45.7	125	85.77	zirconium dioxide ⎭	
1943	15.60	230	79.6	silica gel ⎫	Hoerig, Hanson, and
1943	11.20	270	76.8	silica gel ⎭	Kowalke
1947	305	45	92	vapor pressure ⎫	Gol'danskiĭ
1947	196	75	92	vapor pressure ⎭	

gel, a yield of 90.6% ester was obtained, but on continuous running over a 6-day period this dropped to 83.5%, at which value it remained constant for 5 days (34).

Hoerig, Hanson, and Kowalke have studied the rate of esterification of acetic acid and ethyl alcohol in equimolar quantities in a dynamic system using silica gel catalyst at 150–270°C (35). Experimental evidence indicates that the rate of the vapor-phase reaction is controlled by the rate of mass transfer or diffusion through a condensed phase present in the capillaries of the catalyst rather than by actual chemical rate of esterification.

Gol'danskiĭ and Chirkov investigated the reaction of ethyl alcohol and acetic acid vapors at 75°C in a glass vessel at reduced pressures (36). Without a catalyst the reaction velocity is immeasurably slow, but upon addition of hydrogen chloride (1–36% by wt of the acetic acid) an equilibrium is reached at 92 mole % ester. The rate of esterification up to 40% conversion was independent of time (indicating a zero-order reaction); this was confirmed by inserting glass tubing to increase the surface area; the reaction rate was increased proportionally. The velocity was increased exponentially with increase in the ratio of total gas pressure to the pressure at which droplets appear on the walls of the reactor. The temperature coefficient of the reaction was constant and corresponded to an activation energy of 15,000 cal. From these factors, it was concluded that the reaction takes place in the liquid adsorption layer and is an example of heterogeneous catalysis.

Ethyl Acetate. Some differences of opinion have been expressed as to which catalyst is the best for the vapor-phase production of ethyl acetate. Catalysts proposed have included silica gel, zirconium dioxide, activated charcoal, and potassium hydrogen sulfate.

Ethyl Benzoate. Vernon and Brown have studied the vapor-phase esterification of benzoic acid and ethyl alcohol using a number of difficultly reducible oxides suspended on silica gel, alumina, and silicon carbide, and found that the activity of the catalyst mass varies with the carrier for the same oxide (37). A ratio of 5 moles of alcohol per mole of benzoic acid was used with a temperature range of 370–450°C. Data are given in Table 7 for esterifications with titanium dioxide and the different carriers. A 6-hr run made with titanium dioxide on alumina at 370°C and a space velocity of 276 liter benzoic acid vapor/hr per liter of catalyst gave 85% conversion of the acid to ester and 7% to side reactions at the start. After 4.5 hr, the side reactions were nil and the conversion to ester increased to 99%, at which value it remained.

Table 7. Esterification with Titanium Dioxide and Different Carriers

Carrier	Temperature, °C	Space velocity[a]	Acid to ester, %	Acid to side reactions, %
silica gel	390	278	84	0
		139	85	6
		70	87	10
silicon carbide	390	278	28	2
		139	36	0
		70	49	2
alumina	370	270	98	0
		135	97	0
		68	88	3

[a] Space velocity in liters of benzoic acid vapor/hr per liter of catalyst at the reaction temperature.

Most of the oxides tested indicated increasing extent of esterification with decreased space velocity. However, titania on alumina at 370°C and manganous oxide on silicon carbide at 410°C showed increasing yields of ester with increased space velocity over the range investigated (up to 360 liter acid vapor/hr per liter of catalyst). Manganous oxide on alumina at 390°C, and zirconium dioxide on alumina at 430°C and on silica gel at 410°C show no variation in yield with space velocity. In general, as the space velocity is decreased, a larger amount of the acid was diverted to side reactions.

Other Esters. Spangenberg has studied the esterification of acetic acid with various alcohols in the vapor phase using several catalysts precipitated on pumice (38). The maximum yields with thoria and titania are given in Table 8.

Table 8. Esterification of Acetic Acid with Various Alcohols

	Yield of ester, %	
Alcohol	Thoria catalyst	Titania catalyst
propyl	86.9	95.2
isopropyl	17.2	39.8
isobutyl	87.1	34.9
sec-butyl	13.9	15.9
tert-butyl	14.7	
n-amyl	94.3	

Esterification of Other Compounds

Acid Anhydrides. Esters are produced from acid anhydrides of monobasic acids according to the following equation:

$$(RCO)_2O + R'OH \rightarrow RCOOR' + RCOOH$$

The acid produced cannot hydrolyze the ester, and hence this reaction goes to completion. Because of the higher cost of the anhydrides, however, this method is applied only when esterification cannot be effected by the usual means. Typical reactions involving the use of acid anhydrides are the esterification of tertiary alcohols, phenols, polyhydric alcohols such as cellulose and sugars, and long-chain unsaturated alcohols such as geraniol and linalool. The production of cellulose acetate (see Cellulose derivatives) and aspirin (acetylsalicylic acid) are two examples of the large-scale use of acetic anhydride.

The speed of acylation is greatly increased by the use of catalysts such as sulfuric acid, perchloric acid, trifluoroacetic acid, trifluoropropionic acid, phosphorus pentoxide, zinc chloride, ferric chloride, sodium acetate, and tertiary amines. In the reaction of the lower aliphatic acid anhydrides with sulfuric acid, Murray and Kenyon believe that a mixed anhydride of sulfuric acid and the aliphatic acid is formed, which reacts with the material to be acylated, liberating sulfuric acid, which reacts again with the anhydride and the cycle is repeated (39). Sodium acetate is preferred as the catalyst for esterifying unsaturated alcohols, such as geraniol, which would undergo rearrangement in the presence of stronger agents.

Swanson and Coss refluxed the alcohol, the acid catalyst, and the acid anhydride for one hour (40). In the preparation of allyl acetate, concentrated sulfuric acid was used as the catalyst, giving a yield of 90.9% ester. With benzyl alcohol, phosphoric acid was used and the conversion to ester was 86%; with sulfuric acid, the alcohol was resinified; and with hydrochloric acid, benzyl chloride was formed.

Ketene (qv) may conveniently be discussed together with acid anhydrides. Ketene unites with alcohols to form acetate esters:

$$CH_2=CO + ROH \rightarrow CH_3COOR$$

Ketene is an efficient acetylating agent with some alcohols, but in the absence of catalysts may be either nonreactive or sluggish with others, especially phenols and tertiary alcohols. Morey has studied the reaction of ketene with n-butyl alcohol and obtained a yield of 93 mole $\%$ of butyl acetate (41). Hurd and Roe found that only a trace of sulfuric or p-toluenesulfonic acid was necessary to effect conversion of tertiary alcohols with ketene at room temperature (42). Yields of 86–89% of esters resulted with these catalysts, ketene and phenol, and $tert$-butyl and $tert$-amyl alcohols. β-Phenylethyl alcohol, geraniol, α-ethylbenzyl alcohol, cyclohexanol, and linalool have been esterified with ketene.

Carbon monoxide, which may be considered the anhydride of formic acid, may be combined with lower aliphatic alcohols to produce low-boiling formic acid esters, as shown below:

$$CO + CH_3OH \rightarrow HCOOCH_3$$

The reaction is effected at temperatures of 60–$100°C$ under pressures of 200–700 atm (43). At higher temperatures (300–$400°C$) and in the presence of suitable catalysts, 2 molecules of methanol combine with carbon monoxide to give methyl acetate (3).

$$2 CH_3OH + CO \rightarrow CH_3COOCH_3$$

Dibasic acid anhydrides such as phthalic anhydride and maleic anhydride readily react with alcohols to form the monoalkyl ester:

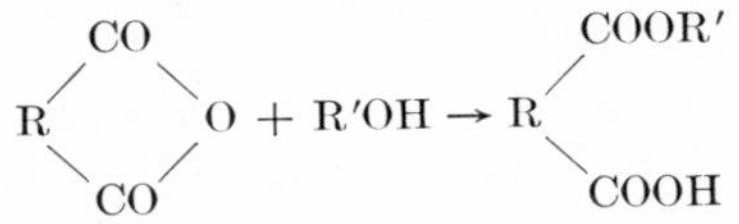

$$R\begin{array}{c} CO \\ \diagup \quad \diagdown \\ \quad\quad O + R'OH \rightarrow R \\ \diagdown \quad \diagup \\ CO \end{array}\begin{array}{c} COOR' \\ \diagup \\ \\ \diagdown \\ COOH \end{array}$$

The formation of monoalkyl phthalates from methyl through eicosyl has been investigated by Goggans and Copenhaver (44). Because of the wide variations noted in the melting points of these monoalkyl esters up to the dodecyl derivative, they suggest this method for identification of individual alcohols.

This reaction is also useful in separating alcohols of various classes (3): Primary alcohols diluted with benzene react completely with phthalic anhydride at $80°C$ in 1 hr, while the secondary alcohols require heating to 130–$140°C$ for several hours. Tertiary alcohols are dehydrated before they combine.

The monoesters are converted into the normal diesters by heating with an excess of alcohol and a catalyst. The diesters are generally formed directly, however. The phthalic anhydride with 1–1.3% of sulfuric acid is melted at 133–$135°C$, 2–4 times the theoretical amount of alcohol is added, and the mixture heated for 6–8 hr. The water is distilled off as formed, with the excess alcohol. Yields of 94–98% of the ethyl, n-propyl, isopropyl, and isobutyl diesters are reported (45).

The Schotten-Baumann benzoylation method may be adapted to the esterification of aromatic acid anhydrides according to the following equation:

$$(C_6H_5CO)_2O + C_6H_5OH + NaOH \rightarrow C_6H_5COOC_6H_5 + C_6H_5COONa + H_2O$$

The reaction mixture must be heated to melt the anhydride. An excess of the acid anhydride (double the calculated amount) does not materially increase the yield of phenyl esters. The amount of sodium hydroxide is critical; with none the yield is nil, with the theoretical quantity the conversion is poor, but with twice the calculated amount of sodium hydroxide the best yields of esters are obtained from phenols. Alcohols, on the other hand, are not easily esterified by this method; 10% aqueous solutions of methanol and ethyl alcohol result in only small amounts of the corresponding benzoate esters.

Polyhydric alcohols such as ethylene glycol, diethylene glycol, propylene glycol, and glycerol react with polybasic acids and acid anhydrides to form esters of high molecular weight. The derivatives are of importance as coatings, resins, plastics, and textiles. The Glyptals (see Alkyd resins) are formed by reacting glycerol with phthalic anhydride. Unsaturated polyester resins used in reinforced plastics are produced by reacting phthalic and maleic anhydrides with ethylene or propylene glycols and dissolving the polyester in styrene monomer. Other acids such as isophthalic and fumaric are sometimes incorporated also. These products are converted into hard, thermosetting resins by peroxide-catalyzed polymerization of the unsaturated linkages. Saturated linear polyesters are formed by condensing terephthalic acid (*p*-phthalic acid) with ethylene glycol. Terylene and Dacron fibers, Mylar film, and Cronar sheeting are poly(ethylene terephthalates). Industrially, these products are made by reacting dimethyl terephthalate with ethylene glycol by ester interchange (qv).

Acid Chlorides. Acid chlorides react with alcohols to form esters:

$$RCOCl + R'OH \rightarrow RCOOR' + HCl$$

The use of sodium alcoholate in place of the alcohol is often practiced. The acid chlorides are generally more reactive than the corresponding acid anhydrides; the hydrogen chloride liberated acts as a catalyst. However, because of this, the acid chlorides are not used with alcohols susceptible to rearrangement.

Acid chlorides are used for the quantitative determination of hydroxyl groups and for acylation of sugars. Industrial applications include the formation of the alkyl or aryl carbonates from phosgene (see Carbonic and chloroformic esters) and phosphate esters such as triethyl, triphenyl, and tricresyl (tritolyl) phosphates from phosphorus oxychloride (see Phosphoric acids).

The reactivity of different acid chlorides with water varies considerably. The lower aliphatic and inorganic acid chlorides react very violently with water. The aromatic acid chlorides react much more slowly and the arylsulfonyl chlorides (*p*-toluenesulfonyl chloride) even more slowly. Ether alcohols or hydroxy ethers such as the Cellosolve (monoalkyl ethers of ethylene glycol) and Carbitol (monoalkyl ethers of diethylene glycol) ethers are readily esterified by means of acid chlorides (see Glycols).

Tertiary alcohols are readily esterified by acid chlorides by the method of Abramovitch, Shivers, Hudson, and Hauser (46): One mole each of dry *tert*-butyl alcohol and *N*,*N*-dimethylaniline in 150–200 ml of dry ether is treated slowly with one mole of acid chloride (with cooling if necessary) with final heating on a water bath for 1–2 hr and standing for several hours. Yields of *tert*-butyl esters prepared are: acetate, 63–76%; propionate, 63%; isobutyrate, 71%; isovalerate, 33%; cinnamate, 58%; and bromoacetate, 70%.

The use of anhydrous aluminum chloride or bromide in anhydrous sulfur dioxide with other diluents such as benzene, toluene, and xylene has been suggested for accelerating the esterification of phenols with acid chlorides at 35–70°C (47). Phenol, alkyl phenols, resorcinol, pyrogallol, salicylic acid, and hydroxyquinoline, as well as cyclohexanol and heptyl, decyl, oleyl, and stearyl alcohols may be used with acid chlorides such as valeric, stearic, melissic, lauric, cerotic, oleic, and ricinoleic, in this process.

The reaction of alcohols and acid chlorides in the presence of magnesium has been investigated by Spasov (48). With primary and secondary alcohols the reaction is very smooth, with high, sometimes quantitative, yields. Difficultly esterifiable hydroxy compounds like tertiary alcohols and phenols can be esterified by this method. The reaction, which is carried out in ether or benzene, is usually very vigorous, with evolution of hydrogen:

$$R'COCl + R_3COH \rightarrow R'C(OH)(OCR_3)Cl \rightarrow R'COOCR_3 + HCl$$

$$2 HCl + Mg \rightarrow MgCl_2 + H_2$$

According to the above, the presence of magnesium favors the esterification by removing the hydrogen chloride formed; however, with isobutyl alcohol no hydrogen is evolved, and with phenols only part of the hydrogen chloride is removed. Magnesium has a specific action; other metals behave differently under the same conditions, as will be shown. The presence of magnesium greatly represses the dehydrating action of acetyl chloride, especially with easily dehydrated tertiary alcohols; generally only very small amounts of unsaturated hydrocarbons are formed.

The tertiary aliphatic alcohols, *tert*-butyl alcohol, *tert*-amyl alcohol, 1-ethyl-1-methyl-1-propanol, and 1,1-diethyl-1-propanol, all acetylate smoothly and rapidly with more than 60% yield. With aromatic tertiary alcohols esterification was slower and more difficult. Triphenylmethanol did not esterify at all, giving chiefly triphenylmethyl chloride. Tribenzylmethanol gave a 50% yield of acetate ester.

Of the acid chlorides, acetyl, propionyl, butyryl, and isobutyryl chlorides reacted with the primary, secondary, and tertiary alcohols smoothly and easily with 50–90% yields. Phenylacetyl (α-toluyl) chloride reacted smoothly with tertiary alcohols but benzoyl chloride did not. Yields of 50 and 20% of benzoate esters were obtained with isobutyl and *sec*-butyl alcohols, respectively. With phenol, *o*- and *p*-cresol, 1-naphthol, resorcinol, and thymol, the yields of esters from all six of the above acid chlorides were in the range of 92–98% (48,49).

Spasov has also investigated the action of sodium, calcium, aluminum, and zinc in the esterification of secondary and tertiary alcohols with acid chlorides (48). The reaction proceeded with the evolution of hydrogen chloride and hydrogen with all these metals except aluminum, in which case only hydrogen chloride was produced. Comparing the results of these esterifications with controls in which no metals were present, sodium decreases the yield of ester, probably through condensation of the product. Zinc increases the yield from secondary alcohols, but is unfavorable with the tertiary alcohols. With aluminum, the ester yields are lower than without the metal. Calcium is similar to magnesium, but not as effective. With magnesium, the yield of ester is increased, ranging from 17% improvement with *sec*-butyl acetate to a 91% improvement with *tert*-butyl phenylacetate over the control with no metal.

Paquot and Bouquet have reported that in the presence of magnesium, yields of better than 90% are obtained with long-chain esters such as ethyl laurate, myristate, palmitate, and stearate, and *n*-hexadecyl acetate and palmitate (50). The acid chloride is diluted with anhydrous ether and added to the alcohol (10% excess) in anhydrous ether with 3–5% excess magnesium ribbon. The mixture is refluxed for a few hours and the resulting complex decomposed with water or concentrated ammonium chloride solution. In the decomposition step much heat is liberated and magnesium hydroxide precipitates. The magnesium is believed to be combined in the complex in a manner similar to that of the Grignard reagents.

Schotten-Baumann Reaction. Esters are produced in the Schotten-Baumann reaction by allowing an acid chloride to react with an alkaline mixture of water and alcohol. Part of the acid chloride is converted into a salt of the acid by alkaline hydrolysis. From quantitative studies on this reaction, Menalda recommends the following conditions to get maximum yields of ester (51): (*1*) The temperature must be kept as low as possible (0–25°C); (*2*) the acid chloride must be added in small portions to prevent the sudden evolution of heat; (*3*) potassium hydroxide should be used in preference to sodium hydroxide, although the latter gives excellent results; (*4*) the alkali must be as concentrated as possible; (*5*) in order to prevent hydrolysis, the ester should be removed from the reaction mixture as quickly as possible; and (*6*) an excess of acid chloride is to be used to obtain a reasonable yield of ester, as a rule, 1.2–1.5 times the calculated amount being necessary.

The yields of ester vary with different acid chlorides, and are best with benzoyl chloride and poorest with acetyl chloride. Benzenesulfonyl chloride gives intermediate yields. The hydroxy compound used also influences the yield of ester under the same experimental conditions; the amount of ester is increased in the order: ethyl, allyl, methyl, and benzyl alcohols, glycerol, sucrose, and phenol, the latter being converted almost quantitatively into esters. In all cases, the amount of ester increases with increasing concentration of the alcohol. In general, the conversion to ester decreases with increasing excess of alkali used, although the influence of this factor is not considerable.

Amides. Amides may be converted to esters by the following reaction:

$$RCONH_2 + R'OH \rightleftharpoons RCOOR' + NH_3$$

This is a reversible reaction and in order to produce high yields of ester it is necessary to remove the ammonia produced, either by heating or by combining with a mineral acid, such as sulfuric or hydrochloric.

Taylor and Davis measured the velocities of esterification of formamide, acetamide, and benzamide at 25°C in dry and in aqueous alcoholic solutions with hydrogen chloride as the catalyst and reported the reaction to be bimolecular (52). Addition of small quantities of water accelerates the reaction, the maximum effect appearing between 8 and 12%.

The structural relationships involved in esterification of amides have been studied by Toole and Sowa (53). With 0.75 mole of the amide in 1.5 mole of absolute methanol and 0.75 mole of boron trifluoride, and with cooling during the absorption followed by heating for 45 min, the yields of ester listed in Table 9 were obtained. For comparison, 0.75 mole of the corresponding acid, 1.5 moles of absolute methanol and 7 g of ethyl ether–boron trifluoride complex were refluxed for 45 min at 64 ± 1°C. There is no direct relationship between ionization constant and quantity of ester formed.

Table 9. Comparative Yields of Esters from Amides or Acids

Methyl ester	Yield of ester, %	
	From amide	From acid
formate	34	
acetate	70	56
monochloracetate	64	65
dichloroacetate	57	70
trichloroacetate	53	73
phenylacetate	50	86
propionate	80	44
benzoate	15	37

Amides react with halogen compounds such as ethyl, *n*-butyl, isobutyl, amyl, isooctyl, dodecyl, β-phenylethyl, and naphthylmethyl chlorides, and ethylene and butylene dichlorides, to form esters at temperatures of 170–270°C. In general, 5–20 mole equivalents of the amide is required per mole of the halide (54).

Nitriles. Direct saponification of nitriles with alcohols offers a convenient way to produce esters without isolating the acid:

$$RCN + H_2O + R'OH \rightarrow RCOOR' + NH_3$$

Acid catalysts are used to combine with the ammonia formed. A large excess of alcohol is used, but the amount of water is generally kept small.

With aromatic nitriles, a single ortho substituent inhibits practically completely the conversion of the nitrile with methanol or ethyl alcohol using hydrochloric acid as the catalyst (55). The chemical nature of the substituent plays only a minor role; methyl, nitro, chloro, phenyl, and vinyl groups all show this property. Yields of esters obtained by refluxing various nitriles with a large excess of anhydrous alcohol for 2 hr with gaseous hydrogen chloride introduced into the mixture are shown in Table 10. With olefinic nitriles of the type $C_6H_5CH{=}CHCN$, the trans compound esterified easily, but the cis form esterified very slowly or not at all.

Mahon has esterified nitriles with olefins in the presence of water and an acid such as sulfuric, phosphoric, or benzenesulfonic at 40–200°C under sufficient pressure to ensure a liquid-phase reaction (56). From propionitrile and dodecene with sulfuric

Table 10. Yields of Esters from Nitriles

Ester	Yield, %	
	Methyl ester	Ethyl ester
benzoate	65.4	35.1
o-toluate	0	0
m-toluate	92.1	58.7
p-toluate	83	80
o-nitrobenzoate	0	0
m-nitrobenzoate	87	45
o-phenylbenzoate	8.4	5.6
p-phenylbenzoate	82	70.4
o-chlorobenzoate	0	0
p-chlorobenzoate	97	67.9
1-naphthoate	0	0
2-naphthoate	77.1	77.4

acid, a yield of 16% propionic ester was obtained at 45–55°C. With 1 mole *trans*-3-pentenenitrile, 2 moles ethylene, and 1.5 moles sulfuric acid, with 4.4 moles pentane as diluent, a 17% yield of ethyl pentenoate was obtained by heating the mixture to 70–100°C under 300–350 psi. Cyclohexene (3 moles) refluxed with 1 mole of propionitrile, 1.5 moles of concentrated sulfuric acid, and 3.5 moles water gave 20% cyclohexyl propionate.

Ross and Bibbins have described the preparation of ethyl malonate according to the following equations (57):

$$ClCH_2COOH + NaOH \rightarrow ClCH_2COONa + H_2O$$

$$ClCH_2COONa + NaCN \rightarrow NCCH_2COONa + NaCl$$

$$2\ NCCH_2COONa + 4\ C_2H_5OH + 2\ H_2SO_4 \rightarrow 2\ C_2H_5OOCCH_2COOC_2H_5 + Na_2SO_4 + (NH_4)_2SO_4$$

Esters of acrylic and methacrylic acids may be prepared by reaction of an alcohol with the reaction product of oleum and acetaldehyde cyanohydrin, $CH_3CH(OH)CN$, and acetone cyanohydrin, $(CH_3)_2C(OH)CN$, respectively (58).

Unsaturated Hydrocarbons. The direct esterification of olefins with organic acids has attracted considerable attention because of the availability of large quantities of unsaturated hydrocarbons from petroleum cracking. Olefins from ethylene through octene have been converted into esters, but the most desirable ones are those from the C_4 and C_5 olefins, since these esters are in demand as lacquer solvents.

With ethylene and propylene, only a single ester is produced (ethyl acetate and isopropyl acetate, respectively). With the butylenes, two products are possible: *sec*-Butyl esters result from 1- and 2-butenes, whereas *tert*-butyl esters are obtained from isobutylene (2-methylpropene). The C_5 olefins give rise to three *sec*-amyl esters and one *tert*-amyl ester.

As the carbon chain is lengthened, the reactivity of the olefin with organic acids increases. Thus ethylene and propylene are much more difficult to esterify than are the butylenes and pentylenes, the latter esterifying readily with sulfuric acid catalysts. The tertiary olefins, $(H_3C)_2C{=}CH_2$, $(H_3C)_2C{=}CHCH_3$, or $(H_3C)_2C{=}C(CH_3)_2$, are much more rapidly esterified than the secondary olefins, $H_3CCH{=}CH_2$ or $H_3CCH{=}CHCH_2$. Polymerization of the olefins must be minimized in order to produce high yields of ester.

Altschul has cited the following requirements for optimum esterification yields with olefins (59): low reaction temperatures, high concentrations and a liberal excess of the more abundant reactant, a relatively large quantity of catalyst, and anhydrous conditions.

Pure Olefins. In the case of ethylene, it is necessary to use high temperatures and pressures as well as active catalysts to effect esterification. Bearse and Morin have obtained a 40% yield of ethyl acetate from a mixture of 480 parts of glacial acetic acid, 420 parts of ethylene, 90 parts of boron trifluoride, and 90 parts of hydrogen fluoride, which was heated for 3 hr at 150–170°C in an autoclave under an initial pressure of 1800 psi (60). With propylene and acetic acid, esterification is much more readily accomplished. With boron trifluoride and hydrogen fluoride as catalyst, heating the mixture to 100°C in a bomb gave a 72% yield of isopropyl acetate in 10–15 min.

Dorris, Sowa, and Nieuwland have studied the reaction of propylene with acetic acid, mono-, di-, and trichloroacetic acids, and benzoic acid using small amounts of boron trifluoride as catalyst (61). The yields of esters resulting at a pressure of 110 cm Hg and 70°C, compared with data obtained by treating isopropyl alcohol and the

Table 11. Comparative Yields of Esters from the Olefin or the Alcohol

Isopropyl ester	Yield, %	
	From olefin	From alcohol
acetate	7	16.8
monochloroacetate	34.2	38.8
dichloroacetate	39.5	48.6
trichloroacetate	48.4	57.8
benzoate	88	60

acid with the same catalyst, are given in Table 11. With cyclopropane in place of propylene and a pressure of 90 cm Hg, the n-propyl esters are formed with the following yields (62): acetate, 65%; dichloroacetate, 59%; and benzoate, 47%.

Isopropyl esters of aliphatic acids are obtained by treating anhydrous aliphatic acids, such as acetic acid, with propylene at temperatures of about 125°C in the presence of sulfuric acid, with arylsulfonic or chlorosulfonic acids, or with a lower alkyl ester of sulfuric, arylsulfonic, or chlorosulfonic acid (63).

Brooks has reported yields of up to 60% of theoretical of *sec*-butyl acetate by heating 2-butene under pressure at 115–120°C with an excess of glacial acetic acid containing 10% sulfuric acid (64). *sec*-Butyl esters of acetic, propionic, butyric, isovaleric, monochloro- and trichloroacetic, oxalic, succinic, tartaric, benzoic, and phthalic acids were prepared in good yields using boron trifluoride–ethyl ether complex as catalyst at 97°C (65). With this catalyst and isobutylene, no esters were formed at 50 and 97°C because of polymerization, but at room temperature a 58% yield of *tert*-butyl ester was obtained with acetic acid.

Tertiary butyl acetate was prepared by Kerr and Throckmorton by passing isobutylene and acetic acid (2:1 mole ratio) in the liquid phase over a silica catalyst impregnated with vanadium pentoxide and potassium sulfate at 250 psi. Conversion of isobutylene to ester increased with increasing temperature and ranged from 10% at 125°F to 24% at 200°F. Based on the acetic acid charged, yields of from 31 to 43% of *tert*-butyl acetate resulted at 200°F (66).

Using zinc chloride as the catalyst, Aldoshin obtained esters by heating 2-butene, 2-pentene, and 2-hexene with acetic acid and monochloroacetic acids for 8 hr at 100°C (67). Except with 2-butene, considerable polymerization also occurred.

Altschul has studied the reversible esterification of isobutylene with acetic, benzoic, and p-nitrobenzoic acids, and trimethylethylene (2-methyl-2-butene) and benzoic acid at 25 and 35°C using sulfuric acid as catalyst with dioxane as solvent (59). In every case, the esters were formed in strict accordance with Markovnikov's rule, without formation of isomers.

Simons and Meunier have used hydrogen fluoride as a condensing agent in the proportion of 5 moles per mole each of olefin and acid at 0°C (68). Under these conditions, yields of 70% of esters were obtained from cyclohexene with acetic and butyric acids, with stirring for a few hours. With 1- and 2-octenes, 29% yield of octyl acetate and 47% yield of octyl butyrate resulted. Polymerization was greater with the octenes than with cyclohexene.

Petroleum–Olefin Mixtures. Evans, Edlund, and Taylor have investigated the preparation of *sec*-butyl and *sec*-amyl acetates using olefin mixtures obtained from petroleum cracking (69). The composition of such cracked-gas mixtures varies considerably, but mixtures of 50% saturated hydrocarbons, 30% *sec*-olefins, and 20% *tert*-olefins are common. Because the reactivity of the *tert*-olefins is much greater than that of the *sec*-olefins, it is impractical to esterify both types of olefins in one operation, since they require different conditions. Since the esters derived from *tert*-olefins have not proved as desirable commercially as those from *sec*-olefins, it is generally necessary to remove the former by selective polymerization or adsorption in acid prior to esterification.

The esterification is carried out with sulfuric acid as a catalyst, although this may cause extensive polymerization unless proper conditions are used. Nevertheless, this agent is one of the best because of its low cost, high activity, and ease of handling.

In a typical experiment, a mixture of 106 g acetic acid, 109 g sulfuric acid (95%), and 419 g pentene–pentane cut (containing 65% pentanes, 35% pentylenes) is charged to an autoclave and stirred under pressure at 60°C for 2 hr and then cooled. Two liquid phases are obtained: The upper phase amounts to 422 g and contains 18.3% amyl acetate, 9.9% pentene, 60.6% pentane, 3% polymers, 3% acetic acid, and small amounts of sulfuric acid, sulfur dioxide, diamyl sulfate, and acid sulfate. The lower layer amounts to 212 g and contains most of the sulfuric and unreacted acetic acids. Only the upper layer is used for recovery of the ester; the lower phase is reused as catalyst with fresh olefin and acetic acid after addition of a small amount of sulfuric acid to compensate for the losses in the upper layer.

Increasing the concentrations of either the olefin or acetic acid tends to increase the concentration of ester (up to 44.5% with *sec*-amyl acetate). It is practical to operate with a free acidity in the range of 0.3–1.5N. By operating near the middle of this range, the process is more flexible than at either extreme; this is an important factor when variability of olefin concentration in the starting material is considered.

The choice of operating temperature is a compromise: Higher temperatures increase the rate of reaction but give a less favorable equilibrium and increase polymerization. Sulfuric acid concentrations of 100%, 80%, or less, are satisfactory. The weaker acid has the advantage that smaller amounts of sulfuric acid and diamyl sulfate occur in the upper layer; on the other hand, the stronger acid gives a higher reaction velocity.

The recovery of ester from the upper layer presents additional problems because the small amount of sulfuric acid present concentrates along with the ester on distillation and promotes decomposition. One method involves contacting the upper layer with aqueous acetic acid of a concentration in equilibrium with the upper layer and containing sodium or calcium acetate in solution. By this means, the sulfuric acid is extracted readily into the aqueous phase while no exchange of acetic acid takes place. Any alkyl hydrogen sulfate present is also removed in this step. Dialkyl sulfates are removed by addition of small amounts of barium or calcium acetate during the final distillation. In this manner, pentene–pentane, acetic acid, and amyl acetate may be recovered.

The above process cannot be used in separating *sec*-butyl acetate and acetic acid because of the proximity of their boiling points. The upper layer is freed of sulfuric acid, as above; the butane–butene is distilled off. The remaining ester–acetic acid mixture is fed into a distilling column. Sufficient water is present in this column to remove the ester as the overhead binary with water, while at the base of the column anhydrous acetic acid is recovered. Upon condensation, the overhead splits into two phases; the lower, water-rich phase is fed back to the column as reflux. The upper layer (butyl acetate saturated with water) is neutralized to remove traces of free acid and redistilled. Esters of 97–100% purity are obtained, the impurities being hydrocarbons and alcohols caused by slight hydrolysis of the ester.

Acetylene combines with organic acids in the presence of catalysts according to the following equations:

$$CH{\equiv}CH + RCOOH \rightarrow CH_2{=}CHCOOR$$
$$CH{\equiv}CH + 2\ RCOOH \rightarrow CH_3CH(COOR)_2$$

Although millions of pounds of vinyl acetate (see Vinyl compounds) and ethylidene diacetate have been produced by these reactions, little has been published on this process.

Morrison and Shaw reported that vinyl acetate is first formed and reacts with a second mole of acetic acid to give the diester (70). Production of vinyl acetate is favored by the rapid removal of the product from the reaction mixture, as well as by the use of specific catalysts. High yields of diester are obtained by recirculation of the vinyl acetate.

For the formation of vinyl acetate, acetylene is passed into a catalyst mixture, which consists of an oxide of mercury dissolved in acetic acid and to which is added phosphoric acid. Another catalyst used in a similar manner is a mixture of mercury compound with an organic trisulfonic acid obtained by treating a liquid organic acid with excess sulfur trioxide, or by treating an acid anhydride with fuming sulfuric acid (71). Vinyl acetate is also formed by passing a mixture of acetylene and acetic acid vapor over catalysts such as zinc or cadmium acetate on activated alumina at 200–270°C (72). The activity of this catalyst is maintained by increasing the operating temperature whenever the absorption of reactants drops.

Metal carbonyls promote reaction between acetylene, carbon monoxide, and alcohol, to produce esters:

$$CH{\equiv}CH + CO + C_2H_5OH \rightarrow CH_2{=}CHCOOC_2H_5$$

Thus nickel carbonyl (0.25 mole) added dropwise to a mixture of ethyl alcohol (1 mole) and concentrated hydrochloric acid (0.5 mole) saturated with acetylene gives a practically quantitative yield of ethyl acrylate. Other alcohols may be used, giving the corresponding acrylate esters or, if water is substituted, free acrylic acid, all in substantially quantitative yields. The nickel is reclaimed from the nickel chloride solution by adding ammonia in slight excess to form the complex hexammine, which is treated with carbon monoxide at 80°C and 50–100 atm to regenerate nickel carbonyl. Cobalt carbonyl will also catalyze this reaction, but iron carbonyl will not (73).

In the presence of a Lewis acid type of catalyst, monoolefins will add on to acid esters of organic polycarboxylic acids to produce neutral esters, useful as plasticizers for vinyl chloride resins. Thus butyl acid phthalate, prepared by reacting 74 parts of phthalic anhydride with 37 parts of *n*-butanol at 20°C for 1.5 hr, was mixed with 126 parts of 1-dodecene at 80°C for 5–10 min and treated with 10 parts of BF₃.Et₂O (containing 44% by weight of BF₃), kept at 80–85°C for 10 hr, cooled to 0°C, filtered, washed with warm alkali and twice with water, and distilled in vacuo, giving 92.3% butyl 2-dodecyl phthalate (73a). A number of mixed esters of succinic, pyromellitic, adipic, sebacic, and isophthalic acids were also produced by this technique.

Organic acids such as formic and acetic add to double bonds of unsaturated fatty acids, esters, alcohols, and glycerides to produce the corresponding acyloxy derivatives, which are useful as plasticizers, lubricants, and hydraulic fluids. A mineral acid such as perchloric or sulfuric acid speeds up the reaction. Formoxystearic acid is obtained in 80% conversion from oleic acid by refluxing with anhydrous formic acid containing 0.5–2% of 70% perchloric acid for 5–30 min. Saponification yields monohydroxy-stearic acid in 90% yield, based on the oleic acid consumed. Substituting acetic acid for formic acid gave a 40% conversion to monohydroxystearic acid on saponification. Elaidic acid and methyl oleate gave substantially the same results as oleic acid. Sulfuric acid was less effective than perchloric acid; in the absence of an acid catalyst, 24 hr reaction time is required for the addition of formic acid to oleic acid (73b).

Ethers. Although ethers are generally regarded as inert compounds, in the presence of anhydrous agents such as zinc chloride or hydrogen bromide, and of acid chlorides, reaction takes place resulting in the formation of esters. Underwood and Toone have shown that when aliphatic ethers are heated with anhydrous zinc chloride, small amounts of the corresponding alcohols and unsaturated hydrocarbons are formed (74). The alcohol thus liberated combines with acid chlorides and the splitting of the ether continues. Some alkyl chlorides are also formed by the hydrogen chloride resulting from the esterification. Only very small amounts of zinc chloride are needed. Dry hydrogen bromide also reacts with aliphatic ethers to produce the corresponding alcohols and alkyl bromides; excessive amounts of hydrogen bromide, however, produce only the alkyl bromide.

Underwood and Wakeman have obtained the yields of ethyl esters listed in Table 12 by treating ethyl ether with acid chlorides, acids, and acid anhydrides (75). With the acid chlorides, finely powdered zinc chloride was used as the catalyst with 10–15% excess of ether and the mixtures refluxed for 2–3 hr. In the other tests, ether was saturated with dry hydrogen bromide and the acid or acid anhydride added. The mixtures were allowed to stand for 10–12 days, after which the mixtures were refluxed for 3 hr.

Table 12. Yields of Ethyl Esters Obtained by Splitting Ethyl Ether (75)

Ester	Yield of ester, %		
	From acid chlorides	From acids	From acid anhydrides
acetate	40	8	13
chloroacetate	35	30	
propionate	15	34	23
butyrate	21	41	38
isovalerate	20	42	41
benzoate	60	28	49
phenylacetate	79	56	
diphenate	77	16	25
hydrocinnamate		80	

Benzenesulfonyl and *p*-toluenesulfonyl chlorides, and stearic, picric, *p*-toluenesulfonic, and 2,4,6-trinitrobenzoic acids did not react. Diphenyl ether and anisole (methyl phenyl ether) formed ketones in place of esters when heated with zinc chloride and acid chlorides. The yields of esters obtained from other aliphatic ethers with various acid chlorides and zinc chloride are as follows: isopropyl acetate, 30%; isopropyl benzoate, 10%; *n*-butyl acetate, 68%; *n*-butyl benzoate, 45%; *n*-butyl propionate, 28%; *n*-butyl butyrate, 57%; isoamyl acetate, 48%; and isoamyl benzoate, 40%.

Meerwein and Maier-Hüser have studied the effect of various catalysts for the reaction of ethyl ether with benzoyl chloride and acetic anhydride and reported the following yields (76):

Catalyst	Ethyl benzoate, %	Ethyl acetate, %
ZnCl$_2$	100	2.84
SnCl$_4$	98.66	36.93
ZrCl$_4$	84.67	
TiCl$_4$	82.67	26.7
SbCl$_5$	82	19.88
FeCl$_3$	50	35.24
AlCl$_3$	50	17

Boron trifluoride produced only traces of ester, and no splitting occurred with silicon tetrafluoride, phosphorus pentachloride, boron trifluoride, phosphorus trichloride, arsenic trichloride, or magnesium chloride.

Brown and Lorette obtained nearly quantitative yields of methyl esters by treating propionic, adipic, and oxalic acids with acetone dimethyl acetal in the presence of a catalytic amount of water or methanol and hydrochloric or *p*-toluenesulfonic acids (77). The reaction proceeds smoothly at room temperature and no water is formed.

Esters may also be produced by interaction of ethers with carbon monoxide according to the equation

$$CH_3OCH_3 + CO \rightarrow CH_3COOCH_3$$

Dreyfus utilizes alkali alcoholates or alkali formates as catalysts at 200–450°C and 50–300 atm (78). By adding water to the reaction mixture, acetic acid is produced in place of the ester. Esters are obtained by heating *n*-butyl or isoamyl ether with acetic acid in the presence of catalytic proportions of sulfuric acid under superatmospheric pressure (79). Boron trifluoride may also be used as a catalyst for this reaction (80); in this case, the ether and boron trifluoride are caused to react at ordinary temperature and pressure, and the product is treated with carbon monoxide at 900 atm. After heating 2 hr at 150–190°C, the product is distilled, during which more ether is added to liberate the ester from its addition compound with the boron trifluoride by formation of an ether–boron trifluoride complex. The latter is again treated with carbon monoxide to form more ester.

Aldehydes and Ketones. Esters are obtained readily by condensation of aldehydes in the presence of alcoholate (alkoxide) catalysts such as aluminum ethylate (ethoxide), Al(OC$_2$H$_5$)$_3$, following the Tishchenko reaction. In 1923–1925, Child and Adkins studied this reaction with acetaldehyde, butyraldehyde, enanthaldehyde, furfural, and benzaldehyde, and obtained yields of 90–95% ester. The rate of formation of esters was most rapid with acetaldehyde and enanthaldehyde and was slowest with furfural. Aluminum butylate and isobutylate are better activators than aluminum ethylate for this reaction. Variations in the relative amounts of aldehyde and catalyst taken have a very small effect on the rate of reaction. Evidently an aldehyde–catalyst complex is rapidly formed, which then decomposes slowly into ester and catalyst.

According to Kagan and Sobolev, the alcoholates may be prepared from commercial aluminum and n-butyl or isobutyl alcohol in the presence of 2–2.5% aluminum chloride (81). With isoamyl alcohol, an amalgam of aluminum is recommended. Any of these alcoholates may be used as a catalyst for preparing ethyl acetate from acetaldehyde. The reaction is carried out with dried acetaldehyde at 25–40°C for 2–3 hr with a yield of 86%. The consumption of catalyst is 7 g aluminum and 2 g aluminum chloride per kg of ethyl acetate produced.

Paquot and Perron produced methyl and ethyl palmitate in yields of 37 and 16%, respectively, by heating 400 ml of a 30% solution of formaldehyde with 200 g palmitic acid in an autoclave at 300°C for 5 hr in the absence of a catalyst (82).

Galat has described a method for the synthesis of α,β-unsaturated esters by condensing aldehydes with an acid ester of malonic acid under the conditions of the Doebner reaction (83);

$$\text{RCOH} + \text{HOOCCH}_2\text{COOR}' \rightarrow \text{RCH}{=}\text{CHCOOR}'$$

Thus, 3.2 g m-nitrobenzaldehyde, 4.8 ml monomethyl malonate, 0.25 ml piperidine, and 10 ml dry pyridine are heated on a steam bath for 6 hr, giving a yield of 86.5% of methyl m-nitrocinnamate (methyl m-nitrophenylacrylate). The ethyl ester was obtained in 85–89% yield from monoethyl malonate. Yields of esters of 75% or higher were obtained with benzaldehyde, p-tolualdehyde, p-chlorobenzaldehyde, m-nitrobenzaldehyde, p-hydroxybenzaldehyde, 3,4-dihydroxybenzaldehyde (protocatechualdehyde), anisaldehyde, 1-naphthaldehyde, and furfural.

Esters may be made from methyl aryl ketones by a process involving degradation. Thus methyl phenyl ketone (acetophenone) is converted into the oxime of phenylglyoxal with hydrogen chloride and amyl nitrite; this is methylated with dimethyl sulfate, forming an unstable substance which decomposes, as shown below:

$$\text{C}_6\text{H}_5\text{COCH}_3 \rightarrow \text{C}_6\text{H}_5\text{COCHNOH} \rightarrow \text{C}_6\text{H}_5\text{COCHNOCH}_3 \rightarrow \text{C}_6\text{H}_5\text{COOCH}_3$$

The yield of methyl benzoate is higher than 90%. Naphthoates may be prepared in the same way (84).

Trihalomethyl ketones react with alcohols in the presence of alkaline catalysts even at room temperature (85) according to the equation

$$\text{RCOCCl}_3 + \text{R}'\text{OH} \rightarrow \text{RCOOR}' + \text{CHCl}_3$$

Substances such as alkali metal organic acid salts (acetates, formates, and benzoates) and inorganic carbonates, bicarbonates, sulfites, and nitrites may serve as catalysts. Water up to 10% has no effect. This reaction takes place with primary and secondary alcohols, glycols, and glycerol. With potassium hydroxide as catalyst and trichloromethyl phenyl ketone, a yield of 90–93% benzoate ester was obtained in 2–4 days at 20°C, with methyl, isobutyl, n-hexyl, and allyl alcohols. With phenol, and o- and m-cresols, the yield of benzoate esters ranged from 80–90% with heating for 4 hr at 120–130°C. A variety of trihalomethyl ketones have been studied in this reaction. With tertiary alcohols and phenols, especially those requiring heating, magnesium salts are preferred to the stronger alkali metals to ensure milder conditions.

Dehydrogenation of Alcohols. The direct synthesis of esters by dehydrogenation of alcohols offers a simple method for the preparation of certain types of esters, such as ethyl acetate and butyl butyrate. The overall reaction is represented by the equation

$$2\ \text{RCH}_2\text{OH} \rightarrow \text{RCOOCH}_2\text{R} + 2\ \text{H}_2$$

The reaction is catalyzed by copper with various promoters or activators and is carried out in the vapor phase at 200–300°C at normal pressures. Although a number of U.S. patents have been issued in this field since 1928, most of the studies on this process have been carried out by Russian investigators, notably Dolgov, Lel'chuk, and Ivannikov, using laboratory or pilot-sized equipment.

The equipment required for this process is relatively simple, consisting of a pre-heater to vaporize the alcohol, a heated tube or chamber containing the catalyst mass, and condensing facilities. With ethyl alcohol, the products consist of ethyl acetate, with smaller amounts of acetaldehyde, acetic acid, unreacted alcohol, and hydrogen. The composition of the product varies greatly, depending upon the catalyst composition and reaction conditions.

Reaction Mechanism. The mechanism of the esterification was at first believed to proceed through the intermediate formation of acetaldehyde, followed by esterification by the Tishchenko reaction:

$$2 \; C_2H_5OH \rightarrow 2 \; CH_3CHO \rightarrow CH_3COOC_2H_5$$

Based on subsequent studies, Lel'chuk and co-workers have proposed the following mechanism (86):

$$C_2H_5OH \rightarrow CH_3CHO + H_2$$
$$CH_3CHO + H_2O \rightarrow CH_3COOH + H_2$$
$$C_2H_5OH + CH_3COOH \rightarrow CH_3COOC_2H_5 + H_2O$$

Acetic acid may also be produced by reaction of alcohol and water, liberating hydrogen, but this apparently plays only a secondary role.

The above reaction mechanism is based on tests with 96% alcohol, using catalysts containing various promoters, carried out at a constant space velocity of 400 ml/(hr) (liter of catalyst), and with reaction temperatures of 250, 275, and 300°C. From analysis of the products obtained, the quantities of acetaldehyde, acetic acid, and ethyl acetate primarily formed according to the above equations were calculated. This permitted calculation of the yields of the reactions, and assuming the yield to be representative of the reaction velocity constant k, plots of log k versus the reciprocal of the absolute temperature were made. These resulted in straight lines, which permitted calculation of apparent activation energies for each of the reaction stages.

Catalysts. The method and technique used to prepare the catalyst mass are reported to be important factors in determining the life and mechanical stability as well as the activity of the mass. One method involves coprecipitation of copper acetate and the nitrate of the corresponding promoter with alkali, washing to neutral, and drying at 100°C (86). In another method, equal parts of copper and aluminum are melted together with the addition of activators, such as cerium or zirconium, and the alloy leached with dilute sodium hydroxide until all the aluminum is removed. Activation of the catalyst with hydrogen at 180–200°C is usually desirable.

Effect of Promoters. Lel'chuk and co-workers have studied the effect of a number of promoters and found the addition of 0.1% of uranium to the copper contact mass to give the highest yield of ester (55.7%). Zirconium (0.9%), thorium (0.2%), and cerium (0.2%) are also effective; titanium and chromium show a promoting influence when present in somewhat larger quantities (2–4%). The introduction of a third component into a binary copper-base catalyst has also been investigated. Addition of barium oxide, aluminum oxide, manganese oxide, silver, and nickel, to a copper catalyst promoted with 2% of cerium all caused a marked reduction in yield of ester. On the other hand, addition of up to 5% of titanium dioxide to a catalyst composed of copper and 10% aluminum oxide increased the yield of ester from 22.5 to 30.6%. This is a true case of coactivation, since the activity of the ternary mixture is higher than that of either of the binary pairs. Chromium oxide and thorium oxide also show coactivation with the copper–alumina (90:10) catalyst.

Optimum Yields of Ethyl Acetate. The yield obtained by dehydrogenation of ethyl alcohol varies considerably depending upon the promoter, space velocity, and temperature. Considering the effect of the promoter, uranium is the most effective with regard to the highest yield of ester, but requires the use of low space velocities, 40–50 ml/(hr)(liter of catalyst), and lower temperatures: 25% yield at 140°C, 45% at 160°C, 56% at 180°C, and 64% at 200°C (87). The copper–cerium catalyst is the least sensitive with respect to space velocity on yield of ester, but this catalyst is most rapidly deactivated (due to acetic acid or acetaldehyde) and produces some acetal and butyl acetate as by-products. The ternary copper–aluminum oxide–chromic oxide catalyst has been reported to give a conversion of 53.9% ester at 275°C with a space velocity of 165 ml/(hr)(liter of catalyst) and is said to approach the stability of the copper–uranium contact masses, which have been used for 1100 hr of continuous operation at 200–290°C.

The yield of ester may be increased by recirculation of the condensate over the catalyst mass. With the copper–aluminum oxide–chromic oxide catalyst, a yield of 75% of ethyl acetate was obtained with three passes over the contact mass at 275°C.

Use of Other Alcohols. In addition to ethyl alcohol, the behavior of the following aliphatic alcohols has been studied by Ivannikov: *n*-propyl, *n*-butyl, isobutyl, *n*-amyl, isoamyl, and *n*-hexyl. Using a catalyst composed of copper oxide with 10.8% of uranium oxide, yields of 51–75.6% of esters were obtained from these alcohols at 220–310°C with feed rates of 300–2400 ml alcohol/(hr)(liter of catalyst). With slower rates of feeding 40–50 ml/(hr)(liter of catalyst), and lower temperatures the following conversions to ester were obtained: 64% from *n*-propyl alcohol at 200°C and 45% at 180°C, 76% from *n*-butyl alcohol at 200°C and 70% at 180°C, and 73% from isoamyl alcohol at 200°C (87).

Treatment of Mixtures of Alcohols. By passing a mixture of two alcohols over the catalyst, four different esters should be possible, according to the equation

$$4 \text{RCH}_2\text{OH} + 4 \text{R}'\text{CH}_2\text{OH} \rightarrow \text{RCOOCH}_2\text{R} + \text{R}'\text{COOCH}_2\text{R}' + \text{RCOOCH}_2\text{R}' + \text{R}'\text{COOCH}_2\text{R}$$

Thus, with a feed of ethyl and butyl alcohols, the products should include ethyl acetate, butyl acetate, ethyl butyrate, and butyl butyrate. However, butyl acetate was found as the predominant product using a copper catalyst promoted with 0.2% cerium at 250–300°C (88).

Ivannikov has investigated the systems ethanol–1-butanol, ethanol–isoamyl alcohol, and ethanol–1-hexanol, with copper oxide catalyst containing 10.8% uranium oxide at 270°C. With a feed velocity of 1200 ml/(hr)(liter of catalyst), the esterified products represented 56.3–65.2% of the alcohols used. At low velocities, 40–50 ml/(hr)(liter of catalyst), the reaction proceeds even at temperatures below 200°C with active catalysts (87).

Technical Preparation of Esters. Although it is generally acknowledged that the choice of the process to obtain a maximum yield of a given ester is dependent upon many factors, some methods of more or less general applicability have been described. It must be emphasized, however, that no single process has universal applicability; in most cases, modifications in the proportions of reactants or other variables are required for optimum yields with different acids and alcohols. The methods given in this section are representative of both laboratory and plant-scale techniques used in batch esterifications.

Methyl Esters. Clinton and Laskowski have reported that methyl esters are obtained in good yield using methylene dichloride or ethylene dichloride as solvent (89). The latter is generally preferred but the choice of the solvent depends to some extent upon the boiling point of the desired ester. The general procedure is as follows: For each mole of aliphatic carboxyl group, 96 g (3 moles) commercial methanol, 300 ml ethylene dichloride, and 3 ml concentrated sulfuric acid are used. With aromatic acids, the amount of sulfuric acid is increased to 15 ml/mole of carboxyl group. The mixture is refluxed for 6–15 hr, although in some cases the time limit may be as short as $\frac{1}{2}$ hr. Progress of esterification is usually, but not invariably, indicated by the development of cloudiness and separation of an upper layer containing water, methanol, and sulfuric acid. After the reaction is completed, the mixture is cooled and is washed successively with water, sodium bicarbonate solution, and again with water. The ethylene dichloride layer is then distilled at atmospheric pressure or in vacuo and the residual methyl ester is purified by distillation or crystallization.

The substitution of a milder catalyst, such as ethanesulfonic acid (0.5–1.0 ml/ mole of carboxyl group) for the sulfuric acid permits the preparation of esters such as methyl pyruvate with no difficulty. Yields of methyl esters prepared by this method are as follows: cyclohexane acetate, 93–95%; adipate, 87%; benzoate, 95%; coumarin 3-carboxylate, 98%; salicylate, 92%; 2,4-dinitrophenyl acetate, 91%; and pyruvate, 73%.

Ethyl Esters. The method of Locquin and Elghozy is often used for the preparation of ethyl esters (90). In the production of diethyl adipate, 400 g ethyl alcohol (95%), 200 g toluene, 146 g adipic acid, and 2.5 ml concentrated hydrochloric acid are mixed in a 1-liter flask equipped with a short distillation column head and downward condenser. The flask is heated on a water bath until the azeotropic mixture of alcohol, water, and toluene stops distilling; at this point about two-thirds of the organic acid is esterified. The same charge, omitting the hydrochloric acid, is added to the residue in the flask and the process is repeated, increasing the yield of ester. The residue is distilled under reduced pressure (125–150°C at 177 mm Hg) giving 85–88% of diethyl adipate.

The advantages of this method are that ordinary commercial alcohol can be used, small amounts of catalyst are required, and no decantation, extraction, or alkali washing is required. The azeotropic distillate may be dried and reused. This process is applicable to esterifications of many organic acids and may also be used with n-propyl alcohol.

Sugasawa reported the following yields of ethyl esters by this method (91): malonate, 85%; suberate, 93%; azelate, 85%; pelargonate, 83%; and tartrate, 90%. With cinnamic, benzoic, and 11-bromoundecylic acids, hydrochloric acid was not satisfactory as a catalyst; sulfuric or hydrobromic acid was substituted with yields of 92–95% of ethyl esters.

Mićović used a similar procedure for diethyl esters of dicarboxylic acids and recommends the following proportions (92): 1 mole dicarboxylic acid, 360 ml absolute alcohol (6 moles), 180 ml toluene, and 1–2% concentrated sulfuric acid. The mixture is heated on an oil bath (at 100–120°C) and the ternary mixture of alcohol, water, and toluene is distilled off at 75–78°C. The distillate is dried with potassium carbonate and returned to the distilling flask. After removing the ternary mixture a second time, the residue was distilled in vacuo after addition of anhydrous sodium carbonate to suberic and higher acids. Yields of diethyl esters from malonic, succinic, glutaric, adipic, pimelic, suberic, azelaic, and sebacic acids were almost quantitative. Diethyl oxalate was obtained in 90–95% yield and good yields were reported with chlorosuccinic and α,α-dibromoadipic acids.

With monocarboxylic aromatic acids, 1 mole of sulfuric acid is recommended for every 10 moles of water, which must be eliminated with the double distillation. A triple distillation is required to give a 95–97% yield of ethyl fumarate. In this case, 39 g fumaric acid is used with 160 ml absolute alcohol, 80 ml toluene, and 1 g concentrated sulfuric acid. Similar yields are obtained using this technique with ethyl maleate. Comparatively good yields of esters of levulinic, palmitic, and oleic acids result under these conditions.

Medium-Boiling Esters. Steffens described a technique for esterifying ethyl and propyl alcohols, ethylene glycol, and glycerol with lactic, tartaric, oxalic, citric chloroacetic, maleic, malic, and succinic acids using a third component such as benzene toluene, hexane, or carbon tetrachloride to remove the water produced (93). For the preparation of ethyl lactate, he recommends using 1 mole of 80% lactic acid, 2.3 moles of 95% ethyl alcohol, and a volume of benzene equal to half that of the alcohol. The vapors from the reaction kettle are rectified to give a mixture of 7% water, 74% benzene, and 19% alcohol. Upon condensing, two layers are formed: The upper one contains 81% benzene, 15% alcohol, and 4% water, and the lower one contains 35% water, 55% alcohol, and 10% benzene. The lower layer is extracted to recover the benzene and alcohol and the water is discarded. The upper layer is returned to the column as reflux. After all the water is removed, the excess of alcohol and benzene is distilled off and the ester is fractionated. With esters such as ethyl butyrate, valerate, propionate, benzoate, and salicylate, a similar procedure is employed except that a catalyst (hydrochloric, phosphoric, or sulfuric acid, or zinc chloride) is used.

Esters of the type of triacetin, and di-*n*-butyl and diisoamyl tartrates and citrates are prepared by heating the alcohol and the acid without a catalyst and continuously removing the water formed by distillation. Thus, in the case of triacetin, 92 lb glycerol and 270 lb glacial acetic acid are charged to a distilling apparatus provided with a rectifying column. The mixture is distilled slowly, giving a distillate of water and very weak acetic acid. The distillation is continued until strong acetic acid is given off. The yield of ester is said to be practically quantitative. For the preparation of dibutyl tartrate, 150 lb tartaric acid and 296 lb butyl alcohol are charged to the still pot, and the water–alcohol binary is distilled out. When no more water is given off, the reaction is completed. The ester is washed with dilute alkali and distilled under reduced pressure, giving an almost quantitative yield.

High-Boiling Esters. Bannister recommends the following procedure for making diethyl phthalate and other high-boiling esters (94): One equivalent of phthalic anhydride and 2.5 equivalents of ethyl alcohol are refluxed for 2 hr in the presence of 1% of concentrated sulfuric acid (based on the acid anhydride). To produce the monoester, the excess of alcohol is distilled off at a temperature below 100°C. For the diester, a mixture of 67% benzene and 33% alcohol is introduced continuously below the surface of the reaction mixture and the resulting alcohol–water–benzene ternary is distilled off and condensed. A yield of diester of over 99% is obtained by passing 3.4–7 equivalents of alcohol through the mixture in 4.5–7 hr.

Esters of stearic, benzoic, citric, caproic, malonic, succinic, cinnamic, tartaric, salicylic, malic, and fumaric acids may be made in this manner. Cyclohexane, cyclohexadiene, and cyclohexene are recommended as entrainers for ethyl and isopropyl esters. Heptane, methylcyclohexane, and toluene are suggested with n-propyl esters.

Crowell and Ebe have employed the following procedure for di-n-butyl phthalate: 1000 lb phthalic anhydride, 1250 lb butyl alcohol (about 25% excess), and 10 lb sulfuric acid are allowed to react at 82–87°C for 24 hr. The mixture is then slowly distilled under a vacuum of 20–26 in. Hg to remove the water as the binary azeotrope. The crude ester is washed with sodium carbonate solution and then with water and dried. To deodorize the product, the ester is heated to 118°C while agitating with a current of dry steam. Decolorizing is achieved by filtering the mass through carbon. A yield of 97% of diester is reported. This procedure is also applicable to di-n-butyl tartrate, oxalate, and stearate.

Organotitanium and -zirconium compounds are effective catalysts for the esterification of carboxylic acids or anhydrides with higher-boiling monohydric alcohols at temperatures which permit the continuous distillation of the water formed (95). Refluxing 1 mole phthalic anhydride with 3 moles 2-ethyl-2-hexanol under stirring with these agents and removing the water by a trap separator gave the following yields:

Catalyst agent	Amount, g	Reflux time, min	Yield, %
tetraisopropyl titanate	2	93	99.7
tetraethyl zirconate	2	93	99.8
tetraphenyl titanate	3	162	99.0
tetrastearyl titanate	4	180	99.0
monostearyl titanate	2.7	240	99.0

In the absence of a catalyst, 19-hr reaction time was required for a 99% conversion to di-2-ethylhexyl phthalate.

Two excellent examples of how the esterification technique must be altered for different members of the same series are shown in the following preparations of esters of lactic acid and of ethylene chlorohydrin.

Esters of Lactic Acid. Smith and Claborn have described the esterification of lactic (α-hydroxypropionic) acid with various alcohols (96). The lactic acid was obtained from the fermentation of whey as the calcium or sodium salt. The calcium or sodium lactate was treated with an equivalent amount of sulfuric acid to liberate the lactic acid. Three procedures are recommended, depending upon the boiling point of the ester. For the low-boiling, water-soluble esters (methyl, ethyl, n-propyl, and isopropyl), the proportions are as follows: 1 mole lactic acid, 5 moles alcohol, and 0.02 mole sulfuric acid. The mixture is heated for 4–8 hr at refluxing temperature to complete the esterification. The mixture is filtered and the residue is washed with fresh alcohol to recover the adhering esters; these washings are then used in the next esterification charge. The filtrate is rapidly distilled at atmospheric pressure without neutralization to remove the excess of alcohol. When most of the alcohol is removed, the distillation is continued under reduced pressure. The distillation is stopped before the occurrence of charring due to excess sulfuric acid. The residue in the still is returned to the reaction kettle for the next charge. The distillate is refractionated, distilling the esters under reduced pressure. Yields of 70–90% are obtained.

For esters insoluble in water (butyl, amyl, hexyl, octyl, and lauryl lactates), 5 moles (1090 g) calcium lactate, 1.5–2 moles alcohol, and an equivalent amount of sulfuric acid plus 10 g for catalytic purposes are taken with 50 g benzene or toluene. The mixture is slowly stirred during the esterification. The water is removed as an azeotrope and is drawn off as it separates in a Betz-Holden-type trap. The reaction is completed in 1–8 hr. The ester is purified in the above manner, giving a yield of 88–95% based on the lactic acid.

In the preparation of pure lactic esters that are too high to fractionate in vacuo without decomposition, it is necessary to start with a refined type of lactic acid. β-Phenylethyl, benzyl, and stearyl esters are examples of this type. No sulfuric acid catalyst is needed with these esterifications. An excess of acid is removed by washing with water, and the last traces of water are removed by heating in vacuo. Any color that develops during esterification may be removed by heating the ester with decolorizing carbon and subsequent filtering. The yield of water-white ester, based on the alcohol, is nearly quantitative.

Esters of Ethylene Chlorohydrin. Rodier has prepared the esters of ethylene chlorohydrin (2-chloroethanol) and a number of fatty acids, and in order to obtain maximum yields used three procedures (97): For the long-chain esters, the acids are used; the acid chlorides are employed for the medium range; and the lower members require the use of acid anhydrides.

Direct esterification in the presence of anhydrous hydrogen chloride was used for the esters of acids from pelargonic through stearic. A 10% excess of ethylene chlorohydrin was dissolved with the acid in carbon tetrachloride. After saturation with hydrogen chloride, the mixture was allowed to stand 3–5 hr in the cold. The excess of hydrogen chloride was neutralized with 7% aqueous sodium bicarbonate, discarding the upper aqueous and intermediate salt layers. The carbon tetrachloride layer was washed with water, dried over calcium chloride, and then concentrated until the ester crystallized out. The esters were purified by recrystallization.

The acid chlorides, with hydrogen chloride as catalyst, were used to prepare the esters from propionate through caprate, with 30-min reaction time in the cold, followed by heating 1–1.5 hr at 40–100°C. Yields of these esters ranged from 70 to 80%.

Acetic anhydride was required to prepare the β-chloroethyl acetate, by refluxing 20 ml of ethylene chlorohydrin with 30 ml of acetic anhydride for 1 hr. β-Chloroethyl formate was made by treating 44 g of ethylene chlorohydrin with formic acetic anhydride (obtained from 23 g of formic acid and 51 g of acetic anhydride) at 40°C.

Difficultly Esterifiable Acids. The sterically hindered acids, such as 2,6-disubstituted benzoic acids, cannot usually be esterified by the conventional means. Prelog and Piantanida developed a process for the synthesis of the methyl esters of such acids (98). The acid is dissolved in methanol and is titrated with pure tetramethylammonium hydroxide in methanol using phenolphthalein as indicator. The excess methanol is removed in vacuo and the salt is decomposed by heating until all the trimethylamine is driven off. The residue is practically pure methyl ester. This method may be used for other acids as well: Yields of 71–95% of methyl esters of oleanolate, acetyloleanolate, palmitate, oleate, and nicotinate have been obtained. With hindered acids such as 2,4,6-trimethyl- and -triethylbenzoic acids, yields of 63–90% of the methyl esters resulted by decomposing the tetramethylammonium salts at 200–250°C (99).

Newman has prepared esters of certain sterically hindered acids by dissolving 2 g of the acid in 14–20 ml of 100% sulfuric acid (prepared by mixing approximately equal weights of 96% sulfuric acid and 20% oleum (100). After standing a few minutes at room temperature, the solution is poured into an excess of cold absolute alcohol. Most of the alcohol is removed under reduced pressure, about 50 ml of water is added, and the distillation continued under reduced pressure to remove the remainder of the alcohol. The organic matter is extracted with ether and treated with sodium carbonate solution. The ester is then distilled. Yields of esters made in this manner are methyl 2,4,6-trimethylbenzoate, 78%; methyl 2,4,6-triethylbenzoate, 80%; methyl 2,4,6-triisopropylbenzoate, 81%; ethyl 2,4,6-trimethylbenzoate, 66%; and isopropyl 2,4,6-trimethylbenzoate, 57%.

Bibliography

"Esterification" in *ECT* 1st ed., Vol. 5, pp. 776–817, by C. E. Leyes, Celanese Corporation of America.

1. H. A. Goldsmith, *Chem. Rev.* **33**, 257 (1943).
2. D. B. Keyes, *Ind. Eng. Chem.* **24**, 1096 (1932).
3. E. E. Reid, "Esterification" in P. Groggins, *Unit Processes in Organic Synthesis*, 4th ed., McGraw-Hill Book Co., New York, 1952.
4. P. Petrenko-Kritchenko, W. Bogatsky, and N. Lubman, *Z. Physik. Chem.* **115**, 289 (1925).
5. G. Cauquil, *J. Chim. Phys.* **23**, 586 (1926).
6. H. A. Smith, *J. Am. Chem. Soc.* **61**, 254 (1939); **62**, 1136 (1940).
7. R. J. Hartman, L. B. Storms, and A. G. Gassmann, *J. Am. Chem. Soc.* **61**, 2167 (1939).
8. A. G. Gassmann and R. J. Hartman, *J. Am. Chem. Soc.* **63**, 2393 (1941).
9. H. A. Smith and C. H. Reichardt, *J. Am. Chem. Soc.* **63**, 605 (1941).
10. N. Shlechter, D. F. Othmer, and S. Marshak, *Ind. Eng. Chem.* **37**, 900 (1945).
11. C. E. Leyes and D. F. Othmer, *Ind. Eng. Chem.* **37**, 968 (1945).
12. S. Berman, A. A. Melnychuk, and D. F. Othmer, *Ind. Eng. Chem.* **40**, 1312 (1948).
13. R. A. Troupe and K. A. Kobe, *Ind. Eng. Chem.* **42**, 801, 1403 (1950).
14. R. A. Troupe and E. DiMilla, *Ind. Eng. Chem.* **49**, 847 (1957).
15. D. F. Othmer and S. A. Rao, *Ind. Eng. Chem.* **42**, 1912 (1950).
16. W. C. Ling and C. J. Geankoplis, *Ind. Eng. Chem.* **50**, 939 (1958).
17. S. Poznanski, *Roczniki Chem.* **8**, 377 (1928); *Chem. Abstr.* **23**, 1559 (1929).
18. W. Swietoslawski, *J. Phys. Chem.* **37**, 701 (1933).
19. P. E. Coria, *Rev. Fac. Cience. Quim. Univ. Nacl. La Plata* **10**, 67 (1935); *Chem. Abstr.* **36**, 7427 (1942).
20. C. A. Durruty, *Anales Asoc. Quim. Arg.* **19**, 227 (1931); *Chem. Abstr.* **26**, 3721 (1932).
21. H. M. Trimble and E. L. Richardson, *J. Am. Chem. Soc.* **62**, 1018 (1940).
22. L. H. Horsley, *Ind. Eng. Chem., Anal. Ed.* **19**, 508 (1947).
23. J. C. Konen, E. T. Clocker, and R. P. Cox, *Oil & Soap* **22**, 57 (1945).
24. E. Thielpape with A. Fulde, *Ber.* **B66**, 1454 (1933).
25. P. L. Gordon and R. Aronowitz, *Ind. Eng. Chem.* **37**, 780 (1945).
26. C. L. Levesque and A. M. Craig, *Ind. Eng. Chem.* **40**, 96 (1948).
27. S. Sussman, *Ind. Eng. Chem.* **38**, 1228 (1946).
28. M. J. Astel, B. Schaeffer, and C. O. Obenland, *J. Am. Chem. Soc.* **77**, 3643 (1955).
29. C. E. Leyes and D. F. Othmer, *Trans. Am. Inst. Chem. Engrs.* **41**, 157 (1945).
30. S. Berman, H. Isbenjian, A. Sedoff, and D. F. Othmer, *Ind. Eng. Chem.* **40**, 2139 (1948).
31. L. E. Schniepp, J. W. Dunning, and E. C. Lathrop, *Ind. Eng. Chem.* **37**, 872 (1945).
32. U.S. Pat. 2,426,968 (Sept. 2, 1947), H. W. Grubb, L. M. O'Hara, and K. Atwood (to Seagram & Sons).
33. C. Venkateswarlu, M. Satyanarayana, and M. N. Rao, *Ind. Eng. Chem.* **50**, 973 (1958).
34. H. C. Tidwell and E. E. Reid, *J. Am. Chem. Soc.* **53**, 4353 (1931).
35. H. F. Hoerig, D. Hanson, and O. L. Kowalke, *Ind. Eng. Chem.* **35**, 575 (1943).

36. V. I. Gol'danskiĭ and N. M. Chirkov, *J. Phys. Chem. (USSR)* **20**, 1333 (1946); *Chem. Abstr.* **41**, 2973 (1947).
37. A. A. Vernon and B. M. Brown, *Ind. Eng. Chem.* **32**, 534 (1940); **33**, 1289 (1941).
38. J. F. Spangenberg, *Ind. Quím. Buenos Aires* **7**, 393 (1945); *Chem Abstr.* **41**, 4028 (1947).
39. T. F. Murray Jr., and W. O. Kenyon, *J. Am. Chem. Soc.* **62**, 1230 (1940).
40. J. W. Swanson and J. Coss, *Proc. Iowa Acad. Sci.* **45**, 123 (1938).
41. G. H. Morey, *Ind. Eng. Chem.* **31**, 1129 (1939).
42. C. D. Hurd and A. S. Roe, *J. Am. Chem. Soc.* **61**, 3355 (1939).
43. U.S. Pat. 2,117,600 (May 17, 1938), J. L. Brill and R. W. Plummer (to E. I. du Pont de Nemours & Co., Inc.).
44. J. F. Goggans, Jr. and J. E. Copenhaver, *J. Am. Chem. Soc.* **61**, 2909 (1939).
45. I. M. Ezrielev and O. L. Katstov, *Narodnyĭ Komissariat Tyazheloĭ Prom. SSSR, Nauchni Izsled. Inst. Plasticheskikh Mass., Platicheskie Massy, Sbornik* **2**, 307 (1937); *Chem Abstr.* **31** 3898 (1937).
46. B. Abramovitch, J. C. Shivers, B. E. Hudson, and C. R. Hauser, *J. Am. Chem. Soc.* **65**, 986 (1943).
47. U.S. Pat. 2,345,006 (March 28, 1944), J. Ross, R. L. Brandt, and J. H. Percy (to Colgate-Palmolive-Peet Co.).
48. A. Spasov, *Ber.* **B70**, 1926 (1937); **B75**, 779, 780 (1942).
49. A. Spasov, *Annuaire Univ. Sofia II, Fac. Phys. Math., Livre 2*, **35**, 289 (1940).
50. C. Paquot and F. Bouquet, *Bull. Soc. Chim. France* **1947**, 321.
51. F. A. Menalda, *Rec. Trav. Chim.* **49**, 967 (1930).
52. H. A. Taylor and T. W. Davis, *J. Phys. Chem.* **32**, 1467 (1928).
53. S. G. Toole and F. J. Sowa, *J. Am. Chem. Soc.* **59**, 1971 (1937).
54. U.S. Pat. 2,375,301 (May 8, 1945), R. M. Joyce (to Du Pont).
55. P. Pfeiffer, I. Engelhardt, and W. Alfuss, *Ann.* **467**, 158 (1928).
56. U.S. Pat. 2,408,940 (Oct. 8, 1946), J. E. Mahan (to Phillips Petroleum Corp.).
57. A. A. Ross and F. E. Bibbins, *Ind. Eng. Chem.* **29**, 1341 (1937).
58. Brit. Pat. 561,969 (June 13, 1944), L. Jilk (to Du Pont).
59. R. Altschul, *J. Am. Chem. Soc.* **68**, 2605 (1946).
60. U.S. Pats. 2,414,999; 2,415,000 (Jan. 28, 1947), A. E. Bearse and R. D. Morin (to Standard Oil of Indiana, Inc.).
61. T. B. Dorris, F. J. Sowa, and J. A. Nieuwland, *J. Am. Chem. Soc.* **56**, 2689 (1934).
62. T. B. Dorris and F. J. Sowa, *J. Am. Chem. Soc.* **60**, 358 (1938).
63. U.S. Pat. 2,224,809 (Dec. 10, 1940), G. H. Coleman (to Dow Chemical Co.).
64. B. T. Brooks, *Ind. Eng. Chem.* **27**, 278 (1935).
65. S. V. Zavgorodnii, *Trudy Voronezhsk. Gos. Univ.* **10** (2), 41 (1938); *Chem. Abstr.* **33**, 5805 (1939).
66. U.S. Pat. 3,014,066 (Dec. 19, 1961), E. R. Kerr and M. C. Throckmorton (to Texaco, Inc.).
67. T. D. Aldoshin, *J. Gen. Chem. (USSR)* **8**, 1385 (1938); *Chem. Abstr.* **33**, 4194 (1939).
68. J. H. Simons and A. C. Meunier, *J. Am. Chem. Soc.* **63**, 1921 (1941).
69. T. W. Evans, K. R. Edlund, and M. D. Taylor, *Ind. Eng. Chem.* **30**, 55 (1938).
70. G. O. Morrison and T. P. Shaw, *Trans. Electrochem. Soc.* **63**, 425 (1933).
71. Brit. Pat. 539,235 (Sept. 2, 1941), Du Pont.
72. U.S. Pat. 2,398,820 (April 23, 1946), P. D. Coppock and D. J. Hadley (to Distillers Co.).
73. J. W. Reppe, *Mod. Plastics* **23** (3), 162 (1945).
73a. U.S. Pat. 2,975,210 (Mar. 14, 1961) L. O. Raether and H. R. Garmrath (to Monsanto Chemical Co.).
73b. U.S. Pat. 2,759,953 (Aug. 21, 1956), H. B. Knight, R. E. Koos, and D. Swern (to the United States of America, as represented by the Secretary of Agriculture).
74. H. W. Underwood Jr. and G. C. Toone, *J. Am. Chem. Soc.* **52**, 391 (1930).
75. H. W. Underwood Jr. and R. L. Wakeman, *J. Am. Chem. Soc.* **52**, 387 (1930).
76. H. Meerwein and H. Maier-Hüser, *J. Prakt. Chem.* **134**, 51 (1932).
77. U.S. Pat. 2,978,469 (April 4, 1961), J. H. Brown Jr. and N. B. Lorette (to Dow Chemical Co.).
78. U.S. Pat. 1,879,605 (Sept. 27, 1932), H. Dreyfus.
79. U.S. Pat. 2,030,835 (Feb. 11, 1936), H. L. Cox and P. S. Greer (to Union Carbide & Carbon Corp.).
80. Brit. Pat. 486,560 (June 7, 1938), Du Pont.

81. M. Y. Kagan and I. A. Sobolev, *J. Chem. Ind.* (*Moscow*) **1933** (2), 35; *Chem. Abstr.* **27,** 4215 (1933).
82. C. Paquot and R. Perron, *Bull. Soc. Chim. France* **1948,** 855.
83. A. Galat, *J. Am. Chem. Soc.* **68,** 376 (1946).
84. G. Darzens and C. Mentzer, *Compt. Rend.* **214,** 113 (1942).
85. J. Houben and W. Fischer, *Ber.* **B64,** 240, 2636 (1931).
86. S. L. Lel'chuk, D. N. Vaskevich, A. P. Belen'kaya, and F. A. Dashkovskaya, *Bull. Acad. Sci. USSR, Classe Sci. Chim.* **1946,** 191, 411; **1947,** 235; *Chem. Abstr.* **42,** 4436, 6630 (1948).
87. P. Ivannikov, *J. Gen. Chem.* (*U.S.S.R.*)**17,** 1103 (1947); *Chem. Abstr.* **42,** 1561 (1948).
88. B. N. Dolgov, M. M. Koton, and S. L. Lel'chuk, *J. Chem. Ind.* (*Moscow*) **12,** 1066 (1935); *Chem. Abstr.* **30,** 1027 (1936).
89. R. O. Clinton and S. C. Laskowski, *J. Am. Chem. Soc.* **70,** 3135 (1948).
90. R. Locquin and F. Elghozy, *Bull. Soc. Chim.* **41,** 445 (1927).
91. S. Sugasawa, *J. Pharm. Soc. Japan* **550,** 1050 (1927); *Chem. Abstr.* **22,** 1572 (1928).
92. V. M. Mićović, *Bull. Soc. Chim. Mém.* **4** (5), 1661 (1937).
93. U.S. Pat. 1,421,604 (July 4, 1922), J. A. Steffens (to U.S. Industrial Alcohol Co.).
94. U.S. Pat. 2,076,111 (April 6, 1937), W. J. Bannister (to Commercial Solvents Corp.).
95. Brit. Pat. 852,110 (Oct. 26, 1960), B. F. Goodrich Co.
96. L. T. Smith and H. V. Claborn, *Ind. Eng. Chem.* **32,** 692 (1940).
97. I. G. Rodier, *Bull. Soc. Chim. France* **1948,** 637.
98. V. Prelog and M. Piantanida, *Z. Physiol. Chem.* **244,** 56 (1936).
99. R. C. Fuson, J. Corse, and E. C. Horning, *J. Am. Chem. Soc.* **61,** 1290 (1939).
100. M. S. Newman, *J. Am. Chem. Soc.* **63,** 2431 (1941).

CHARLES E. LEYES
Newark College of Engineering

ESTER INTERCHANGE

Ester interchange (re-, trans-, or interesterification) may be defined as a reaction between an ester and another compound, characterized by an exchange of alkoxy groups or of acyl groups, and resulting in the formation of a different ester. It is thus an esterification process, if esterification is taken in its broadest sense to include all processes by which esters are produced (see Esters, organic; Esterification).

In the best-known types of ester interchange, the compound with which the ester reacts is an alcohol (eq. 1), an acid (eq. 2), or another ester (eq. 3). These ester interchanges may be called, more specifically, ester–alcohol interchange or alcoholysis, ester–acid interchange or acidolysis, and ester–ester interchange, respectively.

$$RCOOR' + R''OH \rightleftharpoons RCOOR'' + R'OH \tag{1}$$

$$RCOOR' + R''COOH \rightleftharpoons RCOOH + R''COOR' \tag{2}$$

$$RCOOR' + R''COOR''' \rightleftharpoons RCOOR''' + R''COOR' \tag{3}$$

These reactions are reversible and ordinarily do not involve large energy changes.

Ester–Alcohol Interchange (Alcoholysis)

REACTION CONDITIONS

The reaction commonly takes place in one liquid phase, sometimes with one of the reactants being only partially soluble and going into solution gradually as the reaction proceeds. Unless an excess of one of the reactants is used, or unless one of the products is withdrawn from the reacting phase by vaporization or precipitation, the reaction does not proceed to completion, but comes to a standstill with substantial proportions of both alcohols and both esters in equilibrium. The concentrations present at equilibrium depend upon the characteristics of the alcohols and esters involved, but in most practical uses of the reaction, one or both of the devices mentioned are used to force the reaction toward completion.

Temperatures. A wide range of temperatures has been used in alcoholysis reactions. With alkaline catalysts, the reaction often takes place at room temperature or even at lower temperatures. With acid catalysts, temperatures near 100°C are more commonly used. With no catalyst, temperatures around 250°C or higher may be required for a practical reaction rate. The structures of the alcohol and the ester involved, as well as the catalyst used, have an effect upon the rate of reaction at a given temperature. Some esters will interesterify with methanol at 100°C or lower with no catalyst added (1,2).

Pressure. The selection of the pressure to be used is governed largely by the volatility of the reactants at the reaction temperature and by the concentrations which must be maintained. In alcoholysis of an ester with an excess of a volatile alcohol such as methanol, for example, it may be convenient to use a pressure higher than 1 atm (3). On the other hand, when the reaction is to be forced toward completion by vaporization of one of the products, a reduced pressure may be best.

Catalysts. Alkalies and acids are the most commonly used catalysts. Of the alkaline catalysts, alkali metal alkoxides are the most effective; ordinarily, the sodium or potassium alkoxide of the alcohol entering the reaction is preferred. When sodium hydroxide, potassium carbonate, and similar materials are used to catalyze alcoholysis, it is likely that the actual catalyst is the alkoxide, formed by reaction of the added alkali with the alcohol. In solution in alcohol, especially in methanol, alkoxides can exist in equilibrium with hydroxides in the presence of considerable concentrations of water (4).

Various other catalysts of milder alkalinity are said to be preferred in special cases. For example, the use of sodium methyl carbonate as catalyst in the methanolysis of poly(vinyl acetate) is said to yield a poly(vinyl alcohol) having improved color (5). Aluminum alkoxide has been proposed as catalyst for the alcoholysis of certain unsaturated esters (6); other sensitive esters have been made with the Grignard reagent as catalyst (7). Various other metals whose oxides, alkoxides, etc, have more or less catalytic effects include calcium, magnesium, lead, tin, and zinc. Zinc is reported to be an efficient catalyst in the alcoholysis of ethyl esters of α-halogenated aliphatic acids by allyl and methallyl alcohols (8); conventional catalysts would favor undesirable side reactions.

Among the acid catalysts, sulfuric acid, sulfonic acids, and hydrochloric acid are most used. With polyhydric alcohols, sulfuric acid is preferred to hydrochloric because of the tendency of hydrochloric acid to form chlorohydrins.

EQUILIBRIUM

Alcohols and acids differ in their activity in esterification and ester interchange. For example, if equivalent quantities of methanol and isopropyl acetate are heated together until no further change takes place, under conditions which prevent the escape of any of the constituents of the mixture, the equilibrium composition contains larger molar concentrations of methyl acetate and isopropyl alcohol than of isopropyl acetate and methanol. Various alcohols have been compared in this way (9,10). In general, primary alcohols are more active than secondary alcohols (that is, they tend to displace them), and secondary alcohols tend to displace tertiary alcohols, but in addition, there are considerable differences among different members of the same class. Among the primary alcohols, methanol is one of the most active. Similarly, different acids show varying degrees of activity.

REACTION RATES

A notable feature of the alcoholysis reaction is the speed with which it takes place in the presence of an alkaline catalyst. As an example of this, in the saponification of glycerides with alcoholic lye, alcoholysis is faster than saponification, so that the glycerides are converted largely to ethyl esters and glycerol before much soap is formed (11). Methyl benzoate dissolved in 10 equivalents of ethyl alcohol containing 0.05 equivalent of potassium ethoxide is converted almost entirely to ethyl benzoate in one hour at room temperature. These same reaction conditions, on the other hand, are too mild to produce much reaction between methyl benzoate and secondary or tertiary alcohols, or between o-substituted methyl benzoates and primary alcohols (12), facts that illustrate the effect of structure on reaction rates.

REACTION MECHANISM

In the alcoholysis of an ester, as in hydrolysis, the alkoxy group remains intact; the bond between the —OR group and the carbonyl carbon atom is the one that is broken. The only exception is the alcoholysis of esters of tertiary alcohols in neutral or acid medium, but when an alkaline catalyst is present, the rule holds even for tertiary alcohol esters (13).

Various mechanisms have been proposed for ester hydrolysis (14) and for alcoholysis, which may be assumed to proceed according to an analogous mechanism. The formulations given below are believed to give a useful picture, which is in satisfactory agreement with known facts and current ideas.

Reaction with an Alkaline Catalyst. The following is believed to represent this mechanism:

$$RCOOR' \; + \; {}^{-}OR'' \; \rightleftharpoons \; R{-}\underset{\underset{\displaystyle OR''}{|}}{\overset{\overset{\displaystyle OR'}{|}}{C}}{-}O^{-}$$

$$R{-}\underset{\underset{\displaystyle OR''}{|}}{\overset{\overset{\displaystyle OR'}{|}}{C}}{-}O^{-} + HOR'' \rightleftharpoons R{-}\underset{\underset{\displaystyle OR''}{|}}{\overset{\overset{\displaystyle H\overset{+}{O}R'}{|}}{C}}{-}O^{-} + {}^{-}OR''$$

$$R{-}\underset{\underset{\displaystyle OR''}{|}}{\overset{\overset{\displaystyle H\overset{+}{O}R'}{|}}{C}}{-}O^{-} \rightleftharpoons RCOOR'' + HOR'$$

According to this view, the first step in the reaction is an attack on the carbonyl carbon atom of the ester by the anion of the alcohol. The activation energy may be considered to be the energy required to bring the anion up to the carbonyl group; substituents in R or R' that tend to lessen the basicity of the CO group would be expected to facilitate reaction by lowering the activation energy.

Reaction with an Acid Catalyst. The mechanism is as follows:

$$RCOOR' + HOR'' \rightleftharpoons R-\underset{\underset{OR'}{|}}{\overset{\overset{H\overset{+}{O}R''}{|}}{C}}-O^- \overset{HA}{\rightleftharpoons} R-\underset{\underset{OR'}{|}}{\overset{\overset{H\overset{+}{O}R''}{|}}{C}}-OH + A^-$$

$$R-\underset{\underset{OR'}{|}}{\overset{\overset{HOR''}{|}}{C}}-OH \rightleftharpoons R-\underset{\underset{\underset{+}{H\overset{}{O}R'}}{|}}{\overset{\overset{OR''}{|}}{C}}-OH \overset{A^-}{\rightleftharpoons} RCOOR'' + R'OH + HA$$

APPLICATIONS

The applications of alcoholysis in analysis, research, and manufacturing are too numerous to mention in detail. A few examples follow.

n-**Butyl Oleate.** Olive oil, 3 kg, consisting mainly of the glyceryl esters of oleic acid, is refluxed for 20 hr with 7 liters of *n*-butyl alcohol containing 150 g of concentrated sulfuric acid. After removal of the sulfuric acid by repeated washing with saturated sodium chloride solution and of the excess butyl alcohol by distillation, the residue is distilled under reduced pressure. The yield is 2242 g of esters boiling at 204–208°C at 3 mm, about 70% of theoretical based on the olive oil used. The product contains a small proportion of saturated esters (15).

Methanolysis of Glycerides. This proceeds smoothly with excess methanol and sodium methylate as catalyst (16).

Plasticizers are made by reactions of higher alcohols with lower alkyl phthalates (17). Higher esters of tertiary amino alkanoates (18) can be made from higher alcohols and methyl esters using sodium as catalyst. Sodium catalyzes the reaction of dialkylamino alcohols with ethyl esters of pyridinedicarboxylic acids (19). Higher phosphite esters are made from higher alcohols and diethyl phosphite using phosphorous acid as catalyst (20). Alkyl orthocarbonates are prepared from methyl orthocarbonate and alcohols using *p*-toluenesulfonic acid as catalyst (21). Orthotitanic esters are similarly prepared (22). Higher esters of amino acids are prepared by ester interchange with sodium methylate as catalyst (23,24). Aluminum alcoholates catalyze the reactions of acid, alkali, and water-sensitive compounds (25). Sterol esters are made by reaction of sterols with methyl esters of keto or cyano acids (26).

Regeneration of Carbohydrates from Acetylated Carbohydrates. In the investigation of sugars and other carbohydrates it is often advantageous to stabilize the material by acetylation and at the end of the desired manipulations or transformations to recover the free carbohydrate. For this recovery the well-known method of Zemplén is usually preferred because the reaction is rapid and can be carried out at room temperature if desired, with minimum damage to the carbohydrate (27). In the case of sugar acetates, these are dissolved in an excess of anhydrous methanol, to which a small quantity of sodium is added to form sodium methoxide. The quantity of sodium is a small fraction of the quantity equivalent to the acetate. The free sugar separates almost immediately. At waterbath temperature the reaction is complete in less than three minutes.

Cellulose esters as fibers and film can be deacetylated to cellulose by refluxing with methyl alcohol and sodium methylate catalyst.

Completeness of removal of the acetate groups from the carbohydrate to form methyl acetate is favored by the use of an excess of methanol, and by the fact that the free carbohydrate is insoluble in methanol and precipitates from the solution.

Sucrose Esters. These can be prepared by reaction of sucrose with methyl esters of fatty acids, with potassium carbonate as catalyst, and dimethyl formamide as solvent, at 80–90°C and 80–100 mm vacuum to remove methanol (28).

Quantitative Estimation of Acetyl in Carbohydrate Acetates. The foregoing procedure has been made the basis of a method for the quantitative estimation of acetyl groups in carbohydrate acetates, including cellulose acetate. Methyl acetate formed in the methanolysis of a weighed sample, using sodium methoxide as catalyst, is distilled from the mixture and determined by saponification (29,30).

Poly(vinyl Alcohol) (see also Vinyl compounds). Poly(vinyl alcohol) is more easily prepared, in a form which can be filtered and washed in a practical way, by alcoholysis of poly(vinyl acetate) than by its saponification in an aqueous system:

$$\left[CH_2CH\underset{\underset{OOCCH_3}{|}}{}\right]_n + CH_3OH \rightleftharpoons CH_3COOCH_3 + \left[CH_2CH\underset{\underset{OH}{|}}{}\right]_n$$

The use of a catalytic quantity of alkali equivalent to only a small fraction of the acetate has the advantage that contamination of the poly(vinyl alcohol) with salts, which are difficult to remove, is minimized. An interesting variant of the process is the use of a mixture of alcohol with the acetate ester produced by the alcoholysis as the alcoholyzing agent. This provides a means of controlling the completeness of removal of the acetate groups from the poly(vinyl acetate).

"In an enamel-lined vessel equipped with an anchor-type agitator, 600 grams of highly polymerized poly(vinyl acetate) was dissolved in 470 grams of methanol and 1830 grams of methyl acetate. After cooling the solution to a temperature of 20°C., a solution of 13 grams of sodium hydroxide in 200 grams of methanol was added. The resultant solution was agitated for a period of 3 hours and 45 minutes, whereupon the hydrolysis product was precipitated in the form of white shreds, which were easily separated from the liquid by filtration. After drying, a uniform, white, water-soluble product was obtained which had a saponification number of 58, corresponding to approximately 95% hydrolysis of the vinyl acetate" (31).

Monoglycerides. Monoglycerides, which are used extensively as intermediates in the manufacture of alkyd resins, as oil-soluble emulsifying agents, and as ingredients in shortening, are made from fats (triglycerides) by alcoholysis with glycerol (32,33).

An edible grade of monoglyceride can be made by heating refined, hydrogenated, deodorized cottonseed oil, 100 parts, in a stainless-steel vessel with a solution of 0.2 part sodium hydroxide in 20 parts of distilled glycerol, derived from edible fat. A pressure of about 2 in. of mercury is maintained in the vessel and the mixture heated and agitated vigorously with dry steam until the temperature reaches about 190°C and the mixture becomes clear and homogeneous. The catalyst is neutralized with phosphoric acid and the mixture is cooled and filtered. Such a product contains monoglycerides, diglycerides, triglycerides, and free glycerol approximately in the proportions calculated for a simple statistical distribution of fatty acid radicals among the hydroxyl groups in the mixture at equilibrium (34).

Acrylic Esters. A procedure has been described for preparation of higher esters from methyl acrylate, which illustrates the use of an acid catalyst together with the removal of one of the products by azeotropic distillation (35). Aluminum isopropoxide catalyzes the reaction of amino alcohols with methyl acrylate and methyl methacrylate (36,37).

Polyesters. The commercial development of poly(ethylene terephthalate) as a fiber and film is an excellent example of ester interchange as a method of making simple esters as well as making polyesters (38,39). In this reaction excess ethylene glycol is reacted with dimethyl terephthalate in the presence of a catalyst to form bis(2-hydroxyethyl) terephthalate at a temperature high enough to remove the methanol produced. The temperature is then raised and vacuum applied and further reaction takes place to release ethylene glycol and produce high-molecular-weight polymer. Catalysts are needed for both stages of this reaction (see Polyester fibers).

Usually, mildly alkaline substances are best for the first reaction, and mildly acidic substances are best for the second reaction. However, some substances are suitable for both. Very often mixtures are used in which one substance is intended to catalyze the first stage and the other substance to catalyze the second (polymerization) stage.

Substances reported as catalysts for these reactions include litharge (40), mixtures of litharge (PbO) and zinc borate (41), litharge and antimony oxide (42), lithium hydride, zinc acetate, and antimony oxide (43), alkali hydrides and fatty acid salts (44,45), alkali aluminates (46,47), manganous acetate (48,49), calcium hydride and antimony oxide (50), zinc, cadmium, and manganese salts (51), lanthanum oxide (52), cobalt salts plus antimony oxide (53), lead salts (54), low-melting alloys of tin and lead (55), stannous formate (56,57), titanates and silicates (58,59), manganous formate (60), lanthanum titanate (61), mixtures of magnesium carbonate and antimony fluoride (62), and uranyl nitrate and manganous acetate (63).

The ester interchange can be carried out as a continuous process (64,65).

Copolymers are also made by ester interchange (66,67).

1,4-Cyclohexanedimethanol interchanges with dimethyl terephthalate with quaternary ammonium compounds as catalyst (68).

On the other hand, poly(ethylene terephthalate) can be converted back to dimethyl terephthalate by using a large excess of methanol and high temperature and pressure. Crystalline dimethyl terephthalate separates on cooling (69–71).

Polycarbonates (qv) can be prepared by ester interchange between 4,4′-isopropylidenediphenol (bisphenol A; see Vol. 1, p. 912) and diphenyl carbonate using either alkaline or acidic catalysts (72), or by using tetrabutyl titanate as catalyst (73).

Ester–Acid Interchange (Acidolysis)

This reaction requires the use of an elevated temperature or the use of an acid catalyst, or both. Alkaline catalysts, of course, cannot be used. Like alcoholysis, the reaction is reversible and requires the use of an excess of the replacing acid or removal of one of the products during the reaction, if a high degree of replacement of the acid radical of an ester by another acid is to be obtained. This can be accomplished by distilling one of the products from the reaction mixture during the acidolysis (74).

In a series of organic acids of similar type, not much tendency exists for one acid to be more active than another. For example, in the replacement of stearic acid in methyl stearate by acetic acid the equilibrium constant is 1.0, and even for the replacement of stearic acid by formic acid, it is only 1.3 (75). Branched-chain acids, and some aromatic acids, especially steric-hindered acids such as *o*-substituted benzoic acids, would be expected to be less active in replacing other acids.

Mixtures of esters are obtained when acidolysis is carried out without forcing the replacement to completion by removing one of the products. For example, a mixture of the mixed triglycerides of acetic acid and coconut fatty acids can be obtained by heating a mixture of coconut oil and acetic acid in a closed vessel at 180–200°C, or by heating the same mixture with sulfuric acid as catalyst at 150–170°C (76).

Materials that are catalysts for ester hydrolysis in neutral or acid medium are in general also catalysts for ester–acid interchange. For example, magnesium oxide and zinc oxide, which catalyze the hydrolysis of fatty esters, also catalyze the replacement of one fatty acid by another from fatty glycerides. Small proportions of water have an accelerating effect on ester–acid interchange (77); in some cases it is advantageous to use blowing steam for the multiple purposes of agitating a reaction mixture, steam-distilling one of the products from the mixture, and accelerating the reaction. The Kaempfe process for making improved-bodied oil from marine oil by blowing the oil with steam at 260°C or higher temperatures probably involves this effect (78). The saturated fatty acids, being the more volatile ones, tend to be steam-distilled preferentially from the oil, while the less-volatile unsaturated acids formed by partial hydrolysis of the glycerides tend to remain in the oil and replace the saturated acids by acidolysis (78,79). Boron fluoride is a catalyst for acidolysis; it is more active than most acids (80). Mercuric sulfate catalyzes the acidolysis of vinyl acetate by higher acids, caproic to stearic (81,82).

Several processes for replacing fatty acids from fatty oils such as linseed oil by acidolysis with resin acids at temperatures above 250°C have been disclosed (83–85).

Ester–Ester Interchange

The reaction between two esters to produce two other esters was described by Friedel and Crafts in 1865, but has not been used as much as alcoholysis. The same general principles apply, as to reversibility of the reaction and means for driving the reaction to completion. In general, the same catalysts are effective as are effective in alcoholysis. Usually the reaction is slower than alcoholysis of the same esters. Without a catalyst, a reaction time of several hours at temperatures above 250°C is required to bring two typical esters to equilibrium. Catalysts are almost essential to bring reaction rates into a practical range so that the use of destructive temperatures can be avoided. Tin compounds, especially stannous hydroxide, have been mentioned frequently as catalysts, and have the merit that they do not produce much decomposition or discoloration of the esters (32). More effective at lower temperatures are the acid catalysts such as sulfuric acid and sulfonic acids, and especially the alkaline catalysts such as sodium alkoxide. With an alkaline catalyst, ester–ester interchange can be carried out at temperatures as low as 0°C (86). Catalytic ester–ester interchange with continuous removal of one of the esters by distillation has been patented (87).

Applications in the Chemistry of Fats. Various proposals have been made for improving the properties of natural fats, or of prepared mixtures of glycerides, by use of the ester–ester interchange process (32,33). In many natural fats, as well as in mixtures of fats, the arrangement of the fatty acid radicals in the triglycerides differs considerably from a pure chance arrangement. Therefore, when such a fat is subjected to ester–ester interchange, it changes in melting point and other properties, even though nothing is removed in the process, because the composition approaches a mixture of all the possible triglycerides in equilibrium (see also Drying oils; Fats and fatty oils).

A process which can be used to produce a wide range of triglyceride compositions from a given natural fat or artificial mixture is based on the withdrawal of one of the products during the reaction. This is done by carrying out the reaction at low temperature and allowing crystallization of part of the mixture to take place simultaneously with the ester–ester interchange (86).

Pure triglycerides or glycol diesters can be made by the reaction of purified methyl esters with triacetin or glycol diacetate (88,89). In high-temperature reactions involving fatty oils, such as varnish cooking, and the heat-bodying of oils and oil mixtures, more or less ester–ester interchange occurs, depending upon the temperature and the presence of catalytic materials (90–92).

Glyceryl Eleostearate. One mole of anhydrous neutral triacetin was mixed with 0.05% by wt of sodium methoxide. The solution was mixed with 3 moles of neutral methyl eleostearate. Methyl acetate was distilled off under vacuum at 60–100°C. The resulting glyceryl trieleostearate was washed with ethyl alcohol to remove the small quantity of soap that was present (88).

Poly(vinyl Acetate). This can be reacted with methyl esters of fatty acids to produce higher esters of poly(vinyl alcohol) (93).

Bibliography

"Ester Interchange" in *ECT* 1st ed., Vol. 5, pp. 817–823, by E. W. Eckey, E. W. Eckey Research Laboratory.

1. F. Adickes et al., *Ber.* **B70,** 2119–2128 (1937).
2. F. Adickes and V. Krawczyk, *Ber.* **B74,** 1389–1394 (1941).
3. U.S. Pat. 2,177,407 (1939), V. L. Hansley (to E. I. du Pont de Nemours & Co., Inc.).
4. J. F. M. Caudri, *Rec. Trav. Chim.* **48,** 422–460, 589–592 (1929).
5. U.S. Pat. 2,464,290 (1949), G. Bowen (to Du Pont).
6. U.S. Pat. 2,251,765 (1941), B. E. Sorensen (to Du Pont).
7. R. L. Frank, H. R. Davis, Jr., S. S. Drake, and J. B. McPherson, *J. Am. Chem. Soc.* **66,** 1509–1510 (1944).
8. U.S. Pat. 2,446,114 (1948), R. W. Strassburg (to U.S. Rubber Co.).
9. P. R. Fehlandt and H. Adkins, *J. Am. Chem. Soc.* **57,** 193 (1935).
10. G. B. Hatch and H. Adkins, *J. Am. Chem. Soc.* **59,** 1694 (1937).
11. G. K. Rowe, *J. Soc. Chem. Ind.* (*London*) **52,** 49–52T (1933).
12. M. Reimer and H. R. Downes, *J. Am. Chem. Soc.* **43,** 945 (1921).
13. S. G. Cohen and A. Schneider, *J. Am. Chem. Soc.* **63,** 3382–3388 (1941).
14. A. E. Remick, *Electronic Interpretations of Organic Chemistry,* 2nd ed, John Wiley & Sons, Inc., New York, 1949, pp. 408–419.
15. E. E. Reid et al., in A. H. Blatt, *Organic Synthesis,* Coll. Vol. II, John Wiley & Sons, Inc., New York, 1943, p. 469.
16. U.S. Pat. 2,543,421 (1951), D. Price and F. J. Spoules.
17. U.S. Pat. 1,993,552 (1935), E. F. Izard (to Du Pont).
18. U.S. Pat. 2,625,547 (1953), E. J. Lawson and A. Addleton.
19. U.S. Pat. 2,596,097 (1952), A. J. Hill, Jr. and J., T. Maynard.
20. B. A. Arbuzov and V. S. Vinogradova, *Dokl. Akad. Nauk SSSR* **83,** 79–80 (1952).
21. B. Smith and S. Delin, *Svensk Kem. Tidskr.* **65,** 10–16 (1953).
22. B. A. Arbuzov and Z. G. Isaeva, *J. Gen. Chem. USSR* **22,** 629–630 (1952).
23. M. Brenner and W. Huber, *Helv. Chim. Acta* **36,** 1709–1715 (1953).
24. Span. Pat. 210,549 (1953), R. R. Astpul.
25. K. W. Rosenmund, F. Zymalkowski, and E. Gussow, *Arch. Pharm.* **286,** 324–330 (1953).

26. U.S. Pat. 2,693,476 (1954), L. O. Cummings, H. A. Vogel, and A. R. Bader (to Pittsburgh Plate Glass Co.).
27. G. Zemplén, A. Gerecs, and I. Hudacsy, *Ber.* **B69**, 1827–1829 (1936).
28. L. Osipow, F. D. Snell, W. C. York, and A. Fancher, *Ind. Eng. Chem.* **48**, 1459–1462 (1956).
29. R. L. Whistler and A. Jeanes, *Ind. Eng. Chem., Anal. Ed.* **15**, 317–318 (1943).
30. F. B. Cramer, T. S. Gandner, and C. B. Purves, *Ind. Eng. Chem.* **15**, 319–320 (1943).
31. U.S. Pat. 2,266,996 (1941), N. D. Scott and J. E. Bristol (to Du Pont).
32. A. E. Bailey, *Industrial Oil and Fat Products*, Interscience Publishers, Inc., New York, 1945, pp. 676–686.
33. K. S. Markley, *Fatty Acids*, Interscience Publishers, Inc., New York, 1947, pp. 292–313.
34. R. O. Feuge and A. E. Bailey, *Oil Soap (Egypt)* **23**, 259–264 (1946).
35. C. E. Rehberg and C. H. Fisher, *J. Am. Chem. Soc.* **66**, 1203–1207 (1944).
36. U.S. Pats. 2,744,884–5 (1956), P. L. de Benneville and H. J. Sims (to Rohm & Haas Co.).
37. H. J. Sims, P. L. de Benneville and A. J. Kresge, *J. Org. Chem.* **22**, 787–789 (1957).
38. U.S. Pat. 2,465,319 (1949), J. R. Whinfield and J. T. Dickson.
39. E. F. Izard, *Chem. Eng. News* **32**, 3724–3728 (1954).
40. U.S. Pat. 2,534,028 (1950), E. F. Izard (to Du Pont).
41. U.S. Pat. 2,623,031 (1952), M. D. Snyder (to Du Pont).
42. U.S. Pat. 2,650,213 (1953), C. F. Hofrichter (to Du Pont).
43. U.S. Pat. 2,921,051 (1960), L. E. Amborski, E. F. Izard, and C. E. Sroog (to Du Pont).
44. U.S. Pat. 2,681,360 (1954), J. L. Vodonik (to Du Pont).
45. Brit. Pat. 729,803 (1955), J. L. Vodonik (to Du Pont).
46. U.S. Pat. 2,711,402 (1955), N. Fletcher (to Imperial Chemical Industries, Ltd.).
47. Brit. Pat. 742,810 (1956), N. Fletcher (to Imperial Chemical Industries, Ltd.).
48. Brit. Pat. 742,196 (1955), N. Fletcher (to Imperial Chemical Industries, Ltd.).
49. Brit. Pat. 742,811 (1956), N. Fletcher and R. L. Heath (to Imperial Chemical Industries, Ltd.).
50. U.S. Pat. 2,739,957 (1956), H. R. Billica (to Du Pont).
51. Brit. Pat. 753,880 (1956), (to Chemstrand Corp.).
52. Brit. Pat. 765,609 (1957), (to Goodyear Tire & Rubber Co.).
53. Japan. Pat. 6291 (1957), Oriental Rayon Co.
54. Japan. Pat. 8644 (1957), H. Nagao and E. Mifune (to Imperial Rayon Co.).
55. Japan. Pat. 4347 (1957), Oriental Rayon Co.
56. Brit. Pat. 791,790 (1958), (to Chemstrand Corp.).
57. U.S. Pat. 2,892,815 (1959), R. H. Hobson (to Chemstrand Corp.).
58. Brit. Pat. 793,111 (1958), E. Isaacs et al. (to Imperial Chemical Industries, Ltd.).
59. Brit. Pat. 799,782 (1958), D. MacLean et al. (to Imperial Chemical Industries, Ltd.).
60. Brit. Pat. 804,753 (1958), (to Du Pont).
61. U.S. Pat. 2,916,474 (1959), R. F. Engle, Jr. (to Du Pont).
62. Brit. Pat. 851,244 (1960), (to Imperial Chemical Industries, Ltd.).
63. Brit. Pat. 861,712 (1961), (to Goodyear).
64. Brit. Pat. 832,088 (1960), (to Glanzstoff-Fabriken, A.G.).
65. U.S. Pat. 2,829,153 (1959), J. L. Vodonik (to Du Pont).
66. U.S. Pat. 2,937,160 (1960), J. K. Sullivan (to Goodyear).
67. U.S. Pat. 2,947,729 (1960), J. K. Sullivan (to Goodyear).
68. A. Mifune, *Kogyo Kagaku Zasshi* **65**, 276–278 (1962).
69. Ger. Pat. 1,169,915 (1964), R. Lotz (to Verein Glanzstoff-Fabriken).
70. Brit. Pat. 755,071 (1956), (to Verein Glanzstoff-Fabriken).
71. Brit. Pat. 787,554 (1958), (to Verein Glanzstoff-Fabriken).
72. H. Schnell, *Ind. Eng. Chem.* **51**, 157–160 (1959).
73. U.S. Pat. 2,789,971 (1958), D. D. Reynolds and K. R. Durham (to Eastman Kodak Co.).
74. U.S. Pat. 1,882,808 (1932), G. D. Graves (to Du Pont).
75. C. Barkenbus et al., *J. Am. Chem. Soc.* **62**, 1251–1253 (1940).
76. U.S. Pat. 1,558,299 (1925), G. L. Schwarz (to Du Pont).
77. U.S. Pat. 2,378,005 (1945), E. W. Eckey (to Procter & Gamble Co.).
78. G. Kaempfe, *Farben-Ztg.* **40**, 1009 (1935).
79. N. N. Brocklesby, *Fisheries Res. Board Can. Bull.* **59**, 292 (1941).
80. F. J. Sowa, *J. Am. Chem. Soc.* **60**, 654–656 (1938).
81. D. Swern and E. F. Jordan, *J. Am. Chem. Soc.* **70**, 2334–2339 (1948).

82. Ger. Pat. 753,029 (1952), W. O. Herman and W. Haehnel.

83. K. Pistor, *Z. Angew. Chem.* **38,** 1118–1121 (1925).

84. Ger. Pat. 555,812 (1932), K. Albert (K. Albert, G.m.b.H.).

85. U.S. Pat. 2,217,363 (1940), A. Greth and F. Lemmer (to Resinous Products and Chemical Co., Inc.).

86. E. W. Eckey, *Ind. Eng. Chem.* **40,** 1183–1190 (1948).

87. U.S. Pat. 1,860,092 (1932), G. D. Graves (to Du Pont).

88. J. C. Konen, E. T. Clocker, and R. P. Cox, *Oil Soap (Egypt)* **22,** 57 (1945).

89. J. L. Overholt and A. C. Elm, *Ind. Eng. Chem.* **32,** 1348 (1940).

90. W. Krumbhaar, *The Chemistry of Synthetic Surface Coatings*, Reinhold Publishing Corp., New York, 1937, pp. 16–19.

91. M. T. Mellier, *Oleagineux* **10,** 335–336 (1955).

92. U.S. Pat. 2,558,547 (1951), E. W. Eckey (to Procter & Gamble).

93. U.S. Pat. 2,558,548 (1951), E. W. Eckey (to Procter & Gamble).

E. W. Eckey

E. W. Eckey Research Laboratory

E. F. Izard

E. I. du Pont de Nemours & Co., Inc.

ESTERS, ORGANIC

Esters can be defined as compounds that, on hydrolysis, yield alcohols or phenols and acids according to the equation

$$RA + H_2O \rightleftharpoons ROH + HA$$

in which R is a hydrocarbon radical and A is the anion of an organic or inorganic acid. For carboxylic acid esters, the reaction may be represented as follows:

$$RCOOR' + H_2O \rightleftharpoons R'OH + RCOOH$$

in which R and R′ are the same or different radicals. The reverse reaction constitutes the usual method for preparing esters.

Although esters have been likened to salts because of the similarity in formulas and preparation, the reaction leading to esters is not a simple ionic one as is salt formation; thus in the formation of esters of carboxylic acids, it is usually the hydroxyl group (rather than the hydrogen atom) of the carboxy group that is replaced by the alkoxy group (rather than the alkyl group) of the alcohol. Hydroxycarboxylic acids in which the carboxy and hydroxyl groups are separated by at least two carbon atoms may form internal esters, or lactones, as shown by

$$HOCRR(CRR)_nCOOH \rightarrow \overline{OCRR(CRR)_nC} {=} O + H_2O$$

in which $n \geq 1$. When $n = 1$ or $n > 4$, hydroxycarboxylic acids have a strong tendency to form polyesters (by intermolecular esterification) rather than lactones:

$$HOCH_2RCOOH \rightarrow H{\left(OCH_2R\overset{\text{O}}{\overset{\|}{C}}\right)_n}OH$$

Mercaptans and carboxylic acids form an analogous series of compounds, the thiol esters:

$$RSH + R'COOH \rightleftharpoons R'COSR + H_2O$$

Esters of polyhydric alcohols in which the hydroxyl groups are on different carbon atoms (as in ethylene glycol and its homologs) may be prepared by the usual methods; they undergo reactions similar to those of esters of monohydric alcohols. Acylals, $RCH(OCOR')_2$, are esters of 1,1-diols or aldehyde hydrates. Neither their methods of preparation nor their reactions are typical of those of ordinary esters. They have little technical or commercial value. The ortho esters, $RC(OR')_3$, resemble acetals more than they do the simple esters with which this article is mainly concerned, although like ordinary esters they give alcohols and carboxylic acids on hydrolysis (1). The methods of preparation and reactions of vinyl esters, in which the carbon atom carrying the alcohol oxygen atom is unsaturated ($RCH{=}CHOCOR'$), are also not typical of those of simple esters.

Since the number and types of acids and alcohols that may react to form them are very great, an extremely large number of esters is theoretically possible. This article deals only with simple esters of carboxylic acids and principally with esters of the fatty acid series. Further information on esters of other organic acids and esters of inorganic acids is given in articles such as Benzoic acid, Citric acid, Phthalic acid, Phosphoric acids (for tricresyl (tritolyl) phosphates and other phosphates), Sulfuric and sulfurous esters, Acetoacetic acid and ester, Carbonic esters and chloroformic esters, Urethans (for esters of carbamic acid), Glycols, Fats and fatty oils (for fatty acid esters of glycerol (called glycerides)), Rosin (for rosin acid esters or glycerol (called ester gums)), Waxes (for esters of certain higher monohydric alcohols and higher acids), Oils, essential, and Perfumes (for esters of terpenes like borneol and geraniol), Cellulose derivatives and Cellulose derivatives—plastics (for cellulose esters, such as cellulose acetate and nitrocellulose (cellulose nitrate)), and Starch derivatives (for starch esters). Polyesters, whether derived from glycols and dibasic acids or from hydroxy acids, are described under Polyesters.

Various types of esters find widespread uses as solvents (qv), plasticizers (qv), perfumes (qv), flavors (qv), and medicinals; certain polymerized esters are used as resins, plastics, and textile fibers. Esters, because of their wide variation in composition and properties, are among the most important classes of organic compounds.

Nomenclature (2). The names of esters are derived from those of the hydroxy compounds and acids they yield on hydrolysis, as ethyl acetate, geranyl acetate (*trans*-3,7-dimethyl-2,6-octadienyl acetate), butyl hydrogen phthalate, dibutyl phthalate, and phenyl salicylate. Esters of complex hydroxy compounds are sometimes designated as derivatives of these compounds by prefixing the name of the appropriate acid radical; for example, acetylcellulose (cellulose acetate) and acetyl triethyl citrate (triethyl citrate acetate). The prefix nitro has been incorrectly used to designate esters of nitric acid, as in nitrocellulose, nitroglycerin, and nitrostarch, which are better called cellulose nitrate, glyceryl trinitrate, and starch nitrate, respectively. In naming esters containing one or more substituents, it is necessary to indicate specifically in which portion of the molecule the substituents occur and to distinguish between isomers, such as ethyl chloroacetate, $CH_2ClCOOCH_2CH_3$, and 2-chloroethyl acetate, $CH_3COOCH_2CH_2Cl$.

Esters, $RCOSR'$, formed by esterification of a carboxylic acid with a mercaptan, are known as thiol esters; the isomers, $RCSOR'$, are thione esters.

Ortho esters, $RC(OR')_3$, are named on the basis of the ortho acids, as $HC(OC_2H_5)_3$, triethyl orthoformate. Imido esters (often called imido ethers or imino ethers), $RC({=}NH)OR'$, are preferably named as derivatives of imidic acids; thus, $C_6H_5C{-}({=}NH)OC_2H_5$ is ethyl benzimidate.

Physical and Chemical Properties

The lower esters are colorless, volatile liquids, and many of them are pleasantly aromatic. Most of the monoesters of the higher saturated fatty acids are colorless, odorless, crystalline solids. Esters of the very long chain acids and alcohols are hard, brittle, lustrous, crystalline solids, which are generally referred to as waxes. Most of the higher esters of this class are not known in pure form, but only as complex mixtures comprising the naturally occurring waxes.

In general, the melting points of the esters of fatty acids are lower than those of the corresponding acids, and the boiling points of the methyl, ethyl, and propyl esters are lower than those of the corresponding acids. With increasing chain length of the alcohol, the boiling points increase and ultimately become much higher than those of the corresponding acids. Since many of the monoesters are relatively stable toward heat in the absence of moisture, they are generally distillable without decomposition. They are, therefore, often employed in processes of separation and identification of mixed fatty acids.

The data for the methyl and ethyl esters of the saturated fatty acid series are fairly complete and relatively well known, but data for the esters of the higher alcohols are often lacking. Data on boiling point, density, molar volume, viscosity, solubility, heat of combustion, and other physical constants of esters of aliphatic acids have been tabulated by Markley (3).

The esters are generally insoluble in water but are soluble in various organic liquids. The lower esters are themselves good solvents for many organic compounds, including most liquids. They are especially good solvents for cellulose-type lacquers.

Reactions

Hydrolysis (4,5). Monoesters are neutral substances but those of low molecular weight slowly hydrolyze in water to form free acids and alcohols. This reaction is accelerated by high temperature and the presence of alkalies, acids, or various other catalysts. As the molecular weight increases, the tendency to hydrolyze decreases, so that elevated temperatures and the presence of an alkali or catalyst are necessary for rapid reaction.

Although esters have been observed to hydrolyze by six different mechanisms, depending upon the ester and the hydrolysis conditions, only two of these are important for most esters (4). Equations 1 and 2 illustrate the most common paths for basic hydrolysis and for acid-catalyzed hydrolysis, respectively:

$$
\text{HO}^- + \underset{\underset{\text{R}}{|}}{\overset{\overset{\text{O}}{\|}}{\text{C}}}\text{—OR}' \underset{slow}{\rightleftharpoons} \left[\text{HO}\text{—}\underset{\underset{\text{R}}{|}}{\overset{\overset{\text{O}}{|}}{\text{C}}}\text{—OR}' \right]^- \underset{fast}{\rightleftharpoons} \underset{\underset{\text{R}}{|}}{\overset{\overset{\text{O}}{\|}}{\text{HOC}}} + \text{OR}'^- \xrightarrow{fast} \text{RCOO}^- + \text{R'OH} \qquad (1)
$$

$$
\underset{}{\overset{\overset{\text{O}}{\|}}{\text{RCOR}'}} + \text{H}^+ \rightleftharpoons \text{RC}\overset{\overset{+}{}}{\text{—}}\text{O}\overset{\text{R}'}{\underset{\text{H}}{<}} \underset{-\text{H}_2\text{O, fast}}{\overset{+\text{H}_2\text{O, slow}}{\rightleftharpoons}} \left[\text{R—}\overset{\overset{\text{O}}{|}}{\underset{\underset{\text{H}\ \ \text{R}'}{\overset{\text{O}}{|}}}{\text{C}}}\text{—}\overset{\text{H}}{\underset{\text{H}}{\text{O}}} \right]^+
$$

$$
\underset{+\text{R'OH, slow}}{\overset{-\text{R'OH, fast}}{\rightleftharpoons}} \quad \text{R—}\overset{\overset{\text{O}}{\|}}{\text{C}}\text{—}\overset{+}{\text{O}}\overset{\text{H}}{\underset{\text{H}}{<}} \rightleftharpoons \overset{\overset{\text{O}}{\|}}{\text{RCOH}} + \text{H}^+ \qquad (2)
$$

The mechanism represented by equation 1 correctly predicts observed steric and electronic effects in ester hydrolysis. In forming intermediate (**1**), both the density of negative charge at the reaction center and the extent of crowding are increased. It would, therefore, be predicted that electron-attracting substituents would facilitate, and bulky substituents retard, hydrolysis.

The following saponification rates, relative to methyl acetate, illustrate the polar effect:

$$k_{ester}/k_{CH_3COOCH_3}$$

CH_3COOCH_3	$CH_2ClCOOCH_3$	$CHCl_2COOCH_3$
1.0	761	16,000
$(COOCH_3)_2$	$CH_3COOC_2H_5$	$CH_3COCOOC_2H_5$
170,000	0.60	10,000

The following two series of saponification rates, relative to ethyl acetate, illustrate the effect of increasing steric hindrance in the acyl and alkyl substituents, respectively:

$k_{ester}/k_{CH_3COOC_2H_5}$	$k_{ester}/k_{CH_3COOC_2H_5}$
$CH_3COOC_2H_5$	$CH_3COOC_2H_5$
1.0	1.0
$C_2H_5COOC_2H_5$	$CH_3COOCH_2CH(CH_3)_2$
0.47	0.70
$(CH_3)_2CHCOOC_2H_5$	$CH_3COOCH_2C(CH_3)_3$
0.10	0.18
$(CH_3)_3CCOOC_2H_5$	$CH_3COOCH_2C(C_2H_5)_3$
0.011	0.031

Steric effects in acid-catalyzed hydrolysis are similar to those in basic hydrolysis, but polar effects are much less important in the acid-catalyzed reactions.

Basic Hydrolysis. The hydrolysis of esters with alkali is one of the oldest known chemical reactions. The early Romans and Gauls treated fats with wood ashes to obtain a solution with detergent properties, but it was not until the time of Scheele (1779) and Chevreul (1813–1823) that the reaction was understood. Today, this reaction is the basis of the soap industry. For complete saponification of esters slightly more than the theoretical amount of alkali is required, but the free acid may be obtained with catalytic amounts (0.3–1.0%) of basic materials, such as the oxides of calcium, magnesium, barium, and lead, by autoclaving at 8–10 atm.

Acid Hydrolysis. Hydrolysis of esters with dilute acid is slow, owing to the poor emulsifying power of acids. However, the Twitchell reagent (the reaction product of benzene, oleic acid, and concentrated sulfuric acid), which was introduced in the early 1900s, markedly increased the efficiency of the acid hydrolysis of esters, particularly fats. A large number of these fat-splitting compounds has been reported.

Hydrolysis by Steam (6). High-pressure steam alone at 185–300°C hydrolyzes fats directly to high-grade fatty acids. This method offers advantages to the soap industry over basic hydrolysis, and continuous commercial processes have been developed.

Hydrolysis by Enzymes. The metabolism of fats in both animal and plant systems is closely associated with enzymes (lipases) which have the ability to hydrolyze fatty esters. There are also certain enzymes that are capable of splitting the lower esters, but which show little activity with the higher esters.

Alcoholysis, Acidolysis, and Ester–Ester Interchange. See Ester interchange.

Ammonolysis. Ammonia reacts with esters to give alcohols and amides. This reaction is analogous to hydrolysis of esters, which gives alcohols and acids (7). The reaction is usually carried out in aqueous or alcoholic ammonia. Simple esters react with ammonia at a satisfactory rate at room temperature; higher esters may require elevated temperatures and pressures. Sometimes ester ammonolysis is carried out at low temperatures to avoid attack of another reactive group:

$$ClCH_2COOC_2H_5 + NH_3 \xrightarrow[\text{(aq)}]{0\text{--}5°C} ClCH_2CONH_2 + C_2H_5OH$$
$$62\text{--}87\%$$

Other ammonia derivatives, such as primary and secondary amines, react analogously to give *N*-substituted amides:

$$RCOOR' + R''R'''NH \rightarrow RCONR''R''' + R'OH$$

Hydrazine reacts the same way to give hydrazides:

$$RCOOR' + H_2NNH_2 \rightarrow RCONHNH_2 + R'OH$$

The mechanism of these reactions has been studied extensively (8).

When esters are passed with ammonia in the vapor phase over contact catalysts at temperatures around 400–500°C, they are rapidly converted to nitriles. Thus, Mailhe in 1920 prepared oleonitrile by passing a mixture of ammonia and methyl oleate over alumina at 500°C or over thoria at 480–490°C. These reactions may also be carried out in the liquid phase in the presence of suitable catalysts. This conversion of esters to nitriles is actually an ammonolysis, followed by catalyzed dehydration of the amide:

$$RCOOR' + NH_3 \rightarrow RCONH_2 + ROH$$
$$RCONH_2 \xrightarrow[\text{catalyst}]{\Delta} RCN + H_2O$$

Reduction (9). Hydrogenation of esters over copper chromite at 200–300°C and 100–300 atm reduces them to alcohols:

$$RCOOR' + 2 H_2 \rightarrow RCH_2OH + R'OH$$

When R is saturated and when no halogen or sulfur is present, the reaction is smooth and almost quantitative; but when R is an aromatic nucleus, such as benzene or pyrrole, the reaction proceeds beyond the alcohol step, as in the reduction of ethyl benzoate to toluene. This cleavage may be minimized by carrying out the reaction at low temperatures with a high ratio of catalyst to ester. An important commercial use of this reaction is the reduction of coconut oil and other fats to alcohols, chiefly lauryl and decyl alcohols, which are used to prepare the sulfated alcohol-type detergent. The reaction may also be used to prepare diols for use as polymer intermediates, as in the reduction of dimethyl 1,4-cyclohexanedicarboxylate to 1,4-cyclohexanedimethanol.

The use of sodium in alcoholic solutions to reduce esters to alcohols was first reported by Bouveault and Blanc in 1904 (10). Since then it has been used for the commercial production of lauryl alcohol, but this process is probably gradually being superseded for the production of saturated alcohols by the catalytic process. Detailed procedures for the reduction of oleic acid esters with sodium in ethyl or butyl alcohol have been given by Adkins, Reid, and co-workers (11,12). Yields of 80–84% were reported. 4-Methyl-2-pentanol is a preferred solvent for the commercial reduction of esters by this method.

Complex metal hydrides, particularly lithium aluminum hydride (lithium tetrahydroaluminate), are exceedingly useful and widely used reagents for reducing esters to alcohols in the laboratory (see Hydrides). Practically any ester can be reduced by this method, and alcohols of high purity are obtained in excellent yield. Carbon–carbon double bonds are normally not affected (13).

Grignard Reaction (14). The reaction of esters with Grignard reagents is similar to that of ketones. The esters of formic acid yield secondary alcohols, whereas other esters yield tertiary alcohols.

$$
\underset{\substack{\text{O} \\ \|}}{\text{RCOR}'} \xrightarrow{\text{R}''^-} \underset{\substack{\text{O}^- \\ | \\ \text{R}''}}{\text{R}-\text{C}-\text{OR}'} \xrightarrow[-\text{R}'\text{OMgBr}]{\text{Mg}^+\text{Br}} \underset{\substack{\text{O} \\ \| \\ \text{R}''}}{\text{R}\text{C}} \xrightarrow{\text{R}''\text{MgBr}} \underset{\substack{\text{OMgBr} \\ | \\ \text{R}''}}{\text{R}-\text{C}-\text{R}''} \xrightarrow{\text{H}_2\text{O}} \underset{\substack{\text{OH} \\ | \\ \text{R}''}}{\text{R}-\text{C}-\text{R}''}
$$

The overall yield in the preparation of triphenyl methanol from ethyl benzoate and phenylmagnesium bromide is 91%.

Acetoacetic Ester Condensation (15). In the presence of certain bases, an ester having hydrogen on the α-carbon atom will react with a second molecule of the same ester or with another ester (which may or may not have hydrogen on the α-carbon atom) to form a β-keto ester:

$$
\text{R}_2\text{CHCOOR}' + \text{R}_3\text{CCOOR}' \rightarrow \text{R}_3\overset{\overset{\text{O}}{\|}}{\text{C}}\text{CCR}_2\text{COOR}' + \text{R}'\text{OH}
$$

This reaction is a special case of the Claisen reaction which includes ketone–ester condensation to form 1,3-diketones.

Preparation of Acyloins (16). When aliphatic esters are allowed to react with metallic sodium in inert solvents, acyloins (α-hydroxyketones) are formed:

$$
2\,\text{RCOOR}' + 4\,\text{Na} \rightarrow \underset{\substack{\text{RC}-\text{ONa}}}{\overset{\substack{\text{RC}-\text{ONa} \\ \|}}{}} + 2\,\text{NaOR}' \xrightarrow{\text{H}_2\text{O}} \left[\underset{\substack{\text{R}-\text{C}-\text{OH}}}{\overset{\substack{\text{R}-\text{C}-\text{OH} \\ \|}}{}} \rightarrow \underset{\substack{\text{RC}-\text{OH} \\ \text{H}}}{\overset{\text{RC}=\text{O}}{}} \right] + 2\,\text{NaOH}
$$

Pyrolysis (17). The pyrolysis of simple esters of the formula $\text{RCOOCR}'\text{R}''\text{CHR}_2'''$ to form the free acid and an olefin is a general reaction which is frequently used for producing olefins. The pyrolysis is generally carried out at temperatures of 300–500°C over an inert heat-transfer agent, such as 96% silica glass chips. Esters of tertiary alcohols pyrolyze more readily than esters of secondary alcohols, and esters of primary alcohols are the most difficult to pyrolyze. Some of the higher-boiling esters of tertiary alcohols cannot be distilled without decomposition. *tert*-Pentyl acetate decomposes to pentenes and acetic acid below 200°C. This reaction does not require a catalyst; it has been shown to be intramolecular and to involve a cyclic transition state:

$$
\underset{\substack{\text{O} \\ | \\ \text{C} \\ \text{R}' \;\; \text{R}''}}{\text{R}-\text{C}}\overset{\text{O}}{\underset{}{}}\cdots\overset{\text{H}}{\underset{\substack{\text{C} \\ \text{R}'''}}{\text{C}}}\text{R}''' \xrightarrow{\Delta} \text{R}-\text{C}\overset{\text{OH}}{\underset{\text{O}}{}} + \text{R}'\text{R}''\text{C}=\text{CR}_2'''
$$

The double bond does not move along the carbon chain, but mixtures of isomeric olefins are produced by pyrolysis of unsymmetrical secondary or tertiary esters which contain more than one carbon atom capable of losing hydrogen by the above mechanism. The production of methyl acrylate by pyrolysis of methyl 2-acetoxypropionate (methyl 2-hydroxypropionate acetate) has been extensively investigated:

$$CH_3CH(OOCCH_3)COOCH_3 \xrightarrow{\Delta} CH_2{=}CHCOOCH_3 + CH_3COOH$$

Methyl esters and esters of the formula $RCOOCH_2CR_3$ which do not contain hydrogen atoms capable of elimination by the mechanism given above must be heated to much higher temperatures before they decompose, and their pyrolysis products are complex. The pyrolysis of these esters is not a synthetically useful reaction. The enhanced thermal stability of these esters makes them very valuable for certain purposes, however. Some acids from which esters are derived are not stable and decompose under the pyrolysis conditions. Diethyl malonate, for example, pyrolyzes to ethylene, methane, and carbon dioxide; *tert*-butyl esters of β-keto acids decompose smoothly to isobutylene (2-methylpropene), carbon dioxide, and a ketone. Two molecules of esters of α-amino acids, such as alanine, lysine, histidine, leucine, and phenylalanine, condense at 150–180°C to give a piperazine derivative and two molecules of alcohol.

Miscellaneous Reactions. Ketones can be obtained in substantial yields from fatty acid esters as well as from the fatty acids by heating them in the presence of certain metals or their oxides. For example, ethyl laurate in the vapor phase over a thoria-gel catalyst at 300°C gives a 92.5% yield of laurone (12-tricosanone), and ethyl undecenoate gives an 86% yield of didecenyl ketone. Other vapor-phase catalysts are manganese chromite and zinc chromite. When the reaction is run in the liquid phase, the yields are lower, and metallic iron is probably the best catalyst. Aluminum and manganese and the oxides of iron, silicon, copper, zinc, titanium, aluminum, and magnesium have all been reported as catalysts for this reaction to give ketones (18).

A few other reactions that esters may undergo can be illustrated with ethyl acetate. Chlorine in boiling ethyl acetate yields acetyl chloride, whereas bromine at 150–160°C yields ethyl bromide and mono- and dibromoacetic acids. Phosphorus pentachloride at 150°C yields ethyl chloride and acetyl chloride. Alcoholic sodium hydrogen sulfide at about 180°C yields ethyl mercaptan (ethanethiol).

Certain esters, particularly those of disubstituted acetic acids, may be dehydrogenated to the corresponding α,β-unsaturated esters. Methyl isobutyrate, for example, gives methyl methacrylate (19):

$$\underset{\displaystyle CH_3CHCOOCH_3}{\overset{\displaystyle CH_3}{|}} \xrightarrow{\text{catalyst}} \underset{\displaystyle CH_2{=}CCOOCH_3}{\overset{\displaystyle CH_3}{|}} + H_2$$

Analysis of Esters

The analysis of esters usually includes the determination of such physical properties as the boiling range, melting point or freezing point, specific gravity, refractive index, the amount of nonvolatile residue or ash, and color; and such chemical properties as free acidity and the actual ester content. The physical properties are determined by well-known methods. The free acidity is determined by titrating a sample in either water or an alcohol–water mixture, with standard alkali. The ester content is generally denoted by the saponification number, which is the number of milligrams of potassium hydroxide required to saponify one gram of the ester, or by the saponification equivalent, which is the number of milliequivalents of potassium hydroxide required to saponify one gram of the ester. The saponification number (SN) and the saponification equivalent (SE) are related by the following formula:

$$SE = \frac{56.1 \times 1000}{SN}$$

The RCOOR′ group of simple esters is comparatively easy to identify from characteristic bands in the infrared spectrum. The carbonyl group absorbs strongly at 1750–1735 cm^{-1}, and a second strong band, characteristic of the ether linkage, is present in the region between 1300–1100 cm^{-1}. The location of this second band gives an indication of the type of acid from which the ester is derived (20).

The phenacyl esters and the p-halo- or p-nitrophenacyl esters have been used as a means of identifying fatty acids and the fatty acid part of esters. The acid portion of the ester is also readily identified by cleaving the ester with hydrazine to form the hydrazide as described previously.

Health and Safety Factors

Esters, as a class, are not considered health hazards, and any harmful effects of esters, other than those based on their solvent properties, are generally due to the toxicity of the acid or alcohol which is formed by hydrolysis of that particular ester. The lower esters are quite volatile and must be kept away from sources of ignition.

Prolonged exposure to the vapors of esters and particularly esters of unsaturated compounds often causes irritation of the skin or mucous membranes. The regulations for rail shipment require that containers for all compounds having a flash point (Cleveland open-cup) below 80°F (26.67°C) have a red warning label and be marked "flammable."

Occurrence and Preparation

Today, most of the simple esters used commercially are of synthetic origin, although a number of them do occur in nature. Some of the naturally occurring esters, other than fats and waxes, and some of their sources are as follows (21,22): ethyl acetate, in many wines, brandy, wine vinegar, and some fruits, as pineapples; amyl acetate, in apples, bananas, and other fruits; geranyl formate and citronellyl formate and acetate, in geranium oil; terpinyl acetate, in cypress oil; bornyl acetate, in pine-needle oil; geranyl acetate, in lemon grass oil; menthyl acetate, in peppermint oil; benzyl acetate, in jasmine, hyacinth, and gardenia; methyl benzoate, in clove oil; methyl salicylate, in the oils of wintergreen and sweet birch; ethyl, benzyl, and cinnamyl cinnamates in oil of styrax; methyl anthranilate, in jonquil, tuberoses, ylang-ylang, jasmine, and mandarin-leaf oil (see Oils, essential). Most of these naturally occurring esters have very pleasant odors and either they or their synthetic counterparts are used in the confectionery, beverage, perfume, cosmetic, and soap industries.

Recovery of naturally occurring esters is accomplished by steam distillation, extraction or pressing, or a combination of these. Synthetic esters are generally prepared by reaction of an alcohol with an organic acid in the presence of a catalyst such as sulfuric acid or p-toluenesulfonic acid. A number of other reactions may be used industrially for preparing certain esters, however. In the presence of certain metal alcoholate catalysts, two molecules of an aldehyde condense to give an ester (23):

$$2 \text{ RCHO} \xrightarrow{\text{ROM}} \text{RCH}_2\text{OCOR}$$

This is the Tishchenko reaction; its potential importance has increased with the ready availability of aldehydes from the oxo reaction.

Esters may also be made by the reaction of an olefin, an alcohol, and carbon monoxide under pressure in the presence of either strong acids, or, preferably, nickel or cobalt carbonyl:

$$RCH{=}CH_2 + R'OH + CO \rightarrow RCH_2CH_2COOR' + RCH(CH_3)COOR'$$

Mixtures of isomeric esters are produced by this reaction since the reaction occurs to some extent on both sides of the double bond of the olefin, and since the double bond itself migrates along the carbon chain. This method for preparing esters has been the subject of a number of patents.

One important variation of this reaction is the preparation of acrylates from acetylene, carbon monoxide, and alcohol in the presence of a nickel catalyst (24):

$$CH{\equiv}CH + CO + ROH \rightarrow CH_2{=}CHCOOR$$

Vinyl esters, which are derivatives of the enol form of aldehydes, cannot be prepared by simple esterification. They may be made from acetylene and an acid in the presence of zinc or cadmium soaps:

$$RCOOH + HC{\equiv}CH \rightarrow RCOOCH{=}CH_2$$

Table 1. Typical Specifications of Representative Commercial Esters

Compound	Ester content (min), %	Color (max), APHA	d^{20}_{20}	Distillation range, 760 mm	Flash pt, °F[a]	Acidity (max), %[b]
ethyl acetate	85.0	10	0.883–0.886	72.0–78.0	30	0.01
	99.0	10	0.900–0.903	75.5–78.0	30	0.01
	99.5	10	0.900–0.903	75.5–78.0	30	0.005
propyl acetate		15 (Pt–Co scale)	0.878–0.883	95–103	70[c]	0.01
isopropyl acetate	95.0	10	0.868–0.872	85.0–90.0	40	0.01
	99.5	10 (Pt–Co scale)	0.882–0.883	122.5–128.0	100	0.01
butyl acetate	90.0	10	0.874–0.880	118.0–128.0	90[c]	0.01
	98.0	10	0.880–0.883	122.0–128.0	100[c]	0.01
	99.5	10 (Pt–Co scale)	0.882–0.883	122.5–128.0	100	0.01
isobutyl acetate	93.0	10	0.867–0.873	112.0–119.0	87	0.01
sec-butyl acetate	89.9	<5 (Pt–Co scale)	0.862	106.6–113.6	68	
amyl acetate (mixed isomers)	95.0		0.871–0.873	125–150	95	
2-ethylhexyl acetate	95.0	15	0.870–0.875	192.0–205.0	190[c]	0.02
isobutyl isobutyrate	98.0	15	0.853–0.857	144.0–151.0	120	0.02
benzyl benzoate	99.0	colorless	1.117–1.120 (25/25)	crystn pt 18.3°C (min)		
butyl oleate	SN[d] 160–170	1 (Gardner scale)				0.2
dibutyl sebacate	99.0	50	0.935–0.939	349	370	0.02

[a] Tag open-cup (ASTM Method D 1310) unless otherwise noted.
[b] Acidity reported as free acid of each ester.
[c] Cleveland open-cup (ASTM Method D 92).
[d] Saponification number.

Vinyl esters may also be made from aldehydes and acyl chlorides or anhydrides in the presence of bases. Higher homologs may be made from lower vinyl esters by transesterification in the presence of mercuric salts and sulfuric acid (25).

Specifications and Standards

The specifications of individual commercial esters vary widely. Typical specifications of several esters, as taken from the manufacturers' trade publications, are given in Table 1. These will illustrate the tolerances commonly allowed.

General Uses of Esters

Solvents (qv) **and Plasticizers** (qv) (26,27). The greatest uses of esters are in the solvent and plasticizer fields. The lower esters are used in the lacquer, paint, and varnish fields, and the higher ones are used primarily as plasticizers. Table 2 shows the production figures for the alkyl acetates, which are indicative of the amount of esters used in solvents, and for the phthalates and tricresyl phosphate which are indicative of the amount of esters used in plasticizers (28).

Resins, Plastics, and Coatings. Many polymeric materials in commercial use are based on esters. These include vinyl polymers made from such unsaturated esters as the acrylates (qv), methacrylates (qv), vinyl acetate (see Vinyl compounds), and their homologs; alkyd resins (qv), which are essentially crosslinked polyesters prepared from polyhydric alcohols and dibasic acids; and the polyester resins and plastics. The latter are usually made by transesterification, by starting with dimethyl or diphenyl esters of dibasic acids, such as terephthalic or carbonic acids, and dihydric alcohols, such as ethylene glycol, 1,4-cyclohexanedimethanol, or 4,4'-methylenediphenol. These polymers are thermoplastic materials which are useful as films, fibers, and molding plastics. Properties of these materials may be varied widely by changing either the dibasic acid or the glycol. Incorporation of an unsaturated acid, such as maleic acid, gives a material which may be crosslinked, and which is, therefore, thermosetting.

Lubricants (29) (see Lubrication and lubricants). Esters, in the form of natural fats, oils, and waxes have been used as lubricants since ancient times. Animal and vegetable fats and oils have largely been supplanted by petroleum hydrocarbons. Petroleum lubricants are not suitable for turboprop and turbojet aircraft engines which must operate under a wide range of climatic conditions and at very high internal engine temperatures. Such aliphatic esters as bis(2-ethylhexyl) sebacate are widely used as base oils for lubricating turbojet engines because of their relatively low rate of change of viscosity with temperature and their wide liquid range.

Perfumes (qv), **Flavors** (qv), **Cosmetics** (qv), **and Soap** (qv) (22). Compared with the tonnage of esters used in solvents and plasticizers, the tonnage of esters used in improving odors and flavors is small, but nevertheless important economically and esthetically.

Medicinals (30,31). Although the ester group itself apparently is inert physiologically, esters are used widely in pharmaceuticals. In general, esterification of a physiologically active alcohol or phenol with an aliphatic acid detoxifies it by decreasing the concentration of active compound present. The active compound is released gradually in the body by hydrolysis of the ester. An example of detoxification is acetylation of salicyclic acid to give acetylsalicylic acid, the sodium salt of which is the common analgesic aspirin. Benzocaine, a local anesthetic, is the ethyl ester of p-aminobenzoic acid. Heroin, an opiate, is the diacetate of morphine. Salicylates, some benzoates, and esters of the fatty acids in chaulmoogra oil are also important medicinally.

Esters of Aliphatic Acids

Most of the following information was obtained from manufacturers' literature. Detailed data on a large number of solvents, including the following esters and many others, have been compiled recently (26). Some of the more important esters of the fatty acid series are given below.

FORMIC ACID ESTERS

Methyl formate, $HCOOCH_3$, molecular weight 60.05, has a pleasant, ethereal, nonresidual odor; mp, $-99.8°C$; bp, $31.8°C$; d_4^{15}, 0.98149; n_D^{20}, 1.344; flash point (open-cup), $-2°F$; electrical conductivity at $25°C$, 3.6×10^{-5} mho/cm; soly in water at room temp, 23% by wt. A red label is required for shipping.

Trimethyl orthoformate, (trimethoxymethane), $HC(OCH_3)_3$, molecular weight 106.12, is similar to triethyl orthoformate and is a convenient source of the methoxymethylene group; bp 103–105°C; d_{20}^{20}, 0.9706; n_D^{20}, 1.3780. The commercial product has a minimum purity of 98.0% and does not require a red label for shipping.

Ethyl formate, $HCOOC_2H_5$, molecular weight 74.08, has a pleasant, nonresidual odor; mp, $-80.5°C$; bp 54.3°C; d_4^{25}, 0.9236; n_D^{20}, 1.35975; flash point (open-cup), $-4°F$; electrical conductivity at $25°C$, $<1.45 \times 10^{-9}$ mho/cm; soly in water at room temp, 10.5% by wt. Ethyl formate is used like the methyl ester as a fumigant and larvicide, as an intermediate in the synthesis of vitamin B_1, and in the formulation of synthetic flavors. Shipment regulations are the same as for methyl formate.

Triethyl orthoformate (triethoxymethane, orthoformic ester, Aethon), $HC(OC_2H_5)_3$, molecular weight 148.20, is a colorless liquid with a pungent odor; mp, $-76.1°C$; bp, 145.9°C; d_{20}^{20}, 0.895; $n_D^{18.8}$, 1.39218; flash point, 86°F; appreciably soluble in water; soluble in alcohol and ether. Since the flash point is above 80°F (26.67°C), no red label is required for shipping. This ester is available in 15-gal and 55-gal drums and also in smaller containers.

Triethyl orthoformate can be obtained by the two general methods for preparing esters of orthocarboxylic acids: (1) heating trihalogen compounds, such as chloroform, with sodium ethoxide in alcoholic solution;

$$CHCl_3 + 3\ NaOC_2H_5 \rightarrow HC(OC_2H_5)_3 + 3\ NaCl$$

(2) treating the hydrochlorides of imido esters with alcohols:

$$HC(=NH)OC_2H_5 . HCl + 2\ HOC_2H_5 \rightarrow HC(OC_2H_5)_3 + NH_4Cl$$

Ortho esters are unique esters in that they closely resemble acetals (qv). They are very stable to alkalies but are readily hydrolyzed by acids to form the ordinary ester or the free carboxylic acid, depending upon the conditions. They undergo ester interchange similarly to normal esters.

Triethyl orthoformate reacts with Grignard reagents to form acetals. It also reacts with some carbonyl compounds in the presence of a catalyst to form acetals or

Table 2. U.S. Production and Sales of Esters, 1962 (28)

Ester	Production, 1000 lb	Sales Quantity, 1000 lb	Sales Value, $1000	Unit/value, $/lb
General				
amyl acetates (90%)	8,225	5,738	1,000	.17
butyl acetates (90%)				
normal	54,400	63,526	8,276	.13
all other	34,167	38,284	4,330	.11
total butyl acetates	88,567	101,810	12,606	.12
cellulose acetate	606,184			
ethyl chloroacetate	1,288			
dibutyl fumarate	4,852			
diethyl malonate		466	347	.74
dilauryl 3,3′-thiodipropionate	352	461	571	1.24
dioctyl maleate	394			
ethyl acetate (85%)	101,879	90,149	10,230	.11
ethyl acrylate	71,842	24,017	7,759	.32
ethyl formate	199	175	59	.34
isopropyl myristate	1,809	1,811	643	.36
isopropyl palmitate	572	651	215	.33
isopropyl acetate	32,650	33,664	3,751	.11
methyl acetate	15,119			
vinyl acetate, monomer	317,912	189,330	26,350	.14
isobornyl acetate	1,065	1,078	438	.41
linalyl acetate	332	203	740	3.64
nopyl acetate (6,6-dimethylbicyclo-[1.1.3]hept-2-enethanol acetate)	31	33	39	1.19
terpinyl acetate	660	573	260	.45
vetiveryl acetate	17	15	348	23.51
allyl hexanoate (allyl caproate)	21	19	65	3.40
ethyl butyrate	247	239	164	.69
ethyl heptanoate (ethyl enanthate)	3	3	5	1.62
isopentyl butyrate (amyl butyrate)	47	44	36	.81
Medicinals				
cyclic benzenoid				
acetylsalicylic acid (aspirin)	27,194	22,874	12,418	.54
2-(dimethylamino)ethyl *p*-(butyl-amino) benzoate (Tetracaine) and hydrochloride	6	3	50	35.00
Plasticizers				
cyclic				
phthalic anhydride esters				
butyl decyl phthalate	3,011	2,880	511	.18
butyl octyl phthalate	17,833	17,084	3,091	.18
dibutyl phthalate	15,486	13,818	3,460	.25
dicyclohexyl phthalate	6,369	3,781	1,518	.40
diethyl phthalate	16,142	10,918	2,330	.21
dihexyl phthalate	1,533	1,173	247	.21
diisodecyl phthalate[a]	62,680	53,093	8,440	.16
bis(2-methoxyethyl) phthalate	3,927			
dimethyl phthalate	4,562	3,756	858	.23
dioctyl phthalates				
bis(2-ethylhexyl) phthalate	171,037	142,576	24,951	.18
diisooctyl and mixed octyl phthalates[a]	63,851	58,329	11,519	.20
total dioctyl phthalates	234,888	200,905	36,470	.18
ditridecyl phthalate	4,398	3,928	886	.23
decyl octyl phthalates				
isodecyl isooctyl phthalate[a]	2,060	2,158	420	.19

Table 2   (*continued*)

Ester	Production 1000 lb	Sales Quantity 1000 lb	Sales Value $1,000	Unit/value $/lb
decyl octyl phthalate	15,415	14,124	2,986	.21
total decyl octyl phthalates	17,475	16,282	3,406	.21
all other	81,692	71,218	16,524	.23
total phthalic anhydride esters	469,996	398,836	77,741	.19
acylic				
adipic acid esters				
bis(2-ethylhexyl) adipate	5,413	4,271	1,254	.29
diisodecyl adipate[a]	4,851	4,730	1,491	.32
diisooctyl adipate[a]	4,205	4,093	1,209	.30
decyl octyl adipate	8,078	7,386	2,137	.29
all other	1,028	949	437	.46
total adipic acid esters	23,575	21,429	6,528	.30
azelaic acid esters	13,090	11,427	3,729	.33
dibutyl maleate	7,395	2,966	742	.25
glycerol monoricinoleate	175	165	61	.37
oleic acid esters				
butyl oleate	2,022	1,572	403	.26
glycerol trioleate (triolein)	1,618	1,674	343	.20
propyl oleate	513	386	80	.21
all other	1,920	1,781	634	.36
total oleic acid esters	6,073	5,413	1,460	.27
sebacic acid esters				
dibutyl sebacate	3,847	2,348	1,493	.64
bis(2-ethylhexyl) sebacate	8,864	8,319	4,426	.53
all other	233	168	137	.82
total sebacic acid esters	12,944	10,835	6,056	.56
stearic acid esters				
butyl stearate	3,003	3,077	759	.25
all other	3,368	2,637	646	.24
total stearic acid esters	6,371	5,714	1,405	.25
Flavor and perfume				
cyclic benzenoid and naphthalenoid				
benzyl acetate	1,180	1,076	470	.44
benzyl butyrate	6	6	7	1.33
benzyl cinnamate		2	8	3.49
benzyl propionate	19	20	23	1.16
isobutyl phenylacetate	15	19	19	.99
isobutyl salicylate	21	31	30	.99
isopentyl salicylate (amyl salicylate)	443	355	252	.71
methyl anthranilate	180	69	151	2.19
α-methylbenzyl acetate	23	25	21	.87
methyl cinnamate	60	64	123	1.93
methyl salicylate (synthetic wintergreen oil)	6,270	4,155	2,277	.55
phenethyl acetate	57	58	64	1.10
phenethyl isobutyrate		6	13	2.09
2-phenoxyethyl isobutyrate	2	5	16	3.49
cyclic-terpenoid, heterocyclic, and alicyclic				
cedryl acetate	120	105	252	2.40
citronellyl acetate	16	14	28	2.03
citronellyl formate		19	60	3.18
citronellyl isobutyrate	3	6	19	3.35
geranyl acetate	38	41	81	1.94
geranyl formate		7	21	3.03

[a] Isooctyl and isodecyl esters are presumably derived from mixtures of alcohols obtained from the oxo reaction.

ketals. It condenses readily with compounds containing an active methylene group, as in the reaction with diethyl malonate:

$$CH_2(COOC_2H_5)_2 + HC(OC_2H_5)_3 \xrightarrow{(CH_3CO)_2O} C_2H_5OCH{=}C(COOC_2H_5)_2 + 2\,C_2H_5OH$$

The ethoxymethylene derivatives formed by such condensations are useful intermediates for members of the B-complex vitamins and for antimalarials. Triethyl orthoformate also serves as an intermediate in the formation of high-molecular-weight resinous substances and in the synthesis of symmetrical carbocyanine dyes and a group of polymethine dyes (qv) called pyranines.

ACETIC ACID ESTERS

Methyl acetate, CH_3COOCH_3, molecular weight 74.08, is a colorless liquid with a pleasant odor; mp, $-98.5°C$; bp, $57.2°C$, d_4^{20}, 0.933; n_D^{20}, 1.3612, flash point (closed-cup), $0°F$. Methyl acetate is used as a solvent for cellulose nitrate, cellulose acetate, and many resins and oils, and in the manufacture of artificial leather. Shipment regulations are the same as for methyl formate.

Ethyl acetate, $CH_3COOC_2H_5$, molecular weight 88.10, is a stable, colorless, flammable liquid with a pleasant odor; mp, $-82.4°C$; bp, $77.1°C$; d_4^{20}, 0.902; n_D^{20}, 1.3719; surface tension at $20°C$, 23.9 dyn/cm; absolute viscosity at $20°C$, 0.45 cP; specific heat at $20°C$, 0.468 cal/$°C$; latent heat of vaporization, 102.1 cal/g; heat of combustion, 537.5 cal/g; crit temp, $250.1°C$; crit pressure, 37.8 atm; coefficient of expansion, 0.00139/$°C$; flash point (Tag open-cup), $30°F$. The solubility of ethyl acetate in water at $20°C$ is 8.7% by wt, and the solubility of water in ethyl acetate at $20°C$ is 3.3% by wt. Ethyl acetate is soluble in the common alcohols, esters, ketones, ethers, chloroform, benzene, toluene, gasoline, and most other common organic solvents. Its dilution ratio (nitrocellulose solution method) is 3.4 with toluene and 1.1 with petroleum naphtha. The binary and ternary azeotropes of ethyl acetate are given in Table 3.

Table 3. Azeotropes of Ethyl Acetate

Other components	Bp, °C	Ethyl acetate, wt %	Other components	Bp, °C	Ethyl acetate, wt %
water	70.4	93.9	cyclohexane	72.8	46
methanol	62.3	56	hexane	65.0	58
ethyl alcohol	71.8	69.2	ethyl sulfide	73.0	77
isopropyl alcohol	75.3	75	1,3-cyclohexadiene	72.8	46
carbon disulfide	46.02	7.3	water	70.3	83.2[a]
ethyl iodide	70.4	24	ethyl alcohol	70.3	83.2[a]

[a] Water, 7.8%; ethyl alcohol, 9.0%.

Ethyl acetate is one of the most widely used esters. It is a fast-drying solvent which possesses excellent solvency for nitrocellulose, ethylcellulose, shellac, chlorinated rubber, and certain grades of vinyl resins, cellulose acetate, cellulose acetate butyrate, and neoprene, and Hycar synthetic rubber (see Elastomers, synthetic). This solvent is also used in duplicator fluids, nitrocellulose inks, lithographic inks, as a solvent and cleaning fluid in the textile industry, as a metal cleaner, as a solvent in the adhesives field, in flavoring extracts, in specially denatured alcohol for the food industry, and in the manufacture of medicinals. Because it can be produced economically, and because it has strong solvent power, it is widely used in spray lacquers, thinners, and dopes. Its rapid rate of evaporation is a distinct advantage in dipping and calendering processes.

Ethyl acetate is the least toxic of industrial organic solvents. No cases of human poisoning by oral ingestion have ever been reported, nor have any chronic systemic effects from industrial use ever been ascribed to the use of ethyl acetate. The vapors act as a temporary local irritant to the eyes, nose, and throat. At concentrations of about 2000 ppm and above, it has some anesthetic action. The Conference of Governmental Industrial Hygienists recommends a maximum allowable concentration of 400 ppm for 8 hr of exposure.

Since it is highly flammable and forms explosive mixtures with air (explosive limits 2.18–11.5% by vol), the precautions normally employed for handling flammable liquids are required for ethyl acetate. The material is noncorrosive to most metals and may be shipped and stored in ordinary steel.

Propyl acetate, $CH_3COOCH_2CH_2CH_3$, molecular weight 102.13, is a colorless liquid; mp, $-92.5°C$; bp, $101.6°C$; d_4^{20}, 0.887; n_D^{20}, 1.3844; soly in water at 20°C, 1.9% by wt; miscible with alcohol and ether (see Table 1). Because of its higher boiling range, its evaporation rate is slower than that of ethyl acetate. In blush resistance propyl acetate is similar to butyl acetate. Since its flash point (Cleveland open-cup) is 70°F, a red label is required for rail shipments. This ester is used in flavoring agents and perfumes, as a solvent for nitrocellulose, other cellulose derivatives, natural and synthetic resins, lacquers, and plastics, and in organic syntheses. In nitrocellulose lacquer solvents, it may be used as a replacement for methyl isobutyl ketone (4-methyl-2-pentanone) or ethyl acetate–butyl acetate mixtures.

Isopropyl acetate, $CH_3COOCH(CH_3)_2$, molecular weight 102.13, is a stable, colorless liquid with general solvent properties closely related to those of ethyl acetate; mp, $-69.3°C$; bp 89°C; d_4^{16}, 0.877; n_D^{20}, 1.3791; flash point (Tag open-cup), 40°F; soly in water at 20°C, 2.9% by wt. Because of its boiling range, which is higher than that of ethyl acetate, and because of its blush resistance, this ester is used in lacquer formulations. A red label is required for rail shipments.

Butyl acetate, $CH_3COO(CH_2)_3CH_3$, molecular weight 116.16, is a colorless, flammable liquid with a pleasant, fruity odor; mp, $-73.5°C$, bp, $126.5°C$; d_4^{20}, 0.882; n_D^{20}, 1.3947; flash point (Cleveland open-cup), 100°F; miscible in all proportions with the common organic solvents (see Table 1). Since the flash point is above 80°F, no red label is required for shipping.

Butyl acetate and mixtures of butyl acetate with butyl alcohol are useful for dehydrating purposes because they form constant-boiling mixtures with water (see Table 4).

Table 4. Azeotropes of Butyl Acetate

Other components	Bp, °C	Butyl acetate, wt %
water	90.2	71.3
butyl alcohol	117.2	53
water	89.4	35.3[a]
butyl alcohol	89.4	35.3[a]

[a] Water, 37.3%; butyl alcohol, 27.4%.

Butyl acetate is an important solvent in the preparation of high-grade nitrocellulose lacquers. It has high solvent power for nitrocellulose, and its evaporation rate is nearly ideal for this purpose. It is a solvent for ethylcellulose, cellulose acetate, camphor, mineral and vegetable oils, pitch, natural resins, chlorinated rubber, and many synthetic resins such as vinyl, polystyrene, and methacrylate. Ester, kauri, Manila, pontianac, and dewaxed dammar gums dissolve completely in butyl acetate; shellac partially dissolves; and gum rubber softens but does not dissolve. Butyl acetate has a high tolerance for diluents and promotes compatibility of all of the ingredients of a lacquer.

The Conference of Governmental Industrial Hygienists adopted a maximum allowable concentration limit of 200 ppm of butyl acetate vapors in air. This limit is similar to that of many other lacquer solvents. Butyl acetate is noncorrosive to ordinary steel, aluminum, copper, brass, tin, and similar metals. It is shipped in steel containers.

Isobutyl acetate, $CH_3COOCH_2CH(CH_3)_2$, molecular weight 116.16, is a water-white liquid with a typical, mild, fruity ester odor; mp, $-98.9°C$; bp, $116.5°C$; d_4^{20}, 0.8712; $n_D^{17.8}$, 1.39114; flash point (Tag open-cup), 87°F; soly in water, 0.6% by wt at 25°C; miscible in all proportions with common organic solvents. Isobutyl acetate, when used as a lacquer solvent, has properties similar to those of butyl acetate, and in many applications it can be substituted directly for butyl acetate without any change in the formula. Its evaporation rate is somewhat higher than that of butyl acetate, but lower than that of methyl isobutyl ketone (4-methyl-2-pentanone) or *sec*-butyl acetate.

sec-**Butyl acetate,** $CH_3COOCH(CH_3)(C_2H_5)$, molecular weight 116.16, is a water-white liquid with a mild, fruity ester odor; bp, $112-113°C$; d_4^{25}, 0.8648; n_D^{25}, 1.3866; flash point (closed-cup), 60°F; insoluble in water; miscible in all proportions with common organic solvents. Like the two isomeric butyl acetates discussed previously, this ester is used in solvents, especially lacquer solvents, textile sizes, and paper coatings.

Isoamyl acetate (banana oil, pear oil), $CH_3COOCH_2CH_2CH(CH_3)_2$, molecular weight 130.18, is a colorless liquid; mp, $-78.5°C$; bp, $142.5°C$; d_4^{25}, 0.8699; $n_D^{17.9}$, 1.40170; soly in water at 25°C, about 2% by wt; soluble in alcohols, ether, benzene, toluene, and gasoline. The commercial material, sold under the name amyl acetate, has a boiling range of 125–150°C, and contains 90–95% ester (chiefly isoamyl acetate; see Amyl alcohols). The flash point of this material is 95°F (Tag open cup). Amyl acetate is used largely by the lacquer industry, where a solvent boiling moderately higher than butyl acetate is desired. It is also used in leather polishes and drycleaning preparations, in mixtures with ethyl acetate as a solvent for cleaning needles in textile mills, and as a solvent for applying phosphors in the manufacture of fluorescent lamps. Its physiological effects are similar to those of butyl acetate.

2-Ethylhexyl acetate (octyl acetate), $CH_3COOCH_2CH(C_2H_5)(CH_2)_3CH_3$, molecular weight 172.26, bp, $198.6°C$; d_4^{20}, 0.8734; n_D^{20}, 1.4201; flash point (Cleveland open-cup), 190°F. This ester has high solvent power for nitrocellulose and resins in comparison with other high-boiling solvents.

Benzyl acetate, $CH_3COOCH_2C_6H_5$, molecular weight 150.17, is a colorless, mobile liquid possessing the distinctive fragrance associated with the odor of jasmine; mp, $-51.5°C$; bp, $213.5°C$; d_4^{16}, 1.057; n_D^{20}, 1.5232; flash point (open cup), 215°F; almost insoluble in water; miscible with alcohol, ether, and similar solvents. Benzyl acetate is a component of the extract of gardenia, hyacinth, ylang-ylang, and the main component of the extract of jasmine. It is prepared by the esterification of benzyl alcohol with acetic acid, or by the reaction of benzyl chloride and sodium acetate.

Benzyl acetate is handled in the same manner as benzyl alcohol and requires no special shipping regulations. The bulk of benzyl acetate is used in soap odors, but it is also a popular item in other perfumes and is used to a minor extent in flavors.

PROPIONIC ACID ESTERS

Methyl propionate, $CH_3CH_2COOCH_3$, molecular weight 88.10, is a colorless liquid with a fruity odor recalling rum; mp, $-87°C$; bp, $79.7°C$; d_4^{20}, 0.9148; $n_D^{18.5}$, 1.37767; flash point (open-cup), 30°F; soly in water at 20°C, 6% by wt. It is used in organic syntheses. A red label is required for rail shipment.

Ethyl propionate, $CH_3CH_2COOC_2H_5$, molecular weight 102.13, is a colorless liquid; mp, $-73.9°C$; bp, $99.1°C$; d_4^{15}, 0.89574; $n_D^{20.2}$, 1.38385; flash point (open-cup), 54°F; soly in water at 20°C, 2% by wt. A red label is required for rail shipment.

BUTYRIC ACID ESTERS

Methyl butyrate, $CH_3(CH_2)_2COOCH_3$, molecular weight 102.13, is a colorless liquid; mp, $-95°C$; bp, $102.3°C$; d_4^{20}, 0.898; n_D^{20}, 1.3879; flash point (open-cup), 57°F; soly in water at 21°C, 1.5% by wt. It is used in the manufacture of artificial rum and fruit essences. A red label is required for rail shipment.

Ethyl butyrate, $CH_3(CH_2)_2COOC_2H_5$, molecular weight 116.16, is a colorless liquid; mp, $-93.3°C$; bp, $121.3°C$; d_4^{20}, 0.879; flash point (open-cup), 85°F; soly in water at 25°C, about 0.7% by wt. It is used in the manufacture of artificial rum, pineapple oil, and in perfumes.

ISOBUTYRIC ACID ESTERS

Methyl isobutyrate, $(CH_3)_2CHCOOCH_3$, molecular weight 102.13, is a colorless liquid; mp, $-84.7°C$; bp, $92.6°C$; d_4^{20}, 0.891; n_D^{20}, 1.3840; slightly soluble in water; miscible in all proportions with common organic solvents.

Ethyl isobutyrate, $(CH_3)_2CHCOOC_2H_5$, molecular weight 116.16, is a colorless liquid; mp, $-88.2°C$; bp, $111.7°C$; d_4^{20}, 0.86930; n_D^{20}, 1.3903; slightly soluble in water; miscible in all proportions with common organic solvents.

Isobutyl isobutyrate, $(CH_3)_2CHCOOCH_2CH(CH_3)_2$, molecular weight 144.21, is a colorless liquid: mp, $-80.7°C$; bp, $148.7°C$; d_4^0, 0.875; n_D^{20}, 1.3999; flash point (Tag open-cup), 120°F. The commercial material contains 98% ester (min) and has a boiling range from 144–151°C. Isobutyl isobutyrate has a distinct fruity odor and flavor. These properties make it an interesting material for the formulation of perfumes and various flavoring preparations and as a bulk component of flavor essences. It is an active solvent for nitrocellulose and several vinyl resins. It may be used as a replacement for a portion of the more expensive retarder solvents in vinyl lacquer systems.

STEARIC ACID ESTERS

Commercial stearic acid esters are normally mixtures of chiefly stearic and palmitic acid esters corresponding to the composition of commercial stearic acid (see Fatty acids).

Methyl stearate, $CH_3(CH_2)_{16}COOCH_3$, molecular weight 298.50, occurs as white crystals; mp, 39.1°C; bp, 215°C; n_D^{45}, 1.4346; insoluble in water; soluble in alcohol, ether, and similar organic solvents. No red label is required for rail shipment. Its uses are similar to those of butyl stearate.

Ethyl stearate, $CH_3(CH_2)_{16}COOC_2H_5$, molecular weight 312.52, occurs as white crystals; mp, 33.9°C; $b_{0.18}$, 152°C; b_{15}, 213–215°C; n_D^{50}, 1.4320; insoluble in water; soluble in alcohol, ether, and similar organic solvents. The commercial-grade ester solidifies at about 20–24°C and boils at 180°C at 4 mm. Its uses are similar to those of butyl stearate.

Butyl stearate, $CH_3(CH_2)_{16}COO(CH_2)_3CH_3$, molecular weight 340.58, is a colorless liquid; mp, 27.5°C; b_{25}, 220–225°C; d_4^{20}, 0.860; n_D^{20}, 1.4456; flash point (open cup), 187.8°C. The commercial-grade ester is water-white, d_{20}^{25}, 0.855–0.860, contains less than 0.5% acidity calculated as stearic acid, and is practically odorless. It is of value in compounding lubricating oils, as a lubricant for the textile and molding trade, in special lacquers, and as a waterproofing agent. In the cosmetic and pharmaceutical fields it is used in vanishing creams, ointments, rouges, lipsticks, and nail polishes. Its oily characteristics have made it of particular value in polishes and in coatings that are to be polished.

Bibliography

"Esters, Organic" in ECT 1st ed., Vol. 5, pp. 824–850, by T. Earl Jordan, Publicker Industries, Inc.

1. H. W. Post, *The Chemistry of the Aliphatic Orthoesters*, Reinhold Publishing Corp., New York, 1943.
2. "The Naming and Indexing of Chemical Compounds from Chemical Abstracts," *Chem. Abstr.* **56** (1962).
3. K. S. Markley, ed., *Fatty Acids, Their Chemistry, Properties, Production, and Uses*, Part 1, 2nd ed, Interscience Publishers, Inc., New York, 1960; Part 2, 1961.
4. E. S. Gould, *Mechanism and Structure in Organic Chemistry*, Henry Holt & Co., Inc., New York, 1959, pp. 314–345.
5. A. W. Ralston, *Fatty Acids and Their Derivatives*, John Wiley & Sons, Inc., New York, 1948, pp. 258–279.
6. R. H. Potts, in S. E. Pattison, ed., *Industrial Fatty Acids and Their Applications*, Reinhold Publishing Corp., New York, 1959, p. 16.
7. L. M. Fieser, *Advanced Organic Chemistry*, Reinhold Publishing Corp., New York, 1961, p. 380.
8. Ref. 4, pp. 329–332.
9. H. Adkins, in R. Adams et al., ed., *Organic Reactions*, Vol. 8, John Wiley & Sons, Inc., New York, 1954, pp. 1–27.
10. M. W. Formo, in S. E. Pattison, ed., *Industrial Fatty Acids and Their Applications*, Reinhold Publishing Corp., New York, 1959, pp. 70–71.
11. H. Adkins and R. H. Gillespie, in E. C. Horning et al., ed., *Organic Syntheses*, Coll. Vol. 3, John Wiley & Sons, Inc., New York, 1955, pp. 671–673.
12. E. E. Reid, F. O. Cockerville, J. D. Meyer, W. M. Cox, Jr., and J. R. Ruhoff, in A. N. Blatt et al., eds., *Organic Syntheses*, Coll. Vol. 2, John Wiley & Sons, Inc., New York, 1943, p. 468.
13. N. G. Gaylord, *Reduction with Complex Metal Hydrides*, Interscience Publishers, Inc., New York, 1956, pp. 391–543.
14. Ref. 7, p. 272.
15. C. B. Hauser and B. E. Hudson, Jr., in R. Adams et al., eds., *Organic Reactions*, Vol. 2, John Wiley & Sons, Inc., New York, 1947, pp. 266–302.
16. S. M. McElvain, in R. Adams et al., eds., *Organic Reactions*, Vol. 4, John Wiley & Sons, Inc., New York, 1948, pp. 256–268.
17. Ref. 4, pp. 500–504; L. T. Smith, C. H. Fisher, W. P. Ratchford, and M. L. Fein, *Ind. Eng. Chem.* **34**, 743–749 (1942).

18. Ref. 5, p. 833.

19. E. L. McDaniel and H. S. Young, *Ind. Eng. Chem. Prod. Res. Develop.* **2**, 287–292 (1963).

20. L. J. Bellamy, *The Infrared Spectra of Complex Molecules*, 2nd ed, John Wiley & Sons, Inc., New York, 1958, pp. 178–191.

21. E. Guenther and D. Althausen, "The Constituents of Essential Oils," Vol. 2 of *The Essential Oils*, D. Van Nostrand Co., Inc., New York, 1949, pp. 618–656.

22. W. A. Poucher, *Perfumes, Cosmetics and Soaps*, Vol. 1, 5th ed., D. Van Nostrand Co., Inc., New York, 1941.

23. M. Hausermann, *Helv. Chim. Acta* **34**, 2172–2181 (1951); *Chem. Abstr.* **46**, 6586d (1952); I. Lin and A. R. Day, *J. Am. Chem. Soc.* **74**, 5133 (1951).

24. S. K. Bhattacharyya and A. K. Sen, *Ind. Eng. Chem. Process Design Develop.* **3**, 169–176 (1964); F. L. Resen, *Oil Gas J.* **51** (52), 92–93, 122, 125 (1953).

25. W. S. Port, in S. E. Pattison, ed., *Industrial Fatty Acids and Their Applications*, Reinhold Publishing Corp., New York, 1959, pp. 190-195.

26. C. Marsden and S. Mann, eds., *Solvents Guide*, 2nd ed, Interscience Publishers, a division of John Wiley & Sons, Inc., New York, 1963.

27. D. N. Buttrey, *Plasticizers*, 2nd American ed., Franklin Publishing Co., Inc., Palisades, New Jersey, 1960.

28. "Synthetic Organic Chemicals, United States Production and Sales, 1962," *U.S. Tariff Comm. Publ. 114*, U.S. Government Printing Office, Washington, D.C., 1963.

29. W. G. Dukek and A. H. Popkin, in R. C. Gunderson and A. W. Hart, eds., *Synthetic Lubricants*, Reinhold Publishing Corp., New York, 1962, pp. 151–245.

30. G. L. Jenkins, W. H. Hartung, K. E. Hamlin, and J. B. Data, *The Chemistry of Organic Medicinal Products*, John Wiley & Sons, Inc., New York, 1957, pp. 169–176.

31. A. Burger, in A. Burger, ed., *Medicinal Chemistry*, 2nd ed., Interscience Publishers, Inc., New York, 1960, pp. 39, 42, 43; J. S. Pierce, in A. Burger, ed., *Medicinal Chemistry*, 2nd ed., Interscience Publishers, Inc., New York, 1960, pp. 470, 491.

EDWARD U. ELAM
Tennessee Eastman Company

ESTROGENS; ESTRONE. See Sex hormones under Hormones.

ETHANE

Ethane, CH_3CH_3, is the second member of the paraffin series. It is a colorless, odorless gas which burns with a slightly luminous flame. It is a simple asphyxiant and a narcotic in high concentrations. Ethane is present as a minor constituent (5–10%)

Table 1. U.S. Production of Ethane

Year	Production, 1000 lb	Unit price, $/lb
1953	144,623	0.010
1954	355,820	0.006
1955	445,214	0.006
1956	562,153	0.010
1957	639,559	0.010
1958	646,089	0.009
1959	690,582	0.008
1960	733,943	0.010
1961	902,752	0.009
1962	980,614	0.008
1963	1,012,990	0.009

Table 2. Typical Specifications of Three Grades of Ethane

	Research	Pure	Technical
composition, mole %			
methane		trace	trace
ethane	99.98	99.35	97.3
ethylene	trace	0.05	0.4
propylene	0.02	0.25	1.8
propane	trace	0.35	0.5
freezing point, triple point, °F	−297.9		
boiling point, °F		−127.5	−127.3
sp gr of liquid at 60/60°F		0.377	0.376
at 20/4°F	0.3623	0.362	0.361
density of liquid at 60°F, lb/gal		3.15	
sp gr of vapor at 60°F and 14,7 psia (air = 1)		1.0469	
sp vol of vapor at 60°F and 14,7 psia, ft³/lb		12.515	
flash point, °F		−211	−210

Table 3. Physical Properties of Ethane

molecular wt	30.068
boiling point, °F	−127.53
freezing point, triple point, °F	−297.89
critical pressure, atm	48.3
critical temp, °F	90.32
critical density, g/ml	0.203
specific gravity, 60/60°F	0.3771
C_p, 25°C, cal/(C°)(mole)	12.585
C_p, 60°F, Btu/lb	0.4097
C_v, 60°F, Btu/lb	0.3436
heat of vaporization, ΔH_v, atm pressure at bp	3.515 kcal/mole
entropy of vaporization, S_v, at bp	19.06 cal/(C°)(mole)
heat of combustion at 25°C,	
$C_2H_6 \rightarrow H_2O$ (liq) + CO_2 (gas)	372.82 kcal/mole
$C_2H_6 \rightarrow H_2O$(gas) + CO_2(gas)	341.26 kcal/mole
heat of formation at 25°C	−20.236 kcal/mole
entropy at 25°C	54.85 cal/(C°)(mole)
free energy of formation at 25°C	−7.860 kcal/mole
heat of fusion	0.6829 kcal/mole
entropy of fusion	7.594 cal/(C°)(mole)
flammable limits, vol % in air	
lower	3.22
upper	12.45
viscosity at 68°F, cP	0.0091
surface tension, dyn/cm	17.93
flash point, °F	−306
solubility in H_2O at 20°C, ml ethane/100 ml H_2O	4.7
solubility in alcohol at 4°C, ml ethane/100 ml alcohol	46

vapor pressure	°C	mm Hg	°C	mm Hg
	−142.90	10	−75.00	1,500
	−119.30	100	−53.60	3,800
	−96.05	500	−7.7	15,200
	−88.63	760		

in some natural gases and can be recovered from the gases produced during the distillation of crude petroleum. The quantity of ethane produced in the United States, as reported by the U.S. Tariff Commission, has been increasing steadily, as can be seen from Table 1.

Most of the ethane produced, however, is used directly by the manufacturer. In 1963, for instance, only 326,860,000 lb of ethane was sold; this represented a market of \$2.9 million. Ethane is shipped unstenched in pint, quart, and 12-gal cylinders but an odorant can be added upon request to the manufacturer. In the smaller containers ethane is shipped under ICC classification as a flammable, compressed gas; the 12-gal containers require a red gas label. Typical specifications for three grades of ethane are given in Table 2.

Ethane is a minor component in commercial fuels such as "bottled gas" and "suburban gas," which contain approx 90% propane, 5% ethane, and 5% butane. Ethane is also used as a refrigerant in some two-stage refrigeration systems in which relatively low temperatures are produced. The pyrolysis of ethane, or more frequently, ethane–propane mixtures leads to the production of ethylene (qv). Oxidation of natural gas leads to the production of acetaldehyde, acetic acid, and lower oxidation products arising from the ethane present in the natural gas. Ethyl chloride can be produced commercially by the direct chlorination of ethane at 300–500°C. Similarly, nitration of ethane in the vapor phase produces 73% nitroethane and 23% nitromethane.

Ethane can be prepared in the laboratory according to the following equations:

$$CH_2=CH_2 \xrightarrow[Pd]{H_2} C_2H_6$$

$$HC\equiv CH \xrightarrow[Raney\ Ni]{H_2} C_2H_6$$

$$2\ CH_3I + 2\ Na \xrightarrow[reaction]{Wurtz} C_2H_6 + 2\ NaI$$

$$CH_3CH_2I \xrightarrow[Na\ +\ C_2H_5OH]{Zn\ +\ HCl,\ or} C_2H_6$$

$$(C_2H_5)_2Zn \xrightarrow{H_2O} C_2H_6$$

$$C_2H_5MgBr + H_2O \rightarrow C_2H_6 + MgBr(OH)$$

$$CH_3CO_2Na \xrightarrow[electrolysis]{Kolbe} C_2H_6$$

$$CH_3CH_2CO_2H \xrightarrow{decarboxylation} C_2H_6 + CO_2$$

$$CH_3N=NCH_3 \xrightarrow{heat} C_2H_6 + N_2$$

The physical properties of ethane are given in Table 3.

ARNOLD P. LURIE
Eastman Kodak Co.

ETHANETHIOL (ETHYL MERCAPTAN), CH_3CH_2SH.   See Thiols.

ETHANOIC ACID

This article discusses ethanoic acid (acetic acid), and some closely related chemicals, as follows:

ACETIC ACID

Ethanoic acid (IUPAC), more commonly known as acetic acid (methane-carboxylic acid), CH_3COOH (abbreviated as AcOH), is a clear, colorless liquid with an acrid taste and pungent odor. As the acid of vinegar, acetic acid is as old as fermented liquors, which sour spontaneously, and which are historically recorded prior to 3000 BC. Today acetic acid is one of the most important industrial organic acids. It is produced mostly synthetically in volume exceeding a billion pounds per year. Acetic acid is most widely known in the form of vinegar, a dilute aqueous solution; it occurs both free and combined in the form of esters of various alcohols in many plants, and has been detected also in animal secretions (1–4). Major uses of acetic acid are in the manufacture of cellulose acetate fiber and plastics, ester solvents, dyes, metal salts, and many other chemicals. "Glacial" is a term applied to acetic acid of high purity (above 99%), which congeals to ice-like crystals at 58–60°F. Contact with concentrated solutions (50% or more) can cause severe skin burns and severe damage to the eyes, possibly resulting in total loss of sight. Exposed areas should be flushed immediately with ample quantities of water. Breathing of concentrated vapors is also harmful and swallowing may cause severe injury or death.

Physical and Chemical Properties

The physical properties of acetic acid are listed in Table 1. Freezing points and specific gravities of aqueous acetic acid solutions of varying concentrations are presented in Table 2, and acetic acid temperatures at selected vapor pressures are listed in Table 3. Figure 1 illustrates some physical properties of acetic acid–water solutions.

Acetic acid is miscible in all proportions with water, ethanol, and ether. It is an excellent solvent for organic compounds and is widely used as such in organic synthesis and in the preparation of acetates, acetone, acetic anhydride, etc. A dipole moment of zero for the unsymmetrical acetic acid structure has been explained by the formation of symmetric dimers via hydrogen bonding in which the dipole moments cancel. Highly dissociated ionic species do not occur in acetic acid solution because of the low dielectric constant of such a solution (10).

Acetic acid also exhibits relatively low basicity, or proton affinity, and as a solvent yields relatively small ionization constants for strong acids such as perchloric acid. Acetic acid serves as a differentiating solvent for strong acids such as perchloric, hydrobromic, sulfuric, hydrochloric, and nitric acids, which have nearly equal strength in aqueous solution, due to the leveling effect of water. Since acetonium ion, $CH_3C-(OH)_2{}^+$, the strongest acid available in solution, is stronger than hydronium ion, acetic

Table 1. Physical Properties of Acetic Acid

melting point, °C	16.6
boiling point, at 760 mm, °C	118.8
density, d_4^{20}	1.0492
refractive index, n_D^{20}	1.37182 (5)
freezing point, see Table 2	
apparent specific gravity, at 20/20°C	1.0510 (6)
coefficient of cubical expansion, at 20°C	1.071×10^{-3}
critical pressure, atm	57.2 (7)
critical temperature, °C	321.6 (7)
dielectric constant	
2°C (solid)	4.1 (7)
20°C	6.15 (7)
electrical conductivity, at 25°C, mho/cm	1.12×10^{-8} (7)
ionization constant, at 25°C	1.753×10^{-5}
$-\log K$	4.76
magnetic susceptibility, cgs	-0.526×10^{-6} (7)
specific inductive capacity, at 18°C	9.7
surface tension, at 20°C, in air, dyn/cm	27.6 (7)
vapor density (air = 1)	2.07
viscosity, cP	
20°C	1.22 (9)
40°C	0.90 (9)
specific heat, at 0°C, cal/(g) (°C)	
liquid	0.468 (8)
solid	0.487 (8)
heat of combustion, kcal/mole	-209.4 (7)
heat of formation, kcal/mole	-116.2 (7)
heat of fusion, at 16.7°C, cal/g	44.7 (7)
heat of solution, at 18°C, kcal/mole	0.375 (7)
heat of vaporization, at 118.1°C, cal/g	96.8 (7)
autoignition temperature, °C	565
explosive limit, in air (lower limit), % by vol	4
flash point (Tag open-cup), °F	130

acid is very useful as a solvent in carrying out reactions that require stronger acids. Acetic acid, however, has a very strong leveling effect on bases and solvolyzes all strong bases to acetate ion, CH_3COO^-. This amphoteric behavior of acetic acid systems is demonstrated by zinc acetate which dissolves in acetic acid solutions of both hydrogen chloride and sodium acetate, although it is only very slightly soluble in acetic acid alone (11).

The characteristic carboxyl group of acetic and other fatty acids has been considered a resonance hybrid in order to explain an acid strength greater than that of water and of the comparable alcohols (12). Further substitution of electronegative atoms, such as chlorine, tends to increase acid constants by inductive effect along the carbon chain to the oxygen atom. For example, the acid constant, K, is 1.86×10^{-5} for acetic acid, 1.5×10^{-3} for chloroacetic acid, 5.0×10^{-2} for dichloroacetic acid, and 2×10^{-1} for trichloroacetic acid (13,14).

CHEMICAL REACTIONS

Since acetic acid may be treated as a resonance hybrid, in the formation of esters protonation is assumed to occur on the carbonyl oxygen by at least three different

Table 2. Freezing Points and Specific Gravities of Water Solutions in Acetic Acid at 15.5/15.5°C

Acetic acid, %	Freezing point, °C[a]	Specific gravity[b]
99.9	16.43	1.0558
99.8	16.24	1.0561
99.7	16.04	1.0564
99.6	15.84	1.0566
99.5	15.65	1.0569
99.4	15.47	1.0572
99.3	15.28	1.0574
99.2	15.10	1.0577
99.1	14.92	1.0580
99.0	14.74	1.0582
98.9	14.57	1.0584
98.8	14.40	1.0587
98.7	14.23	1.0589
98.6	14.06	1.0592
98.5	13.90	1.0594
98.4	13.74	1.0596
98.3	13.58	1.0599
98.2	13.43	1.0602
98.1	13.27	1.0604
98.0	13.12	1.0606

[a] Each 1% propionic acid depresses the freezing point by 0.485°C.

[b] 3.0% propionic acid depresses the specific gravity by 0.0019; 5% depresses it by 0.0032; and 6% depresses it by 0.0040.

Table 3. Acetic Acid Temperatures at Selected Vapor Pressures

Vapor pressure, mm Hg	Temperature, °C	Vapor pressure, mm Hg	Temperature, °C
1	solid	60	50.84
5	solid	100	62.19
10	17.11	200	79.12
20	29.16	400	98.10
40	42.44	760	117.86

mechanisms. The usual method of esterification involves the reaction of acetic acid with an alcohol in the presence of an inorganic acid as catalyst. For example, acid is refluxed with the alcohol in the presence of 5–10% concd sulfuric acid. Phosphoryl chloride has also been demonstrated as a good catalyst for the esterification reaction (see also Esterification). Esters of low molecular weight are fairly soluble in water, and all esters are soluble in most organic solvents (15).

The formation of acetate esters is undoubtedly the most important commercial use for acetic acid. Large quantities of ethyl acetate, butyl acetates, glycol diacetate, steroid acetates, and other alcohol esters of acetic acid are produced and consumed in the U.S. The recent literature includes references to acetic acid ester synthesis starting with acetylene to give vinyl acetate by using residual acetic acid; ethylene glycol esterification in the presence of ion exchange resins; and catalytic esterifications of methanol, ethanol, and butanol in the presence of a variety of catalysts. The discovery that olefins oxidized in acetic acid solvent yield unsaturated esters such as

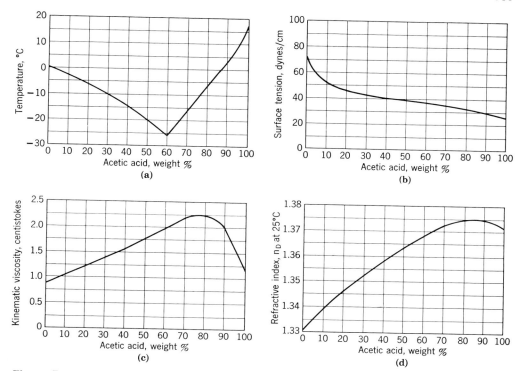

Fig. 1. Properties of acetic acid–water solutions.   (**a**) Freezing points.   (**b**) Surface tension at 25°C.   (**c**) Kinematic viscosities at 25°C.   (**d**) Refractive indexes at 25°C.

vinyl acetate and propenyl acetate, adds to the technical importance of acetic acid (16,17).

A yield of 97% of vinyl acetate based on converted ethylene is reported for the reaction in which palladium chloride is reduced by ethylene in solutions of acetic acid containing sodium acetate:

$$C_2H_4 + PdCl_2 + 2\ CH_3COONa \rightarrow CH_2{=}CH{-}OCOCH_3 + 2\ NaCl + Pd + CH_3COOH$$

Salts of acetic acid are formed directly by reaction with an alkali, or by the saponification or alkaline hydrolysis of an acetate ester. In equimolar proportions sodium acetate and acetic acid provide an excellent buffer solution. Sodium acetate, $CH_3COONa.3H_2O$, and potassium acetate CH_3COOK, are made by neutralization of acetic acid with the corresponding base. Acetates of many mono- and polyvalent metal ions have extensive commercial use. Lead acetate, $(CH_3COO)_2Pb.3H_2O$, one of the few water-soluble lead salts, is widely used in the manufacture of other lead compounds. Copper, zinc, and chromium acetates are commercially available inorganic salts. Copper ammonium acetate derived from either acetic acid or copper acetate is used to absorb butadiene from the butylenes. The industrial chemicals, white lead (basic lead carbonate) and Paris green (a copper acetate–copper arsenite complex), are also made from acetic acid (18).

Typical chemical reactions of acetic acid in addition to the formation of organic and inorganic salts include, halogenation, the formation of amide, nitrile, ketone, anhydride, and acid chloride, as well as acylation and solvolytic reactions.

Halogenation

$$CH_3COOH + Cl_2 \rightarrow CH_2ClCOOH + HCl$$

Substitution occurs at the methyl group and mono-, di-, and trichloroacetic acids are formed in turn when chlorine is passed into hot acetic acid

Amide formation

$$CH_3COOH + NH_3 \rightarrow CH_3CONH_2 + H_2O$$

Nitrile formation

$$CH_3COOH + NH_3 \rightarrow CH_3CN + 2\ H_2O$$

Ketene formation

$$CH_3COOH \xrightarrow{(600°C)} CH_2{=}CO + H_2O$$

Acid chloride formation

$$3\ CH_3COOH + PCl_3 \rightarrow 3\ CH_3COCl + P(OH)_3$$

Substitution of the hydroxyl group by a chlorine atom occurs.

Solvolytic reaction

$$4\ CH_3COOH + SO_2Cl_2 \rightarrow SO_2(OOCCH_3)_2 + 2\ CH_3C(OH)_2{}^+ + 2\ Cl^-$$

Metathetical reactions proceed smoothly in an anhydrous acetic acid medium despite its low dielectric constant. Solutions of, for example, heavy-metal salts, treated with hydrogen sulfide readily precipitate the appropriate sulfides. Silver nitrate solution gives precipitates with solutions of halides, cyanides, and thiocyanates. Sulfates that normally form hydrates are precipitated in anhydrous condition from a solution of almost any soluble metal salt by reaction with anhydrous sulfuric acid. Iron(III) thiocyanate complex is readily formed in acetic acid solution. Neutralization of metal salts with acids is also accomplished in acetic acid solutions; thus, sodium acetate is neutralized by hydrochloric acid with precipitation of sodium chloride.

Manufacture

The methods of producing acetic acid on a commercial scale have multiplied with the rapid expansion of the chemical industry, shifting in the last hundred years from natural fermentation processes to modern synthetic processes. Since the 1950s a growing proportion of the world's acetic acid has been produced by direct oxidation of petroleum fractions. Until then, most acetic acid was produced by the oxidation or dehydrogenation of acetaldehyde. Only minor amounts are still produced by wood distillation. Historically, the acetic acid industry began about 5000 years ago with the production of vinegar—the only acid reagent distinctly recognized by the ancients— by the fermentation of alcohol. It was not until the late nineteenth century that the distillation of wood in retorts was used to obtain acetic acid as well as methanol and acetone. The commercial availability of acetylene in the early 1900s led to a process for the production of acetaldehyde, which can be oxidized to acetic acid; this process was tried as early as 1905 but did not become economically important until 1916 (19,20).

ALCOHOL FERMENTATION PROCESSES

This ancient process employs the aerobic bacterial oxidation of alcohol to dilute acetic acid. Various acetic bacteria (*Acetobacter aceti*, including *A. curvum*, *A. orleanse*, and *A. schuezenbachii*) secrete an enzyme which promotes the oxidation of ethyl alcohol, possibly through acetaldehyde, to acetic acid. The two-stage fermentation reaction proceeds as follows:

$$C_2H_5OH + \frac{1}{2} O_2 \rightarrow CH_3CHO + H_2O$$

$$CH_3CHO + \frac{1}{2} O_2 \rightarrow CH_3COOH$$

The vinegar thus produced from cider, malt, or wine rarely has an acetic acid content greater than 5%; this rises to 12 or 14% if dilute alcohol is used. Modern commercial vinegar production employs the Orleans process or the quick vinegar process.

The quick vinegar process can be used for the commercial production of dilute acetic acid (8–10%). Blackstrap molasses is usually employed as an aqueous solution containing about 10% alcohol and 1% acetic acid. Large wooden tanks about 10 ft in diameter and 15 ft high filled with beechwood shavings are used as the "generators." A false bottom supports the packing and permits the introduction of air as well as the drawoff of the weak acetic acid. The alcohol solution is introduced at the top of the tank through a sparger and is trickled over the beechwood shavings. The weak acid is then recycled until the concentration reaches about 10%. Acid concentrations above approx 12%, however, tend to kill the bacteria. Phosphorus and nitrogen compounds are often supplied as nutrients to promote bacterial growth and thus yield a higher conversion of alcohol to acetic acid. The temperature of the fermenting mass is maintained at 30–35°C by controlling the air-flow rate. A 75–90% conversion of alcohol to acid yields 0.42–0.51 lb of acid per pound of reducing sugar in the molasses. Production by this method was formerly economically practical, up to a capacity of about 10 tons per day (21).

DESTRUCTIVE DISTILLATION OF HARDWOOD

From the destructive distillation of hardwoods, raw pyroligneous acid liquor is produced containing up to 7% acetic acid, 4% crude methanol and acetone, 9% tar and oil, and 80% water. The pyroligneous acid liquor is allowed to settle to separate the clear liquor from the tars. A preliminary distillation removes soluble tars and yields a boiled liquor. In a now obsolete process, after the acids in the distillate are neutralized with lime, methanol is distilled off, and the residue of calcium acetate solution is evaporated to dryness. Distillation of the calcium acetate with strong sulfuric acid and subsequent rectification produce acetic acid of glacial strength together with weaker fractions.

Direct Recovery Processes. Three major methods were worked out for recovering the acetic acid from pyroligneous liquor directly, without first forming calcium acetate, and then using sulfuric acid: (*1*) the extractive distillation process, or Suida system; (*2*) the cold liquid–liquid extraction process or Brewster system and its modifications; and (*3*) the azeotropic distillation process, or Othmer system.

Examination of Figure 2 will show that the vapor composition line for the system acetic acid–water is never far from the 45° line. Therefore, although the difference in boiling point is 18.8°C, separation by distillation to produce either component reason-

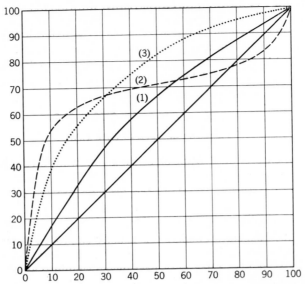

Fig. 2. Vapor–liquid composition curves: (**1**) acetic acid–water at 760 mm; (**2**) acetic acid–cyclohexane at 745 mm; (**3**) acetic acid–isopropyl ether at 742 mm. Value of y = mole % of more volatile component (water, cyclohexane, or isopropyl ether) in vapor phase; x = mole % of more volatile component in liquid phase.

ably pure would require a very large column, and a high reflux ratio and, consequently, a high steam consumption (see Distillation). The three processes described below represent three solutions to this problem. See also below under Acid concentration and recovery.

The Suida extractive distillation process passes the vapors from the distillation of settled pyroligneous acid through a countercurrent scrubbing column to dissolve the acid in a wood-oil tar fraction, while dilute methanol vapor is removed overhead to a recovery system. In a dehydrator water is removed from the acid–wood oil solution, which is then fed to a vacuum exhausting column to separate acid from oil. The oil is recycled and the acetic acid vapor is passed into the bottom of a rectifying column also operating under a vacuum and equipped with reflux condenser. Acid concentrated to 90–95% is withdrawn as liquid from the rectifier to vacuum receivers, and condensate from the top of the column is scrubbed with water to produce a weak 15% acetic acid. The Suida system, one of the first of the direct processes, has been used in Europe and in the United States; it does not yield anhydrous acid (22,23).

The cold-solvent extraction process in the Coahran modification of the Brewster system vaporizes acetic acid and methanol from the pyroligneous acid in a simple primary distillation, leaving soluble tar behind. About 85% methanol is removed overhead in a methanol column while the dealcoholized liquor is cooled and fed to a mechanical extraction column where about 98% of the acid is extracted by an ascending stream of cold ethyl ether (isopropyl ether and ethyl acetate have also been used as extracting agents). From the bottom of the extractor, the water layer (raffinate) is stripped of ether in an exhauster. Separation of the 2–3% acetic acid from the ether in the extract layer is accomplished by distillation in an evaporator and an ether column. Ether is recovered overhead, rectified, and reused, while crude acetic acid (70%) is discharged from the bottom along with wood oils and tar. The crude acetic acid is treated with sodium dichromate as an oxidizing agent, and refined by either continuous or batch distillation to concentrations ranging from 90% to glacial (24–26).

The Othmer azeotropic distillation process pumps the settled pyroligneous acid to a demethanolizing column from which crude methanol is removed overhead, wood oil from a middle plate, and a 7–8% acetic acid solution from the base. This crude acid is fed into a preevaporator to distill off acid and water to an azeotropic dehydrating column. The preevaporator has a conical bottom for the removal of tars polymerized by the addition of small amounts of sulfuric acid. A withdrawing agent (either butyl acetate or ethylene dichloride) forms an azeotropic system with the water and acid vapor in the dehydrator. The withdrawing agent and the water distill off as a low-boiling azeotrope and then are condensed and separated into two phases: The top layer with withdrawing agent is returned to the dehydrating column as reflux wash, and the lower water layer goes to a stripping column to recover the small amount of the remaining withdrawing agent. Crude acid containing acetic, formic, propionic, and butyric acids and some tar is removed near the bottom of the dehydrator and is then rectified in one or two continuous columns from which acetic acid at concentrations of 99.5% or better is distilled. This process requires a minimum of equipment and is economical to operate with relatively small plants (27–31). (See also Vol. 2, pp. 850–853.)

SYNTHETIC METHODS

The major part of the world's production of acetic acid is made today by the synthetic rather than by the natural processes. The principal synthetic processes currently employed include (*1*) oxidation of acetaldehyde (qv); (*2*) direct oxidation of ethanol (qv); (*3*) hydrocarbon oxidation (qv); and (*4*) methanol–carbon monoxide process, as well as other miscellaneous methods.

Oxidation of Acetaldehyde. The production of acetic acid by acetaldehyde oxidation has an extensive patent literature going back more than fifty years. It has been in commercial operation since 1911 in Germany and 1920 in the U.S. Since the bulk of acetic acid in the world today is obtained from acetaldehyde, the acetaldehyde processes enjoy a leading position in any consideration of acetic acid manufacture. In many processes acetaldehyde is essentially an intermediate in the production of acetic acid, and this section of this article should be read in conjunction with the article Acetaldehyde in Volume 1, which describes four main routes to acetaldehyde: (a) the vapor-phase dehydrogenation or partial oxidation of ethyl alcohol; (b) the liquid-phase hydration of acetylene; (c) the high-temperature oxidation of saturated hydrocarbons; and (d) the liquid-phase oxidation of ethylene (32,33).

The continuous oxidation of acetaldehyde in the liquid phase is generally carried out by using air or oxygen in the presence of manganous acetate. The reaction mixture containing acetaldehyde diluted with crude acid and manganous acetate solution is circulated upward through the oxidation tower. Reaction conditions when air is used are 55–65°C at 70–75 psi (about 5 atm); and when oxygen is used, 70–80°C at a pressure sufficient to keep the acetaldehyde liquid. Oxygen is often diluted with 5% air to slow down the reaction and to avoid overoxidation which results in excessive quantities of by-products. The reaction mixture is drawn off the top of the oxidation tower and is distilled continuously in as many as three distillation columns. Crude acid is fed into the top of the distillation column and other volatile components are withdrawn overhead while a residue containing manganese acetate is removed at the

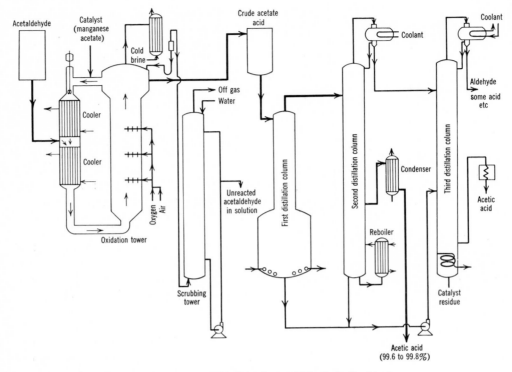

Fig. 3. Continuous oxidation of acetaldehyde in liquid phase.

bottom.   A low-boiling forerun is taken off overhead in the second column and 99.6–99.8% pure acetic acid is then taken off above the reboiler.   Bottoms from the first and the second columns and overhead from the second column go to a third column where acetic acid is taken off as a highly concentrated vapor, which is condensed and delivered to intermediate storage tanks (see Fig. 3).

The older batch process employed large aluminum-clad steel pressure vessels with extensive cooling coil surface to control the temperature.   Oxygen was introduced through a sparger at the bottom to a mixture of acetaldehyde and crude acetic acid, and manganese acetate solution was added to destroy the explosive peroxyacetic acid formed at a temperature of 40°C.   A 9–12 hr reaction time ended with sharp increase in pressure and simultaneous drop in temperature.   The reaction mixture contained 93–94% acetic acid which was purified by distillation for a product yield of about 95% (34–36).

A modification of the acetaldehyde oxidation in which the catalyst is a mixture of copper and cobalt acetates is used for the simultaneous production of acetic acid and acetic anhydride (see below).

Direct Oxidation of Ethanol.   This oxidation proceeds as a highly exothermic reaction of air and vaporized ethanol of high purity; the reaction takes place at 540–550°C and 25–30 psi.   A very short reaction time, influenced by a silver-gauze catalyst, permits conversions of 50–55% per pass with product yields of 85–95%.   Exhaust gases passing into a condenser and a scrubber absorb both the acetaldehyde and the unreacted alcohol into refrigerated water.   Liquid taken from the bottom of the scrubber

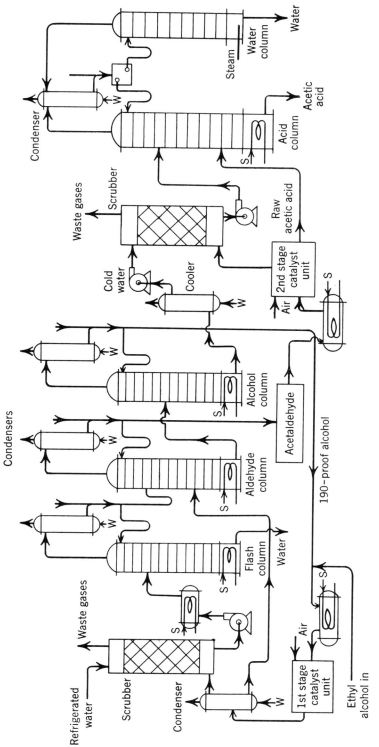

Fig. 4. Direct oxidation of ethanol.

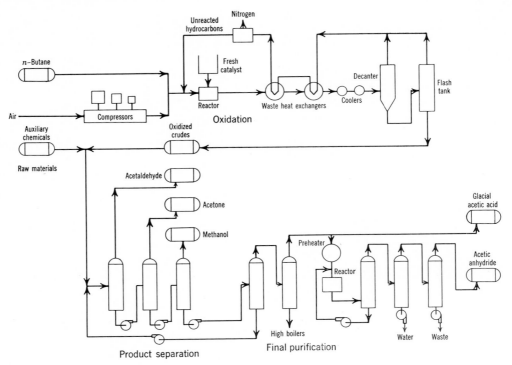

Fig. 5. Liquid-phase oxidation of hydrocarbons.

is a ternary mixture of water, acetaldehyde, and ethanol, the last two being recovered overhead after expansion in a flash column. Both the ternary mixture and the flash-column overhead go to an aldehyde column where acetaldehyde at 99% purity is recovered overhead by ammonia-refrigerated condensers. The bottoms are rectified in another column to recover 190° proof alcohol for recycling to the catalyst chamber (see Fig. 4).

Liquid-Phase Oxidation of Straight-Chain Hydrocarbons. In the presence of a suitable catalyst this oxidation yields acetic acid predominantly as the end product of the oxidation of intermediate oxidation products, such as esters and ketones. Continuous oxidation of lower aliphatic hydrocarbons, such as propane, n-butane, etc, is carried out at temperatures of 125–225°C and under pressures of 200–2000 psia using air, oxygen, or oxygen diluted with an inert gas as oxidizing agent. Acetic acid and other organic acids have been used as solvents for the hydrocarbons that undergo oxidation. Oxidation catalysts include a wide variety of organic acid metal salts. Salts of alkali metal and alkaline earth metals are used in different amounts as catalyst moderators to control reactions of the intermediate oxidation products. Compressed air and butane are fed to the reaction vessels at controlled rates, under conditions that ensure complete consumption of the oxygen. The overhead vapors consisting of water, unreacted hydrocarbon, and oxidation products are fed to a series of condensers that operate at 0–120°C, and include a battery of air-type heat exchangers. Nitrogen and other gases are separated; the nitrogen goes to drive turbines for the compressors used in the process, and the unreacted hydrocarbon is recycled to the oxidation reactors. The condensate is settled out into an upper hydrocarbon phase and a lower aqueous phase. The hydrocarbon phase with dissolved oxidation products is also recycled to the reactor. The aqueous phase, consisting of water of reaction and water-soluble oxidation products, is treated through a separation train including acid concentration and recovery units. The lower-boiling compounds, esters, ketones, and alcohols, are separated from the acid and the water and returned to the reactor. The primary separation of acetic acid and water is made in a distillation tower which concentrates the acetic acid to near 100% in the base. The distillate contains about 15–20% acetic acid, which is recovered by extraction and distillation. The acid is distilled in additional columns to remove the residual water and the higher-boiling compounds (see Fig. 5).

Direct oxidation of light petroleum fractions obtained from refineries, largely butane, has been successfully adapted for commercial production of acetic acid in Europe since 1962 (37–48).

Methanol–Carbon Monoxide Synthesis. This synthesis has been employed by Du Pont and is described in the literature for the direct production of acetic acid in a number of processes involving phosphoric acid, metal oxides on activated carbon, and cobalt carbonyl as catalysts. A new process employed in the United States has been developed by Badische Anilin- & Soda-Fabrik; this process uses methanol and carbon monoxide derived from an acetylene unit based on natural gas. Carbon monoxide is first combined with hydrogen to produce the methanol which is reacted with additional carbon monoxide to yield acetic acid.

$$CH_3OH + CO \rightarrow CH_3COOH$$

The carbon monoxide gas is bubbled up through liquid methanol in a reactor at about 410°F and 7500 psig in the presence of a cobalt carbonyl catalyst. The reaction products in the form of gas and liquid mixtures are drawn off the top of the reactor. The gas stream is cooled to approx 100°F and is passed through a separator to remove unreacted alcohol for recycling; then it is fed to the bottom of a carbon dioxide absorption tower into the top of which cooled reactor liquid products are led. Carbon monoxide is drawn off the top of the absorber for recycling to the reactor. Liquid bottoms are decompressed to release absorbed carbon dioxide. The remaining liquid product contains acetic acid, water, methyl acetate, and catalyst which are separated by distillation in a recovery section. A theoretical yield of 72% acetic acid based on methanol is expected, making allowance for by-product methyl acetate production (49–56).

ACID CONCENTRATION AND RECOVERY

For more than a century the separation and recovery of acetic acid from its aqueous solutions has been of major economic importance to industry. The manufacture of cellulose acetate, aspirin, and the explosive RDX (cyclotrimethylenetrinitramine), as well as semichemical pulping, and other processes that use acetic acid as solvent or raw material, yield large quantities of spent solutions of dilute acid. The high reflux ratio necessary, which leads to high heat costs and excessive column diameter, has generally precluded the use of simple rectification of these dilute solutions. Three modern unit operations, now widely used for separation of industrial liquids, were developed largely for the recovery of acetic acid from spent processing liquors. These processes include (1) azeotropic distillation, in which another liquid increases the volatility of one component of two close-boiling liquids and thus separates them in one column; (2) liquid–liquid extraction, in which differential solubilities of

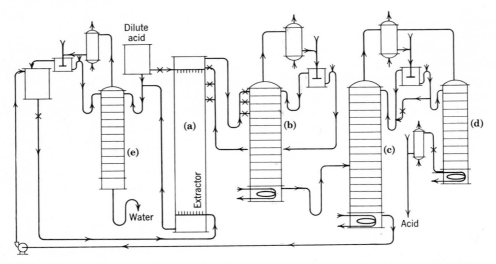

Fig. 6.   Recovery of acetic acid by combination of one extraction and four azeotropic-distillation steps.

the two components in another liquid are used to wash one out of the mixture by countercurrent action; and (3) extractive distillation in which separation is effected by an agent or a solvent that is considerably less volatile than one of the feed components.

Many acetic acid recovery processes employ several of these methods consecutively for optimum heat economy. Extractions and extractive distillations are normally followed by further distillation operations, often azeotropic. A typical process (see Fig. 6) developed by Othmer uses an extraction and several azeotropic distillation steps in order to reduce the heat costs of concentrating acetic acid. A selective solvent separates acid from water in the extractor (a), and then distills the water overhead in a first azeotropic distillation column (b) with low reflux ratio. The condensed overhead, which contains a small amount of acid, is returned to the extractor at a point with the same acid strength. The bottom mixture is discharged to a second azeotropic distillation column (c) to separate acetic acid from the high-boiling solvent by the addition of another liquid which has much less solvent power for the acid than the solvent. Final exhaustion in an azeotropic distillation column (d) separates the second added liquid dissolved in the acid layer in a decanter, and the solvent dissolved in the water from the extractor is finally separated in a fourth column (e). This solvent and the solvent from the base of the second azeotropic column are recycled to the extractor (57–59).

Materials of Construction

Metals.   Steady metallurgical advances tend to shift the emphasis in choice of materials for the handling of acetic acid. Constant improvement in the characteristics of stainless steel and aluminum alloys have led to increased use of these materials in this highly corrosive service. In the past, copper and copper alloys were used most extensively in equipment handling acetic acid, such as distilling columns for shell sections and plates. Copper is favored for its fabricability and low cost, but its corrosion rate is accelerated by high velocity and aeration, which occur in many of the modern commercial processes. Copper may be used in continuous recovery processes where air can be excluded (60).

The impurities present in the acetic acid, their type and concentration, are extremely important factors affecting the life of various materials. Copper and its alloys, as well as Monel and nickel, have exhibited greater length of service in formic–acetic acid mixtures than in glacial acetic acid, although for austenitic stainless steel the reverse is the case. For hot mixtures of acetic acid containing over 2% formic acid, and at temperatures above 250°F, stainless steel may not be as satisfactory as copper alloys or Monel; for dilute acetic–formic acid solutions, however, molybdenum steels are preferred to copper and nickel alloys.

At room temperature aluminum has a corrosion rate of roughly 1 mil/yr in acetic acid of almost any concentration. However, at higher temperatures the rate tends to increase as the acid is diluted. A penetration of 10 mils/yr is reported for 1% acetic acid at 122°F, 7 mils for 60% acid, and 3 mils for 90% acid. Aluminum (Types 2S, 3S, 3003, and 61 ST) is considered suitable for use with the anhydrous acid and for infrequently used equipment, such as storage tanks. A major advantage of aluminum construction is that minute quantities of the metal do not discolor the acid product. When aluminum is used it should be shielded from electrolytic attack (particularly from contact with wet ground) by wrapping or by cathodic protection (61).

The austenitic stainless steels with their superior corrosion resistance are used increasingly in acetic acid service. Low carbon-, molybdenum-, and niobium-containing types (304, 304L, 310, 316, 316L, and 347) can be used for all concentrations of acetic acid at normal temperatures. Type 316 stainless steel is used for many hot acid services. Tests conducted by Eisenbrown and Barbis (62) under heat-transfer conditions in 56% acid indicated that, at various levels of chloride and sulfate ion content, Type 316 stainless steel had the best resistance of the alloys tested. Type 304L showed good resistance with 5.6 ppm chloride and 13.0 ppm sulfate, but at 20 and 25 ppm, respectively, high corrosion rates were obtained. Aluminum bronze and aluminum alloy No. 1100 had high corrosion rates at all levels of chloride and sulfate content. In acid mixtures with 56% acetic acid and 1% sulfuric acid, Type 310 stainless steel showed the best resistance; and with 5% sulfuric acid all alloys had high corrosion rates. The austenitic stainless steels perform well under oxidizing conditions generally because of the formation of an oxide surface film, whose formation has been shown to be a function of time. Reducing conditions as well as chloride ions tend to destroy the film and attack the metal underneath rapidly. High tensile stresses together with chloride-ion attack produce stress-corrosion cracking. Serious intergranular corrosion has also been reported in heat-affected zones adjacent to welds in austenitic stainless steels used for acetic acid service. Columns, bubble caps, stills, tanks, piping, pumps, and valves for acetic acid service are fabricated from stainless steel, preferably of welded and flanged construction. Type 304 stainless steel is used widely for storage tanks and tank cars.

The high alloys, with relatively large percentages of nickel, notably Hastelloy B and C, are suitable for service at all concentrations of acetic acid and at all temperatures. High cost and difficult fabrication, however, limit their use to critical applications where impurities are present. The Chlorimet alloys, which are also high in nickel, have good resistance to acetic acid and are most useful under oxidizing conditions. Inconel, another high alloy, is fairly resistant to the weak acid and is preferred to Monel for dilute, highly aerated solutions, however, it is not recommended for hot, concentrated solutions.

Nickel–copper alloys such as Monel have good resistance to unaerated solutions of acetic acid at all concentrations and at atmospheric temperatures, but the corrosion rate is greatly increased by aeration to about 8 mils/yr in aerated glacial acetic. Its use for hot aerated solutions is not recommended. Monel has been extensively used in pumps, reactors, heating coils, piping, and agitators for acetic acid service in unaerated solutions where sulfuric acid is present. The austenitic cast nickel–iron alloys, called Ni-Resist, have been used for unaerated solutions mostly at room temperature, and also for weak acid service at higher temperatures (63).

Cast iron and carbon steels are not recommended for acetic acid service. High-silicon irons, however, are used extensively in this service for valves, piping, pumps, towers, etc, independent of acid concentration, temperature, and degree of aeration. Brittleness, liability to damage from thermal shock, and costly fabrication methods are the major limiting factors to more widespread use of these materials.

Silver resists corrosive attack by acetic acid at all temperatures and all concentrations. It also has the advantage that its colorless organic compounds do not impair acid color. Where high mechanical strength is required, silver-clad materials or shrunk-fit linings are employed, especially for high-pressure or high-heat-transfer vessels (64).

Where good heat-transfer surfaces are required under severe corrosive conditions, tantalum has also found some application in this service. It shows excellent resistance to all concentrations of the acid at temperatures up to 175°C, and is mostly used in the fabrication of heaters and condensers.

Nonmetallic Materials. Plastic and ceramic materials are used in varying degrees for coatings, linings, and gasketing materials.

Stoneware is inert to acetic acid at all concentrations and temperatures, but has the disadvantages of relatively poor thermal conductivity and high initial cost. Stoneware and porcelain have been used for vessels, pumps, absorption towers, piping, etc.

Glass-lined steel is used in piping and other equipment handling acetic acid at all concentrations at atmospheric temperatures. As temperature increases, however, glass is subject to an increased rate of attack. Brittleness and susceptibility to damage from thermal shock are further drawbacks to the use of glass.

Carbon and graphite in their impervious forms are suitable for use up to the boiling point of acetic acid. Excellent heat-transfer properties have encouraged applications in heaters, evaporators, and condensers particularly. These materials have also found use in contact with acid mixtures such as acetic–formic and acetic–sulfuric acids.

Rubber and synthetic-rubber compounds display a broad spectrum of resistance to corrosion by acetic acid. In general, however, as temperatures and concentrations increase, these materials become less satisfactory, and to some extent may cause discoloration of the acid product. Hard rubber resists all concentrations and can be used at 120°F in contact with glacial acetic acid.

Plastics, although generally lacking in resistance to mechanical abuse, to most solvents, and to high temperatures, do not corrode electrolytically as metals do, and are not as greatly affected by changes in acidity, oxygen content, and impurities. Polytetrafluoroethylene (PTFE), which is used for valve components and valve packings, resists most chemicals and retains its properties up to 500°F. Polyethylene, however, is not suitable for acetic acid service since it permits the acid to diffuse through. Poly-(vinylidene) chloride has been used for pipe lining in service up to 70°C where sufficient regard has been given to increased brittleness at higher temperatures.

Production and Use

Acetic acid exceeded the billion-pound annual production rate in 1963 to become one of the fastest growing of all chemicals—surpassed only by nitric acid and ammonia in rate of growth and total poundage consumed. Acetic acid showed a growth-rate pattern in the period of 1948 to 1963 of 6.2% per year or nearly one and two-thirds times faster than the Gross National Product during the same period. Acetic anhydride achieved an annual growth rate of 3.3% in the same fifteen-year period.

In the five-year period from 1959 to 1964, acetic acid production had grown from 672 million lb to 1112 million lb, amounting to about 75% of total available capacity. In the same five-year interval, sales or consumption of acetic acid grew by about 140%, averaging about 19% growth/yr. All of this growth is attributed to the new synthetic processes, since the production from pyroligneous distillation of wood declined from 20.8 million lb in 1950 to about 17.0 million lb in 1964 (see Table 4).

Table 4. U.S. Acetic Acid Production, 1950–1964, million lb

| Year | Acetic acid | | |
	From wood	Synthetic	Total
1950	20.8	441.2	462.0
1951	19.4	454.0	473.4
1952	23.2	382.9	406.1
1953	20.4	477.7	498.1
1954	19.0	442.0	461.0
1955	22.8	524.0	547.2
1956	22.2	549.8	572.0
1957	19.8	524.4	544.2
1958	20.3	546.2	566.5
1959	23.5	648.7	672.2
1960	23.7	741.0	764.7
1961	19.9	764.0	783.9
1962	17.2	968.6	985.8
1963	17.0	1,028	1,045
1964	17.0	1,095	1,112

The largest single use for acetic acid is the production of acetic anhydride, which in turn is used to manufacture cellulose acetate, plasticizers, and pharmaceuticals. Cellulose acetate accounted for approx 45% of the acetic acid consumption in 1964. This use has grown almost by 40% during the five-year period from 1959 to 1964, averaging about 7% per year. In the same period, anhydride consumption for cellulose acetate production increased from 720 million lb in 1959 to 1 billion lb in 1964. Cellulose acetate finds greatest use in the production of acetate textile fibers, and is also employed in making lacquers, photographic film, transparent sheets, and thermoplastic molding compounds. See Acetate and triacetate fibers; Cellulose derivatives; Cellulose derivatives—plastics.

Vinyl acetate is the second-largest outlet for acetic acid and, from 1959 to 1964, has enjoyed an average annual growth of nearly 11% per year. A major raw material for vinyl plastics, vinyl acetate is also employed in the manufacture of latex paints, adhesives, and textile finishes. See Vinyl compounds and polymers.

The production of acetate esters consumes significant quantities of acetic acid. Methyl, ethyl, butyl, propyl, and amyl acetates find broad industrial use as solvents in the lacquer, plasticizer, and pharmaceutical fields. Ethyl acetate, for example, from 1948 to 1963, enjoyed an average annual growth rate of 3.9% per year and is a general solvent used in lacquer and plastics manufacture, as well as for flavorings, perfumes, and organic syntheses. Acetate esters accounted for roughly 16% of the acetic acid consumption in 1964. See Esters.

Chloroacetic acid (see p. 415) and acetate salts also constitute major outlets for acetic acid. Sodium acetate accounts for 60–65% of the consumption for all acetate salts including ammonium, copper, potassium, and zinc acetates. Sodium acetate finds application as a neutralizer and mordant in the manufacture of leather, textiles, and dyestuffs, as well as in photographic films.

Textile-finishing operations consume considerable quantities of acetic acid. Significant amounts are employed also in the production of nylon and of some acrylic fibers, as well as for dyestuffs and pigments.

The pharmaceutical industry continues to consume appreciable amounts of acetic acid in the production of vitamins, antibiotics, hormones, and similar products. Peroxyacetic acid and various rubber and photographic chemicals constitute a minor fraction of acetic acid usage (69–71).

Analysis and Specifications

The standard method of assay for glacial acetic acid (more than 99.4% acid) is the freezing point method and for dilute acid strengths titration with a standard alkali, such as sodium hydroxide, using phenolphthalein as the indicator. Water content in concentrated acetic acid is normally determined by the Karl Fischer iodine method.

The color of various basic acetates of the rare earths (eg, the blue of lanthanum acetate with iodine) gives a valuable means for unambiguous identification of acetic acid. Increasingly, the use of gas-liquid chromatography, however, has become the method of choice for both separation and identification of acetic acid (65,66).

Sensitive areas of application of acetic acid, such as in the drug, food, and solid-state electronics industries, have increased the importance of analytical procedures for trace impurities. Such impurities may include traces of formic acid, esters, aldehydes, sulfuric acid, sulfates, sulfurous acid, sulfites, chlorides, nitrates, arsenic, copper, lead, zinc, tin, iron, and other metals, depending on both process and equipment used.

Formic acid determination is made with mercuric chloride or lead tetraacetate. Formic acid reduces mercuric chloride to mercurous chloride, which is insoluble and can be determined gravimetrically. Lead tetraacetate (when used in excess) is reduced by formic acid, and the remaining reagent can be determined iodometrically. This method is preferred since it requires less time and is less subject to interferences. For esters, add alcoholic hydroxylamine hydrochloride and alcoholic potassium hydroxide until the solution is alkaline, warm until effervescence begins, and then cool; acidify with hydrochloric acid and add a drop of ferric chloride solution; purple color indicates esters. Aldehydes can be detected as bisulfite addition compounds, or by the addition of 2,4-dinitrophenylhydrazine in methanol solution with hydrochloric acid and neutralization with methanolic potassium hydroxide; a brownish-red color indicates aldehydes. The acid dichromate test may be used to detect formic acid, formaldehyde, and reducing substances such as occur in wood tars.

Sulfates and chlorides, diluted in water, are identified by the formation of precipitates with barium chloride and silver nitrate, respectively; sulfites are identified by the decolorization of starch iodide.

The following specifications indicate the chemical purity of acetic acid: purity, 99.85% by wt (min); specific gravity, at 20/20°C, 1.0505–1.0520; distillation range, 1°C, max; initial bp, 117.3°C, min; drying-up point, 118.3°C, max; freezing point, 16.35°C, min; color, Pt–Co units, max; water content, 0.15% by wt, max; formic acid, 0.05% by wt, max; acetaldehyde, 0.05% by wt, max; iron content, 1.0 ppm, max; heavy metals, 0.5 ppm, max; chlorides, sulfates, and sulfurous acid, 1.0 ppm, max; permanganate time (ACS test), 2 hr min (67,68).

Bibliography

"Acetic Acid" in *ECT* 1st ed., Vol. 1, pp. 56–74, by W. Fred Schurig, The College of the City of New York.

1. K. S. Markley, ed., *Fatty Acids, Their Chemistry, Properties, Production and Uses*, Interscience Publishers, Inc., New York, 1960.
2. F. Haurowitz, *Progress in Biochemistry*, Interscience Publishers, Inc., New York, 1950, pp. 64–69.
3. K. Bloch and D. Rittenberg, *J. Biol. Chem.* **159**, 45 (1945).
4. A. T. James, J. E. Lovelock, and J. P. W. Webb, "The Biosynthesis of Fatty Acids by the Human Red Blood Cell," in H. M. Sinclair, ed., *Essential Fatty Acids*, Butterworths & Co. Ltd., London, 1958, pp. 72–79.
5. *Selected Values of Properties of Chemical Compounds*, Manufacturing Chemists' Association Research Project, Washington, D.C., 1961.
6. I. Johnson, *J. Phys. Chem.* **63**, 2041 (1959).
7. C. J. West and C. Hull, eds., *International Critical Tables*, McGraw-Hill Book Co., New York, 1933, Vol. 3, p. 238; Vol. 4, p. 448; Vol. 6, pp. 84, 143, 361.
8. W. J. Jones, S. T. Bowden, W. W. Yarnold, and W. H. Jones, *J. Phys. & Colloid Chem.* **52**, 753–759 (1948).
9. R. R. Dreisbach, *Physical Properties of Chemical Compounds—III*, Advances in Chemistry Series No. 29, American Chemical Society, Washington, D.C., 1961, p. 437.
10. E. H. Rodd, *Chemistry of Carbon Compounds*, Vol. 1, Part A, Elsevier Publishing Co., Amsterdam, 1951, p. 564.
11. H. H. Sisler, *Chemistry in Non-Aqueous Solvents*, Reinhold Publishing Corp., New York, 1961, pp. 104–108.
12. L. C. Pauling, *The Nature of the Chemical Bond*, 3rd ed., Cornell University Press, Ithaca, N.Y., 1960, p. 314.
13. R. P. Bell, *The Proton in Chemistry*, Methuen Co., Ltd., 1959, p. 64.
14. S. Bruckenstein, *J. Am. Chem. Soc.* **82**, 307–310 (1960).
15. M. L. Bender, *Chem. Rev.* **60**, 53–113 (1960).
16. A. Mitsutani, *Nippon Kagaku Zasshi* **81**, 298–301 (1960).
17. A. D. Kokurin, V. D. Obrezkov, and N. S. Andreew, *Zh. Prikl. Khim.* **36**, 886–889 (1963).
18. B. Notari, V. Cavallanti, and S. Ceccotti, *Chim. Ind. (Milan)* **44**, 978–983 (1962).
19. *Ullmans Enzyklopädie der Technischen Chemie*, Vol. 6, 3rd ed., Urban & Schwarzenberg, Munich, 1955, pp. 778–803.
20. M. Sittig, *Acetic Acid and Anhydride*, Noyes Development Corp., Pearl River, N.Y., 1965.
21. H. T. Herrick and O. E. May, *Chem. & Met. Eng.* **42**, 142 (1935).
22. E. P. Poste, *Ind. Eng. Chem.* **24**, 722 (1932).
23. R. N. Shreve, *The Chemical Process Industries*, McGraw-Hill Book Co., Inc., New York, 1945, p. 685.
24. U.S. Pats. 1,845,128 and 1,845,129 (Feb. 16, 1932), J. M. Coahran.
25. U.S. Pat. 1,865,887 (July 5, 1932), J. M. Coahran.
26. U.S. Pat. 2,197,069 (April 16, 1940), J. M. Coahran.
27. D. F. Othmer, *Chem. & Met. Eng.* **42**, 356 (1935).

28. D. F. Othmer, *Chem. & Met. Eng.* **47**, 349 (1940).

29. U.S. Pat. 2,050,234 (Aug. 4, 1936), D. F. Othmer (to Tennessee Eastman Corp.).

30. U.S. Pat. 2,227,979 (Jan. 7, 1941), D. F. Othmer (to Eastman Kodak Co.).

31. U.S. Pat. 2,395,010 (Feb. 19, 1946), D. F. Othmer.

32. A. S. Hester and K. Himmler, *Ind. Eng. Chem.* **51** (12), 1424–1430 (1959).

33. H. Kalenda, *Ind. Chemist* **37** (43), 13–14 (1961).

34. W. L. Wood, *Production of Acetaldehyde, Acetic Acid, Acetic Anhydride and Acetone from Acetylene*, BIOS (British Intelligence Objectives Subcommittee) Report 75, Item 22 (1947).

35. U.S. Pat. 2,254,725 (Sept. 2, 1941), D. C. Bardwell (to The Solvay Process Co.).

36. U.S. Pat. 2,552,175 (May 8, 1951), D. C. Hull (to Eastman Kodak Co.).

37. H. D. Medley and S. D. Cooley, "Hydrocarbon Oxidation," in K. A. Kobe and J. J. McKetta, eds., *Advances in Petroleum Chemistry and Refining*, Vol. 3, Interscience Publishers, Inc., New York, 1960, pp. 309–338.

38. H. Hofermann, *Chem. Ingr.-Tech.* **36** (5), 422–429 (1964).

39. F. Broich, *Chem. Ingr.-Tech.* **36** (5), 417–422 (1964).

40. U.S. Pat. 2,263,607 (Nov. 25, 1941), J. E. Bludworth (to Celanese Corp. of America).

41. U.S. Pat. 2,369,710 (Feb. 20, 1945), J. E. Bludworth (to Celanese Corp. of America).

42. U.S. Pat. 2,653,962 (Sept. 29, 1953), R. L. Mitchell and O. V. Luke (to Celanese Corp. of America).

43. U.S. Pat. 2,659,746 (Nov. 17, 1953), C. S. Morgan, Jr., and N. C. Robertson (to Celanese Corp. of America).

44. U.S. Pat. 2,704,294 (March 15, 1955), C. S. Morgan, Jr., and N. C. Robertson (to Celanese Corp. of America).

45. U.S. Pat. 2,800,504 (July 23, 1957), A. Elce et al. (to The Distillers Co., Ltd.).

46. U.S. Pat. 2,825,740 (March 4, 1958), G. P. Armstrong et al. (to The Distillers Co., Ltd.).

47. Belg. Pat. 632,398 (May 18, 1962), N. R. Cox (to Union Carbide Corp.).

48. Fr. Pat. 1,339,323 (Nov. 19, 1962), Knapsack-Griesheim A.G.

49. J. W. Copenhaver and M. H. Bigelow, *Acetylene and Carbon Monoxide Chemistry*, Reinhold Publishing Corp., New York, 1949, pp. 267–275.

50. N. von Kutepow, W. Himmele, and H. Hohenschutz, *Chem. Ingr.-Tech.* **37** (4), 383–388 (1965).

51. U.S. Pat. 1,704,965 (March 12, 1929), H. Dreyfus.

52. U.S. Pat. 1,916,041 (June 27, 1933), H. Dreyfus.

53. U.S. Pat. 2,308,594 (Jan. 19, 1943), H. Dreyfus (to Celanese Corp. of America).

54. U.S. Pat. 2,650,245 (Aug. 25, 1953), E. B. Thomas et al. (to British Celanese, Ltd.).

55. U.S. Pat. 2,727,664 (Dec. 13, 1955), E. B. Thomas et al. (to British Celanese, Ltd.).

56. U.S. Pat. 3,014,962 (Dec. 26, 1961), W. Reppe et al. (Badische Anilin- und Soda-Fabrik).

57. D. F. Othmer, *Chem. Eng. Progr.* **54** (7), 48–52 (1958).

58. D. F. Othmer, *Ind. Eng. Chem.* **50**, 143–159 (1958).

59. W. V. Brown, *Chem. Eng. Progr.* **59** (10), 65–68 (1963).

60. G. A. Nelson, *Corrosion Data Survey*, Shell Development Co., Emeryville, Calif., 1954.

61. U. R. Evans, *The Corrosion and Oxidation of Metals*, Edward Arnold, London, 1960, p. 341.

62. C. M. Eisenbrown and P. R. Barbis, *Chem. Eng.* **70**, 149–152 (April 29, 1963).

63. W. D. Staley, *Chem. Eng.* **53** (12), 210 (1946).

64. L. C. Burman, *Chem. Eng.* **53** (11), 262 (1946).

65. F. J. Welcher, ed., *Standard Methods of Chemical Analysis*, Vol. 2, Part A, 6th ed., D. Van Nostrand Co., Inc., Princeton, N.J., 1963, p. 589.

66. *The United States Pharmacopeia* 14th ed., Mack Printing Co., Easton, Pa., 1950, p. 14.

67. *Acids and Anhydrides*, Union Carbide Chemicals Co., New York, 1960.

68. *Acetic Acid*, Celanese Corp. of America, New York, 1964.

69. *Census of Manufactures, 1958, Vol. II—Industry Statistics*, U.S. Dept. of Commerce, Bureau of the Census, U.S. Govt. Printing Office, Washington, D.C., 1959.

70. *Synthetic Organic Chemicals, S.O.C. Series C-64*, U.S. Tariff Commission, U.S. Govt. Printing Office, Washington, D.C., 1962.

71. *Annual Survey of Manufactures*, U.S. Dept. of Commerce, Bureau of the Census, U.S. Govt. Printing Office, Washington, D.C., 1963.

ERNEST LE MONNIER
Celanese Corporation of America

ACETIC ANHYDRIDE

Ethanoic anhydride (IUPAC), more commonly known as acetic anhydride, $(CH_3CO)_2O$ (abbreviated as Ac_2O), is a colorless, strongly refractive, and very mobile liquid with irritating acetic odor. It was first prepared by Gerhardt in 1852 from potassium acetate and phosphorous chloride. Acetic anhydride is slowly hydrolyzed in water to form acetic acid. In acetylation reactions, half of the acetic anhydride molecule goes into the acetylated product, and the other half is converted into acetic acid. As a major acetylating agent, it is used in large quantities for the acetylation of cellulose in the manufacture of acetate fibers, plastics, coatings, and films. It is also used to acetylate salicylic acid to make aspirin, and is employed in the synthesis of sulfa drugs and vitamins. An acetylating agent for animal and vegetable oils, acetic anhydride is also an intermediate in the manufacture of perfume chemicals as well as plasticizers. Acetic anhydride removes impurities from petroleum distillates in the Nalfining process, and is used in the manufacture of acetyl peroxide (a polymerization catalyst and bleaching agent), explosives, and weed killers, and in the chemical treatment of paper and textiles (1).

Table 1. Physical Properties of Acetic Anhydride

melting point, °C	−73
boiling point, at 760 mm, °C	139.6
coefficient of cubical expansion per °C, at 20°C	1.12×10^{-3}
critical pressure, atm	46
critical temperature, °C	296 (3)
dielectric constant, at 20°C	20.5 (4)
electrical conductivity, mho/cm	
0°C	1×10^{-6}
25°C	4.8×10^{-7}
explosive limit, in air, % by vol	2.67–10.13
refractive index	
n_D^{20}	1.3904
n_D^{25}	1.3885
n_{He}^{20}	1.39229
specific gravity	
20/4°C	1.0820
20/20°C	1.0838
surface tension, at 20°C, dyn/cm	32.56
vapor density (air = 1)	3.52
vapor pressure: see Table 2	
viscosity, density, and surface tension: see Table 3	
autoignition temperature, °C	400
flash point, °F	
Tag closed-cup	121
Tag open-cup	148
heat of combustion, kcal/g-mole	431.9
heat of vaporization, at 15°C, cal/g	66.2
specific heat, cal/g	0.434
standard heat of formation, kcal/mole	
gas	−148.82
liquid	−155.16
standard free energy of formation, kcal/mole	
gas	−119.29
liquid	−121.75

Physical and Chemical Properties

The physical properties of acetic anhydride are listed in Tables 1, 2, and 3. Freezing points of acetic acid–acetic anhydride mixtures are illustrated in Figure 1.

Table 2. Vapor Pressure of Acetic Anhydride

Temperature, °C	Vapor pressure, mm Hg	Temperature, °C	Vapor pressure, mm Hg
30	5.5	110	300.0
50	22.0	130	587.0
70	60.0	139.5	760.0
90	145.0	150	1,100.0

Table 3. Density, Surface Tension, and Viscosity of Acetic Anhydride

Temperature, °C	d_4^t	Surface tension, dyn/cm	Viscosity, cP
15	1.0871	33.14	
20	1.0820	32.56	0.9120
25	1.0749	31.90	0.8511
30	1.0690	31.24	0.7962
40	1.0567	30.05	0.7015
50	1.0443	29.00	0.6209

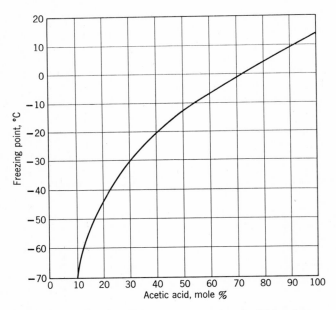

Fig. 1. Freezing points of acetic acid–acetic anhydride mixtures.

CHEMICAL REACTIONS

Acetic anhydride has been the most intensively studied aliphatic anhydride. The bimolecular nature of its uncatalyzed reaction in water and in other solvents has been established by Gold (8) and others, who used a technique in which hydrolysis is carried out in the presence of a primary aromatic amine with varying concentrations of amine and water. The uncatalyzed bimolecular hydrolysis of acetic anhydride occurs when water and anhydride are present in about the same amount. The base-catalyzed reaction is also bimolecular, but progresses at a much greater rate. Using hydrochloric acid as a catalyst the rate of hydrolysis is faster than that of the acetyl chloride which appears to be formed in the reaction. Alcoholysis and ammonolysis proceed relatively slowly by a similar mechanism, resulting in the formation of esters and amides,

$$ROH + (CH_3CO)_2O \rightarrow CH_3COOR + CH_3COOH$$

$$R_2NH + (CH_3CO)_2O \rightarrow CH_3CONR_2 + CH_3COOH$$

$$2\,NH_3 + (CH_3CO)_2O \rightarrow CH_3CONH_2 + CH_3COONH_4$$

Acetylation with acetic anhydride is usually carried out in the presence of a small amount of sodium acetate or concentrated sulfuric acid. Friedel-Crafts acetylation reactions involve the aluminum chloride-catalyzed substitution of the acetyl group for hydrogen on the aromatic nucleus. Other Lewis acids and proton acids have been used as catalysts for this reaction, along with such common solvents as carbon disulfide, nitrobenzene, methylene chloride, and 1,2-dichloroethylene.

$$C_6H_6 + (CH_3CO)_2O \xrightarrow[\text{or BF}_3]{\text{AlCl}_3} C_6H_5COCH_3 + CH_3COOH$$

In other acetylations acetic anhydride reacts with nitrogen pentoxide to form acetyl nitrate, and with aniline to form acetanilide; in the latter case the acetyl group is used to protect the amino group against oxidation in the further nitration of aniline.

Acetic anhydride reacts with aldehydes to form alkylidene acetates.

$$RCHO + (CH_3CO)_2O \rightarrow RCH(OCOCH_3)_2$$

In the Perkin reaction when an aromatic aldehyde such as benzaldehyde reacts with acetic anhydride in the presence of potassium or sodium acetate, the condensation product is a β-aryl acrylic acid. High temperatures are required since a weak base is used with a weakly acidic reagent.

$$ArCHO + (CH_3CO)_2O \xrightarrow{CH_3COONa} ArCH{=}CHCOOH + CH_3COOH$$

If benzaldehyde is used, the product of the Perkin reaction is cinnamic acid. If cinnamaldehyde is used as the substrate in the reaction, vinylogs of cinnamic acid are produced.

$$C_6H_5CH{=}CHCHO + (CH_3CO)_2O \xrightarrow{CH_3COONa} C_6H_5CH{=}CHCH{=}CHCOOH$$

Anhydrides of higher acids that have higher boiling points than acetic acid may be prepared by heating and then fractionating a mixture of the acid and acetic anhydride,

$$2\,RCOOH + (CH_3CO)_2O \rightarrow (RCO)_2O + CH_3COOH$$

Acetic anhydride reacts with hydrogen peroxide forming peroxyacetic acid,

$$H_2O_2 + (CH_3CO)_2O \rightarrow CH_3COOOH + CH_3COOH$$

With metallic peroxides, acetic anhydride forms acetyl peroxide (see Peroxides, organic).

$$BaO_2 + (CH_3CO)_2O \rightarrow (CH_3CO)_2O_2 + BaO$$

Condensation of acetic anhydride with acetone, in the presence of boron trifluoride as catalyst, is used for the preparation of the simplest β-diketone, acetylacetone.

$$CH_3COCH_3 + (CH_3CO)_2O \xrightarrow{\ BF_3\ } CH_3COCH_2COCH_3 + CH_3COOH$$

Acetic anhydride also condenses with acetophenone in the presence of boron trifluoride to form benzoylacetone:

$$C_6H_5COCH_3 + (CH_3CO)_2O \xrightarrow{\ BF_3\ } C_6H_5COCH_2COCH_3 + CH_3COOH$$

Its action on glycidic esters, followed by hydrolysis, is employed as a general method for the preparation of OC-keto esters. Reaction with ethylene, in the presence of the zinc chloride as catalyst, is used to prepare methyl vinyl ketone, the simplest unsaturated ketone and commercial starting material for plastics (see Vinyl compounds and polymers).

$$CH_2{=}CH_2 + (CH_3CO)_2O \xrightarrow{\ ZnCl_2\ } CH_2{=}CHCOCH_3 + CH_3COOH$$

A general method for the preparation of substituted vinyl ketones is by the action of acetic anhydride on the corresponding vinyl magnesium bromide in tetrahydrofuran at -60 to $-70°C$.

$$2\ CHR{=}CHMgBr + 2\ (CH_3CO)_2O \rightarrow 2\ CHR{=}CHCOCH_3 + MgBr_2 + (CH_3CO_2)_2Mg$$

Alkyl cyanides can be prepared by the dehydration of aldoximes with acetic anhydride,

$$RCH{=}NOH \xrightarrow{(CH_3CO_2)O} RCN$$

Acetic anhydride is readily pyrolyzed to ketene,

$$(CH_3CO)_2O \rightarrow CH_2{=}CO + CH_3COOH$$

Manufacture

The earliest commercial route, now largely superseded, involved the heating of anhydrous sodium acetate with an excess of inorganic chloride—such as phosphorus oxychloride, thionyl chloride, or sulfuryl chloride—to convert half of the sodium salt into the acid chloride, which could then react with the sodium acetate to form acetic anhydride. A similar process involved passing chlorine into a mixture of sodium acetate and sulfur dichloride and distilling.

A continuous process was later based on the reaction of acetic acid and phosgene in the presence of 10% of aluminum chloride or magnesium acetate. Acetic anhydride was distilled from the reaction products.

Of the numerous routes to acetic anhydride (see Fig. 2), three emerge as the major economic processes currently employed in the United States as well as abroad. The processes in greatest use in the United States are the two ketene processes, involving either the dehydration of acetic acid or the decomposition of acetone, and the so-called "dual process" or, oxidation of acetaldehyde yielding both acetic acid and acetic anhydride. A fourth general route employing acetylene and acetic acid to produce ethylidene diacetate for decomposition into acetic anhydride and acetaldehyde is less widely used.

Patented processes have also included the synthesis of acetic anhydride from acetone and carbon dioxide; catalytic reaction of ethanol and air, or air and steam; direct

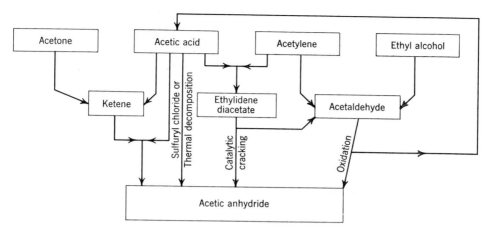

Fig. 2. Various routes to acetic anhydride.

reaction of sulfuric anhydride and sodium acetate; a number of processes using sulfur chlorides and oxychlorides; and the decomposition of vinyl acetate into vinyl ether and acetic anhydride. The oxo process is also potentially suitable for the production of acetic anhydride via the synthesis of acetaldehyde from ethylene and carbon monoxide. Miscellaneous methods of obtaining acetic anhydride were mentioned in the early patent literature; these include several unique reactions involving the reaction of carbon disulfide with silver acetate, and with lead acetate.

Ketene Processes. The addition of ketene to acetic acid provides an industrial

$$CH_2{=\!=}CO + CH_3COOH \rightarrow (CH_3CO)_2O$$

method of synthesizing acetic anhydride. Ketene (qv) is obtained commercially by the catalytic pyrolysis of acetic acid, or by the decomposition of acetone, as follows:

$$CH_3COOH \rightarrow CH_2{=\!=}CO + H_2O$$
$$CH_3COCH_3 \rightarrow CH_2{=\!=}CO + CH_4$$

For higher conversion rates (up to 90% per pass) the acetic acid pyrolysis has been favored, but this process has the disadvantage of operating at reduced pressure. Catalysts employed in this reaction include phosphoric acid and acid phosphates with a relatively short life at the high reaction temperatures; continuous injection of triethylphosphate, however, has proved more effective. The two-step German process using triethylphosphate as catalyst mixes vaporized acetic acid with 0.2% triethylphosphate at a pressure of about 200 mm Hg absolute. The mixed vapors pass through a preheater, emerging at 600°C, and enter a gas-fired or electric resistance cracking furnace to be pyrolyzed at 700–720°C. About 0.02% by wt of ammonia is injected at the furnace exit in order to inhibit the reversal of the ketene reaction. Cracking-furnace exit gases are cooled rapidly to about 0°C in a series of water- and brine-cooled condensers from the bottom of which 30–35% aq acetic acid is drawn. Uncondensed, nearly pure ketene gas, containing only small amounts of ethylene, methane, and carbon monoxide, enters the second stage of the process in which it is reacted with acetic acid in a series of four scrubbing towers.

The first and second towers are used to produce the anhydride, while the third and fourth remove traces of acetic acid and anhydride from the tail gases. In the first tower, ketene gas passes through a mixture of 15% acetic acid and 85% anhydride at 30–40°C and exits to the bottom of the second tower to which fresh glacial acetic acid is added to give a scrubbing mixture of 80–90% acetic acid and 10–20% anhydride at 20°C. The third tower scrubs the gases with raw anhydride and the fourth with 35% acetic acid at 0°C. A single vacuum pump maintains a pressure gradient through the system from 200 mm Hg at the vaporizer to 80 mm Hg at the vacuum pump. Liquids drawn from the bottom of the first and third towers are purified and concentrated to 95% acetic anhydride by vacuum distillation. Conversion of acetic acid is about 90% per pass, and the yield of acetic anhydride on acetic acid reacted reaches approx 90%.

The pyrolysis of acetone produces methane and ketene; the latter can then be reacted with glacial acetic acid in a plate absorption tower or by a method similar to that given above for the acetic acid process. Acetone is thermally cracked at about atmospheric pressure after being vaporized, superheated, and then fed into a tubular reactor heated between 650–800°C. The principal reaction of acetone to ketene and methane can be catalyzed by mixing the acetone with diacetyl or with phosphoric acid esters, or by passing it over heated metal sulfates. However, acetone is also destructively decomposed in a parallel reaction evolving hydrogen, carbon monoxide, and carbon deposits. Rapid cooling of the furnace reaction products by quenching with an acetic acid–acetic anhydride spray to about 550°C is used to prevent subsequent polymerization of the ketene, or its decomposition to ethylene and carbon monoxide. A packed tower cools the quenched gas further to about 200°C in a countercurrent stream of recycle liquid acetic acid and anhydride. Ketene, acetone, acetic acid, and anhydride gases from the top of the quench tower are then condensed in a shell-and-tube heat exchanger. About 90% of the ketene is converted to anhydride by reaction with the condensed acid. Residual ketene and acetone are absorbed into acetic acid in an absorption tower, the bottom liquid of which joins the condensate as mixed feed for a continuous distillation unit yielding acetic acid, acetone, and 95% acetic anhydride as a bottom product. The acetic acid is recycled for use in the quenching and absorption units. The process is carried out with a conversion of roughly 25% per pass.

Dual Process (Acetaldehyde Oxidation). When water is removed immediately and suitable catalysts are employed, the direct oxidation of acetaldehyde in the liquid phase yields a mixture of acetic acid and acetic anhydride. The use of mixed metal catalysts, such as manganese and nickel, manganese and copper, or copper and cobalt, was discovered at about the same time in Germany and Canada. The unique catalytic activity of copper has a very high specificity in this reaction. Esters such as ethyl acetate were subsequently found to remove the water produced in the reaction, which proceeds by the intermediate formation of peroxyacetic acid as shown below:

$$CH_3CHO + O_2 \rightarrow CH_3COOOH$$

$$CH_3COOOH + CH_3CHO \rightarrow 2\ CH_3COOH$$

$$CH_3COOOH + CH_3CHO \rightarrow (CH_3CO)_2O + H_2O$$

The higher the ratio of ethyl acetate to acetaldehyde, the higher the yield of acetic anhydride. This process is used to produce approx 70% acetic anhydride and 30% acetic acid. Continuous azeotropic distillation of the reaction mixture makes it possible to return the acetaldehyde–ethyl acetate layer to the oxidizer (see Fig. 3).

Ethylidene Diacetate Process. This is an older two-stage process that has regained some of its popularity in conjunction with acetic acid processes; it involves the air oxidation of propane and butane. Starting materials in this process are acety-

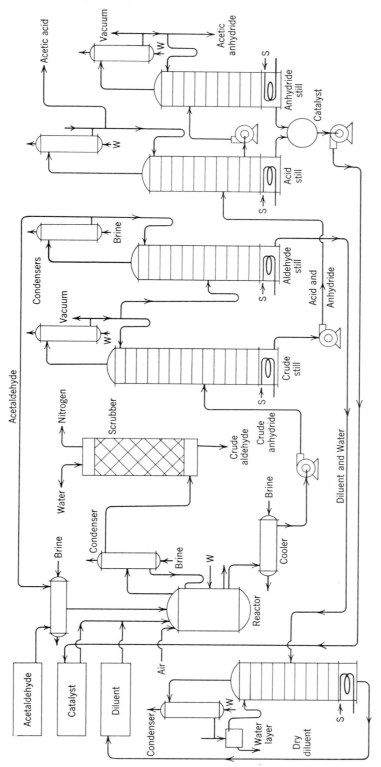

Fig. 3. Dual process (acetaldehyde oxidation).

lene and acetic acid, and acetaldehyde is a coproduct with acetic anhydride. The first-stage liquid-phase reaction proceeds at atmospheric pressure and at 60–85°C in the presence of mercuric oxide, and /or a mercurous salt catalyst, and yields ethylidene diacetate.

$$C_2H_2 + 2\ CH_3COOH \rightarrow CH_3CH(OCOCH_3)_2$$

About 100 lb of ethylidene diacetate is obtained per pound of mercury in the catalyst, which is recovered and converted back to oxide. An excess of acetylene plus a zinc catalyst and temperatures of 170–210°C shift the reaction toward the production of vinyl acetate. Ethylidene diacetate is readily pyrolyzed to acetic anhydride and acetaldehyde with acidic catalysts such as zinc chloride, sodium pyrophosphate, or

$$CH_3CH(OCOCH_3)_2 \rightarrow (CH_3CO)_2O + CH_3CHO$$

sulfuric acid, at about 145°C. Distillation separates acetaldehyde and acetic anhydride from the unchanged ethylidene diacetate (bp 166°C). At 75% conversion, overall yields as high as 97% have been reported for this process. The pyrolysis of ethylidene diacetate is also a significant industrial route to vinyl acetate, an important monomer for the production of vinyl plastics.

Materials of Construction

Final operations and storage of acetic anhydride are usually accomplished in aluminum, Type 316 stainless steel, or glass-lined steel equipment, in order to hold to a minimum the color imparted to the finished product. Copper, aluminum, and aluminum bronze are used for condensers, pipelines, and for refining process steps where air and agitation can be excluded. Type 317 stainless steel has been used satisfactorily in vaporizers, condensers, and pumps of the vapor-phase dehydration process. Silicon-iron columns and centrifugal pumps have been employed in the aldehyde-oxidation process. Both silver and tantalum, although expensive to use even as lining materials, provide complete resistance to acetic anhydride. Molybdenum stainless steels have been considered optimum construction materials in the ketene processes (44).

Analysis and Specifications

Demand for greater and greater purity of acetic anhydride and acetic acid is now pursued to the extent that many users specify their own performance tests which the supplier must meet. Acetic anhydride is usually determined by direct titration, reaction with aniline, or a combination of both to determine total and residual acidity. For total acidity the anhydride is hydrolyzed in the cold with a standard carbonate-free $0.5N$ sodium hydroxide solution. With phenolphthalein as indicator, the refluxed solution is titrated with $0.5N$ sulfuric acid. For residual acidity, the anhydride is reacted with aniline to form acetanilide and acetic acid in the cold, which is then titrated with $0.5N$ sodium hydroxide with phenolphthalein as indicator.

More recently, morpholine, C_4H_9ON, a heterocyclic amine, has to a certain extent supplanted aniline, since the reaction is better and the excess of morpholine can be titrated. Mixed indicators yield better end-point determinations. A blank is required for the morpholine, and different indicators for the blank and the sample overcome the buffering effects of acetic acid.

Specifications for acetic anhydride are as follows: purity, 99.0% by wt (min); specific gravity, at 20/20°C, 1.080–1.085; color, 10 Pt–Co units (max); permanganate time—2-ml sample will not reduce more than 0.1 ml of $0.1N$ $KMnO_4$ in 5 min; phosphate, sulfate, chloride, aluminum, and iron contents—no more than 1.0 ppm each; heavy-metal and nitrate contents, none by test; nonvolatiles, 0.003 g/100 ml (max).

Production and Use

Acetic anhydride production increased 27% in the five-year period 1959–1964, growing at a rate of 5% per year to reach a total of 1.4 billion lb in 1964 (see Table 4). Cellulose acetate production accounted for approx 72% of the acetic anhydride produced in 1964. Roughly 12% of the total production found its way into the production of cellulosic plastics and vinyl acetate, while 1.4% was consumed in the production of aspirin in 1964. Aspirin has continued to maintain a healthy growth rate of 10% per year for the acetic anhydride consumption over the five-year span 1959–1964, during which time cellulose acetate consumption increased by 7% per year.

Table 4. U.S. Acetic Anhydride Production, 1950–1964, million lb

Year	Acetic anhydride	Year	Acetic anhydride
1950	908	1958	965
1951	976	1959	1,097
1952	686	1960	1,096
1953	804	1961	1,260
1954	691	1962	1,242
1955	842	1963	1,272
1956	908	1964	1,395
1957	912		

Bibliography

"Acetic Anhydride" in *ECT* 1st ed., Vol. 1, pp. 78–86, by Gwynn Benson, Shawinigan Chemicals Limited.

Physical and Chemical Properties

1. F. K. Beilstein, *Handbuch der Organischen Chemie*, Vol. 2, Part 1, 4th ed., Springer-Verlag, Berlin, Germany, 1960, p. 371.
2. C. J. West and C. Hull, eds., *International Critical Tables*, McGraw-Hill Book Co., Inc., New York, 1933.
3. J. Timmermanns, *Physico-Chemical Constants of Pure Organic Compounds*, Elsevier Publishing Co., Amsterdam, 1950, p. 375.
4. R. A. McDonald, S. A. Shrader, and D. R. Stull, *J. Chem. Eng. Data* **4**, 311–313 (1959).
5. D. T. Lewis, *J. Chem Soc.* **142**, 32 (1940).
6. D. F. Othmer, *Ind. Eng. Chem., Anal. Ed.* **4**, 232 (1932).
7. S. I. Cherbov, *J. Russ. Phys.-Chem. Soc.* **62**, 1509 (1930).
8. V. Gold, J. Hilton, and E. G. Jefferson, *J. Chem. Soc.* **1954**, 2756.

Manufacture

9. G. V. Jeffreys, *The Manufacture of Acetic Anhydride*, The Institution of Chemical Engineers, London, 1961.
10. *Ullmans Enzyklopädie der Technischen Chemie*, Vol. 6, 3rd ed., Urban & Schwarzenberg, Munich, 1955, pp. 804–815.
11. M. Sittig, *Acetic Acid and Anhydride*, Noyes Development Corp., Pearl River, N.Y., 1965.
12. G. Benson, *Chem. & Met. Eng.* **47**, 150 (1940).

13. *U.S. Dept. Com. Field Information Agency Tech. Rept. 145, Item 22* (1945).

14. *U.S. Dept. Com. Office Tech. Service PB Rept. 208* (1945).

15. Y. Mayer, *Rev. Chim. Ind.* (*Paris*) **45**, 193 (1936).

16. G. O. Morrison and T. P. G. Shaw, *Trans. Electrochem. Soc.* **63**, 425 (1933).

17. *Chemical Safety Data Sheet*, SD-15, Manufacturing Chemists' Association, 1947.

18. U.S. Pat. 2,389,144 (Nov. 20, 1945), T. W. Evans and R. C. Morris (to Shell Dev. Co.).

Ethylene Diacetate Process

19. U.S. Pat. 1,425,500 (Aug. 8, 1922), H. W. Matheson and G. E. Grattan (to Shawinigan Laboratories Ltd.).

20. U.S. Pat. 1,429,650 (Sept. 19, 1922), F. W. Skirrow (to Shawinigan Laboratories Ltd.).

21. U.S. Pat. 1,578,454 (March 30, 1926), M. J. Marshall and G. S. Shaw (to Canadian Electro Products Co.).

22. U.S. Pat. 1,872,479 (Aug. 16, 1932), H. W. Matheson (to Canadian Electro Products Co.).

23. U.S. Pat. 1,986,322 (Jan. 1, 1935), L. V. Clouzeau (to Du Pont).

24. U.S. Pat. 2,264,789 (Dec. 2, 1941), F. O. Cockerille (to Du Pont).

Acetaldehyde Oxidation

25. Brit. Pat. 446,529 (April 27, 1936), N. J. Cermelli (to Shawinigan Chemicals Ltd.).

26. U.S. Pat. 2,170,002 (Aug. 22, 1939), G. Benson (to Shawinigan Chemicals Ltd.).

27. U.S. Pat. 2,225,486 (Dec. 17, 1940), H. L. Reichart (to Carbide and Carbon Chemicals Co.).

28. U.S. Pat. 2,282,209 (May 19, 1942), D. C. Hull and C. A. Marshall (to Eastman Kodak Co.).

29. U.S. Pat. 2,293,104 (Aug. 18, 1942), J. E. Bludworth (to Celanese Corp. of America).

30. U.S. Pat. 2,367,501 (Jan. 16, 1945), D. C. Hull et al. (to Eastman Kodak Co.).

31. U.S. Pat. 2,491,533 (Dec. 20, 1949), H. Dreyfus (to Celanese Corp. of America).

32. U.S. Pat. 2,491,572 (Dec. 20, 1949), S. B. McFarlane (to Celanese Corp. of America).

33. U.S. Pat. 2,514,041 (July 4, 1950), A. Elce et al. (to The Distillers Co., Ltd.).

34. U.S. Pat. 3,119,862 (Jan. 28, 1964), L. Alheritière (to Les Usines de Melle, S.A.).

Ketene Process

35. U.S. Pat. 1,723,724 (Aug. 6, 1929), H. T. Clarke and C. E. Waring (to Eastman Kodak Co.).

36. U.S. Pat. 2,069,243 (Feb. 2, 1937), G. D. Graves and C. H. Greenewalt (to Du Pont).

37. U.S. Pat. 2,176,419 (Oct. 17, 1939), H. Dreyfus (to Celanese Corp. of America).

38. U.S. Pat. 2,202,046 (May 28, 1940), H. Dreyfus (to Celanese Corp. of America).

39. U.S. Pat. 2,232,705 (Feb. 25, 1941), D. C. Hull (to Eastman Kodak Co.).

40. U.S. Pat. 2,249,543 (July 15, 1941), J. Sixt and M. Mugdan (to Tennessee Eastman Corp.).

41. U.S. Pat. 2,258,985 (Oct. 14, 1941), F. J. Hopkinson (to Eastman Kodak Co.).

42. U.S. Pat. 2,688,635 (Sept. 7, 1954), R. K. Eberts (to Allied Chemical & Dye Corp.).

43. U.S. Pat. 2,743,296 (April 24, 1956), E. S. Painter et al. (to Eastman Kodak Co.).

Materials of Construction

44. F. L. La Que and H. R. Copson, Corrosion Resistance of Metals and Alloys, Reinhold Publishing Corp., New York, 1963.

Analysis and Specifications

45. F. J. Welcher, ed., *Standard Methods of Chemical Analysis*, Vol. 2, Part A, 6th ed., D. Van Nostrand Co., Inc., Princeton, N.J., 1963, p. 591.

46. G. S. Shaw, *Can. Chem. Process. Ind.* **25**, 197 (1941).

47. D. M. Smith and W. M. D. Bryant, *J. Am. Chem. Soc.* **58**, 2452 (1946).

48. *Acids and Anhydrides*, Union Carbide Chemicals Co., New York, 1960.

49. *Acetic Anhydride*, Celanese Corp. of America, New York, 1964.

ERNEST LE MONNIER
Celanese Corporation of America

HALOGENATED DERIVATIVES

The derivatives described below are those in which halogen is substituted for hydrogen(s). Substituted halogens are chlorine, bromine, and iodine. For fluorine derivatives, see Fluorine compounds, organic. See also Acetic acid derivatives.

Chloroacetic Acid

Chloroacetic acid (chloroethanoic acid), $CH_2ClCOOH$, is sold commercially as white deliquescent crystals, molecular weight 94.50.

Physical and Chemical Properties. Although commercial chloroacetic acid has a reported minimum melting point of 61°C, three and possibly four different crystalline modifications have been isolated. The α form, monoclinic prisms, freezing point 62.53°C (2), forms by the rapid condensation of chloroacetic acid vapors (3), by crystallization from a strongly cooled aqueous solution (2), or by seeding of the β modification, with the α form (4). The β modification, monoclinic prisms, freezing point 56.3°C (5), is isolated by solidification of molten chloroacetic acid especially when the melt has been preheated to 67°C, or from the γ form by scratching (3). The γ form, monoclinic crystals, freezing point 50.2°C (6), is obtained by cooling molten chloroacetic acid carefully so as to avoid any agitation (3). Pickering (3) reported another possible form (δ) with melting point 43.75°C. The specific heat, c_p, of the liquid shows peaks at 61.215, 56.932, and 50.691°C; these temperature regions correspond to the melting points of the first three polymorphic crystalline modifications (7). The variation of boiling point with pressure is given in Table 1

Table 1. Boiling Point of Chloroacetic Acid at Various Pressures

Pressure, mm	Bp, °C	Pressure, mm	Bp, °C
760	187.85	123.76	134.67
507.5	174.44	75.85	123.19
313.5	159.92	47.16	112.30

(8). In inert solvents of low dielectric constant the acid exists largely as the dimer; solvents which have a high dielectric constant and which facilitate hydrogen bonds lead to considerable dissociation of the dimer (9). Density, d_{65}^{65}, 1.398; d_4^{60}, 1.3764; n_D^{60}, 1.4330; heat of combustion, 1839 cal/g; dielectric constant at 20°C is approximately 21; surface tension at 70.1°C, 31.56 dyn/cm; latent heat of fusion, ΔH_f (α form), 4.630 kcal/mole. The chlorine atom makes it a stronger acid ($K_a = 1.4 \times 10^{-3}$) than acetic acid. For a nomograph relating latent heats and entropies of vaporization with temperature, see reference 10. The solubilities in grams per 100 grams of water, methanol, and ethyl ether, at 25°C, are 510, 350, and 190, respectively (11). Azeotropic systems are formed with a number of organic compounds (12). Because chloroacetic acid is a strong vesicant, contact with the skin should be avoided.

A solution of chloroacetic acid in ethanol, when irradiated with ultraviolet rays, decomposes into a mixture of methanol, acetaldehyde, and hydrogen chloride (13). When heated with thoria at 220–230°C, chloroacetic acid is decomposed into carbon monoxide, carbon dioxide, hydrogen chloride, dichloroethane, and carbon (14). The chlorine atom is readily displaced from aqueous solutions of either chloroacetic acid or its alkali salts. It has been shown (15) that the chloroacetate ion reacts with a wide variety of anions; the reaction with hydroxide, forming glycolic acid, CH_2-OHCOOH, has the greatest velocity constant. Aqueous solutions of chloroacetic acid are hydrolyzed rather slowly under reflux; the reaction is accelerated by neutralizing the acid and is further accelerated by making the solution alkaline (16). In highly alkaline solution, diglycolic acid, $O(CH_2COOH)_2$, is formed. Therefore, when replacement of the chlorine by other groups is desired, excess alkalinity should be avoided. Sodium cyanide reacts with chloroacetic acid to give a 90% yield of cyanoacetic acid. In fact, the chlorine atom is readily displaced by almost any anion if conditions favorable to the formation of alkali chloride or ammonium chloride are established. Thus, the reactions with ammonia (17), alkyl amines, aryl amines, hydrazines (18), and phenols (19) give good yields of the corresponding α-substituted acetic acids. Chloroacetic acid also reacts with the enol form of thiourea to give the S-alkyl derivative (20). Similarly, an S-substituted derivative is produced in the reaction of chloroacetic acid with arylthiocarbamides (21). Chloroacetic acid is reduced with lithium aluminum hydride, in ether solution, to ethanol (16–38%) and less than 5% β-chloroethanol (22). As an acid it is sufficiently strong to catalyze esterification reactions and it forms crystalline salts with a large number of metals. The acid is readily esterified; the methyl and ethyl esters are used extensively in organic syntheses. Like other organic acids, chloroacetic acid is converted to its acid chloride by the action of such reagents as phosphorus oxychloride. Commercially available chloroacetyl chloride has considerable utility in the chloroacetylation of amines. Treatment of chloroacetic acid with phosphorus pentoxide gives chloroacetic anhydride. Dichloro- and trichloroacetic acids are produced by the exhaustive chlorination of chloroacetic acid.

Preparation and Manufacture. The first laboratory preparation of chloroacetic acid, by chlorination of acetic acid in direct sunlight, was reported by Hoffmann in 1857. Since then catalysts such as iodine, sulfur, red phosphorus, phosphorus halides, and sulfuryl halides have been used. The preparation of chloroacetic acid from chloroacetylene, glycerol dichlorohydrin, ketene, tetrachloroethylene, ethylchlorohydrin, chloral, and dichloroacetic acid has been the subject of many papers and patents. Some recent figures on the production of chloroacetic acid are listed in Table 2.

Table 2. U.S. Chloroacetic Acid Production, 1950–1963, million lb

Year	Chloroacetic acid	Year	Chloroacetic acid
1950	27	1957	47
1951	34	1958	38
1952	35	1959	43
1953	38	1960	53
1954	40	1961	55
1955	47	1962	46
1956	45	1963	54

There are two major commercial processes for the production of chloroacetic acid. One is its preparation from trichloroethylene (European method); the other consists in chlorination of acetic acid (the only method used in the United States and Canada). In the European method, equal weights of 95% sulfuric acid (which acts only as a catalyst) and chloroacetic acid are charged into an agitated glass-lined reaction vessel and heated to 135–140°C. A mixture of trichloroethylene (100 parts) and 74% sulfuric acid (96 parts) is continuously fed into the bottom of the reactor. The by-product, hydrogen chloride, is absorbed into water and sold as 35% hydrochloric acid. The chloroacetic acid and sulfuric acid are permitted to overflow into a cascade still where the chloroacetic acid is distilled at 20 mm and the sulfuric acid is recycled. Yields of 90%, based on trichloroethylene, have been reported. The use of glass-lined reaction vessels greatly reduced the cost of maintenance. This process also has the advantage of producing a practically pure monochloroacetic acid free from an acetic acid or dichloroacetic acid impurity. On the other hand, the direct-chlorination process is used extensively in the United States and Canada because of the lower cost of acetic acid as the raw material. Acetic acid is chlorinated in glass-lined or specially designed corrosion-resistant equipment to a maximum content (about 95%) of monochloroacetic acid. Catalysts such as sulfuric acid, phosphorus trichloride, or acetic anhydride are used at temperatures between 85 and 120°C. The chlorination product is upgraded to 99% monochloroacetic acid through recrystallizations (23). The mother liquor, a mixture of acetic acid, chloroacetic acid, and dichloroacetic acid, is customarily converted to trichloroacetic acid by means of exhaustive chlorination.

Uses and Applications. The reactivity of the chlorine atom has led to an increasing use of chloroacetic acid as an intermediate in the preparation of a wide variety of organic and inorganic compounds. Chloroacetic acid was first prepared as the necessary raw material for the synthesis of indigo and related dyes (24). In many syntheses, sodium chloroacetate is first treated with sodium cyanide to give sodium cyanoacetate, which may be used directly, as in the synthesis of coumarin, or which may be hydrolyzed and esterified to give diethyl malonate—the starting material for a long list of barbiturates. Chloroacetic acid has been suggested for the identification of phenols and naphthols as crystalline aryloxyacetic acid derivatives (25). The major use of chloroacetic acid is as the necessary intermediate in the manufacture of (1) selective weed killers such as 2,4-dichlorophenoxyacetic acid (2,4-D) and 2,4,5-trichlorophenoxyacetic acid (2,4,5-T), (2) thiocyanate insecticides, (3) ammonium thioglycolate (used as a cold-permanent wave solution) and (4) pharmaceutical preparations. Medicinally, small amounts have been employed directly as a caustic and vesicant for the removal of warts, corns, etc. The industrial grade (95%) is suitable for most laboratory uses whereas the technical grade (98–99%) is required for pharmaceutical purposes.

Dichloroacetic Acid

Dichloroacetic acid (dichloroethanoic acid), $CHCl_2COOH$, molecular weight 128.95, is a pungent liquid now available in commercial quantities.

Physical and Chemical Properties. Bp, 194.4°C; mp, 9.7–13.5°C (range of values cited in the literature), 10.5°C min for commercial grade (98% min purity); heat of combustion, 1149 cal/g; n_D^{22}, 1.4659; density, d = $1.5924 - 0.01378t$; d_{25}^{25}, 1.560. When dichloroacetic acid is distilled at atmospheric pressure it fumes strongly and contains some acid chloride, phosgene, and tarry materials. When distilled at 17–20 mm (bp 96–102°C) the distillate is colorless and it no longer fumes. This acid is a very strong vesicant and is corrosive to the skin.

Dichloroacetic acid ($K_a = 5 \times 10^{-2}$) is a much stronger acid than chloroacetic acid and is more stable to hydrolysis. Because of the relatively easily replaced chlorine atoms a variety of interesting derivatives is possible. In general, the reactions of dichloroacetic acid resemble those of monochloroacetic acid. For example, dichloroacetic acid reacts with phenol in warm aqueous sodium hydroxide solution to give diphenoxyacetic acid (26). In addition it reacts with hydroxylamine to produce isonitrosoacetic acid, $HON{=}CHCOOH$ (27). With dithioethylene glycol, $HSCH_2$-CH_2SH, on a water bath dichloroacetic acid gives 1,2,5,7-tetrathionane (also called 1,2,5,7-pentamethylene tetrasulfide), $\overline{SCH_2CH_2SCH_2SCH_2CH_2S}$, but in boiling xylene it gives 1,3-dithiolan, $\underline{CH_2SCH_2SCH_2}$ (28). For an interesting discussion of the products derived from the reaction of dichloroacetic acid with aniline and toluidines see reference 29. Dichloroacetic acid undergoes electrolytic reduction to chloroacetic acid (30) in 100% yield; the latter is also obtained, in excellent yield, when aqueous solutions of dichloroacetic acid are hydrogenated over palladium on asbestos (31). The acid chloride, anhydride, amides, esters, and salts of dichloroacetic acid, prepared in the conventional manner, are useful intermediates.

Preparation and Manufacture. Dichloroacetic acid has been prepared, in the laboratory, from the reaction of chloral (qv) with sodium cyanide and sodium carbonate in aqueous solution (32) and by treating trichloroacetic acid or aniline trichloroacetate with hydrochloric acid in the presence of copper powder (33). By a careful chlorination of acetic acid a mixture of dichloro- and trichloroacetic acid is obtained. The latter is destroyed by hydrolysis (see Trichloroacetic acid); the hydrolysis products, chloroform and water, are expelled and dichloroacetic acid is extracted with a water-immiscible solvent such as ethyl ether (34). The crude acid obtained in these processes may be purified to 99.5% by esterification with a low aliphatic alcohol followed by saponification of the isolated ester (35). Mixtures of the three chlorinated acetic acids have been separated rather elegantly by chromatography (36). Dichloroacetic acid is shipped in 13-gallon carboys (150 pounds) with white-label shipping regulations.

Uses and Applications. Simple derivatives of dichloroacetic acid are useful intermediates for the production of a number of organic and pharmaceutical products since reaction may occur at either end of the acid molecule. A study of dichloroacetic acid and its derivatives led to the development of pharmaceutically active chloramphenicol.

Trichloroacetic Acid

Trichloroacetic acid (trichloroethanoic acid), CCl_3COOH, molecular weight 163.4, is sold commercially as white deliquescent crystals.

Physical and Chemical Properties. Mp (theoretical) 59.2°C; mp (commercial product), 55–58°C; bp 197.5°C; d_{60}^{60}, 1.630; heat of combustion, 728.8 cal/g; the solubility per 100 g of water, methanol, and ethyl ether, at 25°C, is 1306, 2143, and 617 g, respectively. Like its lower chlorinated homologs, trichloroacetic acid is a strong vesicant and rapidly attacks the skin. Trichloroacetic acid ($K_a = 0.2159$ to 0.2183, at 20°C) is roughly equivalent to hydrochloric acid in strength. It undergoes rapid decarboxylation when heated with alkali (or even aniline) to produce chloroform. Thus, trichloroacetic acid reacts with alkaline solutions of phenols to produce (in low yields) salicylaldehydic compounds via the Reimer-Tiemann reaction (26). Similarly, trichloroacetic acid undergoes telomerization-polymerization reactions with mono-olefinic compounds, in the same manner as chloroform and carbon tetrachloride, to give $CCl_3(CH_2CH_2)_nCOOH$ (37). Trichloroacetic acid is readily decomposed with mercuric oxide or thoria, at elevated temperatures, into oxides of carbon, chloroform, and other halogenated compounds (14,38). It is partially dehalogenated, with copper, to dichloroacetic acid (33) and undergoes electrolysis to produce trichloromethyl trichloroacetate (39). Its acid chloride, anhydride, amides, and esters are reported in the chemical literature.

Preparation and Manufacture. Trichloroacetic acid was first prepared by Dumas, in 1838, by the chlorination of acetic acid in direct sunlight. Since then it has been prepared by the oxidation of chloral hydrate with nitric acid (40) and by calcium hypochlorite (41). Trichloroacetic acid is manufactured (as described under Chloroacetic acid) by the chlorination of acetic acid; after all of the acetic acid has been chlorinated the chlorination is continued at increasing temperatures of 120–150°C.

Uses and Applications. The major use of trichloroacetic acid is in the form of its sodium salt, which has been found to be a selective weed killer. To a limited extent, it has also been used medicinally for the removal of warts and corns and as an astringent.

Bromoacetic Acid

Bromoacetic acid (bromoethanoic acid), $CH_2BrCOOH$, molecular weight 138.96, is commercially available as a white to pale-yellow deliquescent crystalline material.

Physical and Chemical Properties. Mp (theoretical), 50°C; mp (commercial material), 45–46°C; bp, 208°C; d_4^{60}, 1.880; d_4^{20}, 1.934; $d = 1.93302 - 0.0016482t$ (42); surface tension $= 46.20552 - 0.010910t$ dyn/cm (42); $K_a = 1.35 \times 10^{-3}$. The solubility of bromoacetic acid in 100 grams of water, methanol, ethyl ether, and carbon tetrachloride, at 25°C, is approximately 896, 896, 735, and 26 grams, respectively. Because bromoacetic acid has a sharp and penetrating odor it should be used with adequate ventilation. Aqueous solutions are slowly hydrolyzed with the liberation of hydrogen bromide; the hydrolysis is markedly accelerated by alkali (43). The photochemical decomposition of bromoacetic acid with alkali leads to the formation of methanol, acetaldehyde, and hydrogen bromide (13). In general, the reactions of bromoacetic acid are similar to those of chloroacetic acid. The bromide atom is very readily replaced by thiosulfate ion. The acid chloride, anhydride, esters, amides, and salts are known compounds described in the chemical literature.

Preparation and Manufacture. Bromoacetic acid is synthesized, in 80% yield, by the bromination of acetic acid at 100–105°C in the presence of catalytic quantities of red phosphorus (44). The preparation, on a large scale, is accomplished by adding bromine, in small portions, to glacial acetic acid containing 2% carbon disulfide, in a glass- or lead-lined reactor equipped with a reflux condenser. The temperature must be kept down to a point at which hydrogen bromide boils off smoothly. When sufficient bromine has been added to complete the reaction (theoretical equivalent is 2.66 kg bromine per kg of acetic acid) any remaining hydrogen bromide and carbon disulfide is boiled off and the product is collected by vacuum fractionation. This process is a modification of that described by Michael (45). Chloroacetic acid can be converted to bromoacetic acid by reaction with aluminum bromide (46).

Uses and Applications. Bromoacetic acid is a useful intermediate in the synthesis of other organic chemicals, particularly that of ethyl bromoacetate (lacrimator) which is used in the preparation of β-keto acids via the Reformatsky reaction.

Dibromoacetic Acid

Dibromoacetic acid (dibromoethanoic acid), $CHBr_2COOH$, molecular weight 218.9, is not available commercially and relatively little has been done with it in the chemical laboratory. The white crystalline compound melts at 45–50°C, boils at 234–235°C with decomposition and is relatively soluble in alcohol and ethyl ether. It has been prepared by adding bromine, dropwise, to boiling acetic acid which contains 5% sulfur, and then raising the temperature to 150°C (47).

Tribromoacetic Acid

Tribromoacetic acid (tribromoethanoic acid), CBr_3COOH, molecular weight 298.9, is not available on a commercial scale and, as in the case of its dibromo homolog, very little is known about its physical and chemical properties. Its monoclinic crystals melt at 129–131°C and it decomposes at its boiling point, 245°C. Tribromoacetic acid is very soluble in water, alcohol, and ethyl acetate; it is insoluble in ethyl ether, acetone, benzene, and chloroform. In warm water or alcohol, tribromoacetic acid decomposes rapidly into bromoform. Its amides, esters, acid bromide, and salts are described in the literature.

Tribromoacetic acid has been prepared by the oxidation of perbromoethylene with fuming nitric acid (48), by heating an aqueous solution of malonic acid with bromine (49), and by gently warming bromal with fuming nitric acid (50).

Iodoacetic Acid

Iodoacetic acid (iodoethanoic acid), CH_2ICOOH, molecular weight 185.96, is sold commercially in the form of colorless or white crystals.

Physical and Chemical Properties. Mp 81.9°C; d $= 2.42118 - 0.0017837t$ (42); surface tension $= 48.35779 - 0.11483t$ dyn/cm (42); $K_a = 7.1 \times 10^{-4}$. Iodoacetic acid is soluble in water and alcohol and slightly soluble in ethyl ether. It is oxidized with potassium persulfate to methylene iodide and succinic acid and reacts with formaldehyde to give succinic acid (51). Iodoacetic acid reacts with sulfur-containing amino acids to produce sulfur and/or nitrogen derivatives (52). It is reduced with hydriodic acid, at 85°C, to give acetic acid and iodine (53).

Preparation and Uses. Iodoacetic acid can be prepared by the action of potassium iodide on chloroacetic acid at 50°C (54) or by the reaction of chloroacetic acid or bromoacetic acid with sodium iodide in acetone. More recently, iodoacetic was prepared by the reaction of ketene with iodine monochloride in carbon tetrachloride (55). Iodoacetic acid is a strong muscle poison and has therefore been used in biological and biochemical experimentation.

Diiodoacetic Acid

Diiodoacetic acid (diiodoethanoic acid), CHI_2COOH, molecular weight 311.87, is not a commercial chemical. In the laboratory it has been prepared by treating malonic acid with iodic acid (56) and by warming diiodomaleic acid with water at 100°C (57); mp, 95–96°C. The white crystals are soluble in alcohol, ethyl ether, and benzene; they turn pink on exposure to air.

Triiodoacetic Acid

Triiodoacetic acid (periodoacetic acid, triiodoethanoic acid), CI_3COOH, molecular weight 437.78, is not available commercially. Its preparation by the reaction of malonic acid with iodic acid was reported in 1893 (56). The optimum conditions for a 58% yield were reported recently (58). Triiodoacetic acid is a golden-yellow crystalline compound, mp 150–154°C (dec). It is very soluble in polar organic solvents, but solutions, as a rule, are extremely unstable as evidenced by the rapid generation of the color of iodine. Triiodoacetic acid decomposes rapidly above room temperature to give iodine, iodoform, and carbon dioxide (58,59). It is soluble, with rapid decomposition, in dilute (4%) sodium hydroxide; aqueous suspensions and suspensions in 10–40% sodium hydroxide are quite stable. The sodium salt and lead salt have been isolated (58).

Bibliography

"Acetic Acid Derivatives" treated in *ECT* 1st ed. under "Acetic Acid," Vol. 1, pp. 74–78, by L. F. Berhenke, F. C. Amstutz, and V. A. Stenger, The Dow Chemical Company.

1. F. K. Beilstein, *Handbuch der organischen Chemie*, 4th ed., Springer-Verlag, Berlin, Germany, 1918, Vol. 2, p. 194, and Suppls. 1 and 2.
2. P. W. Bridgman, *Phys. Rev.* **3** (2), 189 (1914).
3. S. U. Pickering, *J. Chem. Soc.* **67**, 664 (1895).
4. B. Tollens, *Chem. Ber.* **17**, 665 (1884).
5. R. Schenck, *Z. Physik. Chem.* **33**, 445 (1900).
6. A. H. R. Müller, *Z. Physik. Chem.* **86**, 177 (1914).
7. S. S. Urazovskiĭ and I. A. Sidorov, *Dokl. Akad. Nauk SSSR* **70**, 859 (1950).
8. R. R. Dreisbach and S. Shrader, *Ind. Eng. Chem.* **41**, 2879 (1949).
9. C. P. Brown and A. R. Mathieson, *J. Chem. Soc.* **1957**, 3625.
10. D. F. Othmer and D. Zudkevitch, *Ind. Eng. Chem.* **51**, 791, 1022 (1959).
11. *Products of the Dow Chemical Company. Their Properties and Uses*, Dow Chemical Company, 1959–1960, p. 16; *ibid.*, 1961.
12. L. H. Horsley, *Anal. Chem.* **19**, 508–600 (1947).
13. H. W. Cassel, *Z. Physik. Chem.* **92**, 113 (1918).
14. J. B. Senderens, *Compt. Rend.* **172**, 155 (1921); *ibid.*, **204**, 209 (1937).
15. H. M. Dawson, E. R. Pycock, and G. F. Smith, *J. Chem. Soc.* **1943**, 517.
16. L. F. Berhenke and E. C. Britton, *Ind. Eng. Chem.* **38**, 544 (1946).
17. N. D. Cheronis and K. H. Spitzmueller, *J. Org. Chem.* **6**, 349 (1941).
18. M. Busch and E. Meussdörffer, *J. Prakt. Chem.* **75**, 121 (1907).
19. U.S. Pat. 2,541,003 (Feb. 6, 1951), H. M. Day and M. H. Bradley (to American Cyanamid Co.).
20. P. C. Ray and F. F. Fernandes, *J. Chem. Soc.* **105**, 2159 (1914).
21. R. D. Desai, R. F. Hunter, and L. G. Koppar, *Rec. Trav. Chim.* **54**, 118 (1935).
22. E. L. Eliel, C. Hermann, and J. T. Traxler, *J. Am. Chem. Soc.* **78**, 1193 (1956).
23. Private communication to author, from The Dow Chemical Company, 1961.
24. H. M. Bunbury, *Chem. Age* (*London*) **7**, 598 (1922).
25. C. F. Koelsch, *J. Am. Chem. Soc.* **53**, 304 (1931).
26. J. Van Alphen, *Rec. Trav. Chim.* **46**, 143 (1927).
27. A. Hantzsch and W. Wild, *Ann. Chem.* **289**, 294 (1896).
28. G. C. Chakravarti and J. M. Saha, *J. Indian Chem. Soc.* **5**, 453 (1928).
29. G. Heller, *Chem. Ber.* **41**, 4264 (1908); I. Ostromisslensky, *Chem. Ber.* **41**, 3019 (1908); H. W. Doughty, *J. Am. Chem. Soc.* **47**, 1095 (1925).
30. Ger. Pat. 848,807 (Sept. 8, 1952), P. Heisel (to Lech-Chemie Gersthofen).
31. U.S. Pat. 2,671,803 (March 9, 1954), K. Sennerwald and A. Wolfram (to Knapsack-Griesheim A.G.).

32. A. C. Cope, J. R. Clark, and P. Connor, *Organic Syntheses* **19,** 38 (1939).
33. H. W. Doughty and A. P. Black, *J. Am. Chem. Soc.* **47,** 1091 (1925).
34. U.S. Pat. 1,921,717 (Aug. 8, 1933), F. C. Amstutz (to Dow Chemical Co.).
35. U.S. Pat. 2,495,440 (Jan. 24, 1950), E. C. Britton and L. F. Berhenke (to Dow Chemical Co.).
36. J. W. Chittum, T. A. Gustin, R. L. McGuire, and J. T. Sweeney, *Anal. Chem.* **30,** 1213 (1958).
37. U.S. Pat. 2,440,800 (May 4, 1948), W. E. Hanford and R. M. Joyce, Jr. (to E. I. du Pont de Nemours & Co., Inc.).
38. K. Brand, *J. Prakt. Chem.* **88,** 342 (1918).
39. R. E. Gibson, *J. Chem. Soc.* **127,** 475 (1925).
40. G. D. Parkes and R. G. W. Hollingshead, *Chemistry & Industry* **1954,** 222.
41. U.S. Pat. 2,443,118 (June 8, 1948), R. E. Plump (to Pennsylvania Salt Manufacturing Co.).
42. J. J. Jasper and L. Rosenstein, *J. Am. Chem. Soc.* **64,** 2078 (1942).
43. H. M. Dawson and E. R. Pycock, *J. Chem. Soc.* **1934,** 778.
44. C. F. Ward, *J. Chem. Soc.* **121,** 1161 (1922).
45. A. Michael, *Am. Chem. J.* **5,** 192 (1883).
46. U.S. Pat. 2,553,518 (May 15, 1951), D. E. Lake and A. A. Asadorian (to Dow Chemical Co.).
47. M. P. Genvresse, *Bull. Soc. Chim. France* [3]**7,** 365 (1892).
48. J. V. Nef, *Ann. Chem.* **308,** 264–328 (1899).
49. W. Petrieff, *Chem. Ber.* **8,** 730 (1875).
50. L. Schaffer, *Chem. Ber.* **4,** 366 (1871).
51. L. Panizzon, *Helv. Chim. Acta* **15,** 1187 (1932).
52. L. Michaelis and M. P. Schubert, *J. Biol. Chem.* **106,** 331 (1934); F. Dickens, *Biochem. J.* **27,** 1141 (1933).
53. K. Ichikawa and E. Miura, *J. Chem. Soc. Japan* **74,** 798 (1953).
54. R. A. Durie, T. Iredale, and J. M. S. Jarvie, *J. Chem. Soc.* **1950,** 1181.
55. U.S. Pat. 2,820,057 (Jan. 14, 1957), A. W. Schnizer (to Celanese Corp. of America).
56. A. Angeli, *Chem. Ber.* **26,** 596 (1893).
57. L. Clarke and E. K. Bolton, *J. Am. Chem. Soc.* **36,** 1899 (1914).
58. R. L. Cobb, *J. Org. Chem.* **23,** 1368 (1958).
59. R. A. Fairclough, *J. Chem. Soc.* **1938,** 1186.

Arnold P. Lurie
Eastman Kodak Company

ETHANOL

Ethanol or ethyl alcohol, CH_3CH_2OH, has been described as one of the most exotic synthetic oxygen-containing organic chemicals known because of its unique properties as a solvent, a germicide, a beverage, an antifreeze, a combustible liquid, a depressant, and especially because of its versatility as a building block, or chemical intermediate, for other organic chemicals.

The name "ethanol" is the IUPAC name for this chemical; the name "ethyl alcohol" is also entirely correct. Similarly, for the lower member of the series, CH_3OH, the names "methanol" and "methyl alcohol" are both correct; but whereas for CH_3OH the name "methanol" is the one almost invariably used in the United States, for C_2H_5OH the more frequently used name is "ethyl alcohol." The name "alcohol" is a generic name derived from two arabic words, *al* and *kohl*, which were used to describe a finely ground powder used by Oriental women to darken their eyebrows. The name was gradually restricted to ethyl alcohol, "spirits of wine rectified to the highest degree" (1).

Ethyl alcohol is, of course, extremely well known as a constituent of alcoholic beverages. See Alcoholic beverages, distilled; Beer; Wine. The word "alcohol," unqualified, is often used to refer to ethyl alcohol.

As a beverage it has been produced and utilized unknowingly as far back as 4000 years ago by the Pharaohs in Egypt (2,3).   An indication of the antiquity of the knowledge of the effect of ethyl alcohol has been traced to Noah, who built for himself a vineyard and grew grapes which he fermented into a sort of alcoholic beverage on which he became drunk with unfortunate results to his respectability (4).

Ethyl alcohol has had a long and illustrious history of progress.   Following is a survey of the more interesting milestones along the way:

1500	First comprehensive book on art of separating alcohol from fermentation products (5).
1790	First correlation between specific gravity and concentration of ethyl alcohol in mixtures of ethyl alcohol and water by Gilpin (6).
1796	First preparation of anhydrous alcohol utilizing anhydrous potassium carbonate (6).
1811	First correlation between percent by volume of ethyl alcohol in spirits by Tralles (7).
1825	First preparation of ethyl alcohol from ethylene and sulfuric acid (8–11).
1855	First published paper on synthesis of ethyl alcohol from ethylene and sulfuric acid (12).
1855	First law to make industrial alcohol taxfree passed in England.
1861	First patent issued covering the synthesis of ethyl alcohol from ethylene and sulfuric acid (13).
1862	First exhibit of one liter of ethyl alcohol obtained from ethylene and sulfuric acid at a London exhibition (14).
1873	First Russian literature reference to ethyl alcohol (15).
1902	First dehydration by azeotropic distillation of ethyl alcohol with benzene.
1903	First commercial development of dehydration by azeotropic distillation of ethyl alcohol with benzene.
1906	First law to make industrial alcohol taxfree passed in United States.
1929	First British patent for the direct catalytic hydration of ethylene to ethyl alcohol (16).
1930	First commercial process for synthesizing ethyl alcohol from ethylene and sulfuric acid.
1943	First commercial production of ethyl alcohol from petroleum refining gases (17).
1945	Maximum annual production of about 580 million gallons of ethyl alcohol.
1951	First U.S. patent for the direct catalytic hydration of ethylene to ethyl alcohol (18).
1954	First commercial production of ethyl alcohol by direct hydration of ethylene.
1962	First in-line blending of denatured ethyl alcohol directly into shipping vehicles (19).

Physical Properties

Ethyl alcohol under ordinary conditions is a volatile, flammable, clear, colorless liquid. Its odor is pleasant, familiar, and characteristic, as is its taste when suitably diluted with water. Otherwise, its taste may be pungent.

The physical and chemical properties of ethyl alcohol are primarily dependent upon the hydroxyl group. This group imparts polarity to the molecule and also gives rise to hydrogen bonding. These two properties account for the abnormal physical behavior of lower-molecular-weight alcohols as compared to hydrocarbons of equivalent weight. Infrared spectrographic studies (20) have shown that, in the liquid state, hydrogen bonds are formed by the attraction of the hydroxyl hydrogen of one molecule and the hydroxyl oxygen of a second molecule. The net effect of this bonding is to make liquid alcohol behave as though it were largely dimerized. This behavior is analogous to the behavior of water, which, however, is more strongly bonded and appears to exist in liquid clusters of more than two molecules. The association of ethyl alcohol, it should be noted, is confined to the liquid state; in the vapor state this alcohol is monomeric.

The molecular association of liquid ethyl alcohol gives rise to an abnormally high boiling point and a high heat of vaporization. Trouton's constant for ethyl alcohols is 26.9, as compared to 21 for unassociated liquids. This constant is the entropy of vaporization at atmospheric pressure and is obtained by dividing the molecular heat of vaporization by the absolute temperature of the atmospheric boiling point.

Ethyl alcohol's polarity and association also manifest themselves in the nonideal behavior of many ethyl alcohol solutions and in the fact that ethyl alcohol forms a large number of azeotropes, a few of which are mentioned in Tables 5–8. Many other examples of ethyl alcohol's abnormalities may be found in the properties of ethyl alcohol solutions appearing in the literature. A summary of physical properties of ethyl alcohol is presented in Table 1.

Table 1. Physical Properties of Ethyl Alcohol (21–29)

Property	Value
freezing point, °C	-114.1
normal boiling point,[a] °C	$+78.32$
critical temperature, °C	243.1
critical pressure, atm	63.0
critical volume, l/mole	0.167
critical compressibility factor, z, in $PV = znRT$	0.248
density,[b] d_4^{20}	0.7893
refractive index, n_D^{20}	1.36143
$\Delta n_D/\Delta t$, 20–30°C, per °C	0.000404
surface tension, at 25°C, dyn/cm	23.1
viscosity,[c] at 20°C, cP	1.17
solubility in water, at 20°C	miscible
heat of vaporization, at normal boiling point, cal/g	200.6
heat of combustion, at 25°C, cal/g	7092.9
heat of fusion, cal/g	25.0
flammable limits in air,	
lower, % by vol	4.3
upper, % by vol	19.0
autoignition temperature, °C	793.0
flash point, open-cup, °F	70.0
specific heat, at 20°C, cal/(g)(°C)	0.579
thermal conductivity, at 20°C, J/(sec)(cm²)(°C/cm)	0.00170
dipole moment, liq at 25°C, esu	1.70×10^{-18}

[a] See Table 2.   [b] See Table 3.   [c] See Table 4.

Table 2. Vapor Pressure of Ethyl Alcohol

Temperature, °C	Pressure, mm Hg	Temperature, °C	Pressure, mm Hg
0.0	12	90	1,187
10	24	100	1,696
20	44	110	2,356
30	79	130	4,320
40	134	150	7,326
50	221	170	11,856
60	351	190	18,178
70	541.5	210	26,821
78.3	760[a]	230	38,176
80	812	240	45,504
		243.1	47,850[b]

[a] Normal boiling point.   [b] Critical point 62.96 atm.

NOTE: For low range (10–1500 mm) the following Antoine equation can be used:

$$\log_{10} P = 8.21337 - 1652.05/(231.48 + t)$$

where P = pressure, mm Hg; t = temperature, °C.

Table 3. Density of Ethyl Alcohol

Temperature, °C	Density, g/ml	Temperature, °C	Density, g/ml
−110	0.9027	−10	0.8147
−100	0.8937	0	0.8063
−90	0.8846	+5	0.8021
−80	0.8757	10	0.7979
−70	0.8668	20	0.7893
−60	0.8580	25	0.7850
−50	0.8492	30	0.7808
−40	0.8405	40	0.7720
−30	0.8319	50	0.7630
−20	0.8233	60	0.7548

NOTE: Density is computed as follows:

$$d_4^t = 0.80632 - 0.00085365\,t - 0.00000001\,t^2 - 0.000000002\,t^3$$

where average deviation = ± 0.00014; t = temperature, °C.

Table 4. Viscosity of Ethyl Alcohol

Temperature, °C	Viscosity, cP	Temperature, °C	Viscosity, cP
0	1.82	40	0.81
10	1.49	50	0.68
20	1.17	60	0.58
25	1.06	70	0.50
30	0.97	80	0.43

Latent Heat of Vaporization.   This constant can be calculated by using the following equation:

$$l_v = 226.27059 - 0.23412409t - 0.00119984t^2$$

where l_v = cal/g, t = °C, average deviation is ±0.24.

Table 5. Selected Binary Azeotropes of Ethyl Alcohol, at 760 mm Hg (29,30)

Second component = B	Azeotrope data (ethyl alcohol = A)		
	Boiling point, °C	Wt % of A or B[a]	
acetonitrile	72.9	43	B
benzene	67.8	32.4	A
2-butanone	74.0	39	A
butyraldehyde	70.7	60.6	A
carbon tetrachloride	65	84	B
chloroform	59.4	93	B
cyclohexane	64.9	40	A
1,2-dichloroethane	70.5	63	B
p-dioxane	78.25	>98	A
ethyl acetate	71.81	30.98	A
ethyl butyl ether	73.8	49.3	A
hexane	58	20.8	A
isopropyl acetate	76.8	53.	A
isopropyl ether	64	17.1	A
methyl acetate	56.9	~3	A
methylcyclohexane	72.1	47	A
nitromethane	76.05	29.0	B
propionitrile	77.5		A
toluene	76.5	66.7	A
trichloroethylene	70.9	72.5	B
water	78.2	95.6	A

[a] Data in reference 30 entered under this compound.

Table 6. Selected Ternary Azeotropes of Ethyl Alcohol–Water–Compound C (30), at 760 mm Hg[a]

Compound C	Boiling point, °C	Composition, wt %	
		Water	Compound C
acetal	77.8	11.4	61.0
acetonitrile	72.9	1	44.0
acrylonitrile	69.5	8.7	71.0
benzene	64.86	7.4	74.1
carbon disulfide	41.3	1.6	3.4
carbon tetrachloride	62	4.5	85.5
chloroform, 20 psig	78.0	3.9	91.2
cyclohexane	62.1		
1,2-dichloroethane	67.8	7.2	77.1
ethyl acetate	70.23	9.0	82.6
heptane	~69.5		
isoamyl acetate	69.0		
trichloroethylene	67	5.5	78.4
toluene	74.55		

[a] Unless otherwise noted.

The three numerical values were computed from a set of selected values for temperatures 0–110°C.

Specific Heat of Liquid. This constant between −100 and 0°C can be calculated by using the following equation:

$$C_p = 0.54247 + 1314 \times 10^{-6}t + 485 \times 10^{-8}t^2$$

Table 7. Ternary Azeotropes of Ethyl Alcohol–Compound B–Compound C (30), at 760 mm Hg

Compound B	Compound C	Boiling point, °C	Composition, wt % B	C
acetonitrile	triethylamine	70.1	34	58
chloroform	acetone	63.2	65.3	24.3
chloroform	hexane	58.3		
ethoxytrimethylsilane	benzene	minimum		
ethyl acetate	cyclohexane	64.3		

Table 8. Selected Binary and Ternary Nonazeotropes of Ethyl Alcohol (30)

acetaldehyde	dioxane
acetic acid	ethyl acetate–carbon
acetone	tetrachloride
aniline–toluene	ethyl ether
benzene–heptane	isopropanol
2-butanone–carbon	methanol
tetrachloride	methanol–acetone
butyl alcohol	pyridine
butyl ether	water–methanol
diethylamine	

For the values between 0 and 80°C, another equation can be used, as follows:

$$C_p = 0.54283 + 1374 \times 10^{-6}t + 224 \times 10^{-7}t^2$$

where t = °C, average error for both equations is ±0.0015.

Chemical Properties

The chemical properties of ethyl alcohol are primarily concerned with the hydroxyl group, namely, reactions involving dehydration, dehydrogenation, oxidation, and esterification. The hydrogen atom of the hydroxyl group can be replaced by an active metal, such as sodium, potassium, and calcium, with the formation of a metal ethoxide (ethylate) and the evolution of hydrogen gas. See Alkoxides, metal.

$$2 C_2H_5OH + 2 M \rightarrow 2 C_2H_5OM + H_2$$

Sodium ethoxide can be prepared by the reaction between absolute ethyl alcohol and sodium, or by refluxing absolute ethyl alcohol with anhydrous sodium hydroxide (31), as shown:

$$CH_3CH_2OH + NaOH \rightarrow CH_3CH_2ONa + H_2O$$

The sodium ethoxide precipitates upon addition of anhydrous acetone (32). This strong base hydrolyzes readily to give ethyl alcohol and sodium and hydroxyl ions.

$$CH_3CH_2O^-Na^+ + H_2O \rightleftharpoons CH_3CH_2OH + Na^+ + OH^-$$

Commercially, water is removed by azeotropic distillation with benzene (33). Sodium ethoxide may also be prepared by reacting sodium amalgam with ethyl alcohol.

Sodium ethoxide is used in organic synthesis as a condensing and reducing agent. The reaction between sodium ethoxide and sulfur monochloride results in the formation of diethyl thiosulfite (34).

$$2 CH_3CH_2ONa + S_2Cl_2 \rightarrow (CH_3CH_2)_2S_2O_2 + 2 NaCl$$

The commercial production of barbiturates (qv) (Veronal, Barbital, Luminal, Amytal), ethyl orthoformate, and other chemicals is dependent upon the use of sodium ethoxide.

Aluminum and magnesium also react to form ethoxides, but the reaction must be catalyzed by amalgamating the metal (adding a small amount of mercury).

$$6 \ CH_3CH_2OH + 2 \ Al \rightarrow 2 \ (CH_3CH_2O)_3Al + 3 \ H_2$$

$$2 \ CH_3CH_2OH + Mg \rightarrow (CH_3CH_2O)_2Mg + H_2$$

Well-cleaned aluminum filings react at room temperature in the presence of mercuric chloride (35,36). In an autoclave metallic aluminum and ethyl alcohol react without a catalyst at 120°C (37). The reaction also may be promoted by the addition of sodium ethoxide (38).

Other reactions involving the hydrogen atom of the hydroxyl group in ethyl alcohol include the opening of epoxide rings to form hydroxy ethers,

$$CH_3CH_2OH + R\!-\!CH\!-\!CH_2 \rightarrow CH_3CH_2OCHRCH_2OH$$
$$\diagdown \diagup$$
$$O$$

and the addition to acetylene to form ethyl vinyl ether,

$$CH_3CH_2OH + HC\!\equiv\!CH \rightarrow CH_3CH_2OCH\!=\!CH_2$$

These reactions are carried out in the presence of acidic and alkaline catalysts. The acid-catalyzed addition of ethyl alcohol to acetylene or to a vinyl ether results in acetals (diethers of 1,1-dihydroxyethane). The acid-catalyzed reaction of ethyl alcohol with an aldehyde or ketone also gives acetals.

$$2 \ CH_3CH_2OH + RCHO \rightleftharpoons RCH(OCH_2CH_3)_2 + H_2O$$

The hydroxyl group can be replaced by halogens from inorganic acid halides and phosphorus halides to give two different products, namely, ethyl esters of the acid, and ethyl halide (39). Phosphorus trihalides, and thionyl chloride, $SOCl_2$, are generally used to make either ethyl phosphite or sulfite (reaction a) or ethyl chloride (reaction b). The yield in (b) is reduced by formation of mixed alkyl esters of phosphites, such as $CH_3CH_2OPO_2$ and $(CH_3CH_2O)_2PO$.

$$(a) \begin{cases} 3 \ CH_3CH_2OH + PCl_3 \xrightarrow[\text{low temp}]{\textit{tert} \ \text{amine}} (CH_3CH_2O)_3P + 3 \ HCl \\[2ex] 2 \ CH_3CH_2OH + SOCl_2 \rightarrow (CH_3CH_2O)_2SO + 2 \ HCl \end{cases}$$

$$(b) \begin{cases} 3 \ CH_3CH_2OH + PCl_3 \rightarrow 3 \ CH_3CH_2Cl + H_3PO_3 \\[2ex] CH_3CH_2OH + SOCl_2 \rightarrow CH_3CH_2Cl + SO_2 + HCl \end{cases}$$

With phosphorus trichloride the predominant product is triethyl phosphite, while ethyl bromide is the principal product with phosphorus tribromide; however, varied reaction conditions strongly affect the composition of reaction products. The halogen acids also produce alkyl halides.

$$CH_3CH_2OH + HX \rightarrow CH_3CH_2X + H_2O$$

The halogen influences the rate of reaction and, in general, the order of reactivity is HI > HBr > HCl. Important uses of ethyl chloride include the manufacture of tetraethyllead and ethylcellulose. Ethyl bromide can be used to produce ethyl Grignard reagent and various amines including mono- and diethylaniline.

Esters are formed by the reaction with inorganic and organic acids, acid anhydrides, and acid halides. If the inorganic acid is oxygenated (sulfuric acid, nitric acid) the ester will have a carbon–oxygen linkage which is easily hydrolyzed (40–42).

$$CH_3CH_2OH + H_2SO_4 \rightarrow CH_3CH_2OSO_3H + H_2O$$

$$CH_3CH_2OH + HONO_2 \rightarrow CH_3CH_2ONO_2 + H_2O$$

Organic esters are formed by the elimination of water between an alcohol and an organic acid.

$$CH_3CH_2OH + RCOOH \rightleftharpoons RCOOCH_2CH_3 + H_2O$$

The reaction is reversible and reaches equilibrium slowly. The technology of esterification with ethyl alcohol is mainly concerned with the removal of the water produced by the reaction to shift the equilibrium to the right. Generally, acidic catalysts are used, such as strong sulfuric acid, hydrochloric acid, boron trifluoride, and p-toluenesulfonic acid (43). Batchwise and continuous processes are used for the esterification reaction.

Ethyl alcohol also reacts with acid anhydrides or acid halides to give corresponding esters.

$$CH_3CH_2OH + (RCO)_2O \rightarrow RCOOCH_2CH_3 + RCOOH$$

$$CH_3CH_2OH + RCOCl \rightarrow RCOOCH_2CH_3 + HCl$$

The direct conversion of ethyl alcohol to ethyl acetate is believed to take place via acetaldehyde and its condensation to ethyl acetate (Tishchenko reaction) (44–50).

$$CH_3CH_2OH \rightarrow CH_3CHO + H_2$$

$$2\,CH_3CHO \rightarrow CH_3COOCH_2CH_3$$

About a 24% yield of ethyl acetate is obtained using a copper oxide catalyst containing 0.1–0.2% thoria at a temperature of 350°C.

Ethyl alcohol may be dehydrated intramolecularly to form ethylene or ethyl ether.

$$CH_3CH_2OH \rightarrow CH_2{=}CH_2 + H_2O$$

$$2\,CH_3CH_2OH \rightarrow CH_3CH_2OCH_2CH_3 + H_2O$$

Generally, both ethylene and ethyl ether are formed to some extent at the same time, but the conditions may be altered to favor one reaction or the other.

The dehydrogenation of ethyl alcohol to acetaldehyde may be obtained by a vapor-phase reaction over various catalysts.

$$CH_3CH_2OH \rightarrow CH_3CHO + H_2$$

The functional methylene group of ethyl alcohol takes an important part in reactions involving the dehydration to ethylene and oxidation to aldehydes and acids.

$$CH_3CH_2OH \rightarrow CH_2{=}CH_2 + H_2O$$

$$CH_3CH_2OH + \tfrac{1}{2}\,O_2 \rightarrow CH_3CHO + H_2O$$

$$CH_3CH_2OH + O_2 \rightarrow CH_3COOH + H_2O$$

Ethyl alcohol reacts with sodium hypochlorite to give chloroform—the haloform reaction. (See Vol. 1, p. 537.)

$$CH_3CH_2OH + NaOCl \rightarrow CH_3CHO + NaCl + H_2O$$

$$CH_3CHO + 3\,NaOCl \rightarrow CCl_3CHO + 3\,NaOH$$

$$CCl_3CHO + NaOH \rightarrow CHCl_3 + HCOONa$$

Similarly, bromoform, CHBr₃, and iodoform, CHI₃, are obtained from sodium hypobromite and hypoiodite, respectively. Ethyl alcohol is the only primary alcohol that undergoes this reaction.

According to Bobtelsky, the reactivity of ethyl alcohol–water mixtures may be correlated with three distinct alcohol concentration ranges (51,52). For example, the chromium trioxide oxidation of ethyl alcohol (53), the catalytic decomposition of hydrogen peroxide (54), and the sensitivity of colloidal particles to coagulation (55) are characteristic for ethyl alcohol concentrations of 25–30%, 40–60%, and above 60% alcohol, respectively. The effect of various catalysts also differs for different alcohol concentrations (51).

Manufacture

Industrial ethyl alcohol is produced either (1) synthetically from ethylene, (2) as a by-product of certain industrial operations, or (3) by the fermentation of sugar, starch, and cellulose materials. There are two main processes for the synthesis of ethyl alcohol from ethylene. The earliest to be developed (in 1930 by Union Carbide Corporation) was the indirect-hydration process, generally referred to as the strong sulfuric acid–ethylene process, ethyl sulfate process, esterification-hydrolysis process, or sulfation-hydrolysis process. The other synthesis process, designed to eliminate the use of sulfuric acid, is referred to as the direct hydration process. As shown in Table 13 (see p. 444), the current synthetic production far exceeds the production by fermentation. Other synthetic methods have been investigated but have not attained commercial realization. These include, for example, the hydration of ethylene in the presence of dilute acids (weak sulfuric acid process); the conversion of acetylene to acetaldehyde, followed by hydrogenation of the aldehyde to ethyl alcohol; the hydration of ethyl ether (under certain circumstances—see p. 437); and the Fischer-Tropsch hydrocarbon synthesis.

Synthetic ethyl alcohol is produced by five domestic companies, by two routes, both of which use readily available and comparatively inexpensive ethylene (qv) as basic raw material. U.S. producers are Union Carbide Corporation (UCC), Enjay Chemical Company (a Division of Humble Oil and Refining Company), Shell Chemical Company, Tennessee Eastman Company (a Division of Eastman Kodak Company), and U.S. Industrial Chemicals Company (USI, a Division of National Distillers and Chemical Corporation). Currently ethyl alcohol production ranks third in the consumption of ethylene; ethylene oxide and polyethylene first and second respectively (56). In view of technological advances in the direct conversion of ethylene to acetaldehyde and acetic acid, announced in 1965, the consumption of ethylene for ethyl alcohol production may radically change (see under Economics). The 1964 ethylene requirement for ethyl alcohol was about 1.4 billion lb. In the fiscal year of 1964 about 82% of the total synthetically produced ethyl alcohol was manufactured by the indirect-hydration process. The remainder was produced by the direct hydration of ethylene.

INDIRECT–HYDRATION PROCESS (ESTERIFICATION–HYDROLYSIS PROCESS)

This process, used by UCC, Enjay, and USI, requires three steps, (1) absorption of ethylene in concentrated sulfuric acid to form mono- and diethyl sulfates, (2) hy-

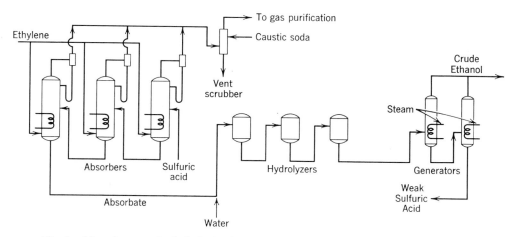

Fig. 1. Manufacture of ethyl alcohol by esterification-hydrolysis (indirect hydration).

drolysis of the ethyl sulfates to ethyl alcohol, and (3) reconcentration of the dilute sulfuric acid. The reactions involved are as follows:

Absorption

$$CH_2{=}CH_2 + H_2SO_4 \rightarrow CH_3CH_2OSO_3H$$
$$\text{ethyl hydrogen sulfate}$$
$$\text{(monoethyl sulfate)}$$

$$2\,CH_2{=}CH_2 + H_2SO_4 \rightarrow (CH_3CH_2)_2SO_4$$
$$\text{diethyl sulfate}$$

Hydrolysis

$$CH_3CH_2OSO_3H + H_2O \rightarrow CH_3CH_2OH + H_2SO_4$$

$$(CH_3CH_2)_2SO_4 + 2\,H_2O \rightarrow 2\,CH_3CH_2OH + H_2SO_4$$

$$(CH_3CH_2)_2SO_4 + CH_3CH_2OH \rightarrow CH_3CH_2OSO_3H + CH_3CH_2OCH_2CH_3$$
$$\text{diethyl ether}$$

Figure 1 depicts a generalized flow diagram of this process. Ethylene is absorbed in 95–98% sulfuric acid at reaction temperatures of 50–80°C and pressures of 150–200 psig. In the U.S.S.R. the conditions include an absorption temperature of 70–80°C at pressures of 375–400 psi (4). The absorption is exothermic and cooling is required. The rate of absorption is increased by stronger acid concentrations, temperature, and, to a lesser extent, by pressure. Agitation to increase the surface area for mass transfer may also increase the absorption rate.

The absorbate containing the mixed sulfates is hydrolyzed with 1–2 vol of water. (In the U.S.S.R. a hydrolysis ratio of 0.8 vol of water to 1 vol of absorbate is used (4).) The hydrolysis time required may be several hours, as the monoethyl sulfate hydrolysis rate is extremely slow compared to the hydrolysis rate of the first ester linkage. Diethyl ether is formed as the principal by-product of the reaction of ethyl alcohol with diethyl sulfate. The formation of ether can be minimized by controlling the temperature and composition of the hydrolysis step.

The crude ethyl alcohol is generated from the hydrolyzate by heating. Ethyl alcohol, ether, and part of the water are stripped overhead. The ethyl ether is removed by steam in a distilling column, and the ethyl alcohol passes to a fractionating column, from which an azeotrope with water, containing 95–96% by vol ethyl alcohol, is removed overhead. The remaining dilute acid, of about 60–70% concentration, is cycled to the absorbers after concentration and removal of carbonaceous decomposition products.

Hatch (1) presents an excellent, thorough review concerning feed materials, absorption, hydrolysis, and acid concentration from which the authors have obtained much of the following material.

Feed Materials. The ethylene feedstock used contains 35–95% ethylene, the remaining gases being saturated hydrocarbons (methane and ethane). Certain unsaturated hydrocarbons give aldehydes and oils. Particularly detrimental, even in relatively small amounts, is acetylene which results in the formation of acetaldehyde, and propylene and butadiene which result in polymer formation. Organic chemicals, such as acetone and acetaldehyde, present in trace quantities in ethylene, affect the quality of the ethyl alcohol obtained.

Absorption. The rate of absorption of ethylene in sulfuric acid is dependent upon the reactor design, acid concentration, ethylene concentration, temperature, pressure, ethyl hydrogen sulfate concentration, and the presence of various metal salts. There seems to be a difference of opinion as to what takes place during the absorption step. One theory claims that ethylene is first dissolved in sulfuric acid and then the dissolved ethylene reacts with sulfuric acid to give ethyl sulfate. The other theory claims direct reaction of gaseous ethylene with sulfuric acid. Under normal operating conditions solution is the slower of the two processes (57).

The absorption may be carried out by passing ethylene countercurrently through sulfuric acid in a column reactor at 80°C under pressures of 180–200 psig (58). A temperature gradient may be maintained by controlling the upper portion of the absorption zone from 65–82°C and the lower portion from about 90–110°C (59).

The absorption rate is increased when ethyl hydrogen sulfate is present in the acid (57,60–62). This may be attributed to the greater solubility of ethylene in ethyl hydrogen sulfate than in sulfuric acid.

Catalysts, such as the oxides of iron, magnesium, copper, uranium, vanadium, and alkaline earth metals, may be used to increase the rate of absorption (63,64). The absorption of ethylene by sulfuric acid is a surface reaction and is inhibited by benzene, m-xylene, naphthalene, phenol, aniline, pyridine, quinoline, acetamide, acetone, water, and ammonium sulfate (65), and by ethyl ether and nitrobenzene (66).

Operating variables such as acid strength, temperature, and pressure have been investigated extensively (67). In general, ethylene absorption by sulfuric acid is slight below 50°C, but increases rapidly with increasing temperature and reaches a maximum at 130°C (68). Formation of ethyl hydrogen sulfate occurs best at about 80°C; above 70°C diethyl sulfate is also formed. The use of 98% sulfuric acid is claimed to be more economical than 94% acid (69). The absorption of ethylene is accelerated under pressure and is roughly a linear function of the pressure (16,70–73). The rate of ethylene absorption, using 95% acid at 80–90°C, increases almost linearly until 1.5 moles of ethylene are absorbed per mole of sulfuric acid (67). Pressures ranging from 250 to 500 psig prevent vaporization loss of diethyl sulfate from concentrated acid mixtures.

Large yields of diethyl sulfate are produced by the solution of excess ethylene in ethyl hydrogen sulfate and its production is affected by pressure. Ethylene under 500 psig pressure (98% acid, 80°C) gives 1.6 moles of ethylene combined with 1 mole of sulfuric acid in 50 min, as compared with 1.18 moles under 20 psig (67). Yields of 35% diethyl sulfate and 51% ethyl hydrogen sulfate, based on the acid, at 525 psig pressure are obtained when 100% acid and 98% ethylene (74) are used. At 150 psig pressure the yields are 62% and 30%, respectively. Low yields of diethyl sulfate are reported using concentrated acid at 65 and 75°C (75). Curme produced diethyl sulfate commercially by using pure ethylene and volatilizing diethyl sulfate in a stream of excess gas (76). The rate of absorption is increased by a more efficient contact between the gaseous ethylene and liquid sulfuric acid (77–80).

Plant and Sidgwick (57) determined the effects of temperature (50 and 70°C) and various acid concentrations on product distribution (see Table 9). At higher temperatures excessive decomposition was evident and the data are inconclusive.

Table 9. Sulfation of Ethylene: Effect of Temperature and Acid Concentration on Product Distribution (57)

Temperature, °C	Acid concn, wt %	Increase in wt of acid, %	Product distribution, wt %			
			Ethyl hydrogen sulfate	Diethyl sulfate	Sulfuric acid	Water
50	93.1	16.6	60.1	nil	33.9	6.0
	97.6	29.2	73.9	15.8	8.4	1.9
	99.3	32.0	72.7	22.2	4.6	0.5
70	93.1	20.8	69.5	2.2	22.5	5 8
	95.8	28.0	79.1	9.4	8.2	3.3
	98.1	34.4	74.8	70.3	3.5	1.4
	98.8	36.2	68.1	29.3	1.7	0.9
	100.1	38.6	70.0	30.0	nil	nil

A review of the patent literature from 1955 to 1964, inclusive, discloses that the absorption of ethylene in sulfuric acid is increased by the suitable design of the absorption tower (81) and by the addition of sodium alkylarenesulfonates (82). Foaming in the esterification-hydrolysis process may be reduced by the addition of isopropyl sulfates (83), or by heating at 150–230°C for 2–24 hr, depending upon the concentration of acid (84). Any deposits of acid-insoluble carbonaceous materials may be removed by flushing with dilute ethyl alcohol (85). Other improvements can be achieved with various combinations of absorption and hydrolysis (86–91).

Hydrolysis. The mixed ethyl sulfates are hydrolyzed by a measured volume of water, sufficient to give an approx 50–60% aqueous sulfuric acid solution after hydrolysis. The hydrolysis mixture containing ethyl alcohol, ethyl ether, sulfuric acid, and water is separated in a stripping column to give dilute sulfuric acid bottoms or tails material and a gaseous alcohol–ether–water mixture overhead. This mixture is washed with water or dilute sodium hydroxide solution. The washed mixture is purified by distillation. The patent literature discloses many modifications of the hydrolysis process, including continuous processes (86,88,89,91,92).

Diethyl sulfate is fairly stable in the presence of water at temperatures below 70°C (93). The hydrolysis is markedly rapid in the presence of free sulfuric acid and results in ether formation. Various methods have been proposed to diminish this, such as a two-step hydrolysis process (94), a single-step process wherein a sufficient concentration of ethyl alcohol is maintained to prevent layering during hydrolysis (95), and vigorous agitation.

Kremann has investigated the hydrolysis of ethyl hydrogen sulfate,

$$CH_3CH_2OSO_3H + H_2O \rightleftharpoons CH_3CH_2OH + H_2SO_4$$

and found that the equilibrium constant of the reaction is apparently independent of temperature. The velocity of the reaction between ethyl hydrogen sulfate and water is proportional to the hydrogen ion concentration (96–98). Ethyl hydrogen sulfate has been hydrolyzed with ammonia gas and steam (99–101).

Acid Concentration. The reconcentration of the dilute sulfuric acid (50–60%) is one of the more costly operations in the manufacture of ethyl alcohol by the indirect-hydration process. Generally a Simonson-Mantius, two-stage, vacuum, acid-concentration system is used for this purpose. The weak acid goes from the stripping column to an acid reboiler in which the acidity is raised to about 70%. This acid is concentrated to 90% via the Simonson-Mantius, two-stage vacuum evaporation operating at pressures of 2.5 and 0.4 in. mercury absolute pressure, respectively. The 90% acid must then be brought to 96–98% strength by fortification with 103% oleum. Dowtherm is the heating medium and heating conditions are maintained at 300°C and 20 psi pressure. The temperature of the acid is kept below 190°C during the concentration.

The buildup of carbonaceous materials in the sulfuric acid presents one of the most serious problems of acid concentration. Insoluble carbon (elemental carbon), as well as liquid organic compounds described as "soluble carbon," are present. The carbonaceous materials can be removed by heating at 175–315°C for about 2 hr (90,102), or by extraction with kerosene (103,104), or ethyl ether (105). The separation of oils and tars from dilute acids is also accomplished by concentrating the dilute acid to 60% strength by distillation, cooling to remove tarry materials, and then reconcentrating to 96% strength (106). Foaming of dilute sulfuric acid may be reduced by adding low-molecular-weight aliphatic alkyl sulfates (83) and by heating at 150–230°C for 2–24 hr (84).

Corrosion. The acid concentration process presents a corrosion problem. Generally, all vessels are mild steel and are lined with lead or brick; the steam-heating elements are composed of either silicon, iron, or tantalum. Many materials have been tried for pipelines, but replaceable lead pipes are generally as economical as any alternative material (107).

DIRECT HYDRATION OF ETHYLENE

The vapor-phase, catalytic hydration of ethylene, used by the Shell Oil Co. and the Eastman Kodak Co., has been covered extensively in the general and the patent literature. Ellis presents a patent literature review through 1937 of the types of catalytic materials used (63,64). A general review of hydration of olefins is given by Tapp (108). Dalin employed a catalyst comprised of phosphoric acid supported on alumina silicate and on a silica gel of coarse porosity (109). Other catalysts include blue tungsten oxide and combinations thereof (110–117), copper fluoborate (118), silicotungstic acid (119), titania and ferric oxide (120), silicophosphoric acid (121), and ion exchange resins (122).

The ethylene hydration process involves the catalytic addition of water to ethylene. Phosphoric acid, impregnated on an inert support such as Celite diatomite, is commonly used as a catalyst. High pressures and temperatures in the order of 1000 psig and 300°C are required. The reaction is exothermic.

$$CH_2{=}CH_2 + H_2O \rightleftharpoons CH_3CH_2OH + 19{,}000 \text{ Btu/lb-mole}$$

The reactor operates at low conversions per pass, so that a large cycle volume of unreacted ethylene is required. Fresh ethylene feed plus recycle ethylene are mixed with 0.5–1.0 mole of water per mole of ethylene and fed to the top of the reactor as vapor. The temperature, pressure, and water-to-ethylene mole ratio, dictate the amount of conversion obtained. The vapor leaving the reactor is slightly hotter than the feed because of the exothermic reaction. The reactor effluent is cooled and neutralized with a small amount of caustic soda (traces of phosphoric acid are present), and the condensed ethyl alcohol and water are separated from unreacted gases. The gases, mostly unreacted ethylene, are scrubbed with water to remove traces of ethyl alcohol, and returned to the reactor. A small vent or purge stream is removed to prevent buildup of impurities in the gas cycle. The condensed ethyl alcohol–water and scrubber liquid are combined and distilled to 190° proof ethyl alcohol by conventional processes. Figure 2 depicts the reaction section for the manufacture of ethyl alcohol by direct catalytic hydration of ethylene.

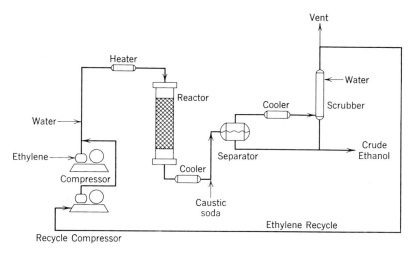

Fig. 2. Manufacture of ethyl alcohol by direct hydration of ethylene.

The Shell Development Company in 1945 discovered that phosphoric acid itself could be employed as a catalyst for the direct hydration of ethylene to ethyl alcohol. The first patent covering the direct hydration of ethylene was issued to Shell in 1951 (18). Since that time a number of patents have been issued covering the use of phosphoric acid catalyst. Recent disclosures have been made by Eastman Kodak Company and by Union Oil Company, encompassing the use of phosphoric acid on various carriers with or without metallic activators (123,124). Montecatini has claimed a continuous, direct-hydration process which comprises a vapor-phase hydration of ethylene at 290°C and at 5100 psi pressure in the presence of a suspension of aluminum hydroxide gel at a pH of 3–4.2. A 25% conversion of ethylene to ethyl alcohol and yields of 92% of ethyl alcohol are reported (125).

The reaction, conditions, purification, and operating variables for the industrial application of the vapor-phase catalytic hydration of ethylene have been described rather thoroughly in the general and patent literature (18,107,126,127). The conditions recommended are shown in Table 10.

Table 10. Recommended Conditions for the Vapor-Phase Catalytic Hydration of Ethylene

reaction temperature, °C	299
reaction pressure, psig	960–1000 (66.3 atm)
reactor feed ethylene concentration, waterfree basis, %	85
ethylene makeup concentration, %	97
water-to-ethylene mole ratio in feed	0.6
space velocity,[a]	26.5–30
ethylene conversion per pass, %	4.2–5
water conversion, %	7.0
overall yield, ethylene to ethyl alcohol, %	$\geqq 97$

[a] Volume of gas at 60°F and 1 atm/(min)(vol catalyst).

Minor side reactions occur which result in the formation of by-products in relatively small amounts. The by-products thus produced include ether, aldehydes, higher hydrocarbons, higher alcohols, and ketones. The principal by-product, diethyl ether, is formed from the ethyl alcohol.

$$2 \; CH_3CH_2OH \rightleftharpoons (CH_3CH_2)_2O + H_2O$$

The ether may be recycled to give ethyl alcohol, since the equilibrium of this reaction leans toward the ethyl alcohol side. Acetaldehyde is formed by the hydration of acetylene present as an impurity.

$$CH{\equiv}CH + H_2O \rightarrow CH_3CH_2O$$

The acetaldehyde undergoes an aldol condensation reaction to give crotonaldehyde.

$$2 \; CH_3CHO \rightarrow CH_3CH(OH)CH_2CHO \rightarrow CH_3CH{=}CHCHO + H_2O$$

The aldehydes may be hydrogenated to the corresponding alcohols. Higher hydrocarbons are formed by the polymerization of ethylene. Any higher unsaturated hydrocarbons are converted to the corresponding alcohols by direct hydration and to the corresponding ketones by dehydrogenation.

Any change in the pressure, temperature, or water-to-ethylene mole ratio results in a change in the concentration of the phosphoric acid supported catalyst (107,126). As the concentration of the phosphoric acid at a given temperature increases, the catalytic activity of the acid also increases. An increase in pressure decreases the concentration of acid on the Celite carrier. The water-to-ethylene ratio also influences acid concentration in the bed. An extrapolated figure of 0.68 mole of water to 1 mole of ethylene appears to give the maximum ethyl alcohol production. Temperature has been found to affect all of the reaction variables.

MISCELLANEOUS METHODS OF PREPARATION

In addition to the esterification-hydrolysis process and the direct-hydration process, various other routes have been investigated for the manufacture of synthetic ethyl alcohol. These include the hydration of ethylene by dilute acids, the hydration of ethyl ether, the hydrolysis of several esters, the hydrogenation of acetaldehyde, and the reaction between carbon monoxide and hydrogen; however, none has proved to be commercially successful. The oxidation of hydrocarbons to produce ethyl alcohol appears to hold some promise on a commercial scale.

Hydration of Ethylene by Dilute Acids. This process is known as the weak acid process. The sulfuric acid concentrations may be 50–70% or 0.5–10%, or other mineral acids may be used. Special equipment is required to control the severe corrosion problems encountered.

A method has been patented which comprises the production of ethyl alcohol by countercurrent absorption of ethylene in 68–72% sulfuric acid at a pressure of 375–600 psi and a temperature of 140–160°C, with subsequent addition of about 7% water (128,129). The total yield is reported to be about 96%, based on the ethylene. The acid leaving the process is at nearly the same concentration as the original feed.

Hydration of Ethyl Ether. Although diethyl ether has up to now frequently been mentioned as an unwanted by-product of ethyl alcohol manufacture, nevertheless there are conditions under which the reverse reaction, manufacture of ethyl alcohol from the ether, may be economical. For example, ethyl alcohol is produced by the hydration of ethyl ether in a reversible reaction catalyzed by acid catalysts and metal oxides.

$$CH_3CH_2OCH_2CH_3 + H_2O \rightleftharpoons 2\ CH_3CH_2OH$$

The acids employed have the following concentrations:

sulfuric acid	10%, or 63–70% (130)
hydrochloric acid	5–6% (131)
phosphoric acid	15–20% (132)

Aluminum oxide has been the most widely used catalyst (132–134). Reaction temperatures of 250–315°C are required. A sulfuric acid concentration of 63–70% permits the use of a 175–230°C reaction temperature. In general, the ethyl alcohol product from the hydration of diethyl ether has a foul odor due to the presence of polymeric hydrocarbon materials.

Hydrolysis of Ethyl Esters. The hydrolysis of esters other than ethyl sulfates has not achieved commercial success. The hydrolysis of chlorosulfonic acid (135), diethyl sulfite (136), and ethyl acetate (137) have also been considered and found to be of little industrial importance.

Hydrogenation of Acetaldehyde. The hydrogenation of acetaldehyde is a possible route for the manufacture of ethyl alcohol and may become more commercially attractive with the recent developments in the direct oxidation of hydrocarbons to oxygen-containing materials. However, at the present time one of the principal uses of ethyl alcohol is the production of acetaldehyde by dehydrogenation (138–141).

Oxidation of Hydrocarbons. In general, a variety of oxygen-containing compounds including ethyl alcohol are produced by the oxidation of hydrocarbons. Ethyl alcohol is reported to be obtained in a yield of 51% by the slow combustion of ethane (142,143). The vapor-phase, partial oxidation of propane, butane, and mixtures with air or oxygen has been reported to give an approx 8% yield of ethyl alcohol (144,145), and other oxygenated organic compounds including acetaldehyde (146–148). See Hydrocarbon oxidation.

Carbon Monoxide and Hydrogen. Ethyl alcohol can be produced, either as a by-product, or in some cases in substantial amounts, by certain modifications of the Fischer-Tropsch process. Although this process is technically feasible, it cannot compete with other more economical methods for producing chemicals from natural gas. The literature is well documented concerning this method (117,149–158). See Carbon monoxide–hydrogen reactions.

Ethyl alcohol can also be synthesized by a process related to the oxo process, which involves the reaction of methanol with carbon monoxide and hydrogen at 180–185°C and at a pressure of 3000 psi in the presence of a cobalt catalyst.   Between 30 and 40% of the reacting methanol is converted to ethyl alcohol, the remaining material consisting largely of diethyl ether and dimethyl acetal (159).

FERMENTATION ETHYL ALCOHOL

Because fermentation ethyl alcohol has been thoroughly and repeatedly discussed in the literature, the coverage here will be illustrative rather than comprehensive. (See Alcoholic beverages, distilled, Vol. 1, pp. 501–531; see also reference 159a).   The following U.S. manufacturers are using the fermentation process: Commercial Solvents Corp., Fleischmann Distillers Corp., Florida Fruit Distillers Inc., Grain Processing Co., Publicker Industries Inc., Joseph E. Seagram and Sons, Inc., Schenley Distillers Inc., and Hiram Walker and Sons, Inc.

Ethyl alcohol can be derived by fermentation processes from any material in which the carbohydrate is present in the form of sugar.   The many and varied raw materials used in the manufacture of ethyl alcohol via fermentation are conveniently classified under three types of agricultural raw materials: sugar, starches, and cellulose materials.   Sugars (from sugar cane, sugar beets, molasses, fruit) may be converted to ethyl alcohol directly.   Starches (from grains, potatoes, root crops) must first be hydrolyzed to fermentable sugars by the action of enzymes from malt or molds.   Cellulose (from wood, agricultural residues, waste sulfite liquor from paper pulp mills which contain sugars derived from cellulose and hemicellulose hydrolysis) must likewise be converted to sugars, in this case by the action of mineral acids.   Once the simple sugars are formed, enzymes from yeast can readily ferment them to ethyl alcohol (160). Even though the fermentation process for making beverages is of such antiquity, old-timers still oppose the intrusion of science (especially chemistry) into the art of whiskey making.   One manufacturer recently emphasized that the old-fashioned way of making whiskey is best as depicted by a sign outside the distillery, "No chemists allowed—this is a distillery, not a whiskey factory" (161).

Molasses. Blackstrap molasses is the principal source of sugars used in the U.S. production of ethyl alcohol (159,160). Blackstrap (derived from Java and the Dutch word "stroop," meaning syrup) is collected as a by-product of cane sugar manufacture. Therefore the availability of blackstrap molasses is limited by sugar production. Also there is currently competition between the alternative uses of molasses in the manufacture of ethyl alcohol and in the preparation of feeds (qv) for livestock.   Molasses, because of its normally low price and high carbohydrate value, is an attractive feed supplement, which is usually added to the extent of about 10%.   It contains about 50–55% of fermentable sugar consisting mainly of sucrose (cane sugar) and invert (about 70% sucrose and 30% invert).

Sugar Cane. Under the current conditions in the world sugar markets, it is somewhat doubtful whether it is economically feasible to produce ethyl alcohol by the direct fermentation of sugar cane juice.

Sugar Beets. In the United States ethyl alcohol is not manufactured directly from beets. The juice of the sugar beet contains a valuable proportion of fermentable sucrose, and beets of good quality should yield about 23 gal of 99.5% ethyl alcohol per ton. Beet molasses, obtained as a by-product in the production of beet sugar, is used in many foreign countries to some extent for the manufacture of ethyl alcohol.

Citrus Molasses. Although the manufacture of ethyl alcohol from the sugar-containing waste products of the fruit industry might appear to be a highly desirable operation—particularly as a means of reducing stream pollution in the vicinity of canning plants—such production is relatively costly. Often these waste products contain as much as 97% water, the bulk of which must be removed. The cost of manufacturing ethyl alcohol from these wastes is such that it cannot begin to compete with operations based on most other raw materials. As a result, the citrus wastes generally account for less than 0.5% of the current total industrial ethyl alcohol production, and pineapple juice, apple pectin residue, and other products are the sources of an even lesser percentage.

Hydrol. Hydrol, a by-product syrup resulting from the manufacture of refined corn sugar, has been utilized on a limited scale as a raw material for alcohol.

Miscellaneous Sugars. Fresh and dried fruits, cane sorghum, whey, and skim milk have been considered as a source of ethyl alcohol, but it is doubtful if they can compete economically with molasses in normal times.

Starches. Because the principal starchy materials used in the manufacture of ethyl alcohol, for example, corn, green sorghum, wheat, rye, barley, and potatoes, ordinarily command much higher prices as foodstuffs, their use as alcohol raw materials is quite limited in normal times. Not only is grain comparatively costly, but it must first be converted to sugar before fermentation may begin. As a rule, grain is a significant factor in the production of ethyl alcohol only when emergency conditions create extraordinary demands, as in World War II and the Korean crisis. Among the disadvantages in the use of grain are its uncertain fluctuations in price. Efforts have been made to bring down the cost of producing ethyl alcohol from grain by employing new agents for saccharification of grain mashes. The industry, however, has been reluctant to accept the fungal amylase process over the malt process normally used (159).

The use of potatoes to manufacture ethyl alcohol proved to be uneconomical because of the low yield of alcohol obtainable (a single gallon of ethyl alcohol requires about 100 lb of potatoes). In addition, high transportation costs make potatoes one of the costliest raw materials available for the production of ethyl alcohol.

Cellulosic Materials. Although such cellulosic materials as corn cobs, cottonseed hulls, peanut shells, and sugarcane bagasse have all, at one time or another, been proposed as potential sources of ethyl alcohol, only wood pulp and wood wastes have been investigated. In the sulfite process for the manufacture of paper pulp, sugars are formed by the hydrolysis of constituents that are dissolved from the wood. About 65% of these sugars (equivalent to 1–2% of the sulfite waste liquor) is capable of being fermented to ethyl alcohol. Ethyl alcohol can be manufactured from sawdust by the Scholler process, the Bergius process, and the modified Scholler process developed at the Forest Products Laboratory at Madison, Wisc.

REFINING

Various distillation and equipment modifications are employed to ensure a pure water azeotrope of ethyl alcohol (95% by wt ethyl alcohol). Hatch presents a review of the patent and trade literature concerning the many methods used for the purification of ethyl alcohol obtained by various synthetic processes (162). Advances made since

1958 in the purification of ethyl alcohol include treatment with alkali (163–165), sodium sulfite (166), organic dicarboxylic acids (167), and improvements in rectification (168). Odor is improved by the partial hydrogenation of ethyl alcohol using Raney nickel catalyst (169), or by contact with unglazed porcelain and iron (170). Carbonyl-containing and unsaturated materials are removed by treatment with sodium borohydride (171,172) and boric acid (173); this results in an improved permanganate time-test (see Table 24). Other methods used to remove carbonyl impurities include treatment with hydroxylamine hydrochloride, potassium permanganate, or N-hydroxylbenzenesulfonamide (173).

MANUFACTURING COSTS

Capital Costs. Inasmuch as all fermentation alcohol plants differ in some respects from each other, no accurate, generally applicable, basic investment cost can be formulated, and no standard production technique exists. In general, plants utilizing molasses apply a much simpler process and require less equipment than do grain plants, since grain handling and by-product feed recovery operations are omitted and since the steam requirements are lower. Under normal price scales, the cost of a plant using molasses may be considered as requiring a capital investment approximating $100 per wine gallon of daily output of 190° proof alcohol (see p. 457). (Here, as elsewhere in this section, prices are to be understood as of 1950, unless otherwise mentioned.) Grain-using industrial alcohol plants, or distilled-spirits plants, cost from $50 to $175 per gallon per day. The lower figure represents old-style plants with wooden open-top fermentors, very simple grain-milling equipment, open mash tube (atmospheric pressure) cooking, and recovery of spent-grain screenings only. The higher figure represents a modern distilled-spirits plant with controlled milling and grain degermination, pressure cooking, recovery of high-grade alcohol in high concentration, and complete recovery and sale of fermentation by-products. Such a plant, fully equipped with instruments, would be largely automatic in operation, and would have extensive control and research laboratories.

Production Costs. The cost of producing alcohol depends upon the location of the manufacturing plant; the design, type, and degree of modernization of equipment; the kind of raw material used; the price paid for the raw material; the relative labor costs represented; the scale of production; and the total investment. It should be emphasized that there is no fixed "alcohol cost," for it will vary between plants and even from day to day in the same plant.

It was estimated that, under the conditions that existed about 1938, the plant-operating (conversion) cost of producing 1 gal of 95% alcohol from molasses might be as low as 3–4¢/gal (exclusive of raw material) for a unit operating at the highest efficiency and producing from 20,000–30,000 gal of alcohol per day. In 1960, for smaller or less efficient operations, such cost may exceed 20¢/gal. With blackstrap molasses at a price of 10¢/gal, and with a yield of 1 gal of 95% alcohol from 2 gal of molasses, the operating and raw material costs would approximate 45¢/gal of alcohol, under good operating conditions (174,175).

Considerable effort goes into the recovery of such by-products as protein feed for livestock, carbon dioxide, and similar items. In any event, a reduction in the conversion cost of molasses alcohol will not necessarily reduce the total cost of production, as the cost of molasses alcohol will depend primarily upon the cost of the raw material. The price of molasses depends upon many factors, not the least of which is that it is a by-product that can be sold profitably at any price in excess of the direct costs of handling. Thus, the supply is relatively stable (although the Cuban situation in the 1960s has distorted the normal pattern) and the price is likely to fluctuate widely, depending upon conditions of demand.

The operating (conversion) cost for producing alcohol from corn in manufacturing plants of 20,000–30,000 gal daily capacity has been estimated to be about 25¢/gal, exclusive of malt cost, which runs at about 5¢/gal of alcohol produced. Assuming a corn price of $1.20/(34-lb) bushel delivered at the plant, a malt price of $1.50/bu, the use of 8% malt, and a yield of 2.5 gal of 95% alcohol per bu, the operating and raw material costs of alcohol from corn can be estimated at approx 70¢/gal. These costs do not include sales expense or freight, cost of subsequent denaturing, or the cost of distribution. Profits to the producer and retailer must be added to determine the price per gal to the consumer. These figures are merely typical and will vary with conditions. Reported figures have varied greatly, particularly since some operators separate certain overhead, management, and supervision items from direct plant costs, so that lower "conversion" costs are indicated.

Since a major problem in the production of alcohol from grain is the fluctuating cost of raw material, the operation of a plant is subject to a great deal of uncertainty. The future outlook for alcohol production from grain does not appear to be favorable in the United States under normal economic circumstances, although it may be different in other countries. However, the full use of by-products is important for the whole national economy. Also the release of government-subsidized corn can temporarily distort the raw material cost figures.

Industrial alcohol from sulfite waste liquor costs at least 30¢/gal depending upon the size of the plant, no value being assigned to the raw material since it is a waste product.

Raw materials constitute an important cost element for alcohol produced by wood hydrolysis. An economically sized plant requires about 200 (short) tons of dry wood substance per day. This, of course, is a waste product, but, even if it is obtained from the sawmill free of charge, it must be loaded on board a freight car or truck, and transported to the alcohol plant; this restricts the area within which the supply of raw material must be obtained.

In addition to the wood substance, other raw materials are required. A plant, converting 200 tons of dry wood substance per day, is said to use in the same time period ten tons of sulfuric acid, six tons of burnt lime, and two million gal of water. Other chemicals are required in smaller quantities. The yield of alcohol resulting from this combination of materials is estimated to be 50–60 gal per ton of wood substance. A yield of at least 55 gal should be obtained from pure wood, but in practice the general run of sawmill waste will include a certain amount of bark which is much less productive.

Total costs including administrative overhead, repair, and maintenance should be about 30¢/gal. The economics of the process hinges on the utilization of lignin, which at present is of little commercial significance.

Synthetic alcohol, produced from ethylene resulting from the cracking of petroleum hydrocarbons, is very probably the cheapest present source of ethyl alcohol. The cost of pure ethylene may be between 3.0 and 5.0¢/lb (4.0¢ as of Jan. 1, 1965). The plant investment required for the separation and purification of ethylene is substantial—more than for any other process.

Since each cent per pound for pure ethylene is equivalent to approx 4¢/gal of alcohol, 4¢ ethylene represents a cost of 16¢/gal of alcohol. The additional cost of processing pure ethylene into alcohol is estimated to be about 10¢/gal. Thus, the maximum cost for synthetic alcohol would be 30¢/gal. These figures, as noted above, do not include such items as administrative overhead, selling expenses, special processing, costs of dehydration, costs of denaturation, and interest on investment (124,125).

It will be seen that the economics of industrial alcohol presents a picture that is very complex, perhaps more so than for any other chemical. The possible raw materials are many, and are connected with large and diverse branches of industry—agriculture, wood industries, and the petroleum industry—so that there are important connections with soil conservation and with mineral resources. The future development of the alcohol industry is therefore a matter of great national interest and importance.

Economics

Ethyl alcohol is produced throughout the world, often under government monopoly. The latest world production figure, which did not distinguish between industrial and beverage alcohol, was estimated to be 940 million U.S. gal in 1938 (176). More than three quarters of this total was produced in five countries: Soviet Union—231 million gal; United States—178; Germany—116; France—108; and United Kingdom—63. Substantial quantities also were produced in Czechoslovakia, Italy, and Poland. Almost all of this production was by the fermentation route with potatoes, beets, molasses, grain, fruit, sawdust, and sulfite liquors providing the raw material. Since World War II, no world production figures have been made available. Some more recent production figures from selected countries are given in Table 11. Although the synthetic route, originally introduced in the United States in 1930, has had some effect on production in such countries as United Kingdom (see Table 12), Denmark, and West Germany, most of the foreign production is still based on the fermentation route.

Before World War II, the normal consumption of industrial alcohol in the U.S. was about 100 million wine gal (190° proof) annually (see Table 13), as pure alcohol, as specially denatured alcohol, or as completely denatured alcohol. There had been no significant development of new markets over a number of years, and occasional new or increased consumption in specific lines usually represented less than 10% of the normal production. Prices remained at low levels, consistent with raw material costs, and it is doubtful if a lowering of prices would have stimulated any significant new markets. During the war, the alcohol requirement for munitions, synthetic rubber, and other war uses, as well as lend-lease, raised industrial alcohol requirements to unprecedented figures, as can be seen from Table 13. This was achieved by the conversion of the distilled-spirits industry, and with the aid of new plants. The effect of the Korean crisis may also be noted in the abnormally high production for the fiscal years 1951–1953. Again, this was achieved primarily through increased utilization of grain fermentation.

Discounting the effect of the two world crises on the production of ethyl alcohol in the United States, a steady growth pattern (see Table 13) has developed since World War II (see also under Uses). More rapidly, the share of the production captured by synthetic routes has steadily increased from zero in 1930 to more than 90% in 1958. This is explained primarily by the stability in the cost of ethylene, (approx 5¢/lb over the last ten years), as compared with the widely fluctuating availability and cost of molasses (from 10–28¢/gal during the same period). Grain, except under unusual circumstances, is not competitive. Historically the price of industrial alcohol in the United States (see Table 14) has been tied closely with both the cost of molasses in normal world conditions and with the cost of grain during emergency times. Now that synthetic ethyl alcohol represents and, will continue to represent, the major portion of U.S. production, greater price stability has been obtained and is to be expected in the future.

Production of fermentation ethyl alcohol has been affected by shortages of raw materials in the United States and abroad. U.S. producers have had to compete with chemical manufacturers and the livestock industry for domestically produced molasses. In other countries, where most ethyl alcohol continues to be produced by the fermen-

Table 11. Selected World Production[a] Figures of Ethyl Alcohol (177,178)

Country	Million wine gal	Year	Remarks
Argentina	43	1960	from fruit, grain, and molasses
Belgium-Luxembourg	3.2	1960–1961	by 16 producers
Brazil	109	1961–1962	from sugarcane or molasses
Canada	3.9[b]	1964	from sulfite waste liquors, by 11 producers
Denmark	3.4	1959	mostly by synthetic process
France	100.3	1960–1961	
Holland	6.6	1960–1961	some by synthetic process
Italy	28.7	1960–1961	
Japan	15[c]	1964	by 13 producers
Peru	8	1964	
Spain	12	1964	by 31 producers
United Kingdom	35.5	1960[d]	24.8 by fermentation, 10.7 by synthetic process
United States	273	1960[e]	
West Germany	38.3	1960–1961	18-million-gal synthetic capacity

[a] Except where otherwise noted, all production is via fermentation.
[b] Consumption.　[c] Capacity.
[d] See Table 12.　[e] See Table 13.

Table 12. Ethyl Alcohol Production in the United Kingdom (177)

Year	Million wine gal, 190° proof		
	Fermentation	Synthetic	Total
1950	37.2	2.5	39.7
1951	44.3	2.5	46.8
1952	25.4	9.6	35.0
1953	17.0	12.9	29.9
1954	22.0	14.1	36.1
1955	28.6	15.0	43.6
1956	26.8	14.5	41.3
1957	23.9	25.0	48.9
1958	9.1	23.8	32.9
1959	11.3	20.0	31.3
1960	10.7	24.8	35.5

Table 13. Ethyl Alcohol Production in the United States, million wine gal, 190° proof (179–182)

Fiscal year[a]	Fermentation				Synthetic		Total alcohol
	Molasses	Sulfite liquors[b]	Grain	Other	Ethyl sulfate	Direct hydration[c]	
1930	96.1				0.9		102.0
1931	76.3				6.9		88.0
1932	65.6		2.9	1.4	7.5		77.4
1933	50.5		2.5	1.9	5.9		60.8
1934	72.5		5.5	2.6	6.4		86.9
1935	81.3		2.6	1.9	9.3		95.1
1936	78.6		7.3	0.8	16.6		103.2
1937	88.9		9.8	0.8	17.8		117.5
1938	77.4		9.6	0.2	18.6		105.8
1939	71.5		8.2	0.9	25.3		105.8
1940	88.0		7.4	0.7	32.2		128.3
1941	110.8		9.2	0.5	36.8		157.3
1942	152.8		71.4	0.6	47.7		272.4
1943	84.3		248.9	1.4	50.9		385.5
1944	113.1		313.6	33.6	59.9		519.9
1945	103.4	0.5	382.2	34.7	58.8		579.6
1946	45.8	1.5	57.2	1.9	67.1		173.4
1947	28.5	2.3	27.7	2.3	70.2		130.9
1948	74.9	2.7	20.8	2.6	73.8		174.9
1949	67.0	2.6	17.3	2.9	86.7	8.2	184.7
1950	56.9	1.8	1.3	1.2	89.7	14.3	165.0
1951	56.0	2.9	60.3	1.5	97.1	16.4	234.2
1952	67.7	3.1	47.0	2.4	109.8	15.8	246.0
1953	97.0	2.7	6.0	2.4	120.5	27.0	255.3
1954	36.8	2.7	4.8	1.2	126.3	27.4	199.2
1955	35.2	2.9	4.5	1.8	144.5	27.7	216.8
1956	66.7	3.4	3.1	1.8	155.0	25.6	255.5
1957	20.8	3.1	6.0	1.4	169.5	22.9	223.9
1958	29.8	3.1	4.1	1.5	188.3	32.1	260.2
1959	20.8	3.3	3.9	1.8	190.6	39.7	260.1
1960	16.1	4.0	4.2	0.7	205.6	42.4	273.0
1961[d]	10.5	3.5	44.7[d]	8.4	208.2	45.5	317.7[d]
1962[d]	1.1	2.3	66.3[d]	10.0	201.5	47.3	317.9[d]
1963[d]	0.8	3.1	47.4[d]	14.6	215.2	46.7	325.7[d]
1964[d]	0.7	4.1	43.9[d]	16.3	232.7	51.7	341.1[d]
1965[d,e]	0.2	1.9	20.0[d,e]		116.5	30.9	174.5[d,e]

[a] Ending June 30.   [b] No production until 1945.   [c] No production until 1949.

[d] Data from 1961 on represent production of alcohol and spirits, 190° proof and over, not directly comparable with previous data; some beverage alcohol is included in grain figures.   Total alcohol is original production plus production by redistillation minus quantity used in redistillation.

[e] First six months.

tation process from molasses, sugarcane, grain, and other carbohydrate agricultural products, adverse weather conditions have been a large factor in keeping the cost of ethyl alcohol high in the early 1960s (183).

Recent U.S. production figures for ethyl alcohol in the fiscal year 1964 are more than 4% higher than in 1963 and nearly 8% higher than in 1962 (Table 13). The U.S. consumption of specially denatured alcohol in the fiscal year 1964 was about 1% higher than in 1963 and nearly 4% higher than in 1961 (Table 15). At the current rate of growth, consumption could reach 287 million gal in 1965 and more than 300 million gal by 1970 (178). Five domestic synthetic alcohol producers with a combined capacity of 308 million wine gal, together with two fermentation producers with a capacity of 33

Table 14. Price History of Industrial Ethyl Alcohol in the United States

Year	Price,[a] ¢/gal, tank quantities		Year	Price,[a] ¢/gal, tank quantities	
	190° Proof	S.D.-1[b]		190° Proof	S.D.-1[b]
1935	30.0	31.0	1950	39.0	41.0
1936	27.0	23.0	1951	89.0	57.5
1937	26.0	27.0	1952	55.0	57.0
1938	24.0	25.0	1953	48.0	50.5
1939	18.5	19.5	1954	40.0	42.5
1940	21.0	22.5	1955	40.0	42.5
1941	26.5	27.0	1956	42.0	44.5
1942	52.0	53.0	1957	47.0	49.5
1943	50.0	50.0	1958	47.0	49.5
1944	50.0	50.0	1959	52.0	54.5
1945	50.0	50.0	1960	52.0	54.5
1946	55.5	54.0	1961	52.0	54.5
1947	98.0	98.0	1962	52.0	54.5
1948	85.0	85.0	1963	52.0	54.5
1949	29.0	31.5	1964	52.0	54.5

[a] Between 1948 and 1955 a 5¢/gal differential existed between 190° and 200° proof; since 1955, the differential has been 7¢.

[b] Typical of denatured formulations.

Table 15. U.S. Consumption of Specially Denatured Alcohol, Fiscal Years 1960–1964[a] (Total disappearance, thousand wine gal, 190° proof alcohol)

Use	1960	1961	1962	1963	1964
acetaldehyde	156,348	148,947	138,334	145,113	104,072[b]
other chemicals	57,760	56,392	61,966	58,317	96,788[b]
solvents					
solvent and thinners for cellulose, shellac, resins, etc	31,961	28,760	29,779	29,969	29,400
toilet preparations	11,621	12,718	16,859	21,977	26,766
processing, foods, drugs, other products	9,034	9,020	9,302	8,765	8,843
parmaceutical products for external use	4,107	3,860	4,614	4,518	4,377
detergents, flavors, disinfectants, and other solutions	10,602	12,174	12,641	11,430	12,160
total	*67,325*	*66,532*	*73,195*	*76,659*	*81,546*
fluid[c]	173	187	184	158	127
fuel	528	434	506	453	477
laboratory and experimental use	1,026	1,204	1,616	1,437	1,812
grand total	*283,160*	*273,696*	*275,801*	*282,137*	*284,822*

[a] Figures published by the U.S. Business and Defense Services Administration.

[b] Changed pattern may be due to change in usage classification.

[c] Antifreezes, brake fluids, cutting oils, etc.

Table 16. U.S.–Foreign Trade in Industrial Ethyl Alcohol (185)

Year	Million wine gal, 190° proof	
	Imports	Exports
1959	0.5	0.3
1960	20.2	3.8
1961	19.9	5.8
1962	4.1	0.2
1963	8.4	14.8

million gal, appear to have sufficient capacity to meet these projected market needs (184).   In the calendar year of 1964 about 2.3 billion lb of denatured alcohol was produced by five U.S. firms operating a total of fourteen plants—eight in Texas, three in Illinois, one in Louisiana, and two in West Virginia.   In addition, small quantities of ethyl alcohol are imported into the country; however, in 1963 exports exceeded imports (see Table 16 (185)).

In 1962 and 1963, 50% of U.S. consumption of ethyl alcohol was used in acetaldehyde manufacture, while in 1964 only 37% was used for this purpose (however, see footnote[b] in Table 15).   This decrease may reflect the recent process developments for the manufacture of acetaldehyde and acetic acid, largest use for acetaldehyde, by direct routes involving ethylene and butane (183).   The phasing out of processes converting ethanol to acetaldehyde, acetic acid, and butadiene, as well as losses to ethylene glycol in antifreeze markets, (see Antifreezes, Vol. 2, p. 542), appears to indicate the end of growth for this use of ethyl alcohol.   The demand for ethyl alcohol as a chemical intermediate thus seems to have reached its peak in 1964.

Consumption of ethyl alcohol in the manufacture of other chemicals, accounting for about 34% of the total consumption, was highest in the fiscal year 1964 (Table 15).   Similarly, solvent usage has shown a steady growth rate from 1960–1965.   Use in detergents, flavors, and disinfectants and in processing foods and drugs was somewhat higher in 1964 than 1963, and somewhat lower than in the peak year of 1962.

Uses

Industrial ethyl alcohol is one of the largest-volume organic chemicals used in a variety of industrial and consumer products (see Table 17).   Its principal use is that of a chemical intermediate, to produce other chemicals.   Millions of gallons each year go into the making of acetaldehyde, acetic acid, ethyl acetate, ethyl chloride, ethylene dibromide, and ethyl ether.   Up to now the most spectacular advances in the use of ethyl alcohol have been the manufacture of butadiene and acetaldehyde.   As a solvent of widespread application, alcohol is second only to water; also its antifreeze characteristics have been utilized.   In the manufacture of drugs, plastics, lacquers, polishes, plasticizers, perfumes, cosmetics, and rubber accelerators, ethyl alcohol is a key raw material.   Currently its use is also finding extensive growth in the aerosols and in mouthwash products.   Alcohol can be used as a motor fuel with considerable success, but it is not competitive in price with petroleum products in the United States.   Around 1960 synthetic ethyl alcohol was the top consumer of ethylene in the United States, but as of 1965 it rates below ethylene oxide and polyethylene.   By comparison, in the United Kingdom polyethylene represents by far the largest single outlet for ethylene, only 8% going to ethyl alcohol (186).   All U.S.-produced synthetic alcohol

Table 17. Uses Authorized for Specially Denatured Alcohol (187g)

Product or process	Code No.	Formulas authorized
acetaldehyde	551	1, 2-B, 29
acetic acid	512	1, 2-B, 29, 35-A
adhesives and binders	036	1, 3-A, 12-A, 23-A, 30
aldehydes, miscellaneous	552	1, 2-B, 29
alkaloids (processing)	344	1, 2-B, 2-C, 3-A, 12-A, 13-A, 17, 23-A, 30, 35-A
animal feed supplement	910	35-A
antibiotics (processing)	343	1, 2-B, 3-A, 12-A, 13-A, 23-A, 30, 32, 35-A
antifreeze, proprietary	760	1
antiseptic, bathing solution (restricted)	220	46
antiseptic solutions, USP or NF	244	37, 38-B, 38-F
bath preparations	142	1, 3-A, 3-B, 23-A, 30, 38-B, 39-B, 39-C, 40, 40-A
bay rum	112	23-A, 37, 38-B, 39, 39-B, 39-D, 40, 40-A
biocides, miscellaneous	410	1, 3-A, 3-B, 23-A, 23-H, 27-B, 30, 37, 38-B, 39-B, 40, 40-A
blood and blood products (processing)	345	1, 3-A, 12-A, 13-A, 23-A, 30
brake fluids	720	1, 3-A
candy glazes	015	13-A, 23-A, 35, 35-A, 45
cellulose coatings	011	1, 23-A
cellulose compounds (dehydration)	311	1, 2-B, 3-A, 32
cellulose intermediates	034	1, 3-A, 13-A, 18, 19, 23-A
chemicals (miscellaneous)	579	1, 2-B, 2-C, 3-A, 6-B, 12-A, 13-A, 17, 20, 29, 30, 32, 36
cleaning solutions	450	1, 3-A, 23-A, 23-H, 30, 39-B, 40
coatings, miscellaneous	016	1, 23-A, 36
collodions, industrial	034	1, 3-A, 13-A, 19, 23-A
collodions USP or NF	241	13-A, 19, 32
colognes	122	38-B, 39, 39-A, 39-B, 39-C, 40, 40-A
crude drugs (processing)	341	1, 2-B, 3-A, 23-A, 30
cutting oils	730	1, 3-A
dehydration products, miscellaneous	315	1, 2-B, 3-A
dentifrices	131	31-A, 37, 38-B, 38-C, 38-D
deodorants (body)	114	23-A, 38-B, 39-B, 39-C, 40, 40-A
detergents, household	450	1, 3-A, 23-A, 23-H, 30, 39-B, 40
detergents, industrial	440	1, 3-A, 23-A, 30
detonators	574	1, 6-B
disinfectants	410	1, 3-A, 3-B, 23-A, 23-H, 27-A, 27-B, 30, 37, 38-B, 39-B, 40, 40-A
drugs and medicinal chemicals	575	1, 2-B, 2-C, 3-A, 6-B, 12-A, 13-A, 17, 29, 30, 32
drugs, miscellaneous (processing)	349	1, 2-B, 3-A, 13-A, 23-A, 30, 35-A, 38-B
duplicating fluids	485	1, 3-A, 30
dyes and intermediates	540	1, 2-B, 2-C, 3-A, 12-A, 29, 36
dyes and intermediates (processing)	351	1, 2-B, 3-A, 12-A
dye solutions, miscellaneous	482	1, 3-A, 23-A, 30, 39-C, 40
embalming fluids, etc	420	1, 3-A, 22, 23-A
esters, ethyl (miscellaneous)	523	1, 2-B, 2-C, 3-A, 6-B, 12-A, 13-A, 17, 29, 32, 35-A

(*continued*)

Table 17 (*continued*)

Product or process	Code No.	Formulas authorized
ether, ethyl	561	1, 2-B, 13-A, 29, 32
ethers, miscellaneous	562	1, 2-B, 13-A, 29, 32
ethyl acetate	521	1, 2-B, 29, 35-A
ethylamines (rubber processing)	530	1, 2-B, 2-C, 3-A, 12-A, 29, 36
ethyl chloride	522	1, 2-B, 29, 32
ethylene dibromide	571	1, 2-B, 29, 32
ethylene gas	572	1, 2-B, 29, 32
explosives	033	1, 2-B, 3-A
external pharmaceuticals (not USP or NF)	210	23-A, 23-F, 23-H, 27-A, 27-B, 37, 38-B, 38-F, 39-B, 40, 40-A
external pharmaceuticals, miscellaneous (USP or NF)	249	23-A, 25, 25-A, 38-B
fluid uses, miscellaneous	750	1, 3-A, 23-A, 30
food products, miscellaneous (processing)	332	1, 2-B, 3-A, 13-A, 23-A, 30, 32, 35-A
fuel uses, miscellaneous	630	1, 3-A, 28-A
fuels, airplane and supplementary	612	1, 3-A, 28-A
fuels, automobile and supplementary	611	1, 3-A, 28-A
fuels, proprietary heating	620	1, 3-A, 28-A
fuels, rocket and jet	613	1, 3-A, 28-A
fungicides	410	1, 3-A, 3-B, 23-A, 23-H, 27-B, 30, 37, 38-B, 39-B, 40, 40-A
glandular products (processing)	342	1, 2-B, 3-A, 12-A, 13-A, 23-A, 30, 32, 35-A
hair and scalp preparations	111	3-B, 23-A, 23-F, 23-H, 37, 38-B, 39, 39-A, 39-B, 39-C, 39-D, 40, 40-A
hormones (processing)	342	1, 2-B, 3-A, 12-A, 13-A, 23-A, 30, 32, 35-A
incense	470	3-A, 22, 37, 38-B, 39-B, 39-C, 40, 40-A
inks	052	1, 3-A, 13-A, 23-A, 30, 32, 33
insecticides	410	1, 3-A, 3-B, 23-A, 23-H, 27-B, 30, 37, 38-B, 39-B, 40, 40-A
iodine solutions (including USP and NF tinctures)	230	25, 25-A
laboratory reagents (for sale)	810	3-A, 30
laboratory uses	810	3-A, 30
lacquer thinners	042	1, 23-A
liniments (USP or NF)	243	27, 27-B, 38-B
lotions and creams (body, face, and hand)	113	23-A, 23-H, 31-A, 37, 38-B, 39, 39-B, 39-C, 40, 40-A
medicinal chemicals (processing)	344	1, 2-B, 2-C, 3-A, 12-A, 13-A, 17, 23-A, 30, 32, 35-A
miscellaneous chemicals (processing)	358	1, 2-B, 2-C, 3-A, 12-A, 13-A, 17, 23-A, 30, 35-A
miscellaneous products (processing)	359	1, 2-B, 2-C, 3-A, 12-A, 13-A, 17, 23-A, 30, 35-A
mouth washes	132	37, 38-B, 38-C, 38-D, 38-F
organo-silicone products	576	2-B, 3-A
pectin (processing)	331	1, 2-B, 3-A, 13-A, 23-A, 30, 35-A
perfume materials (processing)	352	1, 2-B, 3-A, 12-A, 13-A, 30
perfumes and perfume tinctures	121	38-B, 39, 39-B, 39-C, 40, 40-A

Table 17 (*continued*)

Product or process	Code No.	Formulas authorized
petroleum products	320	1, 2-B, 3-A
photoengraving dyes and solutions	481	1, 3-A, 13-A, 30, 32
photographic chemicals (processing)	353	1, 2-B, 3-A, 13-A, 30
photographic film and emulsions	031	1, 2-B, 3-A, 13-A, 19, 30, 32
pill and tablet manufacture	349	1, 2-B, 3-A, 13-A, 23-A, 30, 35-A
polishes	051	1, 3-A, 30, 40
preserving solutions	430	1, 3-A, 12-A, 13-A, 22, 23-A, 30 32, 37, 38-B, 42, 44
proprietary solvents (standard formulas)	041	1
refrigerating uses	740	1, 3-A, 23-A, 30
resin coatings, natural	014	1, 23-A
resin coatings, synthetic	012	1, 23-A
room deodorants	470	3-A, 22, 37, 38-B, 39-B, 39-C, 40, 40-A
rosin (processing)	354	1, 3-A, 12-A
rotogravure dyes and solutions	481	1, 3-A, 13-A, 30, 32
rubber, synthetic	580	29, 32
rubbing alcohol compounds	220	23-H
scientific instruments	710	1, 3-A
shampoos	141	1, 3-A, 3-B, 23-A, 27-B, 31-A, 36, 38-B, 39-A, 39-B, 40, 40-A
shellac coatings	013	1, 23-A
soaps, industrial	440	1, 3-A, 23-A, 30
soaps, toilet	142	1, 3-A, 3-B, 23-A, 30, 36, 38-B, 39-B, 39-C, 40, 40-A
sodium ethylate, anhydrous (restricted)	524	2-B, 2-C
sodium hydrosulfite (dehydration)	312	1, 2-B, 3-A
soldering flux	035	1, 3-A, 23-A, 30
solutions, miscellaneous	485	1, 3-A, 23-A, 30, 39-B, 40, 40-A
solvents and thinners, miscellaneous	042	1, 23-A
solvents, special (restricted sale)	043	1
stains (wood)	053	1, 3-A, 23-A, 30
sterilizing solutions	430	1, 3-A, 12-A, 13-A, 22, 23-A, 30, 32, 37, 38-B, 42, 44
theater sprays	470	3-A, 22, 37, 38-B, 39-B, 39-C, 40, 40-A
tobacco sprays and flavors	460	4
toilet waters	122	38-B, 39, 39-A, 39-B, 39-C, 40, 40-A
transparent sheetings	032	1, 2-B, 3-A, 13-A, 23-A
unclassified uses	900	1, 3-A
vaccine (processing)	343	1, 2-B, 3-A, 12-A, 13-A, 23-A, 30, 32, 35-A
vinegar	511	18, 35-A
vitamins (processing)	342	1, 2-B, 3-A, 12-A, 13-A, 23-A, 30, 32, 35-A
xanthates	573	1, 2-B, 2-C, 29
yeast (processing)	342	1, 2-B, 3-A, 12-A, 13-A, 23-A, 30, 32, 35-A

Table 18. Denaturants Authorized for Completely Denatured Alcohol (C.D.A.) and Specially Denatured Alcohol (S.D.A.) (187f)

Denaturant	Used in formula No.	Denaturant	Used in formula No.
acetaldehyde	S.D. 29	iodine, USP	S.D. 25; 25-A
acetone, NF	S.D. 23-A; 23-H	kerosene	C.D. 18; 19
acetaldol	C.D. 18	lavender oil, USP	S.D. 27-B; 38-B
almond oil, bitter, NF	S.D. 38-B	menthol, USP	S.D. 37; 38-B, 38-C; 38-D 38-F
ammonia solution, strong, USP	S.D. 36	mercuric iodide, red, NF	S.D. 42
anethole, USP	S.D. 38-B	methylene blue, NF	S.D. 4
anise oil, USP	S.D. 38-B	methyl alcohol	S.D. 3-A; 30
bay oil (myrcia oil), NF	S.D. 23-F; 38-B; 39-D	methyl isobutyl ketone	C.D. 18; 19; S.D. 23-H
benzaldehyde, NF	S.D. 38-B	methyl violet (methylrosaniline chloride)	S.D. 33
benzene	S.D. 2-B; 2-C; 12-A		
bergamot oil, NF	S.D. 23-F; 38-B	methyl violet (methylrosaniline chloride), USP	S.D. 33
bone oil (Dipple's oil)	S.D. 17		
boric acid, USP	S.D. 38-F	mustard oil, volatile (allyl isothiocyanate), USP XII	S.D. 38-B
brucine alkaloid	S.D. 40		
brucine sulfate, NF IX	S.D. 40	nicotine solution	S.D. 4
n-butyl alcohol	S.D. 44	peppermint oil, USP	S.D. 38-B
tert-butyl alcohol	S.D. 39; 39-A, 39-B; 40; 40-A	phenol, USP	S.D. 38-B; 46
camphor, USP	S.D. 27; 27-A; 38-A	phenyl mercuric benzoate	S.D. 42
caustic soda, liquid	S.D. 36	phenyl mercuric chloride, NF IX	S.D. 42
chloroform	S.D. 20		
chlorothymol, NF	S.D. 38-B; 38-F	phenyl mercuric nitrate, NF	S.D. 42
cinchonidine	S.D. 39-A		
cinchonidine sulfate, NF IX	S.D. 39-A	phenyl salicylate (salol), NF	S.D. 38-B
cinnamic aldehyde (cinnamaldehyde), NF IX	S.D. 38-B	pine needle oil, dwarf, NF	S.D. 38-B
cinnamon oil (cassia oil), USP	S.D. 38-B	pine oil, NF	S.D. 38-B
		pine tar, NF	S.D. 3-B
citronella oil, natural	S.D. 38-B	potassium iodide, USP	S.D. 25; 25-A; 42
clove oil, USP	S.D. 27-A; 38-B	pyridine bases	S.D. 6-B
coal tar, USP	S.D. 38-B	pyronate	C.D. 18
diethyl phthalate	S.D. 39-B; 39-C	quassia, fluid extract of, NF VIII	S.D. 39
ethyl acetate	S.D. 35; 35-A		
ethyl ether	S.D. 13-A; 19; 32	quassin	S.D. 40
eucalyptol, USP	S.D. 37; 38-B	quinine, NF	S.D. 39-A
eucalyptus oil, NF	S.D. 38-B	quinine bisulfate, NF	S.D. 39-A; 39-D
eugenol, USP	S.D. 38-B		
formaldehyde solution, USP	S.D. 22; 38-C; 38-D	quinine hydrochloride, USP	S.D. 39-A
gasoline	S.D. 28-A		
glycerol, USP	S.D. 31-A	quinine sulfate, USP	S.D. 39-D
guaiacol, NF	S.D. 38-B		

Table 18 (*continued*)

Denaturant	Used in formula No.	Denaturant	Used in formula No.
resorcin, USP	S.D. 23-F	spearmint oil,	
rosemary oil, NF	S.D. 27; 38-B	terpeneless	S.D. 38-B
rubber hydrocarbon		spike lavender oil,	
solvent	S.D. 2-B; 2-C	natural	S.D. 38-B
safrol	S.D. 38-B	storax, USP	S.D. 38-B
salicylic acid, USP	S.D. 23-F; 39	sucrose octaacetate	S.D. 40-A
sassafras oil, NF	S.D. 38-B	thimerosal, NF	S.D. 42
shellac (refined)	S.D. 45	thyme oil, NF	S.D. 38-B
sodium iodide, USP	S.D. 25; 25-A	thymol, NF	S.D. 37; 38-B; 38-F
sodium, metallic	S.D. 2-C	tolu balsam, USP	S.D. 38-B
sodium salicylate,		turpentine oil, NF	S.D. 38-B
USP	S.D. 39; 39-D	vinegar	S.D. 18
soap, hard, NF	S.D. 31-A	wintergreen oil	
soap, medicinal		(methyl salicy-	
soft, USP	S.D. 27-B	late), USP	S.D. 38-B, 46
spearmint oil, NF	S.D. 38-B	wood alcohol	S.D. 1

comes from captive ethylene and, in turn, about half of the ethyl alcohol production is captively consumed. For reasons stated in the following section, almost all of the industrial ethyl alcohol is used in denatured form.

DENATURED ETHYL ALCOHOL

For many hundreds of years in all parts of the world, alcoholic beverages have been taxed. This tax is an important source of revenue for most governments. When ethyl alcohol started to become a key industrial raw material, it was recognized that the alcohol tax was a burden to many essential manufacturing industries. To lift this burden from United States industry, the Tax-free Industrial and Denatured Alcohol Act of 1906 was passed. Today's regulations stem from this first basic act, and the Alcohol and Tobacco Tax Division (ATTD) of the Internal Revenue Service (IRS) now oversees the production, procurement, and use of ethyl alcohol in the United States. For a history of Federal Tax Rates see Alcoholic beverages, Table 1.

Basically, the concern of the government is to prevent taxfree industrial ethyl alcohol from finding its way into beverages. To achieve this, the regulations call for controls of a financial and administrative type—bonds, permits, and scrupulous record keeping; as well as controls of a chemical type—denaturants to make the ethyl alcohol unpalatable. There are four distinct classifications of industrial ethyl alcohol permitted by the regulations, ranging from pure ethyl alcohol, which requires the most stringent financial and administrative controls, to completely denatured alcohol which calls for little control. The available government publications on ethyl alcohol regulations are listed in the bibliography (187a–k). For a list of denaturants currently authorized, see Table 18.

Completely Denatured Alcohol. Completely denatured alcohol (C.D.A.) escapes the involved financial and administrative controls that are required with the other classifications of industrial ethyl alcohol. No tax is applied; no bond is required; no permit is needed to enable a user to purchase C.D.A.; and requirements for keeping records by both producer and user are minimal. These simplified regulations are possible because C.D.A. is denatured with substances that render it totally unfit for beverage purposes.   As a result, however, it cannot be used where odor is objectionable. See Table 19 for the two formulations for C.D.A. currently authorized.

Proprietary Solvents and Special Industrial Solvents.   Proprietary solvents, such as Synasol, Shellacol, Quakersol, Tecsol, Jaysol, Pacosol, Neosol, and Solox solvents and special industrial solvents, like Anhydrol, Paco, Filmcol, Jaysol, and Filmex solvents can also be purchased by users without payment of tax, without posting a bond for tax, or without securing a permit from the ATTD.   Suppliers are required, however, to notify the ATTD of the name, address, type of business, and approximate annual requirements of any user, buying in bulk, as well as the intended end use for the solvent (1,188–190).

Proprietary solvents and special industrial solvents are prepared by adding such denaturants as ethyl acetate, gasoline, methyl isobutyl ketone, butyl alcohol, and others to specially denatured alcohol (see Table 19, formula S.D.-1 and 3-A).   Whereas proprietary solvents may be sold in retail quantities to consumers for such uses as cutting and thinning shellac, special industrial solvents are restricted to industrial and manufacturing use in quantities of 50 gal or more.

Specially Denatured Alcohol.   Specially denatured alcohols (S.D.A.) are formulations of ethyl alcohol containing denaturant substances that generally render them unfit for beverage use but do not limit their use in certain specified applications.   More than sixty different formulations are approved by the ATTD and those with sales greater than 10 million gal per year in 1964 are given in Table 19.   To use a specially denatured alcohol, a manufacturer must make application to the ATTD, giving quantitative formulas and processes.   Specimen labels and a sample of the finished product are also required.   Then the prospective user must post a bond in the amount of $19.95/gal of 190° proof ethyl alcohol ($21.00/gal for 200° proof) for the total amount of specially denatured alcohol on hand or in transit at any given time.   When these re-

Table 19. Compositions of Completely Denatured Alcohols and Certain Specially Denatured Alcohols, gal (187f)

	Specially denatured alcohol[a] (S.D.A.) formula no.					Completely denatured (C.D.A.) formula no.	
	1	2-B	3-A	29	35-A	18	19
ethyl alcohol	100	100	100	100	100	100	100
acetaldehyde[b]				1			
acetaldol						0.5	
benzene		0.5					
ethyl acetate[c]					5		
kerosene or gasoline						1	1
methyl alcohol			5				
methyl isobutyl ketone						2.5	4
pyronate[d]						0.125	
wood alcohol	5						

[a] Sales greater than 10 million gal in 1964.

[b] 100% acetaldehyde or other permissible substances listed in IRS publication No. 368.

[c] Ester content, 85% by wt, min.

[d] Product of destructive distillation of hardwood.

quirements are met and on-site security is inspected, the ATTD will issue an industrial-use permit to the applicant. The ATTD requires detailed records showing both the purchases of specially denatured alcohol and sales of products made from it. The regulations also require the reporting of losses of ethyl alcohol that occur any time during shipment or processing.

Pure Ethyl Alcohol. Undenatured ethyl alcohol can be purchased as either taxfree or taxpaid alcohol. Taxfree alcohol can be purchased by approved educational, scientific, or medical organizations, and by public agencies, by following a procedure roughly similar to the one required of specially denatured alcohol users. Use and withdrawal permits are required, as well as a bond and detailed records. Resale of taxfree ethyl alcohol is not permitted.

Taxpaid industrial alcohol can be purchased by paying the federal tax of $21.00/gal ($19.95 for 190° proof), and by meeting any state requirements that apply. The industrial uses that are approved for pure taxpaid ethyl alcohol include pharmaceuticals, cosmetics, flavoring extracts, and foods. Manufacturers using taxpaid alcohol for any of these uses, except for cosmetics, are eligible for a tax refund, or "drawback," of $19.00/gal providing that prescribed approval and form-filing procedures are followed (187a). Thus, the net tax to manufacturers who are eligible for this refund is $2.00/gal.

CHEMICALS DERIVED FROM ETHYL ALCOHOL

Union Carbide Corporation produces more than seventy organic chemicals based on ethyl alcohol; this illustrates the versatility of ethyl alcohol as a raw material.

Acetaldehyde. The major use of ethyl alcohol is in the production of acetaldehyde (see Table 15). The conversion can be carried out by either an oxidation or dehydrogenation process, or by a combination of these processes. The production of acetaldehyde by oxidation of ethyl alcohol is carried out in the vapor phase in the presence of a silver screen catalyst (191). About an 82% conversion per pass is obtained at a reaction temperature of 480°C. The liquid-phase oxidation of ethyl alcohol takes place in the presence of chloroplatinic acid and in the absence of free oxygen at 80°C and at atmospheric pressure. This reaction results in a selectivity of better than 95% of acetaldehyde (192). The kinetics of the vapor- and liquid-phase oxidation of ethyl alcohol have been described in the literature (193,194). Other processes, such as the direct oxidation of ethylene and ethane to acetaldehyde, may reduce the future consumption of ethyl alcohol (139,141,195–213).

The literature is well documented concerning the reactions and kinetics for the dehydrogenation of ethyl alcohol to acetaldehyde (214–217). The vapor dehydrogenation of ethyl alcohol to acetaldehyde has been carried out in the presence of a copper oxide-chromic oxide catalyst on pumice at 280–340°C to give acetaldehyde in a yield of 89% and a conversion of 72% per pass (138). A lower yield is obtained using neodymium oxide or samarium hydroxide as catalysts (140).

The main use of acetaldehyde is the production of acetic acid and anhydride. See Ethanoic acid. Acetic acid may also be prepared from petrochemicals by the hydration of ethylene, oxidation of ethylene or LPG (liquefied petroleum gas—a mixture of butane and propane), and direct hydration of acetylene.

The recent arc-process for a two-stage pyrolysis of methane or propane to acetylene (218–220) may bear directly on the use of acetaldehyde (and thus ethyl alcohol) as a raw material for acetic acid.

Ethylene. Since ethylene is a major raw material for ethyl alcohol, it may seem surprising that the alcohol is used as a raw material for the manufacture of ethylene. However, in countries where ethylene is in short supply and fermentation ethyl alcohol is available, ethylene may be manufactured by the vapor-phase dehydration of ethyl alcohol. This reaction is generally carried out in the presence of a variety of catalysts such as activated alumina (221–228), hafnium and zirconium oxides (227), and phosphoric and sulfuric acids. An ethylene yield of 96% is reported using aluminum-base catalysts. Ethyl alcohol may be dehydrated by spraying ethyl alcohol and phosphoric acid into a column at 235–240°C to give ethylene in a yield of 30–40% per pass (229).

Ethyl Ether. See Ethers. The literature is well documented on the vapor-phase dehydration of ethyl alcohol to ethyl ether. The maximum yield depends upon the catalyst used and on the temperature. Generally, aluminum oxide is employed to effect the dehydration reaction (230–234). Other catalysts used include sulfuric acid (233), silica-alumina (235,236), copper sulfate, tin chloride, manganous chloride, aluminum chloride, chrome alum, and chromium sulfate (237,238).

Ethyl Chloride. See Vol. 5, p. 140. A major use for industrial ethyl alcohol is in the synthesis of ethyl chloride, used principally as an intermediate in producing tetraethyl lead, an additive to motor fuels to improve anti-knock ratings. Ethyl alcohol is converted to ethyl chloride by direct reaction with hydrochloric acid; however, since about 1960, competitive routes based on the addition of hydrochloric acid to ethylene have been developed. Because the ethylene-hydrochloric acid process is relatively simple, an increased market potential for ethyl alcohol in the manufacture of ethyl chloride appears unlikely.

Butadiene (qv). During World War II the production of butadiene from ethyl alcohol was of the greatest importance. Ostromuislenski reported on a catalytic, vapor-phase reaction in the presence of a mixed catalyst of alumina and zinc oxide at 400°C and at 3.5 psi pressure (239). The yield of butadiene reported was about 50%. The Germans employed a catalyst-mixture of magnesia and cobalt or chromium oxides to get a yield of 60% at 270–300°C and at atmospheric pressure (1). An American one-step process using a catalyst of magnesia, chromic oxide, and silica at 400–425°C gives an over-all yield of 56%. Approximately 60% of the butadiene produced in the United States during World War II was obtained by a two-step process utilizing a mixture of 69% by wt ethyl alcohol and 24% by wt acetaldehyde, and 0.7% water at atmospheric pressure and a catalyst of tantalum oxide and silica gel at 325–350°C (215,239–241). The conversion per pass was 30–35% at an over-all yield of butadiene of 63%. A comprehensive article on this process and catalysts employed is presented by Corson, et al (242). Another catalyst investigated was magnesium oxide-silicon dioxide-chromic oxide-alumina silicate hydrate which resulted in about a 65% yield at 435°C (243). Extensive catalytic studies are reported by Romanovsky, Natta, and Brenman (244–247). A fluidized process is described by Essayan (248). Because of later developments in the manufacture of butadiene by the dehydrogenation of butane and/or butylenes, and by naphtha cracking, the use of ethyl alcohol as a raw material for this purpose has disappeared in the United States and is diminishing abroad (186,249).

Distilled Vinegar. Distilled vinegar is being produced from synthetic ethyl alcohol by bacterial fermentation (250). The quality of vinegar obtained is equal to that obtained by the fermentation of naturally derived alcohol by *Bacterium aceti*.

Chloral. The liquid-phase chlorination of ethyl alcohol at reflux temperature gives a mixture of chloral hydrate $CCl_3CH(OH)_2$, and chloral hemi-acetal, CCl_3CH-$(OH)(OEt)$. The addition of this mixture to 80–85% sulfuric acid gives chloral and chloral hydrate. The principal use of chloral is in the making of DDT. See Insecticides.

Reactions with Epoxides. The addition of one mole of ethylene oxide to ethyl alcohol gives Cellosolve solvent, ethylene glycol monoethyl ether, a reaction catalyzed by acids and bases.

$$CH_3CH_2OH + CH_2{-}CH_2 \rightarrow CH_3CH_2OCH_2CH_2OH$$
$$\underset{O}{\diagdown\diagup} \qquad\qquad \text{Cellosolve}$$

The addition of two moles gives Carbitol solvent, the monoethyl ether of diethylene glycol.

$$CH_3CH_2OH + 2\ CH_2{-}CH_2 \rightarrow CH_3CH_2OCH_2CH_2OCH_2CH_2OH$$
$$\underset{O}{\diagdown\diagup} \qquad\qquad \text{Carbitol}$$

Any amount of ethylene oxide, propylene oxide, butylene oxide, and other epoxy type compounds may be reacted with ethyl alcohol to give reaction products that are liquid, viscous, semi-wax, and hard solids. These products are used in the manufacture of solvents, paints, antioxidants, corrosion inhibitors, and special-purpose polyurethanes. These intermediates have been contributing greatly to the growth of these industries.

Ethyl Acrylate. The condensation reaction of ethyl alcohol, carbon monoxide, and acetylene gives ethyl acrylate (251), which is used in the manufacture of films, hydraulic fluids, oil additives, and pressure-sensitive adhesives.

Ethyl Vinyl Ether. The addition of ethyl alcohol to acetylene gives ethyl vinyl ether (252–255).

$$CH_3CH_2OH + HC{\equiv}CH \rightarrow CH_3CH_2OCH{=}CH_2$$

The reaction is generally run at pressures of 200–300 psi and temperatures of 160–180°C, with alkaline catalysts such as potassium hydroxide and potassium ethylate. The vapor-phase reaction is patented (256). Ethyl vinyl ether can also be made by a transvinylation reaction between methyl vinyl ether and ethyl alcohol (257).

High-molecular-weight polymers of ethyl vinyl ether are used for pressure-sensitive adhesives, viscosity index improvers, coatings, and films; lower-molecular-weight polymers are plasticizers and resin-modifiers.

Amines. Mono-, di-, and triethylamines are produced by the catalytic reaction of ethyl alcohol with ammonia (258). The catalysts used include alumina, phosphoric acid and derivatives, and copper and iron chlorides, sulfates and oxides, in the presence of acids or alkaline salts (259). Piperidine is ethylated with ethyl alcohol in the presence of Raney nickel catalyst at 200°C temperature and 1500 psi pressure, to give N-ethylpiperidine (260).

Acetone. The vapor-phase condensation of ethyl alcohol to give acetone has been well documented in the literature (261–270); however, it is usually obtained as a by-product from the cumene process, by the direct oxidation of propylene, or from isopropyl alcohol.

1-Butanol. The condensation of ethyl alcohol in the presence of sodium ethylate under pressure gives n-butanol (271–274), a reaction known as the Guerbet reaction:

$$2\ CH_3CH_2OH + CH_3CH_2ONa \rightarrow CH_3CH_2CH_2CH_2OH + CH_3COONa + H_2$$

Other catalysts have been used for this type reaction such as, a mixture of potassium hydroxide and boric anhydride (275,276), and alkaline phosphates (277).

Other Derivatives and Reactions. Chemical derivatives of ethyl alcohol, such as ethyl mercaptan, ethyl xanthate, ethyl chloroformate, mercury fulminate, and halogenated ethers are prepared by processes involving alkylation, etherification, alcoholysis, and halogenation.

Units, Specifications, Shipping, and Test Methods

Units. The alcohol content of spirits is usually given in terms of "proof," an archaic term inherited from early distillers of fermentation alcohol. In England the "proof" was to pour some of the spirit over gunpowder, and ignite the spirit; at or above a limiting concentration (eleven parts of alcohol by volume to ten parts of water) the gunpowder would explode. Inasmuch as volumes were much easier to measure accurately than weights, before the development of precise balances and scales, this cumbersome measurement of alcohol persisted, even though there is a considerable volume change on mixing ethyl alcohol with water.

In the United States the proof is twice the alcohol content by volume, thus 188° proof alcohol contains 94% ethyl alcohol by volume. According to Federal statutes, "... proof spirits shall be held to be that alcoholic liquor which contains one-half of its volume of alcohol of a specific gravity of 0.7939 at 60°F." A gallon of proof spirits can

Table 20. Conversion of U.S. Proof to Alcohol by Vol; Alcohol by Wt; and British Proof

U.S. proof at 60°F	Alcohol at 60°F, by vol %	Alcohol, by wt %	British proof[a,b]
0	0.0	0.00	100.0
2	1.0	0.80	98.4
4	2.0	1.59	96.8
6	3.0	2.39	95.2
8	4.0	3.19	93.6
10	5.0	4.00	91.9
20	10.0	8.05	83.5
30	15.0	12.14	75.0
40	20.0	16.27	66.1
50	25.0	20.44	57.0
60	30.0	24.67	48.0
70	35.0	28.97	39.3
80	40.0	33.36	30.6
90	45.0	37.86	21.7
100	50.0	42.49	12.9
110	55.0	47.24	4.0
120	60.0	52.15	4.8[b]
130	65.0	57.21	13.5[b]
140	70.0	62.44	22.3[b]
150	75.0	67.87	31.1[b]
160	80.0	73.53	39.9[b]
170	85.0	79.44	48.6[b]
180	90.0	85.69	57.3[b]
190	95.0	92.42	66.0[b]
200	100.0	100.00	76.0[b]

[a] Underproof, unless otherwise indicated.   [b] Overproof.

be made by mixing 0.5000 gal of absolute alcohol with 0.5373 gal water; it contains 42.49% alcohol by weight.

A wine gallon is a measure of quantity, 231 in.^{3}, of any proof. A proof gallon (tax gallon) is a wine gallon of 100° proof spirits, or its equivalent; thus, a wine gallon of 188° proof spirits is equal to 1.88° proof gallons; 1000 g of 95% alcohol (sp gr 0.816) equals 0.3235 gal.

The determination of the "proof" (the alcohol content) is usually made by means of hydrometers at the standard temperature of 60°F (see under Test methods), since only very small amounts of impurities other than water are usually present. The apparent proof of a formula is the proof of pure alcohol (that is, no impurities other than water) having the same specific gravity as the formula (see Tables 20 and 21).

Table 21. Respective Volumes of Alcohol and Water and Specific Gravity

U.S. proof	Alcohol, vol.	Water, vol	Apparent sp gr, 60/60°F
101	50.50	53.24	0.93320
102	51.00	52.74	0.93222
103	51.50	52.25	0.93123
104	52.00	51.75	0.93023
105	52.50	51.25	0.92923
106	53.00	50.75	0.92822
107	53.50	50.26	0.92720
108	54.00	49.76	0.92618
109	54.50	49.26	0.92515
110	55.00	48.76	0.92409
120	60.00	43.71	0.91333
130	65.00	38.60	0.90190
140	70.00	33.43	0.88986
150	75.00	28.19	0.87714
160	80.00	22.87	0.86364
170	85.00	17.46	0.84927
180	90.00	11.93	0.83362
188	94.00	7.36	0.81963
189	94.50	6.77	0.81775
190	95.00	6.18	0.81582
191	95.50	5.59	0.81385
192	96.00	4.99	0.81184
193	96.50	4.39	0.80979
194	97.00	3.78	0.80770
195	97.50	3.17	0.80555
196	98.00	2.55	0.80333
197	98.50	1.93	0.80104
198	99.00	1.29	0.79866
199	99.50	0.65	0.79620
200	100.00	0.00	0.79365

Table 21 may also be used to determine the quantity of water needed to reduce the strength of ethyl alcohol by a definite amount. Divide the alcohol in the given strength by the alcohol in the required strength, multiply the quotient by the water in the required strength, and subtract the water in the given strength from the product. The remainder is the number of gallons of water to be added to 100 gal of spirits of the given strength to produce a spirit of a required strength.

Example: It is desired to reduce spirits of 191° proof to 188° proof. We find that 191° proof spirits contain 95.5 parts alcohol and 5.59 parts water, and 188° proof spirits contains 94.0 parts alcohol and 7.36 parts water.

$$\frac{95.50 \text{ (the strength of 100 wine gal of spirits at 191° proof)}}{94.0 \text{ (the strength of 100 wine gal of spirits at 188° proof)}} = 1.01$$

$$7.36 \text{ (the water in 188° proof)} \times 1.01 = 7.43$$

7.43 − 5.59 (the water in 191° proof spirits) = 1.84 gal of water to be added to each 100 wine gal of 191° proof spirits to be reduced.

Specifications. The specifications for ethyl alcohol are designed with sufficient latitude to allow for the two principal means of production, synthesis from ethylene and fermentation. The requirements given by the *U.S. Pharmacopeia* (USP) and the American Chemical Society (ACS) generally form the foundation for the most widely used specifications (278,279). A tabulation of the specifications from the major alcohol producers, with consideration for the USP and ACS requirements, is shown in Table 22, a typical ethyl alcohol specification. This specification is further divided to show the requirements for the two most generally used grades, namely, 190° proof and 200° proof.

The major producers of ethyl alcohol also market the specially denatured and completely denatured alcohols, as well as various proprietary solvents in which ethyl alcohol is the basic ingredient. These various products can also be described by rigid and descriptive specifications, but the requirements must make allowances for the chemical and physical character of the denaturants.

Table 22. Typical Ethyl Alcohol Specifications

Requirement	190° proof	200° proof
specific gravity, 60/60°F, max	0.816	0.794
purity, % by vol, min	95	99.9
acidity, % by wt as HOAc, max	0.002	0.002
nonvolatile matter, g/100 ml, max	0.002	0.002
miscibility with water	complete	complete
permanganate time test, minutes, min	50	30
odor	no foreign or residual	
color, APHA, max	10	10
water, % by wt, max		0.1

In addition to these, the following USP requirements are frequently noted. These are qualitative tests for which the absolute limit of detection has not been established:

1. Amyl alcohol and nonvolatile carbonizable substances: to pass test
2. Fusel oil constituents: to pass test
3. Methyl ketones, 2-propanol, and *tert*-butanol: to past test
4. Methanol: to pass test

The two requirements of purity and odor in Table 22 are worthy of particular mention. The use of both purity and specific gravity in this specification is redundant, inasmuch as the purity is generally derived from the specific gravity measurement by reference to standard nomographs published by the U.S. Bureau of Internal Revenue. The use of ethyl alcohol in some medicinal and cosmetic products, requires a very meticulous grade, particularly with reference to odor. In some instances, the odor can be correlated with the concentration of certain minor impurities; in most instances it cannot be directly associated with any measurable contaminant, and the quality can be ascertained only by odor comparison with previously accepted material.

Shipping. Commercial ethyl alcohol is shipped in railroad tank cars, tank trucks, 55-gal and 5-gal drums, and in smaller glass or metal containers having capacities of a pint, quart, U.S. gallon, or Imperial gallon. The 55-gal drums may be of the unlined iron type. If the guarantee of more meticulous quality is desired, the drums may be lined with phenolic resin. All containers, of course, must comply with the specifications of the U.S. Interstate Commerce Commission. Both 190° proof and 200° proof ethyl alcohol are considered as "red label" materials by the ICC, as both have flash points below 80°F by the Tag open-cup method.

Test Methods. The most generally used means of ascertaining the purity of commercial ethyl alcohol is through the specific gravity determination, sometimes referred to as alcoholometry. For this reason, the specific gravity should be determined very accurately to the fourth decimal place by means of a calibrated pycnometer or hydrometer (280) (see Density). The value thereby obtained is referred to standard United States Bureau of Internal Revenue tables relating specific gravity to alcohol content. Of course, this procedure is valid only for undenatured alcohol, since the purity-nomograph is based only on the two-component alcohol–water mixture.

In order to encourage international trade, it is necessary to adapt a uniform method of evaluation of ethyl alcohol. The present system of evaluation is very confusing because of the following factors (4): (*1*) The unit of measurements employed varies from country to country. (*2*) Reference temperature varies in countries where the same general system has been adopted. (*3*) The density or specific gravity data for absolute ethyl alcohol, as adopted for compilation of density or specific gravity tables, temperature correction tables, and for the manufacture of hydrometers, also differ from one country to another.

A thorough re-investigation of alcoholometry measurement was undertaken at the National Bureau of Standards, Washington, D.C., in 1913, by Osborne, McKelvy, and Bearce (281). The investigation involved the preparation of pure anhydrous ethyl alcohol, the determination of the density (expressed in terms of the density of water at 4°C as the unit), and thermal expansion of ethyl alcohol and its aqueous mixtures, and the compilation of tables from these data for convenient use. The results of Osborne were later confirmed by Frost (282) in 1930. The foregoing investigations should help in establishing an international agreement in the analysis of ethyl alcohol.

Although in most countries hydrometers are employed to determine the ethyl alcohol content, confusion is introduced because of different units of measurement (283). The units of measurement currently used are (a) % by weight; (b) % by volume; (c) Cartier; (d) specific volume (the inverse of density); and (e) proof spirit.

Percent by Weight. Germany legalized the percent-by-weight system in 1888. The hydrometers are graduated at 15°C with reference to Mendeleef's table of density. This procedure results in a scale which is independent of the prevailing temperature.

Percent by Volume. Many of the European countries have adopted a percent-by-volume system using a Gay-Lussac hydrometer, at 15°C, graduated to read percentage of ethyl alcohol content by volume. In 1884 a French ministerial decree fixed the conditions that must be satisfied by hydrometers and also prepared tables expressing the relationship between specific gravity at 15/15°C and percent by volume of ethyl alcohol at 15°C. A value of 0.79433 is used as the density of absolute alcohol in vacuum which is not based on Gay-Lussac's original measurements. Belgium, Spain, Sweden, Norway, Finland, Switzerland, Uruguay, Brazil, and Egypt have adopted Gay-Lussac's system, although some of them have recalculated the results obtained by Gay-Lussac and other workers. Thus the Gay-Lussac scales differ appreciably between the countries adopting this system. The Swiss tables use a value of 0.79426 as the specific gravity of absolute alcohol at 15/15°C. Further confusion results from the simultaneous use of tables for percent ethyl alcohol by weight in Switzerland.

Since 1950, the U.S.S.R. has used a 20°C reference temperature for the measurement of ethyl alcohol content by volume in spirits. A value of 0.78927 for the specific gravity of absolute ethyl alcohol at 20/20°C forms the basis of the compilation of the reference tables.

Denmark and Italy have also adopted the volumetric system which is based on a value of 0.79391 as the specific gravity of absolute ethyl alcohol at 60/60°F and using a Tralles alcoholometer.

Cartier System. The Cartier system is in use in some South American countries and the hydrometer is graduated at 12.5°C.

Specific Volume. The Dutch have adopted a specific volume system wherein the hydrometer is graduated to read directly specific volumes (the inverse of density). Double entry tables, based on the researches undertaken by von Baumhauer in 1861, permit conversion from specific volume and temperature into percent by volume.

Proof Spirit. This system is based on a normal proof-spirit mixture containing 49.33% by wt ethyl alcohol. Degrees of underproof and overproof are then calculated accordingly. In the United States proof spirit is defined as the water–alcohol mixture of density 0.93426 containing half its volume of absolute ethyl alcohol with 0.7939 as its specific gravity at 60/60°F. Hydrometers are graduated to read the number of "proof spirit" per 100 parts by vol of the liquid at the reference temperature of 60°F. Pure water is "0"; absolute ethyl alcohol is "200." Thus the U.S. percentage "proof spirit" is double the percentage by volume of ethyl alcohol at 60°F.

British proof spirit corresponds to 57.03° (Gay-Lussac). The British "proof gallon" contains $4.54596 \times 0.5703 = 2.5926$ l of ethyl alcohol at 15°C. The U.S. "proof gallon" is $3.7854 \times 50/100 = 1.8927$ l of ethyl alcohol at 60°F (or 15.6°C). The British "proof gallon" is nearly 1.4 times the U.S. "proof gallon" (283).

Table 23 presents reference temperatures and specific gravity data for absolute ethyl alcohol employed in different countries.

The remainder of the analytical methods that would be necessary to control the typical specification given in Table 21 are, for the most part, relatively simple and common quality control procedures. When a chemical analysis for purity is desired, acetylation or phthalation procedures are commonly employed. In these cases the alcohol is reacted with a measured volume of either acetic or phthalic anhydride in pyridine solution. The loss in titratable acidity in the anhydride solution is a direct measure of the reacting hydroxyl groups present in the sample. These procedures are generally free from interference by other functional groups, but both are affected adversely if excessive amounts of water are present, as this results in depletion of the anhydride reagent strength to a level below that which is necessary to insure complete reaction with the alcohol. Both of these procedures can be adapted to a semi-micro or even micro scale determination. Of course, acetylation and phthalation are not selective for ethyl alcohol, but will determine any reactive —OH group present. Mehlenbocher has prepared a general thesis of methods applicable to the determination of ethyl alcohol (284).

For the determination of smaller concentrations of ethyl alcohol (0–5%) in noninterfering solvents, two colorimetric procedures in particular have been found useful. These involve (a) reaction with ceric ammonium nitrate (285), and (b) reaction with dinitrobenzoyl chloride (286). Both of these reactions have excellent precision for the determination of trace amounts or low percentages of ethyl alcohol.

Table 23. Specific Gravity and Reference Temperature of Absolute Ethyl Alcohol (283)

Established standards	Temperature, °C	Specific gravity
France (1884)	15/15	0.79433
Switzerland (1933)	15/15	0.79426
Holland (1861)	15/15	0.794794
Denmark	15.56/15.56	0.7947
Osborne (1913)[a]	15/15	0.79429
U.S.A.	15.6/15.6	0.7939
Frost (1930)[a]	15/15	0.794254

[a] See p. 459.

Another type of analysis for trace amounts of alcohol is that used in the ACS specification for absolute ether (279). Though this procedure is in reality a measurement of water-soluble oxidizables, in this instance it undoubtedly is designed primarily for the determination of ethanol contamination in ether. In this procedure the sample is extracted with water and the water extract is tested for "oxidizables" content by reaction with nitrochromic acid.

Health and Safety Considerations (287–290)

Ethyl alcohol has found wide application in industry and experience shows that it is not a serious industrial poison. If proper ventilation of the work environment is maintained there is little likelihood that inhalation of the vapor will be hazardous. Prolonged inhalation of ethyl alcohol, resulting from improper handling of the material or inadequate ventilation, results in irritation of the eyes and of the mucous membrane of the upper respiratory tract, headache, nervousness, dizziness, tremors, fatigue, nausea, and narcosis. The powers of concentration and alertness can be impaired with the possible increased likelihood of accidents.

The threshold limit value for ethyl alcohol-vapor in air has been set at 1000 ppm by the American Conference of Governmental Industrial Hygienists (1964 listing). A proposed downward revision to 750 ppm is being considered for the 1965 listing. This reflects the belief that some undesirable effects can result from continuous daily 8-hr inhalation at the 1000-ppm level. The minimum identifiable odor of ethyl alcohol has been reported to be 350 ppm. Exposures to concentrations of 5000–10,000 ppm result in irritation of the eyes and mucous membranes of the upper respiratory tract and, if continued for an hour or more, may result in stupor or drowsiness. Concentrations of this latter order of magnitude have an intense odor and are almost intolerable to begin with, but most people can become acclimated to the exposure after a short time. Table 24 gives the effects of exposure to even heavier concentrations.

Ethyl alcohol is oxidized completely to carbon dioxide and water in the body, thus it is not a cumulative poison. Alcohol poisoning and alcohol intoxication are almost invariably the result of using alcohol as a beverage, rather than inhalation as a vapor. About 75–80 g of alcohol when ingested will produce symptoms of intoxication in an average (154-lb) man. About 150–200 g will cause stupor, while 250–500 g may be a fatal dose.

Table 24. Ethyl Alcohol Vapor Concentration and Its Effects in Man (290)

Concentration		Effects in Man
mg/l of air	ppm/vol in air	
10–20	5,300–10,640	some transient coughing and smarting of the eyes and nose, which disappear after 5–10 min; not comfortable but tolerable
30	15,960	continuous lacrymation and marked coughing; could be tolerated but with discomfort
40	21,280	just tolerable for short periods
>40	>21,280	intolerable and suffocating for even short periods

Some authorities question whether drunkenness can result from the inhalation of ethyl alcohol vapors. Experience has demonstrated that in any event such intoxication is indeed rare. There is no concrete evidence that the inhalation of ethyl alcohol vapor will cause cirrhosis of the liver. Liver function is definitely impaired during alcohol intoxication, making the subject more susceptible to the toxic effects of chlorinated hydrocarbons. It has also been reported that humans consuming ethyl alcohol are especially susceptible to the toxic hazards of ethylene glycol dinitrate.

Repeated exposure to ethyl alcohol results in the development of a tolerance as evidenced by decreasing symptomatic reactions. It has been demonstrated that the symptoms of exposure are less clear and the time required to produce them is greater in subjects accustomed to alcohol. There is no proof, however, of physiological adaptation in man in terms of metabolic changes or resistance to cellular injuries.

The complex subject of the etiology and symptomatology of chronic alcoholism are not pertinent to this discussion. Similarly, the relationship between drinking alcoholic beverages and automobile accidents is not relevant. The accident hazard to, and resulting from, an employee drinking on the job is well known.

Ethyl alcohol is a flammable liquid requiring a red label by the ICC and Coast Guard shipping classifications; its flash point is 70°F. Vapor concentrations between 4.3 and 19.0% by vol in air are explosive. Liquid ethyl alcohol can react vigorously with oxidizing materials.

Bibliography

"Alcohol, Industrial" in *ECT* 1st ed., Vol. 1, pp. 252–288, by R. S. Aries, Consulting Chemical Engineer.

1. L. F. Hatch, *Ethyl Alcohol*, Enjay Chemical Co., a Division of Humble Oil and Refining Co., New York, 1962. (An outstanding reference source.)
2. C. M. Beamer, *Chem. Eng. Progr.* **43** (3), 92–96 (1947).
3. E. Huber, *Z. Spiritusind.* **50**, 164–166 (1927).
4. *Ethyl Alcohol Production Technique*, Noyes Development Corp., Pearl River, N.Y., 1964. (Good reference on chemical industry in India and U.S.S.R.)
5. H. Brunswig, *Liber de Arte Distillandi—Kleines Distillierbuch*, Johann (Reinhard) Gruninger, Strassburg, May 8, 1950.
6. A. Lowitz, *Crell's Chem. Ann.* **1**, 1–22 (1796).
7. M. Martraire, *L'Alcoométrie en France et à l'Étranger: Comparaison entre les divers Systèmes, Alcool et Dérivés*, No. 58–59, 105–120 (July–Aug. 1956).
8. B. Herstein, *Chem. Ind.* (*London*) **13**, 881–884 (1935).
9. M. Faraday, *Phil. Trans. Roy. Soc.* (*London*) **115**, Part II, 440–466 (1825).
10. H. Hennell, *Trans. Roy. Soc.* (*London*) **116**, Part III, 240–249 (1826).
11. H. Hennell, *Trans. Roy. Soc.* (*London*) **118**, 37 (1828).
12. M. Bertholet, *Ann. Chem.* **43** (3), 385–405 (1855).
13. U.S. Pat. 41,685 (Feb. 23, 1864), E. A. Cotelle; *Bull. Soc. Chim.* (*France*) **A4**, 279 (1862).
14. B. T. Brooks, *Ind. Eng. Chem.* **27**, 278–288 (1935).
15. V. Goryainov, *J. Russ. Phys. Chem. Soc.* **5**, 302–305 (1873).
16. Brit. Pat. 308,859 (April 4, 1929), R. E. Slade (to Imperial Chemical Industries Ltd.).
17. Reference 1, p. 4.
18. U.S. Pat. 2,579,601 (Dec. 25, 1951), C. R. Nelson, M. A. D. Taylor, D. D. Davidson, and L. M. Peters (to Shell Development Co).
19. *Chem. Week* **90** (6), 25 (Feb. 10, 1962).
20. D. Hodzi, *Hydrogen Bonding*, Pergamon Press, London, 1957.
21. F. K. Beilstein, *Handbuch der organischen Chemie*, Vol. 1, E III, 1958, pp. 1229–1236.
22. *Selected Values of Properties of Chemical Compounds*, Manufacturing Chemists' Association Research Project Tables, Chemical Thermodynamic Properties Center, Dept. of Chemistry, A & M College of Texas, College Station, Texas.
23. *Selected Properties of Hydrocarbons and Related Compounds*, American Petroleum Institute Project 44, Chemical Thermodynamic Properties Center, Dept. of Chemistry, A & M College of Texas, College Station, Texas.
24. J. Timmermans, *Physico-Chemical Constants of Pure Organic Compounds*, Elsevier Publishing Co., N. Y. 1950, pp. 306–312.
25. K. A. Kobe and R. E. Pennington, *Thermochemistry of Petrochemicals*, Reprint No. 44, University of Texas, Bureau of Engineering Research, Austin, Texas, Jan. 1949–Dec. 1951, pp. 56–59.
26. R. C. Reid and J. M. Smith, *Chem. Eng. Progr.* **47** (8), 415–418 (1951).
27. S. Young, *Sci. Proc. Roy. Dublin Soc.* **12**, 374–443 (1910).
28. A. R. Challoner and R. Powell, *Proc. Roy. Soc.* (*London*) **238A**, 90 (1956).
29. Unpublished physical property data, Union Carbide Corporation, Chemicals Division.
30. "Azeotropic Data," *Advan. Chem. Ser.* **6** and **35**, 1952 and 1962.
31. D. Williams and R. W. Bost, *J. Chem. Phys.* **4**, 251–253 (1936).
32. U.S. Pat. 1,978,647 (Oct. 30, 1934), E. T. Olson and R. H. Twinning, (to Cleveland Cliffs Iron Co.).
33. U.S. Pat. 1,712,830 (May 14, 1929), L. P. Kyrides (to National Aniline Division, Allied Chemical & Dye Corp.).
34. A. Meuwsen, *Ber.* **68**, 121–127 (1935).
35. E. W. Zappi and E. Restelli, *Anales Asoc. Quin. Arg.* **32**, 89–90 (1934).
36. F. Henle, *Ber.* **53**, 719–722 (1920).
37. Brit. Pat. 454,480 (Oct. 1, 1936), (to Consortium für Elektrochemische Industrie G.m.b.H.).
38. Ger. Pat. 602,376 (Sept. 17, 1934), J. Seib (to Deutsche Gold- und Silber-Scheideanstalt vorm. Roessler).

39. Reference 1, p. 71.
40. C. M. Suter and E. Oberg, *J. Am. Chem. Soc.* **56,** 677–679 (1934).
41. M. Gallagher and D. B. Keyes, *J. Am. Chem. Soc.* **56,** 2221–2224 (1934).
42. U.S. Pat. 2,831,882 (April 22, 1958), C. P. Spaeth (to E. I. du Pont de Nemours & Co., Inc.).
43. H. D. Hinton and J. A. Nieuwland, *J. Am. Chem. Soc.* **54,** 2017–2018 (1932).
44. P. Ya. Ivannikov and E. Ya. Gavrilova, *J. Chem. Ind. (USSR)* **12,** 1256–1260 (1935).
45. B. N. Dolgov et al., *Zh. Obshch. Khim.* **25,** 693–697 (1955).
46. B. N. Dolgov et al., *J. Chem. Ind. (USSR)* **12,** 1066 (1935).
47. B. N. Dolgov et al., *Org. Chem. Ind. (USSR)* **1,** 70 (1936).
48. N. M. Beizel et al., *Org. Chem. Ind. (USSR)* **1,** 102–107 (1936).
49. U.S. Pat. 2,004,350 (June 11, 1935), N. D. Scott (to Du Pont); Brit. Pat. 424,284 (Feb. 18, 1935), (to Du Pont).
50. H. Adkins and R. Conner, *J. Am. Chem. Soc.* **53,** 1091–1095 (1931).
51. M. Bobtelsky, *J. Chem. Soc.* **1950,** Part IV, 3615–3617.
52. Reference 1, p. 68.
53. M. Bobtelsky and R. Cohn, *Z. Anorg. Allgem. Chem.* **210,** 225–240 (1933).
54. M. Bobtelsky et al., *J. Am. Chem. Soc.* **67,** 966–975 (1945).
55. Br. Jirgensons, *Z. Physik. Chem.* **158A,** 56–64 (1931).
56. *Chem. Week* **84** (19), 83 (May 9, 1959).
57. S. P. G. Plant and N. V. Sidgwick, *J. Soc. Chem. Ind. (London)* **40** (2), 14T–18T (1921).
58. Brit. Pat. 273,263 (Sept. 15, 1926), (to Compagnie de Bethune).
59. U.S. Pat. 2,545,161 (March 13, 1951), E. C. Morrell and R. F. Robey (to Standard Oil Development Co.); Brit. Pat. 655,475 (July 25, 1951), (to Standard Oil Development Co.).
60. F. Vallette, *Chim. Ind.* **13** (*Paris*) 718–721 (1951).
61. Brit. Pat. 221,512 (Feb. 19, 1925), (to Compagnie de Bethune).
62. P. Fritsche, *Chem. Ind. (London)* **20,** 266 (1897); **21,** 33 (1898).
63. C. Ellis, *Chemistry of Petroleum Derivatives*, Chemical Catalog Co., New York, 1934, p. 301.
64. C. Ellis, *Chemistry of Petroleum Derivatives*, Vol. II, Reinhold Publishing Corp., New York, 1937.
65. W. S. E. Hickson and K. C. Bailey, *Sci. Proc. Roy. Dublin Soc.* **20,** 267–279 (1932).
66. K. C. Bailey and W. E. Calcutt, *Sci. Roy. Dublin Soc.* **21,** 309–315 (1936).
67. B. T. Brooks, *Ind. Eng. Chem.* **27,** 278–288 (1935).
68. B. Neumann, *Gas u. Wasser* **67,** 1–3, 14–16, 53–58 (1924).
69. A. Klima et al., *J. Chem. Prumysl* **7,** 119–122 (1957); (through) *J. Appl. Chem. USSR (Eng. Transl.)* **7** (10), ii–334 (1957).
70. U.S. Pat. 1,885,585 (Nov. 1, 1932), B. T. Brooks.
71. U.S. Pat. 1,919,618 (June 25, 1933), B. T. Brooks.
72. B. G. Simek, *Chem. Prumysl* **7,** 122 (1957); (through) *Erdoel Kohle* **10,** 882 (1957).
73. F. Strahler and F. Hachtel, *Brennstoff-Chem.* **15,** 166–169 (1934).
74. C. Maimeri, *Atti Congr. Naz. Chim. Ind. (Milan)* 1924, 269–271.
75. Brit. Pat. 215,000 (Oct. 16, 1924), S. A. Ledoga and C. Maimeri.
76. U.S. Pat. 1,339,947 (May 11, 1930), H. R. Curme (to Union Carbide Corp.).
77. C. F. Tidman, *J. Soc. Chem. Ind. (London)* **40,** 103R (1921).
78. A. Damiens, *Compt. Rend.* **175,** 585–588 (1922).
79. A. Damiens, *Bull. Soc. Chim.* **33,** 71–81 (1923).
80. H. Hennell, *Ann. Chim.* **35** (2), 154–160 (1827).
81. U.S. Pat. 2,755,297 (July 17, 1956), B. I. Smith and W. H. Rader (to Esso Research and Engineering Co.).
82. U.S. Pat. 2,859,237 (Nov. 4, 1958), S. W. Wilson (to Esso Research and Engineering Co.).
83. U.S. Pat. 2,808,378 (Oct. 1, 1957), F. P. Baldwin and T. H. Hakala (to Esso Research and Engineering Co.).
84. U.S. Pat. 2,849,496 (Aug. 26, 1958), T. H. Hakala and W. R. F. Guyer (to Esso Research and Engineering Co.).
85. U.S. Pat. 2,872,491 (Feb. 3, 1959), S. W. Wilson and W. H. Silver (to Esso Research and Engineering Co.).
86. U.S. Pat. 2,765,347 (Oct. 2, 1956), B. I. Smith (to Esso Research and Engineering Co.).

87. U.S. Pat. 2,779,803 (Jan. 29, 1957), K. C. Bottenberg (to Phillips Petroleum Co.).

88. U.S. Pat. 2,792,432 (May 14, 1957), W. C. Muller and F. D. Miller (to National Petro-Chemicals Corp.).

89. U.S. Pat. 2,792,433 (May 14, 1957), W. C. Muller and J. S. Atwood (to National Petro-Chemicals Corp.).

90. U.S. Pat. 2,302,825 (Nov. 24, 1942), C. B. Wilde (to Stauffer Chemical Co.).

91. U.S. Pat. 2,061,810 (Nov. 14, 1937), W. H. Shiffler and M. M. Holm (to Standard Oil of California).

92. U.S. Pat. 2,038,512 (April 21, 1936), R. N. Graham (to Union Carbide Corp.).

93. V. A. Gutuirya et al., *Azerb. Neft. Khoz.* **16** (5), 72–82 (1936).

94. U.S. Pat. 2,474,568 (June 18, 1949), L. A. Bannon and C. E. Morrell (to Standard Oil Development Co.).

95. U.S. Pat. 2,474,569 (June 18, 1949), L. A. Bannon (to Standard Oil Development Co.).

96. R. Kremann, *Monatsh. Chem.* **31**, 245–274, 275–284 (1910); R. Kremann, *J. Soc. Chem. Ind.* (*London*) **29**, 782 (1910).

97. R. Kremann, *Monatsh. Chem.* **28** (3), 13–32 (1907); **31**, 165–176 (1910); **38**, 53–62 (1917).

98. W. A. Drushei and G. A. Linhart, *Am. J. Sci.* **32**, 51 (1911).

99. Brit. Pat. 229,272 (Sept. 24, 1925), (to Compagnie de Bethune).

100. U.S. Pat. 1,674,891 (June 6, 1928), M. Duchange (to Compagnie de Bethune).

101. Ger. Pat. 413,834 (May 19, 1925), (to Compagnie de Bethune).

102. U.S. Pat. 2,414,759 (Jan. 21, 1947), H. O. Mottern (to Standard Alcohol Co.).

103. U.S. Pat. 2,512,327 (June 20, 1950), T. P. Hawes and A. P. Geraitis (to Standard Oil Development Co.).

104. Can. Pat. 470,593 (Jan. 2, 1951), T. P. Hawes et al. (to Standard Oil Development Co.).

105. U.S. Pat. 2,856,265 (Oct. 15, 1958), G. A. Lescisin (to Union Carbide Corp.).

106. Brit. Pat. 638,547 (June 17, 1950), J. Howlett et al. (to Distillers Co., Ltd.).

107. T. C. Carle and D. M. Stewart, *Chem. Ind.* (*London*), No. 19, pp. 830–839 (1962).

108. W. J. Tapp, *Ind. Eng. Chem.* **40**, 1619 (1948); **42**, 1698 (1950); **44**, 2020 (1952).

109. M. A. Dalin, *Khim. Nauka i Promy.* **1**, 259–272 (1956).

110. C. V. Mace and C. F. Bonilla, *Chem. Eng. Progr.* **50**, 385–395 (1954).

111. Brit. Pat. 691,360 (May 13, 1953), R. C. Thomson and R. K. Greenhaig (to Imperial Chemical Industries, Ltd.); Belg. Pat. 499,676 (May 28, 1951).

112. U.S. Pat. 2,725,403 (Nov. 29, 1955), M. A. E. Hodgson (to Imperial Chemical Industries, Ltd.).

113. Brit. Pat. 665,214 (Jan. 16, 1952), J. Thompson and P. W. Reynolds (to Imperial Chemical Industries, Ltd.).

114. Winkler; *Ind. Agr. Aliment.* (*Paris*) **66**, 159–160 (March–April 1949).

115. U.S. Pat. 2,720,232 (Feb. 15, 1955), H. R. Arnold and J. E. Carnahan (to E. I. du Pont de Nemours & Co., Inc.).

116. U.S. Pat. 2,755,309 (July 17, 1956), P. W. Reynolds (to Imperial Chemical Industries, Ltd.).

117. U.S. Pat. 2,807,655 (Sept. 24, 1957), L. R. Pitwell (to Imperial Chemical Industries, Ltd.).

118. U.S. Pat. 2,763,697 (Sept. 18, 1956), H. J. Hagemeyer, Jr., and W. J. Clegg (to Eastman Kodak Co.).

119. J. Muller and H. I. Waterman, *Brennstoff-Chem.* **38**, 321–329 (1957).

120. U.S. Pat. 2,769,847 (Nov. 6, 1956), R. L. Robinson (to Imperial Chemical Industries, Ltd.).

121. U.S. Pat. 2,876,266 (March 3, 1959), C. Wegner (to Farbenfabriken Bayer A.G.).

122. U.S. Pat. 2,813,908 (Nov. 19, 1957), D. W. Young (to Esso Research and Engineering Co.).

123. U.S. Pat. 2,773,910 (Dec. 11, 1956), R. J. Schrader (to Eastman Kodak Co.).

124. U.S. Pat. 2,756,247 (July 24, 1956), I. J. James, Jr., and A. C. McKinnis (to Union Oil Co.).

125. U.S. Pat. 3,164,641 (Jan. 5, 1965), P. Bazzarin (to Montecatini Società Generale per l'Industria Mineraria e Chimica).

126. *Hydrocarbon Process. Petrol. Refiner* **42** (11), 162 (1963).

127. C. R. Nelson and M. L. Courter, *Chem. Eng. Progr.* **50**, 526–531 (1954).

128. Ger. Pat. 1,035,632 (Aug. 7, 1958), H. G. van Raay (to Farbwerke Hoechst A.G.).

129. *Chem. Week* **84** (6), 58 (1959).

130. U.S. Pat. 3,095,458 (June 25, 1963), C. A. Judice and L. E. Pirkle (to Esso Research and Engineering Co.).

131. U.S. Pat. 2,045,785 (June 30, 1936), W. K. Lewis (to Standard Oil Development Co.).

132. N. S. Kozlov and N. Golubovskaya, *J. Gen. Chem. USSR (Eng. Transl.)* **6**, 1506–1509 (1936).

133. U.S. Pat. 2,519,061 (Aug. 15, 1950), R. B. Mason (to Standard Oil Development Co.).

134. N. Ya. Kagan et al., *J. Gen. Chem. USSR (Eng. Transl.)* **3**, 337–344 (1933).

135. W. Traube and R. Justh, *Brennstoff-Chem.* **4**, 150–154 (1923).

136. U.S. Pat. 2,472,618 (June 7, 1949), A. S. Ramage (to A. A. F. Maxwell).

137. U.S. Pat. 2,317,949 (April 27, 1943), R. E. Burke (to Standard Oil Co. of Ohio).

138. U.S. Pat. 2,861,106 (Nov. 18, 1958), W. Optiz and W. Urbanski (to Knapsack-Griesheim A.G.).

139. U.S. Pat. 2,870,866 (Jan. 27, 1959), G. Baecklund (to Aktiebolaget Chematur).

140. U.S. Pat. 2,884,460 (April 28, 1959), V. I. Komarewsky (to Heavy Minerals Co.).

141. U.S. Pat. 3,073,752 (Jan. 15, 1963), M. Mention (to Les Usines de Melle (S.A.)).

142. D. M. Newitt and A. M. Block, *Proc. Roy. Soc. (London)* **A140**, 426–439 (1933).

143. D. M. Newitt and D. T. A. Townsend, *J. Inst. Petrol. Technologists* **20**, 252A (1934).

144. P. J. Weizevich and P. K. Frolich, *Ind. Eng. Chem.* **26**, 267–276 (1934).

145. U.S. Pat. 1,858,822 (May 17, 1932), P. K. Frolich (to Standard Oil Development Co.).

146. U.S. Pat. 2,700,677 (Jan. 25, 1955), K. D. Bowen, D. R. Keck, and D. C. Lee, Jr. (to Celanese Corp. of America).

147. U.S. Pat. 2,702,298 (Feb. 15, 1955), N. M. Caruthers (to Stanolind Oil and Gas Co.).

148. U.S. Pat. 3,052,731 (Sept. 4, 1962), C. R. Murphy (to Gulf Research and Development Co.).

149. R. S. Aries, *Chem. Eng. News* **25**, 1792 (1947).

150. C. R. Downs and J. H. Rushton, *Chem. Eng. Progr.* **1** (1), 12–20 (1947).

151. P. C. Keith, *Am. Gas Assoc. Monthly* **28**, 253 (1946).

152. M. D. Schlesinger, H. E. Benson, E. M. Murphy, and H. H. Storch, *Ind. Eng. Chem.* **46**, 1322–1326 (1954).

153. R. B. Anderson, J. Feldman and H. H. Storch, *Ind. Eng. Chem.* **44**, 2418–2424 (1952).

154. V. V. Kamzolkin, *Priroda* **45** (11), 93–94 (1956).

155. I. Wender, R. A. Friedel, and M. Orchin, *Science* **113**, 206–207 (1951).

156. Fr. Pat. 1,006,012 (April 18, 1953), H. Grasshof.

157. C. E. Morrell et al., *Ind. Eng. Chem.* **44**, 2839–2843 (1952).

158. *Petrol. Refiner* **36** (10), 241–250 (1957).

159. *Chem. Eng. News* **29** (47), 4932–4938 (1951).

159a. Report of the Task Group on Industrial Alcohol from Grain of the Presidential Commission on Increased Industrial Utilization of Agricultural Commodities, April 25, 1957, 85th Congress, Senate Document No. 45, U.S. Govt. Printing Office, Washington, D.C.

160. *Industrial Alcohol*, Misc. Publ. No. 695, U.S. Dept. Agr., Feb. 1950.

161. *Chem. Eng. News* **43** (11), 130 (March 15, 1965).

162. "Concentration and Purification of Ethyl Alcohol," in reference 1, Chap. III, pp. 33–38.

163. U.S. Pat. 3,156,629 (Nov. 10, 1964), W. Ester (to Bergwerksgesellschaft Hibernia A.G.).

164. U.S. Pat. 2,981,661 (April 25, 1961), W. Sisco and J. S. Wiederecht (to American Cyanamid Co.).

165. U.S. Pat. 3,014,971 (Dec. 26, 1961), S. W. Wilson (to Esso Research and Engineering Co.).

166. U.S. Pat. 2,892,874 (June 30, 1959), C. J. B. Duculot.

167. U.S. Pat. 2,721,874 (Oct. 25, 1955), A. McIlroy (to Stanolind Oil and Gas Co.).

168. U.S. Pat. 2,892,757 (June 30, 1959), A. E. Markham (to Puget Sound Pulp and Timber Co.).

169. U.S. Pat. 2,944,087 (July 5, 1960), E. W. Mommensen et al. (to Esso Research and Engineering Co.).

170. U.S. Pat. 2,857,436 (Oct. 21, 1958), J. R. Mackinder et al., (to Shell Development Co.).

171. U.S. Pat. 2,957,023 (Oct. 18, 1960), W. A. Dimler, Jr. (to Esso Research and Engineering Co.).

172. U.S. Pat. 2,867,651 (Jan. 6, 1959), R. H. Wise (to Standard Oil Co.).

173. U.S. Pat. 2,885,446 (May 5, 1959), S. P. Sharp and A. Steitz, Jr. (to Pan American Petroleum Co.).

174. C. H. Chilton, *Cost Engineering in the Process Industries*, McGraw-Hill Book Co., New York, 1960.

175. W. L. Faith, D. B. Keyes, and R. L. Clark, *Industrial Chemicals*, 2nd ed., John Wiley & Sons, Inc., New York, 1957.

176. *Statistical Year-Book of the League of Nations*, II, *Economic and Financial, 1937/1938*, pp. 109–111, II A.9, Table 43, Geneva, Switzerland, 1938.

177. T. C. Carle and D. M. Stewart, *Chem. Ind. (London)* (9), 830–839 (May 12, 1962).

178. *Chemical and Rubber Industry Report* (U.S. Dept. of Commerce, Business and Defense Services Administration) **11** (2), 10–11 (March–April 1964).

179. *Statistics Concerning Intoxicating Liquors*, Commissioner of Internal Revenue.

180. Annual reports of the Commissioner of Internal Revenue.

181. *Industrial Alcohol*, Pub. No. 695, U.S. Dept. of Agr., Feb. 1950.

182. *Alcohol and Tobacco Summary Statistics*, Bureau of Internal Revenue (issued monthly and annually).

183. *Chem. Week* **94** (16), 59 (April 18, 1964).

184. *Oil, Paint, Drug Reptr.*, **184** (9), 3 (Aug. 26, 1963).

185. Reference 178, p. 11.

186. *European Chemical News, Export and Import Suppl.* **7** (163), 21 (Feb. 26, 1965). (Published by Temple Press, Ltd., London.)

187. Government publications. The Superintendent of Documents, U.S. Government Printing Office, Washington, D.C., makes available several publications that contain ATTD regulations relating to industrial ethyl alcohol. Among these publications are:

187a. *Drawbacks on Distilled Spirits Used in Manufacturing Nonbeverage Products*, Part 197, Title 26, *CFR* (Federal Register), IRS Publication 206.

187b. *Exportation of Liquors*, Part 252, Title 26 *CFR*, IRS Publication 211.

187c. *Returns of Substances or Articles*, Part 173, Title 26, *CFR*, IRS Publication 218.

187d. *Stills*, Part 196, Title 26, *CFR*, IRS Publication 223.

187e. *Rules of Practice in Permit Proceedings*, Part 200, Title 26, *CFR*, IRS Publ. 289.

187f. *Formulas for Denatured Alcohol*, Part 212, Title 26, *CFR*, IRS Publ. 368 (Rev. 1–61).

187g. *Distilled Spirits Plants*, Part 201, Title 26, *CFR*, IRS Publ. 440.

187h. *Gauging Manual*, Part 186, Title 26, *CFR*, IRS Publ. 441.

187i. *Distribution and Use of Denatured Alcohol and Rum*, Part 211, Title 26, *CFR*, IRS Publ. 443.

187j. *Distribution and Use of Tax-Free Alcohol*, Part 213, Title 26, *CFR*, IRS Publ. 444.

187k. *Standard Density and Volumetric Tables*, No. 19, Circular of the Bureau of Standards, Oct. 31, 1924.

188. *Ethanol*, F-41153, Union Carbide Corp., Chemicals Division, New York, June 1965.

189. *Industrial Ethyl Alcohol*, Commercial Solvents Corp., New York, 1962.

190. *Ethyl Alcohol*, U.S. Industrial Chemicals Co., Division of National Distillers and Chemical Corp., New York, 1960.

191. U.S. Pat. 3,106,581 (Oct. 8, 1963), S. D. Neely (to Eastman Kodak Co.).

192. U.S. Pat. 3,080,426 (March 5, 1963), I. Kirshenbaum, E. M. Amir, and E. J. Inchalik (to Esso Research and Engineering Co.).

193. C. F. Cullis and E. J. Newitt, *Proc. Roy. Soc. (London)* **A 237**, 530–542 (1956); **A 242**, 516–533 (1957).

194. J. Klassem and R. S. Kirk, *A.I.Ch.E. Journal* **1**, 488–495 (1955).

195. U.S. Pat. 3,154,586 (Oct. 27, 1964), O. E. Bander et al. (to Farbwerke Hoechst A.G.).

196. U.S. Pat. 3,149,167 (Sept. 15, 1964), L. Hornig et al. (to Farbwerke Hoechst A.G.).

197. U.S. Pat. 3,076,032 (Jan. 29, 1963), W. Reimenschneider and K. Diaier (to Farbwerke Hoechst A.G.).

198. U.S. Pat. 3,057,915 (Oct. 9, 1962), W. Reimenschneider et al. (to Farbwerke Hoechst A.G.).

199. *Chem. Eng. News* **39** (16), 52 (April 17, 1961).

200. U.S. Pat. 3,172,913 (March 9, 1965), L. Hornig et al. (to Farbwerke Hoechst A.G.).

201. U.S. Pat. 3,154,586 (Oct. 27, 1964), O. E. Bander et al. (to Farbwerke Hoechst A.G.).

202. U.S. Pat. 3,122,586 (Feb. 25, 1964), W. Berndt (to Consortium für Elektrochemische Ind. G.m.b.H.).
203. U.S. Pat. 3,106,579 (Oct. 8, 1963), L. Hornig and H. Lenzmann (to Farbwerke Hoechst A.G.).
204. U.S. Pat. 3,119,874 (Jan. 28, 1964), E. Paszthory and W. Reimenschneider (to Farbwerke Hoechst A.G.).
205. U.S. Pat. 3,118,001 (Jan. 14, 1964), W. Reimenschneider (to Farbwerke Hoechst A.G.).
206. U.S. Pat. 3,104,263 (Sept. 17, 1963), W. Reimenschneider (to Farbwerke Hoechst A.G.).
207. U.S. Pat. 3,119,875 (Jan. 28, 1964), A. Steinmetz et al. (to Farbwerke Hoechst A.G.).
208. U.S. Pat. 3,087,968 (April 30, 1958), L. Hornig et al. (to Farbwerke Hoechst A.G.).
209. U.S. Pat. 3,086,994 (April 23, 1963), J. Smidt et al. (to Consortium für Elektrochemische Ind. G.m.b.H.).
210. U.S. Pat. 3,080,425 (March 5, 1963), J. Smidt et al. (to Consortium für Elektrochemische Ind. G.m.b.H.).
211. U.S. Pat. 3,086,052 (April 16, 1963), J. Smidt et al. (to Consortium für Elektrochemische Ind. G.m.b.H.).
212. U.S. Pat. 3,131,223 (April 23, 1964), J. Smidt et al. (to Consortium für Elektrochemische Ind. G.m.b.H.).
213. U.S. Pat. 2,974,173 (March 7, 1961), R. B. Long et al. (to Esso Research and Engineering Co.).
214. U.S. Pat. 1,977,750 (Oct. 23, 1935), C. O. Young (to Union Carbide Corp.).
215. A. Bielanski et al., *Bull. Acad. Polon. Sci. Classe* III **4**, 533–536 (1956).
216. A. Bielanski et al., *Bull. Acad. Polon. Sci. Classe* III **3**, 497–502 (1955).
217. A A. Balandin and P. Titeni, *Doklady Akad. Nauk SSSR* **113**, 1019–1023 (1957).
218. U.S. Pat. 3,168,592 (Feb. 2, 1965), M. T. Cichelli and W. Schotte (to E. I. du Pont de Nemours & Co., Inc.).
219. U.S. Pat. 3,161,695 (Dec. 15, 1964), E. P. Goffinet, Jr. (to Du Pont).
220. U.S. Pat. 3,073,769 (Jan. 15, 1963), G. Doukas (to Du Pont.)
221. A. Kh. Bork and O. A. Markova, *Zh. Fiz. Khim.* **22**, 1381–1384 (1948).
222. S. Abe, *Sci. Papers Inst. Phys. Chem. Res. (Tokyo)* **40**, 331–332 (1943).
223. Ital. Pat. 509,424 (June 14, 1955), V. Martello and S. Ceccotti (to Bombrini Parodi-Defino Società per Azioni).
224. V. M. Nikitin, *J. Gen. Chem. USSR (Eng. Transl.)* **15**, 273–276 (1945).
225. V. M. Nikitin and N. V. Razumov, *J. Gen. Chem. USSR (Eng. Transl.)* **11**, 133–135 (1941).
226. K. V. Topchieva and K. Yun-Pin, *Dokl. Akad. Nauk SSSR* **101**, 305–308 (1955).
227. S. B. Ansimov and G. I. Khaidarov, *Zh. Obshch. Khim.* **18**, 40–42 (1948).
228. Z. E. Kosalapov, *J. Gen. Chem. USSR (Eng. Transl.)* **5**, 307–318 (1935).
229. U.S. Pat. 3,131,212 (April 28, 1964), E. Biller.
230. U.S. Pats. 1,873,536 and 1,873,537 (Oct. 23, 1932), R. L. Brown and W. W. Odel.
231. I. E. Adadurov and P. Ya. Krainii, *J. Phys. Chem. USSR* **5**, 136–144 (1934).
232. J. B. Sendrens, *Ann. Chim. Phys.* **25**, 449–529 (1912).
233. R. N. Pease and C. C. Yung, *J. Am. Chem. Soc.* **46**, 2397–2405 (1924).
234. *Ibid.* **46**, 390–403 (1924).
235. T. V. Antipina and O. V. Isaev, *Zh. Fiz. Khim.* **31**, 2078–2089 (1957).
236. T. V. Antipina and M. D. Sinitsyna, *Vestn. Mosk. Univ., Ser. Mat. Mekh. Astron., Fiz. i Khim.* **12**, 137–142 (1957).
237. Brit. Pat. 332,756 (July 31, 1930), (to N. V. de Bataasche Petr. Maatschappij).
238. Brit. Pat. 350,010 (June 5, 1931), (to N. V. de Bataasche Petr. Maatschappij).
239. I. I. Ostromuislenski, *J. Russ. Phys.-Chem. Soc.* **47**, 1472 (1915).
240. W. M. Quattlebaum, W. J. Toussaint, and J. T. Dunn, *J. Am. Chem. Soc.* **69**, 593–599 (1947).
241. U.S. Pat. 2,421,361 (May 27, 1947), W. J. Toussaint and J. T. Dunn (to Union Carbide).
242. B. B. Corson, H. E. Jones, C. E. Welling, J. A. Hinckley, and E. E. Stahly, *Ind. Eng. Chem.* **42**, 359–373 (1950).
243. I. R. Laszlo et al., *Magy. Kem. Folyoirat* **60**, 65–74 (1944).

244. U.S. Pat. 2,800,517 (July 23, 1957), C. Romanovsky and T. E. Jordan (to Publicker Industries, Inc.).

245. G. Natta and R. Rigamonti, *Chim. Ind. (Milan)* **29**, 239–243 (1947).

246. A. Brenman, *Rev. Chim. (Bucharest)* **8**, 286–290 (1957).

247. U.S. Pat. 2,850,463 (Sept. 2, 1958), C. Romanovsky and T. E. Jordan (to Publicker Industries, Inc.).

248. M. Essayan and I. Ciolan, *Rev. Chim. (Bucharest)* **7**, 31–36 (1956).

249. *European Chemical News*, p. 24, June 29, 1962.

250. *Synthetic Ethyl Alcohol in the Manufacture of Vinegar*, Tech. Bull. No. 19, Enjay Chemical Co.

251. U.S. Pat. 2,964,558 (Dec. 13, 1960), J. M. F. Leathers (to Dow Chemical Co.).

252. C. E. Schildknecht, A. O. Zoss, and C. McKinley, *Ind. Eng. Chem.* **39**, 180–186 (1947).

253. W. G. Hanford and D. L. Fuller, *Ind. Eng. Chem.* **40**, 1171–1177 (1948).

254. U.S. Pat. 1,959,927 (May 22, 1934), W. Reppe (to I. G. Farbenindustrie A.G.).

255. U.S. Pat. 2,021,869 (Nov. 19, 1935), W. Reppe and W. Wolff (to I. G. Farbenindustrie A.G.).

256. U.S. Pat. 2,066,076 (Dec. 29, 1936), W. Reppe and W. Wolff (to I. G. Farbenindustrie A.G.).

257. *Chem. Eng. News* **43** (12), 42 (March 22, 1965).

258. U.S. Pat. 2,085,785 (July 6, 1937), R. R. Bottoms (to the Girdler Corp.).

259. Brit. Pat. 399,201 (Oct. 2, 1933), (to Rohm & Haas Co.).

260. Fr. Pat. 767,771 (July 24, 1934), (to I. G. Farbenindustrie A.G.).

261. Can. Pat. 321,646 (April 19, 1932), G. Bloomfield et al. (to Commercial Solvents Corp.).

262. Brit. Pat. 338,518 (Nov. 19, 1930), H. Dreyfus.

263. Brit. Pat. 347,593 (April 22, 1931), to Holzverkohlungs-Industrie A.G.).

264. Brit. Pat. 359,430 (Oct. 14, 1931), (to Deutsche Gold- und Silber-Scheideanstalt vorm. Roessler).

265. E. Donath, *Chem.-Ztg.* **12**, 1191 (1888); **51**, 924 (1927).

266. U.S. Pat. 1,663,350 (March 20, 1928), K. Roka (to Holzverkohlungs-Industrie A.G.).

267. Brit. Pat. 353,467 (July 16, 1931), H. F. Oxley et al. (to British Celanese Co., Ltd.).

268. St. Bakowski and L. Stepniewski, *Przemysl-Chem.* **20**, 142–145 (1936).

269. B. A. Bolotov et al., *Zh. Priklad. Khim.* **28**, 299–306 (1955).

270. B. A. Bolotov and K. P. Katkova, *Zh. Priklad. Khim.* **28**, 414–421 (1955).

271. M. Guerbet, *Compt. Rend.* **128**, 511–513 (1899).

272. U.S. Pat. 2,457,866 (Jan. 4, 1949), C. A. Carter (to Union Carbide Corp.).

273. E. F. Pratt and D. G. Kubler, *J. Am. Chem. Soc.* **76**, 52–56 (1954).

274. J. Bolle and L. Bourgeois, *Compt. Rend.* **233**, 1466–1467 (1951).

275. Brit. Pat. 655,864 (Aug. 1, 1951), M. Sulzbacher.

276. M. Sulzbacher, *J. Appl. Chem. (London)* **5**, 637–641 (1955).

277. U.S. Pat. 2,762,847 (Sept. 11, 1956), R. E. Miller and G. E. Bennett (to Monsanto Chemical Co.).

278. *The Pharmacopeia of the U.S.A.*, 16th ed., Mack Publishing Co., Easton, Pa., 1960.

279. *Reagent Chemicals, ACS Specifications*, 1960 ed., Applied Publications, ACS, Washington, D.C., 1961.

280. *1964 Book of ASTM Standards*, Part 20,D-891, Method C, American Society for Testing and Materials, Philadelphia, Pa., 1965.

281. N. S. Osborne, E. C. McKelvy, and H. W. Bearce, *Bull. Bur. Stds.* **9**, 327–474 (1913).

282. A. V. Frost, *Recherches dans le domaine du poids spécifique des mélanges d'alcool éthylique et d'eau*, Institut des Réactifs Chimiques Purs, U.R.S.S. Fasc. 9, 1930.

283. Reference 4, p. 46.

284. V. C. Mehlenbocher, "Determination of Alcohols," in John Mitchell, Jr., ed., *Organic Analysis*, Vol. 1, Interscience Publishers, Inc., New York, 1953, pp. 1–65.

285. F. R. Duke and G. F. Smith, *Ind. Eng. Chem. Anal. Ed.* **12**, 201 (1940).

286. D. P. Johnson and F. E. Critchfield, *Anal. Chem.*, **32**, 865 (1960).

287. C. H. Thienes and T. J. Haley, *Clinical Toxicology*, 4th ed., Lea and Febiger, Philaldephia, 1964.

288. F. A. Patty, ed., *Industrial Hygiene and Toxicology*, Vol. II, 2nd ed., Interscience Publishers, a division of John Wiley & Sons, Inc., New York, 1962.

289. N. I. Sax, *Dangerous Properties of Industrial Materials*, rev. ed., Reinhold Publishing Corp., New York, 1962.

290. L. T. Fairhall, *Industrial Toxicology*, 2nd ed., The Williams and Wilkins Co., Baltimore, 1957.

ACKNOWLEDGMENTS. The authors gratefully acknowledge the technical contributions of the following individuals: W. S. Tamplin, Duzanka Zuzic, H. E. Kyle, J. A. Hardy, P. R. Rector, W. G. Rohrbough, N. H. Ketcham, and R. G. Zahn; also personnel from the U.S. Department of Agriculture; Business and Defense Services Administration; and Internal Revenue Service, U.S. Treasury Department were most helpful in providing economic and production information.

C. A. PENTZ, JR., AND G. A. LESCISIN
Union Carbide Corporation, Chemicals Division

ETHANOLAMINES. See Alkanolamines.

ETHERS

Ethers are compounds of the type R—O—R' where R and R' may be the same or different alkyl or aryl radicals. Structurally, ethers have also been classified as oxides. However, they have little in common with inorganic oxides which generally react with water to produce acidic or basic solutions; ethers are very stable under these conditions. Ethers may also be considered as anhydrides of alcohols since they are formed from two molecules of alcohol with the elimination of one molecule of water.

$$2 \text{ ROH} \rightarrow \text{R—O—R} + \text{HOH}$$

If the two R groups are the same, the compound is called a *simple* or symmetrical ether; if they are different, it is a *mixed* or unsymmetrical ether. (The term "ether" (Greek *aither*, air) was chosen because typical ethers are volatile.)

This article discusses those lower aliphatic ethers that are of commercial interest. They are all symmetrical ethers. See also Cellulose derivatives; Vinyl compounds. For ethers of phenol, see Phenolic ethers. For ethers of glycols and of glycerol, see Glycols; Glycerol. Cyclic or inner ethers (epoxides) may be regarded as oxygen heterocycles such as furan, O—CH=CH—CH=CH (see Furfural) and *p*-dioxane,

O—CH₂—CH₂—O—CH₂—CH₂, or in some cases as alkylene oxides such as ethylene

oxide (qv) (oxirane, epoxyethane), O—CH₂—CH₂. See also under Epichlorohydrin, Vol. 5, p. 318, and under Cineole in Terpenes and terpenoids. Cellulose, starches, sugars, saponins, and morphine are representatives of a large number of natural products containing ether linkages.

Simple ethers are named according to the hydrocarbon moiety which they contain; CH_3OCH_3 is called dimethyl ether or methyl ether. Complex ethers may be named as hydrocarbon derivatives (IUPAC), or as ethers; $CH_3OCH_2CH_2CH_3$ may be named 1-methoxypropane or methyl *n*-propyl ether.

In general ethers are pleasant-smelling liquids with densities of less than 1.0. They are neutral, volatile compounds, which have little or no solubility in water but are easily soluble in organic liquids. The lower-molecular-weight ethers boil at lower

Table 1. Physical Properties of Some Representative Ethers

Ether	Formula	Bp, °C	d_4^{20}	n_D^{20}
Aliphatic Ethers				
Simple saturated				
methyl[a]	$(CH_3)_2O$	-23.7		
ethyl[a]	$(C_2H_5)_2O$	34.5	0.7146	1.3527
n-propyl[a]	$(n\text{-}C_3H_7)_2O$	90.5	0.7360	1.3809
isopropyl[a]	$[(CH_3)_2CH]_2O$	68.5	0.7257	1.3682
n-butyl[a]	$(n\text{-}C_4H_9)_2O$	142.0	0.7704	1.3981
sec-butyl	$[C_2H_5CH(CH_3)]_2O$	122.0	0.7590^{25}	$1.3931^{?}$
isobutyl	$[(CH_3)_2CHCH_2]_2O$	123.0	0.7612_{15}^{15}	
t-butyl[a]	$[(CH_3)_3C]_2O$	108.0	0.7622	1.3946
n-amyl[a]	$(n\text{-}C_5H_{11})_2O$	188.0	0.7849	1.4119
isoamyl[a]	$[(CH_3)_2CHCH_2CH_2]_2O$	173.0	0.7777	1.4085
sec-amyl	$[C_3H_7CH(CH_3)]_2O$	161.0	0.7830_{20}^{20}	1.4058
n-hexyl[a]	$(n\text{-}C_6H_{13})_2O$	226.0	0.7936	1.4204
n-heptyl	$(n\text{-}C_7H_{15})_2O$	259.0	0.8008	1.4275
n-octyl	$(n\text{-}C_8H_{17})_2O$	288.0	0.8063	1.4327^{27}
Mixed, saturated				
methyl n-propyl	$CH_3OC_3H_7\text{-}n$	38.9	0.738	1.3579
methyl n-butyl	$CH_3OC_4H_9\text{-}n$	70.5	0.7443	1.3736
methyl t-butyl	$CH_3OC(CH_3)_3$	55.1	0.7406	1.3690
ethyl n-butyl	$C_2H_5OC_4H_9\text{-}n$	91.5	0.7490	1.3818
ethyl n-amyl	$C_2H_5OC_5H_{11}\text{-}n$	118.0	0.7622	1.3927
Simple and mixed, substituted				
bis(chloromethyl)[a]	$(ClCH_2)_2O$	105	1.315	1.4346
1-chloroethyl ethyl	$CH_3CHClOC_2H_5$	28_{57}	0.9495	$1.4021^{28.5}$
2-chloroethyl ethyl	$ClCH_2CH_2OC_2H_5$	106	0.9945	1.412
bis(1-chloroethyl)	$(CH_3CHCl)_2O$	113	1.106^{25}	1.4186^{25}
bis(2-chloroethyl)[a]	$(ClCH_2CH_2)_2O$	178	1.2199	1.4572
bis(2-bromoethyl)	$(BrCH_2CH_2)_2O$	115_{32}	1.8227^{27}	1.5131^{27}
bis(2-chloropropyl)	$(CH_3CHClCH_2)_2O$	188	1.109	1.4467
bis(3-chloropropyl)	$(ClCH_2CH_2CH_2)_2O$	215	1.4120_{20}^{20}	
bis(2-chloroisopropyl)	$(ClCH_2CH(CH_3))_2O$	187	1.1127	1.4505
bis(4-chlorobutyl)	$(ClCH_2CH_2CH_2CH_2)_2O$	$84\text{--}86_{5.5}$	1.0691^{25}	1.4562^{25}
Simple and mixed, unsaturated				
vinyl	$(CH_2{=}CH)_2O$	28–31	0.767^{25}	
vinyl methyl	$CH_2{=}CHOCH_3$	5–6	0.7511	
vinyl ethyl	$CH_2{=}CHOC_2H_5$	35.0	0.7533	1.3739^{25}
vinyl n-butyl	$CH_2{=}CHOC_4H_9\text{-}n$	93.5	0.7735^{25}	1.3997^{25}
allyl[a]	$(CH_2{=}CHCH_2)_2O$	95.0	0.8053	1.4163
bis(2-methallyl)	$(CH_2{=}C(CH_3)CH_2)_2O$	105.4	0.8627	1.4206
allyl ethyl	$CH_2{=}CHCH_2OC_2H_5$	67.6	0.765	1.3881
allyl glycidyl	$CH_2{=}CHCH_2OCH_2CHCH_2O$	75.0_{50}		1.4310^{30}
ethynyl ethyl	$CH{\equiv}COC_2H_5$	49.0	0.8001	1.3796
ethynyl butyl	$CH{\equiv}COC_4H_9\text{-}n$	104.0	0.8078^{25}	1.4033^{25}
Alicyclic Ether				
cyclopropyl methyl	$CH_2CH_2CHOCH_3$	44.7	0.8100	1.3802
Aromatic Substituted Ethers				
benzyl	$(C_6H_5CH_2)_2O$	295–298	1.0428	
benzyl methyl	$C_6H_5CH_2OCH_3$	174	0.9745^{25}	1.5031
benzyl ethyl	$C_6H_5CH_2OC_2H_5$	185	0.9577^{10}	
diphenyl	$(C_6H_5)_2O$	259	1.0863	1.5780^{27}
phenyl methyl	$C_6H_5OCH_3$	153.8	0.9954	1.5179^{20}
phenyl ethyl	$C_6H_5OC_2H_5$	172	0.9792_4^4	1.5076^{21}

[a] These ethers are described in this article in detail.

temperatures than the corresponding alcohol; when R is larger than butyl, the reverse is true. Their boiling points approximate those of hydrocarbons of the same molecular weight and geometry; it can be seen from this, that ether molecules are not associated in liquid form. Ethers form azeotropes with a wide variety of organic compounds (1). Table 1 gives the physical properties of some representative ethers.

Chemically, ethers are relatively inert. They resemble the corresponding alkanes in chemical reactivity, provided there are no functional groups. They do not react with alkali metals at low temperatures, and are not attacked by alkalies. Ethyl ether, therefore, may be dried over metallic sodium. Ethers do not undergo hydrogenolysis (2). On prolonged exposure to air, ethers autoxidize to peroxides, which can be dangerously explosive. Peroxides should be destroyed by alkaline hydrolysis or reduced by shaking with ferrous sulfate or ferrous hydroxide solution before distillation of ethereal solutions. Strong oxidizing conditions cleave ether molecules into at least two fragments (the corresponding aldehyde or the corresponding carboxylic acid; see under Ethyl ether). However, an ether group can survive oxidation of an olefinic or alcoholic group in the same molecule. Hence, hydroxyl groups are often protected by methylation during a synthetic reaction. In general, oxidation of ethers yields the same products as that of the corresponding alcohol.

Cleavage at one or both C—O linkages can be effected by inorganic acids and most readily by hydriodic or nitric acid, by acyl halides, or by phosphorus pentahalides, as illustrated in the following equations:

$$ROR + HI \xrightarrow{\text{cold}} RI + ROH \tag{1}$$

$$ROR + 2\,HI \xrightarrow{\text{heat}} 2\,RI + HOH \tag{2}$$

$$ROR + 2\,HBr \xrightarrow{\text{heat}} 2\,RBr + HOH \tag{3}$$

$$ROR + CH_3COI \rightarrow RI + CH_3COOR \tag{4}$$

$$ROR + PCl_5 \rightarrow 2\,RCl + POCl_3 \tag{5}$$

With hydriodic acid, mixed ethers yield a mixture of alkyl iodides (and alcohols, in the cold only); if one R is methyl or ethyl and the other is a higher hydrocarbon radical other than a tertiary radical, methyl or ethyl iodide is produced.

$$CH_3OCH_2CH_2CH_2CH_3 + HI \rightarrow CH_3I + CH_3CH_2CH_2CH_2OH$$

This reaction is the basis of the Zeisel method for the determination of methoxyl and ethoxyl groups in organic compounds. The amount of methyl or ethyl iodide in the distillate is determined by reaction with alcoholic silver nitrate solution and weighing the silver iodide precipitate. In the Vieboeck-Schwappach modification the alkyl iodide is absorbed in a solution of bromine and potassium acetate in glacial acetic acid which converts iodide to iodate. Addition of potassium iodide (after destroying the excess bromine with formic acid) and acidification produces six iodine atoms for each molecule of alkyl iodide.

$$ROCH_3 + HI \rightarrow ROH + CH_3I$$
$$CH_3I + Br_2 \rightarrow CH_3Br + IBr$$
$$IBr + 2\,Br_2 + 3\,H_2O \rightarrow HIO_3 + 5\,HBr$$
$$HIO_3 + 5\,HI \rightarrow 3\,I_2 + 3\,H_2O$$

The free iodine is titrated by standard thiosulfate solution to give a very accurate methoxy or ethoxy determination.

The relative stability of various alkoxy and aryloxy groups has been studied by cleavage of ethers with hydrogen bromide in glacial acetic acid (4), or acetyl iodide (3), equations 3 and 4, respectively. Cleavage of ethers with hydrobromic acid requires somewhat higher temperatures than with hydriodic acid, but is a convenient method for demethylating nonvolatile methoxy compounds, ie, removing protective methyl groups.

Ethers are also decomposed by heat, especially in the presence of alumina catalyst, to yield olefins, water and sometimes various other products.

$$RCH_2CH_2OCH_2CH_2R \xrightarrow[\Delta]{Al_2O_3} 2\ RCH{=}CH_2 + HOH$$

Similar decomposition occurs on prolonged ultraviolet irradiation, suggesting a free-radical mechanism.

Ethers react with chlorine and bromine considerably more readily than do their corresponding hydrocarbons. By controlling the reaction conditions and the amount of halogen absorbed, the reaction can be stopped at the mono or at the α,α'-bis-halo derivative. Continued addition of halogen produces highly halogenated ethers.

$$RCH_2OCH_2R + X_2 \rightarrow RCHXOCH_2R + HX$$

$$RCH_2OCH_2R + 2\ X_2 \rightarrow RCHXOCHXR + 2\ HX$$

Because α-halogen atoms are very reactive, these α-haloethers constitute a useful class of intermediates. Halogen atoms further removed from the oxygen atom are generally less reactive.

Ethers are nitrated in the vapor phase to yield homologous nitroalkanes as the main products along with some of the nitrated ether (5).

$$(CH_3CH_2CH_2)_2O \xrightarrow[\Delta]{HNO_3} CH_3CH_2CH_2NO_2 + CH_3CH_2NO_2 + CH_3NO_2$$

A characteristic property of ethers is their ability to form addition compounds. This can be attributed to the unshared electrons and the electronegativity of the oxygen atom. With hydrochloric acid and other strong inorganic or Lewis acids, ethers form oxonium compounds with the following general structure:

$$R{:}\overset{\displaystyle ..}{\underset{\displaystyle ..}{O}}{:} + HB \rightarrow \left[R{:}\overset{\displaystyle \overset{+}{..}}{\underset{\displaystyle ..}{O}}{:}H \right] [B^-]$$

Ether dissolves alkylmagnesium halides to give $(R_2O)_2 \cdot MgXR$ and is therefore used as a solvent for preparing Grignard reagents. Not all ethers are suitable solvents since in some cases the complex with the alkylmagnesium halide is insoluble in the ether.

Ethers dissolve in cold concentrated sulfuric acid to form oxonium sulfates; this serves to separate ethers from paraffin hydrocarbons and alkyl halides. Ethers can be recovered from sulfuric acid solution by dilution with water; hydrolysis can be prevented by slowly pouring the solution on ice. Sulfuric acid converts ethers to their corresponding alkyl hydrogen sulfate, which then can be hydrolyzed to the alcohol.

$$ROR \xrightarrow[heat]{H_2SO_4} ROSO_3H + ROH \xrightarrow{H_2SO_4} 2\ ROSO_3H + H_2O$$

$$ROSO_3H + H_2O \rightarrow ROH + H_2SO_4$$

Ethers also form soluble complexes with inorganic halides such as mercuric and magnesium bromides, lithium aluminum hydride, lithium borohydride, and boron trifluoride. The boron trifluoride–etherates (see Fluorine compounds, inorganic) are used in acylation and alkylation reactions, and as catalysts in polymerization, dehydration, and condensation reactions.

Preparation of Ethers

The important general methods for preparing ethers are given below. Many of these (6,6a) have been used for the preparation of most of the aliphatic ethers given in Table 1.

Catalytic Dehydration of Alcohols. This is the oldest and probably most commonly used method. With sulfuric acid as the dehydration catalyst, the reaction takes place in two or three steps—1 and 2, or 1, 3, and 4, respectively.

Step 1. $ROH + HOSO_2OH \xrightarrow{\text{cold}} ROSO_2OH + HOH$

Step 2. $ROSO_2OH + ROH \xrightarrow{\text{heat}} ROR + H_2SO_4$

Step 3. $ROSO_2OH + ROH \xrightarrow{\text{heat}} ROSO_2OR + HOH$

Step 4. $ROSO_2OR + ROH \xrightarrow{\text{heat}} ROR + ROSO_2OH$

This process is used commercially for the production of the lower simple ethers, particularly ethyl ether. It does not give satisfactory yields above propyl, because the higher-molecular-weight alcohols, particularly if secondary or tertiary, are readily dehydrated to the corresponding olefin. In an extensive study of the preparation of ethyl ether, van Alphen found effective catalysis is given by moderately strong acids and salts of weak bases and strong acids (7). He concluded that H^+ or H_3O^+ ions are the active catalysts above 100°C and that the intermediate ester formation (step 1) proposed for the sulfuric acid process cannot be the explanation of all catalytic dehydrations. Phosphoric acid, phosphorus pentoxide, boric acid, and hydrochloric acid also function effectively as dehydration catalysts. High-temperature (240–260°C) vapor-phase-dehydrating catalysts such as alumina were used by Senderens in the preparation of simple ethers (7a).

Williamson Ether Synthesis. The reaction of halogen derivatives of hydrocarbons with sodium alcoholate is probably the most versatile method for preparing simple or mixed ethers.

$$RX + NaOR \rightarrow ROR + NaX$$
$$RX + NaOR' \rightarrow ROR' + NaX$$

Ethylcellulose and other cellulose ethers are made commercially from alkal cellulose and ethyl chloride or another alkyl halide (see Vol. 4, p. 644).

In one modification of the Williamson synthesis, sodionaphthalene is used to prepare the anhydrous sodium alcoholate in situ (8); the yield and ease of preparation were greatly improved. Dialkyl sulfates or sulfonates can replace the alkyl halide.

$$(CH_3)_2SO_4 + NaOCH_2CH(CH_3)_2 \rightarrow CH_3OCH_2CH(CH_3)_2 + CH_3NaSO_2$$

The dialkyl sulfates are especially useful in the preparation of phenolic ethers such as anisole.

Metallic oxides, such as silver oxide, have also been used in place of the sodium alcoholate in the Williamson synthesis of simple ethers.

$$2\,RX + Ag_2O \rightarrow ROR + 2\,AgX$$

A method related to the Williamson synthesis, is the preparation of simple or mixed ethers from alkyl halides and alcohols with or without alkali (9). Allyl ether, for example, is readily obtained by the alkaline hydrolysis of allyl chloride. Mixed allyl ethers have been prepared from an allyl halide, an alcohol and alkali, or from allyl alcohol and an alkylating agent (see below under Allyl ether; see also Vol. 1, p. 920; Vol. 5, p. 208; Allyl starch under Starch).

$$CH_2{=}CHCH_2Cl \xrightarrow{\text{alkali}} CH_2{=}CHCH_2OH \xrightarrow{\text{alkali}} (CH_2{=}CHCH_2)_2O$$

$$CH_2{=}CHCH_2X + ROH \xrightarrow{\text{alkali}} CH_2{=}CHCH_2OR + HX$$

$$CH_2{=}CHCH_2OH + C_6H_5CH_2Br \rightarrow CH_2{=}CHCH_2OCH_2C_6H_5 + HBr$$

Miscellaneous Methods. Mixed ethers in which one of the alkyl groups is tertiary, may be prepared by the reaction of olefins such as isobutylene, with alcohols or phenols in the presence of sulfuric acid (10).

$$(CH_3)_2C{=}CH_2 + C_2H_5OH \xrightarrow{\text{H}_2\text{SO}_4} (CH_3)_3COC_2H_5$$

α-Halo ethers react with organomagnesium or zinc compounds to give a homologous series of mixed ethers (11).

$$C_5H_{11}OCH_2Br + BrMgC_2H_5 \rightarrow C_5H_{11}OCH_2CH_2CH_3 + MgBr_2$$

Boron trifluoride–alcoholates yield the corresponding simple ether when heated in an autoclave at high temperatures and pressures (12).

$$n\text{-}C_4H_9OH.BF_3 \xrightarrow[\text{autoclave}]{\text{benzene}} (n\text{-}C_4H_9)_2O \quad 61\% \text{ yield}$$

Uses and Applications

The greatest use of ethers is as solvents (qv) for organic reactions and extractions, as plasticizers (qv), as vehicles for other products, and as anesthetics (qv). Some ethers when mixed with alcohols, become better solvents for cellulose esters and have been used in the manufacture of cellulose nitrate. They are insoluble in water, but dissolve most organic compounds, and therefore have found wide application in paint and varnish removers, as high-boiling solvents for gums, resins, and waxes, and in lubricating oils. The vapors of certain ethers are toxic to insects and are useful as agricultural insecticides and industrial fumigants. A wide range in solubility, boiling point, refractive index, and density can be achieved by a change in the alkyl group (see Table 1), and an inert ether with a required physical property for a given chemical operation can usually be synthesized. Ethers, thus, find unlimited application as a reaction or extraction medium. The lower-molecular-weight technical-grade ethers are the least expensive and most commonly used in industry.

Table 2 compares the prices and availability of commercial ethers.

Methyl Ether

Methyl ether, CH_3OCH_3, is a colorless gas with an ethereal odor. It burns with a slightly luminous flame; mp, $-138.5°C$; bp, $-23.65°C$; d^{25}, 1.91850 g/l; $n_D^{-42.5}$

Table 2. Price and Scale of Manufacture of Commercial Ethers

Ether	Price, $	Scale of manufacture or availability
methyl	0.11/lb	tank cars
bis(chloromethyl)	16.00/100 g	laboratory quantities
ethyl	0.11/lb (tech)	large
bis(2-chloroethyl)	0.13–0.15/lb	55-gal drums
n-propyl	9.75/100 g	laboratory quantities
isopropyl	0.08/lb	large
bis(2-chloroisopropyl)	0.13/lb	55-gal drums
n-butyl	0.35/lb	55-gal drums
amyl	18.30/100 g or 6.00/500 g, according to grade	laboratory quantities
hexyl	5.50/lb	laboratory quantities
higher alkyl ethers (see p. 493)	6.00/lb	laboratory quantities
allyl	10.90/500 g	laboratory quantities
benzyl	0.15/lb	55-gal drums

1.3441; sp gr of liquid at 20°C, 0.661; flash point (closed-cup), −42°F; heat of combustion, 347.6 kcal/mole. One vol of water dissolves 37 vols of methyl ether; CH_3OCH_3 is miscible with ethyl alcohol or ethyl ether. Gaseous methyl ether has been used as a propellant for sprays and as a refrigerant; it can freeze foods directly without imparting foreign tastes or odors. Methyl ether may be narcotic at high concentrations. It is commercially available for approximately 11¢/lb in tank car quantities and requires a red label for railroad shipment.

Methyl ether is prepared by dehydration of methyl alcohol by the sulfuric acid method or by passage over catalysts such as alumina. Extremely pure methyl ether, prepared by the Williamson procedure from sodium methoxide and methyl iodide, was used for measurements of heat capacities, heat of fusion, densities, melting point and vapor pressure (13). It has also been prepared from trimethyl orthoformate (14), or from sodium methyl carbonate (15).

$$HC(OCH_3)_3 + FeCl_3 \xrightarrow{\text{heat}} CH_3OCH_3 + HCO_2CH_3$$
$$95\% \text{ yield}$$

$$2\ CH_3OCOONa \xrightarrow[\text{tube}]{320°C} CH_3OCH_3 + CO_2 + Na_2CO_3$$
$$58\% \text{ yield}$$

Methyl ether undergoes pyrolytic or photolytic decomposition to give methane, ethane, formaldehyde, carbon dioxide, and carbon monoxide, depending on the reaction conditions and catalysts. Thermal decomposition of methyl ether over alumina–silica in the presence of benzene, gives toluene, xylenes, and polymethylbenzenes (16). Depending on the catalyst, methyl ether reacts with carbon monoxide to form methyl acetate or acetic acid (17), with carbon dioxide to form methoxyacetic acid (18), and with hydrogen cyanide to form acetonitrile (19). Methyl ether forms an isolable complex with boron trifluoride, $(CH_3)_2O \cdot BF_3$, which fumes in air and decomposes in water or alcohol; mp, −14°C; bp, 127°C (dec); d_4^{25} 1.2348; n_D^{20} 1.302.

Methyl ether and its chlorinated derivatives can be selectively chlorinated to give one or more of the polychlorinated compounds (20) given in Table 3.

Table 3. Chlorination Products of Methyl Ether

Product	Bp, °C	n_D^{20}	d_4^{20}
$ClCH_2OCH_3$	61	1.0605	1.3974
$(ClCH_2)_2O$	103–105	1.4421	1.4351
Cl_2CHOCH_3	84.5	1.4299	1.270
Cl_2CHOCH_2Cl	129	1.4622	1.464^{30}
$(Cl_2CH)_2O$	143	1.4728	1.558^{30}
Cl_3COCH_3	106–110.5	1.4536	1.4391
$Cl_3COCHCl_2$	159		

1,1′-Dichloromethyl ether (bis(chloromethyl)ether), the major chlorination product of methyl ether, is a colorless liquid, strongly irritating to the eyes and respiratory tract. It is a mild lacrimator and not a vesicant. It was manufactured in Germany (233 tons between September 1917 and May 1918) as a war gas and chemical intermediate (21). It is most conveniently prepared, in the laboratory, from paraformaldehyde and chlorosulfonic acid as a source of hydrochloric acid (22).

$$2 CH_2O + 2 ClSO_3H + H_2O \rightarrow (ClCH_2)_2O + 2 H_2SO_4$$

Bis(chloromethyl) ether reacts with sodium methoxide to yield bis(methoxymethyl) ether (bp, 64.5° at 200 mm Hg; n_D^{25} 1.3769; d_4^{25} 0.945). Reaction with diethyl malonate and sodium ethoxide gives 1,1,3,3-tetracarbethoxypropane, $CH_2(CH(CO_2C_2H_5)_2)_2$ (22a). With benzyl sodium, bis(phenethyl) ether $(C_6H_5CH_2CH_2)_2O$ is obtained. Under Friedel-Crafts conditions, bis(chloromethyl) ether reacts with anilides to give the corresponding chloromethylated derivative (23).

$$(ClCH_2)_2O + C_6H_5NHCOCH_3 \xrightarrow{H_2SO_4} CH_3CONH\!-\!\!\bigcirc\!\!-\!CH_2Cl$$

Ethyl Ether

Ethyl ether (ethoxyethane (IUPAC)), $C_2H_5OC_2H_5$, is probably the most important member of the ether family. It is a colorless, very volatile, highly flammable liquid with a sweet pungent odor and burning taste. As a commercial product it is available in several grades; it is used in chemical manufacture, as a solvent, extractant, or reaction medium, and as a general anesthetic. Basil Valentine, in the early fifteenth century, and Paracelsus, in the early sixteenth century, described a product from the reaction of "wine spirits" (ethyl alcohol) with "oil of vitriol" (sulfuric acid) as a wonderful medicine and a stupefactive narcotic with an agreeable odor (24). In 1540, Valerius Cordus heated equal weights of ethyl alcohol and sulfuric acid and distilled an upper oily layer which he called "oleum vitrioli dulce verum." This sweet oil of vitriol was probably a mixture of sulfuric esters, ethyl ether, ethyl alcohol, etc. In 1730, Frobenius described the same procedure as the "Sir Isaac Newton process" and called the product "spirit vini aethereus" or "spiritus vini vitriolatus" (sulfuric ether). In 1800, Valentin Rose showed that the product did not contain sulfur, and in 1819, Dalton found that in the combustion of this product 10 volumes required 60 volumes of oxygen, with 40 volumes of carbon dioxide evolved. In 1821, Gaudin arrived at the empirical formula $C_4H_{10}O$ which agreed with Dalton's results since $C_4H_{10} + 6O_2 \rightarrow 4CO_2 + 5H_2O$. In 1851 Williamson demonstrated that ethers have the structure R—O—R.

PHYSICAL AND CHEMICAL PROPERTIES

The physical properties of ethyl ether are given in Table 4.

Ethyl ether is a good insulator and may generate enough static electricity, when shaken in air, to ignite. A saturated water solution, at 20°C, contains 6.5% ethyl ether, by wt; ethyl ether holds a maximum of 1.2% water at this temperature. The two saturated layers constitute an azeotropic mixture which boils at 34.2°C; the

Table 4. Physical Properties of Ethyl Ether

freezing point, °C	−116.3			
boiling point, at 760 mm Hg, °C	34.48			
density at 4 mm,				
0°C	0.7364			
20°C	0.7145			
30°C	0.7019			
refractive index, n_D^t				
15°C	1.3555			
20°C	1.3527			
vapor density (air = 1)	2.55			
viscosity, at 20°C, cP	0.23			
surface tension, at 20°C, dyn/cm	17.30			
specific heat, g-cal/g				
0°C	0.529			
30°C	0.547			
120°C	0.803			
180°C	1.041			
heat of combustion at 20°C, kcal/mole	651.7			
heat of vaporization, at 30°C, kcal/mole	6.215			
heat of formation, at 25°C, kcal/mole	−65.2			
critical temperature, °C	194			
critical pressure, atm	35.51			
critical density, g/ml	0.2625			
flash point (closed-cup), °C	−49			
autoignition temperature, °C	180–190			
explosive range in air, % by vol	1.85–48.0			
coefficient of cubical expansion/°C	0.00164			
dielectric constant, at 26.9°C, 85.8 kc	4.197			
vapor pressure	°C	mm Hg	0°C	mm Hg
	0	184.9	50	1276
	10	290.8	60	1734
	20	439.8	70	2304
	40	921.0		

distillate contains 1.3% water and 98.7% ether. Ethyl ether is very soluble in concentrated hydrochloric acid (oxonium salt formation), but may explode when brought into contact with anhydrous nitric acid (see below). It is miscible with ethyl alcohol, benzene, chloroform, petroleum ethers, oils, and many fat solvents.

Reactions. Although ethyl ether is relatively inert it does undergo several reactions worth noting. Exposure to air and light forms nonvolatile and hazardous peroxides. These remain as a residue when ether evaporates and may explode with extreme violence. Peroxides are pulmonary irritants and must be absent in anesthetic ether. Addition of weak acids or water decomposes ethyl peroxides to hydrogen peroxide and water. Peroxides can be removed effectively by shaking ethyl ether with a suitable reducing agent such as a 5% aqueous ferrous sulfate solution. Other methods for removing peroxides are given in references 25 and 26. The structure and composition of ether peroxides are still uncertain. Among the compounds that have been proposed are oxonium salts, $CH_3CH(OH)OOCH(OH)CH_3$ (bis(1-hydroxyethyl) peroxide), $CH_3CH(OOH)OC_2H_5$ (1-ethoxyethyl hydroperoxide), and ethylidine peroxide polymers. See also Peroxides, organic.

Under vigorous oxidation, ethyl ether undergoes cleavage. Ether vapor and air form acetaldehyde and formaldehyde when passed over a copper catalyst and platinum black at 100°C (27). Chromic anhydride (CrO_3) or nitric acid oxidizes ethyl ether to acetic acid. The reaction with absolute nitric acid can be so violent, as to constitute an explosion hazard; some ethyl nitrate forms at $-15°C$ whereas nitrogen peroxide, carbon dioxide, and water are produced at room temperature due to the decomposition of ethyl nitrate. In the presence of concentrated sulfuric acid, ether and nitric acid explode violently (28).

Ethyl ether can be nitrated safely in the vapor phase (5), to give methyl nitrate, ethyl nitrate, and 2-nitroethyl ethyl ether, $NO_2CH_2CH_2OC_2H_5$, $b_{5.5}$ 58–59°C; n_D^{25} 1.4160; d_{25} 1.079.

Ethyl ether and other ethers can also be cleaved with inorganic acid. Cleavage at one O—R linkage is effected with cold concentrated hydriodic acid, cold nitric acid, concentrated hot sulfuric acid, or dilute acids under heat and pressure; cleavage at both O—R linkages occurs with hot concentrated hydriodic acid or sulfuric acid and phosphorus pentachloride. Ethyl ether reacts with inorganic anhydrides (sulfur trioxide, phosphorus pentoxide, dinitrogen tetroxide), and with organic anhydrides in the presence of ferric chloride to form esters (diethyl sulfate, ethyl acetate, etc). These reactions are reversible; thus ethyl ether can be obtained by heating dimethyl sulfate with cuprous oxide or ethyl esters of organic acids with ferric chloride at 150°C, or by heating diethyl carbonate or diethyl oxalate with zinc chloride (28). Cleavage of ethyl ether occurs by reaction with alkaline carbon disulfide at 60°C, to give potassium ethyl xanthate, $C_2H_5OC(=S)SK$ (29).

With halides such as beryllium chloride, mercuric bromide, aluminum chloride, and titanium tetrachloride, ethyl ether forms crystalline additions compounds, such as $2(C_2H_5)_2O \cdot BeCl_2$. Boron trifluoride reacts with ethyl ether to give boron trifluoride etherate (30), $(C_2H_5)_2O \cdot BF_3$, which is a fuming liquid; bp, 125.7°C; mp, $-60.4°C$; n_D^{20} 1.348; d_4^{25} 1.125. Boron trifluoride etherate is offered commercially at about 34¢/lb, as a catalyst for acylation, alkylation, polymerization, dehydration, and condensation reactions (see Fluorine compounds).

Ethyl ether can be halogenated to yield a variety of derivatives depending on the reaction conditions. Chlorination at room temperature without illumination gives 1,2-dichloroethyl ethyl ether, $ClCH_2CH(Cl)OC_2H_5$, in about 24% yield, bp, 141°C; n_D^{20} 1.4435; d_4^{20} 1.1870. At low temperatures, 1-chloroethyl ethyl ether, $CH_3CH(Cl)$-OC_2H_5 (bp, 98–100°C; n_D^{20} 1.4053; d_4^{20} 0.950) or bis(α-chloroethyl) ethyl ether, $(CH_3CHCl)_2O$ (bp, 113–114°C; n_D^{24} 1.4183) are obtained (31). The β-halo derivatives are prepared from diethylene glycol and phosphorus trichloride, whereas the bis(β-halo) derivatives are prepared from ethylene glycol monoethyl ether (see Glycols). Bromination of ethyl ether in chloroform is reported to give a 55% yield of 2,2-dibromoacetaldehyde diethyl acetal, $Br_2CHCH(OC_2H_5)$ (32).

MANUFACTURE

The continuous dehydration of ethyl alcohol by sulfuric acid (33,34) was first described by P. Boullay in 1809. This process was later standardized in the United States, and called the Barbet process. In this process (see Fig. 1), concentrated sulfuric acid (66° Bé) and 95% ethyl alcohol are charged into a lead-lined steel kettle in the ratio of 3 parts acid to one part alcohol. The reaction is started by heating the mixture to 125-140°C with a steam jacket or internal steam coils. A supply of alcohol vapor is continuously fed into the acid–alcohol mixture at a rate to maintain the temperature at approximately 127°C. The vapor from the still, consisting of ether, alcohol, and water, passes through a caustic scrubber to remove traces of sulfur dioxide and

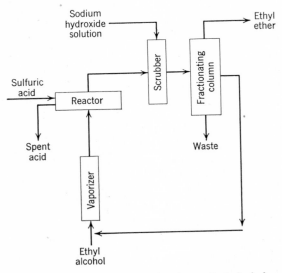

Fig. 1. Manufacture of ethyl ether from ethyl alcohol.

entrained sulfuric acid. The alkaline solution formed, containing small amounts of ether and alcohol, passes from the bottom of the scrubber to the lower level of the fractionating column. At this point, the ether and alcohol are removed as the aqueous solution is discharged as waste. The vapors from the top of the scrubber, consisting of ether, alcohol, and water, are separated in a continuous fractionation. Water passes from the column as waste, while ethyl alcohol (ca 95%) is withdrawn from the center of the column and returned to the vaporizer for recycling. Ether vapors pass from the top of the column through a reflux condenser maintained at 34°C. Fractions boiling above this temperature are returned to the column; ether vapors are condensed and run into a storage tank. This *technical* or *concentrated* ether contains very small amounts of alcohol, water, aldehydes, peroxides, and other impurities (see Table 6). The more refined grades, such as anesthetic ether, are obtained from technical ether by redistillation and dehydration followed by alkali or charcoal treatment.

This process is practically continuous and may be run for months before recharging with sulfuric acid as can be seen from the following reactions:

$$C_2H_5OH + H_2SO_4 \rightarrow C_2H_5HSO_4 + H_2O$$

$$C_2H_5OH + C_2H_5HSO_4 \rightarrow C_2H_5OC_2H_5 + H_2SO_4$$

Side reactions which form tarry products and sulfur dioxide make periodic recharging necessary. The yield of technical ether is 94–95% based upon the ethyl alcohol processed. Benzenesulfonic acid can be used instead of sulfuric acid at somewhat lower temperatures. In a similar process, ethyl alcohol vapor is dehydrated over alumina at 200–230°C, to give a 75% yield of ethyl ether.

Most commercial ethyl ether used today is obtained as a by-product in the synthetic manufacture of ethyl alcohol from ethylene by the sulfuric acid process (see Ethanol). This method may be modified to produce only ether or both ether and alcohol. The principal reactions are shown in the following equations:

$$C_2H_4 + H_2SO_4 \rightarrow C_2H_5HSO_4$$
$$2\ C_2H_4 + H_2SO_4 \rightarrow (C_2H_5)_2SO_4$$

$$C_2H_5HSO_4 + H_2O \rightarrow C_2H_5OH + H_2SO_4$$
$$(C_2H_5)_2SO_4 + H_2O \rightarrow 2\ C_2H_5OH + H_2SO_4$$

$$C_2H_5OH + C_2H_5HSO_4 \rightarrow C_2H_5OC_2H_5 + H_2SO_4$$
$$C_2H_5OH + (C_2H_5)_2SO_4 \rightarrow C_2H_5OC_2H_5 + C_2H_5HSO_4$$

Ethylene (qv), produced by the cracking of petroleum hydrocarbons, is absorbed in concentrated sulfuric acid at fairly high pressures under controlled temperature conditions to yield mixed ethyl hydrogen sulfate and diethyl sulfate (33–36). Ordinarily this mixture would contain 1.0–1.5 moles ethylene per mole sulfuric acid and would be hydrolyzed with water to produce ethyl alcohol, with ethyl ether as a by-product. It will be assumed in this description, however, that only ether is desired as the end product.

In the flow plan shown in Figure 2, the mixed sulfates are pumped into a reactor under pressure with sufficient water to obtain a sulfuric acid strength of about 60% on a hydrocarbon-free basis. A temperature of about 125°C is maintained in the reactor, which should be of sufficient size to permit about three hours' contact time. If a higher temperature is maintained, the contact time can be reduced, but this will result in a higher pressure. The proper balance between temperature and pressure is determined by an economic balance between the expense of the equipment and the cost of operation. The objective is to approach, within reasonable limits, the equilibriums in the ether–alcohol–water–sulfuric acid–ethyl sulfates system, which determines the maximum conversion to be expected. Ethyl alcohol recovered from the alcohol tower is recycled to the reactor. This increases the mole ratio of equivalent ethylene to sulfuric acid that is favorable to high ether conversions. When the process is put into operation, the amount of recycle alcohol increases until the system is in balance. This is usually about 3 moles ethylene per mole sulfuric acid, depending upon the ethylene present in the mixed sulfates, resulting in an ether conversion of about 40%.

The reactor mixture is fed at a uniform rate to a stripping still with sufficient water to reduce the acid strength to about 50% on a hydrocarbon-free basis. The ether, alcohol, and water are removed from the sulfuric acid by stripping with live steam at a pressure slightly above atmospheric. The vapors are passed through a vapor scrubber countercurrent to a dilute (10%) caustic soda solution to remove sulfur dioxide and traces of entrained sulfuric acid. The vapors from the scrubber are condensed, passed through a liquid–gas separator, and run to a storage tank before

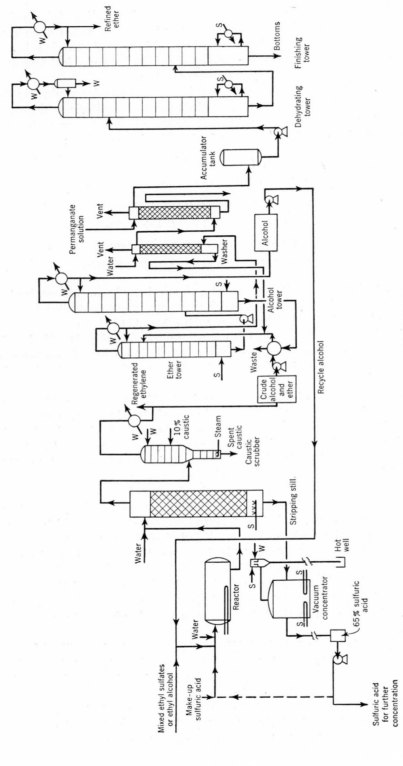

Fig. 2. Manufacture of ethyl ether.

rectification. The ethylene recovered from the separator is sent to a compressor and returned to the ethylene-absorption system. Sulfuric acid from the stripping still is reconcentrated to about 65% strength. If ethylene is the raw material, the 65% sulfuric acid is further concentrated and reused in the absorption of ethylene. If alcohol is the raw material, the 65% acid is returned to the reactor.

The ether–alcohol–water mixture is sent to a finishing system consisting essentially of fractionating towers and washers. The ether is separated from the alcohol and water in the ether tower, and is run through a water washer to remove the alcohol present. Then it is run through a second wash column where it is treated with an alkaline permanganate solution. The treated ether flows to an accumulator tank. The ethyl alcohol–water mixture from the ether tower is sent to the alcohol tower, where a constant-boiling mixture of alcohol and water (95% by volume) distills over. Both the ether and alcohol towers operate at substantially atmospheric pressure. The treated ether, containing a small amount of water, is fed to a dehydrating tower that operates at about 100 psig. The distillate from this tower separates into two layers; the lower aqueous layer is withdrawn. The dry ether passes from the base of the dehydrating tower to the finishing tower, which operates at about 50 psig and gives a highly refined ether as an overhead product, while a very small stream of higher-boiling materials is removed from the base. It is desirable to handle the ethyl ether product in a closed system and store it in pressure drums or spheres. An inhibitor such as 1-naphthol is sometimes added to prevent peroxide formation (37).

The proper choice of the materials of construction is particularly important for the part of the process involving the production and recovery of the crude ether. Because of the presence of sulfuric acid under very corrosive conditions, the reactor, stripping still, and concentrator must be carefully constructed. Lead-lined steel vessels with an inner ceramic lining are satisfactory. The stripping still may be packed with porcelain or carbon rings to secure intimate liquid-vapor contact. The vapor scrubber should be made of Monel or some material resistant to both acid and alkali. The equipment for the remainder of the process may be made of steel, copper, or brass. Neither ethyl alcohol nor ethyl ether are corrosive and these materials are usually handled in steel tanks, lines, and other equipment.

ECONOMIC ASPECTS

Ethyl ether occupies a position of moderate importance in relation to other organic chemicals. Table 5 gives the total production of all grades of ether (as reported by the U.S. Tariff Commission) and the unit price of technical ether (as reported in *Chemical & Engineering News*) in the U.S. from 1940 to 1964.

During World War II, large quantities of ethyl ether were used as a solvent in the manufacture of smokeless powder and butadiene which explains the high production reported for 1945. When the need arises, most synthetic alcohols plants can produce larger quantities of ethyl ether by slight changes in operating conditions (see above). In the period from 1950–1964, the price for anesthetic ether ranged from $0.89 to $1.01/lb; USP grade fluctuated between $0.11 and $0.15/lb.

SPECIFICATIONS, TESTING, AND STANDARDS

Ethyl ether is commercially available in the following grades: USP anesthesia, absolute (ACS), industrial, solvent (concentrated), and synthetic. Specifications vary, depending on the consumers and its intended use. In many instances the ether has to

Table 5. U.S. Production and Price of Ethyl Ether, 1940–1964

Year	Production, million lb[a]	Unit price, \$/lb[b]
1940	17.2	0.11
1945	76.6	0.11
1950	37.9	0.18
1952	65.1	0.16
1954	56.0	0.12
1956	84.5	0.12
1958		0.12
1960	93.7	0.11
1962	88.3	0.12
1964		0.11

[a] Total production of all grades of ether.   [b] Technical ethyl ether.

meet a specific test, written into the specification. For example, it may be important that the ether is completely anhydrous or free from alcohol and aldehyde.

Most of the analytical and testing methods used for ethyl ether are conventional laboratory methods. Ethyl ether that is to be used for anesthetic purposes or in processes that involve heating or distillation must be peroxidefree and should pass

Table 6. Typical Specifications for Various Grades of Ethyl Ether

Specification	Technical refine	ACS, absolute	USP XVI[a]
Color, max	water-white	water-white	colorless
d_{25}^{25}	0.710–0.713	0.7079	0.713–0.716
acidity as acetic acid, wt%	0.0025	0.0010	passes test[b]
peroxides, max wt%	passes test[c]	0.0001	passes test[c]
aldehydes, max wt%	passes test[d]	0.0005	passes test[d]
alcohol, max %	0.5, by vol	0.05, by wt	
nonvolatile matter, max wt%	0.002	0.0010	0.003
water, max wt%	0.3	0.0100	
odor	nonresidual	passes test[e]	passes test[e]
net container contents, lb[f]			
5-gal drum	30	30	30
55-gal drum	324	324	324

[a] Ether, USP XVI, for use in anesthesia. The USP also recognizes slightly less pure grades; ethyl oxide (solvent ether), ether abs, and reagent-grade ether.

[b] Free acid, requiring no more than 0.4 ml of 0.02N sodium hydroxide for 25 ml of ethyl ether.

[c] No color with potassium iodide reagent; USP test.

[d] No turbidity with alkaline mercuric chloride–potassium iodide reagent; USP test.

[e] No foreign odor when last traces of ether evaporate from odorless absorbent paper; USP test.

[f] The tech grade can also be shipped in 103W insulated tank cars of 4000-gal, 6000-gal, 8000-gal, and 10,000-gal capacity.

the USP standard test with potassium iodide (see Vol. 2, p. 396). This test detects about 0.001% peroxide as hydrogen peroxide. If a color is produced, a quantitative determination can be made by titrating the liberated iodine with standard sodium thiosulfate solution. In any case, the peroxides should be destroyed (25).

Typical specifications and containers for various grades of ethyl ether are given in Table 6. For ACS requirements for ether and absolute ether see reference 38.

METHODS FOR HANDLING

Ethyl ether is classified by the ICC as a "flammable liquid." As such it must be packed in ICC specification containers when shipped by rail, water, or highway, and all ICC regulations regarding loading, handling, and labeling must be followed. Each container of ethyl ether must carry an identifying label or stencil. Tank cars and boxcars, either carload or less than carload, must bear the ICC "dangerous" placard. Each drum or each box with inside containers must bear the ICC red label for flammable liquids.

The handling of ethyl ether is hazardous because of its highly flammable properties (26,39). Not only is it highly volatile, but it also has a low autoignition temperature and, as a nonconductor, can generate static electrical charges that may result in ignition or vapor explosion. The area in which ethyl ether is handled should be considered as a Class I hazardous location as defined by the National Electrical Code. All tools used in making connections or repairs should be of the nonsparking type. All possible care should be taken in loading and unloading tank cars. These operations should be conducted by carefully instructed and reliable employees. The tank cars should be properly spotted and the usual caution signs and derails placed in position. Before any connection is made, the tank car should be grounded and bonded. Tank cars should always be unloaded through dome connections rather than through bottom outlets. A pressure-type LPG tank car is preferable, permitting the ether to be handled in a closed system. A positive suction-type pump or natural gas may be used to remove the ether from the tank car. In no event should air pressure be used.

Special containers have been developed for anesthetic ether to prevent deterioration before use. Their effectiveness as stabilizers usually depends upon the presence of a lower oxide of a metal having more than one oxidation state. Thus, the sides and bottom of tin-plate containers are electroplated with copper, which contains a small amount of cuprous oxide (40,41). Stannous oxide is also used in the linings for tin containers (42). Instead of using special containers, iron wire or certain other metals and alloys or organic compounds have been added to ether to stabilize it.

The following caution is given in the USP for the storage of anesthetic ether: "Ether to be used for anesthesia must be preserved in tight containers of not more than 3 kg capacity and is not to be used for anesthesia if it has been removed from the original container longer than twenty-four hours. Ether to be used for anesthesia may, however, be shipped in larger containers for repackaging in containers as directed above, provided the ether at the time of repackaging meets the requirements of the tests of this *Pharmacopoeia*."

HEALTH AND SAFETY FACTORS

The toxicity of ethyl ether is low and its greatest hazards in industry are fire and explosion (39). It is absorbed almost instantly from the lungs and very promptly from the intestinal tract. It undergoes no chemical change in the body. Prevention and control of health hazards associated with the handling of ethyl ether depend primarily upon prevention of exposure to toxic atmospheric concentrations and scrupulous precautions to prevent explosion and fire.

The maximum safe atmospheric concentrations of ethyl ether for prolonged exposure have not been determined under industrial conditions. Concentrations about 3000 ppm and as high as 7000 ppm have been breathed by workers over considerable periods of time without noticeable effect (39). A concentration of 35,000 ppm in the air produces unconsciousness in 30–40 min. This concentration would also constitute a serious fire and explosion hazard and should not be permitted to exist under any circumstance. Any person exposed to ethyl ether vapor of any appreciable concentration should be promptly removed from the area. Recovery from exposure to sublethal concentrations is rapid and generally complete. Except in emergencies, and then only with appropriate protective equipment, no one should enter an area containing ether vapor until the concentration has been found safe by measurement with a combustible-gas indicator.

If an ethyl ether fire occurs, carbon dioxide, carbon tetrachloride, and dry chemical fire extinguishers meeting National Fire Prevention Association Code I and 2 requirements may be used successfully. Water may also be effectively applied. Hose streams played into open tanks of burning ethyl ether serve only to scatter the liquid and spread the fire. Ether fires may, however, be extinguished by a high pressure water spray that cools the burning surface and smothers the fire. Automatic sprinklers and deluge systems are also effective.

USES

Ethyl ether has a wide range of uses in the chemical industry. It is a good solvent or extractant for fats, waxes, oils, perfumes, resins, dyes, gums, and alkaloids (see Solvents). When mixed with ethyl alcohol, ethyl ether becomes an excellent solvent for cellulose nitrate in the manufacture of guncotton, collodion solutions, and pyroxylin plastics. Another important use is as an extractant for acetic acid (see Ethanoic acid) as well as other organic acids. For example, it is used in the cellulose acetate and plastic industries to recover acetic acid from dilute aqueous systems. Ethyl ether has also been used as a denaturant in several denatured alcohol formulas. It has been used as a starting fuel for diesel engines and as an entrainer for dehydration of ethyl and isopropyl alcohol. It may be used as an anhydrous, inert reaction medium for the Grignard and Wurtz-Fittig reactions. Ethyl ether is used as a general anesthetic in surgery (see Vol. 2, p. 396).

Although ethyl ether is made from ethylene, it is useful as a commercial source of ethylene in plants that do not have access to petroleum refinery gases. The ether, being a liquid, is more conveniently transported than ethylene. Ethyl alcohol denatured with ethyl ether may also be used. The vapor is passed over alumina at about 650°F, the yield is very high and the ethylene produced is very pure.

The estimated enduse pattern of ethyl ether in U.S. industries during the late 1950s was as follows: chemical manufacture, 50%; solvent and miscellaneous purposes, 35%; medicinal and pharmaceutical, 15%.

Bis(2-chloroethyl) Ether

Bis(2-chloroethyl) ether (β,β'-dichlorodiethyl ether; Chlorex, registered trademark Union Carbide Corp.), $ClCH_2CH_2OCH_2CH_2Cl$, is the oxygen analog of mustard gas (see Vol. 4, p. 872) but is not a vesicant. It is a colorless, clear nonflammable liquid possessing a chloroform-like odor. Physical constants include fp, −50°C; bp, 176–178°C; b_{23} 82–83°C; d_{20}^{20} 1.22; 10.17 lb/gal at 20°C; n_D^{20} 1.4572; flash point (open-cup), 185°F; viscosity at 20°C, 2.372 cP. It is insoluble in water but soluble in most organic solvents.

Bis(2-chloroethyl) ether is prepared in 75% yield by heating ethylene chlorohydrin (see Vol. 5, p. 307) with sulfuric acid at 90–100°C (43).

$$2 \ ClCH_2CH_2OH \xrightarrow{H_2SO_4} ClCH_2CH_2OCH_2CH_2Cl + H_2O$$

It has also been prepared in very high yield by saturating an aqueous solution of ethylene chlorohydrin with chlorine and ethylene (44).

Bis(2-chloroethyl) ether undergoes a number of very interesting reactions. It dehydrohalogenates over hot potassium hydroxide in the presence of ammonia to give divinyl ether, $(CH_2\!=\!CH)_2O$, and over hot sodium hydroxide flakes to give β-chloroethyl vinyl ether, $ClCH_2CH_2OCH\!=\!CH_2$, and p-dioxane (45,46). Bis(2-chloroethyl) ether reacts with aromatic amines such as aniline to give N-phenylmorpholine (45), with sodium phenoxide to give bis(2-phenoxyethyl) ether, $(C_6H_5OCH_2CH_2)_2O$ (45); with hydrazine to give 4-aminomorpholine (47) and with sodium iodide in acetone to give bis(2-iodoethyl) ether, $(ICH_2CH_2)_2O$ (48), b_{10} 123.5–124°C. Chlorination of bis(2-chloroethyl) ether in sulfuric acid produces 1,2-dichloroethane and 1,1,2-trichloroethane (49); photochlorination gives 1,1′,2-trichloroethyl ether (50), $ClCH_2\text{-}$ $CHClOCH_2CH_2Cl$, or 56% chloral (51) depending on the reaction conditions.

Typical specifications are as follows: color (APHA), 30 max; d_{20}^{20} 1.219-1.224; distillation range, 175–181°C; acidity (as HCl), 0.005 wt %, max; water, 0.10 wt %, max; flash point (open-cup), 185°F.

Bis(2-chloroethyl) ether is an excellent solvent for fats, waxes, and greases, and acts as a good solvent for cellulose esters when mixed with 10–20% alcohol. The solvent action of bis(2-chloroethyl) ether makes it a useful scouring agent for textiles and an additive to oil and grease spotting formulations. It is also used as an insecticide, acaricide, and soil fumigant. The low volatility of bis(2-chloroethyl) ether allows the fumigant to act over a considerable period of time. Because it is phytotoxic it can be used only on a bare soil. It can be used in gasoline to scavenge lead deposits.

Bis(2-chloroethyl) ether is a solvent for the separation of butadiene from butylene by extractive distillation. It is an intermediate in the synthesis of morpholine and N-substituted morpholine compounds (45,47), and of divinyl ether, a basic anesthetic.

Bis(2-chloroethyl) ether is strongly irritating to the skin, eyes, and mucous membranes. It may cause liver and kidney damage.

n-Propyl Ether

n-Propyl ether (dipropyl ether), $C_3H_7OC_3H_7$, is a mobile, highly volatile, extremely flammable liquid, with the following physical constants: mp, $-122°C$; bp, 90.5°C; d_4^{20} 0.7360; d_0^0 0.7661; n_D^{20} 1.3809. It is slightly soluble in water, miscible with alcohol and ether. Propyl ether may form explosive peroxides, and therefore should never be allowed to evaporate to dryness. Methods of preparation are as follows: heating n-propyl alcohol with sulfuric or benzenesulfonic acid; heating the boron trifluoride–alcoholate, $C_3H_7OH.BF_3$ (12); and passing n-propyl alcohol over nickel on magnesium oxide at 200°C. At present there is no market for large quantities of n-propyl ether. Although it reacts with chlorine, its chloro-derivatives (see Table 1) are prepared from the appropriate chlorohydrin (see Bis(chloroethyl) ether).

Isopropyl Ether

Isopropyl ether, $(CH_3)_2CHOCH(CH_3)_2$, is a colorless, moderately volatile, flammable liquid with a characteristic ethereal odor. In 1963 more than 5.25 million lb of isopropyl ether was produced in the United States.

PHYSICAL AND CHEMICAL PROPERTIES

Constants. Fp, $-86.2°C$; bp, $68.47°C$; d_{20}^{20} 0.7244; n_D^{20} 1.3682; flash point (open-cup), $15°F$ ($-9°F$, closed-cup).

Temperature, °C	0	10	20	40	60	68.47
Vapor pressure, mm Hg	41.5	74.5	125	283	600	760

Surface tension at $25°C$ is 19.4 dyn/cm; viscosity at $20°C$, 0.3220 cP; sp heat at $30°C$, 0.528 g-cal/(g)(°C); latent heat of vaporization, 68.2 g-cal/g; heat of formation, 841 g-cal/g; heat of combustion 9.38 kcal/g; cubical expansion coefficient, 0.00144/°C; dielectric constant (E), at 85.8 kc and $25°C$, 4.49; explosive limits at $100°C$, 1.1–4.5% by vol in air; autoignition temp, $443°C$. The solubility of isopropyl ether in water at $20°C$ is 0.94% by wt and that of water in isopropyl ether at $20°C$ is 0.55% by wt. Azeotropes of isopropyl ether are given in Table 7.

Reactions. Isopropyl ether undergoes the usual reactions of ether such as oxidation, chlorination, and cleavage with hydriodic acid, sulfuric acid, or phosphorus pentachloride. Isopropyl ether is nitrated in the vapor phase (5) to give methyl nitrate, isopropyl nitrate, $(CH_3)_2CHNO_2$, and also β-nitroisopropyl isopropyl ether, $NO_2CH_2CH(CH_3)OCH(CH_3)_2$, b_2 $47-49°C$; n_D^{25} 1.4218.

Photochlorination of isopropyl ether at $-20°C$ leads to 1,3-dichloropropane which is a low-melting lacrimatory solid (52). The chloro derivatives of isopropyl ether are best prepared from the appropriate chlorohydrin (see under Bis(2-chloroisopropyl) ether). Isopropyl ether can be used in the alkylation of benzene with hydrogen fluoride to give, 1,4-, 1,2,4-, and 1,2,4,5-isopropylbenzenes (53). At high temperatures and pressures, isopropyl ether reacts with phosphorus pentoxide to give triisopropyl phosphate (54).

Isopropyl ether forms explosive peroxides of uncertain composition. Isopropyl peroxide, $(iso-C_3H_7)_2O,O_2$, is not stable but decomposes to acetone and water (55). When isopropyl ether evaporates, triacetone peroxide and dimeric acetone peroxide, $(CH_3)_2C(O_2H)OC(O_2H)(CH_3)_2$, mp $132°C$, are formed. In the presence of water the dimer reverts to acetone peroxide, $(CH_3)_2C(O_2H)OH$, which is then hydrolyzed to acetone, hydrogen peroxide, and isopropyl alcohol. During the storage of isopropyl ether, acetone and hydrogen peroxide form triacetone peroxide, a highly explosive compound. Storage of isopropyl ether in the dark does not prevent peroxide formation

Table 7. Azeotropes of Isopropyl Ether

Other component	Boiling point, °C	Distillate, wt%	
		Isopropyl ether	Other component(s)
water	62.2	95.4[a]	4.6
isopropyl alcohol	66.2	85.9	14.1
acetone	53.3	43.5	56.5
acetonitrile	61.7	83.0	17.0
ethyl alcohol	64.0	82.9	17.1
isopropyl alcohol ⎱ water ⎰	61.8	90.3[a]	⎰ 6.6 ⎱ 3.1
acetonitrile ⎱ water ⎰	59.0	82.0[a]	⎰ 13.0 ⎱ 5.0

[a] A diphase mixture. See *Azeotrope Data*, American Chemical Society, Washington, D.C., 1952, for other azeotropes.

which occurs at approximately twice the rate as that for ethyl peroxide (56). The formation of peroxide is inhibited by addition of hydroquinone, naphthol, or polyhydric phenols (56,57) to freshly distilled isopropyl ether, and is completely suppressed by storage over 20% sodium hydroxide solution (56). Commercial isopropyl ether may contain p-benzylaminophenol as a stabilizer.

MANUFACTURE AND PREPARATION

Isopropyl ether is manufactured by the dehydration of isopropyl alcohol with sulfuric acid (58). It is obtained in large quantities as a by-product in the manufacture of isopropyl alcohol from propylene by the sulfuric acid process. Small changes in the process of isopropyl alcohol production can result in high percentages of isopropyl ether relative to the alcohol, or the entire production may be isopropyl ether. The manufacture of isopropyl ether from propylene is very similar to that of ethyl ether from ethylene (see above), the first products being the mixed- and diisopropyl sulfates. However, since isopropyl ether forms azeotropic mixtures with water and isopropyl alcohol (see Table 7), it is possible that the alcohol may not be completely removed in the ether tower and washer. If this is so, a portion of the upper phase of the ternary azeotrope from the dehydrating column may also be returned to the washer.

In the laboratory, isopropyl ether can be prepared in 57% yield by hydrogenation of acetone in the presence of isopropyl alcohol (59).

$$(CH_3)_2C{=}O + (CH_3)_2CHOH \xrightarrow[\text{at RT}]{H_2,\ PtO_2} (CH_3)_2CHOCH(CH_3)_2$$

ECONOMIC ASPECTS

Isopropyl ether has little economic importance as compared to ethyl ether. Isopropyl ether production in the United States from 1953–1963 amounted to less than 1% of the isopropyl alcohol produced. In 1963, 5,253,000 lb of isopropyl ether and 1,465,520,000 lb of isopropyl alcohol were produced. Since only 2,876,000 lb of isopropyl ether were sold, it is apparent that a large portion was converted to the alcohol or diverted to motor fuels, etc, without reaching other chemical industries.

SPECIFICATION, TESTING, AND STANDARDS

A typical specification for isopropyl ether is as follows: Color (Hazen), 15 max; d_{20}^{20} 0.7244–0.7260; distillation range, 63–69°C; acidity (as propionic acid) 0.01 wt %, max; peroxides (as isopropyl peroxide) 0.05 wt %, max; nonvolatiles, 0.005g/ 100 ml.

A simple test for the presence of peroxide as active oxygen can be made by treating two volumes of isopropyl ether with one volume of 4% potassium iodide, slightly acidified (60). This test has the following semiquantitative interpretation:

Active oxygen in isopropyl ether, ppm	Qualitative color test
30	very faint yellow
50	faint yellow
70	yellow to brown
100	light brown
145	brown
240	dark iodine color

If a sample of isopropyl ether gives a dark-brown coloration, the ether should not be distilled without first reducing the active-oxygen content with a reducing agent such as sodium sulfite. A typical specification would correspond to an active-oxygen content of 12 ppm of isopropyl ether.

METHODS OF HANDLING

Isopropyl ether is classified by the ICC as a "flammable liquid." It must, therefore, be packed in ICC-specification containers when shipped by rail, water, or highway, and all ICC regulations regarding loading, handling, and labeling must be followed. The containers generally used in commerce are 55-gal drums and tank cars. Each container of isopropyl ether must carry an identifying label or stencil. Tank cars and boxcars carrying isopropyl ether must bear the ICC "dangerous" placard. Each drum and each box with inside containers must bear the ICC red label for flammable liquids.

The handling of isopropyl ether is a hazardous operation because of its flammability. In addition to being fairly volatile, it is a nonconductor and can generate static electrical charges that may cause ignition or explosion. The area in which it is handled should be considered as a Class I hazardous location as defined by the National Electrical Code. All tools used in making repairs or connections should be of the nonsparking type. In loading or unloading tank cars, the same precautions should be exercised as with gasoline or any other flammable liquid. It is especially important to make sure that the tank cars are properly grounded before making any connections.

HEALTH AND SAFETY FACTORS

Isopropyl ether gives a lighter anesthesia than ethyl ether and takes longer to produce unconsciousness. It is about 1.5–2 times as toxic as ethyl ether when administered orally or by inhalation in concentrations above 3% in air. Experiments on monkeys indicate that the fatal concentrations of isopropyl ether in air are between 3 and 6% and that daily exposures of 1 hr or longer to 1% of the vapor could be tolerated for twenty days without permanent damage; 16,000 ppm in air is fatal to rats.

Good ventilation is a necessary precaution and an effective means of control of both fire and health hazards. Any workman exposed to dangerous concentrations of ether should be removed immediately. Except in emergencies, and then only with the proper safety equipment (fresh-air mask), no one should enter a zone containing ether vapor until the concentration is found to be safe by measurement with a combustible-gas indicator.

USES

Isopropyl ether is of moderate importance as an industrial solvent. Being higher-boiling than ethyl ether or acetone, it offers a distinct advantage in certain extraction processes. Low solubility of isopropyl ether in water makes it an attractive extractant for recovering acetic acid, lactic acid, etc, from dilute aqueous solutions. It is an excellent solvent for animal, vegetable and mineral oils, fats, waxes, and resins. The solubility of paraffin wax in isopropyl ether decreases quite rapidly as acetone is added or as the temperature is lowered; the solubility of mineral oil is not appreciably changed. For this reason, isopropyl ether, alone or mixed with other solvents, such as acetone (61), aniline (62), or methyl acetate (63) may be used for dewaxing paraffin-base oils.

In textile spotting, isopropyl ether is preferred to ethyl ether because of its lower vapor pressure and less tendency to form rings. Isopropyl ether extracts nicotine from tobacco. It is used as a solvent in the manufacture of pharmaceuticals, smokeless powder, paint and varnish removers, and rubber cements. Isopropyl ether is a good high-octane blending agent although it has never been widely used. It has a good solvent action on anti-knock compounds, does not show icing tendencies in fuel-feed systems and has a slightly better blending value than technical isooctane (see Gasoline).

Bis(2-Chloroisopropyl) Ether

Bis(2-chloroisopropyl) ether (β,β'-dichlorodiisopropyl ether), $ClCH_2CH(CH_3)$-$OCH(CH_3)CH_2Cl$, is a colorless liquid; bp, 187.1°C; d_4^{20} 1.1127; n_D^{20} 1.4505; flash point (open-cup), 185°F. It is similar in properties to bis(2-chloroethyl) ether, but is less soluble in water (0.17% by weight at 20°C), has a higher boiling point, and lower volatility. Being miscible with practically all oils and organic liquids, it is an excellent solvent and extractant for fats, waxes, and greases. In textile processes, bis(2-chloroisopropyl) ether assists the action of soap solutions without excessive loss by evaporation from the hot solutions. It is also used in paint and varnish removers, spotting agents and cleaning solutions. Because it undergoes the same chemical reactions as bis(2-chloroethyl) ether, bis(2-chloroisopropyl) ether offers numerous possibilities as an intermediate for the manufacture of chemicals which are generally less soluble in water, but more soluble in oil because of the two additional methyl groups.

It is best prepared from β-chloroisopropyl alcohol by the sulfuric acid process.

$$ClCH_2CHOH \xrightarrow{H_2SO_4} ClCH_2CHOCHCH_2Cl$$
$$\quad\quad |\quad\quad\quad\quad\quad\quad |\quad\quad |$$
$$\quad\quad CH_3\quad\quad\quad\quad\quad\quad CH_3\ CH_3$$

Typical specifications for bis(2-chloroisopropyl) ether are as follows: Color (APHA), 40 max; d_{20}^{20} 1.113–1.119; distillation range, 180–190°C; acidity (as HCl), 0.01 wt %, max; water, 0.10 wt %, max; flash point (open-cup), 185°F.

Butyl Ethers

Of the four butyl ethers mentioned in Table 1, only the straight-chain isomer is available in commercial quantities.

n-**Butyl ether,** $CH_3(CH_2)_3O(CH_2)_3CH_3$, is a colorless liquid; mp, −98°C; bp, 142°C; d_4^0 0.7481; d_4^{20} 0.7704; flash point (open-cup), 100°F; viscosity at 15°C, 0.741 cP; surface tension at 15°C, 23.47 dyn/cm;

Temperature, °C	11.3	29.7	66.8	127.7
Vapor pressure, mm Hg	7.5	14.5	57.04	570.5

It is almost insoluble in water (0.03% by wt, at 20°C) but miscible in ethyl alcohol and ether. Like the other ethers, *n*-butyl ether forms explosive peroxides which should be removed before distillation. Azeotropes of *n*-butyl ether are given in Table 8.

Typical specifications are as follows: Color (APHA), 15 max; d_{20}^{20} 0.768–0.771; distillation range, 137–143°C; acidity (as butyric acid), 0.02 wt %, max; water, 0.10 wt %, max; flash point (open-cup), 100°F.

n-Butyl ether is an excellent extracting agent for use with aqueous systems since its solubility in water is less than 1% that of ethyl ether. It is an important solvent

Table 8. Azeotropes of *n*-Butyl Ether

Other component	Bp, °C	Distillate, wt %	
		n-Butyl ether	Other component
water	94.1	66.6[a]	33.4
acetic acid	116.7	19	81.0
butyl alcohol	117.6	17.5[a]	82.5
butyl alcohol \ water	90.6	35.5[a]	$\begin{cases} 34.6 \\ 29.9 \end{cases}$

[a] Diphase system.

for the Grignard and other reactions that require an anhydrous, inert medium. Since it forms many constant-boiling azeotropes, it is useful for purifying other solvents. It is used in the extraction of hormones and of thioglycolic acid and is an intermediate in "cold" hair-waving formulations (see Hair treatment).

As an ether it undergoes oxidation, cleavage, and nitration (5). Butyl iodide can be prepared in high yields by heating butyl ether with a mixture of phosphoric acid, phosphorus pentoxide, and potassium iodide (64); the chloride is obtained in 50% yield by heating with titanium tetrachloride (65). Dibutyl ether can be aminated in the vapor phase to give 80% amines consisting of mono-, di-, and tributylamines (66) and reacts with ethyl diazoacetate to produce ethyl *n*-butoxyacetate and butylene (67). Various simple and mixed chlorobutyl ethers are known. Although butyl ether can be chlorinated, its bis(chloro) ethers are usually made from the chloro alcohol. Thus, bis(4-chlorobutyl) ether (see Table 1) is prepared from 4-chlorobutyl alcohol by the sulfuric acid method, or better, by heating furan with phosphorus oxychloride and sulfuric acid.

n-Butyl ether is prepared by dehydration of *n*-butyl alcohol by sulfuric acid or by catalytic dehydration over ferric chloride, copper sulfate, alum, etc.

sec-**Butyl ether** is not available commercially but can be prepared by dehydration of *sec*-butyl alcohol.

Isobutyl ether is not available commercially but has been prepared by dehydration of isobutyl alcohol and by hydrogenation of methallyl ether, $(CH_2 = C(CH_3)CH_2)_2O$ (68).

t-**Butyl ether,** is not a commercial chemical but its synthesis and properties are worth mentioning. The synthesis of di-*t*-butyl ether was long a vexing problem. Reboul, in 1889, observed that the conventional Williamson technique produced only isobutylene and *t*-butyl alcohol. Until the early 1940s it was felt that two tertiary butyl groups could not be accommodated by one oxygen atom because of the overcrowding of methyl groups. It was finally prepared in 31% yield, by the reaction of *t*-butyl chloride with silver carbonate in dry ether (69).

$$2\,(CH_3)_3CCl + Ag_2CO_3 \xrightarrow{\text{ether}} (CH_3)_3COC(CH_3)_3 + 2\,AgCl + CO_2$$

Di-*t*-butyl ether is a clear, mobile liquid, bp, 108–109°C; n_D^{20} 1.3946; d_{20}^{20} 0.7622; heat of combustion at 25°C, 1268.7 kcal/mole; heat of formation at 25°C, 96.2 kcal/mole for the liquid and 87.2 kcal/mole for gas; heat of vaporization, 9.0 kcal/mole.

Unlike the other ethers discussed in this article, *t*-butyl ether is readily hydrolyzed by dilute acids and gives an immediate Lucas test for *t*-butyl alcohol, with dilute hydrochloric acid.

t-Butyl ether has an odor reminiscent of camphor. This has been attributed to the high steric strain resulting in nearly spherical structure. This strain is approximately 7.6 kcal/mole and is a consequence of the crowding of the opposed methyl groups (70).

Amyl Ethers

n-**Amyl ether**, $CH_3(CH_2)_4O(CH_2)_4CH_3$ (*n*-pentyl ether), is a pale yellowish liquid; mp, $-69.3°C$; bp, $187.5°C$, d_4^{20} 0.7751; d_4^0 0.79881; n_D^{15} 1.4139; surface tension at 20°C, 24.76 dyn/cm; viscosity, 30°C, 1.188 cP; flash point (open-cup), 135°F. It is insoluble in water and soluble in ethyl alcohol and ethyl ether.

Commercial amyl ether, $C_5H_{11}OC_5H_{11}$, is a mixture principally of isoamyl ether and *n*-amyl ether, formed as a by-product in the preparation of amyl alcohols from amyl chloride (see Vol. 2, p. 375). It forms an azeotrope with water which boils at 96–98°C; the distillate contains 59% by wt of water and 41% by wt amyl ether. Amyl ether is available in laboratory samples for $18.30/100 g from two different suppliers. Because a third source lists it at $6.00/500 g, amyl ether is probably available in technical grades differing in amounts of the *n*- and iso-isomers.

Isoamyl Ether, $(CH_3)_2CHCH_2CH_2OCH_2CH_2CH(CH_3)_2$, (isopentyl ether), is a colorless liquid with a pearlike odor; bp, 173.2°C, d_4^{20} 0.7777; n_D^{20} 1.4085; surface tension at 21.7°C, 22.85 dyn/cm. It is extremely insoluble in water (less than 0.02 ml/100 ml water at 20°C) but miscible with alcohol, chloroform, and ether. There is no commercial application requiring large quantities of isoamyl ether. A technical grade is available for $13.05/500 g; bp, 170–173°C. Isoamyl ether can be prepared in the laboratory from 3-methyl-1-butanol by the sulfuric acid method.

sec-**Amyl Ether** (see Table 1) can be prepared in the laboratory by dehydration of 2-pentanol with sulfuric acid. It is not a commercial chemical.

Hexyl Ether

n-Hexyl ether, $CH_3(CH_2)_5O(CH_2)_5CH_3$, is a mild-odored stable liquid; bp, 226.2°C; b_9, 95–97°C; d_4^{20} 0.7936; n_D^{20} 1.4204; flash point (open-cup), 170°F. *n*-Hexyl ether is much less volatile than the lower members of the ether family (see Table 1) and is extremely insoluble in water (less than 0.01% by wt). Its low solubility in water and relatively mild odor make *n*-hexyl ether a convenient solvent for chemical reactions requiring a strictly anhydrous ether medium. Hexyl ether is no longer available as a bulk chemical. Laboratory samples cost $5.50/lb. (In 1962 hexyl ether was available for approximately $0.80/lb in 55-gal drums.)

Higher Alkyl Ethers

The following simple, straight-chain, aliphatic ethers are commercially available for approx $6.00/lb: heptyl ether (bp, 259°C), octyl ether (mp, $-7°C$), decyl ether (mp, 16°C), dodecyl ether (mp, 33°C); tetradecyl ether (mp, 40°C), hexadecyl ether (mp, 54°C), octadecyl ether (mp, 59°C).

Allyl Ether

Allyl ether, $CH_2{=}CHCH_2OCH_2CH{=}CH_2$, (diallyl ether), is a colorless liquid with a radishlike odor; bp, 94.8°C; d_4^{20} 0.8053; n_D^{20} 1.4163 (71), 1.4240 (72); flash point (open-cup), 23°F. It is insoluble in water, but miscible with ethyl alcohol and ether. It forms a binary azeotrope with water boiling at 89.8°C; an azeotrope with water and allyl alcohol (12.4% water, 8.7% allyl alcohol, and 78.9% allyl ether) boils at 77.8°C.

Allyl ether can be prepared in the laboratory by dehydration of allyl alcohol with sulfuric acid. Unlike the preparation of other alkyl ethers, this reaction may result in a violent explosion (73). Among other methods of preparation are the following: heating allyl iodide with mercuric oxide (74); from allyl bromide and 50% aqueous potassium hydroxide (75); from allyl alcohol in liquefied hydrogen chloride (71); and by heating allyl alcohol and hydrochloric acid (75), a strong Lewis acid, or an acid ion-exchange resin (76,76a) in the presence of a cuprous salt. It is conveniently prepared in the laboratory according to the following reaction (72):

$$CH_2{=}CHCH_2OH + CH_2{=}CHCH_2Br \xrightarrow[\substack{acetone, \\ reflux}]{K_2CO_3} CH_2{=}CHCH_2OCH_2CH{=}CH_2$$
$$99\% \text{ yield}$$

Allyl ether forms explosive peroxides on prolonged contact with air, especially in light. Care should be exercised to destroy such peroxides by shaking with ferrous sulfate solution before distillation. Allyl ether is easily oxidized at the olefinic linkage; ie, sodium metaperiodate and potassium permanganate give formaldehyde; this method is useful in determining terminal methylene groups (77). At low temperatures ($-10°C$) allyl ether is chlorinated with the formation of bis(2,3-dichloropropyl) ether, $(ClCH_2{-}CHClCH_2)_2O$; at 27°C allyl 2,3-dichloropropyl ether, $CH_2{=}CHCH_2OCH_2CHClCH_2Cl$, is the chlorination product (78). n-Propyl ether is readily obtained by hydrogenation of allyl ether. It is hydrolyzed in the vapor phase over copper sulfate or alumina to give allyl alcohol (79) and over sodium to give 1,5-hexadiene $(CH_2{=}CHCH_2)_2$, and allyl alcohol (80). Allyl sodium, formed in the reaction of allyl ether with sodium in hexane, reacts with dry ice to form 3-butenoic acid, $CH_2{=}CHCH_2CO_2H$, in 77% yield, and with alkyl halides such as 2-bromooctane to give 4-methyl-1-decene, $CH_2{=}CHCH_2CH(CH_3)(CH_2)_5CH_3$, in 71% yield (81). Hydroxylation and hydrochlorination of allyl ether gives intermediates which may be converted to diglycerol (82); the reaction with hypochlorous acid leads to the di(chlorohydrin) which can be epoxidized to the diglycidyl ether, $OCH_2CHCH_2OCH_2CHCH_2O$, and hydrolyzed to diglycerol, $HOCH_2CH(OH)CH_2OCH_2CH(OH)CH_2OH$. Allyl ether reacts with hydrogen sulfide to give a variety of products depending on the reaction conditions. Photochemically induced reactions of allyl ether with hydrogen sulfide produce polymers, eg, $CH_2{=}CHCHO(CH_2)_3(S(CH_2)_3OCH_2)_3)_4SH$ and $H(S(CH_2)_3O(CH_2)_3)_4SH$ (83) which are oils, greases, or polishes with very low pour points. At high pressures in the presence of catalytic amounts of butylamine, allyl ether reacts with hydrogen sulfide to give a 43% yield of 3,5-dimethyl-1,4-oxathiane, $SCH(CH_3)CH_2{-}OCH_2CH(CH_3)$, b_{16} 113°C; n_D^{20} 1.4850 (84). Allyl ether is readily epoxidized with peracetic acid to form allyl glycidyl ether (see Table 1) in 66% yield (85). Ketones are produced from allyl ether and aldehydes under pressure in the presence of free radicals; allyl ether reacts with butyraldehyde in the presence of benzoyl peroxide to give 3-butyrylpropenyl allyl ether, $C_3H_7COCH_2CH{=}CH_2OCH_2CH{=}CH_2$, b_6 96–98°C; n_D^{20}, 1.4539 (86). Allyl ether is cleaved by Grignard reagents; thus, butylmagnesium bromide gives allyl alcohol (56%), with 5% t-butyl allyl ether $(CH_3)_3{-}COCH_2CH{=}CH_2$ and 7.5% 4,4-dimethyl-1-pentene as by-products; phenylmagnesium bromide gives allyl alcohol (40%) 3-phenylpropene (38%), as well as propionaldehyde (16%) (87).

Limited experimental studies indicate that diallyl ether differs very little from other aliphatic ethers in its toxicity.

Benzyl Ether

Benzyl ether, $C_6H_5CH_2OCH_2C_6H_5$, is a colorless oily liquid; mp, 4–5°C; bp, 295–298°C; d_{15}^{15} 1.036; flash point (closed-cup), 135°C. It is gradually decomposed in moist air with the formation of benzaldehyde. Benzyl ether is insoluble in water but readily soluble in alcohol and ether. The commercial product has the following specifications: color (APHA), 50 max; d_{25}^{25} 1.037–1.040; distillation range, at 20 mm Hg, 170–180°C; fp, −1.5 to +1.5.

The usual reactions may be applied to the benzene nucleus, such as halogenation, nitration, sulfonation, and hydrogenation. The ether linkage is relatively stable under normal conditions. The methylene hydrogens can be replaced by several reactions.

In the presence of zinc chloride and hydrochloric acid at 100°C benzyl ether is converted to benzyl chloride (88). A process has been developed for the conversion of benzyl ether to benzaldehyde, benzoic acid, and benzyl benzoate in 80–85% yield by noncatalytic oxidation in air at 40–250°C (89). When passed over alumina at 340°C, benzyl ether disproportionates to toluene and benzaldehyde in good yields (90). When benzyl ether is heated over sodium or allowed to react with sodamide in liquid ammonia, a rearrangement reaction gives 1,2-diphenylethanol, $C_6H_5CH_2CHOHC_6H_5$, and small amounts of toluene and benzaldehyde or benzyl alcohol as by-products (91). Benzyl ether is readily cleaved, at room temperature, by Grignard reagents, such as butylmagnesium bromide, in the presence of cobalt chloride, to form toluene and benzyl alcohol (92).

Benzyl ether can be prepared in 70% yield by dehydration of benzyl alcohol. When the ratio of benzyl alcohol to sulfuric acid exceeds 1:0.5, hydrocarbon products are produced exclusively (93). When benzyl chloride is reacted with potassium hydroxide at 200°C, benzyl ether is produced (bp, 285–290°C), a colorless liquid with a light-blue fluorescence (94) caused by impurities. A 43% yield of benzyl ether has been obtained by reductive hydrogenation of benzaldehyde in the presence of cobalt hydrocarbonyl, $HCo(CO)_4$ (95).

$$2\ C_6H_5CHO + 2\ H_2 \xrightarrow[\substack{3200\ psi \\ 45\ min}]{cat.HCo\ (CO)_4} C_6H_5CH_2OCH_2C_6H_5 + H_2O$$

It has been prepared in the laboratory, in 63% yield, by the reaction of sodium benzylate, $C_6H_5CH_2ONa$, with p-toluenesulfonimidazolide in benzene at room temperature (96). In this modified Williamson method, bis(p-toluenesulfonates) of glycols can be used (96a).

Benzyl ether serves as a plasticizer for cellulose nitrate and cellulose acetate and as a solubilizer for gums, resins, synthetic and natural rubbers, and waxes. In the perfume industry, benzyl ether is used as a solvent for artificial musks. Mixtures of benzyl ether and zinc oxide in creams, lotions, emulsions, or powders are effective against fleas, mosquitoes, flies, gnats, etc (97).

Bibliography

"Ethers" in *ECT* 1st ed., Vol. 5, pp. 858–876, by Mary A. Magill, Chemical Abstracts, and J. G. Parks and C. M. Beamer, Enjay Co., Inc.

Ethers

1. M. Lecat, *Ann. Soc. Sci. Bruxelles. Sér.* I **61**, 153, 255 (1947); **62**, 93 (1948).
2. H. Gilman, *Organic Chemistry*, John Wiley & Sons, Inc., New York, 1943, p. 822.
3. R. Lydén, *Chem. Rev.* **1**, 1813 (1925).
4. B. V. Tronov and L. V. Laduigina, *Ber.* **B62**, 2844 (1929).
5. H. B. Hass and D. V. Hudgin, *J. Am. Chem. Soc.* **76**, 2692–2694 (1954).
6. A. I. Vogel, *J. Chem. Soc.* **1948**, 616–624.
6a. A. I. Vogel, *A Text-Book of Practical Organic Chemistry*, 3rd ed., Longmans, Green & Co., London, 1957, pp. 309–315.
7. J. van Alphen, *Rec. Trav. Chim.* **49**, 754–761 (1930).
7a. J. B. Senderens, *Compt. Rend.* **181**, 689–700 (1925).
8. P. G. Stevens and S. A. V. Deans, *Can. J. Research* **17B**, 290–292 (1939).
9. *U.S. Dept. Comm. Office Tech. Serv. Rept. PBL-63906* (1933); *Bibliog. Sci. Ind.* **5** (7), 573 (1947).
10. T. W. Evans and K. R. Edlund, *Ind. Eng. Chem.* **28**, 1186 (1936).
11. J. Hamonet, *Compt. Rend.* **138**, 813 (1904).
12. I. Romadane and J. Pelcher, *Izvest. Vysshykh Ucheb. Zavidenii, Khim. i Khim. Tekhnol.* **2** (3), 381–383 (1959); *Chem. Abstr.* **54**, 4357i (1960).

Methyl Ether

13. R. M. Kennedy, M. Sagenkahn, and J. G. Aston, *J. Am. Chem. Soc.* **63**, 2267 (1941).
14. Japan Pat. 214 ('55) (Jan. 21, 1955), T. Tsukamoto and K. Suzuki (to Mitsubishi Chemical Industries Co.).
15. U.S. Pat 2,860,170 (Nov. 11, 1958), J. Criscione and W. H. Bernauer (to Callery Chemical Co.).
16. P. H. Given and D. L. Hammick, *J. Chem. Soc.* **1947**, 931.
17. U.S. Pat. 1,884,628 (Oct. 25, 1933), H. Dreyfus.
17a. J. W. Reppe, *Acetylene Chemistry*, Charles A. Meyer & Co., Inc., New York, 1949, p. 172 (*PB Rept.-18552*, translated from the German).
17b. U.S. Pats. 2,135,449 and 2,135,450 (Nov. 1, 1939), D. J. Loder and A. T. Larson, respectively (to E. I. du Pont de Nemours & Co., Inc.).
18. U.S. Pat. 1,943,375 (Jan. 16, 1934), H. Dreyfus.
19. U.S. Pat. 2,095,224 (Oct. 12, 1935), L. A. Andrussow (to I. G. Farbenindustrie A. G.).
20. A. Rieche and H. Gross, *Chem. Tech.* (*Berlin*) **10**, 515–518 (1958).
21. J. F. Norris, *Ind. Eng. Chem.* **11**, 817–829 (1919).
22. S. R. Buc, in N. J. Leonard, ed., *Organic Syntheses*, Vol. 36, John Wiley & Sons, Inc., New York, 1956, p. 1.
23. U.S. Pat. 2,849,465 (Aug. 26, 1958), D. I. Randall and W. E. Renfrew (to General Aniline & Film Corp.).

Ethyl Ether

24. J. R. Partington, *A History of Chemistry*, Vols. 2 and 3, McMillan & Co., Ltd., 1961, and 1962.
25. *Ethyl Ether*, Chemical Safety Data Sheet SD-29, Manufacturing Chemists' Association, Washington, D.C., 1948.
26. *Ethyl Ether*, Data Sheet D—Chem. 7, National Safety Council, Chicago, Ill.
27. U.S. Pat. 2,477,312 (July 22, 1949), P. T. Parker (to Standard Oil Development Co.).
28. J. van Alphen, *Rec. Trav. Chim.* **49**, 492–500 (1930).
29. U.S. Pat. 2,534,085 (Dec. 12, 1950), B. M. Vanderbilt and J. P. Thorn (to Standard Oil Development Co.).
30. A. W. Laubengayer and G. R. Finlay, *J. Am. Chem. Soc.* **65**, 884–889 (1943).
31. G. E. Hall and F. M. Umbertini, *J. Org. Chem.* **15**, 715–719 (1950).

32. K. Kratzl and K. Schubert, *Monatsh.* **81,** 988–995 (1952).

33. B. T. Brooks, *Ind. Eng. Chem.* **27,** 278–288 (1935).

34. C. Ellis, *The Chemistry of Petroleum Derivatives,* Vol. II, Reinhold Publishing Corp., New York, 1938, pp. 323, 324, 330–337, 360–361, 378–381, 825, 826, 1017, 1202.

35. U.S. Pat. 2,126,952 (Aug. 18, 1938), H. Dreyfus.

36. U.S. Pat. 2,179,092 (Nov. 7, 1939), V. Ipatieff (to Universal Oil Products Co.).

37. U.S. Pat. 2,107,069 (Feb. 1, 1938), T. Evans (to Shell Development Co.).

38. *Reagent Chemicals-ACS Specifications,* American Chemical Society, Washington, D.C., 1952.

39. *Recommended Practice for Unloading Flammable Liquids from Tank Cars,* Manual Sheet TC-4, Manufacturing Chemists' Association, Washington, D.C., 1952.

40. U.S. Pat. 1,632,309 (June 14, 1927), F. W. Nitardy (to E. R. Squibb & Sons).

41. U.S. Pat. 1,813,664 (July 7, 1931), W. G. Christiansen and R. Van Winkle (to E. R. Squibb & Sons).

42. U.S. Pat. 1,814,718 (July 14, 1931), E. Mallinckrodt, Jr. (to Mallinckrodt Chemical Works).

Bis(2-Chloroethyl) Ether

43. O. Kamm and J. H. Waldo, *J. Am. Chem. Soc.* **43,** 2223 (1921).

44. E. A. Shilov, *Dokl. Akad. Nauk SSSR* **47,** 490–492 (1945); *Chem. Abstr.* **40,** 5393 (1946).

45. W. L. Ruigh and R. T. Major, *J. Am. Chem. Soc.* **53,** 2662–2671 (1931).

46. J. H. Cretcher, J. A. Koch, and W. H. Pittenger, *J. Am. Chem. Soc.* **47,** 1173–1177 (1925).

47. W. V. Farrar, *J. Chem. Soc.* **1956,** 782–783.

48. C. S. Gibson and J. D. A. Johnson, *J. Chem. Soc.* **1930,** 2525.

49. U.S. Pat. 3,067,267 (Dec. 4, 1962), D. M. Young and D. N. Glew (to Dow Chemical Co.).

50. Brit. Pat. 744,454 (Feb. 8, 1956), Olin Mathieson Chemical Corp.

51. U.S. Pat. 2,680,092 (June 1, 1954), J. W. Churchill and B. B. Schaeffer (to Mathieson Chemical Corp.).

Isopropyl Ether

52. G. E. Hall and I. Sirel, *J. Am. Chem. Soc.* **74,** 836 (1952).

53. J. H. Simons and S. Archer, *J. Am. Chem. Soc.* **62,** 1623 (1940).

54. Brit. Pat. 649,584 (Jan. 31, 1951), D. C. Hull and J. R. Snodgrass (to Eastman Kodak Co.).

55. A. Rieche and K. Koch, *Ber.* **75B,** 1016–1028 (1942).

56. W. Hunter and J. Downing, *J. Soc. Chem. Ind.* (*London*) **68,** 362–364 (1949).

57. M. Katsuno, *J. Chem. Soc. Japan, Ind. Chem. Sect.* **44,** 903–907 (1941).

58. U.S. Pat. 2,105,508 (Jan. 18, 1939), R. Rosen, H. Berk, and R. B. Lebo (to Standard Alcohol Co.).

59. M. Verzele, M. Acke, and M. Anteunis, *J. Chem. Soc.* **1963,** 5598–5600.

60. E. Hofman, M. Lapeyrouse, and W. Sweeney, *Congr. Mondial Pétrole* **3,** *IIme Congr., Paris, 1937,* Sect 4, 812–819 (1937); *Chem. Abstr.* **34,** 2578 (1940).

61. U.S. Pat. 1,947,359 (Feb. 13, 1934), E. W. Reid (to Carbide & Carbon Chemicals Corp.).

62. U.S. Pat. 2,044,721 (June 16, 1936), F. S. Govers (to Indian Refining Co.).

63. U.S. Pat. 1,938,545 (Dec. 5, 1933), F. W. Sullivan, Jr. (to Standard Oil Co. of Ind.).

Butyl Ethers

64. H. Stone and H. Schechter, *J. Org. Chem.* **15,** 491–495 (1950).

65. P. Mastagli, C. Gnanadickam, and G. Garat, *Compt. Rend.* **250,** 4381 (1960).

66. N. S. Kozlov and M. I. Panova, *J. Gen. Chem. USSR (Eng. Transl.)* **25,** 167–170 (1955); *Chem. Abstr.* **50,** 1572g (1956).

67. G. B. R. deGraaff, J. H. van Dijck-Rothius, and G. van de Kolk, *Rec. Trav. Chim.* **74,** 143–154 (1955).

68. U.S. Pat. 2,122,812 (July 5, 1938), H. P. A. Groll (to Shell Development Co.).

69. J. L. E. Erickson and W. Ashton, *J. Am. Chem. Soc.* **63,** 1769 (1941).

70. E. J. Smutny and A. Bondi, *J. Phys. Chem.* **65,** 546–550 (1961).

Allyl Ether

71. E. Gebauer-Fuelnegg and E. Moffett, *J. Am. Chem. Soc.* **56**, 2009 (1934).

72. R. Riemschneider and H. J. Kotzsch, *Monatsh. Chem.* **90**, 787–791 (1959).

73. J. B. Senderens, *Compt. Rend.* **181**, 698–700 (1925).

74. M. Berthelot and S. de Luca, *Ann. Chem. et Phys.* [3] **48**, 291 (1856).

75. H. Biltz and A. Beck, *J. Prakt. Chem.* [2] **118**, 221 (1928).

76. P. Kurtz, *Ann.* **572**, 23–28 (1951).

76a. Brit. Pat. 913,919 (Dec. 28, 1962), R. J. Stephenson (to Monsanto Chemicals, Ltd.).

77. R. U. Lemieux and E. von Rudloff, *Can. J. Chem.* **33**, 1710–1713 (1955).

78. U.S. Pat. 2,464,758 (Mar. 15, 1949), P. H. Williams and T. W. Evans (to Shell Development Co.).

79. U.S. Pat. 2,434,394 (Jan. 13, 1948), H. A. Cheney, R. Dagley, Jr., and S. H. McAllister (to Shell Development Co.).

80. U.S. Pat. 2,405,347 (Aug. 6, 1946), H. Dreyfus, F. Bryans, and J. G. N. Drewitt.

81. R. L. Letsinger and J. G. Traynham, *J. Am. Chem. Soc.* **70**, 3342–3344 (1948).

82. H. Wittcoff, J. R. Roach, and S. E Miller, *J. Am. Chem. Soc.* **71**, 2666 (1949).

83. U.S. Pat. 2,522,512 (Sept. 19, 1950), D. Harman and W. E. Vaughan (to Shell Development Co.).

83a. U.S. Pat. 2,522,589 (Sept. 19, 1950), W. E. Vaughan and F. F. Rust (to Shell Development Co.).

84. U.S. Pat. 2,562,145 (July 24, 1951), D. Harman and W. E. Vaughan (to Shell Development Co.).

85. F. C. Frostick, Jr., B. Phillips, and P. S. Starcher, *J. Am. Chem. Soc.* **81**, 3350–3356 (1959).

86. Brit. Pat. 635,934 (Apr. 19, 1950), United States Rubber Co.

87. C. H. Hill, L. Haynes, D. E. Simmons, and M. E. Hill, *J. Am. Chem. Soc.* **80**, 3623–3625 (1958).

Benzyl Ether

88. Y. Yamashita and T. Shimamura, *Kôgakuin Daigaku Kenkyû Hôkoku,* **5**, 31–34 (1954); *Chem. Abstr.* **53**, 19988c (1959).

89. F. G. Eichel and D. F. Othmer, *Ind. Eng. Chem.* **41**, 2623–2626 (1949).

90. H. Adkins and K. Folkers, *J. Am. Chem. Soc.* **53**, 1420–1424 (1931).

91. A. J. Weinheimer, S. W. Kantor and C. R. Hauser, *J. Org. Chem.* **18**, 801–805 (1953).

92. M. S. Kharasch and R. L. Huang, *J. Org. Chem.* **17**, 669–677 (1952).

93. J. B. Senderens, *Compt. Rend.* **182**, 612–615 (1926).

94. Ger. Pat. 343,930 (1923), Farbenfabriken A.G.

95. V. N. Davydov, *Chem. Tech.* (*Berlin*) **11**, 431–440 (1959).

96. H. A. Staab and K. Wendel, *Angew. Chem.* **72**, 708 (1960).

96a. J. Lichtenberger and P. Tritsch, *Bull. Soc. Chim. France* **1961**, 363–371.

97. U.S. Pat. 2,469,228 (May. 3, 1949), S. I. Gertler (to the People of the U.S.).

ARNOLD P. LURIE
Eastman Kodak Co.

ETHYL ACETATE, $CH_3COOC_2H_5$.   See Esters, organic.

ETHYL ALCOHOL, CH_3CH_2OH.   See Ethanol.

ETHYLAMINES.   See Amines, Vol. 2, p. 122.

ETHYLATION.   See Alkylation.

ETHYLBENZENE, $C_6H_5C_2H_5$.   See Xylenes and ethylbenzene; Styrene.

ETHYLENE

Ethylene (ethene (IUPAC)), CH_2=CH_2, is the simplest unsaturated or olefinic hydrocarbon. It is a colorless, flammable gas with a faint, pleasant odor. It is one of the world's major growth chemicals, and is used extensively as a raw material in the synthetic organic chemical and plastics industries.

Physical and Chemical Properties

Constants. Melting point, $-169.4°C$; boiling point, $-103.9°C$; d^{-102}_4 0.566; n^{-100}_D 1.363; vapor density (air = 1), 0.9676; surface tension at bp, 16.5 dyn/cm; viscosity of gas at $0°C$, 90.7 μP; heat of vaporization at bp, 115.39 cal/g; heat of combustion (gross), 337.23 kcal/mole; crit temp, $9.9°C$; crit pressure, 50.5 atm; crit density, 0.227 g/cm³; coefficient of thermal expansion (at constant pressure between 0 and $100°C$) $0.003735/°C$; limits of flammability in air: lower limit, 2.75%, upper limit, 28.6%.

Vapor pressure data in the region above the normal boiling point can be satisfactorily correlated by the following equation (1), where T is expressed in °K, $\log P_{atm} = -646.275/T + 1.880472 \log T - 0.00224072 T$.

Below the normal boiling point the Antoine equation should be used. Constants for the Antoine equation (2) are tabulated in Table 1.

Table 1.   Constants of Antoine Equation[a]

Constant	Temperature range, °C		
	-169.2 to -103.7	-103.7 to -70.0	-70.0 to $+9.5$
A	6.76503	6.87477	7.20581
B	590.338	624.240	768.26
C	255.684	260.007	282.43

[a] $\log p = A - B/(t + C)$, where $t = °C$, $p = $ mm Hg.

The constants for the van der Waals equation,

$$(P + n^2a/V^2)\,(V - nb) = nRT$$

for n moles are a, 4.471 (liter)² (atm)/(mole)²; and b, 0.05714 liter/mole.

For the ideal gas state at $298.16°K$, the chemical thermodynamic properties expressed as cal/mole are $\Delta H_f°$, 12.496; $\Delta F_f°$, 16.282; $\log K_f$, μ -11.9345; and $S°$, 52.54.

Values of the molar heat capacity at a pressure of one atmosphere are given by the following equations (3):

$$C_p = 2.71 + 0.0162T - 0.0000028T^2$$

where T is between 500 and $1850°R$, and

$$C_p = 7.95 + 8.13 \times 10^{-11}T^{3.85}$$

where T is between 160 and $660°R$.

References 4–7 give more complete tables of the physical and thermodynamic properties including enthalpy, entropy, and free-energy tables.

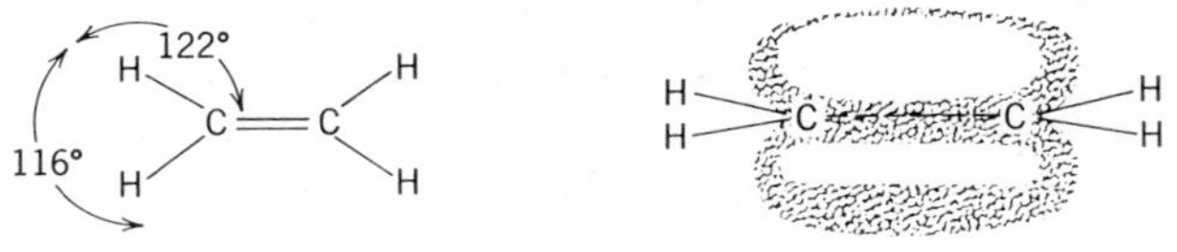

Fig. 1. Ethylene. (a) Structural representation. (b) Schematic diagram of orbital arrangement.

Reactions. The chemistry of ethylene centers about its double bond, which accounts for its reactivity. The geometry of ethylene is relatively simple, since all six atoms lie in one plane (Fig. 1a). The energy barrier to rotation about the carbon–carbon double bond is high enough to hold the four attached hydrogen atoms in a rigid configuration, except at high temperatures.

The picture of ethylene given by the widely accepted molecular orbital theory is shown in Figure 1b, in which the π bond is shown schematically as an electron "cloud" situated above and below the plane of the other three orbitals (bonds).

The nucleophilic character of ethylene is more readily understood from this theory, with its negatively charged π bond, than from the resonance theory which implies equal positive and negative character for the double bond. Ethylene and the higher olefins share the ability to undergo rapid addition reactions. They combine readily with electrophilic reagents such as strong acids (H^+), halogens, and oxidizing agents, and they fail to combine with other nucleophilic reagents such as the Grignard reagents and bases.

Hydrogenation of ethylene may be accomplished at ordinary temperatures and low hydrogen pressures, in the presence of finely divided platinum or palladium. The use of Raney nickel catalyst at high pressure and at temperatures of 150–200°C provides the best hydrogenation conditions for ethylene.

$$CH_2{=}CH_2 + H_2 \rightarrow CH_3CH_3$$

Friedel-Crafts alkylation reactions and acylation addition reactions occur in the presence of ionic catalysts (Lewis acids), which act by polarizing, and perhaps ionizing, the alkylating or acylating agent (8).

$$(CH_3)_3CCl + CH_2{=}CH_2 \xrightarrow[0°C]{SnCl_4} (CH_3)_3CCH_2CH_2Cl$$

tert-butyl chloride   3,3-dimethyl-1-butyl chloride

$$C_2H_5COCl + CH_2{=}CH_2 \xrightarrow{AlCl_3} C_2H_5COCH_2CH_2Cl$$

propionyl chloride β-chloroethyl ethyl ketone

Ethylene may also be alkylated with paraffin hydrocarbons to give a variety of branched-chain paraffins of importance as aviation fuels. The production of 2,3-dimethylbutane from isobutane and ethylene is particularly interesting, since a rearrangement occurs.

$$(CH_3)_3CH + CH_2{=}CH_2 \xrightarrow[550°C]{AlCl_3} (CH_3)_2CHCH(CH_3)_2$$

The Friedel-Crafts alkylation catalysts are also effective in the reaction of ethylene with benzene to give ethylbenzene, an intermediate in the production of styrene.

$$C_6H_6 + CH_2{=}CH_2 \xrightarrow[100°C]{AlCl_3} C_6H_5CH_2CH_3 \xrightarrow[630°C]{metal\ oxide} C_6H_5CH{=}CH_2 + H_2$$

Ethylene (99%+) may be polymerized by means of peroxide catalysts (eg, benzoyl peroxide and di-*tert*-butyl peroxide) at high pressure (1000–2500 atm) and elevated temperatures (100–300°C). Alternate high-pressure processes employ water or aromatic hydrocarbons as solvents. The low-pressure Ziegler process (100 psig, 150°F) employs a catalyst solution composed of alkyl metals, such as triethylaluminum activated with heavy-metal derivatives (eg, titanium tetrachloride),

$$n \ CH_2{=}CH_2 \rightarrow (-CH_2-CH_2-)_n$$

Another polymerization process of increasing importance is the production of an ethylene–propylene copolymer used as a specialty rubber.

Ethylene reacts with halogens at low temperature to give dihaloethanes. The reaction is more rapid with chlorine than with iodine, the latter reaction being incomplete and reversible. Bromine adds irreversibly, but not as rapidly as chlorine.

$$CH_2{=}CH_2 + Cl_2 \xrightarrow{CCl_4} CH_2ClCH_2Cl$$

$$CH_2{=}CH_2 + I_2 \rightleftharpoons CH_2ICH_2I$$

The commercial preparation of ethylene dichloride (1,2-dichloroethane) may be conducted as a vapor-phase or liquid-phase reaction (9). One major process conducted at 40–50°C depends on the action of ethylene dibromide as catalyst. In another process a catalyst of aluminum or ferric chloride is used in a tubular reactor in which gaseous chlorine and ethylene react between 15 and 135°C. Thermal pyrolysis of ethylene dichloride is practiced commercially to produce vinyl chloride and HCl as a by-product. Addition of O_2 in the chlorination (oxychlorination) of ethylene promotes full utilization of Cl_2 (by oxidizing the resultant HCl), and favors substitutive chlorination (10),

$$CH_2{=}CH_2 + Cl_2 + \tfrac{1}{2} O_2 \rightarrow CHCl{=}CHCl + H_2O$$

$$CH_2{=}CH_2 + 2 \ Cl_2 + O_2 \rightarrow CCl_2{=}CCl_2 + 2 \ H_2O$$
$$\text{perchloroethylene}$$

Hydrogen halides also add to ethylene to give corresponding ethyl halides (eg, hydrohalogenation). The order of reactivity is HCl <HBr <HI.

$$CH_2{=}CH_2 + HCl \rightarrow CH_3CH_2Cl$$

The addition of O_2 in the hydrochlorination of ethylene results in the formation of trichloroethylene (11).

$$CH_2{=}CH_2 + 3 \ HCl + \tfrac{3}{2} O_2 \rightarrow CHCl{=}CCl_2 + 3 \ H_2O$$

Commercially, ethyl chloride is produced by addition of hydrogen chloride to ethylene in an anhydrous solution of ethyl chloride and/or ethylene dichloride at 35–40°C, with aluminum chloride catalyst.

Synthetic ethyl alcohol is produced by absorbing ethylene in 90–95% sulfuric acid (which adds as H^+ (SO_4H^-)) to give a mixture of ethyl sulfates, which are then hydrolyzed to ethyl alcohol and dilute sulfuric acid. Small amounts of ethyl ether are formed as a by-product (9).

$$CH_2{=}CH_2 + H_2SO_4 \rightarrow C_2H_5OSO_2OH$$

$$2 \ CH_2{=}CH_2 + H_2SO_4 \rightarrow C_2H_5OSO_2OC_2H_5$$

$$C_2H_5OSO_2OH + C_2H_5OSO_2OC_2H_5 + 3 \ H_2O \rightarrow 3 \ C_2H_5OH + 2 \ H_2SO_4$$

$$2 \ C_2H_5OH \xrightarrow{H_2SO_4} C_2H_5OC_2H_5 + H_2O$$

Fuming sulfuric acid, up to 60% SO_3, gives ethionic acid, $HO_3SCH_2CH_2OSO_3H$ (12) and carbyl sulfate, $O.CH_2.CH_2.SO_2.O.SO_2$.

The most recent synthetic alcohol process is the direct hydration of ethylene over a phosphoric acid catalyst at 1000 psi and 600°F,

$$CH_2{=}CH_2 + H_2O \xrightarrow{H_3PO_4} C_2H_5OH$$

Analogous hydration reactions with 25% sulfuric acid at 200–290°C and 1100–2000 psi can also produce ethyl alcohol (13).

The addition of carbon tetrachloride in the presence of radical-producing catalysts has been used to synthesize 1,1,1,3-tetrachloropropane, which is easily hydrolyzed into β-chloropropionic acid (14),

$$CH_2{=}CH_2 + ClCCl_3 \rightarrow ClCH_2CH_2CCl_3$$

$$ClCH_2CH_2CCl_3 + 2\ H_2O \rightarrow ClCH_2CH_2COOH + 3\ HCl$$

This reaction may become explosive (1,15).

Sulfur monochloride and ethylene unite to give β,β'-dichlorodiethyl sulfide (mustard gas) (16),

$$2\ CH_2{=}CH_2 + S_2Cl_2 \rightarrow (ClCH_2CH_2)_2S + S$$

Ethylene has been employed in the Prins reaction (17) with formaldehyde in acetic acid to produce trimethylene glycol diacetate,

$$CH_2{=}CH_2 + CH_2O + 2\ CH_3COOH \xrightarrow{H_2SO_4} CH_3COOCH_2CH_2CH_2OOCCH_3 + H_2O$$

The latter may be hydrolyzed to trimethylene glycol (1,3-propanediol), which compound was previously available chiefly from the fermentation of glycerol.

Ethylene and hypochlorous acid react to yield ethylene chlorohydrin, which may be converted either to ethylene glycol by hydrolysis, or to ethylene oxide by reaction with alkali.

$$CH_2{=}CH_2 + HOCl \xrightarrow[200\ atm]{20°C} CH_2OHCH_2Cl$$

$$CH_2OHCH_2Cl + NaHCO_3 \xrightarrow[80°C]{H_2O} CH_2OHCH_2OH + CO_2 + NaCl$$

$$2\ CH_2OHCH_2Cl + Ca(OH)_2 \xrightarrow{50°C} 2\ \underset{\diagdown O \diagup}{CH_2{-}CH_2} + CaCl_2 + 2\ H_2O$$

The direct catalytic oxidation of ethylene with air to produce ethylene oxide has substantially replaced the chlorohydrin process in commercial practice,

$$CH_2{=}CH_2 + \tfrac{1}{2} O_2 \xrightarrow[300°C]{Ag} \underset{\diagdown O \diagup}{CH_2{-}CH_2}$$

Some carbon dioxide and water vapor are formed by the complete oxidation of part of the ethylene.

Ethylene also adds ozone to give an ozonide (generally not isolated because of its explosive character), which upon decomposition with water gives a mixture of formic acid and formaldehyde (8).

$$CH_2{=}CH_2 + O_3 \rightarrow \quad \overset{O-O}{\underset{O}{CH_2 \diagup \diagdown CH_2}} \overset{H_2O}{\rightarrow} HCOOH + CH_2O$$

Another reaction of growing commercial importance is the production of straight-chain primary alcohols and olefins in the C_{10} to C_{14} molecular-weight range, by the Ziegler process (see Vol. 1, pp. 560–563).

$$(\text{polymerization}) \; Al(C_2H_5)_3 + n\,CH_2{=}CH_2 \rightarrow Al\begin{smallmatrix} \diagup CH_2CH_2R_1 \\ -CH_2CH_2R_2 \\ \diagdown CH_2CH_2R_3 \end{smallmatrix}$$

$$(\text{displacement}) \; Al\begin{smallmatrix} \diagup CH_2CH_2R_1 \\ -CH_2CH_2R_2 \\ \diagdown CH_2CH_2R_3 \end{smallmatrix} + 3\,CH_2{=}CH_2 \quad \rightarrow$$

$$R_1CH{=}CH_2 + R_2CH{=}CH_2 + R_3CH{=}CH_2 + Al(C_2H_5)_3$$

Manufacture

Substantially all commercial ethylene is made by the thermal pyrolysis of petroleum fractions, except for a small proportion which is recovered as a by-product of refinery catalytic cracking operations. In special situations where small amounts of ethylene are required, ethylene has been manufactured from either ethyl alcohol or ethyl ether by catalytic dehydrogenation. The reaction is carried out at 340–395°C over a specially treated alumina catalyst which must be periodically regenerated with an air–steam mixture to remove carbon. Ethylene is obtained at high purity in yields of approx 95%; it is scrubbed for removal of traces of aldehydes and acids.

Feedstocks. Any feedstock from ethane to heavy gas oil, and even whole crude oil, can be used to produce ethylene. In this country ethane is the most economically attractive feedstock when it is desired to produce ethylene alone. Most of the U.S. ethane supply, available from refinery gases and from natural gas liquids, has already been committed for ethylene production. The result has been a substantial growth of LPG (liquefied petroleum gas) (eg, 95% propane, 5% butane) as a major feedstock for ethylene and propylene production. The rapid growth of propylene derivatives has encouraged this trend. There is also some interest in the U.S. in using naphtha (crude oil fractions with boiling ranges from 90 to 400°F) as a supplementary feedstock.

In industrialized areas of the world outside of the U.S., where ethane and propane generally are not available, liquid feedstocks are used almost exclusively. Naphtha stocks are most commonly used, because of their availability, low cost, and potential for producing high yields of ethylene and its by-products—propylene, butadiene, benzene, and toluene. Higher-boiling petroleum fractions such as kerosene and virgin gas oil have also been used commercially. The use of heavier feedstocks, however, is limited because there are direct markets for them. As ethylene requirements increase and as the market for motor fuels increases, heavier stocks may be used more extensively.

HIGH–TEMPERATURE PYROLYSIS

The pyrolysis reactor operation conditions and the feedstock properties control the composition of the product mixture. It has been established that high selectivity for the desired olefins and diolefins (ie, ethylene, propylene, butadiene), and minimum coke production are promoted by operating at high temperatures, short residence times, and low hydrocarbon partial pressures. The pyrolysis is usually conducted at pressures close to atmospheric and at process temperatures from 1300 to 1600°F. Not all hydrocarbons pyrolyze with equal ease; in general, less severe conditions are required as the molecular weight increases. A complication arises from the fact that different types of compounds, even though they have the same molecular weight, differ in the ease with which they decompose thermally. Most important is the vast difference in product distribution that can result.

For example, in the case of C_6 hydrocarbons, the ease of pyrolysis and the nature of the products varies, depending on whether the compounds are normal paraffins, branched-chain paraffins, naphthenes (cycloaliphatics), or aromatics. Even differentiation by hydrocarbon type can prove insufficient as a criterion for defining cracking patterns. Within the C_6 branched-chain paraffin group, 2-methylpentane and 2,3-dimethylbutane crack to substantially different product distributions. The same is true of the C_6 naphthenes when the reaction products of cyclohexane and methylcyclopentane are compared. Under normal cracking conditions, the C_6 aromatic (benzene) resists cracking and reacts only to produce small amounts of polynuclear aromatics.

Table 2 presents a comparison of the levels of feed conversion and product distributions produced by thermal pyrolysis of selected C_6 paraffins and naphthenes (18). This comparison shows that *n*-hexane produces ethylene most selectively, whereas 2,3-dimethylbutane and methylcyclopentane are least selective. Propylene

Table 2. Cracking Yields of Selected C_6 Paraffins and Naphthenes[a]

Feed	Feed conversion, wt %	Effluent composition, wt %				
		Methane	Ethylene	Propylene	Butylenes	1,3-Butadiene
n-hexane	90	14.0	39.3	18.1	3.9	4.7
2-methylpentane	83	12.5	20.0	23.5	3.6	3.0
2,3-dimethylbutane	94	21.2	15.1	29.9	3.5	9.8
cyclohexane	63	3.7	23.3	6.9	18.2	2.1
methylcyclopentane	33	3.5	6.1	10.9	2.5	3.5

[a]Cracking temperature, 1400°F; gas residence time, 0.5 sec.

butadiene, and methane yields are highest when 2,3-dimethylbutane is the feedstock. Cyclohexane shows the greatest selectivity in producing butylenes. The paraffins are most easily cracked, followed by cyclohexane, methylcyclopentane, and benzene which is totally refractory.

Many types of pyrolysis reactors have been proposed since the middle 1930s, and a number have been put into commercial operation. However, the fired tubular heater has clearly emerged as the primary tool for the production of ethylene and associated by-products. Other commercialized reactor systems which will be discussed briefly are pebble-bed heaters, fluidized-bed cracking, regenerative furnaces, autothermic cracking, and the Catarole catalytic process.

Fired Tubular Heater. The pyrolysis of hydrocarbons is highly endothermic. In order to bring the process gas to the desired reaction temperatures as quickly as possible, convection and radiant sections are provided in the tubular furnace design. The convection section operates by transferring heat from the flue gases to the process stream for vaporization and/or preheating of the feed. The radiant section, or firebox, provides the remaining sensible heat plus the heat of reaction. Based upon the principle mentioned earlier that optimum heater design depends on a short process-gas residence time in the radiant section, high temperatures and high heat flux rates must be obtainable. In addition, control of the firebox burner-firing pattern is desirable to maintain the proper process temperature gradient in the radiant section. These design requirements must be met without exceeding the maximum temperature limitations of the tube metal and tube support materials. New high alloy Ni–Cr cast steels have permitted maximum tube-metal temperatures to reach 1900°F and tube-hanger temperatures to reach 2000°F for long-term operation with vertically hung tubes. (See High temperature alloys.) A number of firms in the U.S. offer fired tubular pyrolysis heaters, including The Lummus Co., The Selas Corporation of America, The M. W. Kellogg Co., and The Foster Wheeler Corp.

In accordance with the classical radiation theory, a single row of tubes fired between two radiant sidewalls would provide the most uniform heat-flux distribution around the circumference of the tubes. With this design, the average heat-flux rates would closely approach the maximum heat-flux rate without exceeding materials temperature. Furnace designs that employ double tube rows fired from two radiant sidewalls or hearth-fired fireboxes containing tubes mounted close to the refractory walls, would provide less uniformity in heat-flux distribution; as a result, they would be limited to lower average flux rates.

Sidewall-fired heaters with burners placed in a checkerboard pattern provide for control of the process temperature profile. In addition, such heaters can be adjusted to accommodate a broad range of feedstocks.

In a given physical tubular heater, feedstocks ranging from ethane through light naphthas all give approximately the same ethylene production, when the heater is operated to maximize ethylene yield. However, the distribution of by-products is very different for ethane, propane, and light naphtha. Ethane makes only about 5 wt % of products heavier than the feed, and relatively high hydrogen yields at normal levels of ethane conversion (55–65%). Propane's major by-products are methane, propylene, and aromatic gasoline. Naphthas produce sizable quantities of butylenes and butadiene, in addition to propylene, gasoline, and some fuel oil. Heavy naphthas and higher-boiling stocks produce proportionately less ethylene with increasing boiling range and with increasing naphthenes and aromatics contents. By-products from cracking these heavy stocks include large quantities of gasoline and fuel oil, and relatively less hydrogen, methane, and propylene. Relative to naphtha feedstocks, a well-designed heater can process 70% as much ethane, 90% as much propane, and 85% as much kerosene or gas oil. Recycling of ethane and propane is often done to maximize the ethylene yield; on occasion, propylene is also recycled to the cracking heaters.

For all feedstocks, a heater operating in the high temperature–short residence time region produces higher yields of ethylene and other olefins (or diolefins) than heaters operating at conventional longer residence times. Short residence time promotes primary reactions (which produce desired olefins and diolefins) relative to secondary reactions (which produce excess hydrogen, methane, and aromatics). The production of aromatics by these secondary cracking reactions leads to the formation of highly condensed aromatic structures which are the precursors of coke. These polynuclear aromatics grow into high-molecular-weight and highly condensed structures. Those in the film along the tube wall are exposed to the highest temperatures and longest residence times. Under these conditions, they continue to condense and eventually become solid. This solid continues to dehydrogenate in the high-temperature atmosphere, and takes the form of hard coke deposits. The fraction of total hydrocarbon material that can be permitted to become coke is very small. For example, if 1 part in 10,000 deposited, the process tubes would be plugged solid over the entire reaction length in several weeks of operation. Steam is added to the hydrocarbon feed to reduce the hydrocarbon partial pressure, which benefits the pyrolysis reaction; it also helps to decrease the rate of buildup of coke deposits within the tubes, by reaction of steam with carbon to form carbon monoxide and hydrogen. Steam-to-hydrocarbon feed ratios (wt basis) are generally 0.2–0.4:1 for ethane and propane, 0.3–0.6:1 for naphthas, and 0.5–1.0:1 for kerosenes and gas oils.

The combination of steam-to-hydrocarbon feed (S/O) ratio and heater-coil pressure level determines the hydrocarbon partial pressure. As mentioned earlier, low hydrocarbon partial pressure favors production of ethylene, propylene, and butadiene. This results from the fact that increasing hydrocarbon partial pressure accelerates the production of secondary products relative to desired primary products, and shortens heater run length by promoting coke buildup. However, lowering the S/O ratio and/or increasing the heater outlet pressure would save investment by decreasing the size of the charge compressors, and would decrease the operating-utilities requirements. Therefore, the selection of optimum pressure conditions depends on an economic balance for the particular plant situation.

One other section of the pyrolysis reactor system warrants discussion, namely the quench and heat recovery. This equipment must provide rapid cooling of the heater effluent to a temperature at which no additional reaction occurs. The design trends have been influenced by both the feedstocks and the fuel value of the recovered heat. In the older U.S. plants, for which ethane and propane were the predominant feeds and fuel was relatively cheap, the common practice was a full quench to approx 600°F by direct injection of water into the heater effluent, followed by water wash in a column. No steam was recovered by heat exchange. In Europe, on the other hand, liquids were the preferred feed, and fuel was relatively expensive. In the older European plants, the effluent was quenched to an intermediate temperature with water, was cooled further in transfer-line heat exchangers, and then scrubbed with circulating oil. In more recent plants, heat recovery has been maximized by elimination of the water-quench step so that the effluent goes immediately into transfer-line exchangers. Now the economics of fuel costs favors the use of transfer-line exchangers in the U.S. also. Progress has also occurred in the design and efficiency of the exchangers. Early units employed hot oil or Dowtherm as an intermediate fluid, and heat was recovered by a secondary steam-waste heat boiler. In current units, steam is raised directly in the transfer-line exchangers. Steam pressures are determined by the feedstocks; lower pressures, 300–600 psig, are suitable for light feeds and higher pressures, 500–

1500 psig, for heavy feeds. The controlling factor is the desired tube wall temperature on the hydrocarbon side of the exchanger.

Pebble-Bed Heater. Mobil Oil Company has developed a thermal pyrolysis system involving the use of refractory pebbles as the heat-transfer medium. The system comprises two main elements, a heater and a reactor, connected by means of a bucket elevator. Preheated pebbles from the heater section are fed into the reactor where they contact the hydrocarbon feed. Thermocracking occurs on the surface of the pebbles and coke is deposited on these surfaces. The pebbles are then elevated to the upper heater unit where the coke is burned off by combustion with air and in the presence of fuel gas introduced directly into the heater. The pebbles having absorbed the bulk of the generated heat are then conveyed back to the reactor section. This is known as the TPC (Thermofor Pyrolytic Cracking) process (19–21).

Phillips Petroleum Company has also developed a very similar process (22). Still another modification of the TPC process has been developed by the Surface Combustion Corporation, which uses a moving bed of coke pebbles and a pneumatic lift principle (23).

Fluidized-Bed Cracking. The use of a fluidized bed of sand as an effective thermal cracking medium has been developed as a cooperative effort in Germany, and is known as the Lurgi-Ruhrgas process (24). In this process preheated feedstock is injected with heated steam into a fluidized bed of hot sand. Any coke which deposits on the surface of the sand particles is burned off in a separate regenerator vessel. During the regeneration with preheated air, the sand particles are heated up to a very high temperature and are then returned via a gas lift to the main reactor. The initial unit has been in operation in Germany since late 1958 and four more units are currently (1965) under construction. The unit is claimed to be extremely flexible with respect to both feedstock and product distribution (25).

The use of fluidized coke particles as a heat-transfer medium has been extensively investigated in Russia on a large pilot-plant scale, employing both light and heavy feedstocks. Badische Anilin- und Soda-Fabrik in Germany has commercialized a crude oil cracking process using the fluidized-coke principle; this has been carried as far as a prototype plant (26,27). The process is an outgrowth of the early Winkler process, which made ethylene from fuel oil and tar. The process feeds crude oil and steam, together with oxygen (which furnishes the heat of reaction by combustion), into a fluidized bed of coke particles. Part of the crude is cracked to lighter hydrocarbons and part is converted directly into additional coke. The products are then separated in a conventional quench and fractionation system.

These processes offer significantly better yields of ethylene (20–25%) than conventional crude pyrolysis, but are still inferior to naphtha. No data have been disclosed about investment costs. It seems likely, however, that these plants will cost appreciably more than current units which are fed with ethane, propane, or naphtha and will be applied only in special situations.

Regenerative Furnaces. A regenerative furnace operates cyclically in the following manner: First, fuel gas is burned directly in the chamber to bring it up to operating temperature. Then, the fuel gas is shut off and feedstock is charged to the chamber and the reaction takes place. When the temperature falls below the desired level, the feedstock is shut off, fuel gas is readmitted, and the cycle is complete. If a continuous system is desired, two furnaces and an elaborate valve system are required.

The regenerative principle is applied to the simultaneous manufacture of ethylene plus acetylene. The Wulff and Koppers–Hasche processes involve the use of two complex tile regenerative furnaces which operate cyclically. The furnaces operate at low pressure, and varying ratios of ethylene and acetylene may be produced from a variety of light feedstocks (28–30). Several Wulff plants of commercial size are currently (1965) under construction in Europe.

Autothermic Cracking. This type of process depends on a balance between the endothermic heat of cracking and the combustion of a portion of the hydrocarbon feed with air or oxygen, so that the overall reaction is self-sustaining. Autothermic cracking has been reported on a wide variety of feedstocks extending to whole crude oil (31,32). The most recent process in this area uses a mixture of hydrocarbons and air at 1 atm pressure (33). The question as to whether to use oxygen or air in the autothermic process is a matter of economic balance; the simpler purification system required for the oxygen system is offset by the cost of the oxygen plant required. A modification of autothermic cracking involves the use of sulfur for dehydrogenation rather than oxygen.

Catarole Catalytic Process. This process has been developed on a large scale by Petrochemicals, Limited, in England (34). The process involves complete vaporization of the hydrocarbon feed, followed by thermal cracking at 20–50 psig in alloy steel tubes which are arranged vertically in the radiant section of a fired heater. The entire effluent then passes on to a soaking section which consists of packed tubes containing metallic copper. At temperatures of 600–700°C extensive formation of aromatics occurs. The effluent is quenched with water to terminate the reaction, and then the gaseous products are sent to a product recovery and purification section.

Du Pont Process. This process permits the pyrolysis of crude petroleum to obtain high yields. It is similar to conventional steam pyrolysis, except that the steam is replaced by ethane recycled to the pyrolysis unit to provide hydrogen. Ethane was chosen in preference to a number of other possible hydrogen donors because it was found to increase the yields markedly and, at the same time, to lower the cracking temperature. Pilot-plant work showed that the process is self-sufficient with respect to ethane (35).

Other Thermal Techniques. The use of various modifications of the electric arc for generation of high temperatures at low contact times has been proposed but never commercialized in this country. During World War II, a process of this type for the production of acetylene from methane was practiced in Germany.

Shock-tube techniques have been employed at very high temperatures and short residence times, to help evaluate the kinetics of the thermal pyrolysis of light hydrocarbons (36). These techniques are presently limited to laboratory studies.

Another technique involves the contact of gaseous charging stocks with molten metals such as lead, either by contact in a packed tower through which the molten metal is circulated, or by bubbling through the metal. The latter method has been used to a limited extent commercially by the Monsanto Chemical Company for the production of ethylene from propane (37).

Yields. When relatively mild pyrolysis conditions are used, similar yield patterns are produced for most pyrolysis methods. Since nearly all new ethylene units are designed for moderate or high-severity pyrolysis (which can be obtained only in fired tubular heaters), the yield data presented are correlated from commercial units operating under those conditions (38). Table 3 compares the yields obtained from

Table 3. Typical Commercial Yields from Fired Tubular Heaters

	Feed			
	Light naphtha	Full-range naphtha	Propane	Ethane
Feed properties				
ASTM boiling range, °F	90–260	90–350		
PONA[a] analysis, wt %				
paraffins	86	73		
olefins				
naphthenes	11	18		
aromatics	3	9		
	Yields, wt % of feed			
	Severity of pyrolysis			
	High	Moderate	High	Moderate	90% conversion	60% conversion
Pyrolysis products						
hydrogen	1.0	0.8	1.0	0.8	1.3	3.5
methane	17.0	13.0	17.0	13.8	22.7	3.8
ethylene	32.0	26.0	28.0	24.0	33.5	48.3
ethane	4.5	4.5	4.5	4.4	6.0	40.0
propylene	18.0	20.0	14.5	16.3	12.5	1.5
propane	0.5	0.6	1.1	1.2	10.0	0.3
butylenes-butanes	10.0	12.5	8.4	11.6	4.5	1.3
C₅–400°F gasoline	14.5	21.5	20.5	24.7	9.5	1.3
fuel oil	2.5	1.1	5.0	3.2		
butadiene in butylenes–butanes stream	45	42	46	39	60	75
aromatics in gasoline						
benzene	38	24	39	25		
toluene	18	11	19	15		
xylene	3	3	7	8		

[a] Abbreviation for a special type of hydrocarbon analysis by structure. PONA is formed from paraffins, olefins, naphthenes, aromatics.

four common feedstocks—ethane, propane, light naphtha, and full-range naphtha. With naphtha feedstocks, it is commercially feasible to obtain ethylene yields in excess of 30 wt %, and total C_2 to C_4 olefin plus butadiene yields in excess of 50 wt %. When processing light hydrocarbon feedstocks such as ethane, ultimate yields of approx 80 wt % are possible with recycle cracking, if once-through conversion is kept below 60% with low-pressure operation. However, increased recycle requirements may offset the ultimate yield advantage.

By-products. The production of ethylene by the pyrolysis of hydrocarbons results in the production of a number of by-products. For all feedstocks except ethane, these by-products occur in large enough quantities to affect the economics significantly. Propylene is produced by pyrolysis of propane or heavier feedstocks. With propane feed, the propylene–propane fraction may contain 40–55% propylene; for heavier feedstocks, the propane–propylene mixture produced may contain 90–94% propylene. Fractionation may be utilized to produce a polymerization-grade material. The pyrolysis fraction containing C_5 to 400°F end-point hydrocarbons is rich in aromatics and, after proper treatment, can be utilized as a gasoline blending agent or as a source of benzene, toluene, and xylenes. Depending upon feedstock and severity of pyrolysis, the clear research octane number may vary from 85 to 98. Catalytic hydrogenation is generally used for the removal of diolefins to produce a stable gasoline. Further hydrogenation of olefins is required if aromatics extraction is to be done. The fraction boiling above 400°F is rich in cyclic compounds such as indene, alkylnaphthalenes, and tricyclics. Considerable interest has developed recently in the 400–550°F boiling-range fraction; after suitable pretreatment this cut may be hydrodealkylated to produce good yields of naphthalene.

The C_4 fraction produced consists essentially of butylenes and butadiene, with concentrations of the latter as high as 40 wt %. The total quantity produced is large enough to warrant a butadiene-extraction plant only for the larger plants which process naphtha or heavier stocks. The C_4 fraction is, therefore, usually shipped to a large butadiene-processing plant or is disposed of as fuel. Acetylene is produced in small quantities in all pyrolysis operations directed toward ethylene production. The quantity is generally insufficient for economical recovery as a usable product, and removal is accomplished by catalytic hydrogenation in order to satisfy the ethylene purity specification. Solvent separation can be used for acetylene recovery where special circumstances make this economic. Hydrogen is produced in all pyrolysis operations. It may be economically purified for use in ammonia synthesis, generally as a supplement to other sources of hydrogen. Hydrogen may also be utilized for the gasoline and aromatics-hydrotreating operations noted above, or for any of the hydrotreating operations in refinery processing.

RECOVERY AND PURIFICATION

Recovery, separation, and purification of the pyrolysis products are major elements of the manufacturing process. The system must treat not only the full range of hydrocarbons indicated in Table 3, but also minor contaminants such as acid gases, acetylene, propadiene, and hydrocarbon polymers. Broadly, there are three principal separations to be made: (1) gasoline and heavier fractions from the C_4 and lighter hydrocarbons; (2) methane and hydrogen off-gases from the ethylene and heavier hydrocarbons; and (3) ethylene from the heavier hydrocarbons. The first separation immediately follows the quench and heat-recovery system previously discussed, and is performed in conventional fractionators at low pressure. Before the subsequent separations can be made, the stream of C_4 and lighter hydrocarbons must be compressed and treated for removal of acid gases. Process and mechanical design conditions for compression are carefully selected to minimize formation and deposition of polymers.

The second and third separations have been performed commercially by four different principal schemes: (a) low-temperature, high-pressure straight fractionation; (b) moderately low temperature absorption and fractionation; (c) low-temperature, low-pressure straight fractionation; (d) ambient-temperature, medium-pressure selective adsorption. Of these, the first is currently favored because it offers an attractive combination of purity, recovery, efficiency, and investment for the larger ethylene plants. One variation of this process is described in detail subsequently under Plant process description. Its distinguishing characteristic is that the separation of methane and hydrogen (demethanization) is carried out by fractionation at temperature–pressure conditions within the range of 400 to 600 psig and -90 to $-140°F$. In scheme (b), however, demethanization is carried out by selective absorption of ethylene and heavier components at temperature–pressure conditions within the range of 450 to 500 psig and $+70$ to $-30°F$. The higher temperatures correspond to the use of a relatively heavy aromatic lean oil, and the lower temperatures to the use of a light lean oil such as ethane, propane, butane, or pentane. This scheme was extensively used during the 1950s, but is less favored currently. Scheme (c) employs the low-temperature techniques derived from air fractionation, that is, temperature–pressure conditions within the range of 25 to 35 psig and -140 to $-220°F$. This scheme has been employed in only a few European plants. Scheme (d) was commercialized as the hypersorption process, which used a moving bed of specially activated charcoal at temperature–pressure conditions within the range of 90 to 100 psig and 120 to 300°F. This scheme was employed at two plants in North America but no other units were built for ethylene recovery.

The fractionation sequence following demethanization varies, depending on product distribution and purity requirements, but generally includes debutanization, depropanization, and splitting between ethylene and ethane and between propylene and propane. A typical sequence is described under Plant process description.

Plant Process Description. A process flow description and diagram for a typical plant using naphtha as a feedstock is given in Figure 2. Naphtha and recycle ethane are cracked separately in vertical tubular heaters in the presence of dilution steam. The heater effluents are cooled in transfer-line exchangers which generate high-pressure steam.

Each radiant section has an independent convection section for steam–naphtha preheat. High efficiencies are obtained by final flue gas cooling against boiler-feedwater preheat, prior to steam generation in the transfer-line exchangers. A separately fired superheater provides superheat for this steam. The effluents from the transfer-line exchangers are combined, quenched with circulating quench oil, and sent to the gasoline fractionator. This column separates fuel oil as bottoms, and takes lighter components overhead. The net fuel oil product is stripped of light components in a separate stripper. The circulating quench oil is used to preheat boiler feedwater and feed naphtha, and to generate low-pressure steam. The gasoline fractionator overhead vapors are condensed and cooled. Net overhead vapors flow to the compression system, and net hydrocarbon liquid is cooled and pumped to battery limits. ("Battery limits" is used generally in the process industries to describe the functional

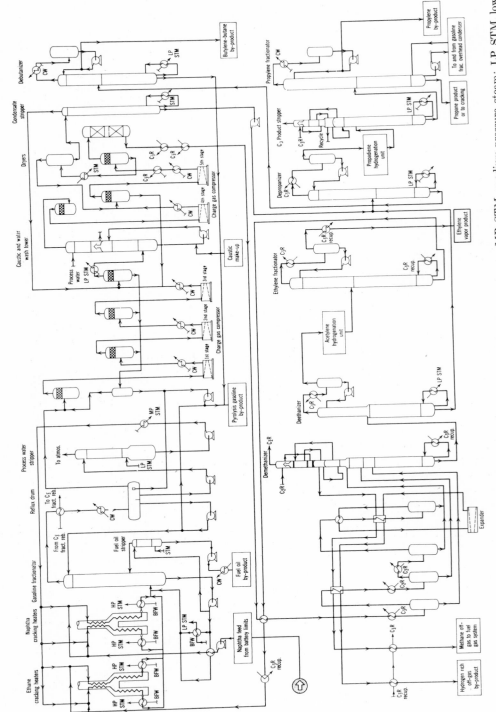

Fig. 2. Ethylene manufacture by naphtha pyrolysis. HP STM, high-pressure steam; MP STM, medium-pressure steam; LP STM, low-pressure steam; BFW, boiler feed water; CW, cooling water; C₂-R, ethylene refrigerant; C₃-R, propylene refrigerant; C₃-R recup, propylene refrigerant recuperation.

physical boundaries of a process unit, beyond which are other process units and the necessary supporting nonprocess facilities such as tankage, boiler house, cooling-water system, maintenance and administration, etc; streams produced within the unit are sent to battery limits for further processing in other areas, for storage and shipping to consumers, for blending into the plant fuel gas system, or for disposal through a vent or flare system.) Condensed water is separated in the gasoline fractionator reflux drum, stripped of hydrocarbons, vaporized against medium-pressure steam, and delivered to the heaters as dilution steam.

The cooled vapors from the gasoline fractionator overhead are compressed in five stages. Between the third and fourth stages the gas is caustic-scrubbed and water-washed for removal of acid gases. The fifth-stage effluent is cooled with water and chilled with propylene refrigeration, and the vapor is sent to the desiccant dryers. The fourth- and fifth-stage hydrocarbon condensates are sent to the condensate stripper where the C_2 and lighter material is removed; stripper bottoms goes to the depropanizer. Condensates from the first three discharge separators are sent back successively to the previous-stage separators to recover the dissolved hydrocarbon gases. From the first-stage discharge separator the water-rich condensate is sent back to the reflux accumulator of the gasoline fractionator.

The final compressor discharge gas is dried in solid-bed dryers before passing to the low-temperature recovery section. Three dryers are provided; each is designed for a 24-hr cycle. Two are onstream, in series, while the third is being regenerated. Both regeneration and cooling of the dryers are accomplished by using a portion of the methane off-gas on a once-through basis. A regeneration heater and a cooler are provided for the regeneration operation. The dry gas is chilled by five successive stages of heat exchange against (1) propylene refrigerant, (2) ethylene refrigerant, (3) hydrogen-rich off-gases, (4) net overhead vapor from the demethanizer, and (5) bottoms liquid ethane product from the ethylene fractionator. The demethanizer is reboiled with condensing propylene refrigerant. Reflux is condensed by using low-level ethylene refrigeration. The demethanizer net overhead is reheated against the demethanizer feed vapors and propylene refrigeration, and delivered to the battery limits. Hydrogen-rich off-gas from the feed separator drum is likewise reheated against demethanizer feed vapors and propylene refrigeration, and delivered to the battery limits. The system used for processing the off-gases depends largely on the particular requirements of the plant. An expander is shown in which the off-gas is expanded to fuel gas pressure to reduce the refrigeration requirements. If hydrogen were required at high pressure, the expander would not be used.

The demethanizer bottoms product flows to the deethanizer where the C_2 compounds are separated from the C_3 and heavier fraction. The reboiler utilizes low-pressure steam; reflux is condensed with propylene refrigerant. The bottoms product is sent to the depropanizer and the net overhead vapors flow to the acetylene converter. Acetylene is removed from the ethylene–ethane vapor stream by selective hydrogenation over a catalyst, in a packed-bed reactor. Hydrogen-rich off-gas is added for this operation. Occasional regeneration of the catalyst is required. Therefore, two reactors are provided, one of which is on stand-by service. Regeneration is accomplished with steam at an elevated temperature. A regeneration heater is provided for this service.

The ethane–ethylene stream that leaves the acetylene-removal system is condensed and charged to the ethylene stripper. The stripper is reboiled with condensing propylene refrigerant, and reflux duty is provided by ethylene refrigeration. The overhead vapor product, containing small amounts of methane and hydrogen, is recycled to the charge gas compressor and the bottoms product is sent to the ethylene fractionator. The tower is reboiled with condensing propylene refrigerant, and reflux duty is provided by propylene refrigeration. The bottoms ethane product is vaporized and superheated against process streams, and recycled to the ethane cracking furnaces. The overhead vapor product is high-purity ethylene which is superheated against propylene refrigerant and sent to battery limits.

The depropanizer receives as feed the deethanizer bottoms and the condensate stripper bottoms. It separates a propylene-rich overhead stream from a C_4 and heavier bottoms. Steam and propylene are the respective reboiling and condensing media. Depropanizer bottoms is charged to the debutanizer. The overhead from the depropanizer is heated and sent to the propadiene converter. Hydrogen-rich off-gas is used for hydrogenation, and regeneration is accomplished in the same manner as in the acetylene converter. The treated C_3 stream is stripped and sent to the propylene fractionator. Propane from the bottom of the fractionator is sent to battery limits, or may be recycled if desired. The debutanizer is charged with the depropanizer bottoms. This column separates a butylene–butadiene overhead from a debutanized gasoline bottoms. Cooling water is the reflux condensing medium, while steam is used for reboiling.

Two refrigeration systems provide the bulk of the chilling and condensing duties for the unit, (a) ethylene and (b) propylene. Each is a multistage system using a centrifugal compressor. The ethylene system has three levels of refrigeration, and propylene refrigerant is the condensing medium. Cooling water and cold off-gases condense and subcool the propylene refrigerant, and some interstage condensing is obtained from reboiling services.

Economics and Uses

Ethylene is one of the most important and largest-volume petrochemicals in the world. Its growth illustrates the complex interplay of technology and marketing that governs the petrochemicals industry, and also the relationships of ethylene with its parent, the petroleum industry. In the economic discussion which follows (which was prepared in 1965), the absolute values will soon be out of date; the trends, however, remain valid and worthy of examination.

Production. The growth of ethylene into one of the largest-volume petrochemicals is shown in Table 4 (39,40):

Table 4. Growth of Ethylene Production in the U.S.

Year	Annual production, short tons
1930	10,000
1940	150,000
1945	400,000
1950	750,000
1955	1,500,000
1960	2,750,000
1965[a]	4,500,000
1970[b]	6,000,000

[a]Estimated.   [b]Projected.

Historically, the major part of the non-Communist world's production capacity has been in the U.S.; the current and projected growth rates for Western Europe and Japan, however, exceed those of the U.S. so that in the future the share of the U.S. will decrease. As of mid-1964, the total installed production capacity in the non-Communist world was approx 7,400,000 (short) tons per year, of which approx 60% was in the U.S. By 1970, world capacity is predicted to reach 12,000,000 tons of which approximately half will be in the U.S. Until recently, the preferred feedstocks in the U.S. have been natural gas or petroleum refinery gases; current designs are based largely upon LPG (liquefied petroleum gas—mixtures of butane and propane) or upon mixtures of ethane and propane. In Western Europe and Japan, however, which lack economic sources of natural gas and LPG, liquid petroleum fractions, especially naphthas, are widely used. Unit capacities of plants have increased along with total installed capacities; the 50,000–75,000 ton/yr plants of the 1950s have been displaced by the 200,000–400,000 ton/yr plants currently being built in Western Europe, in Japan, and in the U.S. All other areas of the world now have less than 5% of the total world production, and although they have plans for additional capacity, their share will not change significantly by 1970 (41).

Costs. Manufacturing costs before taxes for modern large plants in the U.S. generally fall in the range of 2–3.5 ¢/lb of ethylene (42). They depend not only upon the usual factors of raw materials, direct operating, and capital costs, but also upon the credits for by-products such as fuel gas, propylene, LPG, butylenes, butadienes, aromatic gasoline, and fuel oil. Each of these costs will vary with location, market conditions, and corporate policy. Nevertheless, certain general conclusions may be drawn from a comparison of the economics of ethylene production from various feedstocks, by utilizing a uniform cost basis. For this purpose, a pro-forma study is presented for plants with a capacity of 250 million lb/yr of ethylene from ethane, propane, and naphtha feedstocks, using costs representative of U.S. Gulf Coast conditions (43). The other principal assumptions for the comparison are as follows: (a) The feedstocks are delivered by pipeline—ethane in the vapor state, LPG and light naphtha in the liquid state; (b) all major compressors are driven by steam turbines; (c) steam is generated within the battery limits by waste heat recovery and by a conventional boiler installation; (d) raw water is treated as required for plant makeup; (e) cooling water is provided from a conventional cooling-tower system; (f) air cooling is utilized where applicable. Thus all utilities requirements can be reduced to a common cost base of electrical power and fuel. Investment costs are for a "grass roots" installation including all facilities necessary for the operation and administration of the plant.

The results of the comparison are presented in Table 5. Ethane shows the least investment and annual operating costs, but also offers the lowest gross margin (defined as the difference between product sales revenue and feedstock cost). This combination of effects makes ethane the least desirable feedstock, measured by the criterion of percent cash flow return on total investment, after taxes. The sensitivity of the conclusion to the assumed unit cost structure is illustrated by the fact that if the ethane feed were priced at fuel value (approx 0.4¢/lb), the return on investment would increase from 30.7 to 43.1%; for the latter assumption, ethane would be the most desirable feedstock. Feedstocks heavier than ethane show higher investment and operating costs, but also higher margins. The net result of the comparison indicates propane to be the most attractive feedstock, followed closely by naphtha which has been cracked at moderate conversion. Low-conversion naphtha is attractive because of the leverage

Table 5. Pro-Forma Comparison of Economics of Ethylene Production

	Units	Price	Ethane Units	Ethane Value, MM $/yr	Propane Units	Propane Value, MM $/yr	Naphtha, moderate conversion Units	Naphtha, moderate conversion Value, MM $/yr	Naphtha, high conversion Units	Naphtha, high conversion Value, MM $/yr
Feeds^a										
ethane	MM lb/yr	1.2¢/lb	358	4.30						
propane	MM lb/yr	3.5¢/gal			595	4.92				
naphtha	MM lb/yr	$3.30/bbl					1,027	14.08	859	11.77
Products										
fuel gas	MM Btu/hr	20¢/MM Btu	253	0.41	497	0.80	399	0.64	439	0.70
ethylene (polymer grade)	MM lb/yr	4.75¢/lb	250	11.87	250	11.87	250	11.87	250	11.87
propylene (polymer grade)	MM lb/yr	3.0¢/lb			72	2.16	187	5.61	158	4.74
butylene–butadiene	MM lb/yr	3.5¢/lb			16	0.56	122	4.27	80	2.80
aromatic distillate	BPSD	10¢/gal	347	0.49	767	1.07	3,192	4.47	1,831	2.56
fuel oil	BPSD	$2.20/bbl					187	0.14	298	0.21
total				*12.77*		*16.46*		*27.00*		*22.88*
Margin, MM $/yr				8.47		11.54		12.92		11.11
Investment costs, MM $										
process units: pyrolysis and recovery				6.00		7.00		8.00		7.60
OSBL (non-process units)				2.20		2.40		2.70		2.60
initial inventory catalysts and chemicals				0.15		0.15		0.15		0.15
spare parts				0.35		0.35		0.40		0.40
underground storage for ethylene product				1.00		1.00		1.00		1.00
working capital (20% investment)				2.40		2.70		3.05		2.95
total				*12.10*		*13.60*		*15.30*		*14.70*

Operating costs, MM $/yr				
sales expense at 1% of total product value	0.13	0.16	0.27	0.23
operating labor at $7500/yr; 40 men	0.30	0.30	0.30	0.30
supervision service and overhead at 75% of labor[b]	0.23	0.23	0.23	0.23
utilities				
power at 0.7¢/kWh	0.13	0.20	0.24	0.24
fuel gas at 20¢/MM Btu	0.77	0.84	1.00	1.00
catalysts and chemicals	0.13	0.13	0.13	0.13
contract maintenance at 4% (ISBL and OSBL)	0.33	0.38	0.43	0.41
insurance and local taxes at 2% total investment	0.19	0.22	0.25	0.24
depreciation at 10% total investment[b]	0.97	1.09	1.23	1.18
total	*3.18*	*3.55*	*4.08*	*3.96*
Return on investment				
margin	8.47	11.54	12.92	11.11
operating costs	−3.18	−3.55	−4.08	−3.96
gross income	5.29	7.99	8.84	7.15
income tax at 48%	−2.54	−3.84	−4.24	−3.43
net income	2.75	4.15	4.60	3.72
depreciation	0.97	1.09	1.23	1.18
cash flow	3.72	5.24	5.83	4.90
return on total investment, %	$\frac{3.72}{12.10}=30.7$	$\frac{5.24}{13.60}=38.5$	$\frac{5.83}{15.30}=38.1$	$\frac{4.90}{14.70}=33.3$

[a]Includes 2% unaccountable losses.
[b]Excluding working capital.
LEGEND: MM, million; BPSD, barrels per steam day; OSBL, outside battery limits; ISBL, inside battery limits.

of by-product values, particularly with respect to aromatic distillate, a component of high-octane gasoline. This leverage usually exists only when the local gasoline market warrants purchase of the distillate by the naphtha supplier. In Europe, where disposal of the distillate may be a problem, and where the demand for polymer-grade propylene may be less, high-conversion naphtha cracking may be favored.

Derivatives and End Use. The disposition of ethylene in the U.S. to its principal derivatives, for the years 1950, 1960, and 1970 (projected), is shown in Table 6 (40). The growth rate of ethylene and of these derivatives for the decades 1950–1960 and 1960–1970 (projected) is shown in Table 7. Polyethylene (see Olefin polymers) is the main derivative in the U.S. and also in the rest of the world, and its growth is principally responsible for the great expansion in world production capacity. The growth pattern in the U.S. for the decade 1960–1970 is expected to be influenced by the commercialization of new derivatives such as ethylene–propylene rubber, straight-chain alcohols, and acetaldehyde. The pattern of end use for ethylene derivatives extends over a wide range; Table 8 lists the principal end uses, their influences upon the past and projected growth rates of ethylene, and the derivatives which are embodied in them. It can be seen that plastics have dominated, and will continue to dominate, the growth pattern.

Demand vs Capacity. The preceding economic discussion has implicitly assumed that actual production corresponded to the installed production capacity. This, of

Table 6. Ethylene Consumption by Derivatives in the U.S.

Derivative	Ethylene consumption, %		
	1950	1960	1970[a]
ethanol, synthetic	34	19	11
ethyl chloride and ethylene dichloride	15	13	8
ethylene oxide and glycol	30	27	22
polyethylene	5	29	43
styrene	12	10	9
others	4	2	7
total	100	100	100

[a]Projected.

Table 7. Average Growth Rate for Ethylene and Derivatives in the U.S.[a]

Compound	Years	
	1950–1960	1960–1970[b]
ethylene	13.6	5.3
ethanol, synthetic	9	1.8
ethyl chloride and ethylene dichloride	10.5	3.3
ethylene oxide and glycol	12.5	2.3
polyethylene	37.5	9.0
styrene	12.4	5.2
others	1.8	15.3

[a]Percent per year.   [b]Projected.

Table 8. Distribution of Ethylene Growth by End Use in the U.S.[a]

End use	Years 1950–1960	1960–1970[a]	Derivative type
plastics and resins	43.2	63.4	polyethylene, polyesters
detergents	4.8	4.2	straight-chain alcohols
antifreeze	13.8	2.9	ethylene glycol
elastomers	2.7	5.8	ethylene–propylene rubber, styrene–butadiene rubber
solvents	8.8	6.9	chlorinated ethylene
additives	3.5	0.0	tetraethyllead, ethylene dibromide
synthetic fibers	1.2	1.5	polyesters
miscellaneous	22.0	15.3	
total	100.0	100.0	

[a] Percent of total ethylene growth.   [b] Projected.

course, is not so; the true picture is characterized by the ratio of actual production to total installed capacity, which is commonly termed "overall industry operating ratio." This ratio is an average; some producers will operate at substantially higher or lower ratios, depending on individual circumstances. During the decade 1950–1960, the ratio was better than 85%, except for a brief time in 1958. The ratio fell to 78% in 1961–1962 and is expected to continue to fall to a minimum of approx 68% by 1966; by 1970 it is expected to have recovered gradually to approx 73% (40).

This growing overcapacity reflects a rapid increase both in the number of plants and in the size of the individual plants. During the period 1950–1960, ethylene capacity increased in such a way that one new producer entered the industry each year, and the number of plants increased from 14 to 36. The average annual capacity of new plants constructed during that period was 75,000 tons. These increases in capacity were significant, but did not keep pace with demand. In the early 1960s capacity increased at a much faster rate than demand. Part of this is accounted for by the fact that small plants did not remain competitive and producers could afford to shut down several small plants to build a large one. The average annual capacity of plants being built in the first half of this decade will be approx 120,000 tons, with some individual plants as large as 400,000 tons. Each plant of this size represents a significant addition to the total U.S. capacity.

Price Competition. The drive toward larger plants reflects the intense competitiveness of the industry. Unit investment costs are less for larger plants; in addition, labor and overhead costs per unit of product are also less. These advantages are realized only when the larger plant performs at the same operating ratio as its smaller competitor, which imposes a more severe marketing problem for the larger plant. Another factor is that pipeline transport of raw materials (ethane and LPG) and ethylene product is attractive only for large volumes, and correspondingly large plant sizes.

The major expansion in ethylene production capacity which is now (1965) taking place in the U.S., is causing a decline in the price of ethylene (42). During 1963, prices stabilized at 4.75¢/lb, which represented a drop from the previous long-term level of 5¢. It is expected that in areas of the U.S. where major production facilities are being installed, the price will drop to 4¢ or lower.

The nature of the ethylene business also appears to be changing. Very large consumers of ethylene now find it more economical to build their own very large plants, rather than buy ethylene from merchant producers, as they have in the past decade. The declining unit investment costs for very large plants and the benefits of improved technology are largely responsible for this condition. In the future, it seems that merchant ethylene will be sold primarily to small consumers or, on a short-term basis, to large consumers who wish to defer making their own investments. Some small consumers form joint ventures to gain the benefits of large plants.

Ethylene vs Acetylene. One significant aspect of the commercial development of ethylene in the U.S. over the past decade has been its displacement of acetylene as a raw material for the production of chemical derivatives. The price advantage of ethylene has been the motive force which has encouraged users to accept its lower reactivity and, indeed, to develop new derivative processes for which ethylene would be suitable. As noted above, the merchant price of ethylene is less than 5¢/lb, and projections indicate that it may be less than 4¢ in the near future. By contrast, the price of hydrocarbon-based acetylene is approx 10¢/lb, but some recent improvements in technology are expected to reduce its price to the 6¢ range, where it would be superficially competitive with ethylene. One possibility is a new process reported by Othmer (44), which may soon be applied commercially; another is the Wulff process, for which several large plants are currently (1965) under construction. (See Vol. 1, pp. 184–186.)

Superficial price comparison is not the sole factor, as evidenced by the number of hydrocarbon-based acetylene plants built over the past decade. These plants yield valuable coproducts such as hydrogen, ammonia and methanol synthesis gas, and ethylene itself. Furthermore, in the derivatives plants the greater reactivity of acetylene offers certain advantages, but can also be a potential hazard unless special care is taken in its use; this requirement often increases the cost of the derivatives plant.

The current situation is that only one important derivative—neoprene—relies solely upon acetylene. All others, including acetaldehyde, acetic anhydride, acrylonitrile, vinyl chloride, and vinyl acetate, can be made commercially from either acetylene or ethylene. For the first two derivatives, acetylene has been completely displaced by ethylene; for all the rest, important inroads have been made (45). The statistics reveal that the rate of growth for acetylene has been less than for its derivatives, and that a fair portion of new acetylene production capacity currently under construction is of the type (eg, Wulff process) in which both acetylene and ethylene can be produced, in ratios varying from 80:20 to 20:80.

Specifications and Analysis

Prior to the advent of polyethylene, ethylene specifications were keyed to derivatives plants, such as ethyl alcohol plants, which accepted 97–98 wt % ethylene, with maximum propylene and acetylene contents as high as 0.1 and 1.0%, respectively. Because polyethylene is now the predominant derivative, nearly all new ethylene plants are designed to meet the stringent specifications for polymer grade. A typical specification is given in Table 9. (Ethylene USP XIII contains no less than 99% by vol of C_2H_4.)

The classic methods for ethylene determination use absorption in bromine solutions, in fuming sulfuric acid, or in a solution of mercuric sulfate in 25% sulfuric acid,

Table 9. Typical Specification for Ethylene, Polymer Grade

Component	Content
ethylene	99.9%, min[a]
methane + ethane	0.1%, max[a]
propylene and heavier	30 ppm, max[b]
carbon dioxide	20 ppm, max[b]
carbon monoxide	5 ppm, max[b]
oxygen	5 ppm, max[c]
hydrogen	5 ppm, max[c]
water	5 ppm, max[c]
acetylene	10 ppm, max[c]
sulfur	5 ppm, max[c]
oxygenated organics	10 ppm, max[c]
ammonia and amines	10 ppm, max[c]
organic halides	10 ppm, max[c]

[a] Mole %.   [b] By volume.   [c] By weight.

but none of these reagents are selective for ethylene in the presence of other olefins. These methods have been displaced in modern ethylene plants by gas-chromatographic techniques; proposed methods for analysis of trace quantities of acetylene, hydrogen, methane, ethane, other hydrocarbons, and carbon dioxide in high-purity ethylene are given in the *ASTM Standards*, Appendices V, VI, and VIII (46).

Health and Safety Factors

Ethylene's hazards are basically those of a volatile hydrocarbon. It is dangerous when exposed to heat or flame, can react vigorously with oxidizing materials, and has a wide explosive range with air (3–34%). For shipping compressed ethylene in cylinders, the ICC classification is Flammable Gas, Red Gas Label; the containers can shatter with explosive force when shocked (47).

Transportation

Prior to the 1960s, ethylene-derivatives plants either were located immediately adjacent to an ethylene-producing plant, or were fed from a pipeline network belonging to a merchant producer. Except for conventional gas cylinders destined for minor consumers, no other transportation means was available. Then, following the commercial success of large-scale transport under cryogenic conditions of high-vapor pressure liquids such as nitrogen, oxygen, and natural gas, and after successful experience with short trips (10 hr, equiv to about 400 miles), one major U.S. producer offered to ship "anywhere" by tank truck. Such transportation required safety clearance from the Interstate Commerce Commission, who approved a 1600-mile trip from the Gulf Coast of Texas to California, after careful review of the test data and proposed enroute precautions. Experiments had shown that a tank truck containing ethylene at −150°F under its vapor pressure of approx 3 psig, experienced a pressure rise to 79 psig during a 125-hr trip (99 hr on the road, 25 hr parked) with an average ambient temperature of 85°F. Tests under simulated truck breakdown conditions showed that excess vapor could be flared by the driver conveniently and safely. The first commercial 1600-mile trip in 1964 was completely successful, despite unforeseen weather conditions which introduced an 8-hr delay into the 44-hr schedule (48).

Ethylene shipped by truck, even at some premium in price, is expected to be attractive in the special situations of (a) potential users remote from existing ethylene producers or pipeline networks, who currently use alternate raw materials or who could broaden their line of derivatives if ethylene were available; (b) developing users whose needs have outgrown the limitations of cylinders; and (c) large-scale users who need additional ethylene temporarily.   Barge transportation also would appear to be practical, but is not yet done commercially.   Transportation by insulated rail car has been done in Germany since 1957.

Bibliography

"Ethylene" in *ECT* 1st ed., Vol. 5, pp. 880–898, by John Happel, New York University, and E. I. Becker, Polytechnic Institute of Brooklyn.

1. R. M. Joyce, *Chem. Eng. News* **25**, 1866–1867 (1947).
2. V. M. Tatevskii, ed., *Physico-Chemical Properties of Individual Hydrocarbons*, Moscow, 1961.
3. O. A. Hougen, K. M. Watson, and R. A. Tazazt, *Chemical Process Principles*, Part I, 2nd ed. John Wiley & Sons, Inc., New York, 1954, p. 255.
4. W. F. L. Dick and A. G. M. Hedley, "Ethylene" in F. Din, ed., *Thermodynamic Functions of Gases*, Vol. 2, Butterworths & Co. Ltd., London, 1962, pp. 88–114.
5. F. D. Rossini, *Selected Values of Properties of Hydrocarbons*, American Petroleum Institute Project 44, 1953.
6. C. D. Hodgman, ed., *Handbook of Chemistry and Physics*, 45th ed., The Chemical Rubber Publishing Co., Cleveland, Ohio, 1964.
7. J. H. Perry, ed., *Chemical Engineers' Handbook*, 4th ed., McGraw-Hill Book Co., Inc., New York, 1963.
8. D. J. Cram and G. S. Hammond, *Organic Chemistry*, McGraw-Hill Book Co., Inc., New York, 1959, pp. 51, 343, 376.
9. W. L. Faith, D. B. Keyes, and R. L. Clark, *Industrial Chemicals*, 3rd ed., John Wiley & Sons, Inc., New York, 1957.
10. U.S. Pat. 2,327,174 (Aug. 17, 1943), O. W. Cass (to Du Pont).
11. U.S. Pat. 2,308,489 (Jan. 19, 1943), O. W. Cass (to Du Pont).
12. A. Michael and N. Weiner, *J. Am. Chem. Soc.* **58**, 294 (1936).
13. U.S. Pat. 2,296,696 (Sept. 22, 1943), D. F. Babcock (to Du Pont).
14. U.S. Pat. 2,440,800 (May 4, 1948), W. M. Hanford and R. M. Joyce, Jr. (to Du Pont).
15. R. O. Bolt, *Chem. Eng. News* **25,** 1866 (1947).
16. R. C. Fuson et al., *J. Org. Chem.* **11**, 469–474 (1946).
17. J. W. Baker, *J. Chem. Soc.* **1948**, 89–93.
18. J. A. Knaus, J. C. Yarze, and W. M. Campbell, *Paper 31, 6th World Petroleum Congress,* Section IV, Frankfurt/Main, Germany, June 20, 1963.
19. S. C. Eastwood and A. E. Potas, *Petrol. Engr.* **19,** 43 (Aug. 1948).
20. J. M. Reid et al., *Inst. Gas Technol., Res. Bull. No. 16* (Nov. 1963).
21. P. W. Sherwood, *Petroleum (London)* **19,** 161, 309 (1956).
22. M. P. Kilpatrick et al., *Petrol. Refiner* **33,** 171 (April 1954).
23. T. F. Loughry, *Gas (Los Angeles)* **29** (11), 27 (1953).
24. A. J. Andrews and L. W. Pollock, *Chem. Eng.* **66,** 37 (June 29, 1959).
25. P. Schamlfed, *Hydrocarbon Process. Petrol. Refiner* **42,** 145 (July 1963).
26. Anon., *Chem. Eng. News* **37,** 50 (Nov. 9, 1959).
27. A. Steinhofer, O. Frey, and H. Nonnenmacher, *Hydrocarbon Process. Petrol. Refiner* **42,** 119 (July 1963).
28. J. F. Farnsworth et al., *Ind. Eng. Chem.* **47,** 1517 (1955).
29. G. L. Fleming, *Chem. Eng. Progr.* **52,** 249 (1956).
30. M. Bogart and R. Long, *Chem. Eng. Progr.* **58,** 90 (1962).
31. P. H. Calderbank et al., *J. Appl. Chem. (London)* **7,** 425 (1957).
32. R. M. Deanesly and C. H. Watkins, *Chem. Eng. Progr.* **27,** 134 (1951).
33. P. W. Sherwood, *Petroleum (London)* **19,** 1961 (1956).
34. H. J. Andrews and L. W. Pollock, *Petrol. Refiner* **31,** 154 (1952).

35. Anon., *Chem. Week*, p. 95 (April 28, 1963).
36. N. S. Glick, *7th Symposium on Combustion*, London, 1958, pp. 98–107 (1959).
37. J. R. Fair, J. W. Mayers, and W. H. Lane, *Chem. Eng. Progr.* **53**, 433 (1957).
38. Unpublished data, The Lummus Company, New York.
39. *Synthetic Organic Chemicals—U.S. Production and Sales*, U.S. Tariff Commission, U.S. Government Printing Office, Washington, D.C.
40. W. C. King, *Chem. Eng. Progr.* **59**, 22 (1963).
41. Anon., *European Chemical News* (June 19, 1964).
42. Anon., *Chem. Week*, p. 26 (Jan. 16, 1965).
43. W. Tucker, unpublished paper presented at the Mexican Institute of Chemical Engineers, Oct. 1963.
44. D. F. Othmer, *Hydrocarbon Process. Petrol. Refiner* **44**, 145 (1965).
45. *Chemical Economics Newsletter*, Stanford Research Institute (June, July 1964).
46. "ASTM Standards on Petroleum Products and Lubricants," *Book of ASTM Standards*, Vol. 1, 39th ed., American Society for Testing and Materials, Philadelphia, Dec. 1962.
47. N. I. Sax, *Dangerous Properties of Industrial Materials*, Reinhold Publishing Corp., New York, 1957, p. 676.
48. Anon., *Chem. Week*, p. 56 (Dec. 12, 1964).

D. L. CALDWELL AND I. LICHTENSTEIN
The Lummus Company

ETHYLENEAMINES; ETHYLENEDIAMINE. See Diamines and higher amines, aliphatic.

ETHYLENE GLYCOL, CH_2OHCH_2OH. See Glycols.

ETHYLENEIMINE, $NHCH_2CH_2$. See Imines.

ETHYLENE OXIDE

Ethylene oxide was prepared for the first time by Wurtz in 1859. He reacted ethylene chlorohydrin with aqueous potassium hydroxide, thus providing a foundation for the important chlorohydrin process, which is still used today. He also tried to prepare ethylene oxide by direct oxidation. In 1863 he wrote: "It is impossible to obtain ethylene oxide directly by the action of oxygen on ethylene. I tried unsuccessfully to add oxygen directly to ethylene, heating a mixture of both gases in the necessary amounts in a sealed flask in the presence of acetic acid, anticipating to form the glycol acetate" (1). Subsequently, many other investigators were unable to oxidize ethylene directly to ethylene oxide (2–5). In 1904 Walter made an exhaustive study of the oxidation of ethylene by air, but did not observe the formation of ethylene oxide. He tried many metals as catalysts, including silver, platinum, iridium, palladium, uranium, vanadium, manganese, copper, iron, cobalt, nickel, and cerium. He did not attribute any singular, specific properties to silver (6). In 1928 Reyerson and Swearingen reported that oxidation of ethylene over silver on silica gel gave only carbon dioxide and water (4). They established the following order for a number of metals on silica gel for the oxidation of ethylene: Pt>Pd>Cu>Ag. Reyerson referred in 1944 to the possible preparation of ethylene oxide during his earlier studies (7). Lefort, in 1931, was the first to succeed in the direct oxidation of ethylene to ethylene oxide, using silver as the catalyst (8). Lenher, also in 1931, obtained ethylene oxide and formaldehyde as main products from a slow reaction of ethylene with oxygen at 300–525°C (9). This method was patented (9,10) but never used commercially.

Physical Properties of Ethylene Oxide

Ethylene oxide is a colorless gas condensing at low temperatures to a mobile liquid. It is miscible in all proportions with water, alcohol, ether, and most organic solvents. The vapors of ethylene oxide are flammable and explosive. The physical constants are summarized in Tables 1–7.

Table 1. Some Physical Constants of Ethylene Oxide (see also Tables 2–7)

Property	Value	Reference
boiling point, °C		
at 760 mm Hg	10.4	11
at 50 mm Hg	−44.0	
at 10 mm Hg	−66.0	
Δbp/Δp, 740–760 mm Hg, °C/mm	0.036	12
coefficient of cubical expansion		
at 20°C, per °C	0.00147	12
at 55°C, per °C	0.00161	12
critical pressure, psia	1043	11
critical temperature, °C	195.8	11
dielectric constant at −1.0°C, esu	13.9	13
electric moment, $\mu \times 10^{18}$	1.88	14
entropy[a] at 25.0°C, calc, cal/(°C)(mole)	57.94	15
explosive limits in air,[a] % by vol		
upper	100.0	11,16,17
lower	3.0	11,16,17
flash point, Tag, open-cup	below 0 °F	11,16,17
freezing point, °C	−112.5	11
heat of combustion[a] at 25°C, kcal/g-mole	302.09	11,18
	312.55 ± 0.20	19
heat of formation, kcal/g-mole		
vapor	17.0	11,20
liquid	23.3	11,20
heat of fusion, cal/g-mole	1236.4	11,15
heat of solution in water at constant pressure, kcal/mole	1.5	11,20
heat of vaporization,[a] cal/g-mole		
at 10.5°C	6101 ± 6	12,15
at 10.5°C (calc)	6082.0	12,15
ignition temperature in air,[a] °C	429.0	21
melting point, °C	−112.51	12,15
oxygen valence angle	77.0°	14
refractive index, n_D^7	1.3597	22
specific heat[a] at 2.5°C	0.467	12,23
spontaneous ignition temperature,[a] °C	571.0	11,24,17
surface energy, total, dyn	73.2	25
surface tension at 20°C, dyn/cm	24.3	11
thermal conductivity, vapor, at 25°C, cal/(sec)(°C/cm)(cm²)	0.00002961	11
viscosity, absolute, cP		
at 0°C	0.31	12
at 10°C	0.28	

[a] At 760 mm Hg.

Table 2. Vapor Pressures of Pure Ethylene Oxide at Various Temperatures (12)

Temperature, °C	Pressure, mm Hg	Temperature, °C	Pressure, mm Hg
−40.0	62.5	40.0	2,167
−30.0	112.6	60.0	3,919
−20.0	192.6	80.0	6,585
−10.0	314.5	100.0	10,414
0.0	493.2	120.0	15,672
10.44	760.0	140.0	22,635
20.0	1,094	160.0	31,622
30.0	1,559	180.0	43,206
		195.8[a]	54,704

[a] Critical temperature.

NOTE: Antoine equation:

$$\log_{10} p = A - B/(C + t)$$

where p is in mm Hg;
t is in degrees Celsius

Antoine constants:
$A = 7.26100$
$B = 1115.1$
$C = 244.135$

Table 3. Vapor–Liquid Equilibrium Data of the System Ethylene Oxide–Water[a] (12)

Temperature, °C	Ethylene oxide composition, mole %	
	Liquid	Vapor
100	0	0
50.0	4.0	86.00
37.6	6.5	93.70
31.5	8.2	95.95
31.0	9.5	96.48
16.4	21.0	98.16
14.3	43.2	98.53
12.0	87.5	98.88
11.5	95.1	99.27
10.4	100.0	100.00

[a] At 760 mm Hg pressure.

Table 4. Flash Points of Aqueous Solutions of Ethylene Oxide (12)

Ethylene oxide, wt %	Flash point, °F, Tag, closed-cup	Ethylene oxide, wt %	Flash point, °F, Tag, closed-cup
1	87	5	28
3	38	15	28

Structure

Ethylene oxide, the monomolecular cyclic ether derived from ethylene glycol, is the simplest member of the class of alkylene oxides. It is also known as epoxyethane or oxirane. The structure of the compound can be represented satisfactorily by formula (**1**) below, although other, more complex structures have been suggested. With evidence on the interatomic angles of ethylene oxide as computed by Cunningham, three different structural forms of ethylene oxide may be shown (27,28).

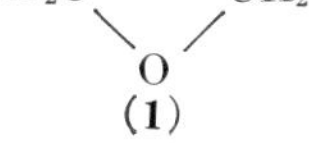

$$H_2C\!-\!\!-\!\!-\!CH_2 \qquad\qquad {}^+CH_2\!-\!CH_2O^- \;\rightleftharpoons\; {}^-OCH_2\!-\!CH_2{}^+ \qquad\qquad CH_2{=}CH_2$$
$$\diagdown\!O\!\diagup \qquad\qquad\qquad\qquad\qquad\qquad\qquad\qquad\qquad\qquad \downarrow O$$
$$(\mathbf{1}) \qquad\qquad\qquad\qquad (\mathbf{2}) \qquad\qquad\qquad\qquad\qquad\qquad (\mathbf{3})$$

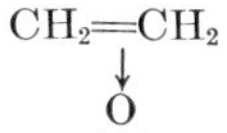

Table 5. Molal Heat Capacity of Ethylene Oxide (15,22)

Temperature, °K[a]	Cal/mole	Temperature, °K[a]	Cal/mole
15	0.60	160.65	19.80
20	1.43	180	19.55
30	3.30	200	19.47
40	5.21	210	19.50
50	6.77	220	19.56
60	8.16	240	19.82
80	10.06	260	20.21
100	11.43	280	20.67
120	12.77	285	20.77
140	14.47	307.18	11.76
160	16.30	337.04	12.74
160.65	16.35	371.23	13.89
melting point			

[a] 0°C = 273.16°K.

Table 6. True Density of Ethylene Oxide (12)

Temperature, °C	Density, g/ml	Temperature, °C	Density, g/ml
−40	0.9488	80	0.7794
−20	0.9232	100	0.7443
0	0.8969	120	0.7052
20	0.8697	140	0.6609
40	0.8413	150	0.6357
60	0.8108		

Table 7. Solubility of Ethylene Oxide in Water, ml Vapor[a]/ml Solvent (26)

Pressure, mm Hg	Water, at °C		
	5°	10°	20°
150	45	33	20
200	60	46	29
300	105	76	49
400	162	120	74
500	240	178	101
600		294	134
700			170
760			195

[a] Reduced to 0°C and 760 mm Hg.

Zimakov (29) suggested that the electrophilic nature of ethylene oxide can be represented best by the resonance hybrid (**2**). Structure (**3**), with the oxygen bonded to the π electrons, is supported by bond-force studies (30,31), but is rejected by Robinson (32), since reduction gives ethanol and not ethylene.

Reactions

Ethylene oxide is highly reactive and is primarily a chemical intermediate for the manufacture of ethylene glycol, polyethylene glycols, glycol ethers, ethanolamines, ethylene cyanohydrin, hydroxyethylcellulose, hydroxyethyl starch, and a wide variety of surface-active agents. It reacts neutral to litmus and forms oxonium salts with strong anhydrous mineral acids. This basicity offers an explanation for the reaction with aqueous solutions of various metallic salts, yielding ethylene chlorohydrin and the corresponding metallic hydroxide:

$$2\ H_2C\!\!-\!\!-\!\!CH_2 + 2\ H_2O + MgCl_2 \rightarrow 2\ ClCH_2CH_2OH + Mg(OH)_2$$

Most reactions involve the opening of the three-membered ring. The oxonium salts mentioned above are among the few exceptions. The great value of ethylene oxide for synthesis is due to two types of reactivity. It introduces the hydroxyethyl group into many compounds having a labile hydrogen atom.

$$H_2C\!\!-\!\!-\!\!CH_2 + RH \rightarrow RCH_2CH_2OH$$

Ethylene oxide also polymerizes to give a polyethylene oxide chain.

$$n\ H_2C\!\!-\!\!-\!\!CH_2 \rightarrow -OCH_2CH_2(OCH_2CH_2)_{n-2}OCH_2CH_2-$$

These two types of reactivity can be combined to give a series of polyethylene glycol derivatives of increasing chain length and water solubility.

$$n\ H_2C\!\!-\!\!-\!\!CH_2 + RH \rightarrow RCH_2CH_2OH$$
$$\rightarrow RCH_2CH_2OCH_2CH_2OH$$
$$\rightarrow R(CH_2CH_2O)_{n-1}CH_2CH_2OH$$

With Hydrogen. Ethanol is obtained by catalytic or chemical reduction, using reagents such as sodium amalgam.

With Water. Wurtz was the first to obtain ethylene glycol, when heating ethylene oxide and water in a sealed tube (1). Lourenço repeated Wurtz's work in 1863 and noticed the formation of by-products, including diethylene glycol and triethylene glycol (33). This was the first synthesis of polymeric compounds of well-defined structure. Hydration is slow at ambient temperatures, but is speeded up by acid- or base catalysts. Smith, Wode, and Widhe published data for the rate of addition of water to ethylene oxide at 25°C in solutions of nitric and perchloric acids of 0.01 and 0.5 molar concentrations. They concluded that the anion of the catalyzing acid is relatively unimportant (34). See Glycols.

With Alcohols. These reactions parallel those of ethylene oxide with water. The principal products are the monoethers of ethylene glycol. By-products are the monoethers of di- and triethylene glycol (35). The ethylene glycol monoethers are excellent high-boiling solvents. Most of them are appreciably soluble in water.

With Organic Acids and Anhydrides. Acids react with ethylene oxide to give mainly the corresponding ethylene glycol monoester. The initial reactions are analogous to those with alcohols. Further treatment with the organic acid gives the ethylene glycol diester, which may be obtained more directly by reacting ethylene oxide with the acid anhydride.

Acyl Halides, Hydrogen Halides, and Metallic Halides. Ethylene oxide reacts with acetyl chloride at slightly elevated temperatures using hydrogen chloride as a catalyst, to give the acetate of ethylene chlorohydrin. Hydrogen halides produce the corresponding halohydrins. Ethylene oxide, in aqueous solutions with certain metallic halides, reacts with the acid freed by dissociation and hydrolysis to precipitate the metallic hydroxide. This reaction serves as a basis of analysis for ethylene oxide (36,37). The halides of aluminum, chromium, iron, thorium, and zinc in dilute solution react with ethylene oxide to form sols or gels of the metal-oxide hydrates and ethylene halohydrin. These can be removed from the solution by ether extraction or distillation (38).

In the presence of aluminum chloride, ethylene oxide undergoes a Friedel-Crafts reaction with aromatic hydrocarbons. Thus, ethylene oxide and hydrogen chloride passed into a mixture of benzene and aluminum chloride yields dibenzyl, $C_6H_5CH_2$-$CH_2C_6H_5$, and a small amount of 2-phenylethanol, $C_6H_5CH_2CH_2OH$ (39). Aryllithiums add ethylene oxide or other epoxides to form the corresponding alcoholate salts which are intermediates for hydroaromatic ketones related to anthracene and phenanthrene (40).

With Grignard Reagents. Ethylene oxide reacts with Grignard reagents, RMgX, to form primary alcohols containing two more carbon atoms, RCH_2CH_2OH, as the principal product. A smaller amount of secondary alcohol, $RCHOHCH_3$, and varying amounts of halohydrin, RCH_2XCH_2OH, are formed (41,42). Grignard (43) proposed that an intermediate oxonium compound is formed when ethylene oxide reacts with an alkyl magnesium bromide, RMgBr. Alcohols can be prepared by reacting ethylene oxide with numerous alkyl and aryl halides (41). Gaylord and Becker offer a comprehensive report on the reactions between Grignard reagents and the oxirane ring (44). The text by Kharasch and Reinmuth is also an excellent source of information on such reactions (45).

With Halosilanes. 2-Haloethoxy groups attach to silicon, when the appropriate silicon halide reacts with ethylene oxide (46–48). The physical properties of the organosilicon alkoxides are very similar to those of analogous organic ethers. Their boiling points are in general about 10–15 degrees higher than those of the corresponding alcohols. A number of these compounds are useful as solvents and lubricants. The reaction of an organosilicon halide with ethylene oxide may involve initial formation of a halohydrin by reaction of ethylene oxide with traces of the hydrogen halide present in the silicon halide. The halohydrin then adds to the silicon chloride in the expected manner (47,48). See Silicon compounds.

With Ammonia and Amines. Ethylene oxide reacts with ammonia to form a mixture of mono-, di-, and triethanolamines. The hydrogen atoms on the nitrogen are more reactive than those of the hydroxyl group (49). A small amount of water is essential to the reaction (50). The proportion of the three ethanolamines in a mixture depends on the ratio of reactants used. A large excess of ethylene oxide favors the formation of triethanolamine. See Alkanolamines.

Complex nitrogen compounds are formed by reacting alkylamines with ethylene oxide. Thus, diethylamine and ethylene oxide react to yield diethylaminoethanol, which is a valuable intermediate for synthesis of procaine. The dialkylaminoethanols react further with ethylene oxide to give amine derivatives of polyethylene glycols.

$$R_2NCH_2CH_2OH + n\ CH_2CH_2O \rightarrow R_2NCH_2CH_2(OCH_2CH_2)_nOH$$

Primary and secondary aromatic amines react like the corresponding alkylamines. Aniline yields 2-hydroxyethylaniline and bis(2-hydroxyethyl)aniline. Ethylaniline yields N-ethyl-N-2-hydroxyethylaniline. These compounds are dye intermediates.

Ethylene oxide adds to hydrazine to give N,N-bis(2-hydroxyethyl)hydrazine (51,52). Hydroxylamine reacts with ethylene oxide at 0°C to yield N,N-bis(2-hydroxyethyl)hydroxylamine and tris(2-hydroxyethyl)amine oxide (53).

$$2\ CH_2CH_2O + H_2NOH \rightarrow (HOCH_2CH_2)_2NOH$$

$$3\ CH_2CH_2O + H_2NOH \rightarrow (HOCH_2CH_2)_3NO$$

With Phenols. The 2-hydroxyethyl aryl ethers are prepared by reacting ethylene oxide with phenols at elevated temperatures and pressures (49,54,55). 2-Phenoxyethyl alcohol is a perfume fixative. The water-soluble alkylphenyl ethers of the higher polyethylene glycols are important detergents. They are made by adding ethylene oxide to the alkylphenol at about 200°C and 2–2.5 atm pressure using sodium acetate or hydroxide as a catalyst. Dodecylphenol reacts with 8–15 moles of ethylene oxide to give a more valuable detergent (49).

With Hydrogen Sulfide. Ethylene oxide reacts with hydrogen sulfide to yield 2-mercaptoethanol and thiodiglycol (bis-2-hydroxyethyl sulfide). Reaction conditions determine the proportions of each derivative. Three moles of ethylene oxide react with 1 mole of hydrogen sulfide to form the strong base, tris(hydroxyethyl)sulfonium hydroxide, $[(HOCH_2CH_2)_3S]^+OH^-$. See Sulfur compounds, organic.

p-Oxathiane and p-dithane are formed from ethylene oxide and hydrogen sulfide at 200°C in the presence of aluminum oxide as a catalyst (56). Culvenor, Davies, and Heath offer considerable information on the reactions of ethylene oxide with sulfur compounds (57).

p-oxathiane　　　　　　　　p-dithiane

With Hydrogen Cyanide. Ethylene oxide reacts readily with hydrogen cyanide in the presence of alkaline catalysts such as diethylamine to give ethylene cyanohydrin (49,58). This is readily dehydrated either under vapor- or liquid-phase conditions to give acrylonitrile in 80–90% yield. Ethylene cyanohydrin can be hydrolyzed or esterified to give acrylic acid or alkyl acrylates.

$$HCN + CH_2CH_2O \rightarrow HOCH_2CH_2CN$$

$$HOCH_2CH_2CN \rightarrow CH_2{=}CHCN + H_2O$$

$$HOCH_2CH_2CN + CH_3OH + H_2SO_4 \rightarrow CH_2{=}CHCOOCH_3 + NH_4HSO_4$$

With aqueous sulfuric acid in the absence of alcohol acrylic acid is obtained (49).

With Carbonyl Compounds. Ethylene oxide reacts with ketones in the presence of metal halide catalysts, such as boron trifluoride or tin tetrachloride under anhydrous conditions only, to give cyclic ketals (59). For example, ethylene oxide reacts with acetone to give 2,2-dimethyl-1,3-dioxolane. Considerable ethylene oxide polymer is formed as a by-product (60–62).

Aldehydes react to give the corresponding acetals. Inert solvents diminish polymer formation. The anhydrous metal halide is added to the chilled carbonyl compound, before addition of the ethylene oxide. The reaction takes place at 40–50°C (80 min). The yield is about 25–35 %.

With Compounds Containing an Active Methylene or Methine Group. Compounds containing active —CH_2— or —CH= groups, such as malonic and monosubstituted malonic esters, ethyl cyanoacetate, and β-keto esters, condense with ethylene oxide and other alkylene oxides to form a wide variety of compounds (63). Ethylene oxide and diethyl malonate, in the presence of sodium ethoxide, form principally diethyl (2-hydroxyethyl)malonate, which loses one molecule of water to form α-carbethoxy-γ-butyrolactone.

$$H_2C\!\!-\!\!-\!\!CH_2 + H_2C(COOC_2H_5)_2 \xrightarrow{\text{NaOC}_2\text{H}_5} HOCH_2CH_2CH(COOC_2H_5)_2$$
$$\underset{O}{\diagdown\diagup}$$
$$\downarrow$$
$$CH_2CH_2CHCOOC_2H_5$$
$$\overset{|}{O}\!\!-\!\!-\!\!\overset{|}{CO}$$

The sodio derivative of ethyl acetoacetate in ethanol reacts at 0°C to give 1-aceto-3-butyrolactone, an intermediate for vitamin B and antimalarials (49).

$$H_2C\!\!-\!\!-\!\!CH_2 + \begin{matrix} CH_3 \\ | \\ CO \\ | \\ CH\!-\!Na \\ | \\ COOC_2H_5 \end{matrix} \rightarrow \begin{bmatrix} CH_3 \\ | \\ CO \\ | \\ CHCH_2CH_2OH \\ | \\ COOC_2H_5 \end{bmatrix}$$

$$\downarrow$$

$$\begin{matrix} CH_3 \\ | \\ C\!=\!O \\ | \\ CH\!-\!CH_2 \\ | \quad \diagdown \\ | \qquad CH_2 \\ | \quad \diagup \\ C\!-\!O \\ \| \\ O \end{matrix}$$

With Organic and Inorganic Acid Halides. Ethylene oxide reacts with acyl halides and with hydrogen chloride as a catalyst to form 2-haloethyl esters (63,64). Thus, acetyl chloride yields 2-chloroethyl acetate. Small amounts of iodine also catalyze these reactions, which proceed slowly without catalysts.

Miscellaneous Reactions. Ethylene oxide isomerizes to acetaldehyde with the evolution of 23.3 kcal/g-mole at 300°–400°C in the presence of catalysts, such as activated alumina, phosphoric acid, and metallic phosphates (49). Twigg showed that ethylene oxide isomerizes over a silver catalyst at 323°C in the presence of oxygen. The aldehyde quickly decomposes to carbon dioxide and water (65).

Phosphorus oxychloride reacts with ethylene oxide in the presence of aluminum chloride to give tris-2-chloroethyl phosphate, a valuable plasticizer (49).

$$H_2C\!\!-\!\!-\!\!CH_2 + POCl_3 \rightarrow OP(OCH_2CH_2Cl)_3$$
$$\underset{O}{\diagdown\diagup}$$

Diborane adds rapidly to ethylene oxide at $-80°C$ to form diethoxyborine and a solid polymer containing about eight ethylene oxide units per molecule. Propylene oxide reacts in a similar manner. Both polymers contain boron and are of the type $H-[CHR-CH_2O]_n-BH_2$ (66).

Potassium thiocyanate or thiourea reacts in aqueous solution with ethylene oxide to give ethylene sulfide. The mechanism of the reaction is not clear (49). Phosgene adds to ethylene oxide and other alkylene oxides with the formation of esters of chlorocarbonic acid (67).

$$H_2C\text{——}CH_2 + COCl_2 \rightarrow ClCH_2CH_2OCOCl$$
$$\diagdown\text{O}\diagup$$

Manufacture

Ethylene oxide is produced commercially by the chlorohydrin and direct-oxidation processes. Badische Anilin- und Soda-Fabrik and other German firms introduced the chlorohydrin process during World War I (68). Union Carbide Corporation became the first large-scale manufacturer in the United States, utilizing the chlorohydrin process in 1925. Union Carbide was also the first company to commercialize the direct-oxidation process in 1937. Considerable information on the early commercial history of both processes can be found in the ACS Monograph on glycols (69).

CHLOROHYDRIN PROCESS

The chlorohydrin process is attractive commercially only when a good supply of captive low-cost chlorine and lime or caustic soda is available; also satisfactory markets are needed to dispose of calcium or sodium chloride and the chlorinated hydrocarbon by-products, 1,2-dichloroethane and bis(2-chloroethyl) ether. These organic derivatives are usually in demand for a variety of applications, such as solvents, gasoline additives, fumigants, and synthesis intermediates. The chlorohydrin process accounted for 50–60% of the ethylene oxide manufactured in the United States in the mid-1950s. However, the advantages of the direct-oxidation process reduced chlorohydrin production to 15% of the total during 1963–1964 (see Table 10).

Chlorohydrin process equipment is designed and operated to minimize the yields of chlorinated hydrocarbon by-products. One thousand pounds of ethylene oxide produced in an 80% yield requires 800 lb of ethylene, 2000 lb of chlorine, and 1600 lb of lime as calcium oxide. Approx 3200 lb of calcium chloride is obtained with each 1000 lb of ethylene oxide. The yield of dichloroethane ranges from 100–150 lb. Seventy to 90 lb of bis(2-chloroethyl) ether and 5–10 lb of acetaldehyde are likely to be obtained from typical large-scale operations (70).

Gomberg indicated in 1919 that hypochlorous acid is stable in water only in low concentrations. Relative yields of ethylene chlorohydrin and dichloroethane are determined by the rates of reaction of ethylene with hypochlorous acid and with chlorine, respectively. Actually, ethylene may react with three of the four components of the following equilibrium:

$$HOH + Cl_2 \rightleftharpoons HCl + HOCl$$

Hypochlorous acid reacts faster with olefins than does molecular chlorine or hydrogen chloride at temperatures of 20–50°C and at pressures of approx 2.5 atm. These are the optimum conditions for the exothermic hypochlorination step. Other conditions, favoring maximum chlorohydrin and minimum by-product formation, include complete dispersion of gaseous reactants, the use of a slight excess of ethylene in the feed, and the maintenance of ethylene chlorohydrin concentrations not above 6% in the reaction stream.

A possible explanation of the hypochlorination step suggests the addition first of positive chloride ion to ethylene to form a carbonium or chloronium ion, and subsequently, of either negatively charged hydroxyl or chloride ion (72–75).

$$CH_2{=}CH_2 + HO^-Cl^+ \rightarrow CH_2CH_2Cl^+ + OH^-$$

$$CH_2CH_2Cl^+ + OH^- \rightarrow HOCH_2CH_2Cl$$

$$CH_2 + Cl^+ \rightarrow \begin{array}{c} CH_2 \\ | \\ CH_2 \end{array}\!\!Cl^+ \quad \xrightarrow[Cl^-]{OH^-} \quad \begin{array}{l} CH_2OH \\ | \\ CH_2Cl \\[6pt] CH_2Cl \\ | \\ CH_2Cl \end{array}$$

$$\begin{array}{c} CH_2 \\ | \\ CH_2 \end{array}\!\!Cl^+ \xrightarrow{HOCH_2CH_2Cl} O\!\!\begin{array}{l} CH_2CH_2Cl \\[6pt] CH_2CH_2Cl \end{array} + HCl$$

Bis(2-chloroethyl) ether can be prepared as a major product by reacting ethylene and chlorine in the presence of chlorohydrin at temperatures above 60°C (74).

Two industrial methods are employed to obtain ethylene chlorohydrin as an intermediate in the production of ethylene oxide (76,77). In the first, ethylene is mixed with a slurry of hydrated lime at 20°C under a pressure of 200 atmospheres. This slurry is pumped to a mixer, where it is treated with a stream of chlorine to form unstable calcium oxychloride, which decomposes in the aqueous media to give hypochlorous acid and calcium chloride. The hypochlorous acid then reacts with ethylene to yield a 35–40% solution of ethylene chlorohydrin.

$$CaO + Cl_2 \rightarrow CaCl(OCl)$$

$$CaCl(OCl) + Cl_2 + H_2O \rightarrow CaCl_2 + 2\,HOCl$$

$$2\,HOCl + CH_2{=}CH_2 \rightarrow HOCH_2CH_2Cl$$

In the second method chlorine is dispersed in water at 15–25°C and a pressure of about 2.5 atm. Ethylene is then sparged into this hypochlorous acid solution to obtain ethylene chlorohydrin in concentrations of 4–6%. See also Chlorohydrins.

The ethylene chlorohydrin, obtained by either method, may be converted directly into ethylene oxide by hydrolysis, using a milk-of-lime slurry or a solution of sodium hydroxide. Sodium bicarbonate solutions for the hydrolysis step present engineering difficulties (76). It is important to remove the ethylene oxide from the alkaline medium as soon as it is formed.

A simplified diagram of a typical chlorohydrin process for manufacturing ethylene oxide is shown in Figure 1. The chlorohydrin reactor must be resistant to corrosion by aqueous solutions of hydrochloric and hypochlorous acids and to the solvent actions of chlorinated hydrocarbons. Therefore steel vessels, lined with rubber, Haveg, a

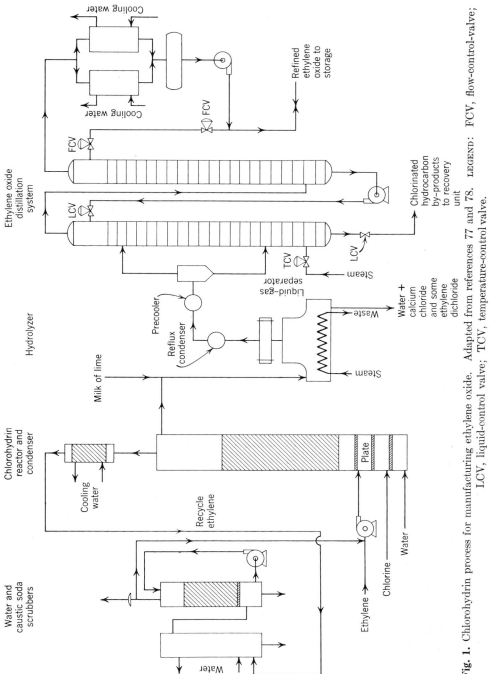

Fig. 1. Chlorohydrin process for manufacturing ethylene oxide.   Adapted from references 77 and 78.   LEGEND: FCV, flow–control–valve; LCV, liquid-control valve;   TCV, temperature-control valve.

chemical and high-temperature resistant plastic and composite type material (Haveg Industries, Inc.), stoneware, or acidproof brick are used. A typical chlorohydrin tower measures 4 ft in diameter and is about 50 ft high. Its lower section contains spargers and porous plates for the effective dispersion of chlorine into water and for injecting ethylene into the hypochlorous acid medium.

Ethylene chlorohydrin formation proceeds rapidly within the lower section of the tower, and is completed in the mid-section, which is packed with 2-in. Raschig rings. Gases are separated from the dilute chlorohydrin solution in the top section. Some dichloroethane is recovered from the vapor in an overhead acid-resistant condenser. The vent gases from this condenser pass in series to acidproof water and caustic scrubbers, where residual chlorine and hydrogen chloride are removed before recycling the unreacted ethylene to the base of the chlorohydrin tower.

The aqueous chlorohydrin solution leaves the acidproof equipment and is mixed with a 10% solution of milk of lime (10–20% in excess) at the inlet to the hydrolyzer. This is usually a horizontal, flat-ended cylindrical vessel with a reflux condenser on top. Steam, at 95–100°C and at 60–80 mm Hg pressure in the hydrolyzer, removes ethylene oxide rapidly from the reaction medium (70).

Thomas and Utley offer an excellent description of a typical ethylene oxide refining system (78). Two columns are used. Each is 5 ft in diameter and contains a total of about eighty bubble-cap trays on 18-in. tray spacings. The first column, 71 ft high, removes chlorinated hydrocarbons from ethylene oxide and contains thirty-seven trays. The second column refines ethylene oxide by removing acetaldehyde. It is 87 ft high and contains forty-five trays. There are thirty-seven 4-in. caps on each tray. Crude feed to the first column contains about 77.5% ethylene oxide; 10% water; 12% chlorinated organic compounds, principally 1,2-dichloroethane; and 0.5% acetaldehyde together with small amounts of hydrocarbon gases. This feed is introduced into the lower section of the first column which is heated with steam. The vapor fraction from the top of the column passes into the base of the second column. Ethylene oxide in 99 mole% purity is distilled off the top of the second column with traces of acetaldehyde as a principal contaminant. The bottoms from the second column (acetaldehyde and ethylene oxide) are recycled to the top tray of the first column. Chlorinated hydrocarbons are taken off of the base of the first column and are pumped to separate recovery systems.

DIRECT-OXIDATION PROCESS

The growth in production capacity and the demand for ethylene oxide since the 1940s can be attributed largely to the commercial success of the direct-oxidation process. Although it has been the subject of considerable research and many patents, its mechanism is not yet fully explained.

The direct-oxidation process obviates a need for large volumes of chlorine. There are no chlorinated hydrocarbon by-products, for which markets must be sought. Processing facilities are in general simpler than those used for the chlorohydrin procedure. The disadvantages of the direct-oxidation process are a lower yield of ethylene oxide and the loss of about one-third of the ethylene fed as carbon dioxide. Therefore operating conditions must be carefully selected and controlled. The main product has to be recovered from a very dilute gas stream, but this separation is not difficult.

Oxygen is absorbed on the surface of a specific, silver-containing catalyst. It then adds across the olefinic bond of ethylene, a most unusual reaction.

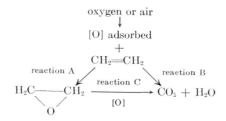

Reaction B liberates about thirteen times as much energy as reaction A. The industrial success of the direct oxidation of ethylene depends accordingly on proper control of the temperature at the catalyst reaction sites.

Conversion of ethylene to ethylene oxide ranges from 50 to 70% for most commercial installations. The two principal reactions occurring at the catalyst surface are as follows:

$$CH_2{=}CH_2 + \tfrac{1}{2} O_2 \rightarrow H_2C\underset{O}{\overset{}{\diagdown\,\diagup}}CH_2 + 1615 \text{ Btu/lb of ethylene}$$

$$CH_2{=}CH_2 + 3 O_2 \rightarrow 2 CO_2 + 2 H_2O + 21,790 \text{ Btu/lb of ethylene}$$

The above energy values are calculated using basic thermochemical data supplied by Kobe and associates (79), and apply to reaction conditions which include a catalyst surface temperature of 327°C (600°K). The following data illustrate the rapid changes in energy released by the oxidation as the selectivity of reaction is decreased by improper control.

selectivity, %	70	60	50	40
total heat, 1000 Btu/lb of ethylene converted	7.67	9.69	11.70	13.72

Using these values, a 50-million-lb-per-year production of ethylene oxide would release about 40 million Btu of heat per hour at an optimum selectivity of 70%. However, the heat release would more than double to 98 million Btu per hour if improper control lowered the selectivity to 50%.

Lack of control of the direct-oxidation reaction is the principal factor contributing to impaired catalyst activity, increased down-time, higher production costs, and lower return on capital invested.

In general, commercial processes for the oxidation of ethylene are operated under recycle conditions in fixed-bed equipment at temperatures of 250–325°C, at pressures of 10–30 atm, and employing contact times of 1–4 sec. Figure 2 shows a typical process and illustrates the salient aspects of fixed-bed conversion systems (70,80–87).

Ethylene (95–98 mole % pure) and air or oxygen are fed separately into a recycle gas stream serving as feed to a bank of one or more primary converters which are operated in parallel. The fresh air/ethylene feed ratio, usually about 10:1, is varied within limits, in order to ensure, after dilution with recycle gas, an optimum air/ethylene feed ratio of 7 (or 8):1 (87). Accordingly, a typical feed stream may contain 3–6 mole % ethylene, 3–6 mole % oxygen, 8–10 mole % carbon dioxide, and the balance a diluent, usually nitrogen (84–86). Reaction takes place over the silver catalyst packed into the tubes of a reactor as shown in Figure 3. The gas stream moves downward over the catalyst countercurrent to the circulation of a heat-transfer fluid in the shell of the reactor. A portion of the fluid (Dowtherm or other high-boiling materials)

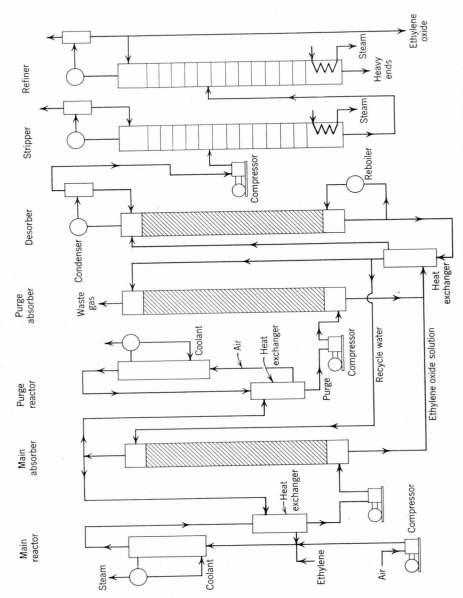

Fig. 2. Direct-oxidation process for manufacturing ethylene oxide (80).   *Courtesy Chemical Engineering.*

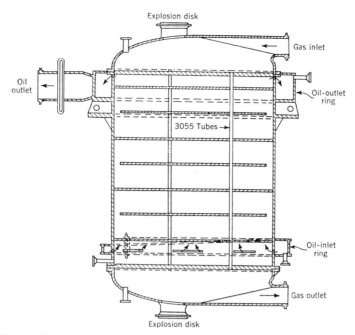

Fig. 3. Oil-cooled reactor for the oxidation of ethylene to ethylene oxide.

is vaporized by the exothermic reaction heat and is condensed in a heat exchanger to provide considerable steam for the ethylene oxide and other processes. Ethylene conversions in the primary reactors are maintained at 30–50% per pass in order to ensure selectivities of 60% or higher. Oxidation inhibitors, such as ethylene dichloride, are added to the inlet gas in ppm concentrations to reduce undesirable carbon dioxide formation (85–87).

The effluent from a primary reactor may contain 1.2–2.0 mole % ethylene oxide and 2–3 mole % ethylene (84–87). This gas is cooled in a shell-and-tube heat exchanger to about 100°F against the recycle stream from the main absorber. The crude product stream is compressed in a centrifugal blower before entering this absorber, generally operated with cold water. However, sulfuric acid, methanol, and carbon may also be used to remove ethylene oxide from crude-product streams (77,87). Dilute sulfuric acid is particularly effective if ethylene glycol is the major product desired. Hydrolysis and recovery take place simultaneously.

The Distillers Company Ltd. and I. G. Farbenindustrie originally recovered ethylene oxide by adsorption on activated carbon. Approx 0.1–0.2 lb of ethylene oxide was adsorbed per pound of carbon. Desorption was accomplished by the use of direct steam. In experiments on the recovery of ethylene oxide by adsorption on activated carbon only 50–60% of the entering ethylene oxide was recovered. The gas stream is so dilute that even with a series of several adsorbers there is some loss of ethylene oxide. Moreover, a portion of the ethylene oxide is converted to ethylene glycol during the desorption by steam. The glycol formation, which occurs in the interstices, deactivates the carbon and reduces the yield (88).

Absorbers using water are usually packed columns about 60 ft high. The effluent from a primary ethylene oxide reactor is cooled by heat exchange to about 100°F, and this stream then passes up the absorption column, countercurrent to the stream of water. Ethylene oxide in the effluent dissolves together with some carbon dioxide in the water. The aqueous stream is removed from the base of the absorber (80). Unabsorbed gas passing overhead is split into two portions. The larger portion recycles first as a coolant for effluent from the primary reactor and then rejoins the fresh feed to the primary reactor. The smaller portion of the gas stream is heat-exchanged to raise its temperature and serves as the main stream for the secondary ethylene conversion system. In the secondary system, air is added to increase the oxygen concentration of the reactor feed. The effluent from the secondary reactor is heat-exchanged against the recycle feed to the system and then enters a purge absorber, wherein ethylene oxide is removed from the stream with water as cited above. The oxidefree gas, low in residual ethylene, is vented overhead from this absorber.

The dilute water solutions containing ethylene oxide, carbon dioxide, traces of hydrocarbons, and chlorinated hydrocarbons from both absorbers are combined. The mixture is fed to the top section of a bubble-plate column, where the absorbate is steam-stripped under vacuum. Only a small portion of the entering steam condenses. The large heat requirements of this phase of the process are circumvented by operating in such a manner that the temperature of the solution does not vary greatly. Ethylene oxide is distilled off on top and is compressed for rectification. The bottoms water is recycled to the absorbers. Rectification of ethylene oxide in the first distillation column removes carbon dioxide and inert gases overhead. Ethylene oxide from the bottom of the column then feeds into the midsection of a second distillation column for refining to 99.5 mole % purity. The desired product is stored under a nitrogen atmosphere (78).

All commercial units operating in 1964 employed fixed-bed conversion systems for the oxidation of ethylene. Adequate heat removal is the controlling feature for successful conversion. This is achieved in properly operated fixed-bed units, but attention has also been given since 1953 to optimum heat control using a fluidized-bed catalyst. The fluidized-bed principle, well known to the petroleum industry since the late 1930s, is used for gas-cracking and gas-reforming operations. The ethylene oxide process was improved by the use of a fluidized catalyst as early as 1947 (89). Corrigan and Foster describe a fluidized-bed process, wherein ethylene is oxidized over a silver catalyst in a multitubed converter, which provides uniform heat transfer to Dowtherm fluid circulating in the shell of the converter and minimizes back-mixing of the fluidized catalyst during operation (82,83). Inhibition of the oxidation reaction and of secondary reactions occurring in conventional fluidized beds are minimized. Further, a greater variety of catalyst formulation is allowed by the fluidized bed because of the absence of reaction "hot spots" and the less stringent requirements of crushing strength placed on the catalyst (82). Pressure differentials which increase during operation across the fixed-bed converter to reduce gas throughput, as well as productivity, are also circumvented. In 1953, the Vulcan-Atlantic fluidized-bed process was supposed to be in the pilot-plant stage, but commercial units were not built by 1964.

Sherwood and Landau compare the merits of operating fixed and fluidized beds of catalysts for oxidation of ethylene (87,90). They conclude that temperature control is excellent in properly operated fixed-bed equipment and that ethylene oxide yields are higher. Catalyst costs, activity, attrition, life, and recovery are major items to be weighed carefully before selecting either a fixed-bed or fluidized-bed process. See also Fluidization.

EFFECTS OF PROCESS VARIABLES

The direct-oxidation process is more complex than is suggested by the description given above for operation of a fixed-bed system. At least eight interdependent variables determine the success of the process. Some latitude can be given to the ranges adopted for several of these variables. However, in practice the reaction system must be rather rigidly controlled and a single set of conditions for ideal operation cannot be specified.

Hydrocarbon Raw Materials. Ethylene, 95–98 mole % pure, is produced without great difficulty and is used as a feed for most industrial operations of the ethylene oxide process (70,87). Its purity is of great importance (87,91). Acetylene, even in trace amounts, is both deleterious and hazardous and has to be removed before the oxidation step by scrubbing the ethylene feed with a solvent, such as acetone or dimethylform-amide, or by selective hydrogenation. Organic sulfur compounds, present in some ethylene derived from petroleum, should be removed because of their irreversible inhibitory effect on the catalyst (87). Propylene and propane should not be present in the reaction feeds (91). The hydrocarbons are separated without great difficulty from ethylene by low-temperature rectification. They burn more readily than ethylene, and their presence in the converter would add appreciably to the reaction heat load. Ethane and methane burn less readily than ethylene. These paraffins are usually present in most ethylene feeds. McKim and Cambron report that methane and ethane provide a synergistic action for the use of ethylene dichloride as a selective oxidation inhibitor. Rapid catalyst deactivation occurs with ethylene dichloride concentrations as low as 0.0001% in ethylene free of methane and ethane (91).

Oxidizing Agents. Most commercial ethylene oxidation units use air as a reactant. Shell Development announced a new process in 1953 which uses 95% oxygen (92). Twelve plants using this process had a total rated annual capacity of 943 million lb of ethylene oxide in 1964 (see Tables 8 and 9). Shell spokesmen claim that the use of oxygen reduces purge losses of ethylene in a cyclic system and results in lower capital investment and operating costs. The ethylene consumption for the Shell process is stated to be 0.93 lb/lb of ethylene oxide in the tank (93). Scientific Design Co. with nineteen installations, having a total capacity of 1216 million lb of ethylene oxide in 1964 (see Tables 8 and 9) claim the superiority of air as an oxidant (90,99). Their conclusions are that oxygen must be diluted with large volumes of inert gas during recycle operation to avoid explosion hazards. Furthermore, building an oxygen plant at an estimated cost of $1.25 million to service a 50-million-lb-per-year oxide production unit is more expensive than the total costs of air compression equipment plus the converter system needed with air to cut purge losses of ethylene (80,87,90).

Catalyst Preparation, Promoters, Supports. Catalysts containing silver are used in all commercial ethylene oxidation units. Catalyst composition may vary considerably (94). For the early history of catalyst development see the ACS monograph on glycols (69). Certain metals such as platinum or palladium adsorb oxygen and are excellent as catalysts for many oxidations, but none of these provides the selectivity of silver for the oxidation of ethylene. Other metals and their oxides, notably those of chromium, nickel or cobalt, and their oxide combinations, such as those of magnesia–chromia, are too active for the complete oxidation of ethylene at the temperatures used in the ethylene oxide process (69,95–97).

The ethylene oxidation catalysts may be prepared by thermal decomposition or by chemical reaction of silver compounds. The various procedures, in general order of importance are as follows: (*1*) precipitation of silver oxide from aqueous silver nitrate or other salt solutions by alkali or alkaline-earth compounds (86,98–101); (*2*) thermal decomposition of silver salts, in particular silver oxalate, also of silver carbonate or cyanide (97,101–104); (3) reduction of silver salts by hydrogen or by reducing agents, such as formaldehyde, hydrazine, or hydroxylamine (100,105,106); (4) electrolysis of silver salt solutions (107,108); and (5) selective removal of a secondary metal from alloys containing silver (105,109–111).

Law and his associates of Union Carbide demonstrated between 1937 and 1945 the catalyst modifications and methods of handling necessary for the efficient production of ethylene oxide (112–117). Silver used alone on a support is not entirely satisfactory. Addition of a promoter enhances and stabilizes its activity. Oxides of alkali and alkaline-earth metals are very effective promoters (115). McKim and Cambron (91), McBee et al. (94), Wan (118), and Margolis (95,97) contributed to the research on the technical and practical aspects of the addition of promoters to silver catalysts.

Many organic compounds, especially halides, are very effective for suppressing the undesirable oxidation of ethylene to carbon dioxide (116). Important "anticatalysts" or inhibitors are ethylene dichloride, ethylene dibromide, other alkyl halides, aromatic hydrocarbons, amines, and organometallic compounds (84,116). McBee, Hass, and Wiseman (94) studied the effects of varying concentrations of ethylene dichloride on catalyst activity, and showed that an excess of ethylene dichloride deactivates a catalyst and also that a chloride-poisoned catalyst can be reactivated successfully in situ (113,114). Methane and ethane facilitate the control of the reaction by the use of ethylene dichloride (91).

The chemical nature and physical state of the catalyst support have an appreciable influence on the activity of ethylene oxide catalysts. The preferred supports are usually inert refractory materials with a large irregular surface. Refractory aluminum oxides, silicates, silicon carbide, and analogous materials, containing inert bonding agents, are used commercially (69,86,94,96). α-Alumina has been found to be very desirable (94,96). Pumice, silica gel, γ-alumina, carbon, magnesia, and analogous high-surface-area materials are deleterious to the selective oxidation of ethylene (69,94,96). Margolis (97,119), Pokrovskii (120), Ostrovskii (121), and Belaya (121a) offer interesting practical and theoretical information bearing on catalyst compositions versus activity for ethylene oxidation; other source material can be found in the monograph on glycols by Curme and Johnston (69).

Temperature. Catalyst surface temperature and proper heat dissipation are the controlling variables for stability and selectivity of the oxidation reaction. Unless temperature can be controlled, localized hot spots, 100–300°C above operating temperatures, are common. These lead to rapid sintering of the silver catalyst, loss of its activity, and costly breakdowns (87,122). Temperature can be controlled by using (a) an excellent heat-transfer medium in the converter shell, (b) a gas diluent, such as nitrogen, to moderate the reaction and reduce explosion hazards; (c) by ethylene dichloride or other anticatalysts to suppress formation of carbon dioxide, the chief source of unnecessary reaction heat; and (d) by use of graded catalyst beds (87,94,122). Although all existing industrial installations use the fixed-bed process, advantage may be taken of the suitability of fluidized-bed techniques for providing for temperature control and optimum heat transfer (82,83).

The effects of operating temperature on catalyst performance are closely related to the age of the catalyst and the contact time. Pressure is also important. Selective oxidation of ethylene can start at temperatures as low as 200°C at atmospheric pressure, using contact times of 5–10 sec, but the commercial process operates above 250°C under superatmospheric pressures with contact times of 1–3 sec (95). Optimum temperatures for large-scale processes are in the range of 260–290°C. The normal surface temperatures of the catalyst, under conditions of proper heat dissipation, may be 20–40°C above the gas or shell temperatures. The reaction is less selective at operating temperatures in the converter shell above 300°C. Catalyst sintering and loss of its on-stream life become serious factors at these more stringent operating conditions (87, 94,122).

Twigg did extensive research on the effects of temperature (65). Oxygen consumption over a silver catalyst increased sharply above 230°C; selectivity of ethylene conversion was optimum at about 270°C. Benton and Drake studied the kinetics of reaction and adsorption in the oxygen–silver system (123). The optimum temperature for conversion of ethylene is about 265°C and that for optimum selectivity is about twenty degrees lower (94). The relative rates for the formation of carbon dioxide from ethylene are about 95 and 60% of the rates for formation of ethylene oxide at temperatures of 274 and 234°C, respectively (124). Therefore, the useful yield of ethylene oxide is limited to the range of 50–55% at 275°C and of 60–64% at 234°C.

Higher yields are obtained with a catalyst composition of maximum superlative activity at low temperatures. A superior catalyst minimizes the combustion of ethylene oxide after formation. Under commercial conditions temperature maxima occur in the catalyst bed close to the converter inlet. The high-temperature peaks subside as the oxidation is slowed by depletion of reactants and by dissipation of heat. Graded catalyst beds reduce the peaks, improving operation and yield (87).

Reactant Concentrations. The rate of oxidation of ethylene is proportional to oxygen concentration (65,91,94). Accordingly, the ratio of air to ethylene has a pronounced effect on conversion and yield. Ideal conditions are approachable under small-scale atmospheric-pressure conditions, with reduced explosion hazards. Catalyst performance improves rapidly as the ratio of air to ethylene reaches 7 (or 8):1. Highest yield is obtained with an ethylene concentration of 30–40% in the Shell process (93). Conversion increases as a nearly linear function of the oxygen concentration until the latter reaches 70% (87). The effects of oxygen–ethylene concentrations must be correlated, of course, with the age of the catalyst, contact time, and temperature of operation (94). Shen-Wu Wan studied the oxidation of ethylene with oxygen using reaction feeds of compositions from 90:10 to 15:85 mole % ethylene and oxygen, respectively (118).

Under commercial conditions the optimum ethylene concentration is determined by the limits of explosibility of the oxygen or air mixture and by the amount of the olefin lost in the purge gas in the recycle operation. Fresh air–ethylene makeup ratios of about 10:1 are practicable when fed into a recycle stream of 3–6 mole % each of ethylene and oxygen at the inlet to a primary reactor. The gases are reacted quickly to safe concentrations. Oxygen values of less than 7 mole % with such ethylene concentrations are fairly safe. Space-time yields in the oxygen–ethylene sytem pass through a steep maximum at a molar feed ratio of about 1:1 (87).

Low ethylene conversions of 40–50% in a primary converter result in optimum selectivities, but also in gas streams that are too rich in ethylene for venting. Many commercial installations operate accordingly under recycle conditions using primary and secondary converters (90). The decrease in ethylene loss in the purge must, of course, be balanced also against increased blower and utility costs for the more complex system and against the effect of large gas throughputs on the efficiency of the ethylene oxide absorption system.

The Shell oxygen process takes advantage of the increased yield possible with decreased conversions by lowering the conversion to less than half that practical with the air process (93).

Contact Time, Space- and Mass Velocity. Temperature, pressure, reactant concentrations, and age and activity of catalyst have a definite interdependent effect on the choice of optimum contact time for commercial installations. Residence times over catalysts in large-scale operations generally are 1–4 sec at 275–325°C. Above 300°C, complications with long contact time determine conversion and also influence selectivity. McBee and co-workers (94) and Shen Wu-Wan (118) studied the inter-related effects of temperature, contact times, and feed mole ratios on optimum catalyst activity. As the contact time decreases, the operating temperature of the catalyst must be raised to obtain maximum conversion with a given air–ethylene ratio.

Recycle vs Single-Pass Operation. A properly designed recycle system operated with several stages produces higher yields of ethylene oxide than does a single-pass system (90,125–127). Lower conversions of ethylene per pass contribute to higher selectivities, as with many vapor-phase oxidations. Air and ethylene are conserved. A practicable single-pass system must be operated in the explosive range of the reactants, requiring large amounts of air and ethylene for a good ethylene oxide yield. Purge losses of ethylene and power requirements would be extremely high.

Atmospheric vs Higher Pressures. The equation for the conversion of ethylene to ethylene oxide is written to show a one-third decrease in volume. Accordingly, such a reaction should be driven more to completion by the use of higher pressures. As a result of concurrent side reactions yielding carbon dioxide and water, the improvement is less than might be expected. The literature states that higher pressures permit improved engineering designs which result in higher productivity per unit volume, improved heat transfer, and excellent recovery of ethylene oxide from the dilute product gas stream. Within certain limits, high throughput per unit reactor space has a significant effect on capital investment and amortization. Obviously lower costs are favored with the higher productivity per unit volume at increased operating pressures.

Some processes have been designed to operate at or near atmospheric pressure, but the ethylene oxide capacities of such installations are too small to be economical, and the recovery of ethylene oxide presents special problems. Most commercial units operate at 5 or more atmospheres pressure, preferably in the range of 10–30 atm, and take advantage of improved heat-transfer at large reaction mass velocities, minimal losses of ethylene, high productivities, and the other advantages accruing with these benefits.

THEORETICAL ASPECTS OF THE OXIDATION OF ETHYLENE TO ETHYLENE OXIDE

The fundamental role of the catalyst in ethylene oxidation is the activated adsorption of oxygen on its extended surface. The formation of ethylene oxide is unique because only one atom of oxygen adds to the olefin bond. Although considerable information exists on the practical and theoretical aspects of ethylene oxidation, the mechanism is not clearly established. The early fundamental studies by Twigg (65) led to many valuable programs of research. A number of these research programs are discussed by Emmett in *Catalysis*, Vol. VII (96). Other excellent sources of theoretical information include papers by the following contributors: Wan (118); McBee, Hass, and Wiseman (94); Margolis (119); Kurilenko (128); Hayes (129); Zimakov (137); Murray (131); Kummer (132); Orzechowski and MacCormack (124); Nault (133); Margolis (134); Schultze and Thiele (122); and Andrianova and Todes (135).

Margolis discusses the theoretical aspects of the oxidation in terms of modifications of the work function of a silver surface, as produced by adsorbed oxygen and by the presence of promoters and anticatalysts at or near this surface (119). The kinetic studies of the oxidation reaction show discrepancies in the data obtained by various scientists wherein the dependence of reaction rates on ethylene and oxygen concentrations is expressed more often than not in fractional powers. Margolis cites a conclusion by Temkin and Associates (136) that this diversity in kinetic data is due to varying oxygen content in the adjacent-to-surface layer.

Proceeding from kinetic considerations, Twigg showed that only oxygen was chemisorbed on silver (65). Thus, if an ethylene molecule reacts with only one adsorbed atom of oxygen, ethylene oxide is obtained at a high selectivity. If ethylene reacts with two adsorbed oxygen atoms, the olefinic bond is ruptured to yield two moles of formaldehyde, which are oxidized to carbon dioxide and water. Ethylene oxide formed must be removed quickly from the site of reaction. Otherwise it may isomerize to acetaldehyde, which also oxidizes to carbon dioxide and water at experimental conditions. Murray confirmed the mechanism proposed by Twigg, wherein ethylene oxide and carbon dioxide are each primary products of the reaction of ethylene with oxygen (131). Orzechowski and MacCormack agree with the above findings but, in contrast to Twigg, conclude that the reaction proceeds by a different scheme wherein only single adsorbed oxygen atoms are involved in the oxidation (124). The two reaction schemes are described as follows:

1. Twigg's reaction (with either one or two adsorbed oxygen atoms):

$$C_2H_4 + O \rightarrow C_2H_4O$$

$$C_2H_4 + 3\,O_2 \rightarrow 2\,CO_2 + 2\,H_2O$$

2. Orzechowski and MacCormack's reaction (with only one adsorbed oxygen atom):

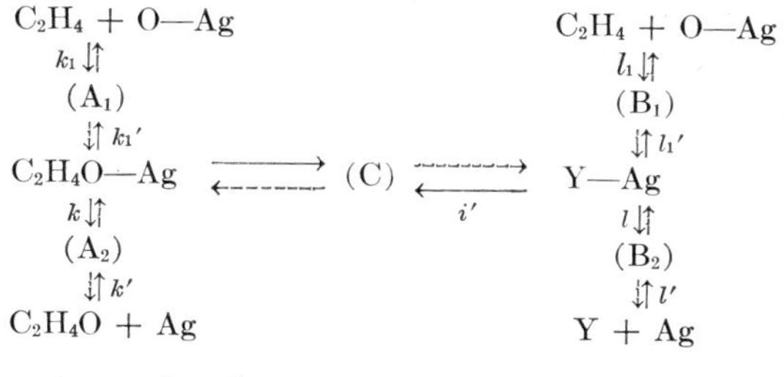

$$
\begin{array}{ccc}
C_2H_4 + O\text{—}Ag & & C_2H_4 + O\text{—}Ag \\
k_1 \updownarrow & & l_1 \updownarrow \\
(A_1) & & (B_1) \\
\updownarrow k_1' & & \updownarrow l_1' \\
C_2H_4O\text{—}Ag \xrightarrow{} (C) \xleftarrow[i']{} Y\text{—}Ag \\
k \updownarrow & & l \updownarrow \\
(A_2) & & (B_2) \\
\updownarrow k' & & \updownarrow l' \\
C_2H_4O + Ag & & Y + Ag
\end{array}
$$

As shown by the above sketch, two parallel reactions can account for the production of ethylene oxide and of carbon dioxide from ethylene and oxygen. Initially, these exist alone, but during the course of the reaction they are also accompanied by the slow consecutive decomposition of ethylene oxide to carbon dioxide and water.

(A), (B), and (C) are used to represent activated complexes with k, l, and i, the velocity constants of the various rate-determining steps. Y is identified as acetaldehyde, and once formed, this aldehyde oxidizes rapidly to carbon dioxide and water. The direct oxidation of ethylene to ethylene oxide follows the route $k_1 k$. Ethylene oxide, either absorbed on the catalyst, or desorbed, may be converted to acetaldehyde and then to carbon dioxide and water by following routes $k'il$. The deep oxidation of ethylene by absorbed oxygen on silver without ethylene oxide as an intermediate is described by the path $l_1 l$. Orzechowski and MacCormack have fitted their mechanism expressions successfully to experimental data.

Kurilenko and Temkin (136) describe a mechanism which is similar to that proposed by Orzechowski and MacCormack, but suggest that the intermediate Y may be vinyl alcohol.

$$O_2 + 4\,e^- \rightarrow 2\,O^{2-}$$
$$O^{2-} + C_2H_4 \rightarrow C_2H_4O + 2\,e^-$$
$$O^{2-} + C_2H_4 \rightarrow CH_2{=}CHOH + 2\,e^-$$
$$CH_2{=}CHOH + 2\tfrac{1}{2}\,O_2 \rightarrow 2\,CO_2 + 2\,H_2O$$

Roginskii and Margolis tagged ethylene with ^{14}C and measured the ^{14}C concentrations in the product. They concluded that 80% of the carbon dioxide comes directly from ethylene, bypassing ethylene oxide, and that only 20% is formed through ethylene oxide as an intermediate (130). Using mixtures of ethylene with formaldehyde and acetaldehyde they concluded that aldehydes increase the rate of ethylene oxide formation and decrease the rate of carbon dioxide formation. Therefore, the aldehydes cannot be the chief intermediate products in the formation of carbon dioxide either from ethylene directly or through ethylene oxide.

Schultze and Thiele, and other contributors, found that the oxidation of ethylene is inhibited by its oxidation products (122). The surface temperature of the catalyst is more important in the oxidation than the temperature of the gas adjacent to the surface. They attempted by diverse means to cover a silver catalyst surface with adsorbed atomic oxygen and then react the adsorbed atoms with ethylene. Although these efforts had only partial success, a preferential reaction of ethylene with adsorbed atomic oxygen was not observed. The conclusions were that oxygen is taken up on the silver surface partly physically and partly chemically as atomic oxygen, and that a peroxidic complex, $C_2H_4O_2$, is involved in the oxidation of both ethylene and ethylene oxide over silver. Zimakov compares the unique properties of silver for the oxidation of ethylene with those properties which exclude other metals as catalysts. His general conclusions are that peroxide groups are more stable on silver than on other metals and that the mechanism of the formation of ethylene oxide is determined by reaction of ethylene with these peroxide groups (137).

Economic Aspects

The production capacity for ethylene oxide in the United States exceeded 2 billion lb a year early in 1964. Production is expected to grow about 3.5% a year through 1970 (138,139). Approx 26% of the 7 billion lb of ethylene produced in the United States during 1963 was used for ethylene oxide (138). Only polyethylene surpassed ethylene oxide as a large-volume derivative of ethylene. World capacities, exclusive of Iron-Curtain countries, for ethylene oxide amounted to 4.77 billion lb during 1965. Information on the types of processes and the numbers of plants as well as their total capacities and locations are shown in Tables 8 and 9. Ethylene oxide production, sales price, and end-use consumption in the United States, 1930–1964, are

Table 8. World Production Capacities[a] for Ethylene Oxide (138–142)

Countries	Total capacity, million lb/yr	No. of companies	Direct-oxidation processes UCC[b]	SD[c]	Shell	Other	Chlorohydrin process
United States	2,920	12	1,400	430	540	200	350
Canada	120	2	60				60
Puerto Rico	130	1	130				
Mexico	26	1		26			
United Kingdom	257	3	33	80	144		
West Germany	374	5		176	88	88	22
France	173	2		173			
Italy	149	3	33	66		50	
Holland	170	2		110	110		
Belgium	45	2		35			10
Spain	56	2		24	22		10
Sweden	33	1		33			
Switzerland	11	1			11		
India	27	1			27		
Japan	210	5		153		57	
Australia	20	1		20			
Total	4,771	44	1,656	1,326	942	395	452

[a] Exclusive of Iron-Curtain countries.
[b] Union Carbide Corp.
[c] Scientific Design Co.
NOTE: Total number of plants: 52. Plants using the direct-oxidation process: UCC, 11; SD, 19; Shell, 12; other, 4. Plants using the chlorohydrin process: 6.

shown in Table 10. The chlorohydrin process attained peak production volumes of 600 million lb in the United States during 1957.

Most of the ethylene oxide is manufactured for captive use and less than 20% of the product is sold. The sales price has been stabilized around 15.50¢/lb since 1955. The success of the direct-oxidation processes reduced the price of ethylene oxide from a high of 19.25¢/lb in 1951 to a low of 13.50¢/lb during 1954. Competition should maintain prices approximately at the 1963–1964 level for several years.

Yields obtainable by the various direct-oxidation processes vary within relatively narrow limits. About 0.9–1.1 lb of ethylene is consumed per pound of oxide produced. The oxidizing agent is consumed at a rate of 1.8 lb per pound of oxide. Sherwood states that ethylene oxide can be produced at 8–9¢/lb using ethylene valued at 4.5¢/lb (87). Landau of Scientific Design Company cites investment costs from 10 to 11¢/lb for direct-oxidation plants producing 40 million lb of ethylene oxide per year (90). Shell estimates indicate that plants producing 60 and 100 million lb of ethylene oxide per year should cost under $3 million and approx $4 million, respectively.

Oxygen is readily available in tonnage quantities from suppliers such as the Linde Division of Union Carbide Corporation. The onstream life of catalysts used for the ethylene oxide process has been improved greatly in the past ten years. Their cost per lb of ethylene oxide produced is negligible in the overall process costs. The active ingredients of the catalyst as well as some of the refractory supports can be reclaimed to provide fresh active catalyst. For a guide of plant costs over a number of years see reference 143.

Table 9. Survey Information on Ethylene Oxide Producers (138–142)

Company	Location	Process[a]	Startup data	Capacity,[b] million lb/yr
United States[c]				
Union Carbide Corp.	South Charleston, W. Va.	d.o.	1937	
	Institute, W. Va.	d.o.	1950	
	Texas City, Texas	d.o.	1941	
	Seadrift, Texas	d.o. (UCC)	1954	1,100
	Whiting, Indiana	d.o.	1950	
	Torrance, Cal.	d.o.	1956	
	Taft, Louisiana	d.o.	1966[d]	300
The Dow Chemical Co.	Freeport, Texas	chlorohydrin	1942	
		d.o.	1965[b]	550
	Plaquemine, La.	chlorohydrin	1959	
Jefferson Chemical Co., Inc.	Port Neches, Texas	SD	1959	
		SD	1964	250
Wyandotte Chemicals Corp.	Geismar, La.	d.o. (Shell)	1958	
		Shell	1966[d]	145
Olin Mathieson Chemical Corp.	Brandenburg, Ky.	Shell	1961	75
Sun Oil Chemical Co.	Claymont, Del.	Shell	1962	75
Houston Chemical Co.[e]	Beaumont, Texas	d.o. (SD)	1961	80
General Aniline & Film Corp.	Linden, N.J.	SD	1958	65
Calcasieu Chemical Corp.	Lake Charles, La.	Shell	1958	80
Allied Chemical Corp.	Orange, Texas	SD	1952	35
Texas Eastman Corp.[f]	Longview, Texas	Shell	1965[b]	35
Shell Chemical Co.	Geismar, La.	Shell	1966[d]	130
Total				*2,920*
Canada				
Union Carbide Canada, Ltd.	Montreal	UCC	1957	60
Dow Chemical Canada	Sarnia	chlorohydrin	1948	60
Total				*120*
Mexico				
Derivados Etilicos	Reynosa	SD	1965[b]	26
Puerto Rico				
Union Carbide Caribe	Ponce	UCC	1959	130
United Kingdom				
Petrochemicals (Shell)	Carrington	Shell	1959	
			1966[d]	143
Union Carbide Ltd.	Hythe	UCC	1959	33
Imperial Chemical Ind. Ltd.	Severnside	SD	1962	80
Total				*256*
France				
Soc. Naphtachimie	Lavera	SD	1953	
			1958	
			1960	120
			1966[d]	
Marles-Kuhlmann	Gonfreville	SD	1958	
			1961	53
Total				*173*
West Germany				
Badische Anilin- und Soda	Ludwigshafen	d.o.	unknown	26
Fabrik		Shell	1965[b]	50
Erdölchemie	Dormagen	SD	1950	
			1960	132
Farbwerke Hoechst	Gendorf	chlorohydrin		22
Chem. Werke Huels	Marl	d.o. (Huels)	1956	88
Chem. Fab. Holten	Oberhausen	SD	1959	44
Total				*362*

Table 9 (*continued*)

Company	Location	Process[a]	Startup data	Capacity,[b] million lb/yr
Holland				
Dow Chemical International	Terneuzen	SD	1966[d]	60?
Shell Netherland	Pernis	Shell	1966[d]	100+
Total				*160+*
Belgium				
Union Chim. Belge	Brussels	chlorohydrin	1936	10?
Petrochim.	Antwerp	SD	1958 ⎫	
			1960 ⎬	35
			1964 ⎭	
Total				*45*
Italy				
Monteshell	Ferrara	Montecatini	unknown	50
S. p. A. Celene	Priolo, Sicily	UCC	1961	33
ANIC Gela, S. p. A.	Gela, Sicily	SD	1964	66
Total				*149*
Spain				
Crosici, S.A.	Puertollano	SD	1965[b]	24
S. A. Derivados de Cok	La Felguera	chlororohydrin		10?
Ind. Quimicas Ass. S. A.	Tarragona	Shell	1966[d]	22
Total				*56*
Sweden				
Mo och Domsjo	Stenungsund	SD	1963	33
Switzerland				
Lonza	Visp	Shell	unknown	11
Australia				
ICI-ANZ, Ltd.	Botany	SD	1964	20
Japan				
Mitsui Petro. Ind.	Iwakuni	SD	1959 ⎫	
			1960 ⎬	40
			1964 ⎭	
Mitsubishi Petro. Co.	Yokkaichi	SD	1960 ⎫	35
			1964 ⎭	
Nisso Petro. Ind. Co.	Goi (Chiba)	SD	1964 ⎫	52
			1965[b] ⎭	
Nippon Soda Co., Ltd.	Kawasaki	SD	1964	26
Japan Catalytic Chem.	Kawasaki	unknown	1964	57
Total				*210*
Grand Total				*4,771*

[a] LEGEND: d.o. = direct oxidation; UCC = Union Carbide Corp.; SD = Scientific Design Co.
[b] As of March 1965.　　　　　　　　　　　　[d] Estimated.
[c] Reference 142a, modified by later　　　　[e] A division of Pittsburg Plate Glass Co.
　announcements in trade publications.　　　[f] A division of Eastman Kodak Co.

The minimum economic capacity for the average ethylene oxide process is about 25 million lb/yr. Borrows and Caplin offer excellent data on the comparative costs of producing ethylene oxide by direct oxidation and by the chlorohydrin route (77). They estimate that capital investment for a direct-oxidation plant is about 50% higher than for a chlorohydrin unit of similar capacity, but that operating costs are lower. The following points are important: (1) As the price of chlorine rises, the chlorohydrin process becomes less attractive; (2) the direct-oxidation process can be made more economical with small improvements in efficiency; and (3) the chlorohydrin process is more economical when ethylene oxide prices are high, but at low ethylene oxide prices the direct-oxidation process gives a better return on ethylene.

Table 10. Ethylene Oxide Production, Sales Price, and End-Use Consumption, 1930 through 1964[a]

	Production, million lb			Sales price,[b] ¢/lb	Consumption, million lb							Nonionic surface-active agents	
Year	Chloro-hydrin process	Direct-oxidation process	Total		Ethylene glycol	Di-ethylene glycol	Tri-ethylene glycol	Poly-ethylene glycol	Glycol ethers	Ethanol-amines	Acrylo-nitrile	Cyclic	Acyclic
1930	16	0	16		14	2	negl.						
1935	60	0	60		53	8	1						
1940	99	11	110		82	9	1		10	7	1		
1945	132	57	189	17.00	136	14	2		14	12	11		
1950	326	153	479	16.75	335	35	4		26	25	26	19	9
1952	466	262	728	19.00	529	56	13		22	39	39	16	14
1954	374	282	656	13.50	430	26	17		35	55	43	26	24
1956	557	535	1,092	15.50	697	79	19	21	52	83	60	49	32
1958	538	684	1,222	15.50	796	88	15	26	60	86	39	63	49
1960	529	941	1,470	15.50	918	79	30	30	79	111	56	102	53
1961	417	972	1,389	15.50	827	88	29	35	79	116	50	115	50
1962c			1,518d	15.50d	1,011	105	34	30	119	120	62	144	55
1963c			1,600d	15.50d	1,092	102	37	30	130	129	71	151	58
1964c	300d	1,345d	1,645d	15.50d	1,256	105	39	32	141	152	71	158	61

a Reference 142b.
b Quotations from *Oil, Paint Drug Reptr.*
c Reference 142c (except for those data marked[d]).
d Estimated values (138).

Table 11. Extra Profitability of the Direct-Oxidation Process over the Chlorohydrin Process,[a] million $/yr

% Selectivity, direct oxidation	Ethylene oxide cost, ¢/lb		
	3.1	6.3	9.4
50	1.05	0.83	0.60
55	1.12	0.96	0.80
60	1.17	1.07	0.96
65	1.22	1.16	1.10
70	1.25	1.23	1.27

[a] BASIS: Chlorine at $62.50/short ton; output—18 million lb/yr; depreciation—10%/yr; plant investment—$1.7 million. No ethylene dichloride credit.

The high capital investment for the direct-oxidation process is largely due to reaction inefficiencies connected with the formation of by-product carbon dioxide. Table 11 compares profitability, which results from improvements in the direct-oxidation process (81).

Using ethylene valued at 5.0¢/lb Aries calculates an ethylene oxide-raw material cost of 6.0¢/lb if a direct-oxidation process is operated at 60% selectivity (88). His comparable raw material cost for ethylene oxide is 9.7¢/lb using the chlorohydrin process.

Health and Safety Factors

Four basic facts must be remembered for the safe handling of ethylene oxide: (1) It is a flammable liquid; (2) it can violently decompose as a vapor; (3) it is toxic and should not be inhaled; and (4) it is highly reactive.

The following information is supplied from a Union Carbide bulletin (16) and from an excellent literature report on the safe handling of ethylene oxide by Hess and Tilton (17).

Explosibility. Liquid ethylene oxide is generally stable to detonating agents, but the vapor explodes when exposed to common igniters. If heated to 571°C in the absence of air or oxygen, ethylene oxide vapor decomposes violently. The upper flammability limit in air is 80% by vol. Ethylene oxide (100%) vapor at atmospheric pressure undergoes 45% decomposition if ignited by a hot platinum coil, and 90% decomposition occurs if ignited by mercury fulminate. Slight dilution with air at higher pressure favors complete decomposition. While explosion pressures are difficult to predict, the surge is immediate and the final pressure can be 16–50 times greater than the initial pressure, depending on the volume-to-surface ratio of the container. In some cases, the pressure rise is too sudden for adequate safety valves and rupture diaphragms.

Among the many sources of ignition are acetylides, static electricity, excessive heat, and open flames which explode ethylene oxide vapor. Glowing carbon and "hot spots" in catalyst beds may also cause explosion. Acetylene may be a trace impurity in diluent gases for ethylene oxide; therefore, acetylide-forming metals such as copper, silver, mercury, and their alloys should not be used to handle ethylene oxide. Mercury fulminate and hot platinum wire coils are convenient for laboratory test explosions.

All mixtures of ethylene oxide and air can be made nonflammable at atmospheric pressures and temperatures by adding 7.15 volumes of carbon dioxide to each volume

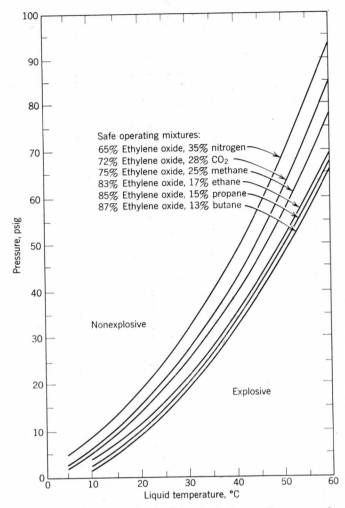

Fig. 4. Safe operating pressures required for mixtures of ethylene oxide vapor and several diluents at various temperatures (17). Courtesy *Industrial and Engineering Chemistry.*

of ethylene oxide (143a). Care has to be taken, when handling ethylene oxide mixtures at reduced pressures (144). Hess and Tilton report that no mixture of air and ethylene oxide is explosive, provided about 40% of nitrogen or 30% of methane is present as diluent (Fig. 4). They also give up-to-date information on safe operating conditions, and storage and handling procedures (17).

Toxicological Properties (16). A threshold limit of 50 ppm ethylene oxide by vol in air for an 8-hr exposure has been suggested as safe concentration. The presence of ethylene oxide in air irritates eyes and nose. Exposure to low concentrations of vapor significantly above the threshold limit may cause delayed nausea and vomiting. Repeated exposure may lower the tolerance level. Exposure to continuous low concentrations results in a numbing of the sense of smell; thus, harmful concentrations may be reached without a warning from odor. High concentrations of ethylene oxide can

Table 12. Specifications for High-Purity Ethylene Oxide (11)

Property	Value
color	10 max Pt–Co
odor	nonresidual
acidity, as acetic acid, % by wt	0.002 max
water, % by wt	0.030 max
aldehyde, as acetaldehyde, % by wt	0.010 max
nonvolatiles, g/100 ml	0.010
suspended matter	substantially free
acetylene	none

produce pulmonary edema and mucous membrane irritation. Ethylene oxide does not accumulate in the body, and therefore, chronic poisoning is not considered possible. Liquid or dissolved ethylene oxide on exposed skin does not cause immediate irritation, but may cause severe delayed skin burns. When absorbed on clothes or shoes, which are not promptly removed, it can also produce delayed skin burns. Liquid or dissolved ethylene oxide may cause severe eye burns.

For rats, the single oral LD_{50} dose was found to be 0.33 g/kg; breathing ethylene oxide at 4000 ppm for 4 hr killed none of six (11). Other information on toxicity is supplied by Hess and Tilton (17), Sexton and Henson (145), and Yant (146).

Specifications and Shipping Data

Specifications. Ethylene oxide is sold only as a high-purity chemical, with the specification limits shown in Table 12.

Shipping Data (12,17). Small shipments of ethylene oxide are made in the following types of cylinders: F2H (ICC-3B-300); CZ (ICC-26-300); CXR (ICC-43-240); and 5P (ICC-5P), containing 1.25; 18.5; 175; and 400 lb net, of ethylene oxide, respectively. Large shipments of 36,000–70,000 lb are made in insulated, Type 105-A-300-W tank cars. A red label is required by the U.S. Bureau of Explosives on all shipments of ethylene oxide.

Analytical and Test Methods

The color of ethylene oxide is determined by use of the platinum–cobalt color standard methods described in *Standard Methods for Examination of Water and Sewerage*, 8th ed., American Public Health Association, 1936. Residual odor is determined by evaporating a few drops at room temperature on a clean filter paper. Acidity is ascertained by titrating a measured sample in water at 0°C with standard 0.02N alcoholic potassium hydroxide, using a phenolphthalein end point. Water is determined by titrating a weighed sample to an electrometric end point, using the standard Karl Fisher reagent. The aldehyde content is obtained by back titration, with standardized iodine, of a cooled sample of ethylene oxide in sodium bisulfite solution. Nonvolatile matter is obtained by evaporating a 100-ml sample to dryness at room temperature and weighing the residue. Suspended matter in a sample of ethylene oxide is examined visually by transmitted light. Any suspended acetylene in ethylene oxide is determined colorimetrically by titrating a sample of chilled ethylene oxide at 0–4°C with alcoholic silver nitrate against a combined methyl red–methylene blue indicator.

If the test is positive, the explosive silver acetylide must be destroyed by adding an excess of acid ferrous sulfate solution before discarding the solution. (For analytical and test methods see references 16 and 147.)

Distillation and chromatographic techniques are employed to determine the purity of an ethylene oxide sample. The latter technique picks up carbon dioxide, ethane, ethylene, and other extraneous materials. The Deckert procedure (148) is used to detect the presence of small quantities of ethylene oxide in air. Fifty milliliters of the sample of air is passed through 1–2 ml of a 40% aqueous solution of potassium thiocyanate containing one drop of 0.1% alcoholic phenolphthalein. If a red color does not appear in 2 min, the test is negative

$$H_2C\underset{\displaystyle O}{\diagdown\diagup}CH_2 + KSCN + HOH \rightarrow \begin{matrix} CH_2OH \\ | \\ CH_2SCN \end{matrix} + KOH$$

Uses

Ethylene oxide has a myriad of uses, due to its relatively low cost and its chemical reactivity (11,149). In most of them it is converted into some derivative, whose manufacture, uses, and further derivatives are discussed elsewhere in this Encyclopedia. See also Table 10.

Ethylene oxide is an excellent fumigant and sterilization agent (11,150). It is generally noncorrosive to metals and leaves no residual odor or taste. As a sterilizing agent, it prevents the microbiological spoilage of foods, colloidal organic materials, soil, and culture media (11,151–155). The addition of more than 7.8 parts of carbon dioxide eliminates the fire hazard (156).

Mixtures of ethylene oxide with dichlorodifluoromethane are also effective sterilizing agents (157). Solutions containing 12% or less by wt of ethylene oxide in dichlorodifluoromethane cannot propagate a flame in the vapor state, either pure or mixed, with any portion of air up to temperatures of 130°F. Carboxide (registered trademark of Union Carbide Corp.) fumigant is a liquefied mixture of 10% by wt of ethylene oxide and 90% by wt of carbon dioxide. It is noncorrosive, nonflammable, and leaves no odors or taste (156). A low concentration of ethylene oxide effectively kills many insect pests at all life stages, yet is only moderately toxic to humans. Carbon dioxide increases the rate of kill by stimulating insect respiration and counteracts the flammability of ethylene oxide vapor. It also renders the mixture nonexplosive, when used under normal conditions in accordance with instructions. The molecular weight and vapor density of the two gases are the same, so that they do not stratify or separate during use or in storage. The vapor mixture is also 1.5 times heavier than air, thus enabling it to penetrate cracks, crevices, furniture, mattresses, and packages. See also Insecticides.

Ethylene Glycol. See Glycols. Traditionally, the main outlet for ethylene oxide has been as an intermediate for ethylene glycol, for which the main market has been as an automotive antifreeze (qv) (139).

Other important uses for ethylene glycol are as a plasticizer for cellophane (see Film materials), as a raw material for ethylene glycol dinitrate for use in low-freezing dynamites (see Explosives), and as a raw material for poly(ethylene terephthalate) (see Polyesters; Polyester fibers; Film materials).

Diethylene Glycol and Triethylene Glycol. See Glycols. These compounds are coproducts of monoethylene glycol. The manufacturing ratio is about 100 parts of mono-, 10 parts of di-, to one part of triethylene glycol. Diethylene glycol is used as an intermediate for polyester resins and for triethylene glycol (by reaction with ethylene oxide); for solvent extractions of aromatic hydrocarbons (Udex process); and for gas purification applications. The preferential use of triethylene glycol is increasing in the latter two applications. Other important markets for diethylene glycol and its derivatives include lubricants; brake fluids; gas dehydration; urethane foams and elastomers; humectants; textile specialties; as a plasticizer in printing inks; low-pressure laminates for glass fibers, asbestos, cloth, or paper; and as an emulsifier, demulsifier, and lubricant (158).

Polyethylene Glycols. See Glycols. These ethylene oxide derivatives, manu-factured by the action of ethylene oxide on water or ethylene glycol, are a series of water-soluble polymers ranging in average molecular weight from 200 to 6000. They are characterized by good lubricity, heat stability, inertness to many chemical agents, and they do not hydrolyze or deteriorate. The lower members of the series (molecular weights of 200–600) are water-white liquids. The higher members of the series (molec-ular weights of 1000–6000) vary in consistency from soft, white, greaselike petrolatum to hard waxy solids. They are used in cosmetics, ointments, and other products where blandness, water solubility, and lubricity are desired. They are used also as water-soluble lubricants for rubber molds, in textile processing and ceramics, and in metal-forming applications. The polyglycols are good plasticizers, and dispersants for casein and gelatin compositions, glues, zein, cork, and special printing inks. They are fine solvents for dyes, resins, proteins, and many medicants.

Glycol Ethers. See Glycols. These are manufactured by the action of ethylene oxide on alcohols. Their applications include de-icing fluids, brake fluids, detergents, and solvents for acrylic lacquers (139).

Ethanolamines. See Alkanolamines. These compounds are manufactured by the reaction of ethylene oxide and ammonia. They have a diverse end-use pattern. About one-third is used for detergent applications. Other important applications include textile chemical intermediates, gas scrubbing, pharmaceuticals, emulsion polishes, and corrosion inhibitors.

Acrylonitrile (qv). This can be manufactured from ethylene cyanohydrin which is obtained from ethylene oxide and hydrogen cyanide. Acrylonitrile production capacity exceeded 515 million lb in the United States in 1962, but only 70 million lb of this capacity depended on ethylene oxide (40 million lb). It is used for acrylic and modacrylic fibers (qv), nitrile rubber (see Elastomers, synthetic), and plastics (see Styrene and styrene polymers).

Nonionic Surface-Active Agents. See Surfactants. Several classes of nonionic surfactants are made from ethylene oxide in addition to the derivatives of ethanol-amine mentioned above. Alkylphenol–ethylene oxide derivatives such as Tergitol NP (registered trademark, Union Carbide Corp.) are used in textile metal-cleaning and many other applications (159). Nonionics are made also by reacting ethylene oxide with tall oil, fatty alcohols, and with various polyols such as sorbitol, mannitol, and cellulose.

The Pluronic (Wyandotte Chemicals Corp.) series of nonionic surface-active agents are block-type polymers formed by adding ethylene oxide to a polypropylene glycol. Niax (Union Carbide Corp.) polyethers and Ucon (Union Carbide Corp.)

fluids and lubricants are essentially random polymers and may contain both ethylene oxide and propylene oxide in their structures. The Polyox (Union Carbide Corp.) series of polymers are constituted of ethylene oxide as the principal monomer with hydroxyl groups ending the chains. The Polyox series has molecular weights significantly higher than are found in the Niax, Ucon, or Pluronic series of polymers.

Bibliography

"Ethylene Oxide" in *ECT* 1st ed., Vol. 5, pp. 906–925, by R. S. Aries, Consulting Chemical Engineer, and Henry Schneider, R. S. Aries & Associates; Koert Gerzon, Cornell University (Structure and Reactions).

1. A. Wurtz, *Ann.* **110**, 125 (1859); *Ann. Chim. et Phys.* **55**, 400 (1859); **69** (3), 355 (1863).
2. E. W. Blair and T. S. Wheeler, *J. Soc. Chem. Ind.* (*London*) **41**, 303 (1922); **42**, 260T, 343T, 415T (1923).
3. W. Bone and R. Wheeler, *J. Chem. Soc.* **85** (2), 1637 (1904).
4. L. Reyerson and L. J. Swearingen, *J. Am. Chem. Soc.* **50**, 2872 (1928).
5. R. Willstatter and M. Bommer, *Ann.* **422**, 36 (1921).
6. Ger. Pat. 168,291; Fr. Pat. 360,785; Brit. Pat. 21941 (1905–1906), J. Walter.
7. L. H. Reyerson and H. Oppenheimer, *J. Phys. Chem.* **48** (5), 290 (1944).
8. Fr. Pat. 729,952 (March 27, 1931) and additions 41,255 (July 4, 1931; 41,724 (Sept. 10, 1931); 41,484 (Sept. 25, 1931); 41,810 and 41,811 (April 21, 1933); also Fr. Pat. 739,562 (Oct. 3, 1931), all by T. E. Lefort (to Société Française de Catalyse Généralisée). *Chem. Zentr.* **1932**, II, 2107; **1933**, I, 2171, 2607; **1933**, II, 607. *Chem. Abstr.* **27**, 312, 2163, 2697, 4546 (1933); **29**, 4029 (1935).
   Brit. Pats. 402,438 and 402,749 (1933), T. E. Lefort (to Soc. Française de Catalyse Généralisée). *Chem. Zentr.* **1934**, I, 2196.
   U.S. Pat. 1,998,878 (April 23, 1935), T. E. Lefort (to Carbide and Carbon Chemicals Corp.); reissued as U.S. Pats. 20,370 (May 18, 1937) and 22,241 (Dec. 29, 1942). *Chem. Abstr.* **29**, 4029 (1935); **31**, 4994 (1937); **37**, 3454 (1943).
9. S. Lenher, *J. Am. Chem. Soc.* **53**, 2420, 3737 (1931).
10. U.S. Pat. 1,995,991 (March 26, 1935), S. Lenher (to E. I. du Pont de Nemours & Co., Inc.). *Chem. Abstr.* **29**, 3350 (1935).
11. *Alkylene Oxides*, Brochure F-40558, Union Carbide Corporation, New York, 1961.
12. Private communication to author from W. S. Tamplin, Research and Development Department, Union Carbide Corp. Chemicals Division, July, 1964.
13. P. Walden, *Z. Physik. Chem.* **70**, 569 (1910); E. W. Washburn, ed., *International Critical Tables*, Vol. VI, McGraw-Hill Co., New York, 1929, p. 84.
14. H. Hilbert and J. S. Allen, *J. Am. Chem. Soc.* **54**, 4115 (1932).
15. W. F. Giauque and J. Gordon, *J. Am. Chem. Soc.* **71**, 2176 (1949).
16. *Ethylene Oxide Storage and Handling*, Brochure No. F7618D, Union Carbide Corporation, New York, 1961.
17. L. G. Hess and V. V. Tilton, "Ethylene Oxide-Hazards and Methods of Handling," *Ind. Eng. Chem.* **42**, 1251–1258 (1950).
18. M. S. Kharasch, "Heats of Combustion of Organic Compounds," *J. Res. Natl. Bur. Std.* **2**, 359–430 (1929).
19. R. S. Crog and H. Hunt, *J. Phys. Chem.* **46**, 1162 (1942).
20. F. S. Bichowsky and F. D. Rossini, *The Thermochemistry of Chemical Substances*, Reinhold Publishing Corp., New York, 1936, p. 46.
21. W. H. Perkin, *J. Chem. Soc.* **63**, 488 (1893).
22. G. B. Kistiakowsky and W. W. Rice, *J. Chem. Phys.* **8**, 618 (1940).
23. E. Peytral, *Bull. Soc. Chim. France* **39** (4), 206 (1926).
24. The Associated Factory Mutual Fire Insurance Companies, *Ind. Eng. Chem.* **32**, 882 (1940).
25. O. Maass and E. H. Boomer, *J. Am. Chem. Soc.* **44**, 1709 (1922).
26. A. Siedell, *Solubilities of Organic Compounds*, D. Van Nostrand Co. Inc., New York, 1941.
27. G. L. Cunningham, *J. Chem. Phys.* **17**, 211 (1949).

28. E. H. Rodd, *Chemistry of Carbon Compounds*, Vol. 1A, Elsevier Publishing Co., Amsterdam, 1951, p. 671.
29. P. V. Zimakov, *J. Phys. Chem. (USSR)* **20**, 133 (1946).
30. A. D. Walsh, *Nature* **159**, 165, 712 (1947); *Trans. Faraday Soc.* **45**, 179 (1949).
31. J. W. Linnett, *Nature* **160**, 162 (1947).
32. R. Robinson, *Nature* **159**, 400 (1947).
33. A. Lourenço, *Ann. Chim. et Phys.* **67** (3), 275 (1863).
34. L. Smith G. Wode, and I. Widhe, *Z. Physik. Chem.* **130**, 154 (1927).
35. *Cellosolve and Carbitol Solvents*, Brochure F-4765F, Union Carbide Corp., New York, 1962.
36. W. Deckert, *Angew. Chem.* **45**, 559 (1932).
37. O. F. Lubatti, *J. Soc. Chem. Ind. (London)* **54**, 424T (1935).
38. W. Ziese, *Chem. Ber.* **66B**, 1965 (1933).
39. A. Schaarschmidt, L. Hermann, and B. Szemzö, *Chem. Ber.* **58**, 1914 (1925).
40. J. W. Cook, C. L. Hewitt, and C. A. Lawrence, *J. Chem. Soc.* **1936**, 71.
41. D. L. Cottle and W. C. Hollyday, Jr., *J. Org. Chem.* **12**, 510–516 (1947).
42. R. C. Huston and A. H. Agett, *J. Org. Chem.* **6**, 123–133 (1941).
43. V. Grignard, *Bull. Soc. Chim. France* **29** (3), 944 (1903); *Compt. Rend.* **136**, 1260 (1903).
44. N. G. Gaylord and E. I. Becker, *Chem. Rev.* **49**, 413 (1951).
45. M. S. Kharasch and Otto Reinmuth, *Grignard Reactions of Nonmetallic Substances*, Prentice-Hall, Inc., Englewood Cliffs, N.J., 1954.
46. R. Whelton, H. J. Phaff, and E. M. Mrak, *Foods Inds.* **18**, 23–25, 174–176, 318, 320 (1946).
47. C. Eaborn, *Organosilicon Compounds*, Academic Press, Inc., New York, 1960, p. 261.
48. U.S. Pat. 2,381,138 (Aug. 7, 1945), W. I. Patnode and R. O. Sauer (to General Electric Co.); *Chem. Abstr.* **39**, 4890 (1945); *J. Am. Chem. Soc.* **67**, 1548 (1945).
49. R. F. Goldstein, *The Petroleum Chemicals Industry*, John Wiley & Sons, Inc., New York, 1958, pp. 342–362.
50. L. Knorr, *Chem. Ber.* **32**, 729 (1899).
51. L. Knorr and H. W. Brownsdon, *Chem. Ber.* **35**, 4474 (1902).
52. G. Benoit, *Bull. Soc. Chim. France* **1947**, 242.
53. L. W. Jones and G. R. Burns, *J. Am. Chem. Soc.* **47**, 2966 (1925).
54. M. Mousseron, R. Jacquier, and A. Fontaine, *Bull. Soc. Chim. France* **1952** (5), 19, 767–776.
55. R. Smith, *J. Am. Chem. Soc.* **62**, 994 (1940).
56. Y. K. Yurlev and K. Y. Novitiskii, *Dokl. Akad. Nauk SSSR* **63**, 285–288 (1948); *Chem. Abstr.* **43**, 2624 (1949).
57. C. C. J. Culvenor, W. Davies, and N. S. Heath, *J. Chem. Soc.* **1949**, I, 278–287.
58. U.S. Pat. 2,453,062 (Nov. 1948), E. L. Carpenter (to American Cyanamid Co.).
59. A. A. Petrov, *J. Gen. Chem. USSR (Eng. Transl.)* **10**, 981–996 (1940); *Chem. Abstr.* **35**, 3603 (1941).
60. G. Willfang, *Chem. Ber.* **74**, 145 (1941); *Chem. Abstr.* **35**, 3226 (1941).
61. M. T. Bogert and R. O. Roblin, Jr., *J. Am. Chem. Soc.* **55**, 3741–3745 (1933).
62. J. A. McRae, E. H. Charlesworth, F. R. Archibald, and D. S. Alexander, *Can. J. Research* **21B**, 186 (1943); *Chem. Abstr.* **38**, 740 (1944); *Chem. Abstr.* **37**, 4056 (1943).
63. E. L. Gusters and P. G. Stevens, *J. Am. Chem. Soc.* **55**, 374–386 (1933).
64. P. Bedos, *Compt. Rend.* **183**, 562–565 (1926).
65. G. H. Twigg, *Trans. Faraday Soc.* **42**, 284, 657 (1946); *Proc. Royal Soc. (London)* **188A**, 92 (1946).
66. F. G. A. Stone and H. J. Emeleus, *J. Chem. Soc.* **1950**, III, 2755–2759.
67. M. S. Malinovski and N. D. Medjanzema, *J. Gen. Chem. USSR (Eng. Transl.)* **23**, 221–223 (1953); *Chem. Abstr.* **48**, 2580 (1954); **49**, 4517 (1955).
68. J. F. Norris, *J. Ind. Eng. Chem.* **11**, 817 (1919).
69. G. O. Curme and F. Johnston, *Glycols*, ACS Monograph No. 114, Reinhold Publishing Corp., New York, 1952, Chaps. 2 and 5.
70. W. L. Faith, D. B. Keyes, and R. L. Clark, *Industrial Chemicals*, 2nd ed., John Wiley & Sons, Inc., New York, 1957, pp. 383–388.
71. M. Gomberg, *J. Am. Chem. Soc.* **41**, 1416 (1919).
72. C. C. Price, *Mechanisms of Reactions at Carbon–Carbon Double Bonds*, Interscience Publishers, Inc., New York, 1946, pp. 35–40.
73. I. Roberts and G. E. Kimball, *J. Am. Chem. Soc.* **59**, 947 (1937).

74. L. F. Hatch, *The Chemistry of Petrochemical Reactions*, The Gulf Publishing Co., Houston, Texas, 1955, pp. 96–97.
75. R. W. Taft, Jr., *J. Am. Chem. Soc.* **70**, 3364–3369 (1948).
76. D. G. Weaver and J. L. Smart, "Ethylene Oxide Derivatives, Glycols and Ethanolamines," in *Modern Chemical Processes*, Reinhold Publishing Corporation, New York, N.Y., 1961, pp. 92–98.
77. E. T. Borrows and D. A. Caplin, "Ethylene Oxide by Direct Oxidation of Ethylene and from Chlorohydrin," *Chem. Ind. (London)* **1953**, 532–537; *Chem. Abstr.* **48**, 587 (1954).
78. C. J. Thomas and J. F. Utley, *Chem. Eng. Progr.* **57** (12), 70–74 (1961).
79. K. A. Kobe and Associates, *Thermochemistry for the Petroleum Industry*, a series of 19 articles appearing in *Petrol. Refiner* **28–30** (Jan. 1949–Dec. 1951); *Chem. Abstr.* **44**, 1679 (1950); **45**, 9841 (1951).
80. C. H. Chilton, *Chem. Eng.* **65** (15), 100–103 (1958); *Chem. Abstr.* **52**, 20109 (1958).
81. *Hydrocarbon Process. Petrol. Refiner* **42** (11), 171–173 (1963).
82. T. E. Corrigan, *Petrol. Refiner* **32** (2), 87–89 (1953).
83. Arch L. Foster, *Petrol. Eng.* **25** (4), C38–C39 (1953).
84. P. W. Sherwood, *Petrol. Refiner* **28** (3), 129–134 (1949); *Oil Gas J.* **55** (39), 80–83 (1957).
85. W. E. Vaughan and R. M. Goepp, Jr., "Proposed Ethylene Oxide Manufacture via Oxidation of Ethylene at Zweckel near Gladbeck," *U.S. Dept. Comm. Office Tech. Serv. PB Rept. 79607* (1947); *FIAT Final Report 875.*
86. U.S. Pat. 2,233,474 (1941), R. W. McNamee and C. M. Blair (to Carbide and Carbon Chemicals Corp.); *Chem. Zentr.* **1942**, I, 1306; Belg. Pat. 429,485 (1939), G. H. Law and H. C. Chitwood (to Carbide and Carbon Chemicals Corp.); Belg. Pat. 429,487 (1939), G. H. Law and C. M. Blair (to Carbide and Carbon Chemicals Corp.); *Chem. Zentr.* **1939**, I, 5043.
87. P. W. Sherwood, *Chim. Ind. (Paris)* **70**, 1078–1080 (1953); *Chem. Abstr.* **49**, 1556 (1955); *Petrol. Process.* **9** (10), 1592–1597 (1954); *Chem. Abstr.* **50**, 3989 (1956).
88. R. S. Aries, "Ethylene Oxide," *Kirk-Othmer Encyclopedia of Chemical Technology*, Vol. 5, 1st ed., The Interscience Encyclopedia, Inc., New York, 1950, p. 915.
89. U.S. Pat. 2,430,443 (Nov. 11, 1947), S. B. Becker (to Standard Oil Co.).
90. Ralph Landau, *Petrol. Eng.* **27** (5), C71–75 (1955); *Chem. Abstr.* **49**, 9910 (1955).
91. F. L. W. McKim and A. Cambron, *Can. J. Research* **27B** (11), 813 (1949).
92. *The Shell Process for Manufacturing Ethylene Oxide and Ethylene Glycol*, The Lummus Company, 1953.
93. U.S. Pat. 3,119,837 (1964), to Shell Development Co.
94. E. T. McBee, H. B. Hass, and P. A. Wiseman, *Ind. Eng. Chem.* **37**, 432–438 (1945).
95. L. Ya. Margolis and O. M. Todes, *Izv. Akad. Nauk SSSR, Otd. Khim. Nauk* **1952**, 52; *Chem. Abstr.* **46**, 5413 (1952).
96. P. H. Emmett, *Catalysis*, Vol. VII, Reinhold Publishing Corp., New York, 1960, p. 246.
97. L. Ya. Margolis, *Usp. Khim.* **28** (5), 615–638 (1959).
98. U.S. Pat. 2,605,239 (1952), G. W. Sears (to E. I. du Pont de Nemours & Co., Inc.).
99. U.S. Pat. 2,752,362 (June 26, 1956), Ralph Landau (to Chempatents, Inc.).
100. U.S. Pat. 2,805,207 (Sept. 1957), F. J. Metzger; *Chem. Abstr.* **52**, 4069 (1958).
101. U.S. Pat. 2,831,870 (April 1958), W. J. McClements and B. E. Elliott (to Allied Chemical & Dye Corp.); *Chem. Abstr.* **52**, 14660 (1958).
102. U.S. Pat. 2,477,435 (July 26, 1949), R. S. Aries; *Chem. Abstr.* **43**, 8399 (1949).
103. U.S. Pats. 2,404,438 (July 23, 1946) and 2,446,132 (July 27, 1948), T. W. Evans (to Shell Development Co.); *Chem. Abstr.* **42**, 7498, 1948. Can. Pat. 432,449 (1946); *Chem. Abstr.* **40**, 3466 (1946).
104. Brit. Pat. 754,593 (Aug. 1954), (to N.V. de Bataafasche Petroleum Maatschappij); *Chem. Abstr.* **51**, 3061 (1957).
105. A. Cambron and W. A. Alexander, *Can. J. Chem.* **34**, 665–671 (1956).
106. Brit. Pat. 811,828 (April 1959), (to Dow Chemical Company); *Chem. Abstr.* **53**, 13456 (1959).
107. U.S.S.R. Pat. 592,446 (July 1960), (to Union Chimique Belge, S.A.); *Chem. Abstr.* **55**, 10,750 (1961).
108. Brit. Pat. 501,278 (1939), (to N.V. de Bataafasche Petroleum Maatschappij).
109. U.S. Pat. 2,562,857 (July 1951), A. Cambron and F. L. W. McKim (to the Honorary Advisory Council for Scientific and Industrial Research of Canada); *Chem. Abstr.* **46**, 1582 (1952).
110. U.S. Pat. 2,686,762 (1954), E. L. C. Tollefson (to National Research Council of Canada).

111. Ger. Pat. 1,139,101 (November 1962), Karl G. Hackstein and Heinz Schmid (to Deutsche Gold- und Silber-Scheidanstalt vorm. Roessler); *Chem. Abstr.* **58,** 2888 (1963).

112. U.S. Pats. 2,142,948 (Jan. 3, 1939) and 2,187,882 (Jan. 23, 1940), G. H. Law (to Carbide and Carbon Chemicals Corp.); *Chem. Abstr.* **34,** 3761 (1940). Brit. Pat. 517,332 (1940), G. H. Law (to Carbide and Carbon Chemicals Corp.); *Chem. Abstr.* **35,** 6570 (1941).

113. U.S. Pat. 2,194,602 (March 26, 1940), G. H. Law and H. C. Chitwood (to Carbide and Carbon Chemicals Corp.); Brit. Pat. 520,170 (1940), G. H. Law and H. C. Chitwood (to Carbide and Carbon Chemicals Corp.); *Chem. Abstr.* **34,** 4870 (1940).

114. U.S. Pat. 2,219,575 (Oct. 29, 1940), R. W. McNamee, G. H. Law, and H. C. Chitwood (to Carbide and Carbon Chemical Corp.); *Chem. Abstr.* **35,** 1063 (1941).

115. U.S. Pat. 2,238,474 (April 15, 1941), R. W. McNamee and C. M. Blair (to Carbide and Carbon Chemicals Corp.); Brit. Pat. 517,333 (1941), R. W. McNamee and C. M. Blair (to Carbide and Carbon Chemicals Corp.); (for both patents see) *Chem. Abstr.* **35,** 4778, 6591, 6596 (1941).

116. U.S. Pats. 2,279,469 and 2,279,470 (April 14, 1942), G. H. Law and H. C. Chitwood (to Carbide and Carbon Chemicals Corp.); *Chem. Abstr.* **36,** 5187 (1942). Brit. Pat. 518,823 (March 8, 1940), G. H. Law and H. C. Chitwood (to Carbide and Carbon Chemicals Corp.); *Chem. Abstr.* **35,** 7414 (1941).

117. Brit. Pat. 524,759 (Aug. 14, 1940) (to Carbide and Carbon Chemicals Corp.); *Chem. Abstr.* **35,** 6597 (1941).

118. Shen-Wu Wan, *Ind. Eng. Chem.* **45** (1), 234–238 (1953).

119. L. Ya. Margolis, "Catalytic Oxidation of Hydrocarbons," in W. G. Frankenberg et al., eds., *Advances in Catalysis and Related Subjects,* Vol. 14, Academic Press, Inc., New York, 1963, pp. 429–501.

120. V. A. Pokrovskii, *Usp. Khim.* **21** (7), 785–807 (1952).

121. V. E. Ostrovskii and Associates, *Kinetics Catalysis (USSR),* (*Eng. Transl.*) **3** (2), 160 (1962).

121a. A. A. Belaya and Associates, *Kinetics Catalysis (USSR),* (*Eng. Transl.*) **3** (2), 171 (1962).

122. G. R. Schultze and H. Thiele, *Erdoel Kohle* **5,** 552 (1952); *Chem. Abstr.* **47,** 291 (1953).

123. A. F. Benton and L. C. Drake, *J. Am. Chem. Soc.* **56** (2), 255, 263 (1934).

124. A. Orzechowski and K. E. MacCormack, *Can. J. Research,* **32,** 388–451 (1954).

125. U.S. Pat. 2,752,363 (June 1956), V. D. Drummond, M. C. Gould, and R. Katzen (to Vulcan Copper and Supply); *Chem. Abstr.* **51,** 1250 (1957).

126. Ital. Pat. 553,704 (January 1957), H. Endler (to Montecatini Soc. Gen.); *Chem. Abstr.* **53,** 2250 (1959).

127. Ger. Pat. 1,059,428 (June 1959), Robert A. Egbert (to Scientific Design Co.); *Chem. Abstr.* **55,** 23562 (1961).

128. A. I. Kurilenko and Associates, *Zh. Fiz. Khim.* **32** (4), 797–805 (1958) (Techn. Transl. 814, National Research Council of Canada, Ottawa, 1959).

129. K. E. Hayes, "The Role of Reaction Products in the Silver Catalyzed Oxidation of Ethylene," *Can. J. Chem.* **38,** 2256–2268 (1960).

130. S. Z. Roginskii and L. Ya. Margolis, "The Use of Marked Carbon in Studying the Mechanism of the Catalytic Oxidation of Ethylene on Silver," *Dokl. Akad. Nauk SSSR* **89,** 515–517 (1953).

131. K. E. Murray, *Australian J. Sci. Research* **3A,** 433 (1950); *Chem. Abstr.* **45,** 6573 (1951).

132. J. T. Kummer, *J. Phys. Chem.* **60,** 666 (1956).

133. L. G. Nault, D. W. Bolme, and L. N. Johanson, *Ind. Eng. Chem. Process Design Develop.* **1** (4), 285–292 (1962).

134. E. Kh. Enikeev, O. V. Isaev, and L. Ya. Margolis, *Kinetics Catalysis (USSR),* (*Eng. Transl.*) **1** (3), 431–439 (1960).

135. T. I. Andrianova and O. M. Todes, *J. Phys. Chem. (USSR)* **30,** 522 (1956); *Chem. Abstr.* **50,** 13582 (1956).

136. A. I. Kurilenko, N. V. Kul'kova, H. A. Rybakova, and M. I. Temkin, *Z. Fiz. Chim.* **32,** 1043 (1958); *Kinetika i Kataliz* **3,** 208 (1962).

137. P. V. Zimakov, "Selectivity in the Catalytic Oxidation of Ethylene to Ethylene Oxide"; *Usp. Khim.* **29** (11), 1343–1352 (1959).

138. H. S. Pylant, *Oil Gas J.* **62** (17), 124 (April 27, 1964).

139. *Chem. Eng. News* **40** (37), 149–161 (Sept. 10, 1962); **42** (14), 30–31 (April 6, 1964).

140. *Chem. Week* **94** (20), Scientific Design Co. ad. (4th cover) (May 16, 1964); **94** (21), 67–70 (May 23, 1964).

141. "ECN Country by Country Survey of Ethylene and Ethylene Derivatives," a supplement to *European Chem. News* **5** (127), 12–43 (June 19, 1964).
142. "Olefins in Europe," Part 1 of a special report in *Chem. Eng. News* **42** (31), 102–134 (Aug. 3, 1964).
142a. *Chem. Week* **95**, 50 (Dec. 19, 1964).
142b. *Chemicals Economics Handbook*, Stanford Research Institute, Menlo Park, Calif., April 1964.
142c. *Ibid.*, April 1965.
143. *European Chem. News* **5**, 26 (Aug. 14, 1964).
143a. H. F. Conrad and C. W. Jones, "Limits of Inflammability in Vapors," U.S. Bur. Mines Bull. 279, rev. ed. (1938).
144. G. Peters and W. Gauter, *Angew. Chem.* **51** (2), 30 (1938).
145. R. J. Sexton and E. V. Henson, *J. Ind. Hyg. Toxicol.* **31**, 297 (1949).
146. C. P. Waite, F. A. Patty, and W. P. Yant, *Public Health Rept. (U.S.)* **45**, 1832 (1930).
147. Private communication to author by R. B. Broadwater, Research and Development Department, Union Carbide Corporation Chemicals Division (July 1964).
148. W. R. Minrath, ed., *International Encyclopedia of Chemical Science*, D. Van Nostrand Company, Inc., Princeton, N.J., 1964.
149. J. R. Skeen, *Chem. Eng.* **57** (7), 331 (1950).
150. C. R. Phillips and S. Kaye, *Am. J. Hyg.* **50**, 270–306 (1949).
151. J. Yesair and O. B. Williams, *Food Res.* **7**, 118 (1942).
152. R. Whelton, H. J. Phaff, E. M. Mrak, and C. D. Fisher, *Food Inds.* **18**, 23, 174, 318 (1946); *Chem. Abstr.* **40**, 5160 (1946).
153. U.S. Pats. 2,189,947–2,189,949 (1943), C. L. Griffith and L. A. Hall (to the Griffith Laboratories); *Chem. Abstr.* **34**, 4178 (1940).
154. J. L. Roberts, L. E. Allison, P. S. Prickett, and K. B. Riddle, *J. Bacteriol.* **45**, 40 (1943).
155. H. N. Hansen and C. Snyder, *Phytopathology* **37**, 369 (1947).
156. R. T. Cotton and H. D. Young, *Proc. Entomol. Soc.* **31**, 97–102 (1929).
157. E. O. Haenni et al., *Ind. Eng. Chem.* **51** (5), 685–688 (1959).
158. *Glycols*, Brochure F4763H, Union Carbide Corp., New York, 1964.
159. *Tergitol Surfactants*, Brochure F5900G, Union Carbide Corp., New York, 1961.

HENRY C. SCHULTZE
Union Carbide Corporation

ETHYLENIC ALCOHOLS. See Alcohols, unsaturated.

ETHYLENIC GLYCOLS. See Alcohols, unsaturated.

ETHYLIDENE DIACETATE, $CH_3CH(OOCCH_3)_2$. See under Ethanoic acid.

ETHYL MERCAPTAN (ETHANETHIOL), CH_3CH_2SH. See Thiols.

ETHYNYLATION. See under Acetylene, Vol. 1, p. 207.

EVAPORATION

Evaporation is the removal of a solvent from a solution by vaporization of the solvent. It differs from distillation (qv) in that no attempt is generally made to separate volatile components. It differs from drying (qv) or sublimation, in that the latent heat required for evaporation is transmitted to a solution or, where a solid phase is involved, to a suspension of the solids in its saturated solution. Sometimes these borderlines between the unit operations are crossed. In Europe, sulfite pulp mill-waste liquor is sometimes fermented. It may then be put through an alcohol still before going to the evaporator or may be fed directly to the evaporator. In the latter case, the condensate from the vapor given off in the first few effects encountered by the feed is rich in alcohol, and hence some distillation separation is accomplished in the evaporator. One means of preparing pure water from hard, brackish, or seawater is commonly called distillation, apparently because the old distinction between evaporation and distillation was based on whether the nonvolatile residue or the vapor was the valuable product (see Water).

The product of an evaporator may be an essentially dry solid, as in the manufacture of common salt, NaCl. Here, the evaporator is fed with a saturated brine so that evaporation causes precipitation of the salt. The evaporator fluid may contain more than 20% salt crystals in suspension. These are removed by a sidestream that is filtered or centrifuged, the clear liquid being continuously returned to the evaporator. Thus, the feed is liquid, the product is solid, but heat transfer is to an essentially liquid mass.

The subject of evaporation can be extended to cover such fields as the near-equilibrium driving forces (evaporation coefficients) needed to evaporate solvent from relatively quiescent surfaces (as under Molecular distillation, see p. 565), the influence of droplet size, velocity, etc, on evaporation from sprays into a gaseous atmosphere (see Drying), and the influence of wind, humidity, solar insolation, etc, on evaporation from lakes and ponds. However, in practically all industrial applications of evaporation, the vapor phase is pure solvent and it is removed at such a rate that "evaporation coefficients" are of no practical significance. In most cases, the solvent is water, the heat required for evaporation is supplied by condensing steam, the heat is transmitted to the solution through metallic surfaces, and the valuable product is that which is left after removal of the water. The principal factors involved in evaporator design are conservation of energy, separation of evolved vapor from residual liquid, heat transfer, and prevention of fouling of the heating surface. Selection of construction materials is also important inasmuch as heat transfer surfaces must be thin to give high conductivity. Corrosion is accelerated by the temperature and concentration gradients developed and by the high fluid velocities used, frequently with solid in suspension. An evaporator is frequently used to produce a crystalline product and its design may then be governed more by its use in effecting crystallization (qv) than as a remover of solvent.

Heat Transfer in Evaporators

The most expensive part of an evaporator is usually that associated with the surface needed to transfer the relatively large amounts of heat required (about 1000 Btu/lb of water). Heat transfer in evaporators is correlated in the usual terms of heat transfer coefficients, $U = Q/A\Delta T$, but the coefficients are frequently a strong function of temperature difference (ΔT), which may in turn be arbitrarily defined (see also Heat transfer).

The temperature difference is usually taken as that between the saturated temperature of steam at the pressure in the steam space (ie, neglecting steam superheat and condensate subcooling) and the temperature of boiling liquid in equilibrium with vapor at the pressure of the vapor–liquid separation space of the evaporator. Actual temperature differences across the heating surface are usually lower than this, primarily because the boiling-liquid temperature is higher. Consider a forced-circulation evaporator where large volumes of liquid are pumped from a flash chamber through a heater and back to the flash chamber, with no boiling occurring in the heater. All heat is absorbed as sensible heat, resulting in a temperature rise that reduces the net temperature difference. Also, in this type, short circuiting may occur in which liquid entering the flash chamber may not flash completely to equilibrium before being recirculated to the heater. In those evaporator types where the heating surface is immersed in the boiling liquid, hydrostatic head raises the boiling temperature above that

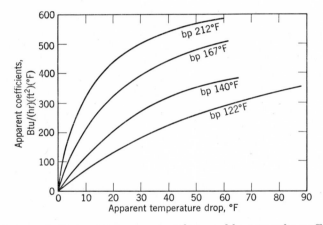

Fig. 1. Relation between boiling point, temperature drop, and heat transfer coefficient in a vertical-tube evaporator (5).

in equilibrium with the vapor space. In evaporators of the long-tube-vertical "climbing film" type, the boiling temperature at the heating surface is higher than that in the vapor–liquid separator due to the combined effects of hydrostatic head, friction, and acceleration of the vapor–liquid mixture generated in the tubes. Even in falling-film-type evaporators, there is evidence that some superheating is involved merely to create bubbles of vapor in the film.

Usually, no allowance is made for these losses of working temperature difference when reporting heat transfer coefficients except in the case of forced-circulation evaporators. Here, coefficients are based either on measured temperatures entering and leaving the heater or else on an equilibrium inlet temperature and an outlet temperature computed from heat input and liquid flow-rate. A further simplification is sometimes used for aqueous solutions whereby it is assumed that the boiling point of the solution is the same as that of pure water. This results in high apparent temperature differences and low apparent coefficients which are termed "uncorrected for boiling point rise."

The area on which evaporator heat transfer coefficients are based is the surface through which heat flows, measured on the liquid side of the surface (1). The total resistance to heat transfer (ie, the reciprocal of the overall heat transfer coefficient) is made up of some or all of the following individual resistances, all operating in series:

1. Steam condensate film, which may be calculated by conventional means (see Heat transfer). Condensation is almost always film type rather than dropwise, especially in units that have been in service for some time.

2. Inert gas film (2,3) due to the presence of gases in the steam, which is frequently vapor evolved in another part (effect) of the evaporator. These gases may have been dissolved in the feed or formed by decomposition reactions within the evaporator. Since most evaporators operate under vacuum, air in-leakage can be a major source of inert gases. These gases are carried by the steam toward the heating surface where they form an insulating blanket through which the steam must diffuse. Properly designed evaporators provide flow paths such that the steam can sweep the gases to a point from which they may be vented.

3. Deposits on the steam side of the heating surface. These may result from oil or boiler treatment compounds in the prime steam, material entrained in the vapor from the preceding effect of the evaporator, or deposits such as sulfur or metal sulfides formed as a result of the presence of hydrogen sulfide in the vapor.

4. Resistance of the tube wall itself, which may readily be calculated from its thickness and thermal conductivity (see Heat transfer), and usually is negligibly small.

5. Deposits on the liquid side of the tube, which may result from salting, scaling, or decomposition of components of the feed. Minimizing, avoidance, or ready removal of such deposits is frequently the most important factor in selecting the type of evaporator to be used.

6. Resistance to heat transfer of the (boiling) liquid film. This is usually the largest and hence the controlling resistance to heat transfer but, unfortunately, is usually the least amenable to calculation. Only in the forced-circulation evaporator, where no boiling occurs at the heating surface, or in the falling-film-type evaporator can the coefficient easily be calculated from conventional film theory.

The principal difference between types of evaporators is in the means used to induce liquid circulation past the heating surface and hence to reduce this last resistance to heat transfer. Some employ mechanical means such as pumps (forced circulation), propellers (propeller calandrias), or wipers (agitated film). Natural-circulation evaporators depend on vapor evolution, either to create bulk density differences to recirculate liquid past the heating surfaces (calandria or short-tube vertical, horizontal tube, basket) or to cause a large increase in volume to force the liquid past the heating surface at high velocity in a once-through operation (long-tube vertical). The falling-film evaporator depends on gravity to carry the liquid across the heating surface.

Many attempts have been made to correlate heat transfer coefficients in natural-circulation evaporators (4). In general, since circulation depends on vapor evolution, the coefficients increase with an increase in the amount of vapor formed and hence with temperature difference. Coefficients also increase with an increase in boiling temperature, partially as a result of the reduced viscosity of the liquid and partially as a result of the steeper slope of the vapor pressure curve, which reduces the temperature difference lost due to hydrostatic head and friction. Figure 1 shows the effect of these variables on coefficients for water boiling in a short-tube vertical evaporator (5). Results for other natural-circulation evaporators are similar and of similar magnitude.

Evaporator Types

Solar evaporation accounts for more total evaporation in the United States than any other method but it is used for only one major purpose—the recovery of salt from seawater. Solar energy is so diffuse that large land areas are needed, and losses due to seepage, etc, limit its use to low-value raw materials such as seawater. Water evaporation rates vary up to 2 lb/(ft²)(day)—several orders of magnitude lower than are normally realized in steam-heated evaporators. In salt manufacture the evaporated water vapor is allowed to diffuse into the atmosphere. When attempts are made to use solar evaporation to recover fresh water from the seawater, a membrane must be employed to retain and condense the water. This reduces water evaporation rates to less than half those otherwise possible. Costs of land and membrane generally make this an unattractive means of making fresh water, even though the energy is "free."

The simplest means of evaporation by conventional heat sources involves bringing the solution into direct contact with the heating medium. In submerged combustion, an oil- or gas-fired burner is immersed in a tank of the solution to be evaporated. Since "no scale can grow on a bubble," these evaporators are well suited to handling severely scaling or highly corrosive solutions, provided that they cannot be harmed by carbonation. More of the heating value of the fuel can be recovered by submerged combustion than by a steam boiler, but the evolved vapor is contaminated by combustion gases and cannot so easily be reused as with a multiple-effect evaporator heated by a steam boiler. Another form of direct-contact evaporator is the Porrion, used in the pulp and paper industry. This consists of a number of rotating discs dipping into a trough of concentrated, viscous black liquor (spent cooking liquor from the pulping process) and carrying the liquor into a stream of stack gases from the boiler in which the liquor effluent is ultimately burned. Direct-contact evaporators have also been built to use electrical heating by immersed electrodes, but the field of application is extremely limited by the high cost of electrical energy relative to fuel.

Most evaporators employ a heating surface to separate the heating medium from the liquid to be concentrated. The simplest is the direct-fired or steam-jacketed kettle, which is suitable only for small loads because of the small surface area that can be employed for heat transfer. Some evaporators have been built with flat, plate-type heat transfer surfaces. One reason for their use is based on the theory that scale will not adhere so readily to such a surface, which can flex to some extent. Another special use has been in the "channel switching" evaporator, where one side of each plate is used sequentially for condensing steam and boiling a scaling liquid. Scale formed during one half of the cycle is then dissolved by condensate during the other half of the cycle.

Most evaporation of industrial significance is accomplished in evaporators that have tubular heating surfaces, and are heated with steam. Thin wall (12–20 gage) plain metal tubes are generally used although heavy-wall impregnated-carbon tubes have found use in highly corrosive acid service, and fluted metal tubes have shown superior heat transfer coefficients in high-performance service such as seawater conversion. Tubes may be arranged vertically or horizontally with the liquid inside or outside the tubes. A great variety of evaporators have been built and are still in use but the field of choice has steadily been narrowed. The following types are usually the only ones that are considered for a new installation except for very limited purposes.

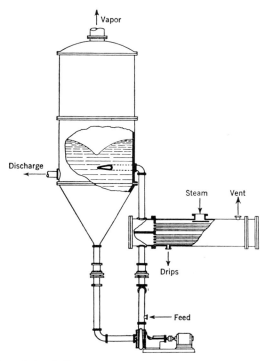

Fig. 2. Forced-circulation evaporator with external heating element (11).

Forced Circulation. This type, although generally the most expensive, is suitable for the widest variety of applications. Circulation is unaffected, or only mildly affected, by boiling action. It is widely used as a crystallizing evaporator since solids will not settle out and plug the evaporator every time the steam supply is interrupted or reduced. The forced-circulation evaporator usually consists of a circulating pump, a heat exchanger, and a flash chamber or vapor head, generally as shown in Figure 2. Volumes of liquid far larger than the volume of feed are pumped from the flash chamber, through the heater, back to the flash chamber. The heater is of conventional shell-and-tube construction and may be arranged vertically (usually single-pass) or horizontally (usually two-pass). Tube dimensions are chosen to give fluid velocities as low as 4–5 ft/sec for thick abrasive slurries. Velocities as high as 8–12 ft/sec are used to obtain high heat transfer coefficients when expensive alloys are required and erosion is not a serious problem. Vertical single-pass heaters are generally preferred when salting or scaling is a problem because it is easier to achieve equal velocities in all the tubes, there is less tendency for solids to settle and plug tubes, and mechanical tube cleaning is easier. For such uses, it is also advisable to locate the heater far enough below the flash chamber so that hydrostatic head will prevent boiling in the tubes, since this reduces the tendency for salts or scale to deposit on the tubes.

The flash chamber may take many forms, especially when used also as a crystallizer (see also Crystallization). That shown in Figure 2 is most common for clear liquids or for crystallizing operations where the crystals are circulated with the liquid. The return line from the heater is usually connected tangentially into the flash chamber below the liquid level. This imparts to the liquid contents both a primary rotary

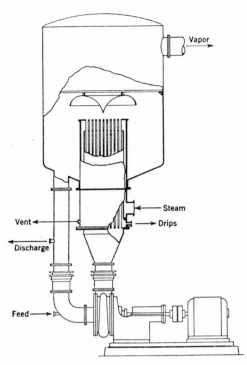

Fig. 3. Forced-circulation evaporation with internal heating element (11).

circulation and secondary toroidal circulation to keep solids in suspension and to bring heated liquid repeatedly to the surface where it can release its vapor more gently. An important advantage of secondary circulation is that it reduces the tendency for short circuiting of heated liquid back to the pump suction before the liquid has had a chance to reach the surface and flash. A disadvantage is that the vortex increases the head required by the circulating pump. Another means of inducing secondary circulation is by an axially located, fan-shaped inlet mounted within the body below the liquid level. Short-circuiting losses can also be reduced by introducing the heated liquid above the liquid level, but this again adds to the circulating pump head.

The volume of liquid handled by the circulating pump must be quite large to keep the temperature rise through the heater within reason. At high temperature rises (on the order of 15°F) flashing may become so violent as to make it difficult to separate the vapor from entrained particles. In some cases, as in saline water conversion, overall temperature differences on the order of 10°F are most economical. Here, a temperature rise through the heater, of 4°F, results in a temperature difference of only 6°F at the heater outlet. The mean temperature difference should then be taken as the log mean, in this case 7.8°F. Thus, 28% more heat transfer surface would be required than would have been needed had there been no temperature rise. Assuming water is evaporated at its atmospheric boiling from a solution having the thermal properties of water, the circulation rate required to keep the temperature rise to 4°F is $\Delta H/C_p \Delta T_r = 970.3/(1.0 \times 4) = 243$ lb/lb evaporation. Pump heads are rarely less than 6 ft, resulting in a power input on the order of 1500 ft-lb/lb evaporation. Sizing of pumps and circulating systems is thus a compromise between the extra cost

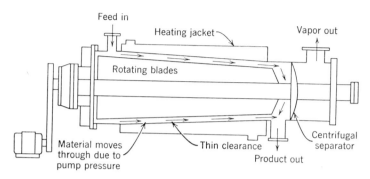

Fig. 4. Agitated-film evaporator used at low absolute pressures. Courtesy The Kontro Company, Inc.

of pumping at the higher circulation rates versus the savings in heating surface due to more complete utilization of the overall temperature difference. The large-volume, low-head circulating requirements are usually best handled by propeller or mixed-flow pumps. For the largest capacities, a number of heaters and propeller pumps may be used with each flash chamber.

When salting, scaling, or crystal size control are not important problems, boiling may be allowed to take place within the tubes. The evaporator then may take the form shown in Figure 3, with the heater extending above the liquid level in the vapor head. With this arrangement, not all the heat is absorbed as sensible heat and so less is lost from the overall temperature difference, heat transfer coefficients are higher, less liquid need be circulated, and head room requirements are lower.

One form of forced-circulation evaporator is an adaption of the short-tube vertical (see below), in which a propeller is placed in the downtake. This "propeller calandria" evaporator was developed originally for salt crystallization, at a time when it was necessary to drill scale from the tubes once a week. This made short, large-diameter tubes almost a necessity, and large volumes had to be circulated by the propeller to achieve reasonable liquid velocities. Propellers 10 ft in diameter and larger have been used. Modern evaporators of this type, used mainly in Europe, employ longer tubes which permit the use of smaller propellers. Propellers are placed at the bottom of the downtake well or in an extension of the well in order to minimize cavitation.

The **agitated-film evaporator** (Fig. 4) might also be classed as a forced-circulation machine inasmuch as it uses mechanical energy to improve heat transfer. The heating surface consists of a single large-diameter, cylindrical or tapered, tube in which is rotated a series of wipers, either maintaining a fixed close clearance from the wall or riding on the film of liquid on the wall. The continuous forming and re-forming of the film permits concentration of materials so viscous that they cannot be handled in other types of evaporators. The short residence time in the evaporator makes it advantageous for extremely heat sensitive materials. The field of application is limited, however, by the small size (about 200 ft² max surface) and expensive construction of this evaporator.

Centrifugal Still. This is another form of evaporator using mechanical energy, in this case centrifugal force to carry liquid as a thin film across the heating surface. It was developed for very high boiling, heat-sensitive materials and usually operates at absolute pressures of the order of 10 μ of mercury (*molecular distillation*). At these

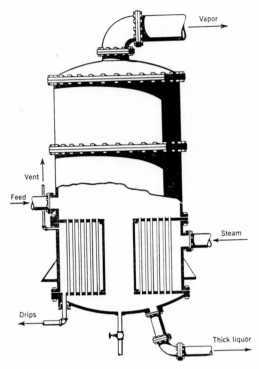

Fig. 5. Vertical-tube calandria evaporator (10). Courtesy Swenson Evaporator Co.

low pressures, the superheat required to form vapor bubbles below the surface is far greater than the temperature difference required to conduct heat through the film, and all evaporation takes place from the free surface of the film. The evaporation rate at this surface is the limiting factor and is given by the Knudsen-Langmuir formula $w = 0.0583\ PA\sqrt{M/T}$; where w = grams evaporated per second, P = solution vapor pressure, in mm Hg, A = solution surface area in m², M = molecular weight, and T = solution temperature in °K.

Molecular Centrifugal Still. This usually takes the form of a rapidly rotating disc or cone, heated on one side and fed at the axis on the other side. The condenser is placed close to the rotor so that the distance for vapor travel is less than the mean free path of an evaporating molecule (so that the molecule has little chance to suffer collisions that might return it to the film on the rotor). Costs are very high and unit capacities low, making these stills suitable only for high-value materials (such as vitamins) not easily amenable to recovery by other methods.

Short-Tube Vertical. The short-tube vertical or calandria evaporator (Fig. 5), was once so widely used that it was called the standard evaporator. Its most important use today is in cane sugar manufacture. Tubes are short (4–6 ft), of large diameter (2–3 in.), and are fitted by expansion into tube sheets that usually extend to the full diameter of the body. Circulation is all by natural convention, being induced by the vapor generated in the tubes. Only a small fraction of the liquid is evaporated in each pass through the tubes; thus, there is need for returning the unevaporated portion to the zone below the bottom of the tubes. The return passage is usually a central downtake as shown. The flow area of the downtake must be almost the same as the combined flow area of the tubes, resulting in a downtake diameter equal to about half the body diameter.

Evaporators of this type give the highest heat transfer when the tubes are not completely submerged—at an apparent liquid level as indicated by an external gage glass about half way up the tubes. However, this involves the risk that occasional lower levels will allow the top sections to be incompletely wetted, which results in baking solids onto the tubes. Consequently, such evaporators are normally operated at higher than optimum levels.

Horizontal Tube. The horizontal-tube evaporator was once widely used in the chemical industry, both because it required little headroom and because it contained a large liquid inventory and hence reacted only very slowly to drastic changes in control settings. Steam condensed inside the tubes with boiling liquid outside, contained in

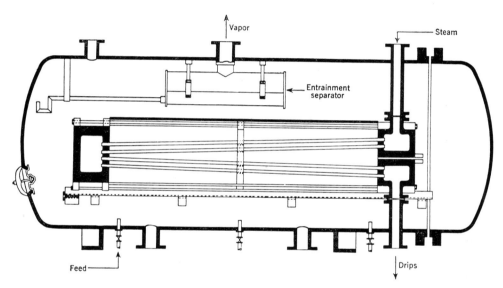

Fig. 6. Power-plant makeup evaporator (11).

either a vertical cylindrical or else horizontal rectangular shell made up of a number of cast-iron segments.

This type is used today mainly for power plant makeup evaporators, in the form shown in Figure 6. The shell is a horizontal cylinder, providing the largest possible vapor–liquid separation area since vapor purity is of prime importance. The bundle of horizontal tubes is generally arranged so that it can easily be removed for cleaning. The tubes may also be installed in a bowed condition, with the tube sheets restrained by tie rods, so that some scale can be cracked off by the flexing that results from spraying with cold water.

Long-Tube Vertical. This type accounts for more total evaporation than all other steam-heated evaporators combined; much of it is for black liquor evaporation in the pulp and paper industry (see Pulp). It is not strictly a natural-circulation type, but relies rather on the large increase in volume accompanying vaporization to push liquid through the tubes at very high (sometimes approaching sonic) velocities.

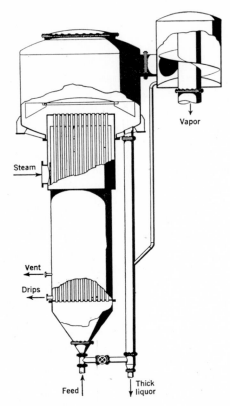

Steam

Vent

Drips

Vapor

Feed

Thick liquor

Fig. 7. Long-tube evaporator (10).

The long-tube vertical (LTV) evaporator consists simply of a vertical single-pass shell-and-tube heat exchanger surmounted by a vapor–liquid separator (Fig. 7).

A dished baffle is positioned above the tube exits to deflect liquid away from the vapor outlet. The baffle is also quite effective as a means of breaking foam. The long tubes make it possible to contain the maximum amount of heating surface in a shippable tube bundle. They also simplify the steam distribution and venting problems since they provide a long flow path for the steam. Operation is usually without recirculation, the feed being concentrated as far as desired in one pass up through the tubes. An extreme example is the caustic high concentrator, going from a 50% solution feed boiling at 300°F, to a 99.5% product boiling at 700°F, in one pass up $\frac{7}{8}$-in. tubes, 20-ft long. As can be seen, no "liquor level" is maintained in the LTV evaporator and residence time is usually very short.

Tube proportions are selected to meet the circumstances, from $1\frac{1}{4}$-in. by 9-ft impregnated carbon tubes on acid service (due to mechanical limitations) to 2 in. by 24–36-ft tubes in black-liquor service. These latter sizes appear to be the cheapest form in which heating surface can be provided in any evaporator.

Heat transfer performance in the LTV is difficult to predict. At the bottom where the feed enters there is no boiling even though the feed has been heated to the boiling point at the pressure in the vapor separator. Velocities of liquid flowing alone are generally low, so heat transfer is poor. As the liquid rises in the tubes it is heated and

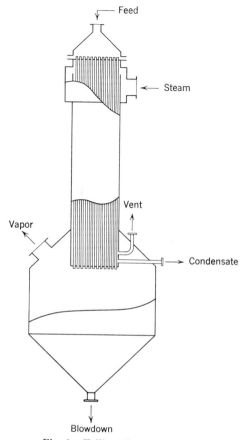

Fig. 8. Falling-film evaporator.

at the same time the pressure is reduced, due to the reduction in the hydrostatic head of the liquid above. At some point the liquid starts to boil, but at a pressure higher than that in the separator due to the hydrostatic head and friction, and acceleration losses of the liquid–vapor mixture still above. From here on up the tube, the temperature decreases due to the portion of these losses left behind. Temperature differences in the nonboiling zone may be high but the coefficients are low. Heat transfer coefficients may be very high in the boiling zone although offset to some extent by the lower-than-terminal temperature differences. Although means of estimating performance have been developed (6), they have not adequately been proved, especially for solutions with properties appreciably different from those of water. In general, however, it can be said that overall heat transfer performance improves radically with increases in temperature difference, since these increase the portion of tube length occupied by boiling liquid.

Falling Film. The conventional LTV evaporator cannot fully utilize the available temperature difference due to the losses incurred by hydrostatic head, friction, and the acceleration of liquid by the vapor. The first of these losses can be eliminated by turning the evaporator on its side (the old Yaryan evaporator). However, this creates hydrostatic head problems in distributing feed equally to all the tubes and the loss due to hydrostatic head in the tubes themselves generally proves to be the smallest of the losses.

An almost complete elimination of these losses can be achieved by turning the conventional LTV upside down, as in Figure 8. The feed now flows down the tube walls as a film, being under most conditions only slightly accelerated by the vapor. Friction losses thus exist essentially only for vapor alone, flowing in a practically empty tube. Friction losses are usually quite small if proper tube proportions have been chosen. Thus very little temperature difference is lost due to the effect of friction and acceleration. Heat transfer coefficients can be predicted from the theories of falling films (see Heat transfer). There is some residual error involved, which is important at a low temperature and which has been attributed either to increased friction (7) or to a degree of superheat needed in order to create vapor bubbles of a size equal to the film thickness (8).

Heat transfer coefficients in the falling-film evaporator are quite high—higher in many cases, especially at elevated temperatures, than in forced-circulation evaporators. Further, these coefficients are achieved at relatively low film velocities and with much less loss in working temperature difference than is the case with forced-circulation evaporators. Entrainment separation efficiency is usually very high, occurring mainly in the tubes themselves where spray from the film on one side of the wall impinges on the film on the other side.

The principal difficulty with falling-film evaporators is that of uniform feed distribution to the tops of all the tubes. Means of distribution include sprays and perforated plates above the top tube sheets or orifices inserted at the inlet to each tube. Any tube or portion of tube that is underfed may boil dry, depositing whatever material was in solution. This problem becomes more serious as the ratio of evaporation to feed increases. In such cases, recirculation may be used to increase the liquid loading. When the solution increases appreciably in viscosity during concentration, the feed chamber and vapor separator may be divided by baffles into a number of portions. The feed is then admitted to only a portion of the tubes, the effluent being pumped to another portion, and so on, with the result that the viscous product need be handled in only the last portion of tubes. A similar arrangement is also sometimes used in rising film LTV's, although in this case no pumps are needed to transfer effluent from one portion of the tubes to the feed chamber of the next portion.

The largest number of falling-film evaporators are used for concentration of citrus juices (see Fruit juices), which are so heat-sensitive that very low evaporating temperatures must be employed. The high heat transfer coefficients even at low temperature, the short residence time, and the freedom from superheating of the falling-film evaporator all are important in this application. The largest falling-film evaporator so far constructed is used for seawater evaporation, where its high heat transfer coefficients, freedom from loss of working temperature difference, and low cost per unit area are the important advantages. This evaporator is a twelve-effect unit with a capacity of more than one million gallons evaporation per day and was built in Freeport, Texas, in 1960–1961, as the first of the United States Department of Interior's demonstration plants for recovering fresh water from seawater (8a).

Energy Conservation in Evaporators

Heat extracted from the steam supplied to an evaporator must be sufficient to heat the feed solution to the boiling temperature, supply any heat required to separate liquid solvent from the solution (the opposite of the heat of mixing), and evaporate the solvent (which is normally water). Usually, the last of these is by far the largest, requiring 80–100% of the total. Thus, the vapor given off is steam in an amount approximating the amount of steam condensed, only somewhat lower in temperature due to the temperature difference required to accomplish heat transfer. This steam given off, which is usually termed "vapor" to distinguish it from the prime steam, may be compressed to serve as part or all of the prime steam (thermocompression operation), or may be used to heat another unit boiling at lower temperature (multiple-effect operation). These means of conserving energy require a more expensive evaporator than would otherwise be needed but sometimes save enough in other investment costs to justify their use on the basis of capital cost alone. Multiple-effect operation reduces the amount of prime steam needed and hence the cost of the boiler. It also reduces the amount of cooling water needed to condense the final vapor and hence the cost of the condenser and water supply system. Thermocompression operation eliminates the need for condenser water entirely and also either eliminates or greatly reduces the size of steam boiler needed.

Thermocompression Operation. Thermocompression evaporators may use high-pressure steam in a steam jet to compress the vapor, but usually use mechanical compression. Thus, evaporation is accomplished by mechanical energy rather than by heat energy. For a perfect compressor, the energy requirement is given by the Carnot cycle equation, $W = Q(T_1 - T_2)/T_2$, where T_1 and T_2 are the absolute vapor temperatures at compressor discharge and suction, and Q is the heat taken in at T_2. To keep power requirements within reason, a low temperature difference $(T_1 - T_2)$ is required across the heating surface, and hence a large and expensive evaporator. For solutions having a boiling point higher than that of pure water at the same pressure (ie, having a boiling point rise), the vapor evolved in the evaporator is superheated. When this vapor condenses, it gives up practically all of its heat at the condensing temperature of pure water. Thus, the boiling point rise is lost from the overall temperature difference. The compression ratio required of the compressor must therefore be sufficient to provide a difference in saturated vapor temperatures which is the sum of the boiling point rise and the temperature difference required for heat transfer. The effect of boiling point rise can in many cases be reduced by compartmenting the evaporator as described for falling-film evaporators so that most of the evaporation is from solutions less highly concentrated than the product.

A thermocompression evaporator is similar to a flywheel; the heat input must exactly equal the heat losses if the operating temperatures are to remain constant. These losses occur mainly as heat in the condensed vapor and the concentrated product which normally leave at temperatures higher than that of the feed, with other losses occurring as heat of concentration, heat leakage, and vapor lost in venting of non-condensable gases. Ideally, the only heat input to the system is the thermal equivalent, W, of the mechanical energy supplied to the compressor. To reduce the need for additional heat input, it is usually economical to employ extensive heat exchanger systems to preheat the feed with both the condensate and the concentrated product. The remaining heat requirements may be supplied by a small steam boiler, which is usually needed anyway to bring the system to operating temperature on startup. When the prime mover is an internal combustion engine, these supplementary heat requirements may be obtained from the exhaust gases, or from the engine cooling water if at sufficiently high temperature.

The largest number of thermocompression evaporators are used by the military for distilling seawater. These are compact, portable, engine-driven units employing positive displacement compressors. For large units in industry, the high specific volume of water makes necessary the use of centrifugal or axial flow compressors. The cost of compressors is a function primarily of inhaled volume. To reduce the vapor volume such evaporators are operated at as high a temperature level as practical, even though this requires a more expensive feed heater installation. By operating the compressor across a double-effect evaporator, the weight of vapor to be compressed can be cut almost in half, although the volume reduction is not as great since the suction pressure is lower (assuming a fixed upper temperature limit). This double-effect thermocompression arrangement does not save on power consumption or evaporator heating surface requirements. Consider both single- and double-effect units boiling pure water and evaporating the same total amount (and hence having substantially the same total Q) under the ideal conditions where one pound of steam evaporates 1 lb of water and where $T_1 - T_2 = \Delta T$ is small relative to the absolute boiling temperature, T. For the single effect, $W = Q\Delta T/T$ and the evaporator heating surface $A = Q/U\Delta T$, where U is the heat transfer coefficient. For the double effect, only half as much vapor need be compressed, but two ΔT's must be overcome,

$$W = (Q/2)(2\Delta T/T) = Q\Delta T/T$$

Each effect of the evaporator now needs to transfer half as much heat so that

$$A_1 + A_2 = (Q/2)/(U\Delta T) + (Q/2)/(U\Delta T) = Q/U\Delta T$$

When very low temperature operation is required as in the concentration of citrus juices, the specific volume of water vapor is so high that the vapor cannot economically be compressed by mechanical means. Steam jet compressors may be used; even though they are quite inefficient, they put to some use the available energy of moderate-pressure boiler steam. Alternatively, a secondary working fluid such as ammonia (or one of the Freon chlorofluorocarbons) may be used to reduce the compressor volume. In this system, the evaporator vapor is condensed in a heat exchanger cooled by boiling ammonia and the ammonia vapor is then compressed to serve as the heating medium for the evaporator. Thus the compressor must overcome the temperature differences across both the evaporator and the condenser-reboiler.

In the mechanical compression of evaporator vapors, the vapor becomes superheated. If the vapor contains any entrained solution, the moisture will evaporate and leave deposits on the compressor blades. A high degree of entrainment separation is required in the evaporator and it is frequently necessary to install an external vapor washer where the vapor can be scrubbed with condensate before it reaches the compressor.

If pure water is evaporated at its atmospheric boiling point and the vapor behaves as an ideal gas in a perfect compressor, the work requirement for a 10°F temperature difference is $W = Q\Delta T/T = 970.3 \times 10/672 = 14.5$ Btu/lb of water $= 35.3$ kWh/1000 gal evaporated. This low energy requirement (one sixty-seventh of that needed in a simple single-effect evaporator) may seem attractive, but unfortunately compressors are far from perfect, steam is not an ideal gas, a boiling-point rise is usually involved, and mechanical energy is usually many times more expensive than heat energy. Thermocompression operation finds its widest use in areas where fuel is expensive and power is cheap, ie, where hydroelectric power is the major source, as in

Switzerland. For most applications and areas in the United States, economic conditions are such that multiple-effect operation is less expensive.

Multiple-Effect Operation. Multiple-effect evaporators have been in use for 130 years and by far the largest number of present industrial installations use this principle. The vapor given off in one unit of the evaporator is used as the heating medium for another unit boiling at a lower temperature (and consequently at lower pressure) and the vapor thus formed may then be used to heat yet another unit boiling at still lower temperature. This reuse of vapor continues until the pressure of vapor given off from the last unit is so low that the vapor can barely be condensed by the available cooling medium, which is almost always water from wells, a river, or a cooling tower. Each unit is called an effect and may be of any type of evaporator described previously.

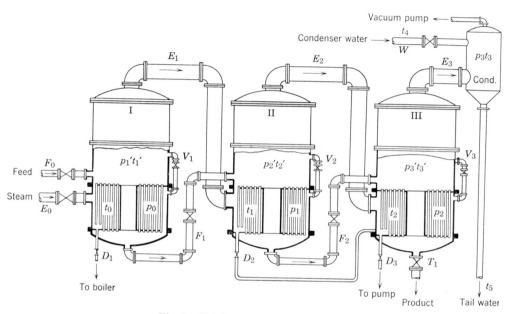

Fig. 9. Triple-effect evaporator (12).

The effects are numbered in order of decreasing boiling temperature, the first effect being the one heated by the prime steam. The entire assembly of effects is considered as one evaporator. In some cases, different evaporator types are used for different effects and in some cases several units (termed bodies) may be connected in parallel on steam and vapor to form one effect. Thus a seven-body sextuple-effect evaporator might have the first five bodies heated in turn by prime steam and then vapor from the preceding effect, with vapor from the fifth effect being split and fed to the two remaining bodies, the vapor from which would then go to the condenser. A compound double-triple effect may have the first effect heated by prime steam with the vapor being split—one part going to a single effect and the other part going to a double effect. These arrangements are most frequently used when the properties of the liquid become less tractable (such as an excessive boiling point rise) as the final concentration is approached—the liquid is fed in a predetermined sequence through the bodies in series flow.

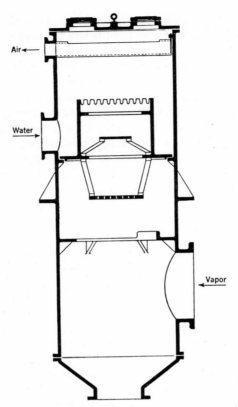

Fig. 10. Countercurrent contact condenser (11).

A simple triple-effect evaporator is shown in Figure 9, using three identical short-tube-vertical effects. Steam at pressure p_0 is fed to the first effect and the vapor formed at pressure p_1 heats the second effect boiling at a lower pressure, p_2'. This vapor then heats the third effect boiling at still lower pressure, p_3', and the vapor thus formed is condensed in a water-cooled condenser. Noncondensable gases in the steam are vented from the steam space to the first-effect vapor space by valve V_1. These gases plus those entering with the feed and as leakage flow with the first-effect vapor to the second effect and are then cascaded down through V_2 and V_3 and are finally removed by a vacuum pump connected to the top of the final condenser. Usually the water is not the valuable product and the last-effect vapor is condensed by direct contact with a cascade of cooling water in the condenser (Fig. 10). Flow is usually countercurrent with the noncondensable gases rising through the cascade of water to cool the gases to as low a temperature as possible and thus strip out most of the water vapor. The condenser is usually elevated so it can discharge the effluent water barometrically against the vacuum in the last effect of the evaporator.

Steam condensate formed in the first effect and removed at D_1 of Figure 9 is usually returned to the boiler as makeup. That condensed in the second effect and leaving at D_2 is usually flashed from pressure p_1 to pressure p_2, either in an external flash chamber or by direct introduction into the third-effect steam space, to recover some of its heat content.

In Figure 9, the liquid to be evaporated is fed to the first effect at F_0 and boiled at temperature t_1'. The residue is fed at F_1 to the second effect where it immediately flashes from temperature t_1' to temperature t_2' and is boiled at this temperature. Similarly, the residual liquid from the second effect is introduced by F_2 into the third effect, and the final concentrate is withdrawn at T_1. The concentration of the final discharge may be regulated by varying either the steam rate, E_0, or the feed rate, F_0, to the first effect, with the levels being controlled by the rates of withdrawal.

Assuming no boiling point elevation (BPE) and no pressure drop in the vapor circuits, the temperature differences available for heat transfer (working temperature differences) will be $t_0 - t_1'$, $t_1' - t_2'$, and $t_2' - t_3'$ across the first, second, and third effects, respectively, and the total temperature difference, $t_0 - t_3'$, where t_0 is the saturation temperature of the steam at p_0. Pressure drop in the vapor circuits may make p_1 lower than p_1', resulting in a lower condensing temperature in the following effect and a loss of temperature difference. This loss is normally very small. The effect of BPE is to make condensing temperature t_1 less than boiling temperature t_1' by an amount equal to the BPE. This reduces the overall working temperature difference to $t_0 - t_3 - \Sigma\text{BPE}$, where t_3 is the condensing temperature at the pressure p_3 in the condenser.

The final condensing temperature is usually determined by the cost of pumping out noncondensables and by the temperature and availability of cooling water. Temperature t_3 cannot be less than tail water temperature t_5 (it is usually about 5°F higher) and this temperature is higher in turn than the inlet water temperature t_4 by the amount needed to absorb the latent heat of the vapor; $t_5 = t_4 + E_3(H_3 - h_5)/W$, where H_3 is the vapor enthalpy at p_3' t_3' and h_5 is the condensate enthalpy at t_5.

The latent heat of water at pressure p_1 is almost as high as that at p_2 within the range of pressures usually encountered. If such secondary factors as heat losses, feed heating, and heats of solution are neglected, then 1 lb of steam condensed in the first effect will generate almost 1 lb of vapor which, when condensed in the second effect, will generate another pound of water. Thus, the total weight of water evaporated should be numerically almost equal to the number of effects. This ratio of evaporation to steam used is termed "steam economy" (sometimes "gained output ratio" or "performance ratio") and is the primary means of expressing evaporator "efficiency." Due to the secondary factors mentioned above, the steam economy is usually appreciably less than the number of effects. Average commercial practice gives steam economies that are 80–85% of the number of effects but this may vary over wide ranges depending on the feed temperature, feed sequence, liquid properties, and percentage of feed evaporated. If the feed temperature is above the average boiling temperature, steam economies greater than the number of effects are possible.

Actual steam economy is determined by heat and material balances around the evaporator. For the flowsheet shown in Figure 9, the equations would be as shown below:

First effect: $E_0 \Delta H_0 = E_1 \Delta H_1 + CF_0(t_1' - t_f)$

Second effect: $E_1 \Delta H_1 = E_2 \Delta H_2 - CF_1(t_1' - t_2') = E_2 \Delta H_2 - C(F_0 - E_1)(t_1' - t_2')$

Third effect: $E_2 \Delta H_2 + CE_1(t_1 - t_2) = E_3 \Delta H_3 - CF_2(t_2' - t_3') =$

$$E_3 \Delta H_3 - C(F_0 - E_1 - E_2)(t_2' - t_3')$$

where C is the specific heat of the corresponding stream and the ΔH's are the latent heats, plus any superheat resulting from BPE and heat effects of concentration. Where the latter is not known and is expected to be small, ΔH is usually taken from the steam tables at the saturation temperature rather than the actual solution temperature. When the intermediate temperatures, t_1' and t_2', are not known, as when designing an evaporator, they can be determined by considering the heat transfer aspects. The amounts of heat transferred are shown by the left-hand side of the equations above. Temperatures are assumed that will give working temperature differences which, in combination with known or assumed heat transfer coefficients, will give a reasonable distribution of heating surface in the several effects of the evaporator. The aim may be to achieve the same heating surface in each effect for reasons of standardization, the minimum total heating surface, or the minimum total cost (as when different types of evaporator or different construction materials are being employed for the several effects).

The feed sequence shown in Figure 9 is termed forward feed because the liquid flows from higher to lower temperature effects in the same direction as the vapor. Other feeding methods are widely used, such as backward feed, mixed feed, and parallel feed (feed introduced to, and concentrated product withdrawn from, each effect). When not dictated by other conditions (such as scaling tendencies, viscosity of the concentrated product, or need to withdraw salts or process liquids at intermediate concentrations and temperatures), the feed sequence is chosen to give the highest steam economy. When the feed is cold, backward feed is usually best because only the smallest volume of liquid needs to be heated to the high first-effect temperature by prime steam, the remaining heating being done by heat that has already accomplished useful evaporation one or more times. When the feed is hot, forward feed is best because the flash evaporation on going from one effect to the next can be used to generate more vapor in each of the remaining effects, which can in turn accomplish more evaporation. When process conditions dictate an "unfavorable" feed sequence, feed preheaters may be incorporated. An example is seawater evaporation where scaling conditions permit only a slight degree of concentration at high temperatures but a considerable degree of concentration at low temperatures. Thus forward feed is necessary if the highest steam temperatures are to be used, even though the feed is cold. The steam economy of such an evaporator can be brought up to that of a backward feed evaporator by passing the seawater feed through a number of heat exchangers, heated in turn by vapor extracted at successively higher temperatures from each effect of the evaporator. Such a system generally requires little or no additional heat transfer surface; it merely means that the total heating surface is split up between more pieces of equipment.

The steam savings of a multiple-effect evaporator are not gained without a considerable increase in capital investment. The reason is that *each* effect must have approximately as much heating surface as a single-effect evaporator operating over the same total working temperature difference. Going from a single- to a double-effect evaporator cuts the steam consumption almost in half, thereby reducing the heat load on each effect by about 50%. Thus, for a single effect, $A = Q/U\Delta T$, and for a double effect, $A_1 + A_2 = (Q/2)/(U\Delta T/2) + (Q/2)/(U\Delta T/2) = 2Q/U\Delta T$, where Q is the total amount of heat that must be transferred and ΔT is the total temperature difference between steam and liquid boiling in the last-effect. A multiple-effect evaporator may be thought of as a number of resistances in series to the flow of heat, since almost the same amount of heat must be transferred in each effect. The driving force is the temperature difference between steam and last-effect saturated vapor temperature. If the resistance of each effect, $1/UA$, is the same and the overall temperature difference remains the same, the flow of heat (steam consumption) will be inversely proportional to the number of resistances or effects. However, since the steam economy is directly proportional to the number of effects, it follows that the total evaporation rate will not change as effects are added. Since each effect must have the same heating surface as a single-effect evaporator (assuming the heat transfer coefficients are the same), the total heating surface required should increase in direct proportion to the number of effects. It is seldom the case that heat transfer coefficients are the same in all effects of an evaporator. As more effects are added, the temperature difference across each effect is reduced and this reduces the heat transfer coefficient for some types of evaporators (Fig. 1). Partially offsetting this is that the addition of effects reduces the amount of evaporation at the lowest boiling temperature, where heat transfer coefficients are generally lowest.

In a multiple-effect evaporator, there are certain losses from the overall temperature difference or driving force that make necessary installation of additional heating surface or limit the number of effects that may be used. These losses, which are quite important in many applications, are mostly proportional to the number of effects. These result from (1) boiling point elevation, (2) pressure drop in vapor lines and entrainment separators, (3) temperature rise of the cooling water, and (4) approach of condensing vapor temperature to the temperature of cooling water leaving the condenser. Additional losses may result from such factors as liquor temperature rise and short circuiting in forced-circulation evaporators.

There are so many factors affecting both the steam economy and capacity of evaporators that the designer must make detailed heat and material balances to determine the best size and arrangement. Basically, however, he inserts as many resistances (effects) as he can economically justify to stem the flow of heat (steam consumption), but he makes the individual resistances low enough (areas large enough) so that the total resistance will allow enough heat through to achieve the desired production. Once in operation, the evaporator establishes its own equilibrium, the temperature drop across each effect being established by the resistance of that effect relative to the overall resistance and the overall temperature difference. If the resistance of one effect doubles due, for instance, to scaling, the production rate is not reduced 50% but only in inverse proportion to the amount that this increases the total resistance of all effects. Also, it follows that any attempt to control temperatures in individual effects can act only by inserting additional resistances (as by throttling vapor between effects) and hence will result in a loss in capacity.

The optimum number of effects used in an evaporator depends on capital write-off policy, cost of steam, and cost of heating surface. Three and four effects are quite common for small installations, where steam is cheap, or where expensive materials of construction are required. Six and seven effects are common for pulp-mill black liquor, where the cheapest type of evaporator (LTV) of primarily steel construction can be used. Under governmental write-off policies, as for water supply, more than twelve effects can frequently be justified. Twelve is the largest number of effects that have been tried to date. This was for the seawater demonstration plant at Freeport, Texas, using a falling-film evaporator (see p. 570). The large number of effects was possible in this case because steel was the primary material of construction (except for heating surfaces), because the falling-film evaporator has a low unit cost, and because low temperature differences do not reduce the heat transfer coefficients.

Combination Operation. It is sometimes practical to combine thermocompression and multiple-effect evaporators to achieve lower energy costs than is possible with either type alone. This is possible because it costs little more to generate steam in a boiler at high pressure than at the low pressures at which it can be used in an evaporator. In this system, the high-pressure steam is used first in a turbine to drive the vapor compressor of a thermocompression evaporator. The steam is expanded in the turbine only to a pressure low enough to permit its use in a multiple-effect evaporator. Such an arrangement permits achieving overall steam economies greater than 20 lb evaporation per lb of boiler steam.

Alternatively, the turbine can be used to generate power for sale or plant use. In normal steam power plant practice, the turbine exhausts to a condenser at as low a pressure as possible. Efficiencies of converting heat to work are only on the order of 30%. By raising the exhaust pressure so the steam can be used in an evaporator, the efficiency of power generation is reduced even further, but this can be offset by placing a value on the exhaust steam. When evaluated in this manner, the cost of exhaust steam is only a fraction of the cost of fuel that would otherwise have to be burned in a low-pressure boiler to generate evaporator steam, without power generation. Such schemes are attractive for production of fresh water from salt water, but would depend on the ability to dispose of the large blocks of power that would be produced. These systems are widely used in industry to generate a plant's own power needs. The choice of the exhaust pressure depends not only on the cost of the exhaust steam, which increases with increasing pressure, but also on the relative amounts of power and steam needed and the effect of steam pressure on the cost of the evaporator.

Multistage Flash Operation. This is a process developed originally as the Alberger process (9) for manufacture of salt from brine and now used for making fresh water from seawater. It is similar to a multiple-effect forced-circulation evaporator but with only one "forced circulation" pump. Feed seawater from one large pump is passed in series through a number of heaters (Fig. 11), where it is heated in turn by vapor at higher and higher temperatures in tubular heat exchangers. The seawater is finally heated to the highest temperature by boiler (or turbine exhaust) steam. It is then flashed down to successively lower temperatures, the vapor going to the heaters to be condensed. The condensate formed in the heaters is also flashed down in stages to the lower-temperature heaters. Due to the high ratio of latent heat to specific heat of water, it is necessary to pump large volumes of seawater through the system relative to the evaporation rate, and power consumption of the feed pump is very high. Only a small fraction of water is flashed off in one pass through the system, so it is necessary to recycle flashed liquid back to the feed pump if the feed is to be concentrated to any appreciable extent. As a result, the liquid in all parts of the system is substantially at the discharge concentration.

In order to achieve the steam economy of a multiple-effect evaporator, the flash evaporator must have approximately three times as many flash stages as there would be effects in the evaporator. However, the construction of flash stages is relatively simple and a number of flash stages with their associated heaters can be combined in a single vessel. Flash evaporators suffer from the same losses as forced-circulation evaporators—temperature rise through the heaters and short circuiting. The loss due to temperature rise through each heater usually amounts to 20–30% of the working temperature difference, even when a large number of stages is used (thirty-six is the largest number used to date). Short circuiting is especially difficult to control because

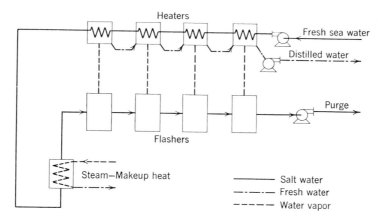

Fig. 11. Multistage flash evaporator.

of the very large volumes of liquid that are flashed only a few degrees per stage. Consider a flash evaporator working over a temperature range between 250 and 100°F. Assuming a specific heat of 1 and a latent heat of 1000, the ratio of feed rate to evaporation rate is approx $1000/[1.0 \times (250\text{--}100)] = 6.67$ (actually somewhat higher because some of the heat comes from reflashing of the condensate). The feed pump must develop sufficient head to overcome not only friction losses in the heaters but also the pressure in the first flash stage (approx 15 psig). The purge pump (or the feed pump if recirculation is used) must also handle a large volume (5.67 lb/lb evaporation), pumping from essentially full vacuum in the last effect. The result is that such evaporators require about twice as much power as is needed by a conventional multiple-effect evaporator having the same steam economy.

The temperature difference available for heat transfer in a flash evaporator may be obtained from the following expression:

$$\Delta t = \frac{\Delta T}{N \ln \left[\dfrac{1 - (\Delta T/2000) - (BR/\Delta T)}{1 - (\Delta T/2000) - (BR/\Delta T) - (R/N)} \right]}$$

where ΔT = the total flashing range, °F

N = the number of flash stages

B = sum of average boiling point elevation and average short-circuiting loss

R = the steam economy desired in lb evaporation/1000 Btu extracted from the steam

For a typical seawater plant where ΔT is 150°F, N is thirty-six stages, B is 2.5°F, and R is 10.2, the temperature difference available is 8.8°F. By comparison, a multiple-effect evaporator for the same conditions would have a steam economy of about 0.85 times the number of effects, requiring twelve effects to reach an R of 10.2. Loss due to boiling point elevation would be lower (about 2°F) because most of the evaporation would be from seawater of much lower concentration than the final purge. For the same temperature difference of 150°F between maximum and minimum brine temperatures there would be interposed eleven of the twelve effects (the first effect and the brine heater of the flash plant being heated by steam at over 250°F), for an average temperature difference of $150/11 = 13.6$°F and a working temperature difference (less B) of 11.6°F.   Thus the flash plant configuration results in losing 24% of the available temperature difference, which is reflected in greater requirements for heating surface.   This is further accentuated by relative heat transfer coefficients. Since all heat transfer takes place under nonboiling conditions, coefficients average only about 540 Btu/(hr)(ft²)(°F) over this temperature range.   Those for a falling-film evaporator, on the other hand, average 640 over the same range.

For relatively small plants, simplicity of vessel construction and the small number of pumps in a flash plant outweigh the disadvantages of high power consumption and extra heating surface needs.   For large plants, the cost of heating surface may exceed 40% of the total plant cost, and power consumption can become a major element of operating cost, making the disadvantages of the flash evaporator much more important.

Bibliography

"Evaporation" in *ECT* 1st ed., Vol. 5, pp. 927–947, by W. L. Badger, Consulting Chemical Engineer.

1. *Equipment Testing Procedures—Evaporators*, American Institute of Chemical Engineers, New York, (1961).
2. S. J. Meisenberg, R. M. Boarts, and W. L. Badger, *Trans. Am. Inst. Chem. Engrs.* **31,** 622 (1936).
3. D. F. Othmer, *Ind. Eng. Chem.* **21,** 576 (1929).
4. F. C. Standiford, "Evaporation" in Perry's *Chemical Engineers' Handbook*, 4th ed., McGraw-Hill Book Co., Inc., New York, 1963.
5. W. L. Badger and P. W. Shepard, *Trans. Am. Inst. Chem. Engrs.* **13** (1), 121–137 (1920).
6. J. R. Fair, *Chem. Eng.* **70,** 119 (July 8, 1963); **70,** 101 (Aug. 5, 1963).
7. Prengle, Dukler, and Crump, Inc., *U.S. Dept. Commerce Office of Saline Water, Res. Dev. Progr. Rept. No. 74* (June 1963); *U.S. Dept. Comm. Office Tech. Serv. PB Rept. 181484.*
8. J. R. Sinek and E. H. Young, *Chem. Eng. Prog.* **58** (12), 74–80 (1962).
8a. F. C. Standiford and H. F. Bjork, *Advan. Chem. Ser.* **27,** 115–127 (1960).
9. W. L. Badger and E. M. Baker, *Inorganic Chemical Technology*, 2nd ed., McGraw-Hill Book Co., Inc., New York, 1941, Chap. 2.
10. W. L. Badger and G. E. Seavoy, *Heat Transfer and Crystallization*, Swenson Evaporator Co., Harvey, Illinois, 1945.
11. *Evaporation* (Film No. 1), American Institute of Chemical Engineers, 1950.
12. W. L. Badger and W. L. McCabe, *Elements of Chemical Engineering*, 2nd ed., McGraw-Hill Book Co., Inc., New York, 1936.

General References

See references 1, 4, 9, and the following:
F. C. Standiford, "Evaporation," *Chem. Eng.* **70,** 158–176 (Dec. 9, 1963).
W. L. Badger and J. T. Banchero, *Introduction to Chemical Engineering*, McGraw-Hill Book Co., Inc., New York, 1955, Chap. 5.

Ferris C. Standiford
W. L. Badger Associates, Inc.

EXINITE.   See Coal.

EXPLOSIVES

An explosive may be defined as a material that can undergo very rapid self-propagating decomposition or reaction of ingredients with the consequent formation of more stable materials, the liberation of heat, and the development of a sudden pressure effect through the action of its heat on produced or adjacent gases. An explosive may be solid, liquid, or gaseous. TNT, glyceryl nitrate, or a mixture of hydrogen and oxygen, respectively, are examples of such states. An explosive may consist of a single chemical compound, a mixture of explosive compounds, or a mixture of one or more explosive compounds with nonexplosive material. TNT, a mixture of TNT and ammonium nitrate, and dynamites are examples of such types.

The products of explosion are generally gases or a mixture of gases and solids. Glyceryl nitrate yields only gaseous products, whereas black powder yields both gases and solids. In several cases, such as that of copper acetylide, all the products are only solids and, therefore, any explosive value of the material depends upon its heating effect on adjacent gases. The gaseous products of explosion generally have a volume much greater than that of the explosive.

Invariably, an explosion results in the liberation of a considerable amount of heat, that is sufficient to cause propagation of the explosion from the initial point or area throughout the mass. The liberated heat greatly raises the temperature of the products of explosion, thereby developing a high pressure that can be applied to doing work. The work done by an explosive is determined primarily by the amount of heat given off during the explosion.

A wide variety of chemical compounds can undergo explosion: nitrates, nitro compounds, nitroso compounds, nitramines, fulminates, azides, chlorates, perchlorates, peroxides, and compounds containing doubly and triply bound carbon are the chief classes of such compounds. However, not all members of these classes undergo explosion; ammonium nitrate and lead azide are explosive, whereas sodium and potassium nitrates and azides are nonexplosive. Basically, explosibility is determined by whether, upon decomposition of a compound, there is a liberation of heat, which thereby represents a positive difference between the sum of the heats of formation of the decomposition products and the heat of formation of the compound.

Among the products of explosion of most explosive compounds are the oxides of carbon and hydrogen; and in the case of some explosives, the oxides of sodium, lead, potassium, and mercury. These oxides are very stable and have no explosive value. However, recent preparations of solid xenon trioxide, XeO_3, and gaseous xenon tetroxide, XeO_4, have proved to be very sensitive explosives.

An important property of all but a few explosives is that of oxygen balance, which largely determines the work capacity of an explosive. Oxygen balance is the oxygen content relative to the total oxygen required for the oxidation of all carbon, hydrogen, and other easily oxidizable elements to carbon dioxide, water, etc. Several explosives, such as lead azide, undergo no oxidation reactions during explosion and thus, have no oxygen balance. If an explosive is less than completely oxygen-balanced, less heat than the maximum will be liberated and the explosive will have less strength than if it were completely oxygen-balanced. Since glyceryl nitrate and ammonium nitrate contain more oxygen than is required to oxidize completely all the carbon and hydrogen present, they possess oxidizing values. Glycol dinitrate is exactly oxygen-balanced, whereas most of the explosives have negative oxygen balances. Oxygen balances can be expressed as positive and negative in terms of the percentage required for complete oxygen balance or in terms of the grams of oxygen required for complete oxygen balance per gram of explosive. Some examples of the calculation of oxygen balance follow.

Explosive	*Oxygen balance*
$C_2H_4N_2O_6 \rightarrow 2\,CO_2 + 2\,H_2O + N_2$ glycol dinitrate	100% or $\pm$ 0.000 g/g
$C_3H_5N_3O_9 \rightarrow 3\,CO_2 + 2\frac{1}{2}\,H_2O + \frac{1}{2}\,O_2 + 1\frac{1}{2}\,N_2$ glyceryl nitrate	105.9% or + 0.35 g/g
$C_4H_8N_2O_7 + 5\,O \rightarrow 4\,CO_2 + 4\,H_2O + N_2$ diethylene glycol dinitrate	58.3% or − 0.408 g/g

By 1000 AD, explosive grenades and bombs containing black powder were being used in China; but it was not until the thirteenth century that it became known in Europe. With the invention of the cannon, black powder began to be used as a propellant; and a short time later, was discovered to be useful for accomplishing mechanical work. Over the next 500 years, it was universally used for priming, as a fuse composition, as a propellant, in shrapnel bursting charges, and as a blasting agent. "Fulminating gold" was first used in 1628, and mercury fulminate was first prepared in the seventeenth century, but it was the year 1846 that marked the modern landmark in the history of the development of explosives. In that year, the explosive properties of cellulose nitrate were discovered and glyceryl nitrate was first prepared. In 1863, Nobel began the production of glyceryl nitrate, and in 1864 Schultze made the first successful smokeless powder. In 1867, Nobel invented dynamite and the mercury fulminate blasting cap; and since that time rapid progress has been made in the field of military and commercial explosives.

The definition of an explosive given earlier, though a general one, actually covers two distinct classes of materials. One of these, known as *low explosives*, undergoes autocombustion at rates varying from a few inches per minute to approximately 400 m/sec. Examples of low explosives are black powder, priming compositions, and colloided cellulose nitrate powders. Low explosives have been used for blasting, but are chiefly used as *propellants* and *priming compositions*. The second class of explosives known as *high explosives* undergoes detonation at rates varying from 1000 to 8500 m/sec. Examples of high explosives are TNT and dynamites.

Interestingly enough, certain explosives, such as cellulose nitrate, can be made to undergo either the relatively slow autocombustion of low explosives or the detonation typical of high explosives.

Low explosives are chiefly subdivided on the basis of composition, whereas high explosives are divided into two categories based on their relative ease of initiation to detonation. One of these categories consists of compounds sufficiently sensitive to heat, impact, or friction to undergo explosion when subjected to such external forces.

These materials, due to their varying capacity to cause the detonation of less sensitive explosives, are termed *initiating explosives, initiating agents*, or *initial detonating agents:* Two examples are lead azide and mercury fulminate. The second category of high explosives, those too insensitive to be detonated by means of impact, friction, or the brief application of heat, and comprising the greater number, are known as *noninitiating high explosives*. These are used on a large scale for military and industrial purposes: TNT and dynamite are examples of this type of explosive.

Priming compositions are low explosives which are very sensitive to impact and friction and are used in small quantities to ignite initial detonating agents and certain other low explosives by means of a burst of flame. Low explosives such as black and smokeless powders can be used as propellants, since their rates of burning can be so controlled that excessive pressures are not developed and desired ballistic effects can be obtained. If such control of the burning rate is not maintained, excessive pressure will build up, whereby autocombustion may be changed into detonation in the propellant, thus rupturing the gun or rocket with consequent loss of ballistic effect.

Noninitiating high explosives are used industrially for blasting, demolition, excavation, seismic exploration, metal forming, metal cutting, metal bonding, and riveting. In military operations they are used in producing fragmentation, air blast, underwater shock, armor penetration, and demolition effects. Such explosives are also used in the ejection of personnel from airplanes and in the functioning of nuclear weapons. The formulation and application of high explosives have become highly developed techniques that are still undergoing improvement and expansion.

In this article, high explosives are treated first, since many high explosive compounds are used in formulating modern low explosives such as propellants. The initiating and noninitiating high explosives that form the bulk of modern explosives are treated separately. Their combinations with each other, with metals, and with binding agents are also treated separately. Commercial blasting explosives comprise a large group of high explosives which receive special consideration. Of the low explosives, black powder compositions are described first; the priming compositions and brief descriptions of the tests used for determining their explosive characteristics are then discussed; and lastly the propellants.

Only the most important members of each class of explosives are considered. For descriptions of the less important explosives and details of manufacture, analysis, testing, and application, the reader is referred to more exhaustive texts which are to be found in the bibliography.

NOMENCLATURE. The names "nitrocellulose" and "nitroglycerin" are not in accord with the best chemical nomenclature; the approved names are "cellulose nitrate" and "glyceryl nitrate." The former names have been, and still are, in universal use in the explosives industry; nevertheless, in this article the correct terms "cellulose nitrate" and "glyceryl nitrate" will be used throughout.

HIGH EXPLOSIVES

Initial Detonating Agents

This class of compounds is distinguished from noninitiating high explosives such as ammonium nitrate, TNT, and cellulose nitrate by their greater ease of detonation on application of impact or friction. Nobel discovered the phenomenon of initiation when he used mercury fulminate to initiate the detonation of glyceryl nitrate. Most

Table 1. Characteristics of Initial Detonating Agents

Characteristics	Lead azide		DDNP	Mercury fulminate
	Crystalline	Dextrinated		
crystal density	α 4.71	4.38	1.63	4.42
	β 4.93			
apparent density	0.8	1.8	0.5–	1.35–
			0.7	1.75
density at 3000 psi	2.9	2.6	1.2	3.0
solubility, %				
in water at 20°C	0.02		0.08	0.01
in ethanol at 18°C	insol	insol		sl s
in ethanol at 50°C			2.43	
hygroscopicity, %	0.03	0.16	0.04	0.02
rate of detonation				
m/sec	5,100		6,900	5,400
at density	4.0		1.58	4.17
sand test,[a] g	17.6	16.7	45.6	22.1
Trauzl test, % TNT	40.0	35	110	51
heat of explosion, cal/g	367		820	429
impact tests				
test A, in.[b]	2	5	2	2
test B, cm[b]		11	5	5
test C, cm[c]	43			24
temp, min, °C to cause				
explosion in				
0.1 sec	383	396	220	263
5 sec	345	340	180	210
75°C international test				
% loss in 48 hr		0.17	0.24	0.18
100°C heat test				
% loss in 1st 48 hr		0.5	0.5	explosive
% loss in 2nd 48 hr		0.1	1.1	
100° vacuum-stability test				
ml gas	0.4	0.2	6.0	
in hr	40.0	40	40	

initial detonating agents have distinctly lower rates of detonation and brisance (shattering effect) values than those of the explosives they are used to initiate; and, in most cases, those termed "detonators" or "blasting caps" have a lower order of stability. Certain compounds that were considered for initial detonating agents were too sensitive or unstable for practical use, and it was not until the mid-1920s that a substitute was developed for mercury fulminate, which had to be used despite its high cost and unsatisfactory stability. The few initial detonating agents being used now have a relatively limited range of sensitivity.

Table 1 summarizes the characteristics of the major initial detonating agents recently and currently used.

Lead Azide, $Pb(N_3)_2$. Hydrazoic acid and its lead, silver, and mercury salts were first prepared by Curtius in the period of 1890–1891. As usually prepared, lead azide consists of needlelike crystals, but it has also been found in orthorhombic, α, and monoclinic, β, forms. The β form is much the more sensitive and the two forms differ in rate of decomposition when heated. The compound can also be produced in the form of

Table 1 (*continued*)

	Lead styphnate	Lead dinitro-resorcinate	Lead dinitroso-resorcinate	Tetracene
crystal density	3.02		3.67	1.7
apparent density	1.0–1.6	0.54		0.45
density at 3000 psi		1.39	2.3	1.05
solubility, %				
in water at 20°C	0.04	0.02	insol	v s
in ethanol at 18°C	insol	0.002	insol	insol
hygroscopicity, %	0.05	0.19	0.73	0.77
velocity of detonation at				
density of 2.9, in./sec	5,200			
sand test,[a] g	10.5	1.6	0.0	2.0
Trauzl test, % TNT	42			53
heat of explosion, cal/g	368	270		658
impact tests				
test A, in.[b]	3	4		2
test B, cm[b]	8		68	7
test C, cm[c]	50			
temp, min, °C, to cause				
explosion in				
0.1 sec	293		274	
5 sec	282	265	205	154
75°C international test				
% loss in 48 hr		0.34	1.78	0.5
100°C heat test				
% loss 1st 48 hr	1.5	0.2	2.43	23.2
% loss 2nd 48 hr	1.5	0.02	0.15	3.4
100°C vacuum-stability test				
ml after 40 hr, gas	0.3	<0.4		

[a] Grams of sand crushed by 0.4 g of explosive.

[b] Minimum height of fall of 2-kg weight to cause an explosion in ten trials.

[c] Minimum height of fall of 1-kg weight to cause an explosion in ten trials.

finely divided amorphous aggregates whose particles range in size from 3 to 4 μ. This form is known as colloidal lead azide.

The structure of lead azide is essentially covalent. Resonance exists between the two structures, which may be shown in either of the following two ways:

$$\text{(a)} \quad \text{Pb}(\ddot{\text{N}}\!=\!\overset{+}{\text{N}}\!=\!\overset{-}{\ddot{\text{N}}}\!:)_2 \longleftrightarrow \text{Pb}(\overset{-}{\ddot{\text{N}}}\!-\!\overset{+}{\ddot{\text{N}}}\!\equiv\!\text{N}\!:)_2$$

$$\text{(b)} \quad \text{Pb}(\!-\!\text{N}\!=\!\text{N}\!\rightarrow\!\text{N})_2 \longleftrightarrow \text{Pb}(\!-\!\text{N}\!\leftarrow\!\text{N}\!\equiv\!\text{N})_2$$

Thus, there is a smaller resonance energy and, hence, less stability than in the purely ionic forms found in the alkali azides (see Hydrazoic acid and azides).

The first efforts, in 1893, to produce crystalline lead azide for military and commercial use resulted in disastrous explosions, and its manufacture was continued only in France and Switzerland. At a later period it was used in England. An amorphous form of lead azide consisting of rounded aggregates and containing a binding agent has been produced in Germany since World War I, and in the U.S. since 1931. This form, known as "dextrinated lead azide," has the following approximate composition: lead azide, 93%; lead hydroxide, 4%; dextrin and impurities, 3%.

The crystalline α form of lead azide is produced by the slow addition of a dilute solution of sodium azide to a dilute, constantly stirred solution of lead acetate or nitrate. Colloidal lead azide is prepared by the very rapid mixing of more concentrated solutions. Dextrinated lead azide is prepared by slowly adding a slightly alkaline solution of sodium azide to a solution of lead nitrate and dextrin. The precipitated lead azide is then washed with water and stored under water or under a 50–50 mixture of water with ethanol or methanol.

Lead azide can also be prepared from the same materials by the Biazzi continuous process.

Pure lead azide consists of colorless crystals or aggregates, whereas the dextrinated azide has a yellowish tint and has no crystal faces that can be observed under a magnification of 50. When it is subjected to high-loading pressures, there is no evidence of desensitization (dead-pressing) as is characteristic of mercury fulminate.

Lead azide is practically insoluble in most of the common solvents, but is very soluble in acetic acid, and somewhat soluble in aqueous ammonium acetate solution. It is insoluble in ammonium hydroxide. Waste lead azide can be decomposed so as to leave no explosive residue, by treatment with a cold 10% solution of sodium hydroxide for 16 hr. It can also be decomposed by suspension in a solution of sodium nitrite with the addition of nitric acid. Aqueous ceric ammonium nitrate (ammonium hexanitratocerate) decomposes lead azide with the evolution of nitrogen; this reaction can be used for determining the purity of lead azide.

The crystalline and colloidal forms of lead azide are almost nonhygroscopic, whereas dextrinated lead azide is slightly hygroscopic, which presents no difficulty in drying it.

Individual crystals or aggregates of lead azide do not burn as do those of mercury fulminate, but detonate when ignited with a flame. If the crystals exceed 0.1 mm in length, they may detonate when merely broken; control of crystal size is therefore essential.

As shown in Table 1, lead azide is less sensitive to impact and heat than is mercury fulminate and also less sensitive to friction, as shown by stab-action tests. The dextrinated form of lead azide, as would be expected, is less sensitive than its crystalline form, but colloidal lead azide is of the same order of sensitivity as the crystalline form. Lead azide is less sensitive to heat than mercury fulminate and this has somewhat limited its applicability, and in some cases a cover charge of a more ignitable material, such as lead styphnate, has been used.

Even at the highest density, the rate of detonation of lead azide is much less than that of TNT. Lead azide, although it has a slightly lower rate of detonation, is less brisant, and has less explosive strength, is a markedly superior initiator of detonation to mercury fulminate. It is also more stable, as shown by the results of tests at 100°C which appear in Table 1. Lead azide remains unimpaired after storage at 80°C for 15 months, whereas at 80°C, the purity of mercury fulminate is reduced to 90% in 1.5 days.

Since lead azide is preferable to mercury fulminate with respect to stability, cost, and availability of raw materials, it has largely replaced mercury fulminate in commercial blasting caps and military ammunition.

Silver azide, AgN_3, is obtained by a method very similar to that used for the preparation of crystalline lead azide, but the product consists of fine, amorphous aggregates that vary greatly in size. Silver azide is of the same order of sensitivity to impact as crystalline lead azide but is much more sensitive to heat. When heated at 251°C, it melts and decomposes into silver and nitrogen, but when heated suddenly to only slightly higher temperatures it detonates. Silver azide is also a somewhat better initiator of detonation than is lead azide, but the relatively high cost of this compound has precluded its extensive use.

Diazodinitrophenol, (DDNP, Dinol, 2-diazo-1-hydroxy-4,6-dinitrobenzene), may have a cyclic diazo oxide grouping. It was first reported by Griess in 1860, but it

was not until Dehn, in 1922, took out a patent for its use as an explosive in mixtures that it gained serious recognition.

A yellow or reddish-yellow amorphous powder, DDNP melts at 157–158°C and explodes at higher temperatures. It is prepared by diazotizing picramic acid, $NH_2(NO_2)_2C_6H_2OH$, with sodium nitrite and hydrochloric acid. The dark-brown, granular product obtained is thoroughly washed with ice water and may be purified by dissolving in hot acetone and precipitating by the addition of a large volume of ice water. DDNP is almost nonhygroscopic and insoluble in water, and is only slightly soluble in methanol or ethanol. It can be stored under water or under an alcohol–water mixture.

When unconfined, DDNP merely flashes on ignition with a flame; but when it is confined, ignition results in detonation. It can be subjected to loading pressures as great as 130,000 psi without being desensitized.

DDNP is as sensitive to impact as mercury fulminate, but less sensitive to friction. Its sensitivity to friction is approximately that of lead azide, whereas it is more sensitive to heat than either mercury fulminate or lead azide. This makes for ease of ignition and thereby renders it slightly more adaptable for use than lead azide. As judged by the sand test and rate of detonation values (see Table 1), DDNP has a brisance essentially equal to that of TNT. It has far greater explosive strength than either lead azide or mercury fulminate as measured by the Trauzl lead-block test.

It is considerably more stable than mercury fulminate, but not as stable as lead azide. Tests have shown that DDNP withstands storage at 50°C for at least thirty months, as compared with nine months for mercury fulminate, and withstands storage under water at 50°C for twelve months. The initiating value of DDNP is considerably greater than that of either lead azide or mercury fulminate, as determined by the minimum detonating charges needed for pressed Tetryl. This superiority is also indicated by its ability to detonate ammonium picrate and cast TNT, neither of which can be detonated in the sand test by lead azide or mercury fulminate.

DDNP is decomposed, with the evolution of nitrogen, by a 0.5% aqueous solution of sodium hydroxide; and this method is suitable for the disposal of waste or surplus material.

Like lead azide, DDNP has largely replaced mercury fulminate in commercial blasting caps and to some extent in ammunition.

Mercury fulminate, $Hg(ONC)_2$, was first prepared by Johann Kunckel von Löwenstern (1630–1703), but it was Howard, in 1800, who first described its preparation and properties in detail. However, it was not until 1864, when Nobel used it to ensure the explosion of glyceryl nitrate, that mercury fulminate was used as an initiator for the detonation of another explosive.

Although it can be prepared from acetaldehyde or nitromethane, mercury fulminate is generally prepared by the reaction of mercury, ethyl alcohol, and nitric acid. The intermediate products formed from the oxidation and nitration reactions involved appear to be acetaldehyde, nitrosoacetaldehyde, isonitrosoacetaldehyde, isonitroso-acetic acid, nitroisonitrosoacetic acid, formonitrolic acid, and fulminic acid. The following procedure has been found effective in the manufacture of mercury fulminate.

A pound of redistilled mercury is added to 8–10 lb of nitric acid (sp gr 1.4) in a 2-liter flask. The flask is maintained at 55–60°C by means of a bath of warm water and is then allowed to stand overnight, or until all the mercury has dissolved. The solution is transferred from the nitrating room to the "fulminate room," and poured into 8–10 lb of 95% ethyl alcohol contained in a large (18–20 in. diam) balloon flask. The flask, which rests in a bath of running cold water, is immediately connected to a suction system which removes any fumes evolved. The reaction begins immediately, with the evolution of white fumes. If colored nitrogen oxide fumes develop, the reaction is considered to be too violent and is checked by the addition of a quantity of ethyl alcohol. After 1.5 hr the reaction is considered to be complete, and when the contents of the flask have cooled to room temperature all of the fulminate has crystallized. The solid material in the flask is then caught on a cloth screen and washed with cold running water until it is free of acid and all fine impurities ("fulminate mud"). The washed fulminate is transferred to cloth bags, which are stored in crocks or concrete tanks of water or packed in barrels of wet sawdust for shipment.

The yield of mercury fulminate is from 120–130 parts per 100 parts of mercury. The fumes from the reaction are drawn through condensers, and the condensed liquid is processed to recover the ethyl alcohol and aldehyde. Ethyl nitrate, ethyl nitrite, and nitroethane are also formed. The acid mother liquor from the reaction and the water washings are neutralized with alkali, evaporated, and then processed for any mercury present.

Mercury fulminate can also be manufactured by the Biazzi continuous process.

Pure mercury fulminate is white, but the material produced by the foregoing process is grayish and only 97–99% pure. It occurs in octahedral crystals. A small amount of cupric chloride added to the nitric acid solution of mercury will improve the color, but not the purity. Military specifications require a minimum purity of 98.0%. Impurities consist chiefly of metallic mercury and complex, water-insoluble compounds. Mercury fulminate can be purified by solution in aqueous potassium cyanide, pyridine, or aqueous ammonia and subsequent precipitation with strong acid, water, or 70% nitric acid, respectively. The latter method is preferred and yields a white product of 99.75% purity.

Mercury fulminate has an apparent density of 1.35–1.75, and when subjected to a pressure of 50,000 psi its density is 4.3 as compared with its crystal density of 4.42. Highloading pressures have a desensitizing effect, so that after being pressed at 25,000–30,000 psi or more, the "dead-pressed" fulminate when ignited will merely burn. However, dead-pressed mercury fulminate is initiated to detonation at a high rate if it is covered with loose or slightly compressed fulminate or another initiating compound and ignited.

Mercury fulminate crystallizes from water with half a molecule of water of crystallization, but is anhydrous when crystallized from alcohol or precipitated from aqueous ammonia by nitric acid. It is soluble in water in the amount of only 0.08% at 20°C and 0.77% at 100°C and is only slightly soluble in cold ethanol. Therefore, mercury fulminate can be stored under water or, in cold weather, under a 50–50 mixture of water with ethanol or methanol. It is easily dried and essentially nonhygroscopic. Drying may be expedited by rinsing with either methanol or ethanol.

The purity of mercury fulminate can be determined by dissolving it in a measured excess of sodium thiosulfate and titrating with potassium iodide the thiosulfate remaining at the completion of the reaction. Starch solution is used as the indicator. A solution of sodium thiosulfate can be used for the disposal, by decomposition, of waste or deteriorated mercury fulminate, since only nonexplosive products are formed.

When a single crystal of mercury fulminate is ignited, it burns very rapidly with an intense flash, but does not undergo the high-order detonation that occurs when a layer of only a few crystals' thickness is ignited. When pressed to densities of 3.0 and 4.17, its rates of detonation are 3975 and 5400 m/sec, respectively. Mixtures of mercury fulminate and oxidizing agents, such as potassium chlorate, detonate at comparable rates; but when mixed with inert materials and/or fuels they merely burn rapidly; such mixtures comprise a number of priming compositions.

Mercury fulminate is among the most sensitive of the initial detonating agents, as shown by the comparative data in Table 1. However, it can be subjected to loading operations without undue hazard. Although not as effective an initiator as lead azide or DDNP, mercury fulminate is so efficient that excessive amounts of it are not needed. As shown by the sand-test values in Table 1, the brisance (shattering effect) of mercury fulminate is greater than that of lead azide, but less than that of DDNP.

The standard grade (98–99% pure) of mercury fulminate deteriorates significantly, even at 30–35°C, but retains a satisfactory purity and initiating value for some years if the storage temperature does not rise above 20°C. It has been found that the purity is reduced at various storage temperatures as given in Table 2.

Mercury fulminate purified to a standard of 99.75% when stored at 50°C is reduced to 95.0% purity after twenty-four months, and to 90.0% purity in approximately thirty months. When its purity has been reduced to approximately 92%, its initiating efficiency is essentially lost, though it will still undergo explosion when ignited.

Lead azide and DDNP have largely replaced mercury fulminate in blasting caps, priming compositions, and military ammunition to a position of secondary importance.

Fulminate–Chlorate Mixtures. Mercury fulminate is relatively expensive, and the admixture of other materials was soon attempted. Oxidizing agents were used since mercury fulminate contains less oxygen than that required for full oxygen balance. Black powder and potassium nitrate were used originally, and somewhat later potassium chlorate was introduced. It was found that 80:20 and 90:10 fulminate: chlorate mixtures are superior to fulminate alone with respect to initiating value,

Table 2. Purity of Mercury Fulminate Determined at Various Temperatures

Storage temperature, °C	Time, in months, to produce a reduction in purity to	
	95.0%	90.0%
80	0.016	0.05
50	8.25	12.0
30–35	20.0	40.0

brisance, and safety in handling. By 1910, in commercial detonators, the use of these mixtures instead of fulminate was widespread, and some use of them is still being made.

Silver Fulminate, $Ag_2(ONC)_2$. This product has never become commercially important due to greater cost and sensitivity than those of mercury fulminate. It has been used to some extent in the manufacture of fireworks and similar materials, such as snaps, and pull-crackers.

Silver fulminate is prepared by dissolving 1 part of silver in a mixture of 8.5 parts of nitric acid (sp gr 1.42) and 1.2 parts of water, heated at 90–95°C, and the solution added to 12.25 parts of 95% ethyl alcohol. The final mixture must have a temperature somewhat above 60°C. The silver fulminate precipitates as the reaction proceeds, the rate of reaction depending upon the temperature maintained. A practically quantitative yield of fulminate is obtained.

Unlike mercury fulminate, silver fulminate as ordinarily produced consists of fine amorphous aggregates rather than crystals. Although normally it is slightly less sensitive to impact and more sensitive to heat than is mercury fulminate, at certain conditions of temperature it has been found that small clusters of crystals are formed which are much more sensitive than the amorphous aggregates. This is the basis of the general conclusion that silver fulminate is dangerously sensitive.

Silver fulminate is a much more efficient initiator of detonation than mercury fulminate, and has essentially the same brisance as measured by the sand test.

Lead styphnate, 2,4,6-trinitroresorcinate, is a relatively poor initiating agent, but because of its ease of ignition it is used to some extent as a cover charge for lead azide and as an ingredient of priming compositions.

The addition of a solution of sodium or magnesium styphnate to a solution of lead acetate results in the precipitation of a basic lead styphnate that has low explosive strength and initiating value, but is used in priming compositions. This may be converted into the normal salt by treatment with dilute nitric acid. The normal salt, first prepared by von Herz in 1914, can also be obtained by treating a solution of lead nitrate and acetic acid with a solution of sodium styphnate.

Normal lead styphnate is a finely divided, rhombic material of light-orange or reddish-brown color, which crystallizes with a molecule of water of crystallization. It is almost insoluble in water and the common organic solvents and can, therefore, be stored under water, or under a mixture of water and an alcohol. It is only slightly hygroscopic. It is dissolved by a sodium hydroxide solution and decomposed by concentrated sulfuric or nitric acid.

When exposed to a flame or subjected to impact, lead styphnate explodes with a loud report. As shown in Table 1, it is less sensitive to impact and friction than both crystalline lead azide and mercury fulminate, but is more sensitive to heat than is lead azide. It has about the same maximum rate of detonation as lead azide, but when subjected to the sand test with ignition by a black powder fuse it crushed only 10.5 g of sand as compared with the 17.6 g crushed by lead azide. However, if it is tested with a cover charge of lead azide, it crushes 24.0 g of sand.   Evidently, the sensitivity of lead styphnate is such that its brisance and rate of detonation are determined by the manner in which it is initiated.

The stability of lead styphnate is excellent as determined by the 100°C vacuum stability test value, but the 100°C heat test indicates it to be somewhat volatile at that temperature.   This evidently is due to loss of water of crystallization.   This compound's high order of stability is shown also by there being no change in its ignitability, stability, or brisance upon storage at 80°C for a period of eight weeks.

Lead styphnate does not initiate the detonation of TNT or Tetryl in the sand test but can cause the detonation of unpressed PETN.   It initiates 40% straight dynamite, but nonuniformity of initiation results when it is used with gelatin dynamite.   These limitations have restricted the application of lead styphnate as an initiator, but it is used somewhat as a cover charge for lead azide in blasting caps, as a primary initiator caused to function by an electric bridge wire, and in priming compositions where certain blast characteristics are required.

Lead dinitroresorcinate, (the 2,4-dinitro compound is the most frequently used). As would be expected, lead dinitroresorcinate is an even less powerful explosive and a less efficient initiator than lead styphnate.   It has been found to be unusually sensitive to friction or stab action without being unduly sensitive to impact; therefore, it is particularly suitable for use as a priming material.   It is prepared by treating lead nitrate in hot aqueous solution with a boiling solution of dinitroresorcinol to which a stoichiometric quantity of sodium carbonate has been added.   After cooling, the precipitated dinitroresorcinate is washed with water, alcohol, and ether before being dried.

When lead dinitroresorcinate is exposed to a flame, it deflagrates, but does not explode with the violence of lead styphnate.   It is of the same order of sensitivity to impact as dextrinated lead azide, but is much more sensitive to ignition.   When subjected to the sand test through ignition by a black powder fuse, it crushed only 1.6 g of sand, but when primed with mercury fulminate it crushed 15.8 g.   It is of the same order of stability as lead styphnate but is less volatile at 100°C.

The relative difficulty involved in its manufacture and the necessary control of the crystal size and form of the lead compound has limited the use of the latter; but it has been found suitable for special designs of ammunition.

Lead dinitrosoresorcinate (probably the 4,6 isomer) has been used since 1940.   It is a nearly black, amorphous material that can be prepared by treating a solution of lead acetate, resorcinol, and acetic acid with sodium nitrite.   A basic salt can be prepared by modifying the conditions of preparation.

Lead dinitrosoresorcinate is much less sensitive to impact than lead azide and slightly less sensitive to friction than mercury fulminate.   When ignited by a flame it undergoes only deflagration.   When it is ignited by a black powder fuse in the sand test it crushes no sand, and when primed with mercury fulminate, it crushes only 3 g.   It is distinctly less stable than lead dinitroresorcinate, since it explodes in less than 2 hr in the 120°C vacuum-stability test, whereas lead dinitroresorcinate does not explode in 40 hr.   The results of heat tests conducted at 75 and 100°C may indicate the presence of combined water rather than decomposition.

The practical value of lead dinitrosoresorcinate is its low ignition temperature, which is essentially that of mercury fulminate.   This property renders it suitable as a cover charge, or in priming compositions.

Tetracene has recently been shown to be 1-(5-tetrazolyl)-4-guanyltetrazene hydrate (see below), rather than the previously assigned structure of 4-guanyl-1-(nitrosoaminoguanyl)-1-tetrazene.

$$\begin{array}{c} N-N \\ \| \quad \diagdown \\ \quad \quad C-N=N-NH-NH-C(=NH)-NH_2 \cdot H_2O \\ \| \quad \diagup \\ N=NH \end{array}$$

Tetracene is a pale-yellow, fluffy, crystalline solid that is prepared by adding 27.6 g of sodium nitrite to a solution, at 30°C, of 34 g of 1-aminoguanidine hydrogen carbonate in 15.7 g of glacial acetic acid in 2500 ml of water. After 24 hr the precipitated Tetracene is caught on a filter, washed thoroughly with water and dried at room temperature.

Tetracene is practically insoluble in water and most of the common organic solvents, but is hygroscopic to the extent of 0.8% and is decomposed by boiling water with the evolution of two molecules of nitrogen per molecule. It is decomposed by aqueous sodium hydroxide and can be stored under water or a mixture of water and an alcohol.

When exposed to a flame, Tetracene undergoes mild explosion producing a large amount of black smoke. Its ignition temperature is much lower than that of mercury fulminate, although the two compounds are of the same order of sensitivity to impact. It does not initiate TNT or Tetryl, but detonates unpressed PETN. The ease of ignition, high heat of explosion, and large volume of gaseous products given off during explosion give Tetracene its practical value as an ingredient for priming compositions.

Tetracene is relatively stable at temperatures no greater than 75°C but at 100°C it undergoes extensive decomposition. It is extremely subject to "dead-pressing." In the sand test unpressed Tetracene detonates PETN and crushes 13.1 g of sand, but when pressed at 3000 psi it does not initiate the detonation of PETN and crushes only 2 g of sand. Tetracene pressed at 3000 psi and initiated with mercury fulminate crushes 21.1 g of sand. Its brisance, therefore, depends upon its physical condition and mode of initiation.

Miscellaneous Initiators. A number of other compounds have been considered for practical use as initiators of detonation, but have not been adopted for such use. These may be mentioned briefly.

Cyanuric triazide is much more sensitive to impact and friction than mercury fulminate and is a very efficient initiator of detonation. It is considered to be too dangerously sensitive for practical use.

$$\begin{array}{c} N_3 \\ | \\ N \diagup \overset{C}{\diagdown} N \\ \| \qquad | \\ N_3-C \diagdown_N \diagup C-N_3 \end{array}$$

1,3,5-Triazido-2,4,6-trinitrobenzene, $C_6(N_3)_3(NO_2)_3$, is of high initiating efficiency and acceptable sensitivity to impact, but undergoes slow decomposition at room temperature. *Mercurous azide*, HgN_3, is an excellent initiator, but is affected by exposure to light. *Mercuric azide*, $Hg(N_3)_2$, is so sensitive and unstable that it frequently undergoes spontaneous explosion during crystallization or at the slightest contact. *Hexamethylenetriperoxide diamine* (HMTD), is as sensitive as cyanuric triazide and under-

$$CH_2-O-O-CH_2-N-CH_2-O-O-CH_2-N-CH_2-O-O-CH_2$$

goes slow decomposition when exposed to atmospheric moisture. *Nitrogen sulfide* (sulfur nitride), N_4S_4, has acceptable initiating sensitivity, brisance, and stability characteristics, but has no distinct advantage over any of the initiators now in use. *Lead picrate*, or trinitrophenolate, $((NO_2)_3C_6H_2O)_2Pb$, is extremely sensitive to impact and is considered to be too dangerous for practical use.

Noninitiating High Explosives

The noninitiating high explosives include a considerable number of organic and inorganic chemical compounds. These are used as such or in the formulation of binary, metalized, plastic, and blasting high explosives; in low explosives they are used as propellants. These explosive compounds are chiefly nitrates, nitro compounds, and nitramines.

Hundreds of explosive compounds are known, but only a few of these have practical value because of the difficult requirements with respect to sensitivity, brisance, stability, volatility, hygroscopicity, reactivity, cost, availability, etc. Only those compounds that have been used in practical applications or are of special interest are discussed in this article.

Binary explosives for military use generally are those designed primarily for purposes of melt-loading into shell and bombs. Some commercial explosives, such as mixtures of ammonium nitrate and dinitrotoluene, are binary explosives.

Metalized explosives for military use are mixtures of TNT with aluminum or mixtures of TNT, aluminum, and another explosive compound. These compositions also are designed to be suitable for melt-loading. Commercial metalized explosives include a wide range of compositions containing much more aluminum or aluminum–magnesium alloy than that required for satisfactory sensitivity to initiation.

Blasting explosives are the dynamites which replaced black powder in blasting operations and were based on glyceryl nitrate. Modifications of these resulted in the use of other explosives, oxidizing agents, fuels, and stabilizers in such compositions. Mixtures of liquid oxygen and carbonaceous material later came into use. The past ten years has seen the extensive use of an ammonium nitrate fuel oil mixture and of slurry compositions.

SINGLE–COMPOUND HIGH EXPLOSIVES

Ammonium nitrate is the only important inorganic high explosive. The organic high-explosive compounds are found among the aliphatic, aromatic, and heterocyclic series. The aliphatic nitrates, such as glyceryl nitrate and cellulose nitrate, were the first to achieve practical importance. Later, the aromatic nitrocompounds such as TNT and picric acid became of major military importance. More recently, the cyclomethylenenitramine compounds have gained importance in this area. These changes in trends in the development of high explosives reflect the early availability of such raw materials as glycerol, cellulose, and sugars, the later appearance of coal-tar products such as benzene, toluene, and phenol, and the relatively recent production, in bulk, of synthetic raw materials such as ammonia and formaldehyde.

Almost all the single-compound high explosives treated in this article are produced by the nitration process to yield nitrates, nitro compounds, and nitramines. Very concentrated nitric acid, a mixture of nitric and sulfuric acids ("mixed acid"), or a mixture of nitric acid and acetic anhydride may be used for such nitrations.

Batch processes generally have been used for the production and purification of such explosives, but *continuous processes* have been developed and their use is increasing. Some ammonium nitrate is now produced by the Stengel continuous process of reaction of ammonia and nitric acid. In this process the molten ammonium nitrate is deposited and cooled on a moving belt, with the heat of reaction evaporating the water from the nitric acid. The best-known continuous processes for producing other explosives are the Biazzi and Schmid-Meissner processes, which were first introduced in Europe.

Schmid-Meissner Process. This continuous process for the nitration of glycerol and the purification of glyceryl nitrate was patented in 1927. It involves continuous nitration, separation of glyceryl nitrate from the spent acid, and purification by neutralization and washing. Schmid-Meissner plants with modern instrumentation are widespread throughout many parts of the world.

The nitrator consists of a closed stainless-steel vessel with a conical bottom that has a capacity of approx 50 gal. It is equipped with a central propeller, cooling tubes, and an overflow pipe near the top. A two-way valve, which connects to the mixed-acid line or may be opened to a drowning tank is centrally fitted to the bottom of the nitrator. A hollow cone is fixed somewhat above the outlet of the valve. Brine at $-5°C$ is circulated through the cooling tubes. As mixed acid is fed in from the bottom, glycerol is fed in from the top at a level below that of the overflow pipe. The propeller mixes the two liquids and this action is enhanced by aeration through the propeller shaft and blades. The mixture then passes through the cooling pipes at such a rate that the temperature at the overflow pipe does not exceed $18°C$.

The glyceryl nitrate–mixed acid mixture flows by gravity to an acid separator; this consists of a tilted rectangular tank which contains baffles and is equipped with a bottom draw-off valve for spent acid, a sight glass near the top, and a steel neck with an overflow pipe for the glyceryl nitrate. The spent acid is discharged to the acid recovery plant, and the glyceryl nitrate flows by gravity to the base of the first of the washing columns. Each column is approx 9 ft from base to overflow and consists of superimposed glass rings separated by perforated steel plates and rubber ring gaskets. The bottom ring is sealed into a steel base equipped with inlet connections for low-pressure air, wash liquid, and glyceryl nitrate. The top ring is fitted with a steel head provided with an overflow to an intermediate separator.

As the glyceryl nitrate from the separator enters the bottom of the first washing column, it is mixed with cold water and emulsified by air injected into the mixture. This also causes the material to rise to the top of the column, where it overflows into the intermediate separator, which discharges glyceryl nitrate by gravity to the bottom of the second washing column. Here, and in the third column, a cold 2.5% solution of sodium carbonate is used instead of water. The fourth column, located in a separate house uses hot water, whereas the fifth column uses cold water. The glyceryl nitrate from the separator next to the fifth-washing column is passed through a four-ply flannel filter bag before being caught in a tank for storage and use. The wash liquors are run through a series of cataract tanks. Glyceryl nitrate which may be held by these is drawn off periodically and rewashed.

Biazzi Process. This process, patented in 1935, has been applied in the manufacture of glyceryl nitrate, glycol dinitrate, diethylene glycol dinitrate, triethyleneglycol dinitrate, trimethylolethane (see Vol. 1, p. 594) trinitrate, PETN, TNT, and Cyclonite. Its advantage is its greater safety over other processes, since a smaller amount of explosive is involved in the system at a given time. Only 25 to 75 lb of separated glyceryl nitrate is present at any given time when 1000 lb of glyceryl nitrate is made in 1 hr in a 10-gal Biazzi nitrator. The equipment for the Biazzi process is manufactured in Vevey, Switzerland.

The nitrator has helical rather than vertical cooling coils and is designed to permit rapid reaction through rapid heat absorption. This also permits the use of a stronger mixed acid. In the separator, provision is made for slowly rotating the intermediate emulsion layer, with consequent improvement in the breaking of the emulsion and the prevention of local overheating and formation of "dead spots." The stainless-steel washing compartments are about half the size of the nitrator and utilize high-speed mechanical agitation instead of compressed air. Glyceryl nitrate used for dynamite is washed only once with sodium carbonate solution; this eliminates the disposal of acidic wash water and appreciably decreases the loss of glyceryl nitrate by solution.

During recent years, Biazzi process plants have been completely automated. Nitration, separation, spent-acid stabilization, washing, transfer, storage, and weighing are carried out in accordance with a time program without the direct intervention of personnel. The presence of an operator is required only for a few minutes at the startup and shutdown operations and for occasional visits to the control room. This operation phase is located at a safe distance from the nitration house. The production rate of the plant can be varied during manufacture from the control room.

A very complete "fail safe" safety system protects the plant in all emergencies. Breakdowns or failures are signaled by a sound alarm and the operator can intervene if necessary. A blink light points out the primary cause of the failure, as distinguished from secondary causes. In the event of a potentially dangerous situation, the plant can be automatically stopped and a shutdown program instituted.

A building only 500 ft^2 and 12 ft high can accommodate a Biazzi glyceryl nitrate plant having a production capacity of 2500 lb/hr.

Ammonium Nitrate, NH_4NO_3 (see Vol. 2, p. 320), has been widely used as an ingredient of bursting charges for shell and bombs, blasting explosives, propellant compositions, as well as in fertilizers. Although first prepared by Glauber in 1659, it was not until 1867 that Ohlsson and Norrbin first used it as an explosive, in what was essentially a dynamite.

Between -16 and $32.1°C$ ammonium nitrate exists as colorless rhombic (β) crystals having a density of 1.725. Between 32.1 and $84.2°C$ it exists as a γ-orthorhombic form which has about 3% greater volume and a density of 1.661. Other forms exist at higher temperatures. The pure compound melts at $169.6°C$ and decomposes at $210°C$ into nitrous oxide and water. The transitions in form at $32.1°C$ are of importance with respect to the caking of the compound in storage.

Ammonium nitrate is soluble in water to the extent of 187 and 843 g per 100 g of water at 20 and $100°C$, respectively. It is soluble in anhydrous methanol and ethanol to the extent of 17 and 2.5 g per 100 g of solvent, respectively, at $20°C$. At $20°C$, 100 g of liquid ammonia dissolves 352 g of ammonium nitrate. Ammonium nitrate is insoluble or only slightly soluble in the common organic solvents. It is extremely hygroscopic, which is an additional factor in its tendency to cake.

Although a number of processes for the manufacture of ammonium nitrate have been used, the most common one in current use consists of passing gaseous ammonia into 40–60% nitric acid. The Stengel process consists of mixing gaseous ammonia and nitric acid to yield the molten nitrate, which is then cooled to freezing on a conveyor belt and crushed.

For use as an ingredient of dynamites ammonium nitrate formerly was coated with approx 1% of waxy material, which was added to the nitrate in the graining kettle. The use of such coatings has decreased greatly for safety reasons. About 0.3% calcium carbonate is added sometimes during the graining operation. Antisetting agents, such as diatomaceous earth, fuller's earth, kaolin, or special organic compounds, sometimes are added in the same manner.

Ammonium nitrate of the grade used in the manufacture of military explosives is required to be at least 99.0% pure and contain no more than 0.02% free nitric acid, 0.05% sulfate, 0.18% water-insoluble material, 0.10% ether-insoluble material, and 0.05% chlorides; it also is to be free of alkalinity and nitrites. The commercial grade used in the manufacture of blasting explosives is of comparable purity. Ammonium nitrate is produced in the form of crystalline aggregates and of "prills" (spherical pellets).

Since it is overbalanced with respect to oxygen content, ammonium nitrate has no heat of combustion. Its heat of formation was calculated to be 1098.46 cal/g or 87.93 kcal/mole at constant pressure. When heated, ammonium nitrate can decompose in a number of ways, depending upon the conditions of heating. The following reactions are the most important:

$$NH_4NO_3 \rightarrow N_2 + 2\,H_2O + \tfrac{1}{2}\,O_2 + 27.72 \text{ kcal}$$

$$NH_4NO_3 \rightarrow N_2O + 2\,H_2O + 10.7 \text{ kcal}$$

$$4\,NH_4NO_3 \rightarrow 2\,NO_2 + 8\,H_2O + 3\,N_2 + 96.0 \text{ kcal}$$

$$4\,NH_4NO_3 \rightarrow \underbrace{3\,NO_2 + 5\,H_2O + N_2 + 2\,NH_3 + NO}_{} - 84.88 \text{ kcal}$$

$$\downarrow$$

$$4\,N_2 + 8\,H_2O + 2\,O_2 + 195.76 \text{ kcal}$$

These different modes of decomposition and thermochemical effects are of some practical importance in view of the insensitivity of ammonium nitrate to detonation.

At ordinary temperatures ammonium nitrate is so insensitive to impact and friction (as shown in Table 10, p. 632) that it is essentially nonhazardous. Its sensitivity to impact increases somewhat with increase in temperature, so that at 150 and 175°C the impact test values are 27 and 12 in. instead of 31 in. The 12-in. value indicates that the molten nitrate is as sensitive as crystalline TNT at ordinary temperatures. As measured by the explosion-temperature test, ammonium nitrate explodes at 325°C in 3 sec, but only decomposes quietly in the standard 5-sec period at a lower temperature. In the sand test, ammonium nitrate is not detonated completely, even with a maximum booster charge. In larger quantities, when properly confined, it can be detonated by a booster charge of Tetryl or PETN, but not by a blasting cap. Unconfined charges must have a minimum diameter of 6 in. for complete detonation; a charge of only 4-in. diam confined in a steel tube undergoes complete detonation. Sensitivity to detonation decreases with increase in loading density, and when this exceeds 1.0, even large booster charges do not cause complete detonation. The sensitivity of ammonium nitrate is partly dependent upon the particle size of the material.

Although the admixture of up to 8% of carbonaceous material sensitizes ammonium nitrate, such mixtures also decrease in sensitivity with increase in density. It has been found that when ammonium nitrate is confined and a certain minimal gas pressure is applied, the nitrate can be detonated by heat alone. A mixture of ammonium nitrate and carbonaceous material under the same conditions requires the development of far less pressure prior to explosion.

Rates determined for the detonation of ammonium nitrate varied from 1000 to 2700 m/sec, depending upon the particle size, loading density, degree of confinement, and the charge diameter. A confined 1.25-in. diam charge of the molten nitrate was found to have a rate of detonation within the above range, and an increase in temperature will produce an increase in the rate of detonation. It may be said that ammonium nitrate has the lowest rate of detonation of any of the explosive compounds considered in this article.

Due to its low rate of detonation, ammonium nitrate would be expected to have a correspondingly low brisance value. However, because of its insensitivity to initiation, the brisance of ammonium nitrate cannot be determined by the sand test. Fragmentation tests of equal weights of ammonium nitrate and TNT at a density of 1.0 have shown that the nitrate produces only 24% as many fragments as TNT; whereas lead-cylinder compression tests have indicated ammonium nitrate to be 55% as brisant as TNT.

Trauzl lead-block tests indicate that ammonium nitrate has only 56% of the explosive strength of TNT, whereas ballistic pendulum tests indicate only 79%, as shown in Table 12; since ammonium nitrate is not used alone as an explosive, its exact strength is not of special interest.

At ambient temperatures ammonium nitrate is very stable, and this is true also at much higher temperatures. It has been heated at 100°C for 100 days without appreciable decomposition. Its 150°C vacuum stability test value as shown in Table 12 indicates it to be quite stable even at that temperature. Decomposition does not appear to begin until after the compound melts. If an organic material such as cellulose is present, decomposition begins at 100°C and becomes pronounced at 120°C, whereas other organic materials such as rosin have much less effect.

Ammonium nitrate is not toxic and the handling of it does not require special precautions. However, it is potentially a fire hazard since it is an oxidizing agent and constitutes an explosive hazard even when packed in paper bags. The "Texas City disaster" and several similar incidents are generally ascribed to the double hazard involved in using ammonium nitrate.

Cellulose Nitrate (more commonly called "nitrocellulose") is a fibrous, white solid which resembles the cotton linters, cotton fibers, or wood pulp, respectively, from which it is prepared. Cellulose mononitrate, dinitrate, and trinitrate have nitrogen contents of 6.75, 11.11, and 14.14%, respectively, representing progressive replacements of the —OH groups in the cellulose unit by —ONO$_2$ groups (see Vol. 4, p. 10). Material which contains 14.0% nitrogen can easily be prepared, but commercial and military grades of cellulose nitrate represent lower degrees of nitration of the anhydroglucose unit of cellulose. The generally recognized grades of nitrocellulose and their respective nitrogen contents are pyroxylin (or collodion) 8–12%; pyrocellulose 12.6%; guncotton 13.0% min.

Pyroxylin is soluble in ethanol to an extent which varies with nitrogen content but is insoluble in water or ether. Pyrocellulose and guncotton are insoluble in ethanol or ether, but are colloidally dispersed by acetone or ethyl acetate. A 2:1 mixture of ether and 95% ethanol disperses pyroxylin and pyrocellulose completely and guncotton partially. Many so-called gelatinizing agents such as dibutyl phthalate, triacetin, and centralite have a dispersing action similar to that of acetone when used alone or diluted with an ether–ethanol mixture. Camphor disperses pyroxylin when the mixture is subjected to heat and pressure, the product being celluloid. Liquid nitric esters such as glyceryl nitrate are colloiding agents for cellulose nitrate; and even aromatic nitrocompounds exhibit some such action, whereas benzene and toluene have no solvent or colloiding effect on cellulose nitrate.

In 1838, Pélouze prepared cellulose nitrate by nitrating paper, but did not recognize it as differing from nitrated starch. In 1846, Schönbein and, later in the same year, Böttger, classified it as a new material and also described its explosive properties. The earliest experiments of Schönbein were involved with its use both as a propellant and as a high explosive. Disastrous explosions of uncolloided cellulose nitrate in storage and in guns ruled out its use for either purpose.

As the various grades of cellulose nitrate are used chiefly in manufacturing lacquers, plastic compositions (see Cellulose derivatives—plastics), and propellant powders, and only a small amount is used for the manufacture of gelatin-type dynamites, the material is not generally recognized as being a powerful detonating explosive. This section of the article will stress this aspect of cellulose nitrate rather than its use as a burning ingredient of propellants (see under Propellants).

In the manufacture of cellulose nitrate, the degree of nitration is controlled by varying the composition of the mixed acid used for nitration. For a greater degree of nitration, a stronger mixed acid with increased sulfuric acid and decreased water content must be used. A representative composition of mixed acids used for the different grades of cellulose nitrate is given in Table 3.

Four different processes have been used for the nitration of cellulose, which are, respectively, the pot, the Thompson displacement, the centrifugal, and the mechanical-dipper processes (see Vol. 4, p. 628). The last, which is the least hazardous of them, is the only one now used in the U.S. In this process, 32-lb batches of cellulose are nitrated with 1500 lb of mixed acid.

The purification of cellulose nitrate is a difficult and tedious operation requiring large amounts of water and heat. During nitration small amounts of nitrated oxycellulose and cellulose sulfate are produced; the latter is considerably less stable than cellulose nitrate. Due to the cell structure of cellulose, it is difficult to remove entrapped spent acid, which renders cellulose nitrate very unstable during storage. It was because of the inability to purify cellulose nitrate properly that early work with it produced disappointing results. It was not until the years of 1866–1867 that Abel worked out a purification method capable of yielding satisfactorily stable cellulose nitrate.

Table 3. Representative Mixed Acids Used in Nitration

Mixed acid, %	Pyroxylin	Pyrocellulose		Guncotton	
sulfuric	45	59.2	57.0	60.5	59.5
nitric	35	21.5	23.5	24.5	28.5
nitrosylsulfuric		3.5	4.4	4.0	3.0
water	20	15.8	15.1	11.0	9.0

In the purification of military grades of cellulose nitrate, the wet material is transferred from a drowning tank to a large wooden tub which contains steam coils and a large volume of water. Here the acid hydrolysis, termed the "sour boil," is carried out by treating the crude cellulose nitrate with boiling water containing 0.025–0.50% acid calculated as sulfuric acid. Pyrocellulose and pyroxylin are subjected to 40 hr of boiling treatment that involves three changes of water. Guncotton is subjected to 60 hr of boiling treatment followed by two 5-hr boiling treatments, with a change of water after each treatment. The cellulose nitrate is then cut and crushed by a pulping or "beating" to liberate any free acid retained in the fiber canals or fine structure of the material. This, generally, is accomplished by means of a type of beater used in the paper industry and known as a Jordan engine (see Paper). This pulping operation is carried out with a large volume of water, with just sufficient sodium carbonate solution added to preserve a slightly alkaline reaction to phenolphthalein. This operation is continued until the cellulose nitrate has been reduced to the desired degree of fineness, as determined by a settling test. After settling and decantation, the cellulose nitrate is subjected to a poaching treatment that consists of one 4-hr, one 2-hr, and two 1-hr boiling treatments followed by settling, decantation, and the addition of fresh water after each treatment. During the 4-hr boiling treatmedt, sodium carbonate is added in the amount of 0.5% of the weight of the cellulose nitrate. The poaching treatment is followed by a minimum of two washes of cold water, each wash consisting of agitation of the cellulose nitrate with fresh water for at least 0.5 hr. After the final washing, the cellulose nitrate is screened through slots no more than 0.022 in. wide, to remove any incompletely pulped fibers.

Cellulose nitrate produced by the foregoing nitration and purification processes is of maximum stability. It generally is faintly alkaline as indicated by an electrometric pH test, and contains less than 0.01% cellulose sulfate.

In times of major crisis the demand for cellulose nitrate for the manufacture of propellants is very great. The insufficient supply, under these circumstances, of easily purified cotton linters led to the development of specially purified and fluffed wood pulp which is as satisfactory as cotton linters.

From the values which appear in Table 11 it is apparent that cellulose nitrate is one of the most potent explosives used. In the dry state, its sensitivity to impact varies somewhat with physical condition but, as shown by Table 10, it is of the same order as that of glyceryl nitrate. Cellulose nitrate is much less sensitive to friction than glyceryl nitrate, but about as sensitive to heat. When ignited, it burns rapidly; and, if the cellulose nitrate is confined, the burning is transformed into detonation unless the rate of burning is controlled to prevent the development of undue pressure. Since dry cellulose nitrate can be ignited by an electrostatic spark, it is a very dangerous material to handle in the dry state. In practice, uncolloided cellulose nitrate generally is not handled in a dry condition, and when shipped is kept wet with no less than 20% water.

Dry, compressed cellulose nitrate can be initiated to detonation by a blasting cap, and wet guncotton can be detonated with dry guncotton. The brisance of guncotton (see Table 11) is approximately that of TNT, but its rate of detonation is greater. Ballistic pendulum and Trauzl lead-block tests indicate that it has about 125% the explosive strength of TNT.

The stability of cellulose nitrate, even when highly purified, is not as great as would be desired. Heat- and vacuum-stability tests at 100°C (see Table 4) show it to be more stable than glyceryl nitrate but less so than PETN. It has been found that cellulose nitrate is inherently unstable, decomposing in the absence of moisture at a rate that increases 3.71 times with each temperature increase of 10°C. The presence of moisture increases the rate of decomposition considerably and the presence of free acid or alkali does so to even a greater degree. At 50 and 97.5°C the rates of thermal decomposition of dry, highly purified cellulose nitrate are 0.45×10^{-5} and 280×10^{-5} %/hr, respectively.

Since the stability of cellulose nitrate is so largely governed by its purity, extreme efforts are made to ensure quality control. Careful control of the quality of the cellulose to be nitrated, is assured by a lengthy purification process, and by submitting the product to certain tests. These tests include the determination of nitrogen content, solubility in ether–ethyl alcohol, acetone-insoluble material content, 65.5°C potassium iodide test, and the 134.5°C heat test. The 65.5°C potassium iodide test is a trace test for acidity or similarly harmful impurities. The 134.5°C heat test employs normal methyl violet paper as an indicator to determine whether cellulose sulfate content has been reduced to a minimum. Cellulose nitrate is normally resistant to heat at this temperature. This test value is not a measure of the low-temperature stability of the cellulose nitrate and has not been correlated with the results of surveillance tests at lower temperatures. Representative values for properly purified cellulose nitrate are shown in Table 4.

Table 4. Representative Values of Purified Grades of Cellulose Nitrate

Test	Pyrocellulose	Guncotton
nitrogen content, %	12.6	13.3
soly in ether–ethyl alcohol, %	99.9	8
acetone-insoluble material, %	trace	trace
ash, %	0.4	0.4
acidity, %	0.00	0.00
cellulose sulfate, %	0.003	0.001
65.5°C KI test, min	45	45
134.5°C heat test		
salmon pink, min	35	30
red fumes, min	45	40
explosion, min	300+	300+

Cellulose nitrate is somewhat hygroscopic. Although the fineness of the material has some effect on the degree of hygroscopicity, pyrocellulose, guncotton, and 14%-nitrogen cellulose nitrates absorb moisture in the amounts of approx 3, 2, and 1%, respectively, when exposed to an atmosphere of 90% relative humidity at 30°C. The greater the degree of nitration of cellulose nitrate, the less is its hygroscopicity and susceptibility to hydrolysis. When subjected to the action of boiling water for 10 days, pyroxylin, pyrocellulose, and guncotton liberated 1.71, 1.22, and 1.03%, respectively, of their nitric acid contents.

Increases in the nitrogen content of cellulose nitrate are accompanied by increases in brisance and heats of explosion as well as decreases in volume of gas evolved and heats of combustion. Representative values are given in Table 5.

Cellulose nitrate is not a generally toxic material, but workers are required to frequently change their clothes and take baths. Explosion hazards are very slight, since cellulose nitrate is always in a wet state during manufacture, purification, and packing. Every effort is made to prevent the accidental drying of cellulose nitrate because of the fire hazard involved. Equipment, floors, etc, are frequently "hosed down" to avoid such accidental drying.

Nitrostarch (starch nitrate) is a finely granular, friable solid which is almost identical in appearance with the starch from which it is prepared. As starch is a mixture of amylose and amylopectin and these are linear and branched polysaccharides, respectively, nitrostarch is not as uniform in composition as cellulose nitrate. The starch molecule is much smaller than that of cellulose, and nitrostarch apparently has a molecular configuration which consists of three dimensional spiral arrangements of the anhydroglucose units.

Starch was first nitrated by Branconnot in 1833. At a later period, European techniques for preparing nitrostarch consisted of dissolving the starch in strong nitric acid and then precipitating the nitrate by the addition of sulfuric acid or the spent acid from another nitration. This nitrostarch, like the cellulose nitrate when it was first prepared, was incompletely purified and highly unstable and was also considered disadvantageous because of the pulverulent, dusty nature of the dry material.

Table 5. Representative Values for Increase in Nitrogen Content

Nitrogen content, %	Sand test, g	Heat of explosion, cal/g	Gas produced, ml/g	Heat of combustion, cal/g
12.60	45.0	845	905	2,415
13.15	48.0	927	878	2,345
13.35	49.0	958	868	2,320
14.00	52.3	1,058	837	2,237

Because of the relatively small size of its molecule, the physical characteristics of nitrostarch are such that it does not yield tough colloids when gelatinized. It is an important ingredient in some commercial blasting explosives, where it, rather than cellulose nitrate, is used in place of glyceryl nitrate. These explosives are nonfreezing and do not undergo the desensitization that accompanies the freezing of glyceryl nitrate dynamites. They also do not undergo leakage nor produce volatility effects on personnel as do glyceryl nitrate explosives (see p. 604). Nitrostarch has been used in this country as an ingredient in dynamites, in military bursting-charge explosives for grenades and trench mortar shell, in demolition explosives, and as a priming composition. It was chiefly used during World Wars I and II and its military uses, therefore, are essentially for emergency situations.

Details of the commercial process for producing nitrostarch have not been published. The starch used is produced from corn, cassava, or potatoes (see Starch). This is purified to some extent by washing with a dilute sodium hydroxide or ammonia solution to remove fats and pectic acid, and then with water. Dried to a moisture content of less than 0.5%, the starch is then added to mixed acid, the temperature being maintained at 38–40°C. The composition of the mixed acid varies with the degree of nitration desired. After nitration is complete, the nitrostarch is drowned in cold water and then caught on a filter. Purification is effected by treatments with boiling and cold water and the use of an alkaline agent such as ammonia. After separation on a filter or a centrifugal wringer, the nitrostarch is dried on trays at a temperature of 35–40°C.

The drying operation is the most dangerous of those involved in the manufacture of nitrostarch, as the dry material is sensitive to ignition by an electrostatic spark.

From a chemical viewpoint, nitrostarch is very similar to cellulose nitrate. It can be produced with nitrogen contents comparable to those of the various grades of cellulose nitrate, and its thermochemical characteristics are similar to those of cellulose nitrates having the same nitrogen contents. Like cellulose nitrate, it is decomposed by aqueous alkali or sulfuric acid. It is insoluble in water, but is completely dispersed by acetone. An ether–ethyl alcohol mixture disperses nitrostarch, the action decreasing with increasing nitrogen content. Nitrostarch can be gelatinized by a wide variety of esters and is hygroscopic to the extent of 1 to 2%.

Nitrostarch is slightly less sensitive to impact but slightly more sensitive to heat than guncotton (see Table 10) but has approximately the same explosive strength (see Table 11). Nitrostarch is more difficult to stabilize by purification than is cellulose nitrate. When subjected to "sour boil" and boiling water treatments, nitrostarch does not give as high potassium iodide- and heat-test values as does cellulose nitrate. Commercially produced nitrostarch is less stable than similarly produced cellulose nitrate, as shown by the 120 and 134.5°C heat-test values given in Table 12. However, such nitrostarch presents no stability problems when used in commercial explosives.

Like cellulose nitrate, nitrostarch is essentially nontoxic and is transported in a wet condition.

Glyceryl nitrate (more commonly called "nitroglycerin") (see Glycerol), $NO_3CH_2CHNO_3CH_2NO_3$, is a colorless liquid at ordinary temperatures. Though first prepared by Sobrero in 1846 or 1847, it was, however, not until 1864, that it was used as an explosive by Nobel. Glyceryl nitrate became the basis of modern commercial blasting explosives and may be considered the first high explosive found suitable for practical application. It is used extensively in propellant compositions as well as dynamites, and to some extent as a medicinal (USP XVI) since a dose of only 0.0006 g causes dilation of the arteries.

Glyceryl nitrate freezes to form dipyramidal crystals which represent a stable form that melts at 13.2°C. Under some conditions, triclinic crystals are formed which represent a labile form that melts at 2.2°C. The labile form gradually changes into the stable form after a period of a week or more.

Pure glyceryl nitrate has the following constants: apparent bp, 145°C (with violent decompn); b_2, 125°C; b_{50}, 180°C; d_{15}^{20}, 1.596; vapor pressure, 0.0015 mm Hg at 20°C, 0.06 mm Hg at 60°C; volatility at 60°C, 0.11 mg/(hr)(cm²); viscosity, 35.5, 21.0, 9.4, and 6.8 cP at 20, 30, 50, and 60°C, respectively; heat of combustion (H_p), 1603 cal/g.

Glyceryl nitrate is soluble in water to the extent of only 0.173 and 0.246 g per 100 g of water at 20 and 60°C, respectively. Its hygroscopicity is only 0.06% at 30°C and 90% relative humidity. Ethanol dissolves 37.5 and 54 g of glycerol nitrate per 100 g at 0 and 20°C, respectively. Hot ethanol and glyceryl nitrate are miscible in all proportions. Glyceryl nitrate is miscible in all proportions with the following: ether, acetone, glacial acetic acid, ethyl acetate, benzene, toluene, phenol, nitrobenzene, chloroform, ethylene chloride, and nitric esters such as glycol dinitrate. Glyceryl nitrate has some solvent action on aromatic nitro compounds such as TNT and dinitrotoluene, and serves as a gelatinizing agent for cellulose nitrate.

Concentrated sulfuric acid decomposes glyceryl nitrate with the formation of nitric acid. In the presence of mercury, nitric oxide is formed quantitatively, and this reaction is the basis of the nitrometer method for the determination of the purity of glyceryl nitrate. The reaction between glyceryl nitrate and aqueous sodium hydroxide is slow due to their immiscibility, but when ethanol is added the reaction is rapid. Glyceryl nitrate is hydrolyzed to a very slight extent by water; the hydrolysis produces less than 0.002% acidity in 10 days at 22°C and only 0.005% acidity in 5 days at 60°C. An aqueous solution of sodium sulfide decomposes glyceryl nitrate with the evolution of much heat, and this reaction can be used for the destruction of waste material.

Glyceryl nitrate is manufactured by the Biazzi and Schmid-Meissner continuous processes as well as the batch process, which is described below.

A charge of about 4.3 parts by weight of mixed acid consisting of 40.0% nitric acid, 59.5% sulfuric acid, and 0.5% water is transferred to an iron, steel, or lead nitrator. Then 1 part of glycerol is slowly added while the acid is stirred constantly with compressed air and kept at 25°C or less by means of brine coils. Should control of the temperature be lost or red fumes evolve, the charge is dumped into a large drowning tank filled with water. After addition is completed, the emulsion of glyceryl nitrate in water and acid is subjected to additional agitation and cooling until the temperature is about 15°C. The charge is then run into a separating tank, where the glyceryl nitrate forms a supernatant layer containing about 8% nitric and 2% sulfuric acids. Agitation of the glyceryl nitrate with water at a temperature as high as 43°C (drowning wash) removes most of the dissolved acid. After settling out, the glyceryl nitrate is given additional washes with water, 2% sodium carbonate solution, and water until the wash waters are free of alkali and the glyceryl nitrate is neutral to litmus. The purified glyceryl nitrate, which appears milky because of the moisture content, is transferred to storage tanks in a heated building. Here, it rapidly becomes colorless and the moisture content decreases to 0.4% or less. The yield is 230 ± 5 parts of glyceryl nitrate by weight per 100 parts of glycerol.

The spent acid from the nitration of glycerol contains approximately 10% nitric acid and 73% sulfuric acid. This is subjected to processing for recovery of the nitric acid and concentration of the resulting dilute sulfuric acid (see under Nitration).

When ignited, unconfined glyceryl nitrate in very small quantities burns without explosion, but if it is confined or of a sufficient quantity to permit local overheating, explosion will result. Its sensitivity to impact is of the same order as that of mercury fulminate (see Table 10) and very great with regard to friction. Its sensitivity to impact is markedly increased by increase in temperature, whereas the frozen solid is much less sensitive than the liquid. However, many accidents have occurred when frozen dynamite was jarred while being thawed; this is attributed to the peculiar sensitivity of glyceryl nitrate in undergoing transition from the labile to the stable form. It has been found that glyceryl nitrate which contains minute bubbles of air is especially sensitive to shock. Glyceryl nitrate can be initiated to detonation, although not uniformly, even by a blank powder squib; thus, it is almost as sensitive to initiation as are lead azide and mercury fulminate.

As measured by the sand test, the brisance value of glyceryl nitrate is one of the highest recorded (see Table 11), almost as great as that of PETN and much greater than that of TNT. Glyceryl nitrate undergoes detonation at rates as low as 1500 to 200 m/sec but, when the diameter of the charge is not too small and a strong detonator is used, rates as high as 8500 m/sec have been obtained. It may be considered that a value of 7700 m/sec is representative of the upper rate of detonation of glyceryl nitrate.

Its explosive strength as measured by the Trauzl lead-block test (see Table 11) is greater than that of PETN or Cyclonite, but ballistic pendulum tests indicate the reverse.

The retention of traces of free acid renders glyceryl nitrate quite unstable with decomposition and the appearance of red fumes taking place within a few days. At temperatures below 50°C, pure nitroglycerin is of such a high order of stability that it will withstand storage for many years. However, its rate of decomposition increases rapidly above 50°C, and at 145°C decomposition is so rapid that the liquid appears to be boiling. As measured by the explosion-temperature test, it explodes at 222°C. Vacuum-stability test values (see Table 13) show glyceryl nitrate to be much less stable than glycol dinitrate, PETN, Tetryl, and TNT.

There are no standard commercial grades of glyceryl nitrate, its quality being determined by that of the glycerol used in its manufacture. Glycerol used in the preparation of dynamite glyceryl nitrate is purified by distillation to a density of 1.262 or greater, a glycerol content of at least 99%, and a moisture content of less than 1%. In the U.S., glyceryl nitrate for military purposes is required to contain no more than 0.002% free acid or alkali and have a nitrogen content no less than 18.40%.

Glyceryl nitrate as such is not transported by common carrier because of its sensitivity to shock. A 70:30 glyceryl nitrate:acetone mixture is relatively insensitive and is sometimes transported by wagons, trucks, etc. The glyceryl nitrate can be separated from the acetone by evaporating the latter with a current of air or by precipitation by the addition of an excess of water.

Glyceryl nitrate is readily absorbed through the skin into the circulatory system of the human body, and the vapors inhaled into the lungs are similarly absorbed by the blood. The effect of such absorption is a severe and persistent headache. Workers in constant contact with glyceryl nitrate soon develop an immunity to such headaches, an immunity which is maintained only by continued contact with the material. Strong black coffee or caffeine citrate affords some relief to workers who suffer from "NG headaches."

Glyceryl nitrate is the most hazardous explosive when handled in relatively large quantities, and extreme precautions are observed in the course of both its manufacture and use. Precautionary measures include barricaded buildings, emergency drowning tanks, remote control of operations, rubber hose connections, rubber-tired transportation buggies, etc.

Diglyceryl tetranitrate (tetranitrodiglycerin), $NO_3CH_2CHNO_3CH_2OCH_2CHNO_3$-$CH_2NO_3$, is seldom prepared in the pure form. It is generally formed by the nitration of a mixture of glycerol and diglycerol obtained by heating glycerol. The presence of about 0.5% of an alkali or sodium sulfite accelerates the condensation of glycerol to diglycerol. Diglyceryl tetranitrate was first prepared in 1861 by Lourenzo, and mixtures of it and of glyceryl nitrate have long been employed in the manufacture of low-freezing dynamites.

Diglyceryl tetranitrate is a very viscous liquid which has a density of 1.542 at 25°C. It freezes at 32°C. Although less soluble in water (0.042 g/100 g at 25°C) than glyceryl nitrate, it is more hygroscopic (0.26% at 30°C—90% rh) and more susceptible to hydrolysis by water (0.025% acidity in 10 days at 22°C). Its volatility at 60°C (0.018 mg/(hr)(cm²)) is less than that of glyceryl nitrate. It is readily soluble in ether or ethanol and is not as good a colloiding agent for cellulose nitrate as glyceryl nitrate.

Diglyceryl tetranitrate is slightly less sensitive to shock, friction, and heat than glyceryl nitrate (see Table 10). It is significantly less brisant, as shown by sand tests, and about 80% as strong as glyceryl nitrate as shown by Trauzl lead-block tests (see Table 3). Heat (100°C) and vacuum-stability tests indicate that it is markedly more stable than glyceryl nitrate (see Table 12).

Glycol dinitrate (ethylene glycol dinitrate, nitroglycol, ethylene nitrate, GDN) $NO_3CH_2CH_2NO_3$ (see Glycols), is a colorless liquid. It was first prepared by Henry in 1870, but was not used commercially until rather recently because of the cost involved. As glycol is now much cheaper than glycerol, glycol dinitrate is now used to a considerable extent in conjunction with glyceryl nitrate in the manufacture of low-freezing dynamites.

Glycol dinitrate has the following constants: fp, $-22.8°C$; b_2, $70°C$; b_{50}, $125°C$; d_{20}^{20}, 1.489; n_D^{20}, 1.4470; vapor pressure, 0.05 mm Hg at 20°C, 1.4 mm Hg at 60°C; volatility at 60°C, 2.20 mm/(hr)(cm²); viscosity, 4.2 cP at 20°C; heat of combustion (H_p), 1753 cal/g; ignition temperature at atm pressure, 195–200°C. Glycol dinitrate is comparable to glyceryl nitrate with respect to solubility in organic solvents and solvent power, but it is more soluble in water (0.52 and 0.85 g/100 g water at 25 and 60°C). It is an even better colloiding agent for cellulose nitrate than is glyceryl nitrate, since it acts at ordinary temperatures, whereas glyceryl nitrate requires a slightly elevated temperature for such action.

The chemical activity of glycol dinitrate is also comparable to that of glyceryl nitrate. Because of its greater solubility in water, glycol dinitrate is slightly more susceptible to hydrolysis than glyceryl nitrate (0.008 and 0.005%, respectively, in 5 days at 60°C). It can be manufactured by the same processes and with the mixed acids used in the manufacture of glyceryl nitrate. The nitration can be carried out at a lower temperature as glycol is less viscous than glycerol. In the batch process, less compressed-air agitation and washing with water are necessary, since glycol dinitrate is more volatile and more soluble in water than is glyceryl nitrate. Most of the glycol dinitrate produced is in the form of a mixture with glyceryl nitrate, obtained by nitrating a mixture of glycol and glycerol.

One of the very few explosives that are exactly oxygen-balanced, glycol dinitrate is similar to glyceryl nitrate with respect to its burning and explosion characteristics, but is slightly less prone to explosion through burning. Impact and pendulum-friction test values (see Table 10) show that glycol dinitrate is much less sensitive than glyceryl nitrate, but must also be classified as a hazardous explosive. It is less sensitive to heat than glyceryl nitrate, as indicated by the difference in their explosion-temperature test values.

Glycol dinitrate has very high brisance as indicated by the sand test (see Table 11), with a value as great as any other single-ingredient explosive treated in this article. The fact that glycol dinitrate has a lower rate of detonation than that of glyceryl nitrate must be attributed to its lower density. Like glyceryl nitrate, glycol dinitrate can detonate at high and low rates—7300 and 2000 m/sec. It has greater explosive strength than any other single-ingredient explosive considered here, as shown by its Trauzl lead-block test value which reflects its perfect oxygen balance.

Though the presence of more than a slight trace of free acid renders glycol dinitrate unstable, vacuum-stability test values (see Table 12) show that it is much more stable than glyceryl nitrate. Its low 100°C vacuum-stability test value appears to indicate that glycol dinitrate is of the same order of stability as diglycerol tetranitrate and trimethylolethane trinitrate.

Due to the hazards in handling, glycol dinitrate is never transported as such beyond the plant in which it is manufactured. Because of the greater volatility of glycol dinitrate, inhalation of its vapors is more difficult to avoid than inhalation of glyceryl nitrate. The effects of absorption of glycol dinitrate are dilation of the blood vessels, acceleration of heart action, and severe headache. There are also indications that continued exposure may cause some organic impairment.

Although glycol dinitrate is somewhat less hazardous with respect to shock than glyceryl nitrate, the same types of equipment and precautions should be used in its manufacture. The sensitivity and volatility of glycol dinitrate would preclude its use in any manufacture other than that of dynamite.

Diethylene glycol dinitrate (dinitrodiglycol, DEGN), $NO_3CH_2CH_2OCH_2CH_2NO_3$, is a colorless liquid which, on cooling, solidifies in a stable form (mp 2°C) or a labile form (mp -10.9°C). It was first described in 1927 by Rinkenbach and was used in German propellant compositions during World War II.

Pure diethylene glycol dinitrate has the following constants: bp, 160°C (when heated rapidly); d_{15}^{20} 1.385; n_D^{20} 1.4517; vapor pressure, 0.0036 mm Hg at 20°C, 0.130 mm Hg at 60°C; volatility at 60°C, 0.19 mg/(hr)(cm²); viscosity at 20°C, 8.1 cP; heat of combustion (H_p), 2792 cal/g. Diethylene glycol dinitrate is similar to glyceryl nitrate with respect to miscibility with and solubility in organic solvents and to solvent action on organic materials. It is distinctly more soluble in water (0.40 and 0.46 g/100 g water at 25 and 60°C) than is glyceryl nitrate, but less so than glycol dinitrate. It is an excellent colloiding agent for cellulose nitrate.

Diethylene glycol dinitrate is similar in chemical reactivity to glyceryl nitrate, but is less subject to hydrolysis (0.003% at 60°C in 5 days) in spite of its greater solubility in water, and is not readily saponified by alcoholic sodium hydroxide.

When prepared by nitrating diethylene glycol (see Glycols) with mixed acid, the yield of diethylene glycol dinitrate is approx 85% of the theoretical value and the spent acid that is left contains an undue amount of dissolved nitrate. This spent acid is unstable and recovery is difficult. This can be accomplished best by adding 20% of 98% sulfuric acid prior to the recovery operation.

Diethylene glycol dinitrate can be ignited only with difficulty, after the liquid is first heated somewhat above room temperature. When so ignited, it burns quietly with a yellow luminous flame. When a small quantity in a capillary tube is thrust into a gas flame, it does not detonate as does glyceryl nitrate, and vapor ejected from the end of the tube burns.

Though considerably less sensitive to impact than glyceryl nitrate or glycol dinitrate, diethylene glycol dinitrate is sufficiently sensitive to friction to explode in the pendulum friction test (see Table 10). Its brisance is equal to that of TNT and 81% of that of glyceryl nitrate (see Table 11). Like glyceryl nitrate, it is capable of detonating at two rates, 1800–2300 and 6760 m/sec. Its explosive strength lies between that of TNT and glyceryl nitrate, as indicated by ballistic pendulum and Trauzl lead-block tests.

Like other aliphatic nitrate esters, diethylene glycol dinitrate is decomposed by free acid. Vacuum-stability test data as shown in Table 13 indicate the pure compound to be of the same order of stability as glycol dinitrate.

Inhalation of its vapors or absorption of liquid diethylene glycol dinitrate through the skin can produce the same effects as those of glyceryl nitrate, but there is some evidence that fewer individuals are so affected than in the case of glyceryl nitrate.

Although diethylene glycol dinitrate has been used in propellant compositions, its volatility may limit its future use for this purpose. Its relatively low oxygen balance and difficulty of manufacture minimize its use in dynamite compositions.

Triethylene glycol dinitrate (dinitrotriglycol, TEGN), $NO_3CH_2CH_2OCH_2CH_2$-$OCH_2CH_2NO_3$, is a colorless liquid which has a freezing point of $-19°C$. It first served as an ingredient in German propellant compositions during World War II.

Triethylene glycol dinitrate has the following constants: d_{15}^{20} 1.33; n_D^{20}, 1.454; viscosity at 20°C, 13.2 cP; vapor pressure, <0.001 mm Hg at 20°C; volatility, 0.04 mg/(hr)(cm²) at 60°C; heat of combustion (H), 3428 cal/g.

Soluble in water to the extent of 0.55 and 0.68 g/100 g water at 25 and 60°C, respectively, triethylene glycol dinitrate is miscible in all proportions with ether, acetone, or an ether–ethanol mixture. It is a good gelatinizing agent for cellulose nitrate. It is hydrolyzed by water to the extent of 0.032% in 10 days at 22°C and 0.029% in 5 days at 60°C.

When triethylene glycol (see Glycols) is nitrated with mixed acid it appears that some diethylene glycol dinitrate is produced. The mixture of nitrate and spent acid must be drowned instead of separated as is done with glyceryl nitrate. The solubility of the dinitrate in the spent acid is from 8 to 9%.

Triethylene glycol dinitrate is quite insensitive to impact and friction (see Table 10), and its brisance as shown by the sand test is low (see Table 11). It failed to undergo detonation when tested in a steel pipe, and vacuum-stability tests (see Table 12) showed it to be as stable as glycol dinitrate at 100°C, but less stable at higher temperatures.

Because it has colloiding value and a degree of explosive strength, triethylene glycol dinitrate may continue to be of interest for use in propellant compositions.

Trimethylolethane trinitrate (1,1,1-trinitroxymethylethane, pentaglycerol trinitrate, metriol trinitrate, TMETN), $CH_3C(CH_2NO_3)_3$, is a colorless liquid which freezes at -3 and $-17°C$ in stable and labile forms, respectively. It was patented in 1927 by von Herz and has been somewhat used as an ingredient in propellant compositions.

Trimethylolethane trinitrate has the following constants: d_4^{20}, 1.4685; $n_D^{17.5}$, 1.4760; vapor pressure at 20 and 60°C, 0.00017 and 0.00427 mm Hg; volatility, 0.024 mg/(hr)(cm²) at 60°C; viscosity at 20°C, 156 cP; heat of combustion (H_p), 2642 cal/g.

It is soluble in water to the extent of less than 0.01 g/100 g water at either 20 or 60°C. Its hygroscopicity values at 30°C are 0.07 and 0.14% at 90 and 100% relative humidity, respectively. It is miscible with either ether or acetone, but is insoluble in 95% sulfuric acid.

Trimethylolethane trinitrate can be prepared by dissolving "trimethylolethane" (2-hydroxymethyl-2-methyl-1,3-propanediol, see Vol. 1, p. 594) in cold 98% nitric acid and drowning the resulting solution in ice water. The yield is about 95% of the theoretical. It can also be prepared by dissolving 1 part of trimethylolethane in 4.7 parts of 98% nitric acid, adding an equal amount of 95% sulfuric acid, stirring for an additional hour, and drowning in ice water. Another method for preparing it is by dissolving trimethylolethane in glacial acetic acid, adding this and 98% nitric acid to acetic anhydride at 20–26°C, cooling to 10°C, and then drowning in water. The yield by means of this process is approx 90% of the theoretical.

Trimethylolethane trinitrate is much less sensitive to impact than is glyceryl nitrate and less sensitive to friction than either glyceryl nitrate or glycol dinitrate (see

Table 10). When frozen, the solid material is of the same order of sensitivity to initiation as the liquid. Its brisance and rate of detonation values are slightly greater than those of TNT, but it has much greater explosive strength as indicated by ballistic pendulum and Trauzl lead-block tests (see Table 11). It is much more stable than glyceryl nitrate as indicated by vacuum-stability tests at 100°C (see Table 12); but markedly more susceptible than glyceryl nitrate to hydrolysis, since it hydrolyzes to the extent of 0.018% in 10 days at 22°C and 0.115% in 5 days at 60°C.

Trimethylolethane trinitrate is a relatively poor gelatinizing agent for cellulose nitrate, although it has such action when the mixture is subjected to pressure. Propellants containing it indicate a high mechanical strength and remain harder at high temperatures and softer at low temperatures than compositions prepared with glyceryl nitrate.

The exceptionally low volatility of the compound is an important property, but its vapors and cutaneous absorption cause headaches similar to those induced by glyceryl nitrate. Like glyceryl nitrate, it has been found to have therapeutic value for cardiac ailments.

Trimethylolethane trinitrate has been found suitable for transportation by common carrier when desensitized with a miscible, inert diluent that is soluble in water. The compound separates from the solution upon dilution with water.

Pentaerythritol tetranitrate (nitropentaerythrite, pentrit, penta, PETN), $C(CH_2NO_3)_4$, forms colorless, prismatic needles which crystallize from water as tetragonal crystals which melt at 141.3°C. It was first prepared by Tollens in 1891, but was not used on a practical basis until after World War I. Since it is made by nitrating erythritol (See Vol. 1, p. 589), which is obtained by reacting formaldehyde and acetaldehyde, it offers certain logistic advantages in not requiring raw material derived from coal. It has been used extensively in admixture with TNT for the loading of small-caliber projectiles and grenades as well as booster charges. PETN itself is used as a filling in detonating fuse and detonators; various countries have prepared mixtures of PETN and a wax by press-loading.

PETN has the following constants: sp gr, 1.765; specific heat (compressed material), 0.4 cal/(°C)(g); heat of combustion (H_p), 1974 cal/g; b_2, 160°C; b_{50} 180°C. It can be pressed to densities of 1.575, 1.638, 1.71, 1.725, and 1.74 under pressures of 5000, 10,000, 20,000, 30,000, and 40,000 psi.

At 25 and 96°C PETN is soluble in water to the extent of only 0.0043 and 0.018 g/100 g, respectively. It is nonhygroscopic when exposed to an atmosphere of 90% relative humidity at 30°C. PETN is soluble in acetone and methyl acetate at 20°C to the extent of 25.4 and 12.9 g, respectively, per 100 g of solvent. It is only slightly soluble in methanol, ethanol, ether, benzene, toluene, and carbon tetrachloride.

PETN is decomposed much more slowly than is cellulose nitrate by a boiling 2.5% solution of sodium hydroxide. At 50°C a solution of sodium sulfide decomposes PETN slowly, but a boiling solution of ferrous chloride decomposes it more rapidly. The most practical method for disposal of waste PETN is dissolving it in acetone and then burning the solution.

Unlike other aliphatic nitrates, PETN is manufactured on a commercial scale by the use of nitric acid rather than a mixture of nitric and sulfuric acids. It is prepared in the U.S. by a batch nitration process in which approximately 75 lb of pentaerythritol is added to 350 lb of 96% nitric acid in a nitrator, with continuous stirring and cooling of the acid by means of a cold-water jacket. The rate of addition of pentaerythritol is controlled so that with an initial acid temperature of 18°C the temperature rises to and is maintained at 22–23°C. After addition of the pentaerythritol is completed, stirring and cooling are continued for 20 min. The solution is then run into about 100 gal of water and agitated, which causes the precipitation of PETN. After being caught on a glass–cloth filter, the precipitated solid is washed with cold water and then suspended in cold water containing a small amount of sodium carbonate. The slurry is then filtered and the solid rewashed with water. The PETN is then dissolved in acetone at 50°C, which contains a small amount of ammonium bicarbonate to neutralize any occluded acidity. After the solution is filtered the tetranitrate is reprecipitated by the addition of cold water and then caught on a filter and washed with water to remove the acetone. The water-wet PETN is considered the final product, as it generally is not dried before being used. The yield of PETN is approximately 93% of the theoretical. The spent acid obtained from the drowning operation contains approximately 20% nitric acid, which is recovered and concentrated for reuse.

PETN is also manufactured by the Biazzi continuous process.

The quality of PETN produced is controlled chiefly by that of the pentaerythritol used. The pure raw material melts at 260.6°C, but that used for plant-scale nitration has a melting point of 254°C or higher, and contains 2–3% dipentaerythritol and a small amount of tripentaerythritol. The PETN produced for military use is required to have a minimum melting point value of 140°C, a minimum nitrogen content of 17.5%, and a maximum acid or alkali content of 0.005%. It must be free of grit; contain no more than 0.10% acetone-insoluble material; and a 2.3-g sample must yield no more than 5.0 ml gas in 20 hr as measured by the 120°C vacuum-stability test. The explosive is required to contain 40% water since it can only be shipped when wet and generally is not used in bulk in the dry state. Thus, it is packed in containers similar to those for lead azide and mercury fulminate.

PETN can be ignited with a flame, but not by the spit of flame from a black powder fuse. In small quantities, when not confined, it melts and burns quietly. Though its explosion-temperature test value of 225°C (see Table 10) is near that of glyceryl nitrate, it is less sensitive to impact and friction than is glyceryl nitrate. When rubbed in a rough porcelain mortar it crackles but does not explode. PETN is extremely sensitive to initiation by lead azide and other initiating agents. In the sand test, only 0.03 g of lead azide is required as compared with 0.10 and 0.26 g for Tetryl and TNT, respectively.

The brisance of PETN is greater than that of glyceryl nitrate and is exceeded only by that of glycol dinitrate as determined by the sand test (see Table 11). This property reflects its high rate of detonation, 8300 m/sec, at a density of 1.70. Its explosive strength is correspondingly great, as indicated by Trauzl lead-block and ballistic pendulum test values which show it to be at least 50% stronger than TNT.

The results of vacuum-stability tests (see Table 12) show PETN to be only slightly more stable than cellulose nitrate, much more stable than glyceryl nitrate, but much less stable than either Tetryl or Cyclonite. Though PETN safely withstands storage for 18 months at 65°C, as indicated by acidity and vacuum-stability tests, continued storage beyond that point has marked effects of instability. The presence of as little as 0.01% free acid or alkali in PETN markedly accelerates its deterioration: It is the least stable of the standard military bursting-charge explosives.

PETN is not unduly toxic, since it is nearly insoluble in water and is usually handled when wet. Various tests have shown that small doses of PETN cause a decrease in blood pressure and larger doses cause dyspnea and convulsions. It currently is widely used as a replacement for glyceryl nitrate in the treatment of cardiac conditions.

Dipentaerythritol hexanitrate (hexanitrodipentaerythrite, dipenta, DPEHN), $(CH_2NO_3)_3CCH_2OCH_2C(CH_2NO_3)_3$, is a colorless, crystalline solid. It has not been used per se, but usually is present in PETN produced on a large scale and, therefore, is of practical interest. The properties of DPEHN were first described by Brün in 1932.

DPEHN has the following constants: mp, 73.6°C; sp gr, 1.630^{15}_{15}; heat of combustion (H_p), 2394 cal/g. It is insoluble in water and hygroscopic only to the extent of 0.03%, but is soluble in acetone.

DPEHN can be prepared by nitrating dipentaerythritol by the same method as that used for the preparation of PETN, or by separation from PETN of ordinary grade by fractional crystallization with moist acetone.

As an explosive, DPEHN is distinguished from PETN by its slightly greater sensitivity to impact (see Table 10) but lesser sensitivity to heat and initiation. Its brisance, as determined by the sand test, is about 90% that of PETN (see Table 11). The rate of detonation of DPEHN at density 1.59 is 94% that of PETN (7860 m/sec) at the same density. The explosive strength of DPEHN is 76% that of PETN as indicated by Trauzl lead-block tests, and 80% on the basis of their heat of explosion values. Vacuum-stability test values (see Table 12) indicate DPEHN to be less stable than PETN. This difference is such that PETN which contains more than 5% DPEHN does not meet the standard 120°C vacuum-stability test required for military-grade PETN.

In manufacturing pentaerythritol, some dipentaerythritol, a smaller amount of tripentaerythritol, and some polypentaerythritol are produced. The tripentaerythritol can be nitrated to form an octanitrate which melts at 82–84°C.

Mannitol hexanitrate (nitromannite, MHN), $NO_3CH_2(CHNO_3)_4CH_2NO_3$, forms colorless, needle-shaped crystals (mp, 110.7°C when pure). The compound has been used for loading commercial blasting caps. It was first prepared by Domonte and Menard in 1847.

MHN has the following constants: sp gr, 1.604; heat of combustion (H_p), 1501 cal/g. It is insoluble in water. Its solubility in ether at 9°C and ethyl alcohol at 13°C is 3.65 and 4.0 g, respectively, per 100 g of solvent. It is readily soluble in acetone and hot ethyl alcohol.

MHN can be prepared by slowly adding mannitol (see Vol. 1, p. 574) to five times its weight of nitric acid (sp gr 1.51), which has been cooled below 0°C. The temperature is not allowed to rise above 0°C and the acid is stirred during the addition. Sulfuric acid (sp gr 1.84) to the extent of five times the weight of mannitol is added slowly with continued cooling and stirring. The precipitated MHN is caught on a filter and washed with water, dilute sodium bicarbonate solution, and finally again with water. The crude material is purified by recrystallization from hot ethyl alcohol, which gives a yield of approx 93% of the theoretical.

Commercially produced MHN has a melting point of 107–109°C. It is kept wet with water until ready for use, and is dried with extreme care. It cannot be stored and must be used immediately.

Although very sensitive to impact, being comparable to lead azide in this respect, and although it has a relatively low explosion-temperature test value (see Table 10), MHN is not detonated by the spit of flame from a black powder fuse. It can be initiated to detonation by the application of heat to its mixture with the feeble initiator Tetracene. MHN is of the same order of brisance and explosive strength as glyceryl nitrate (see Table 11), which it resembles with respect to oxygen balance and nitrogen content. The results of vacuum-stability tests (see Table 12) indicate MHN to be of the same order of stability as glyceryl nitrate. However, when heated at 75°C, MHN envolves red fumes in a few hours while glyceryl nitrate does not do so for several days.

The poor stability of MHN might be expected to preclude its commercial use, but it has been found that the addition of a small amount of a stabilizing agent renders it suitable for such use. Stabilized MHN, when subjected to 75°C-international tests, gave the following values for loss in weight before and after storage at ordinary temperatures:

	Loss in weight, %	
Storage, yr	*Stabilized*	*Unstabilized*
0	0.09	3.5
2	0.25	
5.5	0.44	

After storage for two years, the stabilized MHN required 41 days of heating at 75°C to cause the evolution of red fumes.

When MHN is dissolved in pyridine at 0°C, allowed to stand for about 16 hr at 25°C, and diluted with water, or when treated with an aqueous solution of ammonium carbonate and sodium carbonate, mannitol pentanitrate is formed. This has been found to be present in commercial MHN to the extent of approx 10%.

Mannitol pentanitrate melts at 81–82°C and can be recrystallized from chloroform. It can be esterified to form its acetate, propionate, and phenylacetate, which melt at 77–78, 65–68, and 61–62°C, respectively.

α- or 2,4,6-Trinitrotoluene (Trotyl, Triton, Tritol, Tolite, Trilite, TNT), $CH_3C_6H_2(NO_2)_3$, the most important of modern high explosives, exists in two polymorphic forms; the α form is stable at ordinary temperatures. It forms colorless or light-yellow rhombohedral crystals, with a sp gr of 1.654. TNT has found wide application as a bursting-charge explosive for shells, bombs, and grenades and as an ingredient of binary explosives such as Amatols; of metalized explosives such as Tritonal; of propellant compositions; and of commercial explosives such as dynamites. It was first prepared by Wilbrand in 1863, but was not prepared on an industrial scale until 1891, in Germany. By 1901, it began to displace picric acid and it was adopted by the major military powers. In World War I the use of TNT was expanded to the maximum permitted by the available supply of toluene; and in World War II TNT became even more important and was applied extensively.

Pure TNT has a freezing point of 80.75 ± 0.05°C. This property is determined more reproducibly than is its melting point. Its vapor-pressure values are given below:

temperature, °C	85	100	190	245–250
vapor pressure, mm Hg	0.053	0.106	2	50

At ordinary temperatures, TNT is essentially nonvolatile. It may be distilled in a vacuum without decomposition.

Several specific heat values are given below:

temperature, °C	0	20	50	80
specific heat, cal/(g)(°C)	0.309	0.328	0.353	0.374

Other thermal properties of TNT are heat of fusion, 21.41 cal/g; heat of combustion (H_p), 3589.5 cal/g; thermal conductivity at 25°C, 0.00055 cal/(sec)(cm^2)(°C/cm). The coefficient of linear expansion of cast TNT varies somewhat with crystal size, but for medium-size crystals it is 7.7 × 10^{-5} in./(in.)(°C) in the range of −40 to 60°C.

Crystals of TNT have index of refraction values of $\alpha = 1.5430$, $\beta = 1.6742$, and $\gamma = 1.717$ for sodium light. They indicate a hardness of 1.2 on the Mohs scale. When pressed to a density of 1.6, TNT has a compressive strength of 1400 psi and a modulus of elasticity of 5.4 × 10^{10} dyn/cm^2.

On melting, TNT undergoes an expansion in volume of approx 12%, and the density of the liquid is 1.465. Freezing of the liquid TNT produces a corresponding contraction in volume, a characteristic which presents certain difficulties in the melt-loading of the explosive. The practical importance of TNT has led to extensive studies of its characteristics. It has a viscosity of 9.5 cP at 100°C. The explosive characteristics of liquid TNT will be considered later.

Cast TNT has a density of 1.55–1.56, but the crystalline material can be pressed to a density of 1.6 when subjected to a pressure of 50,000 psi.

TNT is almost insoluble in water (0.010, 0.013, and 0.1475 g/100 g water at 0, 20, and 100°C, respectively) and is hygroscopic to the extent of only 0.03% at 30°C and 90% relative humidity. It is soluble in other solvents at 20°C (see Table 6).

As compared with Tetryl and picric acid, TNT is relatively, but not entirely, nonreactive. Alkalies, alkoxides, and ammonia react with TNT to form dangerously sensitive compounds. A mixture of TNT and solid potassium hydroxide bursts into flame when heated to only 80°C. Sodium sulfide decomposes it completely with the formation of nonexplosive products, and this reaction can be used for the disposal of waste material. Sodium sulfite also decomposes TNT, with the formation of a red, water-soluble product. TNT reacts with formaldehyde to yield 2,4,6-trinitrophenylethanol (2,4,6-trinitrophenethyl alcohol), and with benzaldehyde to form 2,4,6-trinitrostilbene. It forms molecular complexes with amines such as aniline, toluidine, naphthylamine, and carbazole. Upon oxidation with chromic or nitric acid, TNT is converted into 2,4,6-trinitrobenzoic acid. Exposure to sunlight or ultraviolet radiation, particularly in the presence of oxygen, results in decomposition and discoloration with consequent reduction in the freezing point and increase in sensitivity to impact.

Table 6. Solubility of TNT in Various Solvents at 20°C

Solvent	Soly, g/100 g solvent	Solvent	Soly, g/100 g solvent
ethyl ether	3.29	chlorobenzene	33.9
ethyl alcohol, 95%	1.23	carbon disulfide	0.48
acetone	109	methyl acetate	72.1
carbon tetrachloride	0.65	sulfuric acid	4
chloroform	19	benzene	67
ethylene dichloride	18.7	toluene	55
trichloroethylene	3.04		

TNT can be prepared from toluene (qv) by one-, two-, or three-stage processes, and all three processes have been used industrially (see under Nitration). However, it has been found that the three-stage process offers the advantages of maximum yield, greater purity of product, and greater ease of control of acid concentration and temperatures involved. The three-stage process was widely used during World War II, and a general description of it is given below.

Approx 12,500 lb of "mono-mix" acid is transferred to the nitrator in the "mono-house" and is cooled, with agitation, to 36–38°C. The mono-mix acid is prepared by "butting-up" with weak nitric acid the "bi-spent" acid from the second nitration stage, and it contains approx 48% sulfuric acid, 14% nitric acid, 17% nitrosylsulfuric acid, 19% water, and 2% nitro compounds; 1600 lb of toluene is added under the surface of the acid at such a rate as to cause a temperature increase of 1°C/min. The temperature at the completion of nitration is about 55°C and is allowed to increase to 57°C. The stirring is reduced and the charge cooled to 38°C. Stirring is then discontinued, and the spent acid is allowed to separate and settle. The "mono-waste" acid is drawn off and transferred to the recovery system for reworking. The "mono-oil" is transferred to the scale tank of another building some distance away for second-stage nitration.

Spent acid from the trinitration is transferred to the nitrator in the "bi-house" and cooled, with stirring to 77°C. Weak nitric acid is then added so that the nitrator finally contains about 12,500 lb acid composed of 54% sulfuric acid, 13% nitric acid, 17% nitrosylsulfuric acid, 8% water, and 8% nitro compounds. With continued stirring the mono-oil is added at such a rate that the temperature of the mixture rises to 82°C, and then more slowly to 85°C. The charge is "cooked" at this temperature for 8 min and then cooled to 77°C. After the "bi-oil" has separated, the lower layer of bi-spent acid is drained off and transferred to a fortifier for butting-up to form mono-mix. The bi-oil is drained into a storage tank before transfer to the "tri-house" for trinitration.

A "tri-mix" acid is prepared in a scale tank by adding to oleum a "semi-mix" acid containing 62% total (equivalent) sulfuric acid and 43% nitric acid. The tri-mix contains 82.7% total sulfuric acid and 23.3% nitric acid, and generally is at a temperature of about 85°C. Approx 8500 lb of the tri-mix is transferred to the nitrator in the tri-house, agitated, and cooled to 80°C. The bi-oil is now added at such a rate that the temperature of the mixture increases about 0.5°C/min, to a maximum of 90°C. After the completed charge has been held at that temperature for several minutes, it is allowed to rise to 110°C at the rate of 1°C/min. The temperature is maintained at 110°C for about 20 min and then cooled to 107°C with continued agitation. Stirring is then discontinued, and the "tri-oil" is allowed to separate and form a top layer, while the temperature decreases to approx 93°C. The bottom layer of "tri-spent" is drained off to the binitrator, and the tri-oil (approx 3500 lb) is then drained off and pumped to the washhouse for purification.

The quality of the crude TNT may vary widely with the degree of control and efficiency of the third stage of nitration. If this is not complete, a significant amount of dinitrotoluene will be present. The chief impurities normally present are β- or 2,3,4-trinitrotoluene (mp 112°C) and γ- or 3,4,6-trinitrotoluene (mp 104°C). Trinitrobenzoic acid, trinitrobenzene, and tetranitromethane in smaller amounts are also present, due to the oxidizing action of nitric acid. When free from acid, such crude TNT contains 5–7% impurities and has a freezing point of only 75–76°C. The purification of the material is an important step in production, since the crude TNT in the oily state is relatively insensitive to initiation and is subject to exudation when stored at only slightly elevated temperatures.

Before World War I, purification was carried out by washing the crude TNT to remove nitric acid and most of the tetranitromethane and then recrystallizing from ethyl alcohol, carbon tetrachloride, or sulfuric acid. Another method involved washing the TNT free of acid while in the molten condition, crystallizing, and then washing with hot acids, to dissolve the impurities on the surfaces of the crystals. During World War I, the Sellite (sodium sulfite) process of purification was introduced, which became standard during World War II. The Sellite process permits the rapid and very effective purification of crude TNT.

In this process, the tri-oil is agitated for several minutes with a small amount of hot water to dissolve any free acid present. Sufficient cold water is added to cool the mixture to 68°C and cause crystallization of the TNT. Sufficient alkali is added to neutralize any free acid in solution, but care is taken to avoid an excess, since this would decompose some of the TNT. To the agitated suspension of crystalline TNT in the water is now added, first slowly and then more rapidly, a calculated quantity of a solution containing 16–17% sodium sulfite, and 0.1–0.3% sodium hydrogen sulfite. Usually, this requires 15 min and the color of the liquid becomes deep red. Agitation is continued for about 15 min, and the mixture is then transferred to a "melt tank," where it is melted and washed thoroughly with hot water and then dried by agitation with dry air at 100°C or more. The molten TNT is then cooled and flaked, or grained.

Since sodium sulfite does not react with dinitrotoluene, the nitration process must be controlled so as to ensure practically complete nitration to the trinitro condition. It reacts with β-TNT and γ-TNT, present on the surfaces of the α-TNT crystals, to form the sodium salts of the corresponding dinitrotoluenesulfonic acids. Since these salts are easily soluble in water, they are removed. The hot sodium sulfite reacts with a small amount of the α-TNT to form hexanitrobibenzyl, which reddens the water. Another purification reaction employs sodium sulfite and tetranitromethane to form sodium trinitromethanesulfonate and sodium nitrite, both of which are readily soluble in water. Any small amount of dinitrotoluene present generally is removed by the mechanical action of washing. The sodium hydrogen sulfite is not involved in the purification reactions, but is added as a buffer to maintain neutrality.

The TNT obtained by the Sellite purification process generally has a freezing point of 80.3 ± 0.1°C; but, by increasing the duration of the Sellite treatment, a product with a freezing point as high as 80.6°C can be obtained.

Until 1940, the capacity of any country for producing TNT was limited by the availability of toluene as a by-product of the coke industry. The development of special hydrogenation and polymerization processes has since made it available from petroleum fractions and by-products. Thus, since the U.S. has both coal and petroleum resources, its TNT production potential was greatly enhanced; and, during World War II, this country had available any amount of toluene that was required. In World War I, TNT was critically needed in all countries, and was diluted with weaker explosives in order to extend its use as far as possible. Germany, during World War II, suffered from a shortage of TNT, having limited petroleum resources; but the U.S. had such large quantities of TNT available that TNT was used as the suspension agent for more powerful explosives, such as PETN and Cyclonite, which could be applied in ammunition by melt-loading methods.

Different countries produce various grades of TNT, which are determined chiefly by purity, as reflected by the freezing point. Other requirements limit the free acidity to 0.01%, alkalinity to nil, and insoluble matter to 0.05%. To ensure efficient final washing of the purified TNT, the sodium content is not permitted to exceed 0.001%. This is determined by ashing a sample, dissolving the ash, and then precipitating sodium magnesium uranyl acetate.

TNT, with the exception of ammonium picrate, is the least sensitive to impact of the standard military explosives (see Table 10). It explodes only occasionally when subjected to the rifle-bullet test, is quite insensitive to friction, and has a very high explosion-temperature test value. Like picric acid, it is much less sensitive to initiation than Tetryl, PETN, or Cyclonite. Sublimed TNT is sometimes deposited during plant operations in cold weather. It is of high purity and exists in a state of very fine subdivision; moreover, it has been found to be only slightly less sensitive to impact than Tetryl, but nearly as insensitive to initiation as ordinary TNT. Foreign materials, particularly those of a gritty nature, render TNT much more sensitive to impact. A mixture of equal parts of TNT and rust is as sensitive to impact as Tetryl, although not noticeably more sensitive to friction than TNT. Molten TNT is a dangerously sensitive material when confined, as shown by the impact test values in Table 7.

The three lowest impact values indicate confined molten TNT to be of the same order of sensitivity as mercury fulminate. Because of this, special care must be observed in the handling of large quantities of molten TNT, as in melt-loading operations.

The brisance of TNT, as judged by the sand test, is distinctly less than that of Cyclonite, PETN, or Tetryl, with which it is chiefly used (see Table 11). Its rate of detonation also is lower than those of the other three explosives, as is confirmed by shell fragmentation tests. However, the brisance effects of TNT are equal to those of picric acid and ammonium picrate and considerably greater than those of the 50:50 Amatol in which it was formerly used. A comparison of their ballistic pendulum and Trauzl lead-block test values shows that TNT has approx 77% the explosive strength of Tetryl.

TNT is a very stable explosive. Vacuum-stability tests (see Table 12) show that it undergoes relatively little, if any, decomposition in 40 hr at 150°C; and it has been stated that decomposition does not begin until the temperature has reached 180°C. TNT has been found to be unchanged after twenty years of storage at ordinary temperatures. It has been stored at 65°C for one year, and at 75°C for six months, without undergoing any deterioration. TNT in the molten state has been kept at 85°C for four weeks without decomposing. Samples of TNT have been solidified and remelted as many as fifty times without deterioration as determined by tests for freezing point, acidity, vacuum stability, and impact. The chemical stability of TNT presents no practical problem; but storage at elevated temperatures may cause physical in-

Table 7. Impact Test Values of TNT

Temperature, °C	State	Impact test, in.
−40	solid	17
20	solid	14
80	liquid	7
90	liquid	3
105–110	liquid	2

stability, as reflected by the exudation of an eutectic mixture of impurities and α-TNT as an oil. TNT that has a freezing point of 80.2°C withstands storage at 50°C, but exudes at 65°C when loaded in shell. Under such conditions a freezing point greater than 80.4°C is necessary to prevent exudation at 65°C. TNT with a freezing point of 80.75°C undergoes no exudation at 70°C. Although continued exposure to light produces some discoloration and deterioration, this is only a surface effect and of no practical importance, since TNT is rarely subjected to such exposure in very thin layers.

TNT is mildly toxic, but produces neither vesicant nor lacrimatory effects. A maximum concentration in air of 1.5 mg/m³ has been suggested to avoid undue toxicity. Daily changes of clothing and frequent baths are required of those working with large quantities of TNT. It is classified as not being dangerous with respect to hazard from sparks that result from static charges of electricity.

α- or 2,4-Dinitrotoluene (DNT), $CH_3C_6H_3(NO_2)_2$, is not employed as a single explosive but has found extensive use as an ingredient in military and commercial explosive compositions, for its gelatinizing and water proofing action, as well as for its explosive potential.

The pure compound has a melting point of 69.5–70.5°C, but that used for military compositions has a freezing point as low as 66°C. Commercial blasting compositions contain similar material or even an oily mixture of isomeric dinitrotoluenes that becomes completely liquid at 26°C. An intermediate commercial grade is a solid and has a freezing point of 44°C.

Pure DNT forms yellow needles having a sp gr of 1.521 and refractive index values of $\alpha = 1.442$, $\beta = 1.662$, and $\gamma = 1.756$, for sodium light. Its solubility in water is 0.03 and 0.087 g/100 g water at 20 and 60°C, respectively. It is soluble to the extent of 3.8 g/100 g ethyl alcohol at 15°C; 13.2 g/100 g ether at 22°C; and 35 g/100 g glyceryl nitrate at 20°C. It is readily soluble in benzene and carbon disulfide. Its heat of combustion (H_p) is 4682 cal/g.

When toluene is subjected to dinitration, the oil obtained contains approx 75% of the 2,4-isomer. After being washed free of acid, this oil is used as is in commercial compositions or is purified by fractional freezing in order to obtain a solid product of desired purity.

DNT is a good gelatinizing agent for cellulose nitrate. It is very insensitive and difficult to initiate to detonation. In the sand test it crushes only 5 g of sand (see Table 11), but the lead-block compression test indicates it has only 77% the brisance of TNT, and a rate of detonation 85% that of TNT. Ballistic pendulum and Trauzl lead-block tests indicate DNT to have 64–71% of the explosive strength of TNT. Stability-test data for DNT are not available, but DNT should be at least as stable as TNT.

1,3,5-Trinitrobenzene (*sym*-trinitrobenzene, TNB), $C_6H_3(NO_2)_3$, forms rhombic plates of slightly yellowish color when crystallized from benzene. It was first prepared by Hepp in 1876. Because of its high cost of manufacture and only slight superiority to TNT, it has lost its practical importance with the development of Cyclonite and PETN.

Pure 1,3,5-trinitrobenzene has the following properties: mp, 123.25°C; sp gr, 1.688; vapor pressure, 2 mm Hg at 175°C, 50 mm Hg at 250°C; nonvolatility at room temperature; heat of combustion, 3113 cal/g. When pressed at 75,000 psi, TNB has an apparent density of 1.67. The cast material has a density of 1.60–1.61.

It is almost insoluble in water (0.028 and 0.102 g/100 g water at 15 and 100°C, respectively). It is hygroscopic to the extent of only 0.04%. At 17°C it is soluble to the extent of 59 g/100 g of acetone, 29.8 g/100 g of ethyl acetate, 11.8 g/100 g of toluene, 6.2 g/100 g of benzene or chloroform, 3.76 g/100 g of methanol, and 2.1 g/100 g of ethyl alcohol. It is less soluble in 95% ethyl alcohol, ether, and carbon disulfide.

When treated with an alkoxide or alcoholic sodium hydroxide, TNB forms a sensitive metallic derivative, and continued treatment with alkali yields 3,5-dinitrophenol.

Trinitrobenzene can be prepared by the nitration of m-dinitrobenzene, the reduction of trinitrochlorobenzene (picryl chloride), or the oxidation of trinitrotoluene (TNT) to trinitrobenzoic acid and subsequent decarboxylation. The last of these methods is the most economical.

The explosive properties of trinitrobenzene are comparable to those of TNT and picric acid rather than those of Cyclonite or PETN. Trinitrobenzene is more sensitive to impact than TNT, but of the same order of insensitivity to friction and initiation (see Table 10). The brisance and explosive strength of trinitrobenzene are greater than those of TNT, as judged by the sand test and Trauzl lead-block test values (see Table 11). TNB is a very stable explosive, and its explosion-temperature test value of 550°C is greater than that of TNT.

Trinitrobenzene has been reported to be toxic. It should, therefore, be handled with some care, and inhalation in dust form should be avoided.

m-**Dinitrobenzene** (1,3-dinitrobenzene), $C_6H_4(NO_2)_2$, in the pure form, consists of almost colorless crystals which melt at 89.75°C. The material produced on a commercial basis (mp 80–81°C) generally consists of a mixture of isomers containing 91–94% of the m-compound. It has been used as a substitute for TNT and other high explosives in shell, generally in mixtures with ammonium nitrate or other high explosives. Because of its toxicity and the availability of more powerful explosives, it no longer is of practical importance.

Pure m-dinitrobenzene has the following properties: b_{770} 302°C; sp gr, 1.571_4^0; heat of combustion (H_p), 4145 cal/g. It is soluble in water to the extent of only 0.05 and 0.32 g/100 g of water at 15 and 100°C. It is slightly soluble in alcohol, more so in ether, and fairly soluble in benzene, toluene, chloroform, and ethyl acetate.

Dinitrobenzene is readily prepared by slowly adding 1 part by wt of nitrobenzene to a mixture of 2.5 parts of sulfuric acid (sp gr 1.84) and 1.5 parts of nitric acid (sp gr 1.52). After partial cooling, the mixture is poured into cold water, and the precipitated dinitrobenzene is caught on a filter. It is washed with water and recrystallized.

Dinitrobenzene has about 86% of the explosive strength and only 54% of the brisance of TNT (see Table 11). It therefore could be of practical importance only as an emergency material. It is extremely toxic. It has an irritating effect on the respiratory system and causes the skin to become bluish in color. It is considered unsuitable for handling on a mass-production basis and should be handled with care even on a laboratory scale. Contact of dinitrobenzene solution with the skin particularly should be avoided.

Picric acid (2,4,6-trinitrophenol, Melinite, Lyddite, Pertite, Shimose), $HOC_6H_2(NO_2)_3$, exists in two polymorphic forms. When crystallized from alcohol, picric acid takes the form of yellow, orthorhombic, flattened rods. First prepared in 1771 by Woulff, it was used as a yellow dye for silk and wool; and not until after 1885 did the French first begin to use it as a bursting charge for shell, under the name of Melinite. In 1888, it was first used in Great Britain, under the name of Lyddite. Thus, it was the first modern high explosive employed for this purpose. Picric acid, alone or in admixture with other materials, was the chief high explosive of the military powers until it was displaced by the development of TNT. It has also been used as the explosive in detonating fuse and as an ingredient of pyrotechnic compositions. In addition, picric acid served as a raw material for the manufacture of ammonium picrate. It has now been displaced entirely by more modern and superior explosives.

Picric acid is of very low volatility at ordinary temperatures, but because of its bitter taste and dustiness it has the effects of a more volatile material; mp, 122.5°C; dec above 300°C; sp gr, 1.763; vapor pressure, 2 mm Hg at 195°C, 50 mm Hg at 255°C; heat of fusion, 20.4 cal/g; heat of combustion (H_p), 2671.5 cal/g; specific heat, 0.234 cal/(g)(°C) at 0°C, 0.274 cal/(g)(°C) at 50°C, and 0.318 cal/(g)(°C) at 100°C. The density of cast picric acid is approx 1.64, but the material can be compressed to a density of 1.725 when subjected to a pressure of 100,000 psi.

Although soluble in water to the extent of 1.4 and 6.8 g/100 g water at 20 and 100°C, respectively, picric acid is almost nonhygroscopic (0.05%). Its solubility in ether is only 1.43 g/100 ml ether, and, in ethyl alcohol, 4.9 g/100 ml alcohol at 20°C. The compound is easily soluble in benzene, nitric acid, and sulfuric acid.

Picric acid is chemically active. It decomposes carbonates and may be titrated with bases by the use of sodium alizarinsulfonate as an indicator. When copper ammonium sulfate solution is added to an aqueous solution containing as little as 0.01% picric acid, a green precipitate is produced. Picric acid reacts with all the common metals to form picrates, some of which are extremely sensitive.

The direct nitration of phenol is so vigorous that it can be controlled only with great difficulty, and therefore the manufacture of picric acid is carried out by first treating phenol with sulfuric acid to form a mixture of phenolsulfonic acids and by subsequent nitration. Various processes have been described, varying from one-stage to three-stage nitration. The best yield claimed is 200 parts of acid per 100 parts of phenol. Another process involves the conversion of dinitrochlorobenzene into dinitrophenol by means of sodium hydroxide and nitration of the dinitro compound. The catalytic process for producing picric acid directly from benzene involves the use of mercuric nitrate and nitric acid.

The grade of picric acid standard for military use requires it to have a minimum melting point value of 120.0°C and no more than 0.2% ash, 0.2% water-insoluble material, 0.1% sulfuric acid, and 0.0004% lead. Picric acid must be free from nitric acid.

Picric acid has sensitivity, brisance, explosive strength, and stability characteristics that are intermediate between those of TNT and trinitrobenzene (see Tables 10, 11, and 12).

Picric acid strongly stains the skin, but is not as toxic as some of the comparable nitro compounds. Nevertheless, its dust should not be inhaled, and frequent baths and changes of clothing are prescribed.

Ammonium picrate (ammonium trinitrophenolate, explosive D), $(NO_2)_3C_6H_2ONH_4$, exists in stable yellow and metastable red forms of orthorhombic crystals. The two forms are easily interconvertible, and appear to differ only in color. The compound has been used as a military explosive for the loading of armor-piercing shell because of its relative insensitivity to impact. It was formerly used in admixture with potassium nitrate as a substitute for black powder. It was first prepared in 1841 by Marchand;

but it was not until 1869 that ammonium picrate was used as an explosive by Brugère, in admixture with potassium nitrate. The material is no longer used as a bursting-charge explosive in shell, having been displaced by more modern explosives of greater strength.

Ammonium picrate has the following properties: mp, 265–271°C (dec); sp gr, 1.717 (the compound can be pressed to a density of 1.64 by the application of a pressure of 100,000 psi); heat of combustion (H_p), 2745 cal/g. It is soluble in water to the extent of 1.1 and 74.8 g/100 g water at 20 and 101°C, respectively, but is only slightly soluble in ethyl alcohol and practically insoluble in ether. It is more soluble in acetone and less soluble in ethyl acetate than in ethyl alcohol. The yellow form is produced by recrystallizing the red form several times from water. The red form is obtained when ammonium picrate is produced in the presence of an excess of ammonia.

Chemically, ammonium picrate is not very reactive. It is decomposed into picric acid and ammonia by strong alkalies. At 0°C it absorbs one molecule of ammonia, but loses this at 26°C. When maintained at its melting point, it decomposes. The manufacture of ammonium picrate is relatively simple. Picric acid is suspended in hot water and neutralized by the addition of gaseous or aqueous ammonia. As the picrate is formed, it goes into solution; when the solution is cooled, the picrate crystallizes out. To remove any excess of ammonia, the crystals are washed with water and dried.

As an explosive, ammonium picrate is remarkable chiefly for its insensitivity to shock, which permits its use in armor-piercing projectiles. It has a relatively low explosion-temperature test value, and is slightly sensitive to frictional impact as indicated by rifle bullet-impact test results (see Table 10). It is relatively insensitive to initiation, as it cannot be detonated completely in the sand test by lead azide or mercury fulminate alone, but it can be detonated by DDNP. When stored at 50°C for two years, ammonium picrate is sensitized so that it can be detonated with mercury fulminate alone. Subsequent storage at ordinary temperature restores its previous insensitivity.

Ammonium picrate is approx 80% as brisant as TNT, as indicated by sand tests (see Table 11), but fragmentation tests in shell have shown it to be about 95% as brisant. Both explosives have about the same rate of detonation at a density of 1.56; hence, approximate equality of brisance would be expected. The rate of detonation of ammonium picrate has been found to be somewhat affected, particularly at lower loading densities, by the granulation of the material, but this effect is not pronounced. The explosive strength of ammonium picrate is 98% that of TNT, as shown by the ballistic pendulum test.

As judged by vacuum-stability test data (see Table 12), ammonium picrate is of a very high order of stability. The material has been found to withstand storage at ordinary temperatures for a period of twenty years with no evidence of deterioration, and at 50°C for more than five years without marked deterioration.

Ammonium picrate is not particularly toxic, but it discolors the skin and, in the case of some individuals, may cause a dermatitis to develop. Frequent baths and changes of freshly laundered clothes are prescribed for those who work with large quantities of ammonium picrate. Inhalation of the dust should be minimized.

Tetryl (2,4,6-trinitrophenylmethylnitramine, N-methyl-N,2,4,6-tetranitroaniline (C.A.), Tetralite, Pyrenite, CE), $(NO_2)_3C_6H_2N(CH_3)NO_2$, is colorless when freshly prepared and highly purified, but rapidly acquires a yellow color when exposed to light. As manufactured, it has a light-yellow or buff color. When crystallized from benzene it forms monoclinic prisms. Tetryl has been used chiefly as a booster explosive, and to some extent in the formulation of binary explosives. The compound was first described in 1877 by Martens, but it was not until World War I that Tetryl appears to have been used as an explosive. In the early literature, it frequently was referred to as tetranitromethylaniline.

Chemically pure Tetryl has a melting point of 129.45°C, but that manufactured for military use may have a melting point as low as 128.75°C. Crystals of Tetryl have a hardness of less than 1 on the Mohs scale. Tetryl undergoes slight decomposition when melted; repeated melting and cooling rapidly increases the degree of decomposition. The cast material has a density of 1.62, whereas the crystalline compound (true sp gr 1.73) can be pressed to a density of 1.71 under a pressure of 30,000 psi. Tetryl has specific heat values of 0.213, 0.217, 0.223, and 0.231 cal/(g)(°C) at 0, 20, 50, and 100°C, respectively. Other thermal property values are heat of fusion, 20.6 cal/g, and heat of combustion, 2914 cal/g.

Tetryl is hygroscopic to the extent of only 0.04% at 30°C and 90% relative humidity. Its solubility in water is only 0.005, 0.0195, and 0.184 g/100 g water at 0, 50, and 100°C, respectively, but Tetryl is very soluble in acetone. Benzene will hold a greater amount of solid Tetryl in solution if the two are mixed at a high temperature and then cooled to and maintained at a given temperature than when they are heated up to and maintained at that given temperature. Representative values for the two equilibria are given in Table 8. The solubility of Tetryl in ethylenedichloride is 1.5, 3.8, 7.7, 18.8, and 64.5 g/100 g solvent at 0, 20, 40, 60, and 80°C, respectively. Tetryl is only slightly soluble in ethyl alcohol, ether, carbon tetrachloride, chloroform, or carbon disulfide. The spent acid which results from the production of Tetryl holds only 0.3% of its weight of Tetryl in solution.

Table 8. Solubilities of Tetryl in Benzene at Different Temperatures

Temperature, °C	Subsolubility, g/100 g benzene	Supersolubility, g/100 g benzene
15	3.9	10.2
25	5.5	12.2
35	7.4	14.9
45	9.7	19.25
55	13.25	22.5

An aqueous solution of an alkali reacts with Tetryl to form a metallic picrate and nitrite and methylamine. Prolonged boiling with dilute sulfuric acid has no effect, but, when a solution of Tetryl in cold concentrated sulfuric acid is allowed to stand, 2,4,6-trinitrophenylmethylamine (N-methylpicramide) and nitric acid are formed. In the nitrometer, in the presence of mercury, the nitric acid is reduced to nitric oxide, which can be measured. Tetryl reacts with aniline in benzene solution, at ordinary temperatures, forming 2,4,6-trinitrodiphenylamine (mp 179.5°C) and methylnitramine (N-nitromethylamine). When heated under certain conditions, Tetryl yields picric acid with or without the simultaneous formation of N-methylpicramide. Sodium sulfide completely decomposes Tetryl into nonexplosive, water-soluble products, and this reaction can be used for the disposal of waste material. The Tetryl is added slowly, with stirring, to an aqueous solution containing 13% by wt of hydrated sodium sulfide. Tetryl is decomposed into nonexplosive products by a 10% by wt solution of sodium sulfite, but the reaction is relatively slow unless the solution is heated to 80–90°C.

The most apparent method for producing Tetryl—the nitration of N-methylaniline—has not proved practical because of the difficulty involved in producing the raw material on a large scale, at low cost, and in a necessary state of purity. For many years, the standard method of manufacture involved the nitration of N,N-dimethylaniline, as shown in the following equation:

$$C_6H_5N(CH_3)_2 + 10\ HNO_3 \rightarrow (NO_2)_3C_6H_2N(NO_2)CH_3 + 6\ NO_2 + CO_2 + 8\ H_2O$$

This method has the disadvantage of requiring nitric acid for the removal of one methyl group by oxidation. In practice, one part of dimethylaniline is dissolved in 14.4 parts of 96–99% sulfuric acid at 20–30°C, with the formation of dimethylaniline sulfate. The nitration is carried out by the addition, at 68–72°C, of 9.2 parts of mixed acid containing 66.7% nitric acid and 15.8% sulfuric acid. Care must be taken to keep the amount of water present low so as to prevent the formation of benzene-insoluble impurities, which are benzidine derivatives. Because of the formation of some of the tetranitro compound during nitration and the extremely deleterious effect of occluded acidity on the stability of Tetryl, the crude material must be subjected to a careful purification process. This involves removal of most of the acidity by washing with cold water, and treating with boiling water to hydrolyze any tetranitro compound present. Residual acidity is removed by solution in benzene, washing of the solution with water, and recrystallization, or by solution in acetone and precipitation of the Tetryl by mixing of the solution with water. The benzene is recovered by distillation for subsequent use; when acetone is used, the purification process can be made continuous.

The development of methylamine as a cheap commercial bulk chemical made possible the production of Tetryl by a method less wasteful of nitric acid. This involves the reaction of methylamine with 2,4- or 2,6-dinitrochlorobenzene to form dinitrophenylmethylamine (N-methyldinitroaniline), which is nitrated to Tetryl. In recent years considerable practical use has been made of this process.

The only standard grade of Tetryl is that used for military purposes. The essential requirements for this grade of Tetryl are a minimum melting point of 128.8°C, a quantity not greater than 0.02% of free acid, and 0.10% of benzene-insoluble material. In order to prevent the presence of any sodium or other metallic derivatives, it is specified that no sodium carbonate or other alkali should be added to the wash waters.

As an explosive, Tetryl possesses a combination of characteristics that renders it suitable for use as a booster charge. It is distinctly more sensitive to impact, frictional impact, heat, and initiation than is TNT (see Table 10). This degree of physical sensitivity does not require it to be packed or stored in a water-wet condition. Its much greater brisance, as judged by sand-test values, reflects Tetryl's much higher rate of detonation (see Table 11). This has been confirmed by fragmentation tests of shell charges. Tetryl has about 128% the explosive strength of TNT, as indicated by ballistic pendulum and Trauzl lead-block tests. Although Tetryl is slightly less stable than TNT, as judged by vacuum-stability tests (see Table 12), and undergoes slight decomposition, which TNT does not, the compound has satisfactory stability. At ordinary temperatures, it has been found to withstand storage for twenty years, at 65°C for 12 months, at 75°C for 6 months, and at 100°C for 100 hr without significant deterioration. Because the melting point of Tetryl is so much higher than any practical storage temperature and because of the almost complete absence of inpurities that could form eutectic mixtures, the physical deterioration and desensitization of Tetryl by exudation has never been a problem.

Tetryl strongly colors human skin and can produce dermatitis. The use of a cold cream containing 10% sodium perborate has been found to minimize these effects. Protective clothing and frequent baths are standard precautions for protecting workers in direct contact with quantities of Tetryl. Inhalation of Tetryl dust is recognized as producing toxic effects, and the suggested permissible maximum concentration of the dust in air is 1.5 mg/m^3 of air.

Tetranitrocarbazole (1,3,6,8-tetranitrocarbazole, TNC), is a yellow powder that melts at 300.6°C. As manufactured, it melts at 285–300°C because of the presence of

$$(NO_2)_2C_6H_2—C_6H_2(NO_2)_2$$
$$NH$$

about 10% of the 1,2,6,8-isomer and trinitrocarbazole. TNC was first prepared in 1880 by Graebe and von Adlerskron and later patented in Germany in 1914; but it was first used extensively in World War II, in pyrotechnic, igniter, and modified black powder compositions. It is now used also as an insecticide.

Tetranitrocarbazole is manufactured by sulfonating one part of carbazole with 5.7 parts of 93% sulfuric acid and adding the solution to 3.5 parts of 98% nitric acid at 50–60°C. After drowning in 40 parts of water, filtering, and washing, the crude product is digested with 5% ammonium hydroxide and again washed with water.

TNC is soluble in hot acetone and fairly soluble in nitrobenzene, but is insoluble in water, benzene, ether, ethanol, and carbon tetrachloride. It is hygroscopic to the extent of only 0.01% at 30°C and 90% relative humidity, and has a heat of combustion of 3773 cal/g.

TNC is less sensitive to impact and initiation than is TNT but equally insensitive to heat (see Table 10). It is less brisant than TNT as judged by the sand test (Table 11) but has the same high order of stability as TNT as judged by vacuum-stability tests (see Table 12).

Cyclotrimethylenetrinitramine or Cyclonite (hexahydro-1,3,5-trinitro-s-triazine (C.A.), Hexogen, T4, RDX), $(CH_2)_3(NNO_2)_3$, forms colorless orthorhombic crystals. It has been widely used as a base charge for detonators and as an ingredient of bursting charge and plastic explosives. First prepared by Henning in 1899, it was not until 1920 that von Herz discovered its value as an explosive. In World War II, the major powers used it on a large scale.

Cyclonite has the following properties: mp (when pure), 204.1°C; sp gr, 1.816, density when pressed at 30,000 psi, 1.73; hardness (Mohs scale), 2–3; sp heat at 20°C, 0.30 cal/(g)(°C); heat of combustion (H_p), 2307.2 cal/g. Cyclonite is almost insoluble in water and is hygroscopic to the extent of only 0.04% at 35°C and 100% relative humidity. It is only slightly soluble in ethyl alcohol, ether, benzene, toluene, chloroform, carbon tetrachloride, carbon disulfide, and the esters of glycols. It is readily soluble in hot aniline, phenol, or warm concentrated nitric acid. In cold concentrated sulfuric acid, Cyclonite dissolves very slowly, and the solution decomposes on standing. The solubility of Cyclonite in the best solvents is shown in Table 9.

Boiling dilute sulfuric acid or sodium hydroxide solution hydrolyzes Cyclonite. Twenty parts by wt of a 5% solution of sodium hydroxide can be used to decompose waste Cyclonite. Upon reduction, Cyclonite yields methylamine, nitrous acid, and hydrocyanic acid; or methylamine, ammonia, nitrous acid, and formaldehyde, depending upon the experimental conditions.

Since Cyclonite is obtained from the raw materials formaldehyde, ammonia, and nitric acid, it offers distinct logistic advantages over explosives dependent upon petroleum as a basic material. Cyclonite, like PETN, can be produced when only coal, water, air, and electrical energy are available. For this reason, Germany and Italy emphasized its production and use it under the names Hexogen and T4. The British also used it under the name RDX, which is its military name in this country.

Cyclonite can be produced by a number of processes. The two most important are the nitration of hexamethylenetetramine and a similar nitration in the presence of ammonium nitrate and acetic anhydride.

Table 9. Solubility of Cyclonite

Solvent	Solubility in g/100 g solvent at			
	20°C	25°C	50°C	97°C
cyclohexanone	6.6	7.5	13	44
cyclopentanone	8.9	9.9	17	60
acetone	7.3	8.3	14.7	
methyl acetate	2.9		6.0	
nitrobenzene		1.5		12.4
mesityl oxide		3.0		12.0

With the first of these methods Cyclonite can be obtained with a yield of 68% by slowly adding 1 part by weight of hexamethylenetetramine to 11 parts of 100% nitric acid that is stirred vigorously, while the temperature is maintained at 30°C or less. After being cooled to 0°C, the mixture is stirred for 20 minutes more and then drowned in ice water. The crude product is then caught on a filter and washed with water to remove most of the acid. Removal of all but a trace of acid is important and purification is accomplished by grinding the wet material and subjecting it to treatments with boiling water or by recrystallization. The product obtained by this method has a melting point of approximately 200°C and contains about 2% of cyclotetramethylenetetramine (HMX).

In the second method, 40 parts by weight of hexamethylenetetramine is treated with 30–50% nitric acid and the resulting dinitrate is dried. This is dissolved in 240 parts of acetic anhydride, and acid ammonium nitrate, prepared by treating 43 parts of ammonium nitrate with 100% nitric acid, is added to the solution. The chief products are Cyclonite and acetic acid. The yield of Cyclonite is approximately 80% on the basis of the formaldehyde used to manufacture the hexamethylenetetramine. After washing and recrystallization from acetone or cyclohexanone, the product has a melting point of about 190°C and contains about 10% of HMX.

Military grades of Cyclonite are produced by both these processes. Both types are required to have no more than 0.05% acetone-insoluble material and 0.03% inorganic insoluble material. Acidity content in the first grade must not exceed 0.05% and in the second grade 0.02%.

The sensitivity to impact of Cyclonite approximates that of Tetryl (see Table 10), but Cyclonite is somewhat more sensitive to friction and rifle-bullet impact. Both are equally sensitive to heat. Cyclonite is more sensitive than Tetryl to initiation by lead azide or DDNP.   An increase in temperature increases the sensitivity of Cyclonite to impact; at 105°C its impact-test value is 5 in.

Cyclonite is of the same order of brisance and explosive strength as PETN and distinctly superior to Tetryl as determined by the sand, rate of detonation, ballistic pendulum, and Trauzl lead-block tests (see Table 11).   It may be considered, therefore, to be at least the equal of, if not superior to, any of the solid bursting-charge explosives available in quantity.

The stability of Cyclonite is considerably superior to that of PETN and nearly equal to that of TNT, as indicated by the vacuum-stability test (see Table 12).   It withstands storage at 85°C for 10 months or at 100°C for 100 hr without measurable deterioration; hence, from the viewpoint of stability, Cyclonite must be considered highly satisfactory.

Cyclonite does not appear to be markedly toxic; but daily changes of clothing and baths are prescribed for workers continuously exposed to large quantities of it.

Cyclotetramethylenetetranitramine (octahydro-1,3,5,7-tetrazocine (C.A.), 1,3,5,7-tetranitro-1,3,5,7-tetrazacyclooctane (RRI), HMX, Octogen), $(CH_2)_4(NNO_2)_4$, is a white crystalline material which exists in at least four polymorphic forms.   It is formed in the course of the production of Cyclonite and has found some special uses because of its very high melting point and great stability at elevated temperatures.

The most important characteristics of the four forms of HMX are shown below. Ordinarily the least sensitive β form is produced, and this will be the form discussed.

Forms of HMX	α	β	γ	δ
specific gravity	1.96	1.87	1.82	1.77
stability (room temp)	metastable	stable	metastable	unstable
relative insensitivity to impact	60	325	45	75

HMX has the following properties: mp, 276–277°C; hardness (Mohs scale), approx 2; heat of combustion (H_p), 2230.7 cal/g.   It is practically insoluble in water and nonhygroscopic.   Its solubility in other solvents is comparable to that of Cyclonite. Its chemical reactivity is also comparable to Cyclonite, except that it is not easily decomposed by alkaline hydroxide.   It is prepared by the nitration of hexamethylene-tetramine, the nitrating conditions differing from those used in preparing Cyclonite; a mixture of the two explosives results.   The HMX is separated by fractional crystallization or by decomposing the Cyclonite with sodium hydroxide.   Dimethyl-sulfoxide has been found suitable for such separation.

HMX is of the same order of sensitivity to impact and friction (see Table 10,) but is less sensitive to initiation by lead azide.   As judged by sand-test values, HMX is 92% as brisant as Cyclonite, and ballistic-pendulum tests indicate that the two compounds have equal explosive strength (see Table 11).   Vacuum stability-test values indicate that HMX is even more stable than Cyclonite (see Table 12), and the tests at 150°C indicate HMX to be of the same order of thermal stability as TNT and ammonium picrate.

The presence of HMX in Cyclonite, therefore, cannot be considered to impair significantly the brisance or stability of the latter; and, if conditions of crystallization are such that the β form of HMX is produced, its presence does not have an undesirable effect with respect to sensitivity to impact or friction.

Nitroguanidine, $HN{=}C(NH_2)NHNO_2$, was first prepared by Jousselin in 1877, but was not used for practical purposes until World War II. It has found some use in propellant compositions. It exists in two crystal forms having the same melting point. The α form or flat-needle form is the one usually produced. The β form, obtained in clusters of plates, can be transformed into the α form by dissolving it in sulfuric acid and pouring the solution into water. Neither form is converted into the other by solution in water, and the two forms can be separated by fractional crystallization from water.

Nitroguanidine is white and has a crystal density of 1.715. Its melting point varies somewhat with the rate of heating, but when this is moderate the pure material melts at 232°C. Its heat of combustion (H_p) is 1997 cal/g. The two forms differ slightly with respect to solubility in water but are similar at 25 and 100°C, where the solubility is about 0.44 and 8.25 g/100 g water, respectively. The compound is nonhygroscopic. Nitroguanidine is insoluble in ether and only very slightly soluble in ethyl alcohol, methanol, or acetone. It is somewhat soluble in sulfuric acid, its solubility increasing with increase in concentration of the acid. In 45% sulfuric acid, nitroguanidine is soluble to the extent of 5.8 and 10.9 g/100 ml acid at 3 and 25°C, respectively.

Upon reduction, nitroguanidine is converted first into nitrosoguanidine and then into aminoguanidine. Upon solution in hot, concentrated nitric acid, nitroguanidine yields a nitrate that melts at 147°C with decomposition. Nitroguanidine gives a blue color with diphenylamine reagent. In sulfuric acid solution it acts as if it had decomposed into nitramide and cyanamide. When the solution is warmed, first nitrous oxide and some nitrogen are evolved and then carbon dioxide. At a more elevated temperature, ammonia and carbon dioxide are evolved. Upon treatment with ammonium carbonate, nitroguanidine yields guanidine carbonate.

Nitroguanidine is prepared by the dehydration of guanidine (qv) nitrate with sulfuric acid. The guanidine nitrate may be prepared by the reaction of guanidine and nitric acid or that of dicyanamide and ammonium nitrate. To effect the dehydration of guanidine nitrate, 500 ml of 95% sulfuric acid is cooled with ice and 400 g of dry guanidine nitrate is added in small portions while stirring, so that the temperature does not rise above 10°C. As soon as all the crystals have been dissolved, the milky solution is poured into 3 liter of cracked ice and water. The mixture is kept ice-cold until precipitation is complete. The nitroguanidine is then caught on a filter, washed with water, and recrystallized from water. The yield is about 93% of the theoretical.

Since guanidine nitrate can be produced from the raw materials coal, limestone, atmospheric nitrogen, and water, the production of nitroguanidine does not depend upon the availability of special natural resources such as petroleum or an industrial by-product such as coke-industry toluene.

The standard military grade of nitroguanidine is at least 99.5% pure and contains no more than 0.20% water-insoluble material, 0.06% acid, and 0.30% ash. Purity is determined by means of a nitrometer.

Impact tests of nitroguanidine by different methods give contradictory results (see Table 10), but it is less sensitive to initiation than TNT and is not detonated in the pendulum-friction and rifle-bullet impact tests. In the sand test it requires a minimum detonating charge of 0.72 g of DDNP as compared with 0.29 g for TNT. Nitroguanidine in larger amounts can be detonated by means of a blasting cap. At a density of 1.55 it has a rate of 7650 m/sec as compared with rates of 7300 and 6800 for Tetryl and TNT, respectively, at the same density. The brisance of nitroguanidine, however, is less than that of TNT as judged by the sand test and its explosive strength is only 104% that of TNT as measured by the ballistic pendulum test (see Table 11). Nitroguanidine is very stable as judged by vacuum-stability test values (see Table 12), having the same order of stability as TNT; but its explosion-temperature test value of 275°C is much lower than that of TNT.

Nitroguanidine has only limited application as an explosive. Its high nitrogen content and the relatively low temperature developed by its explosion (approximately 2100°C) limit its importance to propellant compositions having low-temperature, nonflashing characteristics.

Ethylenedinitramine (N,N'-dinitroethylenediamine (C.A.), Haleite, EDNA), $NO_2NHCH_2CH_2NHNO_2$, is a white, orthorhombic, crystalline solid. It was first described by Franchimont and Klobbie in 1887, and in World War II was standardized for military use by the U.S. under the name of Haleite. In a 55–45 mixture with TNT, it forms a bursting-charge explosive that can be cast-loaded and is called Ednatol.

Ethylenedinitramine has the following constants: mp, 177.3°C (dec); sp gr, 1.75; n_D^{20} (of crystals obtained from alcohol), $\alpha = 1.427$, $\beta = 1.686$, and $\gamma = 1.730$; heat of combustion (H_p), 2506 cal/g. Ethylenedinitramine is soluble to the extent of 0.3, 1.25, 4.95, and 16.4 g/100 g water at 25, 50, 75, and 95°C, respectively, but its hygroscopicity is only 0.01%. It is soluble to the extent of 1.25, 3.45, and 10.1 g/100 g ethyl alcohol (95%) at 25, 50, and 75°C, respectively. It is insoluble in ether, but soluble in nitrobenzene, dioxane, and acetone.

A solution of ethylenedinitramine in water is slightly acid, and it forms neutral lead, silver, and potassium salts by replacement of the N-hydrogen atoms with metal. On treatment with hot, dilute sulfuric acid, ethylenedinitramine decomposes with the formation of nitrous oxide, acetaldehyde, and glycol.

Ethylenedinitramine is obtained by nitrating 1,3-ethyleneurea (2-imidazolidone (C.A.)), which is prepared from ethylenediamine (see Diamines) and diethyl carbonate (see Vol. 4, p. 390), and hydrolyzing the dinitroethylene urea as shown below:

$$
\begin{array}{c}
CH_2-NH \\
| \quad\quad\quad >CO \\
CH_2-NH
\end{array}
\xrightarrow{HNO_3}
\begin{array}{c}
CH_2-N(NO_2) \\
| \quad\quad\quad\quad\quad >CO \\
CH_2-N(NO_2)
\end{array}
\xrightarrow{H_2O}
\begin{array}{c}
CH_2NHNO_2 \\
| \\
CH_2NHNO_2
\end{array}
+ \; CO_2
$$

Ten parts by weight of mixed acid (74.0% sulfuric acid, 15.4% nitric acid, and 10.6% water) is cooled to 10°C or lower and agitated, and 1 part of ethyleneurea is added in small portions at such a rate that the temperature does not rise above 10°C. Stirring is continued for five minutes after the addition of the last portion of ethyleneurea. The resulting solution is poured into a large volume of ice water and the precipitated dinitroethyleneurea is caught on a filter and washed well with water. The dinitro compound is suspended in water which is heated to boiling. Boiling is continued until the evolution of gas ceases. When the solution is cooled to room temperature, the ethylenedinitramine separates as shining crystals which are caught on a filter, washed with cold water, and dried.

The standard grade of ethylenedinitramine is required to be no less than 94.0% pure and melt at no less than 174.0°C.

Although ethylenedinitramine has a very low explosion-temperature test value, it is less sensitive than Cyclonite or Tetryl to impact, rifle bullet impact, and initiation (see Table 10). Its brisance and explosive strength are very similar to that of Tetryl, as judged by the sand, ballistic pendulum, and Trauzl lead-block tests (see Table 11). It is also similar to Tetryl with respect to stability as indicated by the vacuum-stability tests (see Table 12). Ethylenedinitramine has been found to withstand storage at 50°C, and when heated with boiling water, it slowly undergoes partial hydrolysis.

Ethylenedinitramine is not particularly toxic and no special precautions are required in its handling and manufacture.

The lead salt of ethylenedinitramine is of the same order of sensitivity to impact as mercury fulminate, but cannot be detonated by flame or stab action. Therefore, it is not suitable for use in blasting caps or detonators. The lead and silver salts are insoluble in water, but the sodium and potassium salts are readily soluble in water.

Ammonium perchlorate, NH_4ClO_4, is generally regarded as an oxidizing agent; but, like ammonium nitrate, it is a very insensitive explosive that is not used per se. It is extensively used as an ingredient in propellant and blasting compositions.

The rhombic, colorless crystals of ammonium perchlorate have a density of 1.95 and a refractive index of 1.482. The compound is soluble to the extent of 12.4 and 88.2 g/100 g water at 0 and 100°C, respectively. It is slightly soluble in ethyl alcohol and soluble in acetone. When heated above 300°C it decomposes with the evolution of oxides of nitrogen.

Ammonium perchlorate (see Vol. 5, p. 67) can be prepared by reacting sodium perchlorate and ammonium chloride in aqueous solution and separating the ammonium perchlorate by fractional crystallization.

As an explosive, ammonium perchlorate is similar to ammonium nitrate with respect to sensitivity to impact, friction, heat, and initiation (see Table 10). Because of its insensitivity, its brisance cannot be determined by the sand test, but its rate of detonation (see Table 11) is similar to that of ammonium nitrate. Ballistic pendulum and Trauzl lead-block tests show that the two materials have about the same explosive strength. Vacuum-stability test values (see Table 12) show ammonium perchlorate to be very stable at temperatures as high as 150°C.

The available oxygen content of ammonium perchlorate is 35% greater than that of ammonium nitrate on a weight basis, and this renders ammonium perchlorate of interest for special uses despite its greater cost.

BINARY EXPLOSIVES

The first military binary explosive may have been the 60:40 picric acid:dinitrophenol mixture developed by the French to overcome the difficulties involved in the melt-loading of picric acid due to its high melting point. With the later development of TNT, and the general shortage of this explosive in all countries during World War I, the ammonium nitrate–TNT mixtures termed Amatol were developed to utilize as efficiently as possible the available supply of TNT. The sudden increase in the available TNT realized at the beginning of World War II made possible the practical development of new binary explosives. These were designed to utilize TNT as a carrier for more powerful explosives, rather than to economize on the use of TNT, and have the added advantage of being suitable for melt-loading.

Amatol. During World War I, 80:20 and 50:50 ammonium nitrate:TNT mixtures designated as 80:20 Amatol and 50:50 Amatol were used. The 80:20 Amatol is an essentially oxygen-balanced mixture that has 30% more explosive strength than

TNT. Since it could not be melt-loaded, it was necessary to mix the hot materials so that the nitrate crystals were coated with the TNT, and load shell by extrusion of the hot plastic mass. The 50:50 Amatol, however, is fluid enough to permit melt-loading in the same manner as TNT. During World War II, some 50:50 Amatol was used, particularly by Germany, which had a limited supply of TNT.

Preparation of 50:50 Amatol is carried out by melting TNT and adding an equal weight of ammonium nitrate which has been heated to remove surface moisture and prevent the over rapid cooling of the TNT. The mixture is stirred, with some cooling, until the desired fluidity is obtained and then loaded directly into shell or bombs.

Amatol of 50:50 composition is of the same order of sensitivity to impact, friction, and rifle bullet impact as TNT, but is slightly less sensitive to initiation and has a much lower explosion-temperature test value (see Table 10). It is distinctly less brisant than TNT, as judged by sand-test values (see Table 11) and fragmentation tests. It has about 123% the explosive strength of TNT, but is not as satisfactory as TNT with regard to blast effect. The heat of combustion (H_p) of 50:50 Amatol is 2073 cal/g.

Tetrytol. Tetryl and TNT form a eutectic mixture that melts at 67.5°C. During World War II, a 70:30 Tetryl:TNT composition was developed, known as Tetrytol, which was used as a demolition explosive and bursting charge for mines because of its greater ease of initiation and brisance than TNT. When melt-loaded, the cast material has a density of 1.60 to 1.61 and so permits the use of a slightly greater weight of charge than TNT.

Tetrytol of 70:30 composition is less sensitive to impact than Tetryl, and is distinctly less sensitive to initiation (see Table 10). It is nearly as brisant as Tetryl as judged by the sand test (see Table 11) and fragmentation tests. It has 120% the explosive strength of TNT, as compared with 128% for Tetryl. Vacuum-stability tests (see Table 12) show 70:30 Tetrytol to be less stable than Tetryl, but capable of withstanding storage at 65°C without change in stability, acidity, sensitivity, or brisance, though there is some separation of an oily exudate and physical distortion.

Picratol. During World War II, a 52:48 mixture of ammonium picrate and TNT was developed that could be melt-loaded in armor-piercing shell and had a desired insensitivity to shock. As judged by explosion it afforded no advantage over either of its forming ingredients, and its later use was reduced by new developments in the loading of such shell.

Pentolite. With the standardization of PETN during World War II, PETN–TNT mixtures were developed known as Pentolites. Of these, the one composed of equal weights of the two explosives, is the most important and has been used as a bursting charge for grenades, a booster-surround charge, and commercial boosters.

PETN and TNT form a eutectic mixture that freezes at 77°C and contains 86.5% TNT. Cast 50:50 Pentolite has a density of 1.64–1.66 and offers the advantage of 6% more charge weight than cast TNT when loaded in the same volume.

Pentolite is manufactured by either of two methods. In the slurry method, the PETN is suspended by agitation in water heated above 80°C. When TNT is added, it melts and coats the particles of PETN; and on cooling the slurry with rapid stirring, the TNT solidifies. The granules then are caught on a filter or centrifugal wringer and dried at a temperature below 75°C. In the coprecipitation method, the PETN and TNT are dissolved separately in acetone, the solutions are mixed and filtered, and the two explosives are precipitated simultaneously by pouring the solution into water, with vigorous agitation. The precipitated solid is then separated and dried. The dried Pentolite can be pelleted for use in detonators, boosters, etc, or melt-loaded.

The two impact tests yield contradictory data with respect to the sensitivity of Pentolite (see Table 10), but rifle-bullet impact tests indicate its impact sensitivity to be more similar to that of PETN than TNT. However, it is not nearly as sensitive to friction as is PETN. Its sensitivity to initiation is intermediate between that of PETN and TNT. The presence of rust or grit increases its sensitivity to impact. Sand, ballistic pendulum, and Trauzl lead-block tests (see Table 11) indicate 50:50 Pentolite to be 114% as brisant as and to have about 124% the explosive strength of TNT, but fragmentation tests have shown it to be 131% as brisant as TNT. Vacuum-stability tests show Pentolite to be less stable than PETN, but after storage at 65°C for two years it showed no excessive acidity and was of satisfactory stability. However, it undergoes some exudation when stored at temperatures greater than 50°C. This may be due to the TNT forming an eutectic mixture (mp 57.9°C) with the di-pentaerythritol hexanitrate normally present as an impurity in the PETN.

Cyclotol (Mixtures). Cyclonite and TNT mixtures of various ratios are termed Cyclotol and have found limited special uses. As shown by Tables 10, 11, and 12, the characteristics of 70:30 Cyclotol are intermediate between those of its separate ingredients. The tendency of such mixtures to segregate during melt-loading operations led to the development of Composition B.

Composition B. This is a 60:40 Cyclotol to which 1% of a wax is added that retards segregation during the melt-loading operation. The composition is hygroscopic to the extent of only 0.02%. Composition B is manufactured by heating TNT to about 100°C, adding moist Cyclonite with stirring, pouring off any separated water, and then continuing the stirring and heating until all the water has been removed by evaporation. The wax is then added and mixed thoroughly with the other ingredients by stirring and the mixture is then cooled with continued agitation until a satisfactory fluidity for casting is reached.

When cast, Composition B has a brownish-yellow color and a density of 1.65–1.66. Its sensitivity to impact, friction, rifle-bullet impact, and initiation is closer to that of TNT than that of Cyclonite (see Table 10). Sand, ballistic pendulum, and Trauzl lead-block tests (see Table 11) indicate its brisance and explosive strength to be intermediate between that of Cyclonite and TNT; but fragmentation tests show it to be 1.31% as brisant as TNT, and its blast effect is 110% that of TNT. Vacuum-stability tests show that at 120°C Composition B is as stable as Cyclonite, but at 150°C it is distinctly less stable (see Table 12). Storage at 75°C for one month produces no decrease in stability, and storage at 65°C for one year produces no change in acidity, sensitivity to impact, or brisance. However, 5 months of such storage results in slight exudation.

Because of the superiority of its brisance and blast effect, Composition B replaced Amatol and became the most important bomb-charge explosive used in World War II.

METALIZED EXPLOSIVES

During World War II, the recognition of the tactical advantages of explosives which had high blast rather than fragmentation effects led to the development of metalized explosives. Since these had to be melt-loaded, the direction of formulation was the addition of powdered aluminum to the already available explosives that could be melt-loaded.

Tritonal. An 80:20 TNT:flaked aluminum composition, Tritonal has a density of 1.70–1.73 when cast and is of a silvery appearance. It is manufactured by melting TNT and then adding slowly, with mixing, the requisite quantity of flaked aluminum. After some cooling, the mixture of liquid TNT, crystals of TNT, and aluminum can be cast without segregation of the aluminum.

As aluminum is insoluble in TNT, Tritonal does not begin to melt until the melting point of TNT has been reached. Like TNT, it undergoes considerable expansion upon melting and contraction upon freezing. Its heat of combustion (H_p) is 4315 cal/g and its thermal conductivity is twice that of TNT.

In the presence of moisture, the ingredients of Tritonal undergo a slight reaction with the evolution of gas. This is not of practical importance because of the very slight hygroscopicity of TNT and the fact that any moisture present in it is driven off during the manufacture of Tritonal.

The sensitivity of Tritonal to impact, friction, and rifle-bullet impact is intermediate between that of TNT and Cyclonite, but Tritonal is less sensitive to initiation than TNT (see Table 10). Sand tests show Tritonal to be less brisant than TNT (see Table 11), and fragmentation tests confirm this; but it has 124% the explosive strength of TNT and its blast effect is greater than that of TNT. Vacuum-stability tests (see Table 12) indicate Tritonal to be as stable as TNT. The tendency of Tritonal to exude when stored at elevated temperatures is less than that of TNT.

Torpex. A composition developed during World War II and designated as Torpex was standardized for use in bombs. It contains 41% Cyclonite, 41% TNT, and 18% aluminum and has the greatest blast effect of any of this class of explosives. It is suitable for melt loading and is a silvery-white solid when cast.

Torpex has a density of 1.81 when cast. When it undergoes solidification, there is a decrease in volume of 6%. It is nonhygroscopic when exposed to air at 30°C and 90% relative humidity. At 15°C, it has a specific heat of 0.24 cal/(g)(°C). As in the case of Tritonal, any moisture present in cast Torpex reacts with the aluminum present to evolve gas.

Torpex is manufactured by melting TNT and heating it to about 100°C. Cyclonite slightly wet with water is added slowly, and mixing and heating are continued until all the water has been driven off. Grained aluminum is added and the mixture stirred until uniformity is obtained. The mixture is then cooled, with continued stirring, until its fluidity is such as to render it suitable for loading by pouring. Torpex of slightly different composition can be manufactured by melting 12.5 parts of TNT, adding 69.5 parts of Composition B, and after further heating and stirring, adding 18 parts of aluminum.

Torpex is more sensitive to impact, rifle-bullet impact, and initiation than Composition B (see Table 10). Although sand tests show it to be more brisant than Composition B (see Table 11), fragmentation tests indicate the opposite. The two compositions have the same explosive strength, as indicated by ballistic pendulum and Trauzl lead-block tests, but Torpex is much the superior of the two in blast effect. As judged by vacuum-stability tests (see Table 12), Torpex is of the same order of stability as Composition B. Storage of Torpex at 75°C for 1 month produces no change in its stability, nor does storage at 65°C for 13 months.

Because of the sensitivity of Torpex, the U.S. and Great Britain developed an alternate composition designated as DBX, which is suitable for melt-loading. It represents a replacement of half the Cyclonite in Torpex by ammonium nitrate. Another modification of Torpex is a composition designated as HBX-1 which contains 39.6% Cyclonite, 37.8% TNT, 17.1% aluminum, 5.0% waxy desensitizer, and 0.5% calcium chloride. DBX is somewhat hygroscopic, but HBX-1 is nonhygroscopic. Minol is a castable mixture which contains 40% TNT, 40% ammonium nitrate, and 20% powdered aluminum. Its disadvantage is that in the presence of moisture there is reaction between the nitrate and aluminum.

Ammonal. Products of this type are TNT–ammonium nitrate–aluminum compositions originally developed for commercial blasting purposes, but then adapted to military use in World War I because of the scarcity of TNT. During World War II, the U.S. used, to a certain extent, a composition containing 67% TNT, 22% ammonium nitrate, and 11% powdered aluminum; Great Britain used a composition containing 64% TNT, 15% ammonium nitrate, and 18% aluminum, and Germany used compositions intermediate between these two. The first of the foregoing compositions was castable, whereas the latter two were press-loaded.

Though Ammonal products were found to have acceptable brisance, they proved undesirably insensitive at high densities. The development of high-blast explosives such as Tritonal resulted in their displacement.

PLASTIC EXPLOSIVES

During World War II, the availability of Cyclonite and PETN led to the development of new semiplastic and plastic explosives of high brisance and explosive strength values which could be used for press-loading operations and as easily conformable demolition explosives.

Composition A-3. Great Britain developed an explosive composition containing 91% Cyclonite and 9% beeswax that was designated as Composition A. When this was standardized by the U.S., for logistic reasons, the beeswax was replaced with wax from petroleum and this modified composition was designated as Composition A-3. This explosive is manufactured by heating a water slurry of Cyclonite to nearly 100°C, with agitation. The wax, which contains a wetting agent, is added with agitation, which is continued while the mixture cools to a temperature lower than the melting point of the wax. After being caught on a filter, the composition is air-dried at a temperature of 77°C.

The granules of Composition A-3 are suitable for press loading and have density values of 1.46 and 1.63 when pressed at 3000 and 12,000 psi, respectively. It is completely soluble when benzene and acetone are used successively; and is of the same order of sensitivity to impact, friction, rifle-bullet impact, and initiation as is TNT (see Table 10). Although sand-test values indicate Composition A-3 to be only 7% more brisant than TNT (see Table 11), fragmentation tests show it to be 44% more brisant. Ballistic pendulum tests indicate that its composition has an explosive strength 132% that of TNT; whereas vacuum-stability tests show it to be as stable as Cyclonite (see Table 12). Since Composition A-3 is nonhygroscopic, it is not affected by the absorption of moisture during storage, but it should not be stored at temperatures above 75°C due to the softening effect on the wax.

Composition C-4. During World War II, the British used a plastic demolition explosive that could be shaped by hand and had great shattering power. It was designated as Composition C and contained 88.3% Cyclonite and 11.7% nonexplosive

Table 10. Sensitivity Characteristics of High Explosives

| Explosives | Impact tests[a] | | PF test[b] | Rifle bullet test[b] | ET test, °C[c] | Detonating charge, g, min | | |
	in.	cm				Lead azide	Mercury fulminate	Tetryl
ammonium nitrate	31	100+			325			d
cellulose nitrate (13.3% N)	3	9			230	0.10		
nitrostarch (13.0% N)	5				217			
glyceryl nitrate	1	15	100	100	222			
diglyceryl tetranitrate	<1	43	78		215			
glycol dinitrate	<2	56	70		257			
diethylene glycol dinitrate	2	100+	100		237			
triethylene glycol dinitrate	7	100+			223			
trimethylol-ethane trinitrate		47	20		235			
PETN	6	17	50	100	225	0.03	0.17	
DPEHN	4	14	100		255	0.18		
mannitol hexanitrate	3	8			205	0.10	0.20	
dinitrotoluene		100+						
TNT	14	100		2	475	0.26	0.24	
dinitrobenzene		100+			550	0.26	0.23	
trinitrobenzene	11	46			322	0.24	0.26	
picric acid	13	82		50				
ammonium picrate	17	100+		10	318			0.06
Tetryl	8	26		10	257	0.10	0.19	
tetranitro-carbazole	18	100+			470			0.25
ethylene-dinitramine	10	43			190	0.13	0.21	
nitroguanidine	26	47			275			0.10
Cyclonite	8	33	20	100	260	0.05	0.19	
HMX	9	32	20		335	0.17		
50:50 Amatol	12	95			265			0.05
50:50 Pentolite	13	29		80	220	0.13	0.19	
70:30 Cyclotol		58		60	280			
Composition B	13	75		15	278	0.17	0.22	
70:30 Tetrytol	11	28		30	320	0.23	0.23	
80:20 Tritonal	10	73		60	470	0.30		
Torpex	8	40		100	260	0.18		
Ammonal	11	91			265	0.20		
Composition A-3	16	100+			250	0.25	0.22	
Composition C-4	19	100+			290			0.10
ammonium perchlorate	24	91			427			d

[a] Minimum fall of a 2-kg weight to cause at least one explosion in 10 trials.

[b] Percent explosions in 10 trials.

[c] Temperature required to cause explosion in 5 sec.

[d] Cannot be detonated completely in this test.

oily plasticizer. Modified in this country, it became standardized in the form of a composition designated as C-4. This composition contains 91.0% Cyclonite, 2.1% polyisobutylene, 1.6% motor oil, and 5.3% di-(2-ethylhexyl) sebacate or di-(2-ethylhexyl) adipate. Its method of manufacture has not been published.

Table 11. Explosive Characteristics of High Explosives

Explosives	Sand test, g	RT[a] Density	RT[a] m/sec	BP test,[b] % TNT	TLB test,[c] % TNT	Result of explosion[d] Heat, cal/g	Result of explosion[d] Gas, ml/g
ammonium nitrate		0.9	2,700	79	75	346	980
cellulose nitrate (13.3% N)	48.7	1.2	7,300	125	130	965	883
nitrostarch (13.0% N)		0.9	5,600	120	130		
glyceryl nitrate	58.7	1.60	7,700	140	185	1,486	715
diglyceryl tetranitrate	47.8				157	1,407	840
glycol dinitrate	62.7	1.49	7,300		205	1,655	737
diethylene glycol dinitrate	47.6	1.38	6,760	127	148		
triethylene glycol dinitrate	14.7	1.33					
trimethylolethane trinitrate	49.4	1.47	7,050	136	143	1,073	966
PETN	61.2	1.70	8,300	145	170	1,385	790
DPEHN	55.5	1.59	7,410		129	1,092	903
mannitol hexanitrate	59.5	1.73	8,260		176	1,454	694
dinitrotoluene	5.0	1.52	5,900	71	64		
TNT	47.5	1.56	6,900	100	100	925	730
dinitrobenzene	25.5	1.50	6,000		86	820	727
trinitrobenzene	49.7	1.61	7,440	110	113	1,065	670
picric acid	47.9	1.70	7,350	109	103	1,000	675
ammonium picrate	36.8	1.63	7,150	98		800	
Tetryl	54.0	1.71	7,850	128	129	1,120	760
tetranitrocarbazole	41.3					1,310	
ethylenedinitramine	52.0	1.55	7,750	136	122	1,276	908
nitroguanidine	36.8	1.55	7,650	104	78	721	1,077
Cyclonite	59.0	1.70	8,350	150	170	1,300	908
HMX	54.4			150	153		
50:50 Amatol	38.5	1.55	6,435	122	124	980	860
50:50 Pentolite	54.0	1.65	7,450	126	122	1,220	
70:30 Cyclotol	53.8	1.73	8,060	135	140		
Composition B	53.0	1.66	7,800	133	130	1,240	
70:30 Tetrytol	52.7	1.60	7,300	120			
80:20 Tritonal	46.0	1.72	6,700	124		1,470	560
Torpex	58.2	1.81	7,600	134	131	1,500	
Ammonal	47.8			122			
Composition A-3	51.0	1.59	8,100	132			
Composition C-4	55.7	1.59	8,040	130			
ammonium perchlorate			ca 3,000	81	75	266	810

[a] Rate of detonation.   [c] Trauzl lead-block test.

[b] Ballistic pendulum test.   [d] Water produced in gaseous state at STP.

Composition C-4 has a density of 1.59 and is odorless. It does not harden at −57°C or undergo exudation when stored at 77°C. It is less sensitive to impact, rifle-bullet impact, and initiation than is TNT (see Table 10). Sand tests (see Table 11)

Table 12. Stability Characteristics of High Explosives

Explosive	75°C IT,[a] % loss	100°C HT,[b] % loss in		Sample, g	Vacuum stability test, ml[c]		
		1st 48 hr	2nd 48 hr		100°C	120°C	150°C
ammonium nitrate		0.1		5	0.3	0.3	0.3
cellulose nitrate (13.3 % N)		0.3		5	0.9	11+ 16	
nitrostarch (13.0 % N)		0.6	0.5				
glyceryl nitrate		3.5	3.5	1	11+ 16		
diglyceryl tetranitrate		1.0	1.1	1	2.0		
glycol dinitrate		28.8	25.4	1	0.7	0.7	
diethylene glycol dinitrate		4.0	3.0	1	0.8		
triethylene glycol dinitrate		1.8	1.6	1	0.2	4.6	
trimethylolethane trinitrate		2.5	1.8	1	1.9		
PETN	0.02	0.1		5	0.5	11+	
DPEHN				5	3.7	11+ 16	
mannitol hexanitrate	3.5	73.0	4.8	1	11+ 16		
TNT	0.04	0.1	0.1	5	0.1	0.4	0.7
trinitrobenzene						1.0	
picric acid	0.05	0.03	0.09	5	0.2	0.5	
ammonium picrate	0.12	0.1	0.1	5	0.2	0.4	0.4
Tetryl	0.01	0.1	0.0	5	0.3	1.0	11+ 12
tetranitro- carbazole		0.15	0.05	5	0.2	0.2	
ethylene- dinitramine	0.1	0.2	0.1	5	0.5	1.5	11+ 24
nitroguanidine	0.05	0.2	0.1	5	0.4	0.5	
Cyclonite	0.03	0.03	0.0	5	0.7	0.9	2.5
HMX				5		0.4	0.6
50–50 Amatol				5	0.3	1.0	
50–50 Pentolite			0.2	5	2.5	11+ 16	
70–30 Cyclotol		0.1	0.1	5		0.9	
Composition B		0.1	0.1	5	0.7	0.9	11+ 16
70–30 Tetrytol		0.1	0.1	5	3.0	11+	
80–20 Tritonal				5	0.1	0.2	0.8
Torpex		0.0	0.1	5	0.2	1.5	11+ 16
Composition A-3		0.15	0.15	5	0.3	0.6	
Composition C-4		0.1	0.0	5	0.3		
ammonium perchlorate		0.02		5	0.1	0.2	0.3

[a] International test.   [c] ml liberated in 40 hr except when more than 11 ml are liberated in the number of hours.
[b] Heat tests.

indicate it to be 117% as brisant as TNT, whereas fragmentation tests show it to be 133% as brisant. It has 130% the explosive strength of TNT as indicated by ballistic pendulum tests; and the vacuum-stability tests have shown it to be as stable as Cyclonite and Composition A-3.

Since it contains no aliphatic nitrate or arylnitro compound, Composition C-4 is nontoxic. It is nonhygroscopic and easily formed by hand and, therefore, is suitable for demolition work.

BLASTING EXPLOSIVES

Blasting explosives, used chiefly for industrial and engineering operations, are explosive compositions designed to perform mechanical work such as quarrying, ore dislodgment, ditching, excavating, etc, with a low expenditure of time and money.

Black powder, which has less than half the explosive strength of TNT, was the sole blasting explosive until the applicability of glyceryl nitrate was discovered by Nobel in 1863. This was the first demonstration of the phenomenon of detonation as distinguished from the autocombustion of black powder; and it involved discovery of initiation to detonation by another explosive. It was not until 1883 that Berthelot and Vieille succeeded in measuring rates of detonation.

Economic Aspects of Blasting Explosives

There is no general appreciation of the importance of commercial blasting explosives in the development and maintenance of our civilization. If they did not exist and we were dependent upon only manpower and mechanical equipment for mining, tunneling, and construction and excavation work, the costs in time and money would be much greater.

The U.S. Bureau of Mines compiles statistics of the consumption of industrial explosives in the U.S., and Table 13 gives a summary comparison of such statistics from 1935 to 1962. From these it is apparent that there is, on the average, a considerable annual increase in the amount of blasting agents used.

Table 13. Apparent Consumption, lb

Industrial explosives	1935–1939 (av)	1948	1961	1962
black blasting powder	65,351,700	33,239,700	1,520,800	1,222,000
high explosives permissible	45,683,634	126,282,153	73,438,888	72,883,973
fixed, other than permissible	253,624,298	550,085,616	460,224,123	436,990,610
unprocessed grained and/or prilled ammonium nitrate[a]			484,652,380	554,774,628
completely processed ammonium nitrate blasting agents[a]			181,550,069	244,291,227
liquid-oxygen explosives[b]		15,619,704	2,234,657	2,243,384
total	364,659,632	725,227,173	1,203,620,917	1,312,406,032

[a] Data not collected before 1956.   [b] Data not collected before 1947.

The coal-mining industry consumed 33% of the total production of explosives during 1962, as compared with 46% in 1947. This reduction is attributable to the increasing use of liquid fuels rather than of coal. Quarrying and nonmetal mining operations consumed 22%, and railway and construction work 21%. Metal mining operations required 19% of the total production; 4% of this was used in seismographic work.

It is apparent from Table 13 that liquid-oxygen explosives now are of minor importance, and that since 1948 ammonium nitrate explosives have appeared that have replaced large proportions of the black powder, dynamites, and related explosives previously used. The ammonium nitrate explosives are much safer and cheaper to manufacture and handle, and some are suitable for mechanical loading.

Manufacture of Blasting Explosives

The manufacture of the explosive raw materials glyceryl nitrate, cellulose nitrate, etc, of dynamites and similar explosives has already been described (see under Noninitiating high explosives). The operations involved in the production of blasting explosives consist mainly in thoroughly mixing the ingredients, packing them into cartridges of the desired size and shape, and packing the cartridges into shipping containers.

In the manufacture of blasting gelatin, the glyceryl nitrate and cellulose nitrate are mixed in specially built machines. The preferred type has two blades that rotate separately to produce thorough mixing of the ingredients and which are so arranged that the mixing blades are driven by connecting gears that do not come in contact with each other. In some types of mixing machines, the mixing blades hang from vertical shafts and the bowl, which is movable, is elevated hydraulically at the beginning of the mixing operation until the blades are submerged in the glyceryl nitrate–cellulose nitrate mixture. The bowl is lowered when the mixing operation is completed. Positive stops are provided to prevent the mixing bowl being elevated so far that the rotating blades make contact with either the bottom or side of the bowl. In certain other types of mixing machines, the bowl is fixed in position and the stirring blades are lowered and raised; in still a third type of machine, horizontal mixing arms are employed and the mixing bowl is tilted at the end of the mixing operation to discharge its contents.

The time required to produce complete dispersion of the cellulose nitrate in the glyceryl nitrate may vary from 10 min to an hour, depending upon the type of mixing machine used. The viscosity of the glyceryl nitrate is greatly increased during mixing, and the thick, viscous mix is extruded in special machines of the sausage-machine type. The design of the extrusion equipment provides special precautions to avoid frictional or other effects that would cause heating of the mixture. The doughlike mass is usually extruded as a continuous rod of circular cross section, and this is cut off in lengths desired for the final cartridges. These lengths of blasting gelatin may be extruded directly into the cartridge wrapper or may be wrapped in paper. In either case, the ends of the paper cartridge are folded over or crimped, and the cartridges are packed, usually in 50-lb boxes. The manufacture of gelatin dynamite and ammonia gelatin dynamite is quite similar to the manufacture of blasting gelatin.

In the manufacture of dynamite, the constituents are mixed very thoroughly in mixers without any rubbing or friction. Since these explosives are not of the firm consistency of blasting gelatin or gelatin dynamites, the mixing machines do not have to be of as heavy construction. The cartridge wrappers are made separately in automatic machines. The large sizes of wrappers are spirally wound tubing. The packing of the explosive into the cartridges may be done in either of two distinctly different types of packing machines. One type uses augerlike rotating screws for carrying the explosive into the paper shell and packing it at the desired density. The other type uses a reciprocating rammer or tamping member in conjunction with a feeding device. In some packing machines, the cartridges move away from the filling member as they are filled. In most types, however, the rotating screw or the reciprocating tamping member rises automatically as each cartridge is filled, and the machine automatically stops the further filling of the cartridges when they have been filled to a certain height. The packing machines, which are of the gang type, load a considerable number of cartridges at one time. After a group of cartridges has been filled, the member that holds the cartridges is moved to another position on the machine, and the filled cartridges are then closed by a device that either automatically folds over the unfilled portion of the shell, or crimps it so tightly that the explosive does not work out of the cartridge as the result of ordinary handling. The resistance of explosive cartridges to water may be increased by making the cartridge wrappers of water-resistant paper, and spraying paraffin upon the finished cartridges or dipping them in molten paraffin maintained at a temperature only slightly above its melting point. Cartridge paper should be strong, water-resistant, and relatively light in weight, since any excess in the weight of the paper or the paraffin used tends to decrease the oxygen balance of the explosive and to increase the amount of carbon monoxide present in the gases produced by explosion.

The most modern ammonium nitrate blasting agents are considerably safer and easier to manufacture than are dynamites. Dry compositions of this category can be made in simple mixing machines with equipment for adding oil. Mobile mixing units in trucks are used to a certain extent for mixing at the place of use. This is done in some cases in mixers comparable to mobile concrete mixers. The slurry then is pumped directly from the mixer into the borehole. Water-gel compositions also require relatively simple mixing equipment and are extruded into polyethylene bags or tubing.

Dynamites

The explosive strength of glyceryl nitrate is 140% that of TNT, but its extreme sensitivity to shock prevented its successful use on a practical basis. This led Nobel to invent the first modern blasting explosive—dynamite—for which he was granted a patent in 1867. His first dynamite compositions were mixtures of glyceryl nitrate and kieselguhr (diatomite, qv), in which the absorption of the glyceryl nitrate yielded a dry, much less sensitive material. This was found to be relatively safe for transportation and handling. He found that such dynamite could contain a maximum of 75% glyceryl nitrate without the occurrence of exudation.

Nobel graded these dynamites on the basis of their percentage contents of glyceryl nitrate; and this was the origin of the so-called "weight basis" of grading blasting explosives. The 75% guhr dynamite has since been found to have 97% of the explosive strength of TNT. As shown in Table 14, the explosive strengths of the guhr dynamite compositions were not in direct proportion to their glyceryl nitrate contents. Blasting explosives are also graded on the basis of "bulk strength," this being their relative

Table 14. Compositions and Characteristics of Typical Dynamites

	Strength of dynamite							
	20%	30%	40%	50%	60%	75%	80%	100%
Straight dynamites								
glyceryl nitrate,%	20.2	29.0	39.0	49.0	56.8			
sodium nitrate, %	59.3	53.3	45.5	34.4	22.6			
carbonaceous combustible material, %	15.4	13.7	13.8	14.6	18.2			
sulfur, %	2.9	2.0						
antacid, %	1.3	1.0	0.8	1.1	1.2			
moisture, %	0.9	1.0	0.9	0.9	1.2			
ballistic pendulum test, % TNT	83	90	95	103	114			
rate of detonation, m/sec	3,600	4,300	4,800	5,150	5,900			
Gelatin dynamites[a]								
glyceryl nitrate, %	20.2	25.4	32.0	40.1	49.6		65.4	91.0
sodium nitrate, %	60.3	56.4	51.8	45.6	38.9		19.5	
cellulose nitrate soluble, %	0.4	0.5	0.7	0.8	1.2		2.6	7.9
carbonaceous combustible material, %	8.5	9.4	11.2	10.0	8.3		10.1	
sulfur, %	8.2	6.1	2.2	1.3				
antacid, %	1.5	1.2	1.2	1.2	1.1		1.7	0.8
moisture, %	0.9	1.0	0.9	1.0	0.9		0.7	0.1
ballistic pendulum test, % TNT	70	78	86	93	101		112	143
rate of detonation, m/sec	4,000	4,600	5,150	5,600	6,200			7,400
Ammonia dynamites								
glyceryl nitrate, %	12.0	12.6	16.5	16.7	22.5			
ammonium nitrate, %	11.8	25.1	31.4	43.1	50.3			
sodium nitrate, %	57.3	46.2	37.5	25.1	15.2			
carbonaceous combustible material, %	10.2	8.8	9.2	10.0	8.6			
sulfur, %	6.7	5.4	3.6	3.4	1.6			
antacid, %	1.2	1.1	1.1	0.8	1.1			
moisture, %	0.8	0.7	0.7	0.9	0.7			
ballistic pendulum test, % TNT	81	87	92	99	109			
rate of detonation, m/sec	2,780	3,000	3,780	4,000	4,700			
Ammonia gelatin dynamites								
glyceryl nitrate, %		22.9	26.2	29.9	35.3		38.3	
ammonium nitrate, %		4.2	8.0	13.0	20.1		34.7	
sodium nitrate, %		54.9	49.6	43.0	33.5		19.1	
cellulose nitrate, soluble, %		0.3	0.4	0.4	0.7		0.9	

(*continued*)

Table 14 (*continued*)

	20%	30%	40%	50%	60%	75%	80%	100%
				Strength of dynamite				
carbonaceous combustible material, %		8.3	8.0	8.0	7.9		4.3	
sulfur, %		7.2	5.6	3.4				
antacid, %		0.7	0.8	0.7	0.8		0.9	
moisture, %		1.5	1.4	1.6	1.7		1.8	
ballistic pendulum test, % TNT		81	86	90	95		103	
rate of detonation, m/sec		4,400	4,800	5,200	5,600		6,150	
Guhr dynamites								
glyceryl nitrate, %	20	30	40	50	60	75		
kieselguhr, %	80	70	60	50	40	25		
ballistic pendulum test, % TNT	13.5	27.7	42	57.5	73.5	97		
rate of detonation, m/sec						6,800		

[a] The 100% member of the series is blasting gelatin.

explosive strengths on the basis of equal volumes rather than equal weights. Dynamites as manufactured have a wide range of density values, and their "bulk strengths" afford a better comparison of their relative effects when loaded in boreholes, etc, of fixed volume. The "stick count" of dynamite is the number of cartridges in a 50-lb case.

Straight dynamite or active dope dynamite was the next type invented by Nobel in 1869. Glyceryl nitrate is slightly overbalanced with respect to oxygen content, and kieselguhr is an inert material that decreases the explosive strength of the glyceryl nitrate in a guhr dynamite. It was found that if the kieselguhr was replaced by a mixture of finely ground sodium nitrate and an absorbent, combustible material such as wood pulp, the resulting composition was considerably stronger than the kieselguhr–glyceryl nitrate mixture containing the same proportion of glyceryl nitrate. Later, it was found advantageous to include a small percentage of sulfur in the combustible material and an even smaller percentage of an antacid such as calcium carbonate or zinc oxide. Representative straight dynamite compositions are presented in Table 14.

The formulation of straight and other types of dynamite takes into account the oxygen balance of the composition when packed in paper cartridges that have been waterproofed with paraffin. This is done by adjusting the proportions of the ingredients and the paper cartridge so that detonation results in the formation of nitrogen, carbon dioxide, water, and the oxides of sodium, sulfur, calcium, etc. If the cartridged composition is overbalanced with respect to oxygen, the explosion tends to produce poisonous oxides of nitrogen and does not liberate as much heat as it would if it were oxygen-balanced. The presence of too high a proportion of combustible material, with consequent underbalance with respect to oxygen, results in the production of excessive amounts of carbon monoxide. This also is undesirable, particularly when the dynamite is to be used in underground mining work. In some states, legislation has been enacted which classifies explosives into certain "fume groups," depending upon the amounts of noxious gases, particularly carbon monoxide, hydrogen sulfide, and nitrogen oxides, produced when the explosive is detonated under prescribed test conditions.

The straight dynamites are characterized by relatively high rates of detonation which render them suitable for use in blasting hard and tough rock. Since the cost of straight dynamites is somewhat higher per unit of explosive strength than that of other types of dynamite, they no longer are in general use in the U.S.

Blasting gelatin and gelatin dynamites were both covered by a patent issued to Nobel in 1875. He found that cellulose nitrate containing about 12% nitrogen was colloided by glyceryl nitrate when the mixture was warmed, with the formation of a rather tough gel.

If a mixture containing about 92% glyceryl nitrate is so colloided, it is termed "blasting gelatin" and is considered to be the 100% gelatin dynamite. This has the highest rate of detonation of the glyceryl nitrate dynamites, a high density, and excellent resistance to water. Its explosive strength is very much greater than that of TNT, and it is suitable for use with very hard rock, and in submarine operations.

Blasting gelatin and the other gelatin dynamites are somewhat less sensitive to initiation than straight dynamites and tend to lose some sensitivity when stored. They have been replaced to a large extent by ammonia gelatin dynamites, which can be manufactured at lower cost.

Ammonia dynamites or ammonium nitrate dynamites contain substantial amounts of ammonium nitrate, which usually replaces part of the glyceryl nitrate or other sensitizing agent, also part of the sodium nitrate. The replacement of part of the sodium nitrate by ammonium nitrate increases the volume of gas produced by detonation. A slightly higher proportion of antacid generally is present in ammonia dynamites than in straight dynamites, as it has been found that mixtures of ammonium nitrate and glyceryl nitrate tend to produce acidity more readily than do mixtures of sodium nitrate and glyceryl nitrate.

The ammonia dynamites represent one of the most generally used types of mining and quarrying explosives. Although they are less water-resistant than straight dynamites and distinctly less so than gelatin dynamites, ammonia dynamites have sufficient water resistance for most mining and quarrying purposes. They have approximately the same explosive-strength values as do the gelatin dynamites, but have lower rate of detonation and brisance values. Since the ammonia dynamites are somewhat cheaper than other types of dynamites on the basis of both weight and energy output, they have become one of the most favored of dynamites for ordinary mining and quarrying purposes.

Ammonia gelatin dynamites were patented by Nobel in 1879. They are formulated so as to combine, as far as is practicable, the best characteristics of ammonia and gelatin dynamites. The ammonium nitrate and glyceryl nitrate contents are intermediate between those of the other two types of dynamites (see Table 14). Ammonia gelatin dynamites are more resistant to water than the ammonia dynamites, but less so than the gelatin dynamites. They are superior to the gelatin dynamites, but are slightly inferior to the ammonia dynamites with respect to the volume of gas produced. Conversely, they have lower rates of detonation than the gelatin dynamites but higher rates than the ammonia dynamites.

Semigelatin dynamites are intermediate in composition between ammonia gelatin and ammonia dynamites, and are essentially ammonia dynamites to which insufficient cellulose nitrate has been added to form a stiff gel. They are more plastic than ammonia dynamites and are somewhat less sensitive to shock and friction than gelatin dynamites, although more sensitive to initiation.

Nitrostarch dynamites began to be manufactured in this country shortly after the turn of this century, and they are made nowhere else. In these dynamites nitrostarch is used as the sensitizing agent instead of the glyceryl nitrate, glycol dinitrate, etc, used in other dynamites.

Nitrostarch, being a pulverulent solid, does not freeze at atmospheric temperatures, as does glyceryl nitrate. Moreover, headaches do not result when it comes in contact with the skin, or when small amounts of muck-pile gases (those remaining after an explosion in rock, etc) are inhaled. Nitrostarch dynamites do not undergo exudation as do some glyceryl nitrate dynamites under adverse storage conditions. They have been used successfully in the Arctic and Antarctic regions, where glyceryl nitrate dynamites can freeze and become desensitized.

In general, nitrostarch dynamites are less sensitive to shock, friction, and heat than are the glyceryl nitrate dynamites, and, therefore, are less hazardous when subjected to transportation and handling. Truckloads of nitrostarch dynamite have undergone accidental burning without detonation, whereas glyceryl nitrate dynamites usually undergo detonation under such conditions.

Nitrostarch dynamites are formulated so as to be comparable with the various types of glyceryl nitrate dynamites with respect to conditions of use and explosive effects. As measured by the ballistic pendulum test, the higher grades of nitrostarch dynamites have slightly greater explosive-strength values than the corresponding grades of gelatin, ammonia, and ammonia gelatin dynamites.

"Permissible dynamites" are dynamites so formulated as to be suitable for use under conditions where explosive gas mixtures or dust–air mixtures may be present, as in coal mines.

The ignition of a combustible material requires time. Even such combustible systems as a mixture of a flammable gas and air or a suspension of bituminous coal-dust in air, require for ignition a temperature greater than a specified minimum and the subsequent maintenance of this temperature over a very short but measurable period of time. Explosives can be so formulated that the maximum temperature developed during explosion is relatively low and of short duration. Thus, it is important that coal-mining explosives, when detonated under prescribed conditions of loading and weight of charge, be substantially free from the danger of igniting mixtures of flammable gas and air such as sometimes occur in coal mines, and such suspensions of coal dust in flammable mixtures of gas and air as may be stirred up in mines when a shot "cannons" or blows out through the borehole instead of "pulling" the burden of coal properly. Such explosives are classified as "permissible" by the U.S. Bureau of Mines after having passed a series of special and carefully controlled tests.

There are a number of ways by which explosives which have low flame temperatures may be obtained. In general, this is done by either formulating the explosive so that the explosive reactions are not strongly exothermic, or by adding to the explosive composition ingredients that are inactive and have high specific heat values.

The reaction between carbon and oxygen which yields carbon dioxide is highly exothermic, whereas that which yields carbon monoxide liberates much less heat but an equal volume of gas. Similarly, the explosion of an underbalanced mixture with respect to oxygen yields the same volume of a mixture of gaseous water and hydrogen as if all the hydrogen were converted to water, but less heat is liberated. As a result of these effects, an underbalanced composition produces a flame which has a lowered temperature. The production of excessive amounts of carbon monoxide and hydrogen is undesirable, and this approach to formulate a permissible dynamite composition usually is combined with the addition of inert ingredients.

Such inert ingredients may be either finely divided materials such as diatomaceous earth, clay, or sand, or materials that volatilize at the temperature produced by the explosive reaction. Volatile materials include free water, water of crystallization in compounds such as magnesium sulfate, the alums, and calcium sulfate; and salts such as sodium chloride that are themselves volatile at the temperature produced by the explosive reaction.

Rather than including temperature-reducing constituents in the explosive composition itself, assemblies have been made (particularly in Germany, Belgium, and Great Britain) that comprise an inner explosive cartridge surrounded by an annular layer or "sheath" of a mixture that has flame-reducing properties. The primary explosive should be a composition that itself produces upon detonation only a relatively low explosive temperature. As a surrounding sheath, a mixture of 15 parts glyceryl nitrate, 50 parts sodium bicarbonate, and 35 parts sodium chloride has found wide acceptance in Germany.

In the manufacture of sheathed cartridges, the outer cartridge wrapper is rolled by a machine that fills it with the sheathing composition; a cylindrical cutter removes the sheathing composition from the portion of the charge that is to be filled with the primary explosive composition, and this is then inserted. The portion of the sheathing composition removed by the cutter is reused.

Permissible dynamites are formulated with either glyceryl nitrate or nitrostarch as the sensitizing agent. Because of the very high temperature of explosion of glyceryl nitrate, the proportion of this is kept at a practicable minimum. Permissible dynamites, like the general blasting dynamites, are manufactured in grades having explosive strength values varying from 60 to 110% that of TNT.

Ammonium Nitrate Blasting Explosives

In 1867, Ohlsson and Norrbin laid the basis for this type of blasting explosives with a patent for ammonium nitrate and mixtures of ammonium nitrate with materials other than glyceryl nitrate. Some of these materials were nonexplosive fuels such as charcoal, sawdust, and naphthalene, whereas others were explosives such as picric acid and nitrobenzene.

Since that time an extremely wide variety of compositions which contain no glyceryl nitrate have been developed and used. Such blasting agents generally were produced at lower cost and with reduced hazard in manufacture than the glyceryl nitrate dynamites. The changing nature of these compositions have reflected the changes in availability at low cost of the material to be mixed with ammonium nitrate.

Ammonium nitrate has only 79% the explosive strength of TNT, but the addition of a fuel usually sensitizes the ammonium nitrate to initiation; and such mixtures have more explosive strength than does TNT.

Ammonium nitrate blasting explosives generally contain a greater percentage of the nitrate than do the ammonia dynamites; and some sodium nitrate usually is also used to increase the available oxygen content. Many are characterized by relatively low rates of detonation (2000–3500 m/sec) and high gas-volume values. Despite this, their shattering powers in quarry blasting are greater than would be expected. Their explosive-strength values generally are from 115 to 125% that of TNT. They are not graded for strength in the same manner as glyceryl nitrate and nitrostarch dynamites.

Ammonium Nitrate with Nonexplosive Sensitizers. There are many of these which greatly increase the sensitivity and explosive strength of ammonium nitrate. Among these are powdered metals and alloys. Combustible organic materials such as rosin, hexamethylenetetramine, paraffin oils, fuel oils, and waxes are relatively efficient sensitizers for ammonium nitrate.

During the past ten years, an explosive termed AN-FO has been used in very large amounts. This is an oxygen-balanced mixture, containing 94.5% prilled ammonium nitrate and 5.5% fuel oil, that cannot be detonated by a blasting cap when unconfined, but can be detonated by a booster charge of high explosive. Under the confinement of a steel pipe it can be detonated by a no. 8 blasting cap. Its explosive strength is 120% that of TNT as judged by the ballistic pendulum test, and it detonates at a rate of 2100 m/sec when confined in a steel pipe. Because of its very low cost, ease of manufacture, and suitability for mechanical loading AN-FO has replaced dynamites to a very considerable extent in quarrying, ore mining, and salt mining operations. It has even been used by charging boreholes with ammonium nitrate and fuel oil simultaneously. It is generally packed in multiwall paper bags.

Ammonium Nitrate with Detonatable Sensitizers. Many dry-blasting explosives of this type have been manufactured at various times. Some modern examples of these and their compositions are given in Table 15.

Table 15. Compositions of Various Modern Dry-Blasting Explosives

ammonium nitrate, %	86.0	74.0	29.0	92.5
sodium nitrate, %		11.0	33.0	
dinitrotoluene, %	8.5	7.0		5.0
trinitrotoluene, %			28.0	
ground coal, %	5.5	6.0	10.0	
wax, %		2.0		2.5

Such compositions vary widely with respect to sensitivity to initiation; some are detonatable and others nondetonatable by a blasting cap when in an unconfined state. Their explosive strengths vary from 95 to 125% that of TNT, and their rates of detonation vary from 2200 to 4200 m/sec when confined.

Since 1954, pourable *slurry explosives* have been developed which are based on ammonium nitrate with an explosive sensitizer; these are now used to a considerable extent as replacements for dynamites. Slurry explosives consist of suspensions of undissolved nitrate, organic fuel, and an insoluble sensitizing agent in sufficient nitrate solution to form a slurry. In some cases an organic thickening agent also serves as a fuel. The water contents of slurry explosives generally vary from 11 to 20%.

Slurry explosives are effective because the water present, while decreasing the heat liberated by explosion, increases the volume of gases produced so as to compensate in part for the decrease in heat of explosion. These compositions generally have high densities and are quite insensitive, requiring a booster charge of dry high explosive for initiation, even when confined. Their explosive-strength values are from 90 to 105% that of TNT. When confined in steel pipes they detonate at rates which vary from 4400 to 5800 m/sec.

Slurry explosives have been developed which contain TNT, cellulose nitrate, or nitrostarch as the insoluble sensitizing agent. Both ammonium nitrate and sodium nitrate generally are present. Starch, cellulose, and flake aluminum are the most important fuels used. Guar gum is used as a suspending agent and as a fuel.

Water-gel explosives, based on ammonium nitrate and nitrostarch, are of recent development. They are intermediate between the nitrostarch dynamites and the nitrostarch slurry explosives and are used as replacements for dynamites. They contain less water than a slurry explosive, and this is gelled by materials comparable with gelatin. Such compositions are more resistant to water than are ammonia dynamites, but have some of the characteristics of slurry compositions. Being of a plastic nature, they have the advantage of undergoing plastic flow when loaded in a borehole and thus filling it completely.

A representative water-gel explosive cannot be detonated by a blasting cap and is very insensitive to shock and friction. It has an explosive strength value about 115% that of TNT and is of satisfactory stability. Water-gel explosives are packed in polyethylene tubes.

Liquid-Oxygen Explosives

Liquid-oxygen explosives (LOX) became important blasting agents after World War I, when they replaced dynamites to a certain extent. Using liquefied oxygen and a combustible, absorbent fuel such as granular lampblack or carbon black, LOX was economically competitive with dynamites when a liquid-oxygen plant could be run continuously on a large scale. Since the introduction of the very low cost AN-FO and slurry explosives, use of LOX in this country has decreased to about 15% of its previous maximum.

The carbonaceous fuel of LOX is contained in paper or cloth cartridges which are immersed in liquid oxygen of at least 95% purity shortly before use. After a sufficient time to permit their saturation by the liquid oxygen, the cartridges are loaded in boreholes and detonated.

Evaporation begins from the moment the cartridge is removed from the liquid oxygen, and therefore the cartridge must be used within a short time after removal. With cartridges of 5–8 in. diameter, a soaking period of 0.5 to 1 hr is usually allowed, and the cartridges should be detonated within 45 min after removal from the soaking box. Electric blasting caps are used for initiating small charges of LOX, and large charges are initiated with the same or Primacord (PETN detonating fuse).

Maximum effect is obtained when the mixture is oxygen-balanced. This condition exists for a very short time, and both before and after this period a lesser explosive effect is produced. An oxygen-balanced mixture of charcoal and oxygen contains approx 72.9% liquid oxygen.

Tests have shown that compositions of LOX have rates of detonation of 4400–6200 m/sec; they are considered to have about the same explosive strength as 40% dynamite.

Chlorate and Perchlorate Explosives

In 1788, Berthollet attempted the substitution of potassium chlorate for potassium nitrate in black powder with disastrous results. After the invention of dynamites, blasting explosives based on potassium chlorate were developed. Later, sodium chlorate was substituted for potassium chlorate, and ammonium perchlorate was used to

Table 16. Examples of Chlorate and Perchlorate Explosives

Composition, %	A	B	C	D	E
potassium chlorate	80		87.5		
sodium chlorate		79			
potassium perchlorate				56	
ammonium perchlorate					82
nitronaphthalene	12			12	
dinitrobenzene				32	
dinitrotoluene		16			13
castor oil	8	5			5
oxidized rosin			12.5		

some extent. During World War I, Germany developed potassium perchlorate explosives. Various types of these explosives are given in Table 16.

Other compositions contained ammonium nitrate, glyceryl nitrate, sodium nitrate, or TNT in addition to some of the above ingredients.

Chlorate and perchlorate explosives are unduly sensitive to shock and friction; and their manufacture in the U.S. was abandoned after a long history of plant and field accidents. They are, however, still manufactured in Europe. Their preparation is particularly dangerous when carried out by unskilled workers.

SEISMIC EXPLOSIVES

Explosives are used on a large scale in carrying out seismographic explorations, chiefly in the location of petroleum deposits. These tests are made both on land and below the surfaces of bodies of water. In 1962, no less than 27,000 tons of explosives were used in the U.S. for this purpose.

The particular explosives used vary greatly, depending upon the various conditions of use, the types of seismographic equipment involved, etc. One ton of black powder was used because of the legal restrictions in certain regions. AN-FO and related compositions were used to the extent of 7,800 tons for both land and submarine explorations, and dynamites and special compositions were used to the extent of 19,300 tons. These latter compositions varied from gelatin dynamites to special compositions having a wide range of carefully controlled rates of detonation.

Since there is a large element of secrecy involved in seismographic exploration, the relative applicability of the various types of explosives under specific conditions has not become generally known.

OIL-AND GAS–WELL EXPLOSIVES

Despite its long-established record of extreme sensitivity to shock and disastrous episodes in transportation, glyceryl nitrate for many years was the traditional explosive for "bringing in" oil wells after being drilled to the oil formation. Today, less hazardous explosives are used for enlarging well bottoms, cracking strata to rejuvenate wells, and for the bringing in of dry wells.

Most of these replacements for glyceryl nitrate are solid explosives similar to 75% gelatin or 70% nitrostarch dynamite, which have high explosive-strength values and rates of detonation. In some cases, a special dynamite is used which contains as much as 87% ammonium nitrate and only 2.5% glyceryl nitrate.

Explosives are sometimes used to increase the rate of flow of gas wells, and for this purpose explosives similar to those employed in oil wells are generally used.

Index to High Explosives

LOW EXPLOSIVES

The "low explosives" are those which, as normally used, undergo autocombustion at rates which are low as compared with the rates of detonation of high explosives. They are divided into *black powders, priming compositions*, and *propellant compositions*. Some pyrotechnic compositions are low explosives, but are not used in this capacity, since they are formulated so as to develop maximum light effects rather than explosive strength.

Black Powder

Black powder is a mechanical mixture of potassium or sodium nitrate, charcoal, and sulfur. None of these ingredients are explosive, and the mixture undergoes autocombustion that cannot be transformed into detonation.

Black powder is the oldest explosive known, since it apparently was used in China, 2000 or more years ago. By 700 AD it had reached Eastern Europe; it or an analogous composition constituted the famous "Greek fire." It was not until about 1250 that black powder became known in Western Europe through the work of Roger Bacon. Black powder was used only for producing pyrotechnic and incendiary effects until 1313, when the invention of the cannon in Germany marked the beginning of its use as a propellant. It was not until about 1613 that it was first used in Saxony, as a blasting explosive in mines.

From then until nearly 1870, black powder was the universally used explosive. When used in firearms, a loose charge above the borehole or in the priming pan served as the priming composition. The charge of black powder in the borehole acted as the fuse composition to advance the ignition to the propellant charge of black powder in the tube of the gun. When the projectile was of the shrapnel type, black powder in the delay fuze was ignited, and in turn ignited the bursting charge of black powder.

As a blasting explosive, ignited by a delay fuse containing black powder, it was used for mining, quarrying, and demolition purposes.

The development of a cellulose nitrate propellant by Schultze in 1864, and of dynamite in 1867, by Nobel, marked the introduction of modern explosives for the replacement of black powder. Since that period the importance of black powder, on the basis of proportion of explosives produced, has declined steadily. During the past ten years, with the advent of cheaper, safer, and more easily manufactured ammonium nitrate explosives, this decline has been precipitate. In 1962, the production of black powder in the U.S. was only 3.7% that of 1948 and less than 2% that of the years immediately prior to World War II. Today, it is used chiefly in ignition charges for propellants, saluting charges, delay charges in blasting (miners') fuse and blasting in mines.

MANUFACTURE OF BLACK POWDER

Because of the large number of disastrous explosions that have occurred, the manufacture of black powder is carried out in a series of buildings carefully spaced so as to prevent the propagation of fire or explosion from one building to another. The general method of manufacture is described below.

In one house, the potassium nitrate is ground in a ball mill, while the charcoal and sulfur are pulverized together in a ball mill located in another house. The sulfur thereby is "incorporated" or worked into the cellular openings of the charcoal. The nitrate and charcoal–sulfur mixture are transferred to a mixing building, where they are sieved to remove foreign materials and then mixed. Mixing is accomplished by dampening the materials and mixing by hand or mechanically. The mixed materials are transferred to a millhouse which contains a wheel mill. Each of the two wheels, made of cast iron, is 7–8 ft in diam, has a width of 18 in., and weighs approx 10 tons. The wheels are so assembled that the path of one overlaps that of the other by several inches. A plough behind the inner wheel is turned so as to throw the material being mixed away from the center of the mill, while a plough behind the outer wheel throws the material toward the center. About 300 lb of mixture is spread on the bed of the wheel mill and moistened so as to contain a moisture content of approx 4%. The mill is then operated for 4–6 hr at the rate of 10 rpm. The milling operation serves to increase the degree of incorporation of the nitrate and sulfur into the charcoal.

At the conclusion of the milling operation, any wheel cake or clinker is broken up manually. The milled material is then transferred to a presshouse and pressed into cakes 18–24 in. square and 0.75–1 in. thick. This is done by means of a hydraulic press with a spread of about 6 ft between platens, and aluminum plates 0.37 in. thick. The powder is placed on the plates and an aluminum rack is used to hold the powder in place while the depth of layer is adjusted. Successive layers and plates are built up until about 4000 lb of powder has been put in the press. Pressure of 6000 psi is then applied for a period that varies with the type of powder desired.

The resulting cakes are transferred to a corning mill building, where they are unloaded in a room that is partitioned from the corning mill by a steel barricade. The cakes are fed into the mill by means of a conveyor, which carries them over the top of the barricade. The first rolls of the mill have corrugated surfaces and are adjustable. The broken cakes are then fed to another pair of rolls that further reduces the material to the desired grain size. The powder then passes over mechanically operated shaker screens, the dust and fines being caught in bags. This material is returned to the wheel mill. The coarse material from the screens is passed through the rolls a second time and rescreened. The corning mill operation is considered the most hazardous in the manufacture of black powder.

After being transferred to the blending house, the powder is placed in rotating drums of hardwood about 8 ft long and 4 ft in diameter. Tumbling of the powder produces heat due to friction, and temperatures as high as 65°C are developed. This heating produces evaporation of any moisture present without any further drying of the powder. When the powder is to be glazed, graphite is added to the contents of the drum after the moisture has been reduced to a point, where the powder has not become too dry; the success of this technique depends upon the experience of the operator. Drying and glazing require approx 8 hr. The powder is separated into standard granulations by sieving before packing. The finished powder is packed in airtight metal kegs that hold 20–25 lb of powder.

In the manufacture of black powder it is customary to employ extreme caution in the grounding of machinery, in wearing of nailless shoes, etc, in order to avoid the formation of sparks.

Black powders are graded on the basis of grain size rather than quality. The grades are classified in size, as C (coarse), CC, CCC, F (fine), FF, or 2F, 3F, 4F, etc. The average diameter of the CCC granulation is about 14 mm, whereas that of the 4F granulation is 1–2 mm.

BLACK POWDER COMPOSITIONS

The basic modern black powder compositions are shown in Table 17.

Black powders burn at rates dependent upon combustion, degree of incorporation, density, and degree of confinement. The sodium nitrate powder burns more slowly than that which contains potassium nitrate. Increase in the proportion of charcoal causes a decrease in burning rate. A small change in the sulfur content does not affect the rate of burning, but moisture in excess of 0.2% does cause some decrease. The type of charcoal has a pronounced effect on the rate of burning; powders that are made from willow or alder charcoal burn much more rapidly than those made from oak charcoal. Powders made by simple mixing burn much more slowly than incorporated powder, the rate increasing with increase in degree of incorporation. Increase in grain density has the effect of decreasing the rate of burning. At a pressure of 25,000 psi, black powder burns at a rate of approx 4 in./sec, as compared with rates of 7–12 in./sec for single- and double-base smokeless powders. Efforts to cause detonation of black powder by initiation with a booster explosive have yielded a maximum rate of approximately 400 m/sec, as compared with rates from 2000 to 8500 m/sec for most high explosives. This difference may be considered as due to the explosion of black powder representing a chemical reaction between its ingredients rather than an exothermic decomposition.

Table 17. Basic Formulas of Modern Black Powder Compositions

Ingredient	A	B
potassium nitrate, %	74.0	
sodium nitrate, %		71.0
charcoal, %	15.6	16.5
sulfur, %	10.4	12.5

For some applications, it is desirable that black powder burn at a rate less than that normal for the standard composition at atmospheric pressures. This usually is accomplished by changing the type of charcoal used, substituting barium nitrate for potassium nitrate, increasing the proportion of sulfur present, or by the inclusion of inert materials such as borax.

Upon explosion, black powders produce gases and a wide variety of solid products which are represented by the following empirical equation:

$$74 \text{ KNO}_3 + 16 \text{ C}_6\text{H}_2\text{O} + 32 \text{ S} \rightarrow 35 \text{ N}_2 + 56 \text{ CO}_2 + 14 \text{ CO} + \text{C} + 19 \text{ K}_2\text{CO}_3 + (\text{NH}_4)_2\text{CO}_3 +$$
$$3 \text{ CH}_4 + 7 \text{ K}_2\text{SO}_4 + 8 \text{ K}_2\text{S}_2\text{O}_3 + 2 \text{ KSCN} + 2 \text{ K}_2\text{S} + 2 \text{ H}_2\text{S} + 3 \text{ S} + 4 \text{ H}$$

Having a heat of combustion of 1425 cal/g, potassium nitrate black powder, upon explosion, liberates approx 680 cal/g and produces 0.6 g of solids and 278 ml of gas per gram.

Black powders are very sensitive to ignition, but this varies considerably with the degree of aggregation. In dust form black powder is ignited by an electrostatic spark or a spark from a flint. When dropped on hot metal at 510°C black powder ignites in 0.1 sec. In the explosion-temperature test it ignites in 5 sec at 427°C.

Different methods of testing indicate black powder to be less sensitive to impact than TNT. Sodium nitrate black powder is slightly less sensitive to impact than the potassium nitrate powder. As determined by pendulum-friction tests, both types of powder are of the same order of insensitivity to friction as TNT.

Black powders have very little brisance as measured by the sand test, in which they crush no sand when ignited by a flame and crush only 8 g of sand when initiated with Tetryl or PETN, as compared with 47.5 g for TNT.

Because of the poor confinement of the Trauzl lead-block test and the low rate of explosion of black powder, this test indicates black powder to have only 10% of the explosive strength of TNT. However, ballistic pendulum tests have shown potassium nitrate and sodium nitrate black powders to have 42.5 and 45% of the explosive strength of TNT, respectively.

In the absence of excessive moisture, black powder is of a high order of chemical and physical stability. The ingredients of the powder are essentially nonreactive with each other even at temperatures as high as 120°C. However, it is not desirable to heat black powder above 70°C because of the rapid increase in vapor pressure of the sulfur, with consequent increase in volatility, and the resulting change in composition or uniformity of composition of the powder.

Black powders are undesirably hygroscopic, and especially so in the case of sodium nitrate. This hygroscopicity, which varies widely with the conditions of exposure to atmospheric humidity, has been generally attributed to the hygroscopicity of the nitrate in the powder. Although the nitrate does contribute to the hygroscopicity of the powder, it has been found that the charcoal is chiefly responsible for this. Evidently this is due to the large specific surface of charcoal and its known adsorptive capacity for gases. The substitution of noncellular carbon, such as soot or sugar carbon, yields powders of much lower hygroscopicity. Since the sulfur and nitrate of such powders cannot be incorporated into the particles of carbon, they are much less satisfactory with respect to uniformity of burning rate, and burn much less rapidly than do powders made with charcoal.

Ignition Powder. The potassium nitrate composition given above is used for ignition purposes in military ammunition. The powder is granulated so as to pass

Table 18. Composition of Benite

cellulose nitrate (13.5% N), %	40.0
potassium nitrate, %	44.3
charcoal, %	9.4
sulfur, %	6.3
ethyl centralite, %	0.5

through a no. 4, and be retained on a no. 8 screen. It is loaded in a cloth bag attached to the base of a charge of smokeless powder. In some cases, the black powder is pressed to form pellets before it is loaded in the primers.

Benite is an ignition powder which consists of the ingredients of black powder in a matrix of gelatinized cellulose nitrate. It is manufactured in the form of strands by a solvent extrusion process. Its composition is given in Table 18.

The presence of a large number of finely divided, incandescent, solid particles in the products of explosion of black powder render it an efficient ignition agent for smokeless powder. It has been found that black powder is more effective in igniting smokeless powder than is a quantity of smokeless powder itself.

Fuse Powder. This powder is used in commercial miners' fuse, used for delays in exploding detonators (blasting caps). The powder may have the potassium nitrate composition shown above or may represent a variation in the proportion of ingredients so as to decrease the rate of burning. In some cases, inert diluents such as graphite, brick dust, or borax may be present which serve to decrease the rate of burning.

Fuze Powders. These are black or modified black powder compositions that are loaded in time-train rings of military time fuzes that serve to produce a predetermined delay between firing of the round and detonation of the charge in the shell or bomb. To obtain maximum uniformity of burning at a minimum rate, the powder is loaded in rings under high pressures. These may be of the order of 100,000 psi.

If a lesser rate of burning is required than is obtainable with the standard powder composition, the desired rate may be obtained by modifying the composition or by blending the standard powder with a powder that burns too slowly for direct use in fuzes. Modification of the composition in this direction can be accomplished by the substitution of barium nitrate for part of the potassium nitrate in the standard composition. The modified powder must then be blended with the standard powder in experimentally determined proportions. A powder that has a very low burning rate and can be blended with standard black powder contains 70% potassium nitrate, 14% bituminous coal, and 16% sulfur. The manufacture of such a coal powder is similar to that of standard black powder, but, due to the noncellular structure of bituminous coal, there is no incorporation of the nitrate and sulfur.

Black Blasting Powder. Sodium nitrate black powder burns more slowly than does the potassium nitrate type, and its lower cost makes it more suitable for certain blasting purposes. However, it is more hygroscopic, and is well glazed with graphite to retard the absorption of moisture.

The manufacture of black blasting powder is the same as that described for potassium nitrate black powder. The graphite-glazed grains are sieved to sizes designated as C, CC, CCC, F, FF, FFF, and FFFF. Black blasting powder is also produced in the form of cylindrical pellets which have central perforations. Several such pellets may be wrapped together to form a cartridge of desired diameter and length. Pelleted black blasting powder contains some starch as a partial replacement for charcoal, the starch being added to the mix in the form of a paste. Since it is practicable to make pellets from the mix as it comes from the wheel mill, generally a "press cake" is made and granulated before the pellets are made. The moisture in the pressed pellets is removed by drying on trays before cartridges are made up. Pelleted black blasting powder is produced in several "grades," which differ in density and, therefore, in burning rate. The granulated powder has an apparent density of approx 1.8, but that of the pelleted powder is only 1.35–1.50.

Miscellaneous. The potassium nitrate type of black powder is used to some extent in base charges for fuzes, friction primers, as smoke-puff charges, and in practice projectiles. It is an important material in the fabrication of fireworks (see Pyrotechnics).

The sodium nitrate type of black powder, in airtight assemblies, has been used in saluting charges and practice bombs.

Priming Compositions

Priming compositions are mixtures which provide a sudden burst of flame that serves to ignite an initial detonating agent, propellant, fuze powder, or pyrotechnic composition. Their action is thus distinct from that of initial detonating agents, which transmit detonation waves. Priming compositions must function when subjected to impact, stab action, percussion, friction, or flame, and are used in commercial and military devices such as blasting caps, fuzes, small-arms cartridges, artillery and rocket igniters, incendiary compositions, and pyrotechnics (qv).

A priming composition must deliver a relatively large volume of hot gas and solid particles without the development of a detonating wave. The ideal priming composition would consist of a single chemical compound of uniform granulation that would undergo rapid, highly exothermic decomposition when subjected to one of the physical forces mentioned. At the present time, the only compound that meets this requirement is lead dinitroresorcinate; however, the sensitivity of the material is such that it can be used in the desired manner only under somewhat restricted conditions.

The next most desirable type of priming composition would be a mixture of compounds that, although individually nonexplosive, sensitize each other to ignition and rapid burning. Such compositions have been developed. In practice, most priming compositions consist of mixtures of one or more initial detonating agents with oxidizing agents, fuels, sensitizers, and binding agents. Potassium chlorate, antimony sulfide, and gum arabic are examples of the classes of "addends" mentioned. In some cases an addend may serve two purposes. Whereas antimony sulfide acts as a fuel as well as a sensitizer to friction, gum arabic acts as a fuel and as a binding agent. The net effect of the addends is so to dilute the initial detonating agent as to convert its decomposition from detonation into rapid combustion. The addends may also serve to increase the volume of gas produced per unit weight of priming composition, to prevent the gases from having too high a temperature, and to contribute incandescent solid particles to the products of decomposition.

Table 19 gives examples of typical priming compositions. The classes of compositions given are intended for use where ignition is caused by impact, stab action, or percussion. In addition, compositions in certain assemblies are required to function through friction. An example is the friction primer for a pyrotechnic flare. This consists of a braided wire coated with red phosphorus and shellac, which is pulled through a pellet consisting of 88% potassium chlorate, 10% charcoal, and 2% dextrin.

Table 19. Typical Priming Compositions

Constituents	A	B	C	D
Mixtures of nonexplosive ingredients, %				
potassium chlorate	55	60	50.5	
lead thiocyanate	45			
antimony sulfide		30	26.3	
cuprous thiocyanate		3		
sulfur		7	8.8	
ground glass			12.4	
shellac			2.0	
Mixtures based on mercury fulminate, %				
mercury fulminate	19	32	28	11
potassium chlorate	33	45	14	52.5
antimony sulfide	43	23	21	36.5
black powder	2.5			
sulfur	2.5			
ground glass			35	
shellac			2	
Mixtures of nonexplosive ingredients with noninitiating or weak initiating explosives, %				
potassium chlorate	53	52.7		
lead thiocyanate	25	24.8		
antimony sulfide	17	11.9	5	
barium nitrate			42	
calcium silicide			18	
TNT	5			
PETN		9.9		
lead styphnate			35	
gum		0.7		
Mixtures based on lead azide. %				
potassium chlorate	53	33.4		
lead thiocyanate	25			
antimony sulfide	17	33.3		
silicon carbide		5.0		
lead azide	5	28.3		

Other friction primers consist of a roughened wire or rod, which is pulled through a pellet of priming composition. A typical composition of this type consists of 56.2% potassium chlorate, 24.6% antimony sulfide, 9.0% sulfur, and 10.2% ground glass.

Of the compositions listed in Table 19, those containing mercury fulminate are the least stable; however, even these may be considered satisfactory in this respect when not stored at temperatures above those normally encountered in temperate climates. The other compositions, which contain nonexplosive compounds only, or lead styphnate, lead azide, TNT, or PETN, are of a high order of stability even at 100°C. The presence of moisture may cause some acceleration of deterioration and, in some cases, lead to segregation and nonuniformity. As priming compositions are used frequently in conjunction with a water-wet binding agent, subsequent thorough drying of the composition is important. Binding agents that are used include gum tragacanth, gum arabic, glue, dextrin and, sodium alginate.

The sensitivity of priming compositions varies widely, but that of an individual composition can be varied somewhat by careful control of the granulation of each of the ingredients. This, in some cases, is more important than the proportions of the ingredients. Nonuniformity of composition due to mechanical segregation of ingredients can cause great variations in sensitivity and failures in function. The presence of a binding agent prevents such segregation and fixes the composition in the desired position in the assembly.

The weight of priming composition used may be of the order of only 0.15 g, and the rate of burning, volume of gases, and weight of solid particles produced, as well as the duration of the flame, are the properties of major importance with respect to efficient functioning. The volume of gas, at STP, is of the order of only 1.5 ml. The percentage of the weight of the composition carried as incandescent particles by the hot gases will vary with the composition, but is approx 70% in the case of the above composition which contains 5% TNT. Such incandescent particles are considered to promote ignition by thermal radiation.

Flame bursts from various primer compositions similarly loaded were found to have effective durations varying from 400 to 750 μsec, with total durations varying from 650 to 1500 μsec. Short as these periods may appear, they are thousands of times as great as would be required for detonation of composition of equal thickness. The priming composition in a round of military ammunition must function with the great speeds indicated by the above duration values. This can be recognized from the fact that in the firing of a 75-mm round, only 0.05 sec is required for ignition, burning of the black powder igniter charge, and complete controlled combustion of the propellant charge.

TESTING OF EXPLOSIVES

The most important tests used for establishing the suitability of explosives for commercial or military use, or for the comparison of various explosives, are those that determine the sensitivity, stability, brisance, and explosive-strength characteristics. If on the basis of these tests an explosive is found acceptable, additional tests for hygroscopicity, volatility, solubility, density, and compatibility with other materials are then necessary. Further investigation involves the determination of the following characteristics: mechanical properties; setback sensitivity; heat and gas production values; rate of detonation; detonation pressure; fragmentation effects; the velocity and distribution of fragments from shell and bomb casings; and blast effect. Propellants are tested especially for stability, since their sensitivity is of secondary importance; ballistic potential is determined by performance tests in weapons and rockets. Brief descriptions of the tests for the determination of explosive and stability characteristics are given below.

Sensitivity

Impact Tests. Sensitivity to impact is determined by subjecting a small quantity of confined explosive to the transmitted shock of a falling weight—usually 2 kg—and determinining the minimum height of fall that will produce at least one explosion in ten tests. Another approach is to determine the height of fall that will cause explosions in 50% of the tests. With the Bureau of Mines apparatus (Test B), 0.02 g of the material is spread evenly over an area 1 cm in diameter and confined by means of a 2-kg plunger with a tip 1 cm in diameter. The falling weight strikes the upper end of the plunger. If the explosive is liquid, the sample is held in position by being absorbed in a disk of dried filter paper 1 cm in diameter. With the Picatinny Arsenal apparatus (Test A), the cavity in a steel cup is filled with the solid or liquid explosive; the cup is then covered with a cylindrical brass cover which has a slip fit and a small steel plug is placed on the center of the brass cover. In this test, the falling weight strikes the steel plug.

Explosion Temperature Tests. Sensitivity to explosion when heat is applied is determined as the temperature required to produce explosion in either 5 sec, or in less than 0.1 sec. In the first case, a sample of 0.02 g is placed in a gilding-metal, blasting-cap shell, and the lower end of this shell is plunged into a bath of molten Wood's metal at a measured temperature. The time required to cause explosion, flashing, or very rapid decomposition is measured with a stop watch. The temperature for producing an explosion in 5 sec can be obtained by making a number of tests at various temperatures and plotting a temperature–time curve. The temperature required for instantaneous (less than 0.1 sec) explosion is determined by dropping small particles of the explosive on the surface of molten metal held at a measured temperature. The time required for explosion is determined, and the temperature is varied to determine the minimum temperature required for instantaneous explosion, flashing, or decomposition. Not all explosives undergo detonation in explosion temperature tests; in some cases, decomposition is accompanied by a puff of gas or smoke, whereas in other cases, no violent evolution of gas or smoke takes place.

Sensitivity to Initiation. This is determined by a modification of the sand test. A 0.40-g sample of the explosive is pressed into an empty blasting cap, and successive charges of 0.10 g Tetryl and 0.20 g lead azide are pressed on top. Five such assemblies are fired in the sand-test bomb, and the average amount of sand crushed, after correction for that crushed by the Tetryl and lead azide, is determined. Successive, tests determine the minimum amount of either Tetryl or lead azide that is required to crush the same amount of sand.

Pendulum Friction Test. This test determines sensitivity to friction. A 7-g sample of the explosive is spread evenly over a scored steel-base plate, and a 20-kg steel shoe suspended from a height of 1.5 m is allowed to sweep back and forth pendulumwise across the base plate. The rod which carries the shoe must have been adjusted so that the shoe will slide across the plate 18 ± 1 times when no explosive is present. Tests of ten samples are then made and the number of snaps, cracklings, ignitions, and/or explosions is noted. If positive results are obtained, further tests employ a fiber rather than a steel shoe, the frictional effect being less with the fiber shoe.

Rifle-Bullet Impact Test. A bomb is prepared by screwing a closing cap to one end of a 2-in.-long piece of cast-iron pipe that is 2 in. in diameter and threaded at both ends. The bomb is filled with the liquid, pressed or cast explosive and is closed by screwing on a closing cap. With the bomb in a vertical position, a .30-caliber bullet is fired through it from a distance of 30 ft. At least five such tests are made and the number of explosions is noted.

Brisance

Sand Test. Brisance (shattering power) can be determined by the sand test. A 0.40-g sample of the explosive is pressed into a metal blasting cap under a pressure of 3000 psi. Charges of 0.10 g Tetryl and 0.20 g lead azide are added under the same pressure, and a reinforcing cap is then pressed against the top charge. An 8-in. length of miners' fuse is inserted in the cap and crimped tightly in place. The detonator so assembled is centered in a bomb containing 80 g of Ottawa sand of such fineness that all of it will pass through a no. 20 sieve, whereas none of it will pass through a no. 30 sieve. Then, 120 more g of Ottawa sand is added, the bomb is closed, and the charge is fired by igniting the fuse protruding through a hole in the top plate. The amount of sand crushed is determined by weighing the portion that passes through a no. 30 sieve. This is corrected by subtracting the separately determined weight of sand crushed by 0.10 g of Tetryl and 0.20 g of lead azide, respectively. The net weight obtained is representative of the 0.40-g charge of explosive under test. Flame-sensitive initiating explosives such as lead azide or mercury fulminate require no superimposed charges for this test.

Rate of Detonation. The rate of detonation of an explosive varies greatly with its density, diameter of charge, and degree of confinement. However, each explosive has a characteristic maximum rate of detonation under optimum conditions that reflects its brisance. There are a number of methods for determining rates of detonation. The simplest method is that of Dautriche, which depends upon a comparison of the unknown with a standard, such as a measured length of cordeau detonating fuse of known rate of detonation. A more precise method is that in which the passage of a detonation wave through the unknown detonating fuse breaks successive wires which carry electric currents. These wires are spaced through the explosive charge at carefully measured distances. The time interval between successive breakages is determined precisely by a Mettegang recorder, or modern electronic equipment. Recent developments in this area permit such measurements to be made with relatively short lengths of explosive rather than with the 1-m lengths previously used, as well as the determination of variations in the rate of detonation with numerous current inserts (pin method). High-speed photographic methods are also used under certain conditions of confinement of the explosive charge.

Explosive Strength

Ballistic Pendulum Test. This test utilizes the equality of action and reaction to measure explosive strength. A sample of the explosive is detonated in a heavy mortar suspended by a pendulum bar and closed by means of a loosely fitting steel cylinder weighing 36 lb. An adjacent scale is provided to show the angular deflection of the mortar from its position of rest when the steel plug is ejected in the opposite direction. In practice the deflection caused by 10 g of TNT, and the weight of the sample explosive required to produce approximately the same deflection, are determined. The relative strength of the sample explosive is calculated by comparison with the 10 g of TNT.

Trauzl Lead-Block Test. This test is made by exploding a 10-g charge of the explosive in a cylindrical cavity, 25 mm in diameter and 125 mm deep, in a cylindrical lead block 200 mm in height and diameter. The sample is wrapped in tin foil, with a detonator embedded in the charge, and is placed at the bottom of the cavity. The cavity is stemmed with sand. After the charge is fired, the volume of the cavity is determined by pouring in water from a graduate. The enlargement caused by the explosive sample is found by subtracting, from the determined volume, the original volume plus the enlargement caused by the detonator alone. The latter is determined separately in the same manner.

Heat of Explosion. The work capacity or strength of an explosive or propellant can be determined by measuring the heat liberated during detonation or autocombustion in an inert atmosphere. With high explosives, this is done with a very large calorimetric bomb, which permits explosives to be detonated without rupture of the bomb. Propellants can be tested in much smaller calorimetric bombs, in which samples of only 1–2 g are ignited by means of an electrically heated wire.

Stability

65.5°C Surveillance Test. This test is applied chiefly to propellants, but can be applied to high explosives as well. A 45-g sample is placed in a flint-glass bottle which has a ground-glass stopper. The bottle is placed in an oven or chamber maintained at 65.5 ± 1.0°C. Daily observations are made to note the appearance of red fumes, which mark the end of the test. The number of days required for the liberation of red fumes is taken to represent the relative stability of the propellant or explosive, and tests of 30 days or less indicate hazardous instability. Deterioration during storage can be established by periodic tests of the propellant.

75°C International Test. A 10-g sample of the explosive is transferred to a tared weighing bottle, 35 mm in diameter and 50 mm deep. A watchglass is placed over the top of the bottle so that it is loosely covered. The bottle and contents are heated at 75°C for 48 hr, cooled, weighed, and examined for fumes or decomposition, as indicated by appearance or odor. If the loss in weight exceeds the moisture content of the sample, volatility or decomposition is indicated.

100°C Heat Test. The moisture content of the sample explosive is determined by drying a weighed 10-g portion in a desiccator until constant weight is obtained, and calculating the loss in weight as percentage of moisture. Weighed 0.60-g portions of the sample are transferred to each of two test tubes, 75 mm in length and 10 mm in diameter, one of which has been tared. The tubes and contents are placed in an oven maintained at 100 ± 1°C. At the end of 48 hr, the tared tube is removed, cooled, weighed, and replaced in the oven. After an additional 48 hr of heating, the tube and contents are again cooled and weighed. The percentage of loss during each heating period is calculated on the basis of the original weight, correcting the first value for the moisture present as previously determined. The untared tube and contents are heated at 100°C for 100 hr, and any ignition or explosion is noted.

Vacuum-Stability Tests. A weighed 5-g or 1-g sample of the explosive is transferred to a glass heating tube so designed that the ground neck can be sealed with mercury, after a calibrated capillary tube with a ground stopper end has been connected to the heating tube. The capillary tube is of $\frown\!\!\!\frown$ shape and the lower end consists of a cup. About 7 mm of mercury is placed in the cup, and the system is evacuated until the pressure is reduced to approx 5 mm. The level to which the mercury has risen in the capillary tube is recorded, and the heating tube is inserted in a constant-temperature bath maintained at 100, 120, or 150°C. If an excessive amount (11+ ml) of gas is not liberated, heating is continued for 40 hr. After the apparatus has cooled, the level to which the mercury in the capillary tube has fallen is noted. The volume of gas liberated during heating is calculated from the difference between the initial and final levels and the volume of the capillary per unit of length. If the explosive is very sensitive, a 1-g sample is used in making this test.

Bibliography

"Explosives" in *ECT* 1st ed., Vol. 1, pp. 1–91, by Wm. H. Rinkenbach, D. R. Cameron (Propellants), both of Picatinny Arsenal, U.S.A. Ordnance Department, and W. O. Snelling (Blasting Explosives), Trojan Powder Company.

1. C. Beyling and K. Drekopf, *Sprengstoffe und Zündmittel*, Springer-Verlag, Berlin-Wilmersdorf (West), 1936.
2. *Blasters' Handbook*, 14th ed., E. I. du Pont de Nemours & Co., Inc., Wilmington, Del., 1958.
3. H. Brunswig, *Das Rauchlose Pulver*, de Gruyter, Berlin, 1926.
4. L. V. Clark, "Absorbents for Liquid-Oxygen Explosives," *U.S. Bur. Mines Rept. Invest. No. 3169* (1932).
5. E. W. S. Colver, *High Explosives*, Technical Press, London, 1938.
6. M. A. Cook, *The Science of High Explosives*, Reinhold Publishing Corp., New York, 1958.
7. T. L. Davis, *The Chemistry of Powder and Explosives*, John Wiley & Sons, Inc., New York, 1943.
8. R. Escales, *Ammonsalpetersprengstoffe*, von Veit, Leipzig, 1909.
9. R. Escales, *Nitroglyzerin und Dynamit*, von Veit, Leipzig, 1908.
10. R. Escales, *Nitrosprengstoffe*, von Veit, Leipzig, 1915.
11. R. Escales, *Schwarzpulver und Sprengsalpeter*, von Veit, Leipzig, 1914.
12. R. Escales and A. Stettbacher, *Initial Explosivstoffe*, von Veit, Leipzig, 1917.
13. A. P. van Gelder and H. Schlatter, *History of the Explosives Industry in America*, Oxford University Press, London, 1927.
14. T. J. Hayes, *Elements of Ordnance*, John Wiley & Sons, Inc., New York, 1938.
15. *Transportation of Explosives and Other Dangerous Articles by Freight*, Interstate Commerce Commission Regulations, and Supplements, New York, 1941.
16. W. C. Lothrop and G. R. Handrick, "The Relationship Between Performance and Constitution of Pure Organic Explosives" *Chem. Revs.* **44**, 419–445 (1949).
17. A. Marshall, *Explosives*, 2nd ed., The Blakiston Co., Inc., Philadelphia, Pa., div. McGraw-Hill, 1917.
18. L. Metz, *Chemische Untersuchung der Spreng- und Zündstoffe*, Vieweg, Braunschweig, 1931.
19. C. E. Munroe and J. E. Tiffany, "Physical Testing of Explosives," *U.S. Bur. Mines Bull. No. 346* (1931).
20. P. Naoúm, *Nitroglycerine and Nitroglycerine Explosives*, transl. by E. M. Symmes, The Williams and Wilkins Co., Baltimore, Md., 1928.
21. P. Naoúm, *Schiess- und Sprengstoffe*, Steinkopff, Dresden, 1927.
22. C. S. Robinson, *Explosions, Their Anatomy and Destructiveness*, McGraw-Hill Book Co., Inc., New York, 1944.
23. A. Stettbacher, *Spreng- und Schiesstoffe*, Rascher Verlag, Zürich, 1948.
24. C. G. Storm, *Analysis of Explosives*, in Scott, Vol. 2, 5th ed., 1939, pp. 1660–1700.
25. J. Taylor, *Detonation in Condensed Explosives*, Oxford University Press, New York, 1952.
26. N. A. Tolch and G. St. J. Perrott, "Dynamites: Their Propulsive Strength, Rate of Detonation and Poisonous Gases Evolved," *U.S. Bur. Mines Rept. Invest. No. 2975* (1929).
27. W. E. Tournay, F. M. Bower, and F. W. Brown, "Safety and Performance Characteristics of Liquid-Oxygen Explosives" *U.S. Bur. Mines Bull. No. 472* (1949).
28. R. N. Wimpross, *Interior Ballistics of Solid-Fuel Rockets*, McGraw-Hill Book Co., Inc., New York, 1950.

WM. H. RINKENBACH
Consulting Chemist

PROPELLANTS

1. Introduction

Propellants may be defined as explosive materials which are formulated, designed, manufactured, and initiated in such a manner as to permit the generation of large volumes of hot gas at highly controlled, predetermined rates. This is often referred to as deflagration, or more simply, as burning, to differentiate its relatively slow rate of gas evolution from the extraordinarily high rates associated with the detonation process. The chemical reaction that results in gas and heat formation is readily started by a variety of simple ignition systems. Furthermore the reaction does not require atmospheric oxygen, since the oxidizing element is contained in the propellant components. Because of their ease of initiation, control, and independence of atmospheres, propellants are excellent materials for providing energy to systems where such energy must be rapidly delivered; and they meet the primary requirements of compactness, economy of weight, and self-sufficiency with respect to oxygen. Propellants are primarily employed to provide the working fluid for driving projectiles from guns of all sizes and for the propelling of rockets and missile systems. Propellant-actuated devices have numerous other uses: to drive turbines; to move pistons; to eject pilots from jet planes; to shear bolts and wires; to operate vanes in rockets; to act as sources of heat in special operations; to operate pumps in missiles; to start aircraft engines; to jettison stores from aircraft; and generally for systems that require well controlled sources of high force applied over relatively short periods of time. Although, the major use of propellants is for military purposes, they are being used increasingly in industrial operations because of their safety and simplicity of application (1–9).

Propellants may be broadly classified as either solid or liquid oxidizer-reductant systems, and may be classified further in terms of the number and types of components within the systems.

Solid propellants have great versatility of use due to their compactness, safety, storability, and ease of handling. As a result, they are the only propellants used in military and sporting weapons and in a wide variety of military and industrial propellant-actuated devices. Solid propellants are also widely used in rockets and missile systems.

Propellants used in guns, mortars, howitzers, rifles, and small arms almost invariably contain plasticized cellulose nitrate as the major oxidizing ingredient. Various other chemicals may be added for the following specific purposes: (1) high-energy oxidizing plasticizers such as glyceryl nitrate to increase performance; (2) fuel-type plasticizers such as dibutyl phthalate to provide improved physical and processing characteristics; (3) organic crystalline chemicals such as nitroguanidine, $CH_4O_2N_4$, to moderate the ballistic characteristics of the propellant; (4) stabilizers such as diphenylamine and ethyl centralite to increase chemical stability by combining with decomposition products; and (5) a number of inorganic additives such as graphite, potassium sulfate, and potassium nitrate to improve ignitability, facilitate handling, and minimize gun flash.

Conventionally, gun propellants that contain plasticized cellulose nitrate as the only oxidizer are referred to as *single-base propellants;* propellants that contain both cellulose nitrate and glyceryl nitrate or other explosive plasticizers as the energy-producing components are referred to as *double-base propellants*. Triple-base gun propellants are produced when substantial quantities of an organic, energy-producing crystalline compound such as nitroguanidine are incorporated in double-base propellants.

Propellants for rockets fall into two broad groups: (1) double-base compositions with various additives formulated to meet specific system requirements; and (2) compositions containing inorganic crystalline oxidants in some type of polymeric matrix which acts as both fuel and binder. The crystalline oxidant–fuel matrix systems are referred to as *composite propellants*. Single-base propellants are not used because of the difficulty of initiating and sustaining burning at the low pressures encountered in rockets. The range of oxidizing plasticizers in double-base rocket propellants increases to include chemicals such as diethylene glycol dinitrate, triethylene glycol dinitrate, and metrioltrinitrate; fuels such as dibutyl phthalate, dimethyl phthalate, and triacetin are used; organic and inorganic energy-producing salts such as *RDX* (cyclotrimethylenenitramine) and $KClO_4$ may be added. A large number of inorganic additives may also be included in double-base propellants to permit control of ballistic properties, a requirement that is more imperative in rocket propellant performance than in gun propellants.

Composite rocket propellants have been developed and have found extensive use in the last twenty years. Oxidizing salts such as ammonium perchlorate, potassium perchlorate, and ammonium nitrate are incorporated in a variety of linear or crosslinked polymeric binders such as poly(vinyl chloride), polysulfide rubbers, and crosslinked polyurethanes. In addition, aluminum, boron, and boron hydrides may be added to increase the energy evolved; and a variety of plasticizers, extenders, special additives, and catalysts are introduced to influence mechanical and ballistic properties as well as processing characteristics (10–17).

Liquid propellants are more restricted in use than solid propellants because of their reactivity and the special handling precautions required. Although efforts as yet have been unsuccessful in using liquids in gun propulsion systems, they have been most commonly applied in high-performance missile systems where major advantages are obtained in the ease of thrust control through valving. Liquid systems may also offer advantages in energy delivered per pound of propellant, which warrants consideration where maximum performance is required. Liquid systems are either *monopropellants* which consist of a single oxidizer-reducer compound or of stable mixtures of oxidizing-reducing agents; or *bipropellants*, in which the chemical oxidizers and the fuels are kept apart until reaction is required in the rocket engine. Monopropellants find their chief use in producing gases to provide supplemental power in missiles and for driving turbines used to pump liquid oxidizers and fuels in bipropellant systems. Monopropellants that have been investigated include hydrazine and hydrazine derivatives, concentrated hydrogen peroxide, ethylene oxide, propyl nitrate, nitromethane, mixtures of methyl alcohol and methyl nitrate, and mixtures of nitric acid, nitrobenzene, and water. Monopropellant systems offer considerable advantages in system simplicity, but their performance is not likely to measure up to the best bipropellant systems.

Bipropellant systems contain liquid fuels which are ordinarily inert and non-hazardous, and liquid oxidizers which may be corrosive but are not shock sensitive and are usually thermally stable. Bipropellants may either ignite spontaneously on contact or require an input of external energy for initiation. The terms *hypergolic* and *diergolic* are used respectively to describe these conditions. A large number of liquid oxidizers and fuels are available; selection of a specific combination is dictated by cost and operational requirements. Liquid oxidizers include such relatively common materials as liquid oxygen, concentrated nitric acid, and variants of the acid-containing oxides of nitrogen. More unusual materials such as fluorine and various fluorine compounds are also being considered for systems where maximum performance is required. Fuels for use in bipropellant systems are relatively numerous; their selection is based on system compatibility, ease of handling, and the optimization of performance with the oxidizer selected for the system. Of chief use and greatest interest have been the hydrocarbon fuels such as gasoline and kerosene, commonly referred to as the jet propulsion or JP types; ethyl alcohol, hydrazine, hydrazine derivatives; aniline, and ammonia. Considerable amount of experimentation has also been conducted with hydrogen, the borohydrides, and a variety of light metals such as beryllium and boron (18).

PROPELLANT CHARACTERISTICS

The criteria for selection of propellants for various systems depend upon matching the characteristics of the propellant to the special requirements of the system. This involves consideration of the physical and chemical characteristics of the propellant, its burning characteristics, and the amount of energy that can be made available. Criteria for selecting solid propellants include consideration of the mechanical properties, ease of manufacture and inspection of the propellant, its performance under the environmental conditions to which the system is subjected, and "lot-to-lot" variations in performance. On the other hand, the use of liquid propellants is governed by factors often quite different than those associated with solid propellants, such as the fluid-flow properties of the propellant, its boiling and freezing points, heat of vaporization, corrosiveness, and toxicity. A fuller treatment of the factors involved in selecting solid and liquid propellants is given in Section 2.

The rate at which energy must be delivered to a propulsion system and the total energy requirements of the system are fundamental factors influencing propellant selection and design. An extremely rapid liberation of all the available energy would result in either catastrophic detonation or in the development of intolerably high pressures. The problem of metering the energy of liquid propellants at the required rate is handled relatively simply by employing well-established techniques of pressurization and valving to control fluid flow and thereby regulate the energy release. By contrast, the rate at which energy is delivered by solid propellants depends upon the physical characteristics of the propellant, its intrinsic burning characteristics, and the geometric form of the propellant structure. These characteristics are treated in Section 3 in terms of the physical and chemical factors which affect burning, the burning-rate equations which apply, and the various techniques for the control of burning which are available for the design of propellants.

The total energy required by the system and the system design depend both on the energy characteristics of the propellant and on such characteristics of the gases as their heat capacity and volume, and their actual performance within a gun or rocket system. Since propellant energy is delivered in the form of hot gases, a set of simplified thermochemical–thermodynamic techniques have been developed that enable design engineers to assess the performance of propellants in various systems rapidly and within several percent of experimental findings. The most significant properties of gun and rocket systems that relate to propellant performance are reviewed in Section 4, where a rapid procedure is given for calculating the important propellant characteristics from a knowledge of propellant composition.

The specific physical, chemical, and operational characteristics of liquid monopropellant and bipropellant components and systems are given in detail in Section 5. Section 6 similarly treats the most widely used solid propellants and their important components. Moreover, since the techniques used in the manufacture of solid propellants are relatively unusual, these are also described in this Section in some detail. They include procedures for making the older gun propellants as well as the more recently developed gun and rocket propellants. Section 7 presents the most important and unusual experimental procedures used in propellant evaluation.

Bibliography

1. J. Corner, *Theory of the Interior Ballistics of Guns*, John Wiley & Sons, Inc., New York, 1950.
2. F. R. W. Hunt, *Interior Ballistics*, Philosophical Library, Inc., New York, 1950.
3. C. F. Curtis and J. W. Wrench, *Interior Ballistics:* A consolidation and revision of previous reports, *Interior Ballistics I to VII inclusive, NDRC Report A-397, OSRD Report 6468*, Geophysical Laboratory, Carnegie Institute of Technology, Washington, D.C., 1945.
4. G. P. Sutton, *Rocket Propulsion Elements*, 3rd ed., John Wiley & Sons, Inc., New York, 1963.
5. B. Kit and D. S. Evered, *Rocket Propellant Handbook*, The Macmillan Co., New York, 1960.
6. M. J. Zucrow, *Aircraft and Missile Propulsion*, Vol. 2, John Wiley & Sons, Inc., New York, 1958.
7. D. Altman, J. M. Carter, S. S. Penner, and M. Summerfield, *Liquid Rocket Propellants*, Princeton University Press, Princeton, N.J., 1960.
8. C. Hugget, C. E. Bartley, and Mark M. Mills, *Solid Propellant Rockets*, Princeton University Press, Princeton, N.J., 1960.
9. S. S. Penner and J. Ducarme, eds., *The Chemistry of Propellants*, Pergamon Press, Inc., New York, 1960.
10. H. W. Ritchey, "Solid Propellants and the Conquest of Space," *Astronautics* **3**, 39–41, 75–77 (1958).
11. *Propellant Actuated Devices, Engineering Design Handbook AMCP 706-282*, U.S. Army Materiel Command, Washington, D.C., 1963.
12. M. J. Zucrow, *Propulsion and Propellants, Engineering Design Handbook, AMCP 706-282*, U.S. Army Material Command, Washington, D.C., 1963.
13. A. M. Ball, *Solid Propellants, Part 1, Engineering Design Handbook, ORDP 20-175*, Ordnance Corps (now U.S. Army Materiel Command), Washington, D.C., 1961.
14. *Military Explosives, TW-1910*, Dept. of Army Technical Manual (1955).
15. O. A. Colitti, *Processing of High Energy Solid Rocket Propellants*, Picatinny Arsenal, Dover, N.J.
16. A. J. Qachringer, "Composite Propellants," *Missiles and Rockets* **4**, 16 (1959).
17. *The Chemistry and Chemicals of Composite Solid Propellants, Report RK-TR-64-6*, U.S. Army Missile Command, 1964.
18. D. D. Armstrong, "Liquid Propellants for Rockets," in S. Penner and J. Ducarme, eds., *The Chemistry of Propellants*, Pergamon Press, Inc., New York, 1960, pp. 121–168.

2. Major Factors Affecting Selection of Propellants

The choice of a propellant system is, in theory, based on optimization of the energy weight relationship for the system. Since propellant energy is produced in the form of hot gases, the requirement for optimizing performance leads to maximizing the flame temperature of the gases and the volume of gas produced per unit weight of propellant. In practice, propellants are subject to a number of practical considerations relating to use and handling which significantly affect selection. A description of some of the major factors involved in the choice of liquid- and solid-propellant systems is presented below; and a summary list of factors appears at the end of this section in Table 2.3.

LIQUID PROPELLANTS

Density. The overall density of monopropellants or of bipropellant mixes must be maximized so that the dimensions and weight of the metal parts required for containing and operating the propellant can be minimized. Calculations of impulse on a density basis rather than on a weight basis can be highly revealing of weight economics which may be obtained on a systems basis. Variations of density with temperature occurring as a result of storage conditions or aerodynamic heating must be allowed for in design. For comparison, an indication of the range of densities of important oxidizers with a variety of commonly used fuel systems are shown in Table 2.1.

Table 2.1. Range of Density for Various Oxidizers

Combination	Density range
liquid oxygen–fuel	1.00 ± 0.20^a
red fuming nitric acid–fuel	1.20 ± 0.20
hydrogen peroxide–fuel	1.25 ± 0.15

[a] Exceptions: ammonia 0.88, hydrogen, 0.26.

Reactivity. High chemical reactivity between oxidizer and fuel in a bipropellant system is essential for smooth and complete burning. Elimination of supplementary ignition systems and uniform combustion are obtained by use of hypergolic reactants. For repetitive motor operation, it is necessary to have mixtures which are spontaneously combustible with a minimum time lag. Several combinations have ignition delays of less than two msec; the maximum acceptable ignition delay for most hypergolic combinations is less than 50 msec. Tests have been designed to assess in a relative fashion the ease with which liquid propellants may be ignited. Although similar considerations apply to monopropellants, the advantages of high reactivity are offset to some extent by increased explosiveness. Implicit in high chemical reactivity are problems of corrosiveness and chemical instability (1).

Corrosiveness. Chemical reactivity is also manifested in its effect on the metallic and nonmetallic components of the system and on the storage and shipping containers required. A considerable number of long-term, high-low temperature compatibility tests must be conducted to qualify metallic and nonmetallic system components for use in contact with the propellant components. The choice of adequate materials becomes most critical where long-term storable systems are being designed.   In general, monopropellants and oxidizers for bipropellant systems present the most serious problems of compatibility. However, even relatively stable fuels must be carefully examined for effect on such materials as gaskets, bushings, and for long-term deposition of sludge.

Corrosion can often be markedly decreased by the use of additives to the propellant or by coatings applied on the contact material (2).

Stability and Sensitivity. Tests are conducted to determine stability under ambient conditions of use and performance as well as under shock and thermal impact. Decomposition during storage necessitates use of heavy-walled containers and of techniques for venting. Decomposition at the elevated temperatures encountered in flight may result in clogging of passages, gas bubble formation, or explosion. Monopropellants that readily detonate on application of shock and thermal loads are unsuitable for most purposes. Card-gap tests have been developed to measure the sensitivity of high-energy liquid propellants to mechanical or hydrodynamic shock. Drop-weight tests, comparable to those used for solid explosives, are also used to obtain indications of sensitivity of liquid explosives. Similarly, tests have been developed to measure thermal stability and the tendency to ignite under a variety of conditions (3,4).

Toxicity. The toxicity of liquid propellants and their products of reaction is of considerable importance in the selection of a system. Chemicals such as liquid fluorine and fluorine compounds, mixed oxides of nitrogen, and beryllium are highly toxic and extreme care must be used in their handling. Similarly, highly toxic or corrosive exhaust products jeopardize ground crews and equipment.

Boiling and Freezing Points. Military applications to missiles and rockets which are expected to be used under worldwide field and flight conditions dictate maximum boiling point-minimum melting point systems. Temperature limits of 60 to $-65°C$ have been established as desirable objectives. Low-boiling propellants must be stored in heavy-weight tanks; special precautions must be taken to pressurize propellant reservoirs in missile systems to avoid vapor locks in auxiliary delivery equipment. Propellants with high vapor pressures present serious disadvantages to the rocket engineer (6).

Heat of Vaporization and Specific Heat. Propellants used for regenerative cooling should have high heats of vaporization and high specific heats.

Viscosity. The propellant should be sufficiently fluid to pump easily at the temperatures encountered. Materials having a viscosity of up to 20 cP are considered acceptable, although most materials used have a viscosity on the order of 1 cP.

SOLID PROPELLANTS

Large, solid rocket-propellant grains (see p. 674) must have exceptionally good mechanical properties to withstand the severe stresses imposed during firing as well as in operational use. In addition, characteristics are required that will permit satisfactory performance after experiencing severe thermal stresses produced during long-time exposure and cycling at high–low temperature conditions. Solid propellants tend to be used over a much greater range of environmental conditions than liquid propellants. High physical performance characteristics are essential. The requirements imposed on the very much smaller gun propellant grains are, on the other hand, considerably less severe because of the lower magnitude of forces imposed on individual grains. Since solid propellants are often stored in very large quantities, considerable care must be taken to prevent catastrophic damage in the event of fire or detonation (7,8).

Physical Uniformity. It is of critical importance that propellant grains do not contain any nonuniformities such as cracks, pores, and cavities since the internal grain burning which results may produce gun and rocket motor blows, or high-order detonations in exceptionally severe cases. Small, gun-propellant grains are examined microscopically and density determinations are conducted. Closed-bomb burning tests (see Section 7) give an even more valuable indication of the adequacy of propellant consolidation. Larger rocket grains are inspected with x-ray and supersonic equipment; and firings may be conducted in full scale or reduced scale motors. An interrupted burner that permits recovery of partially burned propellant may also be used for experimental evaluation to determine the uniformity of combustion.

Ultimate Tensile Strength, Elongation, and Modulus in Tension. A variety of methods have been established for determining ultimate tensile strength, elongation, and modulus of rocket propellants by use of the same test and by empirically correlating these data with satisfactory performance in specific rocket engines. Techniques are available for high-rate load application in an effort to simulate rocket acceleration forces. Low-rate tests simulate stresses produced by differential thermal expansion. The mechanical characteristics of double-base propellants are greatly affected by the percentage and type of cellulose nitrate present and the plasticizer–cellulose nitrate ratio. Increases in plasticizer decrease strength; increases in temperature produce similar effects. The characteristics of composite propellants depend upon the nature of the binder, upon the binder-oxidizer ratio, and upon the mixing and curing techniques used (9,12).

Compressive Strength, Deformation, and Modulus in Compression. Artillery grains and rocket grains supported at the aft end of the engine experience compressive stresses and shock loading on ignition, on acceleration of the system, and in logistic handling of the munition. Mechanical properties of propellants under compression are generally related to those of the propellants under tension. In addition to tension tests functioning tests of rocket propellants are also conducted. Drop tests of loaded motors are conducted from various heights, at various angles, and at high and low temperatures; vibration tests are conducted under conditions that simulate those of actual use; and sled tests are conducted in which rockets are used to impose accelerational forces comparable to those expected in use.

Thermal Expansion. The coefficient of thermal expansion of solid propellants is important in rocket systems in which the propellant is coated with an inhibitor or bonded to the case. Inhibitors must be selected to match the characteristics of the propellant. On the other hand, the very large differences between the coefficients of expansion of the metallic motor and of the propellant require the use of relatively elastic propellant in case-bonded engines.

Thermal Conductivity and Diffusivity. The thermal conductivity of solid propellants is quite low. Propellant burning proceeds faster than heat is conducted

Table 2.2[a]. Representative Thermal Characteristics of Propellants

Propellant type	Specific heat, Btu/(lb)(°F)	Thermal conductivity, Btu/(hr)(ft)²(°F/ft)	Thermal diffusivity, ft²/hr	Linear thermal coefficient, in./°F(10^5)
vinyl polyester,				
75% NH_4ClO_4	0.307	0.185	0.0059	2.68
75% NH_4NO_3	0.413	0.152	0.0040	
polysulfide,				
63% NH_4ClO_4	0.307	0.163	0.0052	3.47
double base, JPN	0.365	0.130	0.0035	

[a] Adapted from reference 14.

Table 2.3. Characteristics to be Considered in Propellant Selection

1. Manufacturing characteristics
   a. Availability and cost of raw materials and processing equipment
   b. Simplicity and cost of manufacture and inspection
   c. Manufacturing hazards
2. Energy delivery requirements
   a. Specific impulse or force
   b. Loading density in terms of required burning characteristics
   c. Metal parts requirements in terms of operating pressure over required temperature range
3. Temperature dependence
   a. Ignition, pressure, and thrust characteristics over temperature range
   b. Mechanical characteristics over temperature range
   c. Effect of high–low temperature cycling
4. Reliability of performance
   a. Lot-to-lot variations in thrust and pressure
   b. Effect of small variations in metal parts on performance
   c. Effect of small variations in composition and dimensions on performance
5. Long-term storage characteristics
   a. Deformation changes
   b. Gassing characteristics
   c. Performance changes
   d. Moisture absorption
   e. Exudation of plasticizer
6. Mechanical characteristics
   a. Variation on long term storage
   b. Variation on high-low temperature cycling
   c. Effect of acceleration forces
   d. Effect of rough handling
   e. Effect on case bonding
7. Compatibility
   a. With process equipment
   b. With personnel (toxicity)
   c. With metal and plastic parts and other components
   d. Of reaction products with personnel, metal parts and electronic equipment
   e. Erosive effects of reaction products
   f. Smoke and flash

behind the burning surfaces. As a result, propellant grains have approximately the same initial temperature throughout the burning process. However, their low conductivity also produces thermal stresses which may crack large rocket grains when subjected to abrupt changes in ambient temperatures. As much as 24 to 48 hr may be required for uniform temperature to prevail in large grains on changing the temperature from −40 to 60°C. The introduction of metallic powder such as aluminum significantly changes thermal characteristics. Typical values for thermal conductivity and diffusivity as well as specific heats are shown in Table 2.2 (13).

Stability. The term stability as applied to propellant grains has different denotations. The *safe storage life* refers to the period during which autocatalytic decomposition has not reached a sufficient level to present a storage hazard. A variety of tests are available for measurement of the decomposition of cellulose nitrate propellants; fewer are available for satisfactory measurement of composite-propellant decomposition. In general, no serious problem is encountered with the safe storage life of rocket propellants. Although the problem of autocatalytic decomposition and "runaway" fires is more serious with the large masses of small gun propellant grains, cellulose nitrate gun propellants made before World War II are still in satisfactory storage. The *safe use life* presents considerably more problems, particularly with rocket propellants. The formation of cracks and voids in propellant grains, as a result of thermal cycling and gas formation, causes the propellant to malfunction during firing. Inhibitor failure and failure of the propellant bond to the motor case as a result of long term storage are equally serious. Significant changes in burning rates may also occur as a result of plasticizer loss or migration into the inhibitor (15–18).

Bibliography

1. *Liquid Propellant Test Methods*, Test No. 2, "Minimum Pressure for Vapor Phase Ignition," Liquid Propellant Information Agency, John Hopkins University, Md.
2. F. Bellinger et al., "Chemical Propellants–Corrosion and Stability Studies," *Ind. Eng. Chem.* **38**, 310–320 (1946).
3. S. Krop et al., *Liquid Propellant Safety Manual*, Liquid Propellant Information Agency, Johns Hopkins University, Md. 1958.
4. *Liquid Propellant Test Methods*, Tests No. 4, 5, and 6, "Drop Weight Test," "Adiabatic Compression Sensitivity Test," "Thermal Stability Test," Liquid Propellant Information Agency, Johns Hopkins University, Md., 1958.
5. S. Krop, "The Toxicity and Health Hazards of Rocket Propellants," *Jet Propulsion* **24**, 223–227 (1964).
6. D. R. Bartz, "Factors which Influence the Suitability of Liquid Propellants Rocket Motor Regenerative Coolants," *Jet Propulsion* **28**, 46–63 (1958).
7. *United States Army Ordnance Safety Manual ORDM-7-224*.
8. W. F. Haite, "Propellant Explosives Classification and Effect of Field Handling of Missiles," *Jet Propulsion* **27**, 489–491, (1958).
9. *Methods for Determining the Tensile Properties of Solid Rocket Propellants*, Solid Propellant Information Agency, Johns Hopkins University, Md.
10. K. W. Bills, Jr. and J. H. Wiegand, "Relation of Mechanical Properties to Solid Rocket Motor Failure," *AIAA J*, 2116–2123 (1963).
11. R. N. Wimpress, *Internal Ballistics of Solid Fuel Rockets*, McGraw-Hill Book Co., Inc., New York, 1950, pp. 150–166.
12. R. F. Landel and T. L. Smith, "Viscoelastic Properties of Rubberlike Composite Propellants and Filled Elastomers," *Rubber Chem. Technol.* **35**, 227–230 (1962).
13. *Ibid.*, pp. 183–208.
14. K. Klager, *Solid Propellants*, Aerojet General Corporation Publication.
15. G. Lianis, "Stresses and Strains in Solid Propellants During Storage," *ARS* (*Am. Rocket Soc.*) *J*. **29**, 148–150 (1959).
16. Carl Boyars, "Surveillance of Solid Propellant Rockets," *ARS J*. **29**, 148–150 (1959).
17. *Military Explosives, TW-1910*, Department of Army Technical Manual, 1955, pp. 238–248.
18. *Data Presentation Requirements for Determining Safe Handling, Storage, and Shipping Procedures: Aeronautical Rocket Motors and Components*, U.S. Air Force Specification MIL-D-26389, 1958.

3. Propellant Performance: The Burning Process

The Transition from Burning to Detonation. Since propellants consist largely of explosive components, the burning process which is required for controlled propellant performance may transform to an uncontrollable detonation under certain conditions. For example, a chemical compound such as cellulose nitrate may detonate violently when in the fibrous form or burn quietly when properly plasticized. A propellant which burns satisfactorily in a rocket may detonate when initiated with a sufficiently powerful booster or even under certain conditions with a mild igniter at low temperatures. In view of the disastrous consequences involved in propellant detonations, considerable attention has been paid to those factors that cause the burning process to convert to detonation. In general, the available evidence indicates that detonation will occur only if the conditions are such as to lead to the initiation and maintenance of a high-pressure shock wave. When this occurs, burning proceeds at so high a rate that it provides the energy required to sustain a detonation system. Two of the most important characteristics of solid propellants leading to detonation are the presence of porosity and fissures in the propellant and mechanical breakup during the burning process. The large burning surface produced by porosity or cracks arising from low mechanical strength results in a high rate of gas evolution with correspondingly high pressures. An increasingly steep pressure front is produced; a pressure wave develops which transforms to a shock wave; steady state detonation occurs shortly thereafter. Pressurization rates on the order of 10^8 psi/sec have been observed with some materials during the initiation stage of the detonation process. Detonation is most likely to occur with maximum energy propellants that have a high crystalline filler content. Since mechanical strength is lowest at low temperatures, eg, $-40°C$, the frequency of malperformance increases as the temperature decreases. Many liquid bipropellant systems and some solid propellants will also detonate where ignition is not effective and rapid, and intermediate propellant decomposition products are allowed to accumulate. A great deal of consideration is given to igniter designs for gun-propellant systems to ensure fast, shockfree, and simultaneous initiation of the large number of propellant grains present. Detonation potentials may be minimized by selecting propellants that have high mechanical strength at all temperatures, by paying careful attention to the elimination of cracks and voids through appropriate manufacturing and inspection procedures, and by designing for simultaneous, rapid, shockfree ignition systems. All conditions which can lead to a very rapid pressure buildup have to be avoided (1–4).

Chemical Processes in Propellant Burning. The rate of evolution of gas during burning is very much less than that during detonation. The rate of burning of well colloided cellulose nitrate used as a propellant is measured in in./sec; its detonation rate is at least several miles/sec. In both instances, the total quantity of gas and heat evolved and the composition of the gaseous products are quite similar. The oxidation-reduction reaction mechanism of propellant breakdown results in gas formation; the rate is greatly affected by the pressure of the gaseous products above the propellant surface. The great difference in reaction rate between deflagration and detonation arises from, and is in turn contributory to, the gas pressure prevalent under the two conditions. Propellant gas pressures in rocket systems are generally of the order of 500 to 1500 psi; and up to 60,000 psi in gun systems. Shock wave pressures in detonation are about three–four million psi. Although the reaction rate is not directly proportional to pressure, as will be seen when burning-rate equations are considered, the two are very intimately related.

The mechanism of energy release in propellant burning is comparable to that of explosive detonation. Initiation results in endothermic decomposition of molecular components. All gun and many rocket propellants contain nitrated esters such as cellulose nitrate and glyceryl nitrate which decompose. If a stepwise mechanism is assumed, for simplicity, on application of heat the initial low-temperature reaction results in the splitting off of nitrogen dioxide and the formation of miscellaneous low-molecular-weight alcohols and aldehydes.

$$2\ RH_2CONO_2 \rightarrow RCHO + RCH_2OH + 2\ NO_2$$

As the temperature increases, exothermic oxidation reactions occur between NO_2, the alcohols and aldehydes with the evolution of gaseous products such as NO, CO, CO_2, and H_2O. With further increase in temperature, the final oxidation reactions occur with maximum evolution of heat to yield primarily N_2, CO, CO_2, H_2O, and H_2 under the equilibrium conditions existing at the prevailing pressure and temperature of the system. Contributing to the speed with which the reaction occurs is the presence of a variety of free radicals and chain reactions which are believed to occur in the process. Differences between the products of detonation and the products of deflagration are relatively small and may be accounted for largely in terms of equilibrium shifts that result from pressure and temperature differences. Activation energies on the order of 40–50 kcal/mole have been established for the low-temperature, low-pressure decomposition of nitrate esters such as glyceryl nitrate, cellulose nitrate, and diethylene glycol dinitrate. The mechanism of decomposition and oxidation of more complex nitrates as well as aromatic nitro compounds at high pressures and temperatures is undoubtedly more involved, but it probably follows the pattern of decomposition of aliphatic nitrates (5–7).

The decomposition of the newer, heterogeneous composite propellants is more complex and requires consideration of both oxidizer and fuel decomposition. Solid oxidizing agents such as ammonium nitrate, ammonium perchlorate, and potassium perchlorate, now used in composite rocket propellants decompose at considerably higher temperatures than do organic nitrates. Ammonium nitrate decomposition produces nitrous oxide and water at low temperatures and follows the unimolecular rate equation

$$k = 10^{13.8}\ e^{-40,500/RT}$$

Ammonium perchlorate decomposition starts at about 200°C and proceeds in accordance with the following equation above 350°C: $2NH_4ClO_4 \rightarrow 4H_2O + Cl_2 + O_2 + 2NO$. Potassium perchlorate decomposes to produce potassium chloride and oxygen at about 500°C in accordance with

$$k = 10^{14.0}\ e^{-60,800/RT}$$

In any homologous series of propellant, those which contain potassium perchlorate burn faster than those with ammonium perchlorate; ammonium nitrate propellants burn slowest. The relative burning rates of the propellants seem to be related to the oxygen content of the gas mixture (produced by decomposition of the oxidizer), rather than to the ease of decomposition of the oxidizer (8–10).

Physical Processes in Propellant Burning. Considerable study has been made of the burning process of propellants, particularly for understanding the variety of aberrant phenomena encountered in the performance of gun and rocket systems. Spectroscopic examinations have been made of the gases evolved by thin rods of cellulose nitrate and composite-type rocket propellants burning under pressure conditions approximating those in a rocket motor. Photographic studies have been conducted of the relationship between the distance of the flame from the propellant and the luminosity of the gases produced as functions of the pressure of gases above the propellants. The mechanisms of burning for solid rocket propellants are broadly comparable for homogeneous and heterogeneous compositions. Differences in detail exist, particularly with respect to the decomposition rates of the individual components of heterogeneous compositions such as those containing aluminum, perchlorates, and fuel binders.

Initiation of a solid propellant is commonly accomplished by the use of an igniter that applies heat to the propellant by radiation, conduction, and convection from the hot gases produced. The most effective igniters such as black powder and metal oxidant mixtures also form hot particles which contribute to the heat transferred. The surface of cellulose nitrate-type propellants consists of nitrate esters. These decompose as their temperature increases to form liquid and gaseous products which volatilize and leave the propellant surface. The interaction of these products is exothermic, so that a hot environment continues to exist above the propellant. As a result, heat is transferred to the propellant surface with continuous propellant breakdown. Interaction among the gaseous products continues with maximum evolution of

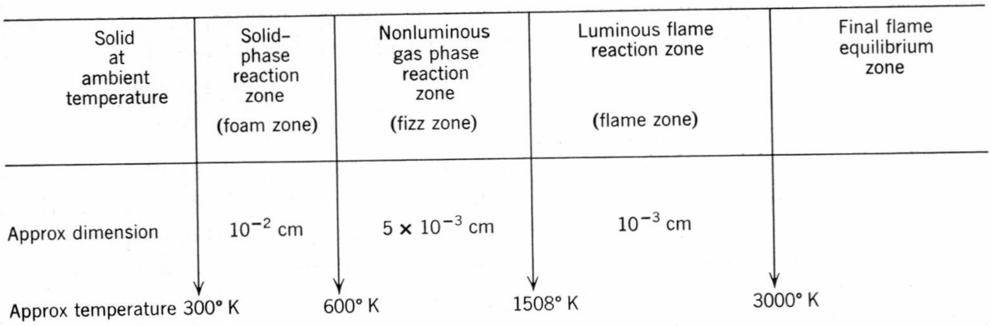

Solid at ambient temperature	Solid–phase reaction zone (foam zone)	Nonluminous gas phase reaction zone (fizz zone)	Luminous flame reaction zone (flame zone)	Final flame equilibrium zone
Approx dimension	10^{-2} cm	5×10^{-3} cm	10^{-3} cm	
Approx temperature 300° K	600° K	1508° K		3000° K

Fig. 3.1. One-dimensional model of propellant burning process.

heat and the establishment of final equilibrium conditions. The flame temperature of the propellant is equal to the temperature of these equilibrium products. Solid propellants are poor conductors of heat, having thermal conductivity values on the order of 3×10^{-5} Btu/(sec)(ft)^2(°F/ft). Heat transferred by the gases to the propellant surface results in molecular breakdown at a rate greater than that which permits transfer of heat to the propellant interior. Burning is an ablative process (see Ablation) with only the exposed surface being heated and burning away; thermocouple measurements have shown that the propellant temperature, 0.01 cm below the surface is essentially unchanged. Consideration of the overall process of cellulose nitrate propellant burning on a one-dimensional basis indicates that it may be thought of as proceeding in accordance with the following model:

(1) The surface of the solid is a reaction zone or *foam zone* approx 0.01 cm in thickness and ranging in temperature to about 600°K. Molecular bond breakage occurs in this zone, primarily the —O—N bond in cellulose nitrate propellants. The rate of bond breakage is a function of temperature in accordance with the applicable Arrhenius equation; (2) above the foam zone is a nonluminous gaseous reaction zone or, *fizz zone*, several thousandths of a centimeter in thickness. This zone attains a temperature of approximately 1500°K as a result of partial reaction of the materials ejected from the foam surface. About half the total heat evolved by the propellant is

liberated in the fizz zone; (*3*) the reaction continues to completion and thermodynamic equilibrium is established in the *flame zone*. This zone, approx 0.001 cm in thickness, defines the flame temperature of the propellant, which may range from 1750°K for cool propellants to 3500°K for very hot ones. Figure 3.1 summarizes the essential features of this model of the burning process (11,12).

The case of composite propellants is considerably more complex and has not been completely clarified. A two-temperature postulate has been proposed for ammonium nitrate propellants which assumes that the heat required for decomposing the propellant is provided solely by oxidizer decomposition that occurs close to the burning surface. According to this model, the burning rates of oxidizer and fuel are about the same, though their temperatures are different. The flame supplies little heat to the propellant.

The burning rate of pure, pressed ammonium perchlorate is comparable to that of propellants with fuels, which suggests primary dependence on the oxidizer. However, since burning rate is also influenced strongly by the mixture ratio which determines flame temperatures, the influence of heat diffusion from the flame is also indicated. More complicated models have also been developed in which the vapors of fuel or oxidizer are presumed to be formed in pockets of a specific mass content. These pockets then burn in the surrounding medium of the opposite reactant (13,14).

FACTORS AFFECTING THE BURNING PROCESS

The rate of propellant burning is dependent, on one hand, upon the characteristics of the propellant surface which affect the rate at which the decomposition reactions will occur. On the other hand, it is dependent upon the characteristics of the environment above the propellant which affect the rate at which heat is transferred to the propellant surface to cause chemical breakdown. The two are intimately related and both surface theories and gas phase theories have been evolved to explain burning. Each may be considered somewhat independently for purposes of simplicity.

The composition of the propellant determines both the rate of molecular breakdown on the propellant surface as well as the energy evolved by the product gases and transferred to the surface. As the rate of reaction increases, the rates of heat production and transfer are increased with appropriate increases in the linear burning rate of the propellant. The heat evolved per gram of propellant as a result of the decomposition process is commonly referred to as the heat of explosion, Q, or the calorific value. It may be rapidly calculated or determined by conventional methods in the calorimetric bomb. Values obtained range from about 500 cal for very cool propellants to 1500 cal for high-energy propellants. As may be expected, the flame temperature, $T°K$, of propellants of similar composition is generally proportional to the calorific values since the gases formed are similar in composition and in heat capacity (Fig. 3.2). Furthermore, the greater the calorific value, or heat of explosion of the propellant, the higher the burning rate of the composition in any homologous series (Fig. 3.2). The ambient temperature of the propellant has the expected effect upon the propellant burning rate, the higher the temperature, the higher the burning rate. It may be assumed that the quantity of heat which must be delivered to raise the propellant surface temperature to the value required for decomposition depends in part upon the heat already available within the propellant. Propellants at high temperatures require less energy for initiation of the decomposition action and therefore consummate this

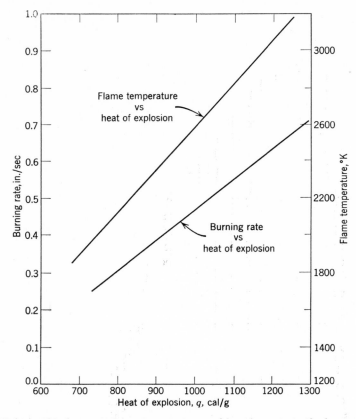

Fig. 3.2. Relationship between flame temperature and burning rate to the heat of explosion.

reaction more rapidly.   Depending considerably upon the propellant composition, burning rates change up to approx 0.5%/°C under constant pressure conditions (15).

The effect of pressure has a predominant influence on the burning rate of propellants.   Photographic evidence indicates that increasing pressure decreases the thickness of the flame and fizz zones.   The distance between these zones and the propellant surface also decreases approximately inversely to the cube of the pressure for cellulose nitrate propellants.   The rate of heat transfer to the propellant surface increases accordingly.   In addition, the rate of reaction among the gaseous components of the zones above the propellant increases in agreement with established relationships between pressure and the rate of gas reactions in equilibrium.   The addition of various inorganic salts can significantly affect the burning rate of rocket propellants so that it differs considerably from that anticipated from the heat of explosion.   The use of lead salts in double-base propellants may actually result in a burning regime which is relatively independent of pressure (*plateau* propellants) or in which the burning rate may decrease as the pressure increases (*mesa* propellants).   The addition of catalysts such as copper chromite to composite rocket propellants may substantially increase the burning rate.   The burning rate of composite propellants is also markedly affected by the particle size of the oxidizer, increasing as the particle size decreases. The effects of temperature and pressure on the burning rates of com-

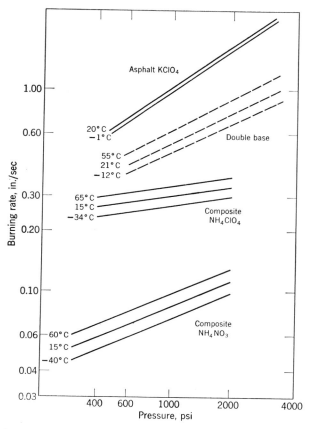

Fig. 3.3. Relation of burning rate to pressure and temperature for typical propellants (29).

posite and double-base propellants are shown in Figure 3.3 (16,17). The effect of composition, temperature, and pressure on burning rates is of primary importance. Any factor that will influence heat transfer from gas products to solid propellant will effect burning. A secondary factor influencing burning rate is the velocity of the gases passing over the propellant under the dynamic conditions prevailing in a rocket or in an artillery tube. When a turbulent flow of gas occurs behind the reaction zone, part of the turbulence may penetrate the zone and increase heat transfer to the propellant surface. This appears to occur, generally, when the flow of gases over the propellant surface exceeds about 10% of the velocity of sound. Increase in heat transfer increases the burning rate. Observations of the interior surfaces of tubular sticks of rocket and artillery propellant show that the aft internal openings over which gas velocity is greatest appear to have been eroded by gas wash. Since the thickness of the reaction zone varies inversely with the rate of burning, propellants with low burning rates are more readily susceptible to the erosion effects attributable to gas velocity than are high-burning rate propellants (18,19).

Burning-Rate Equations. The design of propellants for gun or rocket performance requires a knowledge of the exact rate at which gas is produced under the prevailing conditions of pressure and temperature. Burning-rate equations have been developed

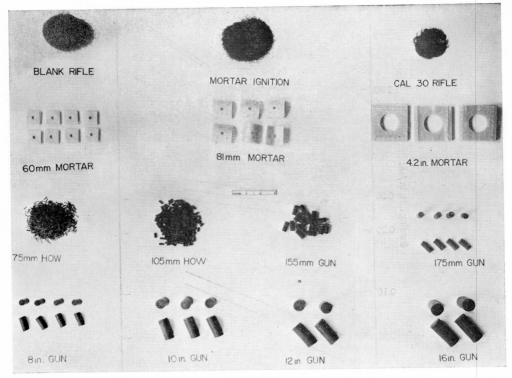

Fig. 3.4.

to describe the performance of solid propellants. These equations are based on the assumption that all the exposed propellant surfaces burn up and therefore recede at the same linear rate (Piobert's Law). This type of burning has been confirmed experimentally by examination of partially burned and recovered rocket and gun propellants. The mass rate of burning can be expressed exactly by $m = lSr$; where l is the propellant density (approx. 0.059 lb/in.^{3}), S is the burning surface, in.^{2}, r is the linear rate of surface regression, in./sec, and m is the mass rate of burning of the propellant, lb/sec. Since density is a constant characteristic and the burning surfaces are controllable by the propellant design, the factors that influence the rate of surface regression or linear burning rate are of paramount importance to the propellant designer.

The relationship between the linear burning rate and pressure has been intensively explored experimentally for a large number of solid propellants under the low-pressure conditions characteristic of rocket performance and the high-pressure conditions associated with gun propellants. The two most commonly established linear burning-rate equations are (1) $r = a + bp$; and (2) $r = bp^n$, where r is the linear burning rate, p is the pressure, n is the pressure exponent, and a and b are constants which vary with temperature. Equation (1) is more often used with gun-propellant design at high pressures and is a variant of equation (2). The pressure exponent ranges from about 0.06 to 0.95. Equation (2) is associated with low-pressure rocket propellants where the pressure exponent generally varies from 0.1 to 0.75. Burning rates at 1000 psi vary from 0.05 to 1.5 in./sec. Plots of log p vs log r are linear as shown in Figure 3.3, but may show different slopes at low and high pressures. The effect of various additives to

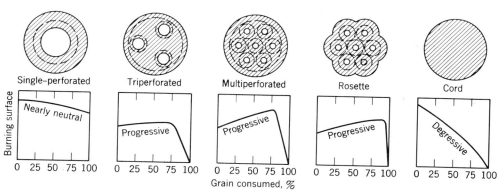

Fig. 3.5. Effect of grain shape on surface exposed during burning.

cellulose nitrate and composite propellants appears to be catalytic, increasing the burning rate at low pressures beyond that to be expected from extrapolation of burning rates at high pressures. The significance of a low pressure exponent is particularly critical in rocket propellant design. The pressure in a rocket system can be defined as

$$P = K\ (S_b/A_t)\ \exp 1/(1 - n)$$

where S_b = the propellant burning surface
A_t = the rocket nozzle throat area
K = a constant

Fig. 3.6.

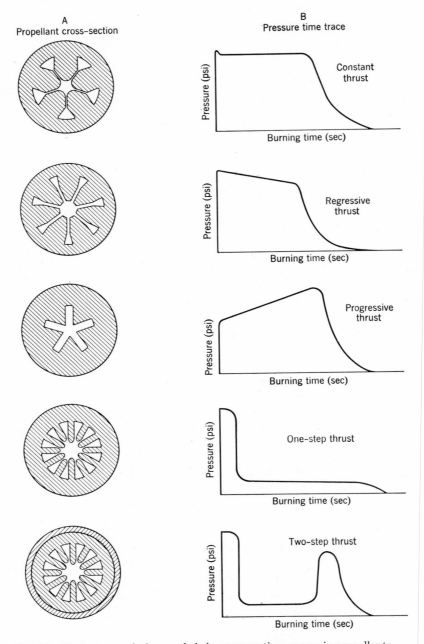

Fig. 3.7. Various granulations and their pressure–time curves in propellants.

The pressures produced by propellants with high pressure exponents, n, are very sensitive to changes in the available burning surface area of the propellant, variations in nozzle throat area, and changes in propellant temperature. Since it is highly desirable to minimize rocket motor weight for maximum performance, the penalty paid in over-design for high pressures required by propellants with high pressure exponents has led to considerable research to develop rocket propellants with very low—and even negative, pressure exponents over the anticipated operating pressures.

Control of Burning. The process of metering out propellant gas at a predetermined rate involves the selection of a propellant composition with the required burning rate at the operating pressures in the gun or rocket, and then designing the propellant so that the necessary burning surface is available to provide the required mass rate of gas evolution. The individual propellant structure is referred to as a grain; grains may be very small and numerous as are the 0.02-in. diam grains used in some small arms propellants, or, they may be very large and of complex geometries as are the 200-in. diam perforated cylinders that are used in some rocket boosters (Fig. 3.6). Control of the burning surface of the propellant is achieved by establishing the number of grains to be used, their geometrical configuration, and in the case of rocket propellants, the cementing of noncombustible inhibitors such as ethyl cellulose on specific grain surfaces to prevent their burning. Propellant grains may have to be formulated that provide a uniform rate of gas evolution during the burning process. The geometric form of such grains is so designed that as the grains are consumed the area of the burning surface remains essentially constant, eg, long, hollow tubes, or thin sheets. This type of burning is known as neutral burning and the geometric forms of the grains that produce it as neutral geometries. Such geometries are often characteristic of rocket propellant grains. Artillery propulsion systems frequently require an increasing rate or gas evolution during burning and the multiperforated small cylinders that produce this progressive type of burning are based on geometrics referred to as progressive geometries. Grains which decrease in surface area during burning are said to have degressive geometries, eg, spheres and rods, and are used in the propellants for small arms and rifles. (Fig. 3.5). Various granulations ranging from those used in sporting-type ammunition to the type employed for large artillery appear in Figure 3.4; whereas typical granulations used in rocket propellants and characteristic pressure–time curves obtained therefrom, appear in Figure 3.7. In general, rocket-propellant burning requires a constant pressure–time curve; whereas gun-propellant burning requires a pressure–time curve which peaks near the gun breech and then decreases as the projectile travels down the gun tube and the gases expand. A number of special techniques have been developed for obtaining high burning rates in rocket propellants. One method consists of embedding metallic wires or strands of black powder axially in propellant grains to increase the rate of heat transfer to the surrounding propellant and thereby increase its burning rate. Undesirably high pressure peaks obtained with some type of tubular rocket grains may be eliminated by the insertion of thin rods in the central perforations, or by drilling lateral holes through the grain. The use of chemical additives to produce plateau and mesa propellants in double-base propellants and burning-rate control through the control of particle size and the use of catalysts in composite propellants have been mentioned (21–25).

Bibliography

1. A. Macek, "Transition from Deflagration to Detonation in Cast Explosives," *J. Chem. Phys.* **31**, 162 (1959).
2. W. H. Anderson and R. F. Chaiken, "Detonability of Solid Composite Propellants," *ARS (Am. Rocket Soc.) J.* **31**, 162 (1959).
3. J. E. Crump and E. W. Price, "Catastrophic Changes in Burning Rate of Solid Propellants During Combustion Instability," *ARS J.* **30**, 707 (1960).

4. Stanley Wachtel, "Prediction of Detonation Hazards in Solid Propellants," *Paper 145th Natl. Meeting, Div. of Fuel Chem., New York, 1963.*

5. R. E Wilfong, S. S. Penner, and F. Daniels, "An Hypothesis for Propellant Burning," *J. Phys. & Colloid Chem.* **54**, 836 (1950).

6. O. K. Rice and Robert Ginell, "Theory of Burning of Double-Base Rocket Powders," *J. Phys. & Colloid Chem.* **54**, 885 (1950).

7. B. L. Crawford, C. Hugget, and J. F. McBrady, "The Mechanism of Burning of Double Base Propellants," *J. Phys. & Colloid Chem.* **54**, 847 (1950).

8. O. R. Irwin, P. T. Salzman, and W. H. Anderson, "Deflagration Characteristics of Ammonium Perchlorate at High Pressures," *9th Symp. Combust. Ithaca, 1962* (1963).

9. J. Pawling and W. A. W. Smith, "The Surface Temperature of Ammonium Perchlorate in a Stream of Combustible Gas," *10th Symp. Combust. Cambridge, England, 1963* (1964).

10. M. Barrère and L. Nadaud, "Combustion of Spheres of Ammonium Perchlorate in a Stream of Combustible Gas," *10th Symp. Combust. Cambridge, 1963* (1964).

11. Clayton Huggett, C. E. Bartley, and Mark M. Mills, *9th Symp. Combust. Ithaca, 1962* (1963).

12. F. R. W. Hunt, *ARS J.* **31**, 23–37 (1959).

13. R. Schultz, L. Green, and S. S. Penner, "Studies of the Decomposition Mechanism, Erosive Burning, Sonance and Resonance for Solid Composite Propellants," *Paper AGARD Combust. Panel Colloq., Palermo, Sicily, 1958.*

14. Martin Summerfield et al., "Burning Mechanism of Ammonium Perchlorate Propellants," *Am. Rocket Soc. 13th Ann. Meeting, New York, 1958.*

15. B. L. Crawford et al., "Rocket Fundamentals," *Office Sci. Res. Develop. Rept. 3992*, pp. 121–126, 1944.

16. K. Klager, *Solid Propellants*, Aerojet General Corporation.

17. R. F. Preckel, "Plateau Ballistics in Nitrocellulose Propellants," *ARS J.* **31**, 1286–1287 (1961).

18. L. Green Jr., "Erosive Burning of Some Composite Solid Propellants," *ARS J.* **24**, 9 (1954).

19. R. J. Thompson and F. T. McClure, "Erosive Burning of Double-Base Powders," *Office Sci. Res. Develop. Rept. 5831*, 1945

20. A. M. Ball, *Paper AGARD Combust. Panel Colloq., Palermo, Sicily*, 1958, pp. 12–15.

21. J. A. Vanderkerhove, "Recent Advances in Solid Propellant Grain Design," *ARS J.* **29**, 483–491 (1959).

22. Max W. Stone, "A Practical Mathematical Approach to Grain Design," *Jet Propulsion* **28**, 236–244 (1958).

23. W. H. Avery and J. Beek, Jr., "Propellant Charge Design of Solid Fuel Rockets," *Office Sci. Research and Develop., Rept. 5890*, 1946.

24. F. L. Schuyler, "Analytical Investigations of Combustion Instability in Solid Propellant Rockets," *Ill. Inst. Technol. Rept. IITRI—A 6002*, Chicago, Ill., 1963.

25. R. D. Geckler and D. F. Sprenger, "The Correlation of Interior Ballistic Data for Solid Propellants," *ARS J.* **24**, 22 (1954).

4. Propellant Performance: Energy Characteristics of Gun and Rocket Propellants

The effective use of a propellant for gun and rocket systems requires an assessment of the thermal and kinetic energy that can be made available from the chemical energy of the propellant. It is desirable to know with reasonable approximation such characteristics as the energy evolved during propellant burning, the quantity of gaseous products, their composition, molecular weight, heat capacity, and flame temperature. Through the use of readily available thermochemical data and a number of simplifying assumptions, it is possible to quickly calculate these and other characteristics of propellants and thereby estimate performance characteristics with an accuracy of about three per cent. Although it is not possible to calculate the burning rate of a propellant from a knowledge of its thermochemical–thermodynamic characteristics, a fair estimate may be obtained by comparison with other propellants of analogous composition whose burning rate and calorific value have already been established.

System Compatibility. Propellant designers are required to deliver a total amount of energy to comply with overall system performance requirements. The energy must be metered out at very specific rates to meet pressure and acceleration limitations established in advance. The optimization process is a complex one in which the interior ballistics of the propellant, ie, the rate at which energy is delivered and pressure produced over the time available, are intimately related to the dimensions, weight, and overall performance of the system. For example, gun designers generally desire to obtain maximum projectile velocity. The use of high energy propellants, increased quantities of propellants, maximum pressures in the breech, and maximum gas expansion in long gun tubes all increase maximum velocity substantially. However, any of these approaches may lead to intolerable increases in weight in order to withstand the pressures developed or to accommodate the longer charges and greater gun-tube length. Other problems, such as erosion of the gun tube and excessive flash, may also be encountered; similar considerations apply to rocket systems. Selection of a propellant is, therefore, necessarily a compromise between the requirements of the system and the performance of the propellant. Although guns are far more efficient than rockets in the utilization of propellant energy, the absence of recoil in rockets as well as the simplicity and lightness of the launcher make the use of rockets particularly attractive for both military and industrial purposes. The overall system advantages of the rocket frequently offset the disadvantages of low efficiency of conversion of propellant chemical energy to kinetic energy (1,2).

Gun Equations. Gun design involves consideration of the conversion of propellant chemical energy to kinetic energy in what amounts to an expanding chamber. All propellant energy must be delivered within the confines of the gun tube and maximum projectile velocities must be achieved by the time the projectile reaches the end of the tube. The projectile forms a reasonably gas-tight seal with the walls of the gun tube. On ignition of the propellant in the breech, the pressure rises gradually, and then more rapidly, as the burning rate increases with the increase in pressure. The projectile is propelled along the length of the tube at an acceleration proportional to the pressure on its base. The movement of the projectile increases the volume available to the gases. The tendency of the pressure to rise begins to be offset by the increasing volume after the volume has about doubled. The pressure then begins to fall and the temperature of the gases decreases, although the propellant is still burning. After the projectile has traveled about two-thirds of the distance from the breech to the muzzle, the propellant has been completely consumed and the pressure drops much more rapidly. Propellant grains must be sufficiently small so that they are entirely consumed within the gun tube and all available energy evolved. The important ballistic equations are those for the burning rate of the propellant, the motion of the projectile, the energy balance, the equation of state of the propellant gases, and the force, or impetus equation. The first four equations must be solved simultaneously since the events in the tube are simultaneous. The equation of motion is $AP = W(d^2x/dt^2)/g$ where A is the cross-sectional area of the tube; P is the pressure on the projectile base; W/g is the projectile mass; x is the distance along the length of the tube behind the projectile base; and t is the time of motion of the projectile. The total volume available to the gaseous products is Ax. The equation of state is the Nobel-Abel simplified equation which is adequate for ballistic purposes,

$$P\left(\frac{1}{\Delta} - \eta\right) = nRt_v$$

where P is the average pressure; Δ, the loading density or weight of propellant in the volume available, η an empirical covolume correction for gas pressure; n the number of moles of gas; t_v, the adiabatic isochoric flame temperature, and R, the gas constant. This equation is also essentially the force equation, $F = n\,RT_v$ where force or impetus is conventionally used as a measure of potential available in foot pounds per pound of propellant. The energy-balance equation portrays the conversion of internal energy to kinetic energy of the projectile:

$$N \int_t^{t_o} C_v dt = \frac{1/_2 W}{g} V^2 \quad \text{or} \quad NC_v\,(t_o - t) = \frac{1/_2 W}{g} V^2$$

where N is the amount of propellant burned, V is the projectile velocity, C_v is the heat capacity of the gases over the temperature range indicated and t_0, the flame temperature of the gases. Inspection of these equations reveals that the chief thermodynamic–thermochemical characteristics of the propellant affecting gun performance are the gas volume n, the adiabatic isochoric flame temperature of the gases, t_v, their heat capacity, C_v, and the heat capacity ratio γ, (C_p/C_v) which is involved in conversion of energy. The covolume of the gases η is significant in pressure calculations. Although the burning rate of the propellant does not enter these considerations and is not amenable to calculation, it is critically important in determining the rate at which the various processes described occur (3–5).

Rocket Equations. Rocket design involves consideration of the conversion of propellant chemical energy to kinetic energy in a chamber of constant volume. Rearward ejection of the gases from the nozzle imparts a forward velocity to the rocket motor. The thrust on a rocket motor is given by the approximate equation $F = (P_e - P_a)\,A_e + \dot{m}V_e$, where F is the thrust, P_e and V_e the pressure and velocity of the gas stream at the nozzle exit, A_e the cross-sectional area of the nozzle exit, $\dot{m}$ is the mass rate of discharge, and P_a the pressure of the atmosphere into which the gases efflux. Of immediate interest to the propellant designer is the quantity $F/\dot{m}$, the thrust obtained per unit mass rate of gas discharge. This quantity, commonly called the specific impulse of the propellant, depends primarily on the thermodynamic properties of the gaseous products and is affected by the motor only in terms of the nozzle motor operating pressure and the nozzle design. It may be expressed as

$$I = \sqrt{\frac{2\gamma nRt_v}{(\gamma - 1)g} \left[\left(\frac{P_a}{P_e}\right)^{(\gamma-1)/\gamma} \right]}$$

where I is the specific impulse and all other symbols are as defined above.

In rocket motor operation, an equilibrium rate of gas production and gas efflux is reached at an equilibrium pressure in the motor. The pressure in the nozzle throat is proportional to the pressure in the rocket and the thermodynamic properties of the gas; however, the temperature of the gases in the throat and their velocity are independent of chamber pressure and may be estimated thermodynamically from the temperature of the gas in the chamber and its thermodynamic properties. The following equations apply:

$$P_t = 2/(\gamma + 1)P_c \qquad T_t = 2/(\gamma + 1)t_c \qquad V_t = \sqrt{\gamma nRT}$$

P_t and P_c are throat and chamber pressures, T_t and t_c, throat and chamber temperatures, respectively, and V_t, the velocity of gases in the throat.

Table 4.1. Thermochemical Additive Constants for Propellant Components[a]

Components	Q_i cal/g	C_{vi} cal/g	E_i cal/g	n_i mol/g	η[b] in./lb
cellulose nitrate[c] A	1,033	0.3421	283.1	0.03920	27.56
B	−140	0.006	−153	0.00218	1.00
glyceryl nitrate	1,785	0.3438	952	0.03082	22.78
m-dinitrotoluene	−148	0.3210	−668	0.06040	40.44
1,3,5-trinitrotoluene	491	0.3037	−110	0.04843	34.31
diethanolnitramine dinitrate	1,340	0.3651	529	0.04164	
nitroguanidine	721	0.3709	−49	0.04804	31.77
metriol trinitrate, tri-methylolethane trinitrate	1,189	0.3052	377	0.04318	
ethyl centralite, N,N'-diethylcarbanilide	−2,412	0.3905	−2,766	0.10434	62.60
methyl centralite, N,N'-dimethylcarbanilide	−2,200	0.3683	−2,640	0.9988	
diphenylamine	−2,684	0.3471	3,010	0.10637	65.44
diphenylurethane, ethyl N,N'-diphenylcarbamate	−2,739	0.3608	−3,187	0.09533	
ethyl N-phenylcarbamate	−1,639	0.4280	−2,249	0.10132	
N,N'-diphenylurea	−2,227	0.3402	−2,620	0.90423	
2-nitrodiphenylamine	−1,813	0.3226	−2,201	0.08411	
mineral jelly	−3,302	0.5811	−4,175	0.1426	
diethyl phthalate	−1,760	0.3866	−2,349	0.0855	
dibutyl phthalate	−2,071	0.4258	−2,656	0.09701	56.97
diamyl phthalate	−2,187	0.4401	−2,809	0.1102	
triacetin, glyceryl triacetate	−1,284	0.4191	−1,973	0.0733	43.77
ether	−2,007	0.5790	−2,958	0.1243	
acetone	−1,938	0.5104	−2,842	0.1033	57.33
ethyl alcohol	−1,716	0.6083	−2,785	0.1085	56.35
water		0.6507	−1,568	0.0555	24.60
graphite	−3,370	0.1349	−3,224	0.08326	60.53
carbon black	−3,330	0.1349	−3,188	0.08326	
ammonium chlorate	1,603	0.3167	800	0.2128	
potassium nitrate	1,434	0.2158	25	0.00989	23.61
barium nitrate	1,139	0.1574	131	0.00765	15.34
potassium sulfate	300	0.125	−800	0.00574	9.36
ammonium nitrate	1,450	0.4424	405	0.0375	
potassium chlorate	1,667	0.2000	800	0.0072	
poly(methyl acrylate)	−1,404	0.4231	−2,111	0.0814	
polyisobutylene	3,228	0.5798	−3,981	0.1426	
polystyrene	−2,983	0.3739	−3,309	0.1152	
polyurethane	−3,296	0.4073	−3,773	0.1080	
poly(vinyl chloride)	−1,614	0.2080	−1,850	0.0560	

[a] Adapted from references 7,17.

[b] Covolume values given only for common components of gun propellants.

[c] The values for cellulose nitrate depend linearly on the degree of nitration; the table gives the two constants of the linear expression: $X = A + B\,(13.15 - \% \text{ N})$; eg, for 12.6% N cellulose nitrate $Q_i = 1033 - 140\,(13.15 - 12.6)$.

The foregoing equations reveal the characteristics of the propellant which affect rocket performance to be the gas volume n, the adiabatic isobaric flame temperature t_p, the heat capacity of the gases C_v, the heat capacity ratio γ, and the total energy evolved in propellant burning (6,7).

Factors Affecting Performance in Guns and Rockets. Comparison of the thermo-chemical-thermodynamic factors affecting gun- and rocket-propellant performance reveal that they are essentially the same and involve common properties. If certain of these properties are known, as for example the energy evolved, the volume of gas produced, and the flame temperatures of the gas and its heat capacity, it is possible to make calculations of the force of gun propellants and the specific impulse of rocket propellants at specified rocket conditions. In addition, knowledge of the calorific value Q is valuable as an index to the burning rate and flame temperature of the propellant. Since the thermodynamic properties of the gases produced are known, it is possible to calculate accurately the performance of propellants by a series of successive approximations in which the products formed, the energy evolved, and the equilibria which prevail at the estimated temperature and pressure are continuously equated in an iterative sequence of calculations. However, accurate calculations require computers and are very tedious. Using a number of simplifying assumptions, various techniques have been developed which permit rapid calculations to be made. These approaches involve the use of precalculated additive constants to determine the desired parameters. One system originated by Hirschfelder and Sherman establishes gas volume n, calorific values Q, mean heat capacity C_v in the temperature range of interest (2000–3000°K), and the relative energy of the gas at 2500°K (E_{2500}). An example of such calculations is presented which demonstrates the ease with which the important and revealing thermochemical dynamic data may be obtained by a series of simple calculations (9–17).

Calculations. The following equations are useful for estimating the required parameters:

$$n = (C) + \tfrac{1}{2}(H) + \tfrac{1}{2}(N)$$

$$C_v = 1.62(C) + 3.265(H) + 5.193(O) + 3.384(H)$$

$$Q = H_c - 67{,}421(2C + \tfrac{1}{2}H - O)$$

$$E_{2500} = H_c - 13{,}2771(C) - 40{,}026(H) + 51{,}819(O) - 6724(N)$$

where C, H, N, and O are gram atoms of carbon, hydrogen, nitrogen, and oxygen per gram of compound in which the element exists (no. atoms/molecular weight), n is moles of gas per gram, C_v is the average heat capacity in the temperature range 2000–3000°K, Q is the heat of explosion in a calorimetric bomb with water formed in the liquid state, H_c is the heat of combustion of the compound, and E_{2500} is the relative energy of the gases using 2500°K as the reference temperature. Table 4.1 lists values which have been calculated in this manner for representative compounds used in propellants. In addition, the following equations apply with terminology as described above:

$$\gamma = 1 + nR/C_v$$

$$t_v = 2500°K + \frac{E_{2500}}{C_v}$$

$$t_p = t_v/\gamma$$

Calculate Q, n, E, C_v, γ, t_v, t_p, and I for the following composition, using individual values taken from Table 4.1.

1. *Nominal composition*

	Wt, %	Q	n_i	E_i	C_{vi}
cellulose nitrate (12.6% N)	59.1	956	0.04040	198.9	0.3454
glyceryl nitrate	29.8	1,785	0.03082	951.9	0.3438
triacetin	9.5	−1,284	0.07333	−1,973	0.4191
2-nitrodiphenylamine	1.6	−1,813	0.08411	−2,201	0.3226

2. *Summation*

	Q	n	E	C_v
cellulose nitrate	565.0	0.02388	117.5	0.2041
glyceryl nitrate	531.9	0.00918	283.7	0.1025
triacetin	−122.0	0.00697	−182.4	0.0398
2-nitrodiphenylamine	−29.0	0.00135	−35.2	0.0052
Propellant	945.9	0.04138	178.6	0.3516

The above propellant has a calculated heat of explosion of 945.9 cal/g (H_2O), produces 0.04138 moles of gas per gram, has a relative energy at 2500°K of 178.6 cal/g, and an average heat capacity of 0.3516 cal/(g)(°K) between 2000–3000°K. The positive relative energy at 2500°K shows that heat is available to raise the temperature of the gases above 2500°K.

3. Heat capacity ratio $\gamma = 1 + nR/C_v$

$$\gamma = 1 + \frac{0.04138 \times 1.987}{0.3516} = 1.23$$

4. Heat capacity at constant pressure, C_p

$$C_p/C_v = 1.23$$

$$C_p = 1.23 \times C_v = 1.23 \times 0.3516 = 0.4339 \text{ cal/(g)(°K)}$$

5. Adiabatic isochoric flame temperature, t_v

$$t_v = 2500°K + (E/C_v) = 2500°K + (178.6/0.3516) = 3008°K$$

At temperatures considerably higher than 3000°K, a correction is made for gas dissociation in accordance with the following equation:

$$t_v = 3000°K + 6046 \left[-(C_v + 0.01185) + [(C_v + 0.01185)^2 + (3.308 \times 10^{-4})(E - 500\, C_v)]^{1/2} \right]$$

6. Adiabatic isobaric flame temperature, t_p

$$t_p = t_v/\gamma$$

$$t_p = 3008/1.23 = 2446°K$$

7. Specific impulse I, at $P_c = 1000$ psi, $P_a = 14.7$ psi

$$I = \sqrt{\frac{2\gamma nRt_p}{(\gamma - 1)g} \left[1 - \left(\frac{P_a}{P_c}\right)^{(\gamma-1)/\gamma} \right]}$$

$$I = 13.153 \sqrt{\frac{1.23 \times 0.04138 \times 2446}{1.23-1} \left[1 - (0.0147)^{\frac{(1.23-1)}{1.23}} \right]}$$

$$I = 226 \text{ lb (f) sec/lb (m)}$$

8.   Force $= nRT_v$

$$= 0.04138 \times 2782 \times 3008$$

$$= 345,920 \text{ ft-lb(f)/lb(m)}$$

Table 4.2 lists the calculated specific impulses obtainable with existing and prospective types of liquid, and solid rocket propellants. The calculated thermochemical and thermodynamic characteristics of a number of gun and rocket propellants are given in Tables 5.1 and 5.2 in Section 5 and Tables 6.4 to 6.12 in Section 6.

Table 4.2. Specific Impulses of Various Liquid and Solid Rocket Propellants[a]

Propellant combinations	I_{sp} range
Monopropellants (*liquid*)	
low-energy monopropellants: hydrazine, ethylene oxide,	
hydrogen peroxide	160–190
high-energy monopropellants: nitromethane	190–230
Bipropellants (*liquid*)	
low-energy bipropellants: perchloryl fluoride–available	
fuel; aniline–acid; hydrocarbon fuel (JP-4)–acid; hydro-	
carbon fuel (JP-4)–hydrogen peroxide	200–260
medium-energy bipropellants: hydrazine–acid; ammonia–	
nitrogen tetroxide	230–260
high-energy bipropellants: liquid oxygen–JP-4; liquid	
oxygen–alcohol; hydrazine–chlorine trifluoride	250–270
very high energy bipropellants: liquid oxygen and	
fluorine–JP-4; liquid oxygen and ozone–JP-4; liquid	
oxygen–hydrazine	270–330
super high-energy bipropellants: fluorine–hydrogen;	
fluorine–ammonia; ozone–hydrogen; fluorine–diborane	300–385
Oxidizer–binder combinations (*solid*)	
potassium perchlorate	
polysulfide rubber	170–210
ammonium perchlorate	
polysulfide rubber	170–210
rubber	170–210
polyurethane	210–250
nitropolymer	210–250
ammonium nitrate	
polyester	170–210
rubber	170–210
nitropolymer	170–210
double base	210–250
boron metal components and oxidant	200–250
lithium metal components and oxidant	200–250
aluminum metal components and oxidant	200–250
magnesium metal components and oxidant	200–250

[a] Adopted from reference 19.

Performance Optimization. In general, about 700–1100 cm³ of gas per gram are produced by propellants commonly used for gun and rockets. Typical gas compositions are shown in Table 4.3. Heat capacity ratios range between 1.20–1.30; flame temperatures between 2000–4000°K. The overall thermal energy available is approximately proportional to the product of the amount of gas produced and the flame

Table 4.3. Typical Propellant Gas Compositions[a]

Composition	Propellant types			
	Double base	Rubber base + NH_4NO_3	Polysulfide base + NH_4ClO_4	Polyurethane base + Al + NH_4ClO_4
CO_2	28	16	17	1
CO	23	2	4	29
H_2	8	28	4	38
H_2O	26	32	42	7
N_2	15	22	9	6
HCl			18	12
sulfur compounds			6	

[a] Approximate values, mole %; adapted from reference 22.

temperature of the gas. Therefore, except where circumstances require special consideration as in certain gun and rocket systems, efforts to produce high energy propellants consist of maximizing flame temperature and gas volume. Since flame temperature is related to calorific value and gas volumes are relatively similar, measures of the available energy of propellants of comparable composition are approximately proportional to their heats of explosion.

Maximum specific impulses of about 265 lb-sec/lb are attainable with flame temperatures of from 3000 to 4000°K, generally by the incorporation of crystalline oxidizers and aluminum in double-base or elastomeric mixtures. The requirements for high-impulse rocket propellants to accelerate heavier payloads necessitate an increase in propellant flame temperature and gas volume in accordance with $(nt_p)^{1/2}$. This may be approached in various ways. Increasing the crystalline oxidizer content of composite propellants consistent with maintaining adequate mechanical strength is one approach. Another is through the use of oxidizer binders. The incorporation of metallic fuels increases impulse when used with crystalline oxidizers, although the increase is often less than the calculated value, perhaps because of inadequate residence time for complete reaction between the metal and the oxidizer in the motor. Incorporation of large quantities of crystalline oxidizers and metallic fuels in double-base mixtures is also accomplished to provide high-impulse propellants. The synthesis of new, high-energy fuels and oxidizers further supports these approaches. Although these techniques are not readily applicable to gun propellants, the recent development of effective procedures for minimizing gun-tube erosion permits consideration of high flame temperature propellants with high force values which could not previously be used. Performance increases have been obtained through the development of the casting process which has led to systems in which the propellants may be cast directly into the rocket motor. Since the propellant bonds directly to the motor wall (case-bonding), the motor wall is thermally protected by the grain. Thinner walls may be used with significant metal weight decrease. Maximum density of loading and maximum motor velocity are achieved through the high propellant-mass ratios obtained from case bonding of propellants. Efforts to maximize performance by combining the advantages of both liquid and solid rocket systems has led to work on hybrid rocket engines. In many such instances, however, the disadvantages of both systems have also been manifest (20–25).

Bibliography

1. *Elements of Armament Engineering*, Part 3, Department of Ordnance, U.S. Military Academy, West Point, 1959, Chap. 1,5.
2. M. J. Zucrow, *Propulsion and Propellants, Engineering Design Handbook AMCP 706-282*, U.S. Army Materiel Command, Washington, D.C., 1963, pp. 27–36.
3. J. Corner, *Theory of the Interior Ballistics of Guns*, John Wiley & Sons, Inc., New York, 1950, Chap. 4.
4. F. R. W. Hunt, ed., *Interior Ballistics*, Philosophical Library Inc., New York, 1950.
5. C. F. Curtis and J. W. Wrench, Jr., *Interior Ballistics, A Consolidation and Revision of Previous Reports, Interior Ballistics I-VII Inclusive P 4-7 NDRC Rept. A-397 N, OSRD Rept. 6468* Geophysical Laboratory, Carnegie Institute of Technology, Washington, D.C., 1945.
7. David Altman, James M. Carter, S. S. Penner, and Martin Summerfield, *Liquid Propellant Rockets*, Princeton University Press, Princeton, N.J., 1960, pp. 108–122.
8. B. L. Crawford et al., "Rocket Fundamentals" *Office Sci. Res. and Develop. Rept. 3932*, 1944.
9. J. George Sotter, "Chemical Kinetics of the Cordite Explosion Zone," presented at the *10th Symposium on Combustion, Cambridge, England, 1964.*
10. G. E. Ellis and G. S. Bahn, "Engineering Selection of Reaction Rate Constants for Gaseous Chemical Species at High Temperatures," *Presented at Fall Meeting of the Combustion Institute, Western States Section, 1962.*
11. *Joint Army-Navy-Air Force Thermochemical Tables*, Dow Chemical Co., Midland, Mich., 1960.
12. A. O. Dekker, "Rapid Estimation of Specific Impulse of Solid Propellants," *Jet Propulsion* **21** (1956).
13. John D. Clark, *The NQD Method of Specific Impulse Calculation 2nd Revision*, Picatinny Arsenal, 1961.
14. B. L. Crawford et al., *Liquid Propellant Rockets*, Princeton University Press, Princeton, N.J., pp. 273–275.
15. F. L. McMains, *A Digital Computer Program for Hirschfelder Interior Ballistics, Techn. Mem. 1404*, Picatinny Arsenal, Dover, N.J., 1964.
16. "Letter Symbols for Rocket Propulsion," *Jet Propulsion* **25**, 636 (1955).
17. J. O. Hirschfelder and J. Sherman, "Simple Calculation of Thermochemical Properties for Use in Ballistics," *NDRC Rept. A-101, Office Sci. Res. Develop., Rept. 935.*
18. A. M. Ball, *Solid Propellants, I, Ordnance Engineering Design Handbook, ORDP 20-175*, Army Materiel Command Washington, D.C., 1961.
19. Staff Report, *Space Handbook: Astronautics and Its Applications*, U.S. Government Printing Office, Washington, D.C.
20. R. O. Wolff, *Reduction of Gun Erosion, Technical Report 3096*, Picatinny Arsenal, Dover, N.J.
21. O. A. Colitti, *Processing of High Energy Solid Rocket Propellants*, Picatinny Arsenal, Dover, N.J.
22. K. Klager, *Solid Propellants*, Aerojet General Corporation.
23. J. W. Wiggens, "The Use of Solid Propellants Engines for Achievement of Super Velocities," *Jet Propulsion* **26**, 1084–1087 (1956).
24. Douglas F. Ordahd, "Hybrid Propulsion System," *Astronautics* **4**, 42–43, 84 (1959).
25. George E. Moore and Kurt Berman, "A Solid–Liquid Rocket Propellant System," *Jet Propulsion* **26**, 958–964 (1956).

5. Propellant Characteristics: Liquid Propellants

Table 5.1 gives data on a number of substances used in liquid propellants. Additional information on the more important of these is mentioned below.

Liquid Monopropellants. The basic problem in the development of high-energy liquid monopropellants consists in finding materials which are stable, simple to handle, and resistant to a wide variety of adverse environmental influences. At the same time, the monopropellant must decompose rapidly when energy is applied, burn smoothly, and deliver its energy under rocket conditions. Of the monopropellant systems described, concentrated hydrogen peroxide and hydrazine are most commonly used to provide power to turbopumps or to auxiliary power units; they are also used as oxidizer and fuel, respectively, in bipropellant systems.

Hydrogen Peroxide. Hydrogen peroxide, H_2O_2, may be used in concentrations from 80–99%. It decomposes in the presence of catalysts such as sodium and calcium permanganate, as follows:

$$H_2O_2 \text{ (liq)} \rightarrow H_2O \text{ (g)} + \tfrac{1}{2} O_2 + 23,300 \text{ Btu}$$

At 300 psia the temperature of the gases is calculated to be 980°C, the theoretical impulse 146 sec. Although concentrated hydrogen peroxide can be handled and stored when considerable care is used, it is unstable, decomposing at ambient temperature, and has an undesirably high freezing point (−0.5°C). It boils at 150°C and has a density of 1.44 g/cm³. Its specific heat at 20°C is 19.7 cal/(°C)(mole); its viscosity is 1.83 cP at 20°C. Storage in vented containers of purified aluminum (99.7%, min) is required and precautions must be taken to prevent contamination from a wide variety of substances which catalyze the decomposition. Hydrogen peroxide is made by electrolysis of sulfuric acid followed by hydrolysis of the resulting peroxydisulfuric acid. The product is purified by fractional distillation and freezing and costs about $1.20/lb (4–6).

Hydrazine. Hydrazine, N_2H_4 decomposes exothermically as follows:

$$3 \, N_2H_4 \rightarrow 4 \, NH_3 + N_2 + 144,300 \text{ Btu}$$

If sufficient time is available, the ammonia formed decomposes endothermically,

$$4 \, NH_3 \rightarrow 2 \, N_2 + 6 \, H_2 - 79,200 \text{ Btu}$$

Since the time of exposure in rocket action is limited, this decomposition occurs only to a small extent. The presence of catalysts such as iron, nickel, and cobalt further accelerates the decomposition of hydrazine. Hydrazine is soluble in water and forms a hydrate, $N_2H_4 \cdot H_2O$, which may be used as a fuel with various oxidizing agents. The material is toxic and has an undesirably high freezing point, 1.6°C. However, the addition of nitric acid and water depresses its freezing point so that a mixture of 74% N_2H_4, 16% HNO_3, and 10% water by weight freezes at approximately −40°C and forms gases which have a flame temperature of about 927°C. This mixture is thermally stable at ambient temperatures and may be readily stored in aluminum or stainless-steel containers. The characteristics of hydrazine are: specific heat and viscosity at 20°C, 19.7 cal/(°C)(mole), and 1.83 cP; density at 15°C, 1.01 g/cm³; heat of formation 12,050 cal/mole. Hydrazine may be made by the modified Raschig process involving reaction of ammonia with sodium hypochlorite. Preliminary purification is by distillation followed by final purification which involves refluxing with potassium hydroxide and vacuum distillation. Approximate cost is $1.25/lb (7,8).

Liquid Bipropellants. It is possible to obtain a significantly greater impulse with bipropellants than with monopropellants without seriously increasing hazards in use. A wide variety of liquid oxidizers and fuels is available; the specific material selected depends upon the performance characteristics desired. The use of liquid systems for large high-performance missiles and boosters often necessitates considerable auxiliary "plumbing" to permit close control of fluid flow and termination of rocket action when required. However highly simplified designs have been developed for use in storable rockets where less stringent performance requirements permit the elimination of much of the componentry often associated with liquid fuel systems (9).

Table 5.1. Properties of Liquid Propellants[a]

Propellants	Formula	Mol wt	Mp, °C	Bp, °C	Critical temp, °C	Critical pressure, psia	Heat of formation, cal/mole, 298°K	Heat of vaporization, Btu/lb
aerozine-50 (50% hydrazine–50% UDMH)		41.8				1,696	11,789	426
ammonia	NH_3	17.0	−78	−33	132	1,636	−17,140	596
anhyd nitric acid	HNO_3	63.0	−42	83	287	1,240	−41,404	216
aniline	$C_6H_5NH_2$	93.0	−6	184	426	771	7,340	203
bromine pentafluoride	BrF_5	174.9	−61	40	197	624	−131,200	74
chlorine trifluoride	ClF_3	92.5	−76	12	174	838	−43,100	128
diborane (6)	B_2H_6	27.7	−165	−93	17	581	7,500	224
diethylcyclohexane	$C_{10}H_{26}$	140.3	−79	174	367	367	−173,560	119
ethyl alcohol	C_2H_5OH	46.1	−114	78	243	925	−66,363	362
ethylene oxide	C_2H_4O	44.1	−112	11	196	1,043	6,010	249
fluorine	F_2	38.0	−221	−188	−128	808	−3,056	71.5
hydrazine	N_2H_4	32.0	16	114	380	2,131	12,050	540
monomethyl hydrazine	$N_2H_3(CH_3)$	46.0	53	87	321	1,195	12,700	377
hydrogen peroxide (100%)	H_2O_2	34.0	−0.5	150	457	3,146	−44,750	596

liquid hydrogen	H_2	2.0	−259	−253	−240	188	−1,895	195
JP-X(40% UDMH/60% JP-4		89.3	<−59	99	285	680	1,171	169
fuming nitric acid max density (56% HNO_3–44% N_2O_4)		73.2	−37	30	241	1,320	−30,413	153
red fuming nitric acid (85% HNO_3–15% NO_2)		59.7	−48	64	271	1,286	−33,500	247
liquid nitrogen	N_2	28.0	−210	−196	−147	492		85.8
nitrogen tetroxide	N_2O_4	92.0	−11	21	157	1,470	−6,800	178
nitrogen trifluoride	NF_3	71.0	−207	−129	−67	729	−31,700	73
oxygen	O_2	32.0	−219	−183	−119	731	−2,896	92
ozone	O_3	48.0	−193	−112	−12	803	28,300	128
pentaborane	B_5H_9	63	−47	58	223	557	7,800	219
perchloryl fluoride	ClO_3F	102	−146	−47	96	779	−10,910	84
n-propyl nitrate	$C_3H_7NO_3$	105	<−101	111	307	588	−47,000	142
RP-1 (H/C = 2.0)		172	−46 to 73	217	407	315	−6,222	125
U-Deta (60% UDMH–40% diethylenetriamine)		72.1	<−84	72	292	805	4,860	191
UDMH	$(CH_3)_2N_2H_2$	60.1	−58	63	249	880	12,724	251

[a] Adapted from reference 25.

Table 5.2.[a]   Calculated Thermochemical Characteristics of Liquid Bipropellant Systems[b]

Oxidizer	Fuel	Mix ratio	Bulk density	Chamber temp, °C	$\bar{M}$	I, lb-sec/lb	γ
oxygen	ammonia	1.30	0.88	2,768	19.2	285	1.23
	92.5 % ethyl alcohol	1.48	0.98	3,035	22.9	274	1.21
	hydrazine	0.74	1.06	3,027	18.3	301	1.25
	hydrogen	3.40	0.26	2,416	8.9	388	1.26
	RP-1	2.24	1.01	3,282	21.9	286	1.24
	UDMH	1.39	0.96	3,171	19.8	295	1.25
fluorine	ammonia	2.80	1.14	4,132	18.6	330	1.33
	hydrazine	1.83	1.29	4,218	18.5	334	1.33
	hydrogen	4.54	0.33	2,791	8.9	398	1.33
	JP-4	2.9	1.19	3,927	24.0	297	1.22
	diborane	5.0	1.07	4,360	21.0	329	1.30
chlorine-trifluoride	ammonia	3.0	1.26	2,749	22.0	251	1.32
	hydrazine	2.16	1.46	3,398	23.0	269	1.33
	RP-1	3.14	1.40	5,855	29.0	251	1.25
hydrogen peroxide, 99.6%	ethyl alcohol, 92.5%	4.0	1.24	2,538	23	251	1.20
	JP-4	6.5	1.28	2,666	22	265	1.20
	hydrogen	1.7	1.24	2,584	19	280	1.22
	ammonia	2.15	1.12	2,326	21	252	1.24
	hydrazine	1.23	1.26	2,726	19.7	277	1.25
	50% UDMH–50% N_2H_4	1.73	1.23	2,725	20.6	272	1.23
	JP-4	4.1	1.30	2,843	25	271	1.23

[a] Conditions: chamber pressure, P_c = 1000 psi; exit pressure, P_e = 14.7 psi; optimum nozzle-expansion ratio; isentropic one-dimensional flow; frozen equilibrium during expansion; mix ratio: wt oxidizer/wt fuel; chamber temperature: adiabatic flame temperature; $\bar{M}$ = average mol wt of combustion gases; I_c = theoretical calculated specific impulse; γ = heat capacity ratio, C_p/C_v; RP−1 = hydrocarbon fuel.

[b] Adapted from references 23,24.

Oxidizers.   The most important existing and potential oxidizers contain oxygen or fluorine. These include low-energy oxidizers such as nitric acid and variants of the acid and concentrated hydrogen peroxide; medium-energy oxidizers such as nitrogen tetroxide and chlorine trifluoride; and high-energy oxidizers such as oxygen and fluorine. The characteristics of the most important of these materials are listed in Tables 5.1 and 5.2.

Liquid Oxygen.   Liquid oxygen has been used in a number of missile systems and is superior on a weight basis to any of the available oxidizers. It has a density of 1.14 g/cm³, a viscosity of 0.19 cP and a specific heat of 13.0 cal/(°C)(mol) all measured at the boiling point of −183°C. Whereas the cost of manufacture of liquid oxygen from liquid air is very low, the overall cost of use involving handling, transport, and storage of a material with a serious fire hazard potential is relatively high. Liquid oxygen is produced by fractional distillation of liquid air at a cost ranging from 3 to 10 ¢/lb (10).

Nitric Acid.   Nitric acid and a number of variants have been used extensively as oxidizers (including white and red fuming acids and a stabilized form of the red acid).

Red fuming nitric acid is one of the most important oxidizers because of its availability and practical use with a variety of fuels. It contains approximately 83% HNO_3, 14% NO_2, and 3% H_2O. The addition of approx 0.5% hydrofluoric acid stabilizes the acid, decreasing its corrosivity, and permitting long-term storage in aluminum or stainless-steel containers. Nitric acid has a density of 1.51 g/cm^3 at 20°C, melts at −41.6°C, and boils at 83°C. Its specific heat and viscosity at 10°C are 26.3 cal/(°C)(mole) and 0.91 cP, respectively. Stabilized red fuming nitric acid has a somewhat higher density, 1.56 g/cm^3. Nitric acid decomposes slowly at ambient temperatures as shown below:

$$2 HNO_3 \rightarrow 2 NO_2 + H_2O + \tfrac{1}{2} O_2$$

The addition of NO_2 and H_2O to nitric acid to form the red acid reverses the reaction and minimizes oxygen formation, thereby reducing storage pressure and eliminating the need for venting. Upon the further addition of hydrofluoric acid, a liquid oxidizer becomes available which can be safely stored at high and low temperatures and can be readily handled in missile systems. Its use does not provide as high an impulse as does liquid oxygen. For example, the reaction between oxygen and hydrazine yields an impulse of 279 sec as compared with 257 sec obtained from red fuming nitric acid and hydrazine under the same conditions. However, its superior storage and handling characteristics make it a most useful oxidizer for all but very high performance applications (11,12).

Hydrogen Peroxide. The characteristics of hydrogen peroxide have been considered under its use as a monopropellant.

Mixed Oxides of Nitrogen. An equilibrium mixture of NO_2 and N_2O_4 has received consideration for use in bipropellant systems. The relatively high freezing point, −11°C, and extreme toxicity make its use generally unwarranted. The mixture has a density of 1.45 g/cm^3 at 20°C, boils at 21°C, and melts at −11.3°C. Its heat of vaporization is 9.1 kcal/mole; the heat of formation at 25°C is 6.8 kcal/mole; at 20°C, the specific heat and viscosity are 33 cal/(°C)(mole) and 0.43 cP, respectively. Nitrogen tetroxide (dinitrogen tetroxide) N_2O_4 has been used in Titan II (13).

Liquid Fluorine. Liquid fluorine at present is an experimental oxidizer which offers the possibility of significant gains in impulse when used in bipropellant systems. As an example, a fluorine–hydrazine mixture has a specific impulse of 316 sec at 500 psia and a density of 1.30 g/cm^3; an oxygen–hydrazine mix under the same condition has an impulse of 279 sec; it also has a lower density, 1.06 g/cm^3. Fluorine has a greater heat of reaction with hydrogen than does oxygen; the hydrogen–fluorine combination is one of the highest performing systems available: a flame temperature of about 4800°K is produced, with the formation of hydrogen fluoride. The specific impulse is 373 sec at 500 psia. Fluorine has three major disadvantages: its unusual chemical activity, its great toxicity, and the high reactivity of its gaseous reaction product, hydrogen fluoride. As a result, use of fluorine by comparison with liquid oxygen is apt to be restricted to a very limited number of instances where maximum performance is essential. Fluorine has the following physical characteristics: density at −187°C is 1.55 g/cm^3; the melting and boiling points are −221 and −188°C. Fluorine has a specific heat of 11.3 cal/(°C)(mole) at −188°C, and a viscosity of 0.28 cP at −193°C (14,15).

Chlorine Trifluoride. The most noteworthy of the oxidizers containing fluorine is chlorine trifluoride. This material closely resembles fluorine in its chemical properties and in its performance in propellant systems. The noncryogenic storage properties of chlorine trifluoride make handling problems much less severe than with liquid fluorine. It has a density of 1.81 g/cm³ at 25°C, boils at 12.1°C and melts at −76°C. At 25°C, its specific heat and viscosity are 28 cal/(°C) (mole) and 0.48 cP, respectively. Chlorine trifluoride may be produced in a one-stage reaction between chlorine and fluorine at temperatures of above 280°C. The current price in small quantities is about $3.00/lb (16).

Fuels. Fuels for use in bipropellant systems are relatively numerous; selection is based on system compatibility, ease of handling, and optimization of impulse to be obtained with the oxidizer chosen for the bipropellant system. Fuels such as the light hydrocarbons, ethyl alcohol, hydrazine, unsymmetrical dimethylhydrazine, and ammonia have been of greatest use and interest. A considerable amount of experimentation is being conducted with hydrogen, the borohydrides, and a variety of light metals such as beryllium and boron.

Hydrocarbon Fuels. The jet propulsion fuels commonly referred to as JP fuels are hydrocarbons particularly of the gasoline and kerosene type. JP-5 is a high-flash kerosene in the 177–288°C distillate range with a maximum melting-point requirement of −40°C; JP-4 is a kerosene with a lower distillate range, 93–288°C, and a melting-point requirement of −60°C. Other JP hydrocarbons vary somewhat in distillate ranges. These fuels have excellent handling and use characteristics; their performance with oxidizers such as red fuming nitric acid, hydrogen peroxide, and liquid oxygen yield impulses varying from 235 to 262 sec at 500 psi. In general, JP fuels require external initiation with most liquid oxidizers and are not used in prepackageable systems because of the tendency to form sludge and gums.

Ethyl Alcohol. Ethyl alcohol was used in the German V2 missile and offers the advantages of availability, ease of handling, and a satisfactory impulse with such oxidizers as liquid oxygen, 257 sec at 1000 psi. Its chief drawback is its low specific gravity, 0.79 at 20°C. Ethyl alcohol is nonhypergolic with liquid oxidizers in common use.

Hydrazine. Hydrazine is a high-impulse fuel whose characteristics have been previously described. As an example, its specific impulse with red fuming nitric acid is 257 sec compared with 235 sec for JP-4 fuel. Hydrazine is hypergolic with most oxidizers except liquid oxygen. Its chief disadvantage is its relatively high freezing point (1.6°C).

Unsymmetrical Dimethylhydrazine (UDMH). This material has a density of 0.786 g/cm³ at 25°C, a freezing point of −58°C, and boils at 63°C. Its specific heat at 25°C is 39.21 cal/(°C)(mole); and its viscosity at 25°C is 0.509 cP. UDMH performs well with liquid oxidizers and yields a slightly lower impulse than does hydrazine. It has a much lower freezing point, −58°C, than does hydrazine, 1.6°C, and ignites more readily with acid. Considerable work has been done to investigate its performance as a monopropellant. The compound shows good stability to heat and catalytic decomposition. Its theoretical performance approaches that of hydrazine, but its lower freezing point offers advantages. The compatibility of UDMH with a wide variety of metals and its long-term storability have resulted in increasing use of this compound in bipropellant systems (17–18).

Liquid Hydrogen. Liquid hydrogen combined with liquid fluorine or liquid oxygen offers the maximum impulse attainable by conventional chemical techniques. Because of the hazards involved in its storage and use, as well as a very low density

(0.07 g/cm³ at 20.4°K), the application of hydrogen as a bipropellant fuel is limited to requirements where maximum impulse is of critical importance. Liquid hydrogen boils at $-252.8°C$, has a viscosity of 1.344×10^{-4} P at 20°K, and a heat capacity of 2.92 cal/(°K)(mole) at 20°K.

Boron Hydrides and Metallic Borohydrides. Boron compounds containing hydrogen have received considerable attention primarily for use in jet plane performance. Both diborane (6), B_2H_6, and pentaborane (9), B_5H_9, are low density materials, 0.43 and 0.61 g/cm³, respectively. Diborane boils at $-93°C$, and melts at $-165°C$; pentaborane, the more stable of the materials boils at 58°C and melts at $-46.6°C$. Decaborane (14), $B_{10}H_{14}$, is a solid substance, the most stable of all the boron hydrides. (See Vol. 3, p. 684 and beyond.) Perceptible decomposition occurs only above 170°C. This material melts at 99.5°C, boils at 213°C and has a specific gravity of 0.92 g/cm³. Boron hydrides offer the possibility of high performance approximating that of hydrogen, if usage problems can be resolved. They burn to produce boron oxide and water as follows:

$$B_5H_9 + 6 O_2 \rightarrow 2\tfrac{1}{2} B_2O_3 + 4\tfrac{1}{2} H_2O$$

However, they are costly, toxic, and inconvenient to handle owing to their extreme reactivity (they react with water). A variety of metallic borohydrides and lithium borohydride have been suggested as fuels; but as yet these have found only experimental use (20,21).

Mixed Fuels. Mixed amine fuels consisting of unsymmetrical dimethylhydrazine and diethylenetriamine in various ratios have been prepared and used. Similarly, a storable fuel blend of 50:50 unsymmetrical dimethylhydrazine and hydrazine has been prepared. Specific mixtures tend to offer advantages in ease of ignition and handling; performance properties generally lie between those of the components.

Fuel Suspensions. Suspensions or colloidal solutions of boron, beryllium, and other substances in petroleum products have been considered for maximizing energy output. The problems of production of colloidal solutions of high concentration and the prevention of settling of solids have as yet rendered this approach impractical for missile systems (22).

Bibliography

1. C. E. Roth and H. M. Polant, "Liquid Rockets for Supersonic Sleds," *Jet Propulsion* **27,** 1006–1011 (1957).
2. D. R. Geehring, "High Energy Fuels," *Ordnance* **42,** 563–566 (1957).
3. K. A. Ehricke, "A Comparison of Propellants and Working Fluids for Rocket Propulsion," *ARS (Am. Rocket Soc.) J.* **23,** 287 (1953).
4. "Hydrogen Peroxide," *U.S. Specification MIL-H-16005*, 1956.
5. *Properties of Hydrogen Peroxide*, Buffalo Electro Chemical Company, Inc., 1955.
6. H. Walter, "Experience with the Application of Hydrogen Peroxide for Production of Power," *ARS J.* **24,** 166 (1954).
7. "Hydrazine," *U.S. Specification MIL-P-26536A*, 1959.
8. L. F. Audrieth and B. A. Ogg, *The Chemistry of Hydrazine*, John Wiley & Sons, Inc., New York, 1951.
9. S. H. Dole and M. A. Margolis, "Sources, Availability, and Estimated Costs of Propellants," *Jet Propulsion* **27,** 1–24 (1957).
10. "Oxygen," *U.S. Specification BB-O-925A*.
11. D. L. Mason, "Properties of Fuming Nitric Acid Affecting Its Storage and Use as a Rocket Propellant" *Jet Propulsion* **26,** 741–744, 756 (1956).
12. "Nitric Acid," *U.S. Specification MIL-P-7254E* (1961).

13. "Nitrogen Tetroxide," *U.S. Specification MIL-P-26539A* (1961).

14. R. Landou and R. Rosen, "Industrial Handling of Fluorine," *Ind. Eng. Chem.* **39**, 281–283 (1947).

15. "Fluorine Figures Big" *Jet Propulsion* **27**, 678–679 (1957).

16. *Perchloride Fluoride, Booklet DC-1819*, Pennsalt Chem. Co., Technical Division, Phila, Pa. (1957).

17. *Storage and Handling of Unsymmetrical Dimethylhydrazine*, Food Machinery and Chemical Corporation, South Charleston, W. Va.

18. S. H. Smith and R. R. Miller, "Some Physical Properties of Diboranes Pentaborane and Aluminum Borohydride," *ARS J.* **76**, 1452–1458 (1950).

19. "Hydrogen," *U.S. Specification MIL-P-27201* (1959).

20. Ya. M. Paushken, *The Chemical Composition and Properties of Fuel for Jet Propulsion*, Pergamon Press, London, 1962.

21. "Pentaborane," *U.S. Specification MIL-P-27403* (1963).

22. J. F. Torney, "Liquid Rocket Propellants" *Aeron. Eng. Rev.* **16**, 55 (1957).

23. *Rocket Engine Propellants*, Rocketdyne Publication 505 X, 1959.

24. M. J. Zucrow, *Propulsion and Propellants, Engineering Design Handbook, AMCP 706-282*, U.S. Army Materiel Command Washington, D.C., (1963).

25. *Performance and Properties of Liquid Propellants, Revision A, Report No. 8160-65*, Aerojet General Corporation.

6. Propellant Characteristics: Solid Propellants

Very large numbers of quite small grains of gun propellant are used in propellant charges to provide the high mass rate of burning required to accelerate projectiles to maximum velocity in the relatively short distances of travel available in the gun tube. The manufacturing processes for gun propellants are designed to produce these grains in enormous quantities essentially by plasticizing cellulose nitrate in simple mixers and extruding long strands of soft propellant which can be readily cut to lengths and dried to a hard, hornlike texture. Performance and quality control are obtained by control of the composition, the volatile material present, and by careful control of grain dimensions through appropriate extrusion and drying techniques. Some variation in burning characteristics is permissible, since it is generally possible to modify the propellant charge to meet gun requirements by the addition or removal of propellant grains. Evaluation of gun propellants and charge establishment are best made in terms of composition analysis and measurements of the heat of explosion, the closed bomb characteristics (relative force and quickness) (see Section 7) and the geometrical dimensions followed by confirmatory weapon firings. The requirements of rocket systems pose a number of problems for the rocket-propellant designer which do not exist in gun propellant designs. Rocket grains are very much larger and have considerably more complex geometric forms. Their burning characteristics must be much more carefully tailored and controlled since the weight–volume–pressure relationships in a rocket are far more restricted and demanding than in a gun. The stresses imposed on large rocket grains as a result of mechanical and thermal shocks find no parallel in the small gun propellant grains. Rocket grains must be free of flaws to avoid the disastrous consequences of internal burning. Manufacturing and inspection procedures are more critical. The cost of firing of a large rocket in order to evaluate its performance is very great. As a result of the stringent requirements imposed on solid rocket propellants and the diversity of rockets used, a large number of different rocket propellants have been developed to meet specific requirements. Performance and quality control must result in satisfactory rocket grains as produced. Composition and particle size of ingredients are carefully controlled; heats of explosion and strand burning rates are established; geometrical dimensional measurements made; physical properties ascertained; extensive radiographic examination for flaws and grain defects are conducted; and small and limited full-scale rocket motor firings made at high and low temperatures. In-process variations of a minor and not readily identifiable nature may produce significant changes in performance (1–3).

Manufacture of Solid Gun and Rocket Propellants. The processing techniques to be described for making solid propellants are essentially those which are unique, or almost so, to the propellants industry. Conventional chemical procedures for synthesis of individual materials will not be described. Many of the procedures for specific components are described in this article under High explosives; others can readily be found in the pertinent literature. In the plan of this Section, after a brief review of the characteristics of black powder and their relationship to modern propellants, a short description is given of Benite, a potential replacement for black powder as an igniter. The characteristics of cellulose nitrate as produced are considered in detail, since this material is common to so many propellants and is of major importance. Similarly, its use in combustible cartridge cases is treated. Consideration is then given to the manufacture of extruded gun propellants. Cellulose nitrate-type rocket propellants are next covered; finally, procedures used for making composite rocket propellants are reviewed.

Black Powder. The use of black powder as a gun propellant is of historical interest only, since it has been completely replaced by cellulose nitrate compositions. The most pertinent properties of interest as a propellant are those relating to use and performance: namely, gas produced per gram—280 cm³; heat of explosion—720 cal/g; flame temp—2800°K; and force—110,000 ft-lb/lb.

Black powder produces a large amount of solid reaction products, primarily potassium carbonate and potassium sulfate. Although black powder had been used exclusively as a gun propellant until 1870, it was rapidly supplanted by the much higher-energy smokeless cellulose nitrate propellants. As an example, commonly used gun propellants have forces from 300,000 to 350,000 ft-lb/lb as compared with a force of 110,000 ft-lb/lb for black powder. Cellulose nitrate formulations can be tailored to meet ballistic requirements; black powder compositions are relatively invariant. Further, the manufacture of black powder is undesirably hazardous because of its sensitivity to electrical sparks and to friction and impact. The advent of cellulose nitrate propellants resulted in high energy, relatively smokeless, nonhygroscopic propellants which could be modified to meet requirements, were relatively easy to manufacture, and had long shelf lives. Until recently, the major military use of black powder was essentially restricted to primers for gun and rocket propellants where the large volume of hot particles produced make it a useful material. At present, black powder is being replaced as a rocket igniter in many instances, by metal–oxidant mixtures such as aluminum–ammonium perchlorate; and in guns by Benite, an extrudable mixture of cellulose nitrate and black powder. These new mixtures offer specialized advantages in controllability of ignition and ease with which formulations may be designed to meet unusually exacting requirements (4,5).

Benite. Benite is a composition consisting of approx 60 parts of black powder in a matrix of about 40 parts of plasticized cellulose nitrate. This composition can be extruded in thin strands with high-capacity automated equipment such as is used in the food industry for the manufacture of spaghetti. When long primer tubes filled with granular black powder are used for ignition of long gun propellant charges the

Table 6.1.[a]   Composition of Benite

Ingredients	Percent
cellulose nitrate (13.15% N)	40
potassium nitrate	44
sulfur	6.5
carbon	9.5
ethyl centralite (added)	0.5
volatiles, max	2.25
moisture, max	1.0

[a] Adapted from references 25, 26.

flow of hot gases through the column may be seriously impeded. As a result, it may be difficult to obtain sufficiently rapid ignition of long gun propellant charges. Delayed and inadequate ignition resulting in propellant smoldering appears to be responsible for occasional detonations at low temperatures. The use of strands of Benite in primer tubes under certain conditions permits the ready flow of gases in the annular spaces formed so that far more nearly simultaneous initiation is obtained. The approximate composition of Benite is shown in Table 6.1.

Cellulose Nitrate.   Cellulose nitrate is the fundamental ingredient used in all gun propellants and in many rocket propellants. For this reason, it is the only propellant component treated in detail in this article with emphasis on the factors involved in its use in gun and rocket propellants. Cellulose nitrate, developed in 1845, by Schonbein, may be prepared simply by treating cotton with a mixture of concentrated nitric and sulfuric acid. Superficially, the product looks like the fibrous cotton from which it is prepared. It soon became evident, however, that the presence of nitric acid trapped in the fibers resulted in exothermic decomposition and occasional detonation of the cellulose nitrate. In addition, the natural thermal decomposition of cellulose nitrate resulted in the formation of oxides of nitrogen which in turn accelerated decomposition. Moreover, whereas fibrous cellulose nitrate could be used as an explosive and detonated, its use as a propellant was not feasible until it could be manufactured in dense grains of a geometric form suitable for ballistic application. Purification of the fibrous cellulose nitrate for removal of acidic contaminants was accomplished by a drastic and prolonged washing, tearing, and beating process comparable to that used in the paper-pulp industry. Removal of acidic oxides of nitrogen resulting from cellulose nitrate degradation was solved through the addition of small quantities, 0.5 to 1.0%, of weak organic bases such as diphenylamine, $(C_6H_5)_2NH$, and ethyl centralite, N,N'-diethylcarbanilide, $OC(N(C_2H_5)C_6H_5)_2$, which are preferentially nitrated by the NO_2 and NO produced. The elimination of the fibrous characteristics of cellulose nitrate by colloiding with plasticizers and the development of simple techniques for fabrication of grains of various sizes and shapes were first accomplished by Vielle in France in 1884, and subsequently, by Nobel in 1888, and Abel in 1891.

The nitration of cellulose to propellant-grade cellulose nitrate poses several special problems not commonly encountered in nitration for other purposes. The fibrous form of the cellulose is retained throughout nitration. The nitration process must therefore establish an equilibrium reaction between the cellulose and the final acid or spent acid composition which will ensure attaining the required nitrogen content. This must be carried out under conditions that do not seriously degrade the chain length of the polymeric fiber, since the mechanical properties of the propellant are dependent, in part, on the degree of polymerization of the cellulose nitrate. The starting cellulose for propellant use may consist either of cotton linters or sulfate wood pulp. The propellant-grade cellulose nitrate that is produced is a mixture of polymers of different chain length, reflecting more or less the polymolecularity of the starting cellulose, and a degree of degradation which occurs during nitration. It is also a mixture of cellulose nitrates of different degrees of nitration as a result of the differing accessibility of the cellulose fibers to the action of the acid as well as the various equilibria between the cellulose nitrate and the spent acid which occur as the concentration of the spent acid changes during the nitration process.

Although the three OH groups in cellulose nitrate can be nitrated with difficulty to form a maximum energy product containing 14.15% nitrogen, the trinitrate is not used in propellant formulations, because its low solubility makes colloiding very difficult either with the conventional alcohol–ether mix, or with explosive and non-explosive plasticizers. Solubility depends on nitrogen content; mechanical properties, burning rate, energy content, and hygroscopicity of propellants are also dependent upon the nitrogen content of the cellulose nitrate used. In general use for propellants are *pyrocellulose* containing 12.6% nitrogen; *gun cotton* 13.4% nitrogen and a mixture of pyrocellulose and gun cotton that forms a military blend containing 13.15% nitrogen. The polymolecularity of cellulose nitrate is responsible for mechanical and physical characteristics which make it a near ideal material for use in propellants. A wide variety of liquid and solid components can be incorporated in substantial percentages while still retaining the mechanical properties required for satisfactory gun performance. A number of relatively simple processes can be used to manufacture grains required in a great many shapes and sizes from small flat sheets to very large grains of intricate geometrical pattern. Energy output can be controlled through modification of the degree of nitration of the cellulose nitrate as well as through the incorporation of high-energy or fuel type plasticizers. As a result of its satisfactory stability, simplicity of energy modification, excellent mechanical characteristics, and ease with which it may be converted to gun and rocket propellants, cellulose nitrate is still used extensively for this purpose more than 100 years after its discovery (8–10).

Combustible Cartridge Cases (8–10). The many advantages of cellulose nitrate have led to its application not only in propellants but also, more recently, to the manufacture of combustible cartridge cases to replace the conventional metallic cartridge cases used in some military weapons. Significant advantages accrue in weight decreases of complete rounds and in elimination of the accumulation of spent cartridge cases at gun sites or in gun turrets. Lighter weapons are also possible since such components as extractor mechanisms and sliding wedge breech blocks may be eliminated. The various processes used, still in the preproduction stages, are based fundamentally on felting fibers over a desired form, removal of water, and drying and final finishing. One such process consists of mixing cellulose nitrate kraft paper, a resin for strength, and a stabilizer such as diphenylamine in a water slurry to a consistency of about 1%. The aqueous slurry of fibers is deposited on a fine mesh wire screen contoured over a perforated mold of the desired shape. The resulting mat of fibers is squeezed to remove some of the water, oven dried, and cooled. The preform may be impregnated at this stage with various materials in volatile solvents and redried. The case is removed and trimmed to final form. Combustible cases are porous and fast burning and have very satisfactory mechanical properties and good chemical stability. Considerable work has been done to automate the process; female molds are used instead of male molds, and a series of carefully monitored transfer stations are used at which water may be expelled from the fibers in the female mold by use of a rubber bladder. The deposited fibers are sized to shape with a sizing mandrel inserted into the mold; the sized case is then separated from the mold by injecting high-pressure air. Typical compositions consist of cellulose nitrate (12.6% N), 65%; kraft paper, 15%; resin, 20%, and diphenylamine (added), 1% (11,12).

Single-Base Solvent Extruded Gun Propellants. Single-base propellants consisting predominantly of cellulose nitrate are used exclusively for guns. The process in use is essentially that developed by Vielle in 1884. It involves thorough incorporation of the ingredients and plasticization of the cellulose nitrate by a mixing and an extrusion process. Colloiding is accomplished by the ether–alcohol solvent used, the fuel plasticizer such as dibutyl phthalate, and the work applied during mixing and extrusion. Removal of ether–alcohol and drying to required levels of solvent and water content are critical for the control of ballistic performance. The presence of 1% moisture decreases the force by approx 1%; the presence of 1% solvent decreases force by approximately 2.5%. The burning characteristics are also seriously affected by the presence of residual volatile materials. The major operations involved in the manufacture of a standard single-base propellant consist of mixing, blocking, screening, extrusion to form, cutting, drying, and blending. Table 6.2 presents the characteristics of a typical single-base propellant. The cost of single-base propellants is about 50¢/lb.

Mixing and Maceration. Alcohol-wet cellulose nitrate in block form or previously broken is placed in a sigma-blade mixer similar to the type used for mixing bread dough (see Mixing). The remaining ingredients are added, including ether, alcohol,

Table 6.2. Characteristics of a Typical Single-Base Solvent Extruded Artillery Propellant: Composition M1

Nominal composition (in %)	
cellulose nitrate (13.15% N)	85.0
dinitrotoluene	10.0
dibutyl phthalate	5.0
diphenylamine	1.0 (added)
total volatiles (residual)	1.25
Physical characteristics	
specific gravity (15.5/15.5°C)	1.57
pressure to produce cracking, 21°C, psi	8,520
compression at cracking, 21°C, %	7.7
Thermochemical characteristics	
flame temperature, °K	
isochoric	2,420
isobaric	1,920
force, ft-lb/lb	305,000
unoxidized carbon, %	8.5
combustibles, %	65
heat of explosion, cal/g	700
gas volume, mole/g	0.045
ratio of specific heats of reaction products	1.26
covolume in.³/lb	30.57
Stability characteristics	
80°C surveillance	265 days
65.5°C surveillance	1,800 days

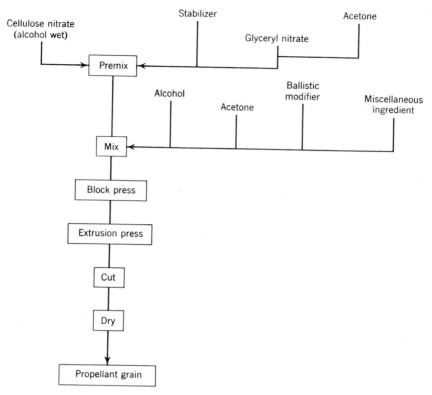

Fig. 6.1. Solvent process flow chart for single-base propellants.

plasticizers such as dibutyl phthalate, stabilizer, and required salts. Mixing is conducted for about 1 hr, during which partial colloiding of the cellulose nitrate occurs. The paste from the mixer may be macerated at low temperature to continue the colloiding process, and to further destroy the fibrous structure of the cellulose nitrate.

Blocking and Screening. The macerated, colloided paste is pressed into blocks about one foot in diameter and two feet long to reduce bulk volume and eliminate trapped air in order to facilitate subsequent handling. The propellant may subsequently be extruded through wire mesh screen into strands or "macaroni" to remove foreign material and uncolloided cellulose nitrate. If "macaroniing" is eliminated, screens are used in the final graining process. "Macaroni" is again blocked prior to the final graining.

Graining and Cutting. The propellant is extruded through a die to form the proper cross-sectional area and geometrical configuration allowing for shrinkage during the drying process. Strands of propellant are cut to proper length.

Drying and Finishing. The "green" propellant is placed in solvent recovery cars. Heated inert gas up to about 65°C is forced through the propellant to drive off about 95% of the ether and alcohol solvent. Solvent vapors are recovered in condensers and activated carbon beds (see Solvent recovery). The gas-dried propellant receives a final treatment in tanks of heated water not exceeding 65°C to reduce the residual solvent by a diffusion process to specification requirements. Drying time may be as long as one month depending on the size of the propellant grain. A final

Table 6.3. Characteristics of a Typical Single-Base Solvent Extruded Propellant for Small Arms Ammunition: Composition IMR

Nominal composition	
cellulose nitrate (13.15% N)	100.0
dinitrotoluene	8.0 (added as surface coating)
potassium sulfate	1.0 (added)
diphenylamine	0.70 (added)
volatiles (residual)	2.50
Physical characteristics	
density, g/cm³	1.62
Thermochemical characteristics (calculated)	
flame temperature, °K	
isochoric	2,835
isobaric	2,285
force, ft-lb/lb	331,000
unoxidized carbon, %	3
combustibles, %	59
heat of explosion, cal/g	868
gas volume, mole/g	0.042
ratio of specific heats of reaction	
products	1.24
covolume, in.³/lb	28.9

air-dry treatment with forced hot air removes surface-occluded residual water. During the drying process, the grains shrink about 25% across the grain and 10% along the length.

Blending. The dried propellant is screened to remove fines and tailings and is glazed with graphite in a rotating barrel, if required. In order to assure uniform ballistics, the propellant must be thoroughly blended. Blending is conducted in large rotating barrels up to 5000/lb capacity or in blending towers consisting of a series of hoppers and inverted cones over which the propellant is dropped. A single-base solvent process flow chart appears in Figure 6.1.

Small Arms Propellant. One technique for the manufacture of small arms propellants is similar to that for the manufacture of gun propellants. Appropriate ballistic performance is obtained by coating the grains with slow burning chemicals such as dinitrotoluene when the grain has a maximum surface area in order to decrease rate of gas evolution. The dinitrotoluene (DNT) is incorporated on the surface of the propellant by tumbling the air-dry propellant and DNT in a rotating "sweetie" barrel similar to that used for sugar-coating various products. The barrel is equipped with a heating jacket to facilitate softening of the coating agent and occlusion on the surface of the propellant grain. Small arms propellant costs approx $1.50/lb. Characteristics of a typical small arms propellant are listed in Table 6.3 (14).

Small Arms Ball Propellant. A second technique for making propellant for small arms and sporting weapons is by means of a process which is entirely different from those previously described for the manufacture of cellulose nitrate propellants for guns or small arms. The basic element of this important process involves solution of cellulose nitrate in a water-immiscible solvent to destroy its fibrous character. The small amounts of acid commonly retained by cellulose nitrate are released and then removed with water. The prolonged and costly purification of cellulose nitrate required in conventional purification techniques is eliminated. The following representative steps occur in the manufacture of ball powder:

Solution of Cellulose Nitrate. Water-wet cellulose nitrate is pumped as a free-flowing aqueous slurry into a steam-jacketed solution still equipped with agitators. Stills vary in capacity from 3000 to 8000 lb of finished propellant. Additional water is added. The cellulose nitrate suspension is stirred and sufficient ethyl acetate is added to dissolve the cellulose nitrate, converting it to a doughlike mass which is suspended in the water phase by the agitator. Diphenylamine dissolved in ethyl acetate is added to stabilize the cellulose nitrate; chalk may be added to neutralize released acid. The batch temperature is raised to 50°C and solution is complete in about 1 hr to form a thick lacquer emulsion in which water is dispersed. In the manufacture of a double-base propellant, a solution of glyceryl nitrate is added at this point; the glyceryl nitrate dissolves in the cellulose nitrate lacquer.

Ball Formation. A gluelike protective colloid is added which stabilizes the lacquer droplets formed as a result of agitation and prevents droplet coalescence. Continuous agitation results in complete breakdown of the doughlike mass to form small dispersed droplets. The size of the droplets or "grains" depends on temperature, solvent–water ratio, agitation speed and time, and the type of colloid added. The grains at this stage are soft because of their solvent and water content.

Grain Dehydration and Hardening. Military uses for rifles require dense grains; sporting ammunition such as shot gun shells use a porous grain propellant. Water removal is accomplished by a "salting" process involving the solution of an inorganic salt such as sodium sulfate in the water phase. Water within the grains migrates to the aqueous phase. After dehydration, the solvent is removed by raising the temperature to about 70°C. The ethyl acetate boils off and is recovered. At this point the "balls" are hard and may vary in size from 0.015 in. to about 0.030 in.

Propellant Sizing. Sizing is accomplished by a wet screening process. Where required, grain size may be also reduced by wet rolling.

Deterrent Addition. The burning rate of the screened propellant is controlled by application of a deterrent or slow-burning plasticizer to the surface, to decrease gas evolution until the total burning surface of the grain has decreased in size. The sized propellant in water suspension is pumped to a coating still. A coating emulsion is added; the coating agent is preferentially absorbed by the propellant. Glyceryl nitrate may be similarly added to the propellant at this stage. The suspension is heated and agitated until the coating has penetrated the required depth.

Finishing. The finishing process consists of filtering of the grains and air drying at about 70°C to remove residual water. The propellant is glazed in "sweetie" barrels with graphite to prevent formation of electrostatic changes after which it is subjected to final screening and blending operations.

Double- and Triple-Base Solvent Extruded Gun Propellants. An increasing number of double-base and triple-base gun propellants are being used to meet requirements for higher energy in systems designed for maximum range and accuracy. The techniques used in the manufacture of glyceryl nitrate gun propellants are comparable to those described for single-base propellants. Differences arise because of the special treatment required as a result of the presence of glyceryl nitrate and volatile solvents which cannot be readily recovered by conventional means. The exact procedures vary somewhat with the composition and the type and capabilities of equipment available.

Preliminary Mixing. Alcohol-wet cellulose nitrate from a block-breaking operation is charged into a Schraeder bowl mixer, especially designed for use with glyceryl nitrate. Glyceryl nitrate dissolved in acetone is added and the contents are mixed briefly to incorporate the glyceryl nitrate into the cellulose nitrate and to start the plasticization process. If nitroguanidine or other crystalline salts are required, a portion may be added during the premix operation.

Final Mixing. The premix and possibly some reworked propellant are added to a double-arm, tilting, variable-speed, water-jacketed, sigma-blade mixer along with additional alcohol, acetone, and such other ingredients as are required, including additional salts. Mixing is conducted for 2 to 3 hr at about 40°C.

Blocking, Screening, Graining, and Cutting. These operations are conducted in essentially the same manner as for single-base propellants.

Drying, Blending, and Glazing. The propellant grains are dried on trays under forced warm air at gradually increasing temperatures to about 60°C. Ten to fifteen days may be required to complete the process. No solvent recovery is attempted because of the presence of glyceryl nitrate in the vapors. Blending and glazing, where required, are accomplished in the same manner as for single-base propellants.

Double-base propellant costs approximately 85¢/lb; triple-base costs are slightly greater, about 87¢/lb. Double-base and triple-base solvent compositions and their characteristics are shown in Tables 6.4 and 6.5. The characteristics of one of the very few solvent-extruded double-base rocket propellant compositions are shown in Table 6.6 (17–19).

Solventless Extruded Double-Base Rocket Propellant. The manufacture of solventless double-base rocket propellant by extrusion was initiated during World War II, to meet a requirement for large grains which could not be met by conventional solvent extrusion processes because of the impossibility of removing volatile solvents by available drying processes. Previously the general technique of aqueous mixing and rolling had been well developed for the manufacture of sheet propellant for trench mortars. Special press procedures were developed for rocket grain extrusion. The

Table 6.4. Characteristics of a Typical Double-Base Solvent Extruded Artillery Propellant: Composition M2

Nominal composition (in %)	
cellulose nitrate (13.25% N)	77.5
glyceryl nitrate	19.5
barium nitrate	0.40
potassium nitrate	0.75
ethyl centralite	0.60
graphite	0.30
total volatiles (residual)	3.00
Physical characteristics	
specific gravity at 15.5/15.5°C	1.65
Thermochemical characteristics (*calculated*)	
flame temperature, °K	
isochoric	3,320
isobaric	2,710
force, ft-lb/lb	360,000
unoxidized carbon, %	none
combustibles, %	47
gas volume, mole/g	0.039
heat of explosion, cal/g	1,080
ratio of specific heats	1.22
covolume, in.³/lb	27.9

Table 6.5. Characteristics of a Typical Triple-Base Solvent Extruded Artillery Propellant: Composition M17

Nominal composition (in %)	
cellulose nitrate (13.15% N)	22.0
glyceryl nitrate	21.5
nitroguanidine	54.7
ethyl centralite	1.5
cryolite	0.3
graphite (glaze)	0.1
total volatiles (residual)	0.3
Physical characteristics	
hygroscopicity at 95% rh	0.3
specific gravity at 15.5/15.5°C	1.67
gravimetric density, lb/ft³	54
Mechanical properties	
compression test, % at rupture	8
pressure to produce cracking, at 21°C, psi	3,500
side impact test, in.-oz	150
Thermochemical characteristics (*calculated*)	
flame temperature, °K	
isochoric	3,015
isobaric	2,430
force, ft-lb/lb	364,000
unoxidized carbon, %	4
combustibles, %	39
heat of explosion, cal/g	960
gas volume, moles/g	0.043
specific heat ratio	1.24
covolume, in.³/lb	29.5
Stability	
134.5°C heat test (in minutes)	
salmon pink	35
red fumes	40
explosion	170
120°C heat test (in minutes)	
salmon pink	115
red fumes	145
explosion	7,300
Taliani (N₂ atmosphere) (see Section 7)	
slope at 100 mm pressure	0.55
time to 100 mm pressure, min	244

mixing procedure, often referred to as the aqueous slurry or slurry mix process, is applicable to the manufacture of a wide variety of double-base propellants both in sheet form and large grains. Depending upon size and geometry, extruded double-base propellant costs about $1.75/lb.

Preparation of Materials. Water-wet cellulose nitrate is reduced to a predetermined water content by centrifuging and blending to form a uniform mass. The remaining chemicals including stabilizers, carbon black, and additives are prepared and may be preblended in water in a small colloid mill.

Slurry Mixing. The slurry tank consists of a large copper tank varying in size up to as much as 20,000 lb total capacity. The tank is equipped with an agitator and is filled with process water at approximately 60°C. All ingredients including glyceryl nitrate are added to the slurry water. The mixture is agitated and circulated through

Table 6.6. Characteristics of a Double-Base Solvent Extruded Rocket Propellant: Composition M7

Nominal composition	
cellulose nitrate (13.15% N)	54.6
glyceryl nitrate	35.5
ethyl centralite	0.9
potassium perchlorate	7.8
carbon	1.2
Thermochemical characteristics (calculated)	
flame temperature, °K	
isochoric	3,815
isobaric	3,160
specific impulse (1000 psi, and expansion ratio 8)	240
heat of explosion, cal/g	1,285
gas volume, mole/g	0.037
ratio of specific heats	1.21
Stability	
120°C heat test (in minutes)	
salmon pink	80–90
red fumes	180–200
explosion	300 +
Burning characteristics	
burning rate at 1000 psi and 20°C, in./sec	0.70
pressure exponent	0.77

pumps for up to 30 min. Excess water is drained off; the liquid components of the propellant, such as glyceryl nitrate and dibutylphthalate are adsorbed on the fibers of the cellulose nitrate. Solids are entrapped and dispersed on the fibers. The wet, fibrous mass is centrifuged to remove excess water and is then placed in cloth bags.

Drying and Blending. The paste from the slurry mixing operation is dried at temperatures up to 60°C to a moisture content of about 10% and then blended in rotating barrels. Water-soluble solids may be added at this time or subsequently during the rolling operations.

Rolling. The dried paste is spread along the length of rolls of differential speed roll mills (American practice: ratio of speeds is typically 1.5:1) controlled at about 90–100°C. The paste rapidly colloids into a sheet which adheres to the rolls. Roll gap, differential roll speed, roll surface, and roll temperature are critical variables which determine the adequacy of colloiding the paste. During the rolling, the paste is dried to a moisture content of less than 0.5% and is formed into long sheets for further rolling to provide satisfactory surface characteristics. Differential speed rolling is followed by rolling of the sheets on an even speed, temperature-controlled roll mill. Final sheets are smooth, and satisfactory for extrusion. The sheets are slit into strips or discs for use in the extrusion press. The rolls may be controlled to produce thin sheet propellant for use in trench mortar munitions or thick sheets for further processing in presses to produce rocket grains.

Pressing. The propellant is extruded from presses varying in size up to 21 in. in diam. The presses may be horizontal or vertical and are equipped with thermostatically controlled barrels, chambers, and dies and can be evacuated during pressing. The propellant may be extruded in a variety of shapes, particularly with respect to the central perforation. The operating pressure may be up to 10,000 psi; pressures will depend upon composition, temperature, grain dimensions, and shape. The objective is to obtain a well consolidated, flawfree grain. Final dimensions depend upon the die

Table 6.7. Characteristics of a Typical Double-Base Solventless Mortar Sheet Propellant: Composition M8

Nominal composition (in %)	
cellulose nitrate (13.25% N)	52.15
glyceryl nitrate	43.00
potassium nitrate	1.25
diethyl phthalate	3.00
ethyl centralite	0.60
volatiles (residual)	0.40
Physical characteristics	
specific gravity at 15.5/15.5°C	1.62
Thermochemical characteristics (*calculated*)	
flame temperature, °K	
isochoric	3,695
force, ft-lb/lb	382,000
unoxidized carbon, %	0
combustibles, %	37
heat of explosion, cal/g	1,244
gas volume, mole/g	0.037
ratio of specific heats	1.21
covolume in.^{3}/lb	2.66
Stability characteristics	
120°C heat test (in minutes)	
salmon pink	60
red fumes	120
explosion	>300
90°C vacuum stability, ml/40 hr	2.50
80°C surveillance, days	19
65.5°C surveillance, days	160

dimensions and the mechanical properties of the propellant. By proper press design, grains may be extruded with diameters approximately equal to one third that of the press.

Finishing. The propellant strand extruded from the press is cut to size with a guillotine cutter. The grains are annealed at elevated temperature to remove stresses, cooled and inhibited as required to obtain the desired mass rate of burning. Ethyl cellulose inhibitors are cemented to the propellant grain. Final trimming is made on a lathe or special cutting machine. Grains are inspected for flaws with x-ray equipment and samples are fired for performance prior to acceptance of the lot of propellant.

Characteristics of double-base solventless propellant for mortars and rockets are shown in Tables 6.7 and 6.8 (20–22).

Double-Base Cast Rocket Propellant. The fabrication of rocket propellants by the casting process enables large solid grains of a variety of compositions and complex geometries to be made simply and economically. Large solvent-extruded grains cannot be dried satisfactorily and large solventless extruded grains require unusually large presses. The development of casting techniques has made feasible the use of very large, solid grain booster motors which would otherwise have required the use of liquid propulsion systems. There is no inherent limitation on the size of grain which can be produced. The techniques used for the manufacture of double-base propellant are well standardized because of similarities in composition; techniques for casting composite propellants described below are somewhat more varied because of the variation in binder characteristics.

The manufacture of cast double-base propellants essentially consists of the preparation of an intermediate product called casting powder or base grain by techniques almost identical to the manufacture of small grains of gun propellant. The casting powder is loaded into the rocket motor and gelled into a solid grain by the addition of a liquid casting solvent consisting of a mixture of explosive and nonexplosive plasticizers such as glyceryl nitrate and diethyl phthalate. The preparation of the casting powder

Table 6.8. Characteristics of a Typical Double-Base Solventless Extruded Rocket Propellant: Composition JPN

Nominal composition (in %)	
cellulose nitrate (13.25% N)	51.40
glyceryl nitrate	42.90
diethyl phthalate	3.23
ethyl centralite	1.00
potassium sulfate	1.25
carbon black	0.20
candella wax	0.02
Physical characteristics	
specific gravity at 15.5/15.5°C	1.62
Thermochemical characteristics (*calculated*)	
flame temperature, °K	
isochoric	3,660
isobaric	3,010
specific impulse (1500 psi, and expansion ratio 4)	236
heat of explosion, cal/g	1,220
heat of combustion, cal/g	2,200
ratio of specific heats	1.22
gas volume, mole/g	0.038
Burning characteristics	
rate at 1000 psi and 21°C, in./sec	0.60
pressure exponent	0.68
Approximate composition of gaseous products	
hydrogen	6.5
water	27.0
carbon monoxide	33.0
carbon dioxide	18.0
nitrogen	14.0
other	1.5
Stability characteristics	
120°C heat test (in minutes)	
salmon pink	80
red fumes	190
explosion	300 +
90°C vacuum stability, ml/40 hr	2.65
80°C surveillance, days	130
65°C surveillance, days	500–700

involves steps similar to those used for making finely divided solvent extruded propellants. Although the cost of cast double-base propellant depends on many factors including size, shape, motor loading, etc, an average cost of approx $2/lb may be used for purposes of comparison. A base grain casting process flow chart is shown in Figure 6.2. The characteristics of typical compositions are shown in Table 6.9, a high-energy composition in Table 6.10 (23).

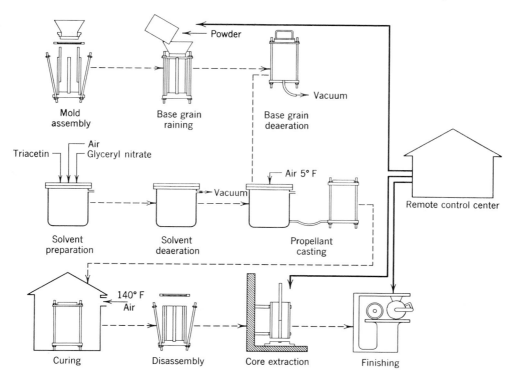

Fig. 6.2. Flow chart for double-base propellants.

Mixing. Cellulose nitrate is mixed in a slow-speed heavy-duty mixer with the required solid ingredients, plasticizer, and volatile solvents to produce a colloided plastic mass. Crystalline and metallic solids such as ammonium perchlorate and aluminum may also be incorporated.

Blocking. The plasticized cellulose nitrate is consolidated in a blocking press to minimize volume and remove air.

Extrusion. The blocked and plasticized cellulose nitrate is extruded from a die to form strands.

Cutting. The strands are cut into short lengths approximately equal to the thickness of the strands to form a finely divided solvent-wet casting powder.

Drying and Blending. The grains formed in the cutting process are dried to remove excess solvent and are blended to remove batch-to-batch nonuniformities.

Casting. To provide external inhibition of the grain, a casting beaker may be used which consists of a cylinder of plastic material such as ethylcellulose. The cylinder is inserted into a brass mold jacket; a core pin of appropriate shape is positioned to provide a central perforation of required geometry. The casting powder is poured into the mold after previous evacuation to remove occluded air. The casting solvent is drawn through the powder to fill the voids between the grains. Vacuum is conventionally applied during the casting process to remove occluded and dissolved gas in order to obtain a flawfree grain. The casting powder begins to coalesce under the plasticizing action of the casting solvent. However, complete solution of the individual grains does not occur.

Table 6.9.   Characteristics of a Typical Cast Double-Base Propellant

Nominal composition (in %)	
cellulose nitrate (12.6% N)	58.6
glyceryl nitrate	24.2
dimethyl phthalate	9.6
dinitrotoluene	6.6
ethyl centralite	1.0
carbon black (added)	0.1
Physical characteristics	
density, at 20°C, lb/in.^{3}	0.056
rupture stress, psi	4,550
stress for 5% compression, psi	690
compression to rupture, %	50
Thermochemical characteristics (*calculated*)	
flame temperature, °K	
isochoric	2,680
isobaric	2,140
specific impulse (1000 psi, and expansion	
ratio 9), lb-sec/lb	213
heat of explosion, cal/g	810
gas volume, mole/g	0.0435
ratio of specific heats	1.25
Burning characteristics	
burning rate at 1000 psi and 20°C, in./sec	0.27
pressure exponent at 500–3000 psi	0.65
Stability characteristics	
110°C Taliani test in nitrogen atmosphere	
pressure-time slope at 100 min	0.65
time to 100 min, sec	145

Curing.   The cast propellant may be cured in its mold at elevated temperatures to about 60°C.   The casting-powder grains continue to absorb the casting solvent. Gelation occurs, as the external surfaces of the propellant grains plasticize and coalesce to form a solid, tough, and voidfree charge of the required geometry.

Finishing.   The grain is trimmed to length and inspected.

Slurry Cast Double-Base Propellant.   The cast double-base process involves the preliminary preparation of the casting powder intermediate in order to eliminate the fibrous form of the cellulose nitrate.   A variant of this approach consists of starting with a granular form of cellulose nitrate which is added directly to the casting solvent along with the remaining solid ingredients.   The process is flexible, and many different formulations can be rapidly prepared.   The manufacture of granular cellulose nitrate has been developed into well standardized processes by a number of companies (24).

Cellulose Nitrate Preparation.   Using the same techniques as those used for the preparation of ball propellant, fibrous cellulose nitrate is converted to granular cellulose nitrate by solution or partial solution in such volatile solvents as ethyl acetate mixed with a nonsolvent such as water.   A lacquer is formed which is then emulsified by the addition of a colloid and rapid agitation or by applying a high shear load to produce the required particle size.   The solvent is removed by distillation or flash evaporation at high temperatures and the resulting slurry is washed to remove adherent impurities.   The required granular size is obtained by wet screening.   Variations of the foregoing technique to produce larger granules are accomplished by eliminating the nonsolvent in the formation of the lacquer and extruding the lacquer into

Table 6.10. Characteristics of a Typical High-Energy Cast Double-Base Propellant[a]

Nominal composition (in %)	
cellulose nitrate (12.6%N)	25
glycerol nitrate	30
ammonium perchlorate	20
aluminum	20
plasticizer	5
stabilizer (added)	1
Physical characteristics	
density at 20°C, lb/in.³	0.063
Thermochemical characteristics (calculated)	
flame temperature, isobaric, °K	4,000
specific impulse at 1000 psi, optimum expansion ratio	265
heat of explosion, cal/g	1,650
gas volume, mole/g	0.035
ratio of specific heats	1.20
Burning characteristics	
burning rate, at 1000 psi and 20°C, in./sec	0.7
pressure exponent at 1000–2000 psi	0.5

[a] Representative values for a variety of compositions.

a nonsolvent to form strands which are cut into appropriate size. The incorporation of some plasticizer in the granular cellulose nitrate facilitates subsequent solution in the plasticizer during the mixing process.

Mixing. The granular cellulose nitrate and the remaining solid ingredients, including solid oxidizers and metallic fuels, are added to the liquid plasticizer consisting frequently of glyceryl nitrate and fuel plasticizers in a mixing pot. The mixture is stirred briefly; vacuum may be applied during the mixing process. Gelation of the cellulose nitrate begins to occur.

Casting. After mixing, the slurry is poured directly into the motor case or into a mold as described in the conventional casting process. The mechanism of plasticization and coalescence of the cellulose nitrate by the liquid plasticizer is similar to that encountered between casting powder and casting solvent.

Curing. Curing is accomplished at elevated temperatures.

Ball Powder Cast Double-Base Propellant. Another important process for the fabrication of double-base cast propellants involves the use of very finely divided ball powder instead of the conventional 0.020-in. cubes as the casting powder. The ball powder is similar to that used for small-arms propellant and is made in the same way. The principal difference is size: gun powder has an average spherical diam of from 0.015 to 0.030 in.; casting ball powder has an average diam of 50 μ or less to

Table 6.11.[a] Composition of Several Types of Ball Powder

Nominal composition (in %)	(1)	(2)	(3)
cellulose nitrate (12.6% N)	98.5	90.1	75.1
2-nitrodiphenylamine	1.5	1.5	1.5
glyceryl nitrate	none	8.0	23.0
carbon black	none	0.4	0.4
coating agent (added)	0.15	0.15	0.15
Particle density, g/ml, min	1.56	1.58	1.58

[a] Adapted from references 25–27.

achieve the required flow and mix characteristics. The compositions of several stand-ard types of ball powder for casting is given in Table 6.11.

Manufacture of Composite Rocket Propellants. Composite propellants may be made by either the casting or the extrusion process depending on the physical char-acteristics of the oxidizer–binder mix. A number of different binders are in use which permit different fabrication techniques to be employed and enable a spectrum of physical characteristics to be obtained. Early in World War II, a simple asphalt binder was developed into which the oxidizer salt could be loaded. The disadvantages of brittleness at low temperature and flow at high temperatures led to the development of a number of replacements. "Poly" binders consist of a plastisol grade of an already polymerized linear poly(vinyl chloride) resin to which plasticizers, oxidants, and other materials are added. The resulting fluid plastisol suspension fuses to a hard mass by plasticizer solvation and absorption at temperatures above 150°C. Polysulfide rubber binders consist of a low- or intermediate-molecular-weight polymeric liquid such as di-ethylformaldisulfide with thiol groups on the ends of the chain. During curing at tem-peratures above 80°C, the groups are oxidized to form high-molecular-weight, cross-linked polymers with elastomeric physical characteristics. These materials have good rubberlike characteristics at low temperatures, can be bonded to motor cases, and are useful in booster rockets. Elastomeric castable binders containing long-chain linear crosslinked polyurethanes may be formed by the catalyzed reaction at elevated tem-peratures between isocyanates and compounds containing OH groups, such as the

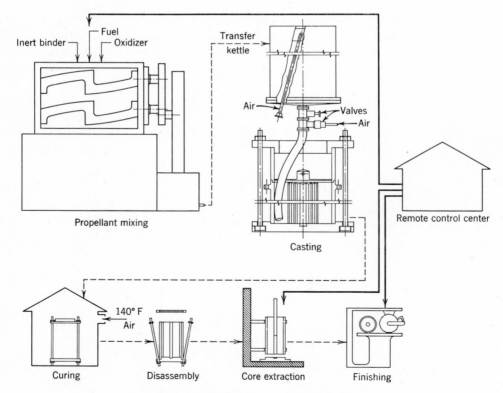

Fig. 6.3. Elastomeric process flow chart.

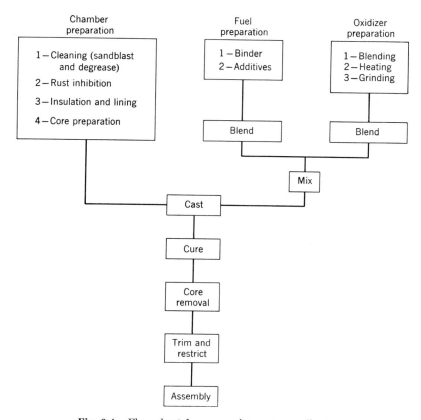

Fig. 6.4. Flow chart for composite cast propellants.

glycols. These binders are curable somewhat above ambient temperature; they do not release heat and shrink very little during cure. Crosslinked elastomeric binders may also be formed by copolymerizing butadiene with 2-vinylpyridine and by curing at elevated temperatures. These high-viscosity binders may be loaded with ammonium nitrate and may be either compression-formed or extruded to produce cartridges for use over a wide temperature range in JATO's, boosters, or gas generators. A large number of other binder formulations are available and may be used in the fabrication of composite propellants to satisfy specific system requirements.

Extruded Composite Propellants. The extrusion process combines elements of material preparation and processing which the cast composite rocket propellant industry uses and extrusion techniques associated with the manufacture of solventless extruded double-base propellants. The process has been applied to the manufacture of a variety of composites including rubber-base compositions which contain ammonium nitrate as the filler (28,29).

Material Preparation. Using conventional techniques, the crystalline salts are ground, dried, and reground to meet particle size and moisture requirements. Flow properties and bulking characteristics of the oxidizer are closely dependent upon these characteristics. The rubber binder and additives, including materials such as carbon black, plasticizers, curatives, accelerators, inhibitors, catalysts, and age resistors, are mixed in conventional heavy-duty rubber mixers. The moisture content of the rubber

Table 6.12. Characteristics of a Typical Cast Composite Propellant

Nominal composition (in %)	
ammonium perchlorate	21
potassium perchlorate	47
rubber-base binder	29
curing agents	3
Physical characteristics	
density, lb/in.^{3}	0.067
thermal diffusivity, cm^2/sec	1.50×10^{-3}
shear strength, psi	120
ultimate compressive strength, psi	4,000
compressive deformation at ultimate compression, %	80
Thermochemical characteristics (*calculated*)	
flame temperature, isobaric, °K	2,410
specific impulse at 1000 psi, optimum expansion	180
gas volume, mole/g	32.0
ratio of specific heats	1.24
Products of combustion, mole fraction (in %)	
potassium chloride	11
hydrogen chloride	6
nitrogen	3
hydrogen	9.5
water	30
carbon monoxide	22
carbon dioxide	11
sulfur compounds	7.5
Burning characteristics	
burning rate, at 1000 psi and 20°C, in./sec	0.70
pressure exponent at 1000–2000 psi	0.78

is reduced in the mixer using a dry atmosphere and as a result of heat evolved in the shearing process.

Mixing. The ground and dried salts are incorporated in the rubber binder in increments, depending on size of mix, ratio of oxidizer to binder, and characteristics of the mixer. Mixing is conducted under vacuum in heavy-duty water-cooled mixers in use in the rubber industry. Mix times vary up to several hours. The specific procedure and equipment used are critical in determining final performance of the propellants. Close process control and performance checks are mandatory.

Extrusion. Using conventional techniques associated with the extrusion of solventless double-base propellants, the mix is preblocked under vacuum. It is then transferred to the extrusion press. The grain is formed by application of pressures to 10,000 psi to the mix which is extruded through a temperature-conditioned die. Vacuum is applied to prevent entrapment of air bubbles, and the press walls as well as the basket may be heated or cooled. Continuous extrusion processes have been developed by a number of companies.

Trimming, Inhibiting, and Curing. The propellant from the press is cut to approximate length with guillotine-type cutters. The grain may be inhibited to prevent burning on predesignated surfaces by use of relatively noncombustible materials, similar to the binder or specially formulated. The inhibitor may be cemented on with the aid of pressure or simply applied by coating in a mold. Bonding to the motor may

Table 6.13. Characteristics of Typical High-Energy Cast or Extruded Composite Propellants[a]

Nominal composition (*in* %)	
ammonium perchlorate	60
fuel binder[b]	25
aluminum	14
additives[c]	1
Physical characteristics	
density at 20°C, lb/in.³	0.060
Thermochemical characteristics (*calculated*)	
flame temperature, isobaric °K	2,700
specific impulse at 1000 psi, optimum expansion ratio, lb-sec/lb	250
gas volume, mole/g	0.04
ratio of specific heats	1.20
Products of combustion, mole fraction, %	
carbon monoxide	30
water	12.5
hydrogen	30
nitrogen	5
hydrogen chloride	15
aluminum oxide	7.5
Burning characteristics	
burning rate, at 1000 psi and 20°C, in./sec	0.30
pressure exponent, at 1000–2000 psi	0.2

[a] Representative values for a range of compositions.
[b] For instance, polybutadiene–acrylonitrile copolymer.
[c] Catalysts, such as iron oxide; curing agents, such as diepoxides.

be accomplished with rubber-base inhibitors. Curing is accomplished at temperatures from 70 to 120°C for periods up to several days. Final dimensioning is accomplished with band saws, rotary cutters, lathes, and contouring machines.

Cast Composite Propellants. A number of procedures are in use in the manufacture of cast composite propellants which differ primarily because of considerable differences in the nature of the binder. The general procedures are quite comparable. A description of one is given; this embodies techniques for material preparation similar to those given for extruded composite propellants. A pictorial representation as well as a more detailed flow chart are shown in Figures 6.3 and 6.4. Typical characteristics of some of composite cast propellants are presented in Tables 6.12 and 6.13.

Materials Preparation. Crystalline oxidizers are dried to control moisture content, are blended for uniformity, and ground to control particle size. Conventional drying procedures and grinding with hammermills are employed. Very close control is exercised over the moisture content and the particle size distribution because of their effect on the processing as well as the physical and burning characteristics of the propellant. Perchlorate manufacturers have developed spherical crystalline perchlorates which have good flow characteristics and may be used in some cases without further size reduction. Dry ingredients, such as curing agents and accelerators, are premixed in the fuel, frequently by the use of a small colloid mill. Proper dispersion in the fuel is ensured in this manner. The viscosity and polymerization characteristics of the fuel binder are carefully controlled.

Mixing and Casting. The oxidizer, premix, and fuel, both polymeric and metallic, are mixed under vacuum and cast directly into assembled motors which have been previously prepared, frequently by coating the interior with a thin layer of the polymeric binder and curing. Mixing is perhaps the most significant and critical manufacturing step in castable propellant manufacture. Sigma-blade and "bear claw" blade mixers as well as "charge can" planetary mixers are in use. In general, batch processes are employed, although several techniques have been worked out for continuous mixing. Liners on the motor may be applied by centrifugal casting, slingers, brushing, or electrostatic-deposition techniques. Casting is conducted under vacuum to deaerate the propellant and remove any entrapped gas and gaseous products formed during the partial polymerization which may have occurred.

Curing. Curing is accomplished at elevated temperatures. The time and temperatures required depend on the binder used, its gel time, and exothermic properties during curing. In some cases, motors may be cured under pressure (30–35).

Bibliography

1. "Propellants, Sampling, Examination and Testing," *U.S. Military Standard 286A* (1961).
2. "Propellants, Solid for Cannon, Requirements and Packing," *U.S. Military Standard 652* (1963).
3. "Propellant, Artillery," *U.S. Specification MIL-P-270A* (1959).
4. "Black Powder," *U.S. Specification Jan P-223A* (1962).
5. J. Taylor, *Solid Propellant and Exothermic Compositions*, Interscience Publishers, Inc., New York, 1959.
6. "Benite," *U.S. Specification MIL B45451B* (1960).
7. E. Huselton and S. Kaplowitz, "Evaluation, Tests and Process Studies Relating to Establishment of Substitute for Black Powder," *Picatinny Arsenal Report DETR 5-60* (1960).
8. "Nitrocellulose," *U.S. Specification MIL-N-244A* (1962).
9. F. D. Miles, *Cellulose Nitrate: The Physical Chemistry of Nitrocellulose*, Interscience Publishers, Inc., New York, 1946.
10. E. Ott, *Cellulose and Its Derivatives*, Interscience Publishers, Inc., New York, 1946.
11. K. H. Russell, "Combustible Cartridge Cases," *Picatinny Arsenal Paper presented to Materials Division, American Ordnance Association* (1946).
12. Edward Daniels and Isidore G. Nadel, "Combustible Igniter Tubes," *Picatinny Arsenal Reports 3052 and 3120* (1963).
13. "Propellant, M1," *U.S. Specifications MIL-P-46650 and MIL-P-46913* (1962).
14. "Propellants for Small Arms Ammunition," *U.S. Specification MIL-P-3984A* (1961).
15. J. J. O'Neill, "Ball Powder," *Ordnance* **46** (1961).
16. Theodore R. Olive, "Ball Powder Process," *Eng. Quart. Univ. Chekiang* (Dec. 7, 1946).
17. "Propellant M2 and M5," *U.S. Specification MIL-P-323A* (1959).
18. "Propellant M15 and M17," *U.S. Specification MIL-P-668A* (1955).
19. A. M. Goldstein and K. H. Russell, "Process Engineering of Triple Base Propellants," *Picatinny Arsenal Report DB-TR-8-60* (1960).
20. "Propellant, Double Base, Type N2," *U.S. Specification MIL-P-18617* (1955).
21. "Propellant, T2," *U.S. Specification MIL-P-45460* (1960).
22. R. Steinberger, *Preparation and Properties of Double-Base Propellants*, Chemistry of Propellants, Pergamon Press, London, 1960, pp. 248–249.
23. Ref. 22, pp. 249–251.
24. D. E. Boynton and J. V. Schowengerdt, *Slurry Casting: A Versatile Process for Double-Base Rocket Propellants, Report B12-182.1*, Hercules Powder Co.
25. *Fluid Ball Propellant Casting Powder*, Olin Mathieson Chemical Corp., East Alton, Ill.
26. U.S. Patent 2,916,775 (1959), J. J. O'Neill, Jr. (to Olin Mathieson Chem. Corp.).
27. U.S. Patent 2,929,107 (1960), E. A. Andrew (to Olin Mathieson Chem. Corp.).
28. Charles F. Dougherty, "Processing Rubber-Base Composite Rocket Propellant," *Chem. Eng.* **53** (1957).
29. A. O. Dekker and G. A. Zimmerman, "Ammonium Nitrate Propellants Based on a Polyester–Acrylate Binder," *Ind. Eng. Chem.* **50**, 22–27 (1962).

30. W. F. Arendale, "Fuel Binder Requirements for Composite Solid Propellants," *Ind. Eng. Chem.* **48**, 725–726 (1956).
31. *Solid Rocket Industry Propellant Processing*, Aerojet General Corporation (internal publication).
32. D. Geckler and R. E. Davis, "Modern Developments in Solid Propellant Rocket Engineering," *Aeron. Eng. Rev.* (August, 1957).
33. *Safety Requirements for the Manufacture and Loading of Castable Composite Propellants*, Ordnance Corps Manual ORDM 7-230 (1960).
34. "Solid Propellant Technology," *Chem. Eng. News* **42**, 50 (1964).
35. T. L. Smith, "Solid Propellants, Elastomeric Binder and Mechanical Property Requirements," *Ind. Eng. Chem.* **52**, 776–780 (1960).

7. Propellant Evaluation

A wide variety of propellant characteristics are of importance to the propellant designer and manufacturer in order to establish performance, to control quality, and to assess hazards in handling and manufacture. Computational and experimental techniques are used to define these characteristics of the propellant and the total energy available. Information regarding the mechanical properties of propellants and their stability and sensitivity are also of interest. A number of tests have been discussed and references given in Section 2. An outline of only the most significant and widely used procedures are treated below.

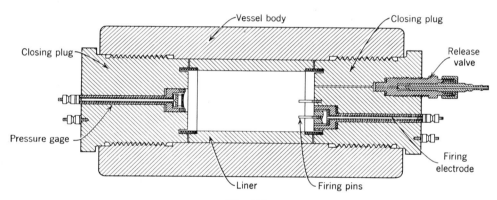

Fig. 7.1.

Computational Techniques. Of greatest importance are those calculations that deal with the impulse of rocket propellants, the force of gun propellants, and the relevant characteristics of the propellant gases produced. Calculation of heats of explosion and flame temperature offer revealing indications of burning-rate characteristics. Of considerable interest is the detailed calculation of the reaction products of gun propellants. Meaningful measurement of the flash and smoke produced by gun propellants is difficult and often misleading because of instrumentation problems and the meteorological conditions during an experiment. Calculation of the percentage of unoxidized carbon and other solids, and of the percentage of flash-producing combustible gases such as carbon monoxide and hydrogen which may exist at the equilibrium conditions prevailing at gun discharge, is considerably simpler and is often more revealing than experimental determination. Conventional iterative calculations requiring the use of digital-computer procedures are used. Even short-form techniques which may be accomplished rapidly with desk calculators are valuable first approxima-

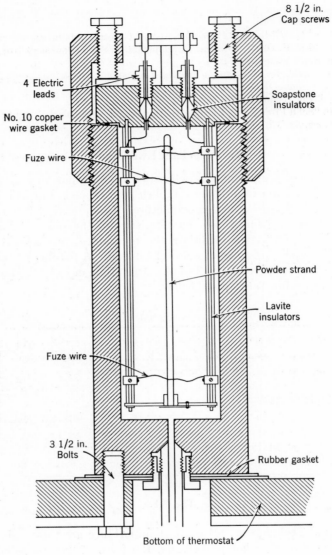

8 1/2 in.
Cap screws

4 Electric
leads

Soapstone
insulators

No. 10 copper
wire gasket

Fuze wire

Powder strand

Lavite
insulators

Fuze wire

3 1/2 in.
Bolts

Rubber gasket

Bottom of thermostat

Fig. 7.2.

tions, provided that the basic assumptions upon which the techniques were developed
are validly used.

Experimental Techniques: Burning Rate. Burning rates of solid propellants are
of essential importance to both the designer and the manufacturer. Since they cannot
be calculated with sufficient accuracy, their experimental evaluation is essential.
Two techniques are widely used: (*1*) the closed bomb for gun propellants, and (*2*)
the strand burner for rocket propellants

The closed bomb is essentially a heavy-walled cylinder capable of withstanding
pressures to 100,000 psi (Fig. 7.1). It is equipped with a piezoelectric gage, a cathode-
ray oscillograph, and associated electrical apparatus required to establish two significant

characteristics of gun propellants: (1) the total pressure, p, produced in the chamber which is related to the force of the propellant; and (2) the rate of pressure rise versus pressure (dp/dt vs p) which is related to the burning rate of the propellant through its geometry. Samples of gun propellant are placed in the bomb and fired. An oscillogram is obtained in which dp/dt, the rate of pressure rise on the Y axis is plotted against the pressure increase on the X axis. The data so obtained may be used on a comparative basis for quality control and charge assessment; or, on an absolute basis to establish the burning rate equation for use in calculations of interior ballistics. A series of firings are conducted, with different weights of a standard propellant, each followed by the same weight of a similar propellant under assessment. Total pressures are compared on the X axis and a "relative force" value is obtained as the ratio of total pressure produced by the propellant being assessed to the total pressure produced by the standard. A "relative force" value greater than 100% indicates a greater total energy available from the propellant under study. Measurements of the relative values of dp/dt on the G axis at four or five comparable pressures on the X axis are made to obtain "relative quickness"; again, a value greater than 100% for a propellant indicates that it is burning faster than the standard. This may be due to compositional or geometrical differences. This relatively simple technique of propellant evaluation by empirical comparison is of great value in control of propellant production and in minimizing gun firings used for propellant proof and assessment. Application of the closed bomb for this purpose depends on the comparison of propellants of very similar composition and granulation. The establishment of the absolute burning characteristics and the burning-rate equation of a gun propellant is a more difficult procedure. It requires absolute calibration of the piezoelectric gage used, and a series of calculations in which the specific data for rate of change of pressure vs pressure is converted to a curve of rate of linear burning vs pressure. This is accomplished through the use of a series of equations involving form functions for the specific geometric form of the grain so that one may proceed from rate of pressure rise through mass rate of burning to linear rate of burning. The burning-rate equation so obtained is applicable to calculations of the interior ballistics of guns (5–8).

The strand burner is used for measurement of burning rates of rocket propellants. It consists of a bomb which can be pressurized with an inert gas and which may be maintained at high, low, and intermediate temperature conditions by immersion in appropriate thermostatic baths (Fig. 7.2). Auxiliary apparatus consists primarily of timers which may be started and stopped by thyratron-actuated brakes leading to thin fuse wires, threaded through the propellant, and separated by accurately known distances on the propellant strand being tested. A strand of propellant approx ⅛ in. in diam and 7 in. long is coated with a resin to restrict burning to only one end. The strand is perforated, threaded at several distances with fine fuse wires, and assembled to a mount which is threaded into the bomb. Appropriate electrical circuitry and leads exist to connect the fuse wires to the timers. After pressurizing the bomb with an inert gas, such as nitrogen, the propellant strand is ignited at one end by a hot wire; on burning linearly at a predetermined pressure the first fuse wire is consumed, thereby activating the timers. Severing of each successive fuse wire stops the timer to which it was connected so that the time elapsed to burn a known linear distance of propellant is established. Within several hours, it is possible to establish complete burning rate curves at pressures from 300 to 5000 psi and at several temperatures. The method is ideally suited for evaluation of small quantities of experimental propellants or for assessment of the adequacy of production propellants to meet specification requirements. Correlation with dynamic performance in rocket motors is quite satisfactory for evaluation techniques. In addition, through use of strand burners with optical ports and associated photographic and spectrographic techniques, highly informative studies have been made on the mechanism of propellant burning (9–11).

Stability and Sensitivity. The tests used to assess the stability and sensitivity of solid propellants are for the most part similar to those used for the explosive components. The Taliani test which measures the rate of pressure buildup by the gases evolved during propellant decomposition has found increasing use for gaging stability, particularly for cellulose nitrate propellants. A number of tests have been developed to determine the tendency of propellants to detonate under shockwave loading or direct impact. All such tests are necessarily relative and provide a basis for comparison with materials of known performance. Extrapolation to service conditions must be done judiciously (12–14).

Mechanical Properties. The major problems in determining the mechanical properties of propellants consists of the application of stresses at rates of loading comparable to those experienced in weapons and rockets. In general, as in the case of measures of stability and sensitivity, the results obtained are relative and assessment is made in terms of comparison with standard materials. Systems may differ considerably in the magnitude and duration of stresses imposed and the effect of various metal parts as well as temperature cycling. The results of tests of mechanical properties may indicate areas of weakness, but cannot provide assurance of satisfactory performance. In general, conventional equipment is used; however, a considerable amount of work has been done to develop high-rate-of-loading testers; and techniques have been established for determining the mechanical properties of propellant specimens over a broad temperature range, eg, from −40 to 60°C (15,16).

Bibliography

"Propellants" under "Explosives" in *ECT* 1st ed., Vol. 6, pp. 74–87, by D. R. Cameron, Picatinny Arsenal, U.S.A. Ordnance Department; "Rocket Propellants" in *ECT* 1st ed., Vol. 11, pp. 761–768, by A. W. Sloan, Atlantic Research Corporation; "Rocket Propellants, Solid" in *ECT* 1st ed., Suppl. 2, pp. 709–715, by W. F. Arendale and T. A. Neely, Thiokol Chemical Corporation.

1. A. G. Edwards and C. R. Grande, *Simulation of Gun Firings by Analog Computer Techniques*, Picatinny Arsenal Report, Dover, N.J., 1960.
2. J. Brinkley, *Computational Methods in Combustion Calculations, High Speed Aerodynamics and Jet Propulsion 2. Sec C.*, Princeton University Press, Princeton, N.J., 1956.
3. A. S. Donegan and M. Farka, "Solution of Thermochemical Propellant Calculations on a High Speed Digital Computer," *Jet Propulsion* **26**, 164–171 (1956).
4. *Joint Army-Navy-Air Force, Thermochemical Tables*, Dow Chemical Co., Midland, Mich., 1960.
5. F. R. W. Hunt, ed., *Interior Ballistics*, Philosophical Library, Inc., New York, 1950, pp. 160–183.
5a. *Ibid.*, p. 161.
6. A. O. Pallingston and M. Weinstein, *Method of Calculation of Interior Ballistic Properties of Propellants from Closed Bomb Data, Report 2005*, Picatinny Arsenal, Dover, N.J., 1959.
7. *Propellant Actuated Devices, AMCP 706-270*, U.S. Army Material Command, Washington, D.C.
8. B. H. Julier, *Form Functions for Use in Interior Ballistics and Closed Bomb Calculation, Mem. Rept. No. 3*, Naval Powder Factory (1940).

9. B. L. Crawford, C. Huggett, F. Daniels, and R. E. Wilfong, "Direct Measurement of Burning Rates by an Electric Timing Method," *Anal. Chem.* **19,** 630 (1947).

10. E. K. Ives, J. Dominek, and W. A. Proell, "Heat Sink Strand Bombs for Determining Ballistic Properties of Solid Propellants, *ARS (Am. Rocket Soc.) J.* **31,** 783–785 (1960).

11. J. P. Picard et al., "Apparatus for Determining Combustion Rate of Solid Propellants," *Ind. Eng. Chem.* **56,** 49–52 (1964).

12. D. Price and I. Jaffee, "Large Scale Gap Test; Interpretation of Results for Propellants," *ARS J.* **31,** 595–599 (1961).

13. R. C. Kopituk, "New Impact Detonability Tester for Evaluating Materials with Highly Reactive Oxidizers," *ASTM (Am. Soc. Testing Mater.) Bull.* **1960,** 51–55.

14. "Propellants Solid, Sampling, Examination and Testing," *U.S. Mil. Std. 286A* (1961).

15. "Propellants Solid for Cannons, Requirements and Packing," *U.S. Mil. Std. 652* (1963).

16. *Methods for Determining the Tensile Properties of Solid Rocket Propellants,* Part I, "Nitrocellulose Propellants"; Part II, "Composite Propellants SPIA/PP8," Solid Propellant Information Agency, Johns Hopkins University, Silver Springs, Md. (1956,1957).

Victor Lindner
U.S. Army
Picatinny Arsenal

EXT D&C DYES. See Colors for foods, drugs, and cosmetics.

EXTRACTION

LIQUID–LIQUID EXTRACTION

Liquid–liquid extraction, or more briefly, liquid extraction, refers to the transfer of one or more components between two liquid phases. Its purpose is to purify one or more compounds or to effect a more economical recovery of a component than is possible by other means. The process in which a component is removed from one solvent by contact with another solvent, immiscible with the first, is called "simple liquid extraction" and is the original type of liquid extraction. In the laboratory, the process is generally carried out in a separatory funnel by successive extractions of the one solution with fresh portions of the other solvent. Frequently an organic compound is produced by chemical reaction in an organic solvent to produce a solution of the desired compound together with acid. The acid may be one of the products of reaction or it may be the catalyst for the reaction, as in the case of some polymerizations. Before the compound can be recovered from the solution by boiling off the solvent, it is usually necessary to remove the acid to prevent decomposition or other undesirable side reactions. The organic solvent is then shaken in a separatory funnel with successive portions of fresh water until the acid concentration is reduced to a desired level. By regulating the quantity of water in a single equilibrium stage or by using a given quantity of fresh water a sufficient number of times, any desired degree of removal of the acid can be obtained.

The converse condition would result from a chemical reaction in water to produce an organic compound and other inorganic compounds. An example is the reaction of sodium acetate with sulfuric acid to produce acetic acid and sodium sulfate. In this case the acid can be extracted from the aqueous salt solution by repeated extractions with an organic solvent such as butyl acetate, ethyl ether, or methyl isobutyl ketone.

Since both the chemical processes previously mentioned are typical of most organic syntheses, liquid extraction is an operation essential to the production of pure organic chemicals. The techniques described above are suitable for laboratory work, and in some cases in the past they have been used for plant-scale operations, due to lack of familiarity with the chemical-engineering operation of continuous countercurrent extraction and with the equipment to carry it out. Thus, in the latter problem of extracting an organic compound from aqueous solution with a solvent, it is found that each successive extract phase is less concentrated than the previous one; if ten such extracts are combined, a relatively dilute extract results. If a second batch of the aqueous solution is to be processed, however, the first extraction can be made with the solvent extract from the second extraction of the first batch, the second extraction made with the solvent extract from the third previous extraction, and so forth, until only the final extraction is made with the fresh solvent. After this operation is carried out through a sufficient number of aqueous batches, a condition is reached where the final concentration in the solvent is ten times that in the combined extracts from the ten separate washes with fresh water. This operation is called countercurrent extraction, and where the solvent and organic solute must ultimately be separated by distillation or some other means, it is obvious that the countercurrent process is far more economical.

When the removal of the organic compound from the aqueous solution must be substantially complete, a large number of batchwise extractions with fresh solvent are required. It will be demonstrated below that 99% removal requires twice the number of extractions as 90% removal, and 99.9% removal requires three times the same number. It is apparent, therefore, that the advantages of a countercurrent operation are more significant the greater the degree of removal required, because this method of operation can reduce the amount of solvent necessary to that used in a single-batch extraction. This is possible whenever the single-batch extraction removes more than half of the solute from the original solution.

If the concentration of solute in the aqueous phase is x and the concentration of solute in the solvent in equilibrium with this aqueous phase is y, it is possible to define a distribution coefficient, D, such that

$$D = y/x$$

If the ratio of solvent phase to aqueous phase is expressed as L/H it can be shown by a material balance that when L/H is greater than $1/D$, more than half the solute is in the solvent phase. Under these conditions it is possible to extract substantially all the solute from the aqueous phase in a countercurrent process if sufficient stages are provided. When the solvent ratio is exactly equal to $1/D$ a substantially complete removal requires an infinite number of stages; at any smaller ratio, complete removal is impossible even if an infinite number of stages were available. Thus it is convenient to consider the solvent ratio equal to $1/D$ as the minimum solvent ratio for complete removal, and at any smaller ratio only a fraction of the solute can be removed even though infinite stages are provided.

By making use of these concepts it is possible to separate two different solutes by countercurrent extraction; this process, called fractional liquid extraction because of the analogy to fractional distillation, has been developed and applied commercially over the past two decades.

For example, if in the acidification previously considered, the starting material consisted of a mixture of sodium propionate and sodium acetate, the addition of sulfuric acid would liberate both propionic and acetic acid. The propionic acid would have a higher distribution coefficient than the acetic acid in the solvent; by way of illustration, assume the values are 2.0 and 1.0, respectively. Operation at a solvent ratio slightly greater than unity would remove both acids completely from the aqueous solution. On the other hand, operation at a solvent ratio greater than 0.5, such as 0.7, would remove all the propionic acid but only a fraction of the acetic acid. The acetic acid, free of propionic acid, remaining in the aqueous solution could be extracted by a second extraction at a solvent ratio greater than unity. Similarly, the original solvent extract could be extracted with water at a solvent ratio of 0.7; all the acetic acid would then be removed by the water, but a fraction of the propionic acid would remain in the solvent to provide a propionic acid solution free of acetic acid. The resulting aqueous solution of mixed propionic and acetic acids would be more dilute than the original. A second similar processing would reduce the concentration proportionately more; however, this dilute solution could be used to start the next acidification and the acid concentrations would build up to the point where the net yield of each acid is equal to the amount in the feed.

In industrial practice this process is actually carried out in a single column, with the mixture to be separated introduced into the center and operated at a suitable solvent ratio. The ratio is such that the light solvent introduced at the bottom removes the component with the higher distribution coefficient when it leaves the top of the column, and the heavy solvent introduced at the top removes the component with the lower distribution coefficient when it leaves the column at the bottom.

This fractional liquid extraction process was first considered on a batchwise laboratory scale in 1925 and rejected as impractical (23). However, Craig developed an apparatus for conveniently carrying out the multiple operations of the batchwise extraction process (14,16). The apparatus was especially suitable for microchemical studies and could be used to ascertain the purity of a compound and to detect mixtures by comparing the distribution curve obtained for a large number of such extractions with the theoretical curve (15). The device was primarily designed to determine distribution data and to ascertain purity. It could not be used to give an appreciable yield of purified product.

In 1948 the first practical equipment was described for carrying out the continuous fractional liquid extraction in a single column (43). With this column products can be obtained that have been subjected to sharp fractionation between two solvents.

The design of extraction processes is analogous to the design of distillation processes because the distribution coefficient is identical in definition to the vaporization constant in the latter processes.

Interpretation of Distribution Data

The design of liquid–liquid extraction operations depends upon a knowledge of the distribution or relative solubility of a solute between two solvents that are not completely miscible. Several methods have been developed for studying these data (50, 55). In the ternary diagram (Fig. 1), the corners A and B represent two solvents of limited miscibility, and C a third substance miscible, in this case, with both A and B.

The curve DEPFG represents the mutual solubility curve and any composition lying inside this envelope separates into two liquid phases. This is called the heterogeneous region, and a mixture of composition M separates into two phases of compositions E and F. The line connecting these two compositions in equilibrium with each other is called the *tie line*. Compositions outside the mutual solubility curve are in the homogeneous region and do not separate into two phases.

It is observed from Figure 1 that it is difficult to interpolate between the tie lines on this type of diagram, and several methods have been developed for accomplishing this interpolation with better accuracy. One method consists of constructing the "conjugate" line (or curve) by laying off EH parallel to side AB of the ternary diagram and

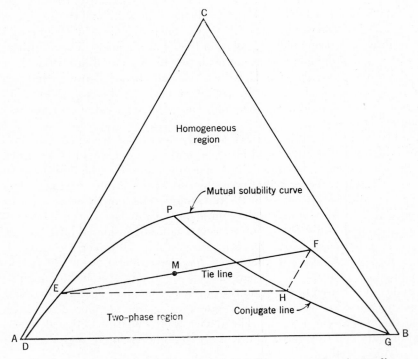

Fig. 1. Ternary diagram showing mutual solubility curve and conjugate line.

line HF parallel to side AC. The intersection, H, of these two lines defines the conjugate curve GHP from which any tie line can be found by reversing the construction just described. The conjugate curve intersects the mutual solubility curve at the point P, known as the "plait point." At this point the two phases in equilibrium are identical and it may be considered to be a limiting condition for extraction. Other methods for constructing the conjugate line have been described; this line allows an extrapolation to the plait point as well as facilitating interpolation of the data.

Another method for accomplishing the same result is to plot the equilibrium conditions as the concentration of the solute in one phase against the concentration in the other phase. This is the most popular type of graph and will be discussed later in its application to design calculations. The plait point on this plot is the intersection of the equilibrium curve with the 45° or $y = x$ line as shown in Figure 5.

Other methods for plotting tie-line data have been proposed. All of these may be conveniently extrapolated to determine the plait point, but it should be noted that slightly different points may be obtained by the different methods, depending upon the extent of the extrapolation required. This is of minor significance because in the design of an extraction operation it is undesirable to approach very close to the plait point.

Numerous methods have been proposed for the correlation of tie-line data and prediction from vapor–liquid equilibria data based on the activity coefficients (50,55). Binary data can be used to predict the activity coefficients for the ternary system by the Gibbs-Duhem relationship, as described in the article Distillation, if the ternary constants are neglected. If any ternary vapor–liquid equilibria data are available these constants can be included, but in many systems they make only a minor contribution to the overall calculation and can be ignored. In addition, all these methods require a knowledge of mutual solubility data. Theoretically predictions could be made by thermodynamic relationships, but sufficiently precise equations are not as yet available to correlate binary and ternary phase equilibria data.

Methods for predicting the activity coefficients for binary systems proposed by Pierotti, Deal, and Derr (42) can also be employed in the preliminary selection of solvents for extraction; this is particularly applicable to the selection of solvents for a fractional liquid extraction to separate two or more solutes.

Simple Liquid Extraction

In simple liquid extraction a component is transferred from one solution into another solution. There may be one or several advantages in transferring a compound into the other solution. Starting, for instance, with a dilute and heavily contaminated aqueous solution of a compound less volatile than water, liquid–liquid extraction with an immiscible organic solvent may lead to a concentrated and highly purified solution of a valuable material. The advantages are obvious. Concentrating a dilute and contaminated aqueous solution by straight evaporation is costly, leads to an impure concentrate, and may be accompanied by a considerable destruction of the product. Concentration after liquid–liquid extraction with an organic solvent is comparatively cheap, leads to a refined product, and avoids destruction.

In some cases the component extracted may be separated more easily from the second solution than from the original solution; this application has many ramifications. It can be used to extract a component from a solvent with which it forms an azeotrope into a solvent with which it does not form an azeotrope. A large-scale commercial application of this type of extraction is the removal of a component present at a dilute concentration in a lower-boiling solvent by extraction with a higher-boiling immiscible solvent. This effects a substantial saving of heat because it is necessary only to distill off the smaller quantity of the component from the final extract solution, as compared to distilling off the larger amount of original solvent. It has been applied extensively to the recovery of acetic acid from dilute aqueous solutions; the higher-boiling ketones have been found to be especially suitable for this extraction (76,77,79). Another important application of this type is the removal of small quantities of phenol from waste aqueous solutions to avoid stream pollution.

MULTIPLE CONTACT WITH FRESH SOLVENT

The laboratory technique for simple liquid extraction consists of providing contact between the solvent and the solution to be extracted by shaking them vigorously in a separatory funnel and then separating the layers. This operation is represented graphically in Figure 2. Assuming that the solvents are completely immiscible and that equilibrium between the two solutions is attained, the concentrations of the two phases correspond to a point on the equilibrium curve. Thus, if H moles of a heavy

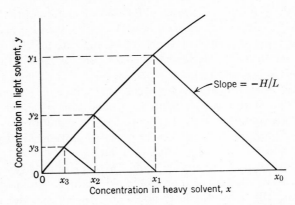

Fig. 2. Graphical solution of multiple batchwise liquid extraction with fresh solvent.

solvent containing a solute at a concentration of x_0 is mixed with L moles of a light solvent and the mixture is shaken to obtain equilibrium, the final concentrations may be assumed to be given by the point (x_1, y_1) on the equilibrium curve. This point can be located by considering a material balance on the two phases such that

$$y_1/(x_0 - x) = H/L \tag{1}$$

The left-hand side of this equation can be seen to be the slope of the line between $(x_0, 0)$ and (x_1, y_1) in Figure 2 considered in the negative direction. The calculation can be repeated as shown by constructing lines of slopes $-H/L$ through the raffinate concentrations to the equilibrium curve for successive treatments of the raffinate with the same quantity of fresh solvent.

For the case of systems obeying the ideal distribution law, so that the concentration in one phase is always proportional to the concentration in the other, the equation of the equilibrium curve is $y = Dx$. It has been shown by Underwood that the relationship between the initial and final concentration in the raffinate after n extractions (36) is

$$x_n = x_0/(1 + LD/H)^n \tag{2}$$

where x_n = final raffinate concentration after n extractions. This equation has been represented graphically (56). From equation 2 it is also possible to determine the number of extractions with a given ratio of solvents necessary to reduce the raffinate concentration to any desired amount. Thus

$$n = \frac{\log (x_0/x_n)}{\log (1 + LD/H)} \tag{3}$$

In the use of partially miscible solvents, account must be taken of the dissolved solvent in each of the phases. The calculations are carried out on a ternary diagram as shown in Figure 3 (50,55). The feed composition is represented by the point F. The point S_0 at the solvent corner of the diagram represents the fresh solvent and coincides with the corner only when the solvent contains none of the other constituents in the feed. The compositions of all mixtures of the feed and the fresh solvent lie along the line S_0F; the location depends upon the relative amounts of each in the mixture. Thus the first mix point M_1 is located so that the ratio of the distance M_1F to S_0M_1 is equal to the ratio of the solvent to the feed quantity in the same units of the ternary

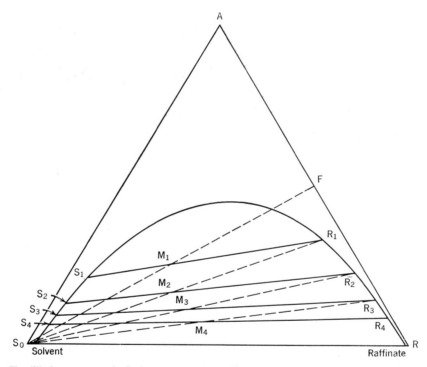

Fig. 3. Equilibrium-stage calculations on a ternary diagram for multiple batchwise extraction with fresh solvent.

diagram. The mixture M_1 must fall in the immiscible region and will then separate into two phases given by the tie line through this point.

The extract composition from the first extraction is designated by S_1 at the solvent end of the tie line, and the raffinate composition is designated R_1 at the opposite end. The raffinate R_1 is mixed with fresh solvent, the mix point M_2 is located as before, and the equilibrium-stage calculations are continued, as shown, until the desired raffinate concentration is obtained. It has been mentioned previously that interpolation of the tie lines on a ternary diagram cannot be made readily by inspection; reference to the conjugate line, or to a separate equilibrium curve as shown in Figure 5, will give a more reliable interpolation. The location of the proper tie line through the mix point is by "cut and try" regardless of which method is used to represent the tie-line data.

Continuous Countercurrent Extraction

Because of the economic advantages of continuous countercurrent extraction this type of operation is preferable for plant-scale operations. In the case of completely immiscible solvents and ideal distribution (so that the concentrations in the two solvents are proportional), it can be shown by material balances and equilibrium conditions that when the fresh solvent contains no solute, the relationship between the solute concentrations in the feed and final raffinate solution is given by

$$x_n = \frac{(LD/H) - 1}{(LD/H)^{n+1} - 1} \, x_0 \tag{4}$$

where x_0 = solute concentration in feed; x_n = solute concentration in raffinate after n equilibrium stages; L = flow rate of light solvent; H = flow rate of heavy solvent; and D = distribution coefficient. Underwood has presented the first chart by which the unextracted fraction, x_n/x_0, can be determined directly from the values of LD/H and the number of equilibrium stages, n, or by which any of these values may be determined from the other two (56). By interchanging parameters, however, Treybal (55) has constructed a similar graph which can be read more accurately in the range of usual commercial practice.

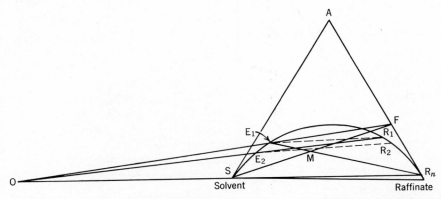

Fig. 4. Graphical stage calculations for countercurrent liquid extraction by the method of Hunter and Nash.

In general, however, the distribution coefficient, D, will vary with concentration even though the solvents are almost completely immiscible. A completely rigorous method for calculating the number of equilibrium stages, taking into account the partial miscibility of the solvents as well as varying distribution coefficient, was developed by Hunter and Nash (29) and is illustrated in Figure 4. A feed composition F is to be extracted with solvent in a countercurrent operation to produce a raffinite of composition R_n. From the flow rates of the solvent and the feed the mix point M is located along line SF. The mix point represents the total material introduced into the column and must also represent the total material leaving the column. It therefore lies on the line between the raffinate composition R_n and the extract composition E_1. Projection of a line through R_n and the mix point M to the mutual solubility curve gives the final extract composition E_1. The relative rates of the raffinate and extract are given by the distances E_1M and MR_n. The raffinate solution from the first stage can be located

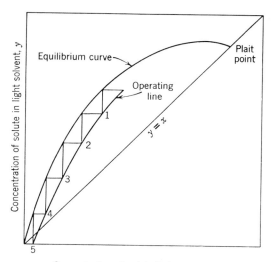

Fig. 5. Graphical stage calculations by the method of Varteressian and Fenske.

by the tie line through the point E_1; this is shown at point R_1. It can also be shown, by rearranging the overall material balance, that the difference between the extract and feed must be the same as the difference between the solvent and raffinate. The point that satisfies this condition lies on the intersection of lines FE_1 and R_nS, and is shown at point O. It can also be shown from a material balance that the difference between the two streams at any point in the column is the same as at the ends. Thus the line through these compositions must also pass through the point O. Accordingly, the line between R_1 and O in Figure 4 intersects the mutual solubility curve at concentration E_2, which is the solvent composition leaving the second theoretical stage. This construction is equivalent to a graphical material balance. The tie line through the point E_2 locates the point R_2, and this is equivalent to a graphical equilibrium calculation. Thus by alternate material-balance and equilibrium calculations the procedure can be repeated until the desired raffinate composition is obtained.

In a similar manner the calculations may be carried out in a reverse order starting at the point R_n. However, the first method is preferable because it immediately shows with the first equilibrium calculation whether the solvent rate used is above the minimum. If the first tie line is above the line E_1F, it is apparent that the raffinate composition cannot be realized and the solvent rate is below a definite minimum. When the tie line coincides with the line E_1F, the solvent rate is a minimum value which would require infinite stages. Any solvent rate above this will give the desired separation in a finite number of stages and therefore represents a practical separation.

Varteressian and Fenske modified the method of Hunter and Nash to eliminate the use of the tie line on the ternary diagram (57). They located the operating line on any xy diagram, as shown in Figure 5, by the intersections of the lines in Figure 4 passing through point O with the mutual solubility curve, and plotted the concentration in the solvent phase against the concentration in the raffinate phase. These concentrations may be in mole or weight fractions as read directly from the ternary diagram, or they may be converted to any other basis. Due to the mutual solubility of the solvents, however, the operating line will not be straight by any method of expressing the concentration; therefore the most convenient basis would be preferred. In Figure 5 the tie-line data are plotted to locate the equilibrium curve. The equilibrium stages required are stepped off between the two curves as in distillation and absorption calculations. This is equivalent to alternate equilibrium and material-balance calculations and is mathematically identical to the method of Hunter and Nash, but it is somewhat more convenient to carry out the graphical operations on the xy plot of Figure 5.

In the case of countercurrent extraction in a packed column the concentrations vary continuously, and if the equilibrium curve and the operating line have appreciably different slopes, the "equilibrium stage" (or the equivalent "theoretical stage," as is generally used in this case since actual physical stages do not exist) is not a good criterion for design. In this case the transfer unit proposed by Chilton and Colburn is a better measure of the difficulty of separation because it is based on an integrated driving force in preference to a constant driving force over the theoretical stage (7). For the technique for determining the proper mean driving force between the equilibrium curve and the operating line see Absorption.

Fractional Liquid Extraction

The analogy between distillation and liquid extraction has been noted above together with the possibility of utilizing liquid extraction to separate a mixture into pure components. The precise analogy to fractional distillation would be a liquid extraction in which a single solvent is used and a fraction of the product removed in the solvent stream is refluxed to the extractor. This was the first fractional liquid process recognized and investigated. It was originally called liquid extraction with reflux; more recently, however, the advantages of reflux in a two-solvent fractional liquid extraction have been recognized, and consequently this designation is not explicit.

FRACTIONAL LIQUID EXTRACTION WITH SINGLE SOLVENT

It is sometimes possible to separate a binary mixture completely into pure components if both of these components are only partially soluble in the solvent. It is then possible to return some of the product removed with the solvent to the column instead of employing an additional foreign solvent. This type of operation is shown in Figure 6 as applied to the separation of methylcyclohexane (MCH) and n-heptane, using aniline as the solvent (58). The MCH is returned to the bottom of the column as "reflux," accomplishing the same effect as reboiler vapor at the bottom of the distilling column. This MCH phase passes upward through the column countercurrent to the aniline, which is introduced at the top of the column. As it passes upward through the column, it dissolves in the aniline and simultaneously extracts or displaces the n-heptane from the aniline solution, so that at the top of the column the hydrocarbon phase consists essentially of n-heptane. At the top of the column, the aniline entering becomes saturated by dissolving the proper amount of the n-heptane, and the excess passes overhead as the n-heptane product. The dissolved hydrocarbon acts as the reflux in the conventional distilling column, although at this end of the column it is actually an internal reflux resulting from the introduction of the solvent. At the other end of the column, the MCH return to the column may be considered as an external reflux stream.

Two other methods have been used to produce this reflux in the extraction column. These should be more clearly defined as fractional liquid extraction with internal re-

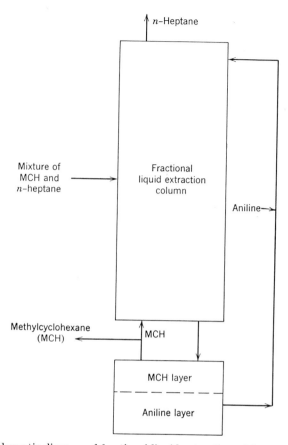

Fig. 6. Schematic diagram of fractional liquid extraction with external reflux.

flux. One method is to change the temperature of the solvent at the discharge end and thus precipitate out the necessary reflux, which then flows back through the column, countercurrent to the solvent, to the other end, where it is dissolved in the incoming fresh solvent and thus is recycled. Another method is to add to the solvent discharge end of the column a second solvent that is soluble in the first solvent but immiscible with the product being removed at this end of the column, so that some of the product precipitates from the solvent and returns through the column countercurrent to the first solvent. This is distinguished from the general case of two solvents, in that this second solvent does not pass countercurrently through the column against the first solvent, but is completely soluble in the first solvent and is immediately eliminated at the same end along with this solvent. The product precipitated from the solution provides the necessary reflux to the column.

Maloney and Schubert (37) developed a method for carrying out these graphical calculations for fractional liquid extraction with a single solvent based on the Ponchon principle, which is well known in distillation. In the application to liquid extraction, the solvent is analogous to the reboiler duty or heat input to the column in distillation in that it provides the return of solutes through the column necessary to effect the separation.

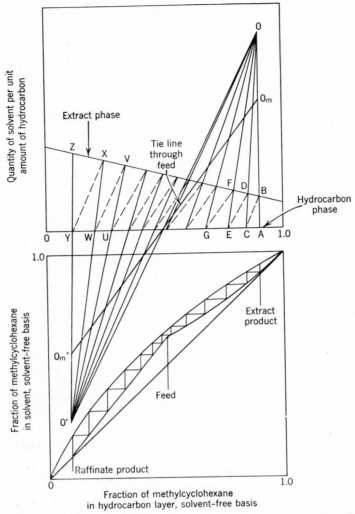

Fig. 7. Graphical stage calculations for fractional liquid extraction by method of Maloney and Schubert (37). Courtesy American Institute of Chemical Engineers.

Figure 7 illustrates the graphical technique for carrying out the stagewise calculations for the separation of n-heptane and methylcyclohexane by the use of aniline. The mutual solubility data and equilibrium or tie-line data are represented on the upper graph of the figure by plotting the ratio of solvent to solute against solute composition on a solvent-free basis (note the analogy to enthalpy in the Ponchon method). When the feed composition is located on this diagram at F, the tie line passing through this point (extrapolated if necessary) intersects the vertical line at the MCH product composition at point O_m such that the minimum reflux ratio, R_m, is equal to O_mB/AB. If the equilibrium data are such that the intersection of any of the tie lines in the area between the lines O_mF and O_mA intersects the line O_mA at a point above O_m, the minimum reflux ratio is calculated using the tie line having the intersection farthest away from B. It can also be shown that the minimum solvent quantity is equal to the ordinate of $E(O_mA)$ where E is the net quantity of solutes after the reflux is returned to the column.

An operating reflux ratio, R, is then selected greater than the minimum and the point O is located such that OB $= R$(AB). It can be shown that all material balances around the extract end of the column pass through point O, so that stagewise calculations can be carried out on the upper part of the figure by alternate tie lines and material-balance lines as shown in Figure 7, where BC and DE are tie lines. Alternatively, they can be carried out on the lower section of the figure by first locating the operating line from suitably spaced lines through point O, and then stepping off the stages by the conventional technique until the feed composition is reached.

Stagewise calculations are carried out for the stripping section of the column in a similar manner; O′ is located by extending line OF to the intersection with the vertical line at the raffinate composition. Either technique may be used and in this figure VW and XY are tie lines. Thus the total number of theoretical stages for any given separation is determined.

FRACTIONAL LIQUID EXTRACTION WITH TWO SOLVENTS

It should be noted that the fractional liquid extraction with a single solvent can produce two pure products only if the solute preferentially soluble in the solvent is partially immiscible with the solvent. The selection of a suitable solvent is not always possible if the components to be separated are so different in solvent properties or polarity that any solvent immiscible in one is soluble in the other under normal operating temperatures. Fractional liquid extraction with two solvents imposes no such restriction, since both solutes may be completely miscible with both solvents. The only requirement is that the two solvents be immiscible in each other. This is a physical requirement for operation of the process. It imposes no excessive restrictions on the solvents because only dissimilar solvents have a selective effect on the components of the original mixture, and all solvents which are immiscible in each other are appreciably dissimilar.

The first consideration of this process on the basis of individual batchwise countercurrent operation led to the conclusion that it was impractical when the relative distribution was small because a large number of contacts would be required for a good separation. Craig developed a relatively simple device for carrying out twenty or more countercurrent extractions simultaneously and improved the yield to make the process practical on a laboratory scale (14,16). The original design employed a circular pattern of extraction stages which became impractical for larger numbers of stages on the order of 100. As applications of fractional liquid extraction as an analytical tool expanded, the need developed for equipment with more stages for sharper separations of components with close distribution coefficients, and Craig subsequently proposed a stage design which could be assembled in a straight line arrangement so that more than 1000 stages would be available and operation of the device could be made fully automatic. A complete survey of the use of this equipment and the interpretation of the data are given by Craig and Craig (15).

The Craig apparatus was used primarily to ascertain the purity of a compound and to identify impurities. Accurate interpretations of the data required that the addition of solute have a negligible effect on the volume of the heavy phase and also that the distribution coefficients remain constant. In order to attain these conditions solute

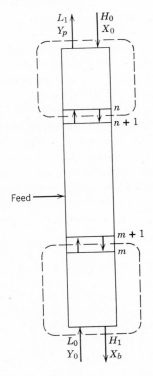

Fig. 8. Schematic diagram of material balances in two-solvent fractional liquid extraction.

concentrations had to be small and thus it was not practical to produce appreciable quantities of purified products, as would be required of a commercial process.

The first recognition of the possibility of separating components by the difference in distribution coefficients between solvents was in a doctoral dissertation by Tiedcke in 1926. Jantzen (31) summarized the work carried on under his guidance and including the work of Tiedcke in a 1932 monograph, which compared the separation of a multicomponent mixture by fractional distillation and fractional liquid extraction and showed the greater potential of the latter method. He used a small internally agitated glass column of a rather delicate design which apparently did not lead to a commercial application.

Other potential applications were demonstrated by Van Dijck (66,67,71) in patents assigned to Royal Dutch Shell. In 1948 Scheibel (43) described the stagewise technique of process calculations for fractional liquid extraction for ideal and nonideal systems. Figure 8 shows the location of the streams in the material balances above and below the feed. The basic equation for the variation of solute concentration above the feed stage can be calculated from the following equation:

$$L_{n+1} Y_{n+1} = (H_n Y_n / D_n) + L_1 Y_p - H_0 X_0 \tag{5}$$

where D is the distribution coefficient for the solute component expressed as the ratio of the quantity of component per quantity of light solvent divided by the quantity of component per quantity of heavy solvent, and where L and H are the quantities of light and heavy solvent, respectively, expressed in the same units as D. Y and X are the concentrations of solute in the light and heavy phases, respectively, also in the same units as D. The subscripts denote the stage of origin of the streams as indicated in Figure 8.

Similarly, the variation of solute concentration below the feed stage can be calculated from the following equation:

$$H_{m+1} X_{m+1} = L_m D_m X_m + H_1 X_b - L_0 Y_0 \tag{6}$$

where X represents the solute concentration in the heavy phase, also expressed in the same units as D.

Ideal Systems

The term "ideal systems," as used here, refers to solvent systems in which the distribution coefficients for the solutes are independent of concentration. It does not imply thermodynamic ideality, since if both phases were ideal, the distribution coefficients on a mole fraction or mole ratio basis would be not only constant but equal to unity. In all immiscible systems, at least one phase is thermodynamically nonideal and distribution coefficients vary with concentration. If solutions are sufficiently dilute, distribution coefficients can be considered constant and by the definition of this section they would be classified as ideal over a limited concentration range. In general, this range is smaller if the individual phases are more thermodynamically nonideal, and the following section on nonideal systems thus implies these deviations from thermodynamic ideality.

The previous relationships are rigorous and difficult to apply. All early work on fractional liquid extraction processes was based on assumptions of constant L and constant H over the two individual sections of the column. Fresh solvents were also assumed to be solutefree ($X_0 = 0$ and $Y_0 = 0$). Thus equations 5 and 6 become

$$Y_{n+1} = (H/LD_n) (Y_n + Y_p) \tag{7}$$

and

$$X_{n+1} = (LD_m/H) (X_m + X_b) \tag{8}$$

If the system can be considered ideal for each component, the distribution coefficients are constant in each stage and the coefficients of the Y_n and X_m terms are constant in each equation; furthermore, if no solvent is introduced with the feed the coefficients are reciprocals of each other. The term LD/H is defined as the extraction factor, E, and is dimensionless.

For this ideal system Bartels and Kleiman (3) derived the relationships

$$R_1 = (E_1^{n+m} - E_1^n)/(E_1^n - 1) \tag{9}$$

and

$$R_2 = (E_2^{n+m} - E_2^n)/(E_2^n - 1) \tag{10}$$

where R is the ratio of the quantity of a solute in the light product stream from the top of the extractor to the quantity of the solute in the heavy product stream from the bottom of the extractor. The subscripts refer to the components of the feed mixture, 1 designating the component whose equilibrium distribution favors the light phase, and 2 the component whose distribution favors the heavy phase. In these equations the feed stage is the nth stage below the top and the mth stage above the bottom. Since the feed stage is counted twice by this system, the total number of stages in the column is $n + m - 1$.

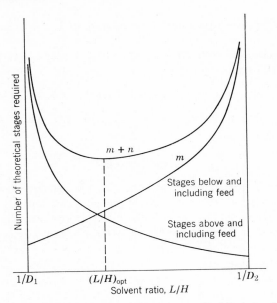

Fig. 9.   Effect of solvent ratio on stages required in two-solvent fractional liquid extraction.

The ratio R is called the rejection ratio, and, in terms of the symbols in Figure 8, it is given as follows:

$$R = L_1 Y_p / H_1 X_b \tag{11}$$

It will be noted that the rejection ratio of component 1 is always greater than unity, whereas the rejection ratio of component 2 is always a fraction less than unity. In order to maintain the symmetry of the equations defining these systems, it is preferable to consider a retention ratio R' which is the reciprocal of R such that

$$R' = H_1 X_b / L_1 Y_p \tag{12}$$

and thus the value of R_2' will always be greater than unity.

It is seen that when the feed is introduced into the center stage of the column, $n = m$, and equations 9 and 10 become

$$R_1 = E_1{}^n \tag{13}$$

and

$$R_2' = 1/E_2{}^n \tag{14}$$

In order for a separation to be effected it is thus necessary that the solvent ratio be selected so that E_1 is greater than unity and E_2 is less than unity. If both are greater or both are less than unity, the two components in the feed appear in the light or heavy phase product, respectively, with no significant change in the composition. There is, however, a range of solvent ratios possible such that

$$D_2 < H/L < D_1 \tag{15}$$

Figure 9 shows the effect of this variable on the number of stages in the column. Calculations were carried out using equations 7 and 8 and matching components at the feed stage as described by Scheibel (43). This figure shows that there is an optimum solvent ratio at which a specified separation can be achieved in fewer stages than at any other solvent ratio.

The first reference to an optimum solvent ratio was by Van Dijck and Schaafsma (75), who suggested operating at the geometric mean of the limiting values:

$$H/L = \sqrt{D_1 D_2} \tag{16}$$

Stene (51) showed that this optimum solvent ratio holds exactly when $R_1 = R_2'$, and under these conditions $n = m$. This is considered a symmetrical system, and the early work in analyzing the fractional liquid extraction process was based on this system.

If a relative distribution, β, is defined as

$$\beta = D_1/D_2 \tag{17}$$

equation 16 becomes

$$H/L = D_2 \sqrt{\beta} \tag{18}$$

and at this solvent ratio

$$E_1 = \sqrt{\beta} \tag{19}$$

and

$$E_2 = 1/\sqrt{\beta} = 1/E_1 \tag{20}$$

Klinkenberg, Lauwerier, and Reman (36) derived equations for calculating the number of stages above and below the feed for the general case of $R_1 \neq R_2'$ and found that the equations could not be solved directly for n and m except in certain special cases. By solving for these special cases, however, it was possible to construct curves similar to Figure 9 for any given separation and thus to determine the optimum solvent ratio graphically.

Klinkenberg (35) applied this technique to a large number of systems and developed empirical correlations for the optimum solvent ratio and the number of stages required above and below the feed at this solvent ratio. Scheibel (45) developed empirical equations from Klinkenberg's curves to permit the calculation of the optimum solvent ratio and number of stages required above and below the feed. At the optimum solvent ratio

$$\log E_1 = \frac{\log \beta}{1 + (\log R_2'/\log R_1)^{1/2}} \tag{21}$$

and

$$n + m = \left(\frac{2 \log R_1 R_2'}{\log \beta}\right)\left(1 - 0.04 \left|\log \frac{R_1}{R_2'}\right|\right) \tag{22}$$

where the term $|\log (R_1/R_2')|$ indicates the positive value of this function regardless of actual size.

The feed stage can be located for the nonsymmetrical system, depending upon whether R_1 or R_2' is greater, as follows. When $R_1 > R_2'$

$$\frac{n}{m} = \left(\frac{\log R_2'}{\log R_1}\right)^{1/2}\left(1 + \frac{\log (R_1/R_2')}{R_2' \log R_1}\right) \tag{23}$$

and when $R_2' > R_1$

$$\frac{m}{n} = \left(\frac{\log R_1}{\log R_2'}\right)^{\frac{1}{2}}\left(1 + \frac{\log (R_2'/R_1)}{R_1 \log R_2'}\right) \qquad (24)$$

These equations permit the complete process design of ideal fractional liquid extraction systems.

Nonideal Systems

Nonideal fractional liquid extraction systems may be of two types. In one the distribution coefficient varies with concentration of one or both components of the mixture, but the solvent quantities may be considered constant over the entire range of operation. In the second type the mutual solubility of the solvents varies appreciably with solute concentration so that the solvent quantities cannot be considered constant throughout the operation.

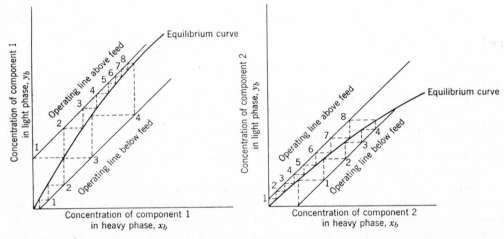

Fig. 10. Graphical stagewise calculations for fractional liquid extraction by method of Martin and Synge (38).

When the solvents are sufficiently immiscible so that their mutual solubilities are not appreciably affected by solute concentrations, the solvent quantities can be considered constant. The simplest nonideal system is one in which the distribution coefficient of each component varies with the concentration of the particular component but is independent of the concentration of the second component. Systems of this type were first studied by Asselin and Comings (2) and Compere and Ryland (10). Stagewise calculations can be carried out graphically according to the method of Martin and Synge (38), as shown in Figure 10. Matching at the feed stage is accomplished by a trial and error technique which provides the same number of stages above and below the feed for each component. Asselin and Comings carried out the calculation by plotting the concentrations of each component by stage numbers above and below the feed from the graphical construction, and matching components at the feed stage as described by Scheibel (43).

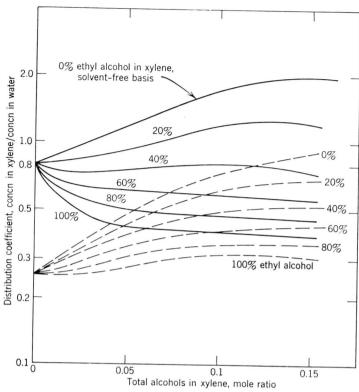

Fig. 11. Distribution coefficients of ethyl alcohol (- - -) and isopropyl alcohol (——) between xylene and water on a mole ratio basis.

If the distribution coefficients for the components vary with the concentration of both components, the equilibria data can be represented by a series of curves, similar to the single ones shown in Figure 10. With the concentration of the other component as the parameter on each plot, the graphical technique of Martin and Synge can be applied. In this case each step must be made simultaneously on both parts of a figure similar to Figure 10 by a trial and error technique which matches the concentrations of both solutes at the equilibrium conditions in each stage. This becomes increasingly difficult as the equilibrium curves vary more with the parameter of the concentration of the other component.   When high degrees of purity are required for each product most of the stages occur at dilute concentration, where the effect of the parameter is small and only the stages in the center of the column present any problems in the matching of the concentrations.

In another method proposed by Scheibel (43), the distribution coefficients are plotted as functions of total solute concentrations with the fraction of one component in the total solute as a parameter, as shown in Figure 11. Distribution coefficients from this figure are then applied to the stagewise technique by application of equations 7 and 8 and by matching the components at the feed stage achieved, as discussed previously (43).

In the case of very closely related compounds, such as isomers, the distribution coefficients frequently vary with total concentration but do not vary appreciably with the relative amounts of the individual solutes, so that the distribution coefficients for each component in Figure 11 lie on a single curve. A system of this type was studied by Karr and Scheibel (33), who applied the Thiele and Geddes method of distillation calculations (53) to the interpretation of the liquid extraction data.

Rigorous stagewise calculation for the quaternary system could be carried out graphically in three dimensions similar to the two-dimensional technique previously applied to the ternary diagram by the Hunter and Nash method. This technique is quite cumbersome, however, and would of course be impossible with systems of more than four components. Thus multicomponent systems involving more than two solutes can be handled by present techniques only by the application of certain reasonable assumptions.

Aromatic and paraffinic hydrocarbons could be considered closely related compounds in a highly polar solvent such as diethylene glycol. Scheibel (48) found that the liquid distribution data for the different hydrocarbons could be correlated thermodynamically on the assumption that the activity coefficient for each component in the solution, including the solvent, is a function only of total hydrocarbon or solvent concentration and independent of the relative amounts of aromatics and paraffins present. This assumption was extended to demonstrate the rigorous stagewise calculations for a multicomponent system in which the mutual solubility of the two phases changed in every stage (48).

Unsteady-State Conditions

In the start-up of a continuous extraction column the solvents are run in to adjust the interface to the desired level, then the feed mixture to be separated is started into

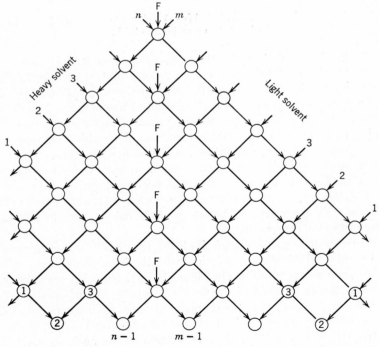

Fig. 12. Development of steady-state conditions by means of continual feed in a batchwise pattern.

the feed stage. Solute is extracted from the light phase above the feed and from the heavy phase below the feed until the concentration at the feed stage builds up to the steady-state concentration calculated by the techniques of the previous sections. Theoretically this requires infinite time, but it is important to determine the time required for a desired approach to steady state so that it is known whether the approach to steady state will be 90 or 99% or better. This is important both in the interpretation of laboratory data and in the analysis of plant operation data.

The calculation for the approach to the steady state is based on a pattern such as that shown in Figure 12; it has been called by Craig (15) the double withdrawal pattern. Craig's pattern considered only a single-feed introduction at the top stage. The development of the steady-state conditions requires the introduction of feed at every center stage, as shown in Figure 12. However, since each feed portion distributes independently to accumulate the steady-state conditions at infinite introductions, the mathematical relationships can be developed from a consideration of a single feed at the top of the pattern. Consideration of the superimposed patterns for all successive feeds shows that the quantity of solute in each product cycle is the sum of all quantities above and including the product cycle in the single-feed pattern. This was first recognized by Stene (51), who developed the relationships for the symmetrical pattern in which the feed is introduced into the center stage so that $n = m$. He concluded that the mathematics of the nonsymmetrical system is too complex to develop a rigorous relationship, and for the following ten years only the symmetrical system was considered. Generalized relationships are possible if the value of the extraction factor is constant. This requires not only a constant solvent ratio but an ideal system in which the distribution coefficient is constant independent of concentrations of all solutes. Thus the variation of the quantity of each solute can be calculated independently.

The first simplification of the Stene relationships was proposed by Scheibel (44), who recognized that the terms for the successive product cycles at a single-feed introduction approach a converging geometric series and that the slowest approach is obtained with an extraction factor of unity. Since the product quantities at steady state could be calculated (eq. 13), it was possible to define the geometric series giving the theoretical sum at infinite terms and to correlate the ratio for an extraction factor of unity so that the deviation from steady state, δ, at any product cycle, t, could be expressed as

$$\delta = \frac{4E \left(1 - \dfrac{1}{2^{n-1}}\right)^t}{(E + 1)^2} \tag{25}$$

and curves were calculated giving the number of product cycles necessary for a 90% approach to steady state for extraction systems up to 15 stages.

Peppard and Peppard (41) pointed out that this equation gave significant errors when used for large numbers of cycles giving a close approach to steady state and for large numbers of stages such that the approach to steady state was slow. They proposed extending the range up to 30 stages with two different empirical equations, each applicable over part of the range; however, these had the same limitations when used for more than 30 stages.

The rigorous solution for the general nonsymmetrical pattern was published simultaneously by Compere and Ryland (11) and by Scheibel (46). The former authors applied the random walk technique, designated by Feller (20) as "gambler's ruin," whereas the latter applied a technique which was noted by Compere (12) to utilize Kelvin's "method of images." The rigorous expression for the fraction of a solute in the light solvent leaving a fractional liquid extraction system, in which the feed stage is n stages below the top and m stages above the bottom, after t cycles, is given as follows:

$$\frac{R_1}{R_1 + 1} = \left(\frac{E}{E+1}\right)^n \left\{\beta_1 + \beta_2 \frac{E}{(E+1)^2} + \beta_3 \left(\frac{E}{(E+1)^2}\right)^2 + \ldots + \beta_t \left(\frac{E}{(E+1)^2}\right)^{t-1}\right\}$$

(26)

where the individual values of β are calculated by the equation

$$\beta_t = \sum_{i=0}^{\infty}\binom{n+2t-3}{t-1-i(m+n)} - \sum_{i=0}^{\infty}\binom{n+2t-3}{t-2-i(m+n)}$$
$$- \sum_{i=0}^{\infty}\binom{n+2t-3}{t-m-1-i(m+n)} + \sum_{i=0}^{\infty}\binom{n+2t-3}{t-m-2-i(m+n)} \quad (27)$$

in which the summation terms are the binomial coefficient such that

$$\binom{n}{r} = \frac{n!}{r!\,(n-r)!}$$

(28)

and

$$\binom{n}{0} = 1$$

(29)

It can be seen that the numbers of terms in all four summations in equation 27 increase for each increment of $n + m$ in t so that when the number of cycles is several times the number of stages in the pattern, the rigorous calculation becomes quite complex. It had been observed previously from experimental data on a continuous multistage extraction column that the column holdup had to be turned over about five times for an approach to within 10% of steady state; for this condition t is approximately $5(n + m)$. In order to simplify the interpretation of experimental data, Scheibel (46) suggested the use of the rigorous equation for the first terms of the series, where the greatest deviations from the geometric series are observed, and then application of the original concept of the geometric series to the deviation remaining after the successive terms approached more closely the constant ratio of the geometric series.

The previous derivations have been made for an ideal system with no change in the mutual solubility of the solvents so that the solvent ratio remains constant. If the latter assumption can be made it is possible to develop the relationships for the nonideal systems by direct calculation, employing the same repetitive techniques of the ideal system and using numerical values in place of the symbols. This is not excessively complicated, but unfortunately, the set of values obtained would have no application to any system other than that for which it was developed. The concept of applying the geometric series to the residual deviation after a reasonable number of cycles is a convenient empirical tool for these systems also, although the nonideality could produce intermediate quantities in excess of the steady-state quantities, and more care should be exercised than is necessary in the ideal system, where no intermediate quantities can ever exceed the steady-state values.

Certain important conclusions are apparent from the calculations for approach to steady state in ideal systems which could be applied qualitatively to the nonideal systems. The approach to steady state is slower with extraction factors approaching unity from either side. The approach to steady state is different if the distribution coefficients and consequently the extraction factors differ; if one extraction factor is the reciprocal of the other, however, the approach to steady state is identical. It has been noted previously that this condition is usually very close to the optimum solvent ratio for a separation.

The approach to steady state is slower with large numbers of stages so that in a nonsymmetrical pattern the side with the larger number of stages will be further from steady state at the same product cycle than the other side. It can be seen also from Figure 12 that at the same horizontal line of stages the product cycle for the side having the smaller number of stages is numerically ahead of the product cycle at the other side, so that approach to steady state during the early periods of developing a pattern could be considerably different at the opposite sides of the pattern. If the optimum solvent ratio is used, however, the approach to steady state is identical for both components. Thus the product composition on a solvent-free basis is the same as the steady-state composition at all cycles on both sides of the pattern, and only the total quantities of solutes varies with product cycles or time in a continuous multistage extractor operated at optimum conditions.

It should also be noted that all mathematical expressions have been derived for the stochastic process involving a stepwise change and can be applied only approximately to the operation of a continuous column. The solution of the relationships for a differential change in this system has not yet been expressed mathematically; however, the basic relationships lend themselves very readily to solution on an analog computer.

Equipment for Liquid Extraction

In the contacting of two liquid phases, the mass transfer necessary for an approach to the equilibrium conditions assumed in the stagewise calculations takes place at a considerably slower rate than in the contacting of a gas and a liquid phase. Consequently the equipment normally used for distillation and absorption processes is not very effective for liquid extraction. This was noted in the early attempts to adapt the principles of distillation design to extraction column design.

Spray Columns. In a spray column one phase is pumped through a spray nozzle and dispersed into small droplets, which then move through the other phase due to the difference in density. Figure 13 shows a design developed by Elgin (78) to improve the capacity of this type of column by providing an enlarged calming area at each end of the column for coalescing the drops. In the column shown, the light phase is dispersed into small droplets which pass upward through the continuous phase to the expanded section at the top of the column, where they coalesce and are removed from the column as a single phase. The enlarged section at the bottom provides a reduced flow rate and additional residence time to permit any fine droplets of light phase to coalesce and rise through the column, so that the heavy solution can be withdrawn from the column as a homogeneous phase.

In this type of equipment, residence time of the dispersed phase is at a minimum. Uneven distribution of the dispersed phase and nonuniform flow of the continuous phase also make this one of the least effective contacting devices. However, its sim-

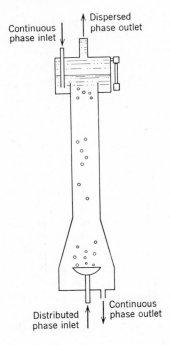

Fig. 13.   Spray column with modified end design.

plicity has made it a useful tool for studying the fundamental mechanism for mass transfer between phases.

Baffle Columns.   To increase the residence time of the dispersed phase in a spray column, segmental baffles have been proposed to provide cross flow, and "disc and doughnut" baffles have been proposed to promote radial flow. Coalescence occurs on the baffles, and redispersing devices have been proposed to increase the area of contact between the phases as the dispersed phase flows off the baffle through the continuous phase.

Packed Columns.   Columns have also been filled with different packings, such as Raschig rings, Berl saddles, intalox saddles, and others, to increase the residence time of the dispersed phase and at the same time to promote mixing of the phases. However, the density difference causing the flow of the dispersed phase through the column is much less than in the case of distillation. Consequently, packing which provides the maximum surface and which is most effective for distillation does not permit any flow of the dispersed phase due to interfacial tension effects. The usable packings are not very effective for distillation.

Plate Columns.   Bubble caps were the first means to improve the efficiency of distillation and absorption columns, but their use in extraction columns has proved impractical.

Perforated tray columns, on the other hand, are the most popular of the nonpowered extractors. In a typical design shown in Figure 14, the light phase is dispersed in the heavy phase. It accumulates under the tray until the pressure difference is sufficient to overcome interfacial tension and pressure drop through the perforations of the tray. Bottom weirs must be sufficient to provide this pressure differential and prevent bypassing of the dispersed phase in the downcomer. Overflow weirs such as required in distillation columns are unnecessary. The light phase is redispersed through every

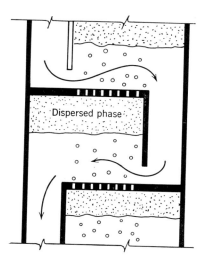

Fig. 14. Perforated tray extractor.

tray, and since data have indicated that a major portion of the transfer in a spray column takes place at the spray nozzle where new surface is created, this perforated tray column is more effective than any of the other previous designs.

If the extractor is to be used to disperse the heavy phase instead of the light phase, the design shown in Figure 14 is inverted.

POWERED EXTRACTORS

In the previous perforated tray column the droplet size is fixed by the fluid properties of viscosity and interfacial tension and within narrow limits by the flow of dispersed phase up to the point where the dispersed phase overflowed the restraining weir of the downcomer. Thus, with a given fluid system, there is very little possibility of improving the contacting efficiency over its normal value, which is generally quite low.

Mixer-Settlers. In the design of liquid extraction processes the concept of the theoretical stage leads logically to the design of individual units for alternately mixing and separating phases. The first commercial application of a fractional liquid extraction process, the Duosol process for the separation of aromatics and paraffins by countercurrent flow of propane and cresylic acid (62), utilized seven separate stages in which the mixing is accomplished by recirculation through an external pump. Guinot (70) patented a similar system in which an inert gas jet is used in place of the pump, as shown in Figure 15.

For small-scale operation, Coplan, Davidson, and Zebroski (13) described a pump-mix mixer-settler (Fig. 16) in which the pump impeller is located in the mixing chamber and circulates heavy phase through light phase by pulling the heavy phase upward from the liquid interface into the eye of the pump. Thus interface level in each stage is automatically controlled, depending upon the speed of the impeller, and countercurrent flow through a battery of consecutive stages is by gravity. A comprehensive survey of the different types of mixer-settlers has been made by Davis, Hicks, and Vermeulen (19).

Internally Agitated Columns. The mixer-settler design and operation described in the previous section is relatively simple because, as long as the settling volume is

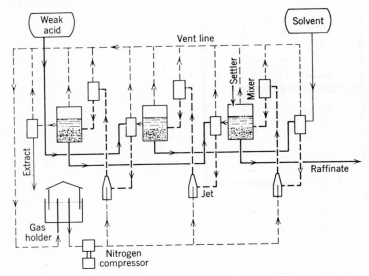

Fig. 15. Multistage mixer-settler utilizing an inert gas jet for mixing.

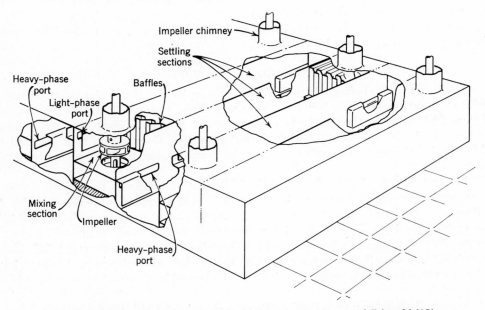

Fig. 16. Pump-mix mixer-settler unit of Coplan, Davidson, and Zebroski (13).

adequate, it is possible to determine the mixer speed which gives a sufficiently close approach to equilibrium so that a theoretical stage can be attained. On the other hand, the multiplicity of equipment makes cost and space requirements excessive for large numbers of stages, and single columns providing any desired number of theoretical stages have been developed.

The first data on the use of internal agitation to promote mixing of the liquid phases were published by Jantzen (31) in 1932. The unit was a small glass laboratory column which gave high efficiency. In 1934 Schöneborn (63) patented a simple agitated extraction column consisting of a series of impellers mounted on a central shaft for pumping the two liquids simultaneously, and stationary intermediate vaned baffles to permit separation of the phases. Weirs on each side of the stationary baffles were so arranged that the heavy phase flowed downward between stages through the central opening while the light phase flowed upward through a series of openings spaced around the circumference of this central opening. Since the impeller was larger than the opening in the stationary baffles, the column was flanged at each baffle to permit assembly of the stages from an end of the column. The following year, Othmer (64) patented a multistage column with internal agitators and cone-shaped dividers with longitudinal fins to permit the dispersed phase to coalesce in the calm section between the wall and the cone and then pass to the next stage through a trap. The base of the cone was also provided with a vertical fin to permit the entrained liquid to settle out of the continuous phase before passing to the next stage through the apex of the cone. One of the obvious aims of the design was to completely eliminate back mixing; this made the internal design considerably more complicated than the present commercial columns of this type, in which back mixing is the biggest thief of efficiency.

Van Dijck (66), in subsequent process patents on liquid extraction, described one of the simplest designs of internally agitated columns, in which the agitators were mounted on a central shaft in compartments separated by perforated plates to permit passage of the phases. In 1948 Scheibel (43,80) presented performance data on a similar design in which the mixing compartments were separated by wire mesh; he noted that, by the use of sufficient thickness, back mixing between the stages could be substantially eliminated. Oldshue and Rushton (39) also described a similar column in which the mixing compartments were separated by doughnut baffles which, because of the back mixing, gave a lower stage efficiency.

In the previous columns agitation was provided by flat, bladed turbine-type agitators in order to minimize any forces which might promote back mixing. In 1952 Reman (82) patented the rotating-disc contactor similar to the Oldshue-Rushton column, except that the agitator was a flat circular disc instead of a turbine.

In all these designs the flow pattern in the mixing stage was such that scale-up required an increase in the spacing between the agitators. Scheibel attempted to restrict the height of the mixing zone but found that a greater height of packing was required between agitators for optimum performance at the larger diameters (44). Reman and also Oldshue and Rushton recommended designs in which the height between stages was proportional to the diameter. As the interest in liquid extraction as a commercial process increased, the need became apparent for a design in which the ratio of stage height to column diameter could be reduced below that acceptable in small-diameter columns. In 1956 Reman (83) patented a column in which horizontal baffles above and below the rotating disc provided a compressed flow pattern from the center of the column to the walls. These baffles were of a diameter less than the inside diameter of the doughnut baffles to the wall of the column, so that the agitator assembly could be withdrawn from the column.

Also in 1956, Scheibel (47,84) published performance data on a similar modification of his original design (Fig. 17) in which the baffles around the agitator were of a larger diameter than the inside diameter of the baffles on the shell. This made it impossible to withdraw the agitator shaft without disassembling, but observation of the flow pattern indicated that the proposed dimensions were necessary to obtain a flow

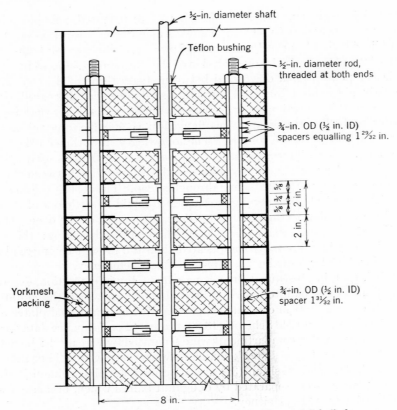

Fig. 17. Modified multistage extraction column of Scheibel.

pattern extending to the wall of the column. This design also proposed a thin layer of wire mesh or screen around the discharge of the impeller and between the inner baffles to promote the formation of small droplets simultaneously with their dispersion in the column.

In all columns in which the internal agitation is obtained by rotation of an impeller there is a tendency for the entire contents of the column to rotate and thus develop centrifugal forces opposing the internal flow pattern desired. In Scheibel's original design (43) this rotation was removed by the return flow through the packing to the center of the column. Oldshue and Rushton provided vertical baffles along the walls of the mixing chambers to remove this rotation (39). Reman's rotating disc column produces the agitation by the viscous drag of the disc on the fluid and consequently depends upon the viscous drag of the walls and baffles on the fluid to restrict the rotation. Scheibel's modified design (47) opposes the rotational force by pumping through the stationary screen around the impellers.

A large number of other internally agitated columns have been proposed without appreciable supporting evidence of their performance. To be practical, all modifications must be considered on the basis of their economics. Complicated designs are justified only if the increase in efficiency is greater than the proportional increase in cost. Obviously a stage design giving half the efficiency but at less than half the cost is more economical. Economics vary with the particular application, as well as with the scale of the application; the present large-scale agitated extraction columns utilize one of the three designs developed by Reman, Oldshue and Rushton, and Scheibel.

Extractors with Mechanical Redistributors.　The major limitation of packed columns when used in distillation is in the channeling of the liquid phase. Efficiencies can be significantly improved by providing redistributors for the liquid periodically over the height of the packing. In liquid extraction channeling is one of two limitations, the other being the droplet size produced by the packing. Although many methods have been proposed to provide redistribution in extraction columns so as to improve the efficiency, practically no data are available to evaluate the effectiveness of the equipment.

In 1937 Robinson (69) proposed various designs of rotating devices which would collect the heavy phase above and the light phase below and permit them to pass through tubes or perforations, so that the channeling of either continuous or dispersed phase would be eliminated. Numerous other devices such as the oscillating grid of Tijmstra (72) and the horizontal shaft propellers of Gallo and Hartvigsen (81) have been proposed to improve the efficiency. In the latter case the spiral action of propellers also increases the length of travel of both phases within the column. In general, mechanical redistributors are characterized by lower speeds than mechanical agitators; in some cases, however, such as the Bottaro design (74), it is difficult to predict the effect of the internal motion. Without data to analyze performance, the increase in efficiency resulting from these innovations cannot be evaluated.

As noted, these columns overcome only one objection of the packed columns and, if any commercial units incorporating these designs are in operation, their advantages have not been publicized.

Pulse Columns.　Agitation also can be induced in an extraction column by means of an external device which imparts a pulsating motion to the contents or by means of a series of reciprocating discs installed in the column. Both these techniques were suggested in 1935 by Van Dijck (66), but interest was not aroused until performance data were reported by Von Berg and Wiegandt in 1952 (59). In a packed column an improvement in efficiency of only about 30% has been indicated; no large-scale commercial columns of this type have been reported.

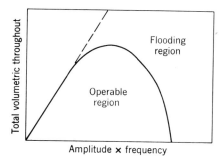

Fig. 18.　Effect of pulse volume on capacity of sieve plate column.

Sieve plate columns have proved more effective when pulsed, and plate efficiencies ranging from 20 to 50% have been reported (5). For best results the perforations in the plates should be so small that there is no flow through them due to gravity alone. The total flow through the column is thus proportional to the frequency and amplitude of the pulsations. This effect of the pulsation is shown in Figure 18. On the upward motion of the contents the light phase is dispersed in the heavy phase above the plate, and on the downward motion the heavy phase is dispersed in the light phase. At low frequencies where substantially none of the dispersed phase is drawn back through the perforations on the reversal of flow, the combined flow of both phases through the column is exactly equal to the volumetric displacement per cycle times the frequency. As the frequency increases, some of the dispersed phase is entrained in the continuous phase as it flows in the opposite direction, and the capacity decreases to the point where there is total back mixing and no net flow through the column.

For maximum capacity the amplitude should be large and the frequency small, but for maximum efficiency the amplitude should be small and the frequency large. Thus this extraction column requires the same compromise of efficiency and capacity necessary in all agitated extraction columns, and each application has an optimum frequency and amplitude, depending upon the same factors of solvent ratio and the density, viscosity, and interfacial tension of the solvent.

In small laboratory sieve plate extractors, plate spacing of 1 in. and hole diameters of about 0.1 in. are used. Larger columns are fabricated with twice this spacing and with larger hole sizes up to $\frac{1}{4}$ in. It can be recognized that there is no transverse mixing induced in this design, and serious channeling can result in columns of 2 ft or more in diameter. To overcome this effect, redistribution plates with louvred openings and vertical baffles to control the transverse mixing have been proposed (61), to be installed every 3–4 ft in the larger-diameter columns.

The converse method of promoting mixing by pulsing a perforated tray through the contents of the column has been studied by Karr (32), who reported HETS values of 5–10 in. in a 3-in. diameter column. The original concept of Van Dijck was based on small holes and thus required a good seal between the column wall and the moving disc. Karr overcame this problem by using large holes and a total open area of more than 50% so that when the optimum amplitude and frequency were determined for this design, the adverse effect of leakage along the wall would be virtually eliminated. Also at optimum conditions, the large amount of transverse motion imparted to the column contents eliminated the redistributing baffles needed in the previous type of pulse column.

Another extraction column utilizing a pulsating perforated disc for agitation was described by Fenske and Long (21,22). All discs were mounted on a vertical shaft and phase separation occurred in separate areas of the column from which the light phase flowed to the stage above and the heavy phase flowed to the stage below. To prevent bypassing, the reciprocating shaft was sealed between mixing stages; at the proper agitator speed and throughput, it was possible to obtain 100% stage efficiency in this column. This design has been used primarily for laboratory and pilot-plant studies.

Centrifugal Extractors. All extractors previously described effected the separation of the phases by gravity settling. Mechanically agitated columns must be operated at a speed below that producing an emulsion of fine droplets, which will not separate readily by gravity. With some solvent systems this requirement severely limits the maximum efficiency attainable.

In 1935, Podbielniak (65) obtained his first patent on an extractor utilizing centrifugal force up to 5000 gravities for the countercurrent flow of two liquid phases through a spiral passageway. Commercial development of this extractor received its impetus in the extraction of penicillin from the fermentation broth. The solvent used to extract the penicillin emulsified readily, due to the suspended solids in the broth; in addition the penicillin was unstable in the acidified broth from which it was extracted.

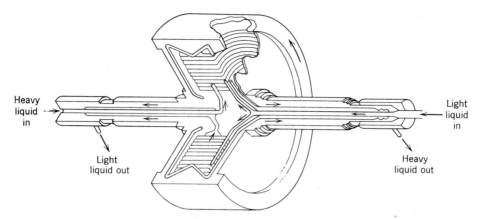

Fig. 19. Podbielniak centrifugal extractor.

The centrifugal extractor solved both problems because the high gravities attainable broke the emulsions and permitted rapid countercurrent flow so that residence times of the penicillin in the acidified broth were at a minimum. There is no doubt that the Podbielniak extractor greatly accelerated the commercial development of penicillin, which otherwise might have been forced to await development of some other suitable extractor.

Figure 19 shows a cut-away picture of the rotor of a Podbielniak extractor. The light solvent enters through the one end of the shaft and moves through a passageway to the outside of the rotor. The heavy phase enters the other end of the shaft to the rotor, where centrifugal force forces it outward against the light phase, which is displaced inward around the spiral path. Performance data indicated that placing louvres in the wall of the spiral, to permit both the light and heavy phases to bypass one turn of the spiral and be dispersed in the other, provided more transfer than obtained across the fixed interface in the spiral. Louvre locations are staggered to prevent complete bypassing of the phases through the rotor. A subsequent design without the staggered louvres has been developed to handle solutions carrying suspended solids, and the efficiency of mass transfer between the stages has been significantly reduced. Thus the same sort of compromise must be made with the centrifugal extractor as with the mechanically agitated units, but in the area of much more difficult extraction problems.

Mass Transfer in Liquid Extraction

The process design of a liquid extraction operation discussed in the previous sections is based on the concept of a theoretical stage in which the concentrations of the solute in the two phases reach equilibrium. Theoretically, perfect equilibrium requires infinite time, and in a continuous flow system this concept serves merely as a reference base for relating different systems. Thus the "height equivalent to a theoretical stage" (HETS) is a useful tool for relating the experimental performance data on a type of packing to the requirements of the designed system. Tray efficiency, or stage efficiency, is also a means of relating the performance of perforated tray columns or multistage extractors to the design requirements.

Considering equilibrium as a limiting condition at which no transfer takes place, the deviation of the two phases from equilibrium can be taken as the driving force for mass transfer. Thus a mass-transfer coefficient between phases may be defined as either

$$dN_A/d\theta = K_d a(C_d - C_d{}^*) \tag{30}$$

or

$$dN_A/d\theta = K_c a(C_c{}^* - C_c) \tag{31}$$

where the transfer is positive in the direction of decreasing concentration and the left-hand term is in lb-mole/(hr)(ft³ of column volume). K_d is the mass-transfer coefficient for the dispersed phase and K_c is the mass transfer, both expressed in lb-mole/(hr)(ft² surface)(lb-mole/ft³ driving force in the respective phase); a is the surface per unit volume; C_d and C_c are the concentrations of the solute in the dispersed and continuous phases, respectively; and $C_d{}^*$ and $C_c{}^*$ are the concentrations in the dispersed and continuous phases, respectively, in equilibrium with the other phase. All concentrations are expressed as lb-mole/ft³.

The overall coefficients are related by the ratio of the equilibrium constants and are not independent, so a design based on either one must give the same result. They represent the transfer from the point of average concentration of one phase to the point of average concentration of the other phase and, in order to relate the coefficients obtained under one set of circumstances to those obtained under different conditions, it is necessary to analyze the transfer in more detail. Several models have been proposed but none has proved entirely satisfactory.

The first model was the two-film theory proposed by Whitman (60) in 1923 and subsequently applied to all transfer between two different phases. This theory assumes the bulk of the phase thoroughly mixed and solute transfer through a stagnant film to the interface so that Fick's first law of diffusion applies. The theory then assumes no resistance to transfer at the interface, so that the liquid on one side is in equilibrium with the liquid on the other side of the interface. Solute transfer from the interface to the bulk of the second phase is also through a stagnant film similar to the first phase.

Under these conditions the solute transfer can be related to the individual film resistance so that

$$dN/d\theta = k_d a(C_d - C_{di}) = k_c a(C_{ci} - C_c) \tag{32}$$

where the terms have the same significance as in the previous equations, the lowercase k refers to the individual film resistance, and the subscript i refers to the respective concentrations at the interface. If the ratio of the equilibrium concentrations over the range of C_d to C_c is constant or can be represented by some average value m such that $C_d = mC_c$ at equilibrium, it can be shown that

$$K_d a = \frac{1}{(1/k_d a) + (1/mk_c a)} \tag{33}$$

or

$$K_c a = \frac{1}{(m/k_d a) + (1/k_c a)} \tag{34}$$

The first extension of this theory was the assumption that the individual film coefficients are functions only of the flow rates of the particular phase and are independent of the flow rates of the other phase. This theory was rather quickly disproved, but a subsequent theory which reduces to the same form as that discussed next is still used. The greatest weakness in the two-film theory was exposed when it was used to interrelate the transfer data on different solutes. It is apparent that if the concept of a stationary film applies, the transfer coefficients for different solutes in each film must be proportional to the diffusivity of the solutes in the respective phases. Performance data indicate a variation proportional to less than the $\frac{1}{2}$ power of the diffusivity.

Chilton and Colburn (7) proposed the concept of a "transfer unit" to replace the theoretical stage, in which the driving force is integrated over the range of concentrations exactly as it would be expected to vary in a packed column if the phase concentrations were perfectly mixed and averaged at every differential height in the column, and if there were no concentration gradients within a phase at right angles to the flow rates. Thus the concentration in each phase at any point in the column can be calculated from the material balance at that point.

The definition of the overall transfer unit is

$$(NTU)_{\text{OL}} = \frac{Z}{(HTU)_{\text{OL}}} = \int_{y_2}^{y_1} \frac{dy(1-y)_{\text{M}}}{(y-y^*)(1-y)} \tag{35}$$

and

$$(NTU)_{\text{OH}} = \frac{Z}{(HTU)_{\text{OH}}} = \int_{x_2}^{x_1} \frac{dx(1-x)_{\text{M}}}{(x^*-x)(1-x)} \tag{36}$$

where $(NTU)_{\text{O}}$ represents the number of overall transfer units and $(HTU)_{\text{O}}$ represents the height of an overall transfer unit and Z is the height of the column. Subscripts L and H refer to the light and heavy phases, respectively, and the subscript M refers to the log mean value between the solvent concentration of the one phase and the solvent concentration at the solute concentration in equilibrium with the other phase. Concentrations y and x have the same significance as above and refer to the light and heavy phases, respectively. The value of the integral is dimensionless and thus independent of the units of concentration in the particular phase; however, they are different for the two phases and can be shown to be related in such a way that

$$(NTU)_{\text{OH}} = (LD/H)(NTU)_{\text{OL}} \tag{37}$$

or

$$(HTU)_{\text{OL}} = (LD/H)(HTU)_{\text{OH}} \tag{38}$$

where D has the same significance as above and is equal to y^*/x.

Applying the definition of transfer units to the two-film theory, the individual HTU for each film can be combined to give the overall HTU as follows:

$$(HTU)_{\text{OL}} = (HTU)_{\text{L}} + (LD/H)(HTU)_{\text{H}} \tag{39}$$

or

$$(HTU)_{\text{OH}} = (HTU)_{\text{H}} + (H/LD)(HTU)_{\text{L}} \tag{40}$$

If the individual HTU values are constant for any system independent of the flow rates of either phase, a straight line is obtained if $(HTU)_{\text{L}}$ is plotted against LD/H or $(HTU)_{\text{OH}}$ is plotted against H/LD. Individual film HTU values are determined from the slope and intercept of the curve. This correlation technique is used in spite of the fact that it frequently gives negative values for one of the individual values of

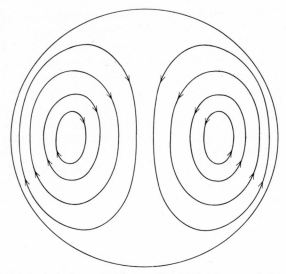

Fig. 20. Internal circulation in falling droplet as derived by Hadamard (55). Courtesy McGraw-Hill Book Co., Inc.

HTU. Reference to the mass-transfer coefficient relationships previously derived show that not only must the individual transfer coefficient be independent of the flow rate of the other phase, but it must also be proportional to the first power of the flow rate of the particular phase. Consequently equations 39 and 40 have less flexibility in correlating data than does the original two-film theory of Whitman.

A third concept for correlating mass-transfer data is the surface renewal theory originally proposed by Higbie in 1935 (28) and subsequently developed by Dankwerts (18). In unsteady-state diffusion into a stagnant medium, with a constant concentration as one boundary condition and an infinite sink on the other side, the amount of mass transfer can be shown to be proportional to the square root of the diffusivity. This concept can be applied, as shown in Figure 20, to the transfer into a droplet if the internal circulation induced by the movement through the continuous phase is as indicated. Thus, if the diffusion is so slow that no solute penetrates the moving film during its period of contact with the other phase, and it enters this period with zero solute concentration,

$$k_D = 2\sqrt{D/\pi t} \tag{41}$$

where t is the life of the film.

By analogy, if the transfer to any liquid phase occurs by eddy diffusion so that at any unit time a fraction s of the surface is renewed by fresh solvent from the interior of the phase, it follows that

$$k_D = \sqrt{Ds} \tag{42}$$

This is the basis for the surface renewal theory, and the concept of individual eddy currents over the entire surface can be applied to a liquid phase of any size and shape.

Hadamard (25,26) considered the internal circulation within a droplet and deduced the internal circulation shown in Figure 20; however, in order to simplify the mathematical model, Handlos and Baron (27) postulated the toroidal flow shown in Figure

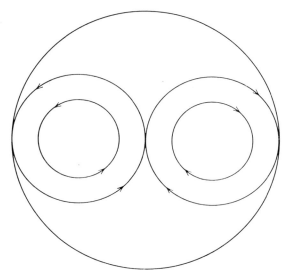

Fig. 21. Internal recirculation assumed by Handlos and Baron.
Courtesy American Institute of Chemical Engineers.

21 and developed the theoretical relationships for mass transfer when the resistance of the continuous phase is negligible, so that the concentration in this phase at the surface of the droplet·is constant.

Based on the modification of the Reynolds analogy similar to that employed in heat transfer, Colburn (9) derived an equation for mass transfer in gases, which was further modified by Chilton and Colburn (6) to provide a better correlation of mass-transfer data. They defined analogous functions for heat and mass transfer, j_H and j_D, respectively, as follows:

$$j_H = (h/C_p \rho U_{AV}) (C_p \mu/k)^{2/3} \tag{43}$$

$$j_D = (k_G\ p_{BM}/G_M) (N/\rho D_G)^{2/3} \tag{44}$$

and found that both functions were approximately equal to one half the Reynolds friction factor. Subsequent studies (24) showed that better agreement was obtained if $j_H = 1.08\ j_D$. This analogy was derived for gas phases and involves only the properties of the gas phase. Heat-transfer studies have indicated the application to liquid phases, and consequently, attempts have been made to apply the corresponding function to mass transfer in liquid phases. If this analogy could be proved applicable in all cases, it would make the large amount of theory and semiempirical correlations of heat-transfer data useful for correlating a relatively small amount of mass-transfer data and for predicting the performance of all other systems of mass transfer. However, mass transfer depends upon the movement of a particular species of molecule from a position in one phase to a location in another phase, whereas the transfer of heat is accomplished mainly by transfer of energy from one molecule to another, rather than by the diffusion of a high-energy molecule. Mass transfer requires a concentration gradient, and the variation of fluid properties with concentration could be either positive or negative, whereas in heat transfer the effect of the temperature gradient on fluid properties is always in the same direction. Thus mass transfer is a much more

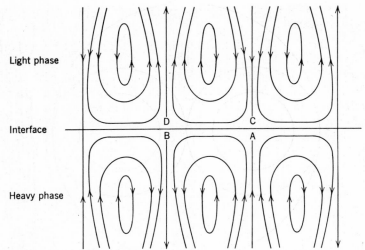

Fig. 22. Schematic diagram of two dimensional roll waves. Courtesy American Institute of Chemical Engineers.

complicated mechanism and cannot be expected to follow the analogy to heat transfer in all instances.

Sternling and Scriven (52) showed that if the surface tension increases with concentration in one phase and the transfer is into this phase, a "roll wave" could be established in this phase, whereas when the transfer is in the opposite direction no such effect is possible. This can be seen by Figure 22, where due to mass transfer, the concentration at B is greater than at A. Thus the surface tension is greater at B and this difference promotes the circulation as indicated. If the variation of surface tension with concentration is the opposite in the other phase, the same circulation pattern is induced in this phase since the concentration at D is less than at C and surface tension at D is greater. Under these conditions a stable roll wave is developed, which will greatly improve the mass transfer between phases. The basic mechanism producing these roll waves was first observed for a gas–liquid interface and has been called the Marangoni effect.

Sternling and Scriven (52) developed the mathematical relationships for two-dimensional roll waves and Orell and Westwater (40) obtained schlieren photographs of the three-dimensional roll waves shown in Figure 23.

Mass transfer in the presence of the violent interfacial turbulence of these waves is considerably greater than when they are absent. Thus it is apparent that the factors producing mass transfer are entirely different from those producing heat transfer, and the analogy proposed by Chilton and Colburn (6) must be applied very cautiously to generalized design.

At the present time no sound mathematical model is available for correlating or predicting the performance of liquid extraction equipment. All correlations proposed are empirical and therefore uncertain when extrapolated beyond the range of the original data. It should be significant that better correlation of mass transfer has been achieved in the gas phase than in the liquid phase. One reason for this failure may be traced to the use of concentration as the driving force for mass transfer in the liquid phase. The true driving force for diffusion is the activity of the solute. In gases of

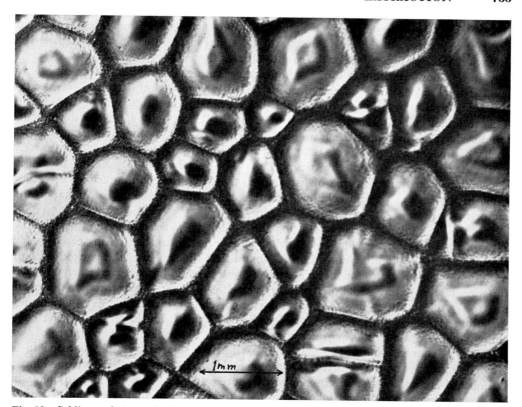

Fig. 23. Schlieren photograph of stationary cells formed by transfer of acetic acid from glycol into ethyl acetate. Courtesy American Institute of Chemical Engineers.

relatively low pressures up to a few atmospheres the activity coefficients for the components are close to unity and the activity is thus accurately expressed as concentration. In liquids, on the other hand, activity coefficients can in some cases be greater than ten without exhibiting immiscibility. Although concentration is a proper criterion for driving force only in ideal systems, it has been used in practically all calculations of mass-transfer coefficients, and the activity coefficient is normally not included in the general correlations.

In 1954 Karr and Scheibel (34), studying the mass transfer between two liquid phases in an agitated chamber at continuous flow conditions, obtained a general correlation of their data when mass-transfer coefficients were calculated using activity as the driving force in systems where the activity coefficients varied more than tenfold. This method has not been extended to other mass-transfer data in liquid systems. It may not apply when appreciable turbulence at the interface results from the transient physical properties and heat effects of the transfer mechanism, but it holds better promise for a general correlation when these effects are minimal.

Capacity of Liquid Extraction Equipment

It is apparent from the previous section that in the transfer of a solute from one liquid phase to another in continuous countercurrent flow there is no sound basis for prediction of the time of contact or height of column required for a given amount of transfer or number of equilibrium stages. Of equal importance in the design is the cross-sectional area required for the countercurrent flow of the two fluids.

In the countercurrent flow of two liquid phases under the influence of gravity there is a terminal velocity for the rate of rise or fall of the droplets of dispersed phase relative to the continuous phase, which establishes the maximum throughput of the column. This terminal velocity, according to Stokes' law, is dependent upon the droplet diameter, density difference of the two phases, density of the continuous phase, and viscosity of the continuous phase. Droplet size is a function of interfacial tension as well as the density difference of the two phases. The relative velocity of the phases is dependent upon the open area of the column available for countercurrent flow, and thus, in the case of packed columns, the free space of the packing is an important factor.

Since the controlling factor limiting the capacity of a column is the relative flow rates of the phase, increasing the flow of one phase decreases the limiting capacity for the other phase. Blanding and Elgin (4) found that the capacity of a packed column at different solvent ratios for the same solvent system could be expressed as an additive function of the square roots of the linear velocities of each phase through the open area. Crawford and Wilke (17) developed a correlation based on this function and including the density difference, interfacial area, density and viscosity of the continuous phases, and ratio of surface to free space in the packing. The square of the sum of the square roots of the velocities of the two phases was incorporated in a Reynolds number as the velocity. Other general correlations usually developed have been based upon the flow measurements with pure solvents. Treybal, in applying four such correlations to an industrial problem (54), found that predicted capacities varied more than twofold, although each was claimed to correlate its own data within 10–15%.

Solute concentration gradients between the phases can affect the capacity of the extraction column much the same as they affect mass transfer. Also, trace quantities of surface-active agents can affect the interfacial tension and significantly alter the limiting capacity of liquid extraction equipment. This is a common problem in industrial applications where solvents are recycled. Extreme caution should be exercised in applying any general correlation obtained on fresh solvents under laboratory conditions to commercial practice. Pilot-plant data are preferred and the problems are thus reduced to those concerned with the scale-up to different sizes. In some cases, even these problems are appreciable.

In perforated tray extraction columns it is possible to exercise some control over the droplet size by changing the sizes of the holes. Within reasonable limits, larger holes produce larger drops and increase capacity, but at the same time the amount of mass transfer decreases, so the final design generally represents a compromise of the two effects.

If the liquid to be dispersed flows through the perforation at a sufficiently low velocity that its kinetic energy is negligible, the droplet size can be calculated exactly from the interfacial tension, the diameter of the hole, and the density difference of the phases; droplet volume would be found to be proportional to the diameter of the perforation. Hayworth and Treybal (30) developed an empirical relationship which takes into account the kinetic energy of the phase entering the droplet as it forms and permits calculation of the droplet diameter. They also presented a graph for the solution of their relationship from which the droplet diameter can be read directly when the other functions have been calculated.

The Hayworth-Treybal correlation was originally proposed for orifice velocities up to 0.33 ft/sec and in one instance was found to apply up to 1 ft/sec. This latter velocity is generally within the range encountered in perforated tray columns, but peak velocities in pulse columns usually exceed this value. Christiansen and Hixon (8) correlated fluid properties, with the nozzle velocity giving maximum droplet surface; presumably this correlation would be more applicable for pulse column design.

In agitated extraction columns the droplet size can be regulated by the degree of agitation, and in this case also, the final operating conditions for a commercial installation represent a compromise of capacity and efficiency to provide the optimum results. At a constant agitator speed, as indicated in Figure 24, the efficiency increases at higher throughputs due to the greater holdup of dispersed phase until the maximum capacity is approached; then just before flooding, the efficiency decreases because excessive entrainment results in considerable back mixing between stages. The similar effect is noted as the agitator speed is increased at a constant throughput, as shown in Figure 25. Also, the capacity decreases with increasing agitator speed, and conversely, at lower capacities a higher agitator speed is possible and is usually required for maximum efficiency.

These columns are far more sensitive to traces of surface-active agents or other foreign materials which accumulate at the interface during extraction. The high degree of agitation and the back mixing tend to perpetuate their retention in the column and thus promote emulsion formation. This can be avoided only by a reduction of agitator speed, which decreases dispersed phase holdup but at the same time reduces the efficiency below that theoretically possible with uncontaminated solutions.

If the foreign material is preferentially wetted by one of the liquid phases the problem can be minimized by controlling the interface at the proper end of the column. Thus, if the solid is preferentially wet by the light solvent, the interface should be maintained at the top of the column; if it is wet by the heavy solvent, the interface should be maintained at the bottom. Since the agitated extractors give maximum capacity

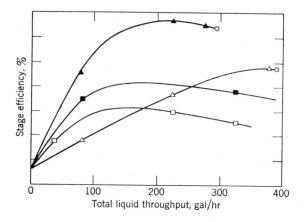

Fig. 24. Effect of throughput on stage efficiency of agitated extraction column at constant agitator speed (300 rpm) in the acetone–xylene–water system (49). Water extractant, □; xylene extractant, △; open points, 9-in. packing; solid points, 13½-in. packing; approximate flooding conditions, O.

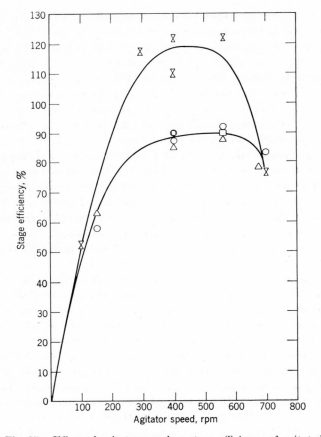

Fig. 25. Effect of agitator speed on stage efficiency of agitated extraction column at constant throughput (240 gal/hr) in the acetic acid–isobutyl methyl ketone–water system (49). Water extractant, water dispersed, □; ketone extractant, water dispersed, △; water extractant, ketone dispersed, ○; ketone extractant, ketone dispersed, X.

when the smaller volume is dispersed, this technique of operation could also seriously reduce column capacity if it requires dispersion of a large flow rate in a phase flowing at a small flow rate.

Centrifugal extractors are also subject to the problems of solids precipitation at the interface, but in this case, the large centrifugal force makes it possible to overcome the surface tension effects; the separation of the solids through the phases is based on density alone, with the result that they deposit on one of the walls of the internal passage and ultimately plug the unit. This has been mentioned previously in the discussion of penicillin extraction.

Liquid Extraction Processes

The petroleum industry employs the largest liquid extraction columns. To produce a high-grade lubricating oil from the crude petroleum fraction, it is necessary to extract the saturated paraffins in a dewaxing operation. Solvent dewaxing can provide the maximum yield of final product. It is also necessary to remove the aromatic, asphaltic, and resinous compounds by a deasphalting operation. Practically every known solvent has been considered for these processes, but those in commercial use are phenol, furfural, propane, nitrobenzene, sulfur dioxide diluted with a small amount of benzene, and a two-solvent (Duosol) process using propane and a mixture of cresylic acids. Similarly, practically every known solvent has been considered for the upgrading of gasoline by separating the aromatics from the low-octane paraffins. The use of sulfur dioxide by the Edeleanu process is the oldest, and many plants using this process are still in operation. However, this refining operation is now, for the most part, carried out with diethylene glycol by the Udex process.

Sulfur compounds, present to some degree in all crude oil, are corrosive, impart an objectionable odor, and in the case of gasoline fraction, reduce the response of the octane rating to the addition of tetraethyllead. Sodium hydroxide solutions in water or water–methanol mixtures are frequently used to extract the sulfur compounds. Potassium hydroxide in water mixed with organic potassium salts are also used. In the manufacture of plastics large extraction columns are also used to recover valuable products from waste streams or to purify recycle solvents. In coke plants, also, columns are used to reduce the phenol content of discarded waste streams to a few parts per million or less, thereby minimizing river pollution. In these same plants aromatic compounds are purified by the Udex process previously mentioned.

Countless other extraction processes employing columns less than 4 ft in diameter are in use in the refining of vegetable oils and fats, in the manufacture of pharmaceuticals and fine chemicals, and in practically every synthetic organic process. Applications in the inorganic field are less extensive, but are sufficiently important to be mentioned. Several different processes have been developed to reprocess spent fuel from the nuclear reactors. All of these depend upon dissolving in an organic solvent some organic compound which will form a complex with one or more of the metal ions and thus alter the distribution coefficients relative to the other metals. Similar fractional liquid extraction separations of metal salts have made the pure metals available at a sufficiently low price to permit their use as a material of construction for corrosion-resistant equipment. The tantalum–niobium and the zirconium–hafnium mixtures are typical, and there are many other potential applications in this field.

Bibliography

"Liquid–Liquid Extraction" under "Extraction" in *ECT* 1st ed., Vol. 6, pp. 122–140, by E. G. Scheibel and A. J. Frey, Hoffmann-La Roche, Inc.; "Extraction, Liquid–Liquid," in *ECT* 1st ed., Suppl. 1, pp. 330–365, by Marcel J. P. Bogart, the Lummus Company.

1. L. Alders, *Liquid–Liquid Extraction*, 2nd ed., Elsevier Publishing Co., New York, 1958.
2. G. F. Asselin and E. W. Comings, *Ind. Eng. Chem.* **42**, 1198 (1950).
3. C. R. Bartels and G. Kleiman, *Chem. Eng. Progr.* **45**, 589 (1949).
4. F. H. Blanding and J. C. Elgin, *Trans. Am. Inst. Chem. Engrs.* **38**, 305 (1942).
5. W. A. Chantry, R. L. Von Berg, and H. F. Wiegandt, *Ind. Eng. Chem.* **47**, 1153 (1955).
6. T. H. Chilton and A. P. Colburn, *Ind. Eng. Chem.* **26**, 1183 (1934).
7. T. H. Chilton and A. P. Colburn, *Ind. Eng. Chem.* **27**, 255 (1935).
8. R. M. Christiansen and A. N. Hixon, *Ind. Eng. Chem.* **49**, 1017 (1957).
9. A. P. Colburn, *Ind. Eng. Chem.* **22**, 967 (1930).
10. E. L. Compere and A. Ryland, *Ind. Eng. Chem.* **43**, 239 (1951).
11. E. L. Compere and A. Ryland, *Ind. Eng. Chem.* **46**, 24 (1954).
12. E. L. Compere, private communication.
13. B. V. Coplan, J. K. Davidson, and E. L. Zebroski, *Chem. Eng. Progr.* **50**, 403 (1954).
14. L. C. Craig, *J. Biol. Chem.* **155**, 519 (1944).

15. L. C. Craig and D. Craig, "Extraction and Distribution" in A. Weissberger, ed., *Technique of Organic Chemistry*, Vol. 3, Part 1, 2nd ed., Interscience Publishers, Inc., 1956, pp. 149–332.
16. L. C. Craig and O. Post, *Anal. Chem.* **21**, 500 (1949).
17. J. W. Crawford and C. R. Wilke, *Chem. Eng. Progr.* **47**, 423 (1951).
18. P. V. Danckwerts, *Ind. Eng. Chem.* **43**, 1460 (1951).
19. M. W. Davis, Jr., T. E. Hicks, and T. Vermeulen, *Chem. Eng. Progr.* **50**, 188 (1954).
20. W. Feller, *Introduction to Probability Theory and Its Application*, Vol. 1, John Wiley & Sons, Inc., New York, 1950.
21. M. R. Fenske and R. B. Long, *Chem. Eng. Progr.* **51**, 194 (1955).
22. M. R. Fenske and R. B. Long, *Ind. Eng. Chem.* **53**, 791 (1961).
23. M. Frenc, *Z. angew. Chem.* **38**, 323 (1925).
24. B. W. Gamson, G. Thodos, and O. A. Hougen, *Trans. Am. Inst. Chem. Engrs.* **39**, 1 (1943).
25. J. S. Hadamard, *Compt. Rend.* **152**, 1735 (1911).
26. J. S. Hadamard, *Compt. Rend.* **154**, 109 (1912).
27. A. E. Handlos and T. Baron, *A.I.Ch.E. J.* **3**, 127 (1957).
28. R. Higbie, *Trans. Am. Inst. Chem. Engrs.* **31**, 365 (1935).
29. T. G. Hunter and A. W. Nash, *J. Soc. Chem. Ind. (London)* **53**, 95T (1932).
30. C. B. Hayworth and R. E. Treybal, *Ind. Eng. Chem.* **42**, 1174 (1950).
31. E. Jantzen, *Dechema Monograph.* **5** (48), 81 (1932).
32. A. E. Karr, *A.I.Ch.E. J.* **5**, 446 (1959).
33. A. E. Karr and E. G. Scheibel, *Ind. Eng. Chem.* **46**, 1583 (1954).
34. A. E. Karr and E. G. Scheibel, *Chem. Eng. Progr. Symp. Ser.* **50** (10), 73 (1954).
35. A. Klinkenberg, *Ind. Eng. Chem.* **45**, 653 (1953).
36. A. Klinkenberg, N. A. Lauwerier, and G. H. Reman, *Chem. Eng. Sci.* **1**, 93 (1951).
37. J. O. Maloney and A. E. Schubert, *Trans. Am. Inst. Chem. Engrs.* **36**, 741 (1940).
38. A. J. P. Martin and R. L. M. Synge, *Biochem. J.* **35**, 91 (1941).
39. J. Y. Oldshue and J. H. Rushton, *Chem. Eng. Progr.* **48**, 297 (1952).
40. A. Orell and J. W. Westwater, *A.I.Ch.E. J.* **8**, 350 (1962).
41. D. F. Peppard and M. A. Peppard, *Ind. Eng. Chem.* **46**, 34 (1954).
42. G. J. Pierotti, C. H. Deal, and E. L. Derr, *Ind. Eng. Chem.* **51**, 95 (1959).
43. E. G. Scheibel, *Chem. Eng. Progr.* **44**, 681–690, 771–782 (1948).
44. E. G. Scheibel, *Ind. Eng. Chem.* **43**, 242 (1951).
45. E. G. Scheibel, *Ind. Eng. Chem.* **46**, 16 (1954).
46. E. G. Scheibel, *Ind. Eng. Chem.* **46**, 43 (1954).
47. E. G. Scheibel, *A.I.Ch.E. J.* **2**, 74 (1956).
48. E. G. Scheibel, *Petrol. Refiner* **38** (9), 227 (1959).
49. E. G. Scheibel and A. E. Karr, *Ind. Eng. Chem.* **42**, 1048 (1950).
50. T. K. Sherwood and R. L. Pigford, *Absorption and Extraction*, McGraw-Hill Book Co., Inc., New York, 1952.
51. S. Stene, *Arkiv Kemi, Mineral., Geol.* **18H** (18) (1944).
52. C. V. Sternling and L. E. Scriven, *A.I.Ch.E. J.* **5**, 514 (1959).
53. E. W. Thiele and R. L. Geddes, *Ind. Eng. Chem.* **24**, 289 (1933).
54. R. E. Treybal, *Ind. Eng. Chem.* **47**, 536 (1955).
55. R. E. Treybal, *Liquid Extraction*, 2nd ed., McGraw-Hill Book Co., Inc., New York, 1963.
56. A. J. V. Underwood, *Ind. Chemist* **10**, 128 (1934).
57. K. A. Varteressian and M. R. Fenske, *Ind. Eng. Chem.* **28**, 928 (1936).
58. K. A. Varteressian and M. R. Fenske, *Ind. Eng. Chem.* **29**, 270 (1937).
59. R. L. Von Berg and H. F. Wiegandt, *Chem. Eng.* **59** (6), 189 (1952).
60. W. G. Whitman, *Chem. & Met. Eng.* **29**, 147 (1923).
61. F. W. Woodfield and G. Sege, *Chem. Eng. Progr. Symp. Ser.* **13**, 14 (1954).
62. U.S. Pat. 1,912,349 (May 30, 1933), M. H. Tuttle (to Max B. Miller & Co.); Reissue 19,763 (Nov. 19, 1935).
63. U.S. Pat. 1,949,496 (March 6, 1934), H. Schöneborn (to Koppers Co.).
64. U.S. Pat. 2,000,606 (May 7, 1935), D. F. Othmer (to Eastman Kodak Co.).
65. U.S. Pat. 2,003,308 (June 4, 1935), W. J. Podbielniak.
66. U.S. Pat. 2,011,186 (Aug. 13, 1935), W. J. D. Van Dijck (to Shell Development Co.).
67. U.S. Pat. 2,023,109 (Dec. 3, 1935), W. J. D. Van Dijck (to Shell Development Co.).

68. U.S. Pat. 2,041,308 (May 19, 1936), M. H. Tuttle (to Max B. Miller & Co.).

69. U.S. Pat. 2,072,382 (March 2, 1937), J. Robinson (to Standard Oil Co., Indiana).

70. U.S. Pat. 2,076,126 (April 6, 1937), H. M. Guinot.

71. U.S. Pat. 2,081,719 (May 25, 1937), W. J. D. Van Dijck (to Shell Development Co.).

72. U.S. Pat. 2,106,366 (Jan. 25, 1938), S. Tijmstra (to Shell Development Co.).

73. U.S. Pat. 2,201,549 (May 21, 1940), W. J. D. Van Dijck (to Shell Development Co.).

74. U.S. Pat. 2,218,080 (Oct. 15, 1940), G. Bottaro.

75. U.S. Pat. 2,245,945 (June 17, 1941), W. J. D. Van Dijck and A. Schaafsma (to Shell Development Co.).

76. U.S. Pat. 2,269,163 (Jan. 6, 1942), D. F. Othmer (to Tennessee Eastman Co.).

77. U.S. Pat. 2,275,862 (March 10, 1942), D. F. Othmer (to Tennessee Eastman Co.).

78. U.S. Pat. 2,364,892 (Dec. 12, 1944), J. C. Elgin (to Research Corp.).

79. U.S. Pat. 2,395,010 (Feb. 19, 1946), D. F. Othmer.

80. U.S. Pat. 2,493,265 (Jan. 3, 1950), E. G. Scheibel (to Hoffmann LaRoche, Inc.).

81. U.S. Pat. 2,562,783 (July 31, 1951), S. G. Gallo and H. V. Hartvigsen (to Standard Oil Development Co.).

82. U.S. Pat. 2,601,674 (June 24, 1952), G. H. Reman (to Shell Development Co.).

83. U.S. Pat. 2,729,545 (Jan. 3, 1956), G. H. Reman (to Shell Development Co.).

84. U.S. Pat. 2,850,362 (Sept. 2, 1958), E. G. Scheibel (to Hoffmann LaRoche, Inc.).

E. G. SCHEIBEL
Cooper Union School of
Engineering and Science

LIQUID–SOLID EXTRACTION

The extraction of a solid with a liquid ranks with evaporation as one of the oldest separation techniques. Most of the modern pharmaceutical, cosmetic, perfume, flavoring, and food industries had their origin in a liquid–solid extraction process to concentrate naturally occurring compounds into more potent mixtures. The same operation is often essential in the winning of metals from their ores, and increased efficiency is one of the keys to the economic utilization of low-grade ores, now that most of the known high-grade ore deposits have been worked out.

Because of the origin of this process in many fields it is known by numerous names, such as leaching, washing, decantation, percolation, elution, digestion, steeping, elutriation, lixiviation, diffusion, decoction, maceration, dissolution, and infusion. Before the advent of liquid–liquid extraction as a separation process, the term solvent extraction referred only to extraction of a solid, and this is still the implied meaning in some industries. However, with the development of liquid–liquid extraction on a large scale under the same title, a less ambiguous name is desirable.

Rickles (13) has attempted to divide the field into categories depending upon the pretreatment of the solid and upon whether chemical reaction is involved in the extraction. Actually the mechanism for dissolving an extractable solid is essentially the same, whether or not chemical reaction takes place, because both depend upon a second component reaching the solid, and this component may be a solvent or a reactant dissolved in the solvent. The term *leaching* has been proposed at times for one or all of these mechanisms.

On the other hand, if the extractable material is a liquid or a material dissolved in a liquid adhering to the inert solid, diffusion outward from the solid can occur without the solvent first penetrating the inert solid or matrix. *Washing* is the conventional term for this case, and although *leaching* has occasionally also been applied, it is suggested here that, because of this similarity of mechanism, "washing" includes

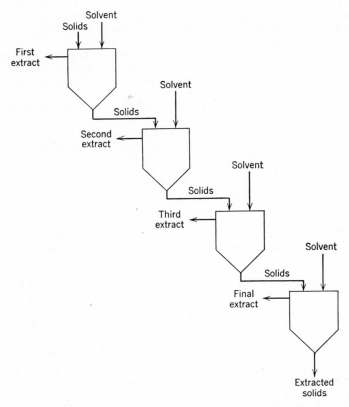

Fig. 1. Extraction of a solid with multiple portions of fresh solvent.

all extractions of liquid solutes. *Elution* of an adsorbed material from an adsorbent is a process intermediate between these two, and if it is recognized as a surface phenomenon and liquid is assumed to reach all parts of the adsorbent as soon as it is wet, diffusion away from the solid could start immediately; thus this particular process would fall in the category of washing.

It is significant that advances in liquid–solid extraction preceded similar developments in other areas. In 1917, Hawley (6) derived the same mathematical relationship for a countercurrent multistage washing or decantation process that was developed fifteen years later for a multistage absorber by Kremser (8) and Souders and Brown (16) and in 1934 was derived by Underwood (17) for a liquid–liquid extraction operation. The lack of communication between the different fields of chemical engineering is evidenced by the fact that one usually refers to this equation by one or more of the latter names.

Actually, all of the mathematical relationships in the previous section on liquid–liquid extraction apply to liquid–solid extraction if no solute remains in the actual solid, if the term H is used for the solvent adhering to the solid leaving the multistage operation, and if the term L refers to the solvent leaving the other end of the countercurrent process. (The liquid adhering to the solid is frequently called underflow, due to the location of its withdrawal after a decantation, and is distinguished from the overflow, which is the solid-free solution from the decanter.)

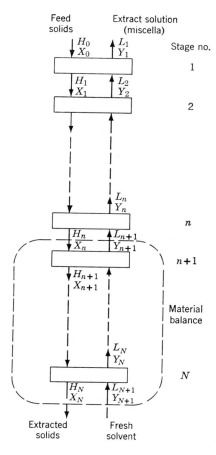

Feed solids

Extract solution (miscella)

Stage no.

Extracted solids

Fresh solvent

Fig. 2. Continuous countercurrent liquid extraction of a solid (15). Courtesy *Chemical Engineering Progress.*

If the liquid and solid in each stage are completely mixed to reach equilibrium, the concentration in L will be the same as in H, and the distribution coefficient may be taken as unity. On the other hand, if the mixing is incomplete so that the concentration in the liquid adhering to the solid is always the same fraction greater than the concentration of the clear liquid, the distribution coefficient will be constant at an appropriate value of D less than unity.

For the case of batchwise leaching with multiple quantities of fresh solvent, equation 2 (p. 724) applies when the same amounts of solvent are used in each step. The amount of solvent adhering to the solid and the concentration ratio between the supernatant liquid and the adhering liquid are both constant in each step. Thus

$$X_N/X_0 = 1/(1 + LD/H)^N \tag{1}$$

where X_N/X_0 is the fraction of the solute adhering to the feed solids remaining after N washings. It is apparent that if the solids are introduced dry, the solvent used in the first stage must be $L + H$ if this equation is to apply. Figure 1 shows the schematic diagram of this process.

Again, as with liquid–liquid extraction, this technique gives a much poorer extraction efficiency than the same amount of total solvent used countercurrently, as shown in Figure 2. Equation 4 (p. 726) can be similarly applied to nonequilibrium conditions as well as the equilibrium conditions for which it was originally derived by Hawley, as previously mentioned:

$$\frac{X_N - Y_{N+1}/D}{X_0 - Y_{N+1}/D} = \frac{(LD/H) - 1}{(LD/H)^{N+1} - 1} \tag{2}$$

where the terms have the same significance as in the batchwise operation but Y_{N+1} refers to the solute concentration in the fresh solvent as shown in the figure; if Y_{N+1} is zero, the left-hand term is the fraction unextracted, identical to that of equation 1 and also equation 4 (p. 726).

It can also be recognized from Figure 2 that if the solids are charged into the first stage dry, the effect is to reduce the solvent quantity from the first stage by an amount H but all other quantities would be the same. In this case equation 2 can be applied to stages 2 through N and a separate calculation is required for stage 1, similar to the stagewise technique for the calculation of liquid–liquid extraction.

Baker (1) took this into account and, assuming all soluble material in the liquid phase in this stage, developed the relationship for the ratio of X_N/X_1.

McCabe and Smith (10) also derived the relationship between number of stages and concentrations of solute in feed and product streams by introducing the overall material balance on the column to derive L/H as $(X_0 - X_N)/(Y_1 - Y_{N+1})$ and taking $D = 1$ so that

$$N = \frac{\log (X_0 - Y_1)/(X_N - Y_{N+1})}{\log (X_0 - X_N)/(Y_1 - Y_{N+1})} \tag{3}$$

If no solvent is introduced in the first stage the material balance on this stage is established separately and equation 3 is used to calculate $N - 1$.

If the solute concentration affects the properties of the liquid solution sufficiently that the solvent retention H of the solid varies and the variation with concentration is known, it is possible to construct a graph similar to the XY plots used in absorption, distillation, and liquid–liquid extraction to represent the stagewise calculations; thus, if the solvent concentration is the same in the free liquor and in the solution adhering to the solids, the equilibrium curve lies along the 45° line as shown in Figure 3. Terminal conditions for the extraction pattern shown in Figure 2 are set by the process specifications and a solute material balance around the top stage gives

$$L_1 Y_1 - L_2 Y_2 = H_1 X_1 - H_0 X_0 \tag{4}$$

whereas a solvent material balance gives

$$L_1 - L_2 = H_1 - H_0 \tag{5}$$

Since X_1 is equal to Y_1 and H_1 is known as a function of X_1, the concentration Y_2 can be calculated as

$$Y_2 = \frac{L_1 - H_1}{L_1 + H_0 - H_1} X_1 + \frac{H_0}{L + H_0 - H_1} X_0 \tag{6}$$

It is easily recognized that if H is constant the locus of all X and Y concentrations passing each other in the column, ie, Y_{N+1} vs X_N, is a straight line between the points (X_0, Y_1) and (X_N, Y_{N+1}), which has a slope of $(L-H)/L$. When H varies, this line is curved similar to the operating lines in other stagewise operations of absorption,

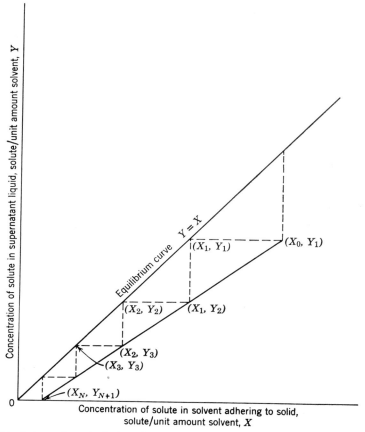

Fig. 3. Graphical stagewise calculations for countercurrent liquid–solid extraction, based on liquid concentrations only.

distillation, and extraction. In washing operations, it is also possible to express solute concentrations as quantity per unit quantity of insoluble solid, as shown in Figure 4. In this figure, if H is constant the slope of the equilibrium line will be S/H and the slope of the operating line will be S/L. It can, of course, be recognized that this plot is more nearly analogous to that used for other diffusional operations. Chen (4) also considered the case of constant H and derived the relationship equivalent to equation 3 in terms of the solvent-to-solid ratio, L/S.

However, if H is not constant, both operating line and equilibrium line will be curved and, although they are readily calculable there is little practical value to this type of plot. Grosberg (5) developed equations for a varying value of H assuming that the reciprocal could be correlated to a linear function with concentration X. Chen (4), using the same functional relationship, simplified the analytical technique for solving the relationships.

A useful graphical technique for stagewise calculations which can handle a variation of H with X was developed by Scheibel (15). A solute balance around the $N + 1$ stage and the bottom of the column gives

$$L_{n+1} Y_{n+1} = H_n X_n - H_N X_N + L_{N+1} Y_{N+1} \tag{7}$$

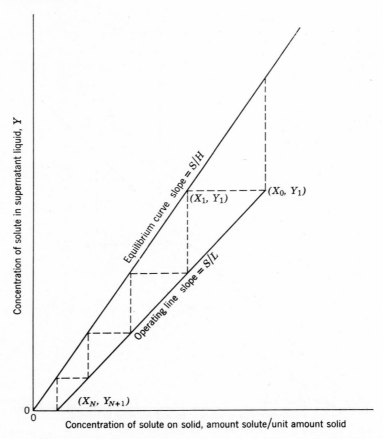

Fig. 4. Graphical stagewise calculations for countercurrent extraction considering the flow of solids as one of the streams.

and a solvent balance around the same section gives

$$L_{n+1} = H_n - H_N + L_{N+1} \tag{8}$$

Substituting equation 8 in 7 and solving for Y_{n+1} gives

$$Y_{n+1} = \frac{H_n X_n - (H_N X_N - L_{N+1} Y_{N+1})}{H_n - (H_N - L_{N+1})} \tag{9}$$

If a point F is located in Figure 5 so that the ordinate is equal to $H_N X_N - L_{N+1} Y_{N+1}$ and the abscissa is equal to $H_N - L_{N+1}$, the value of Y_{n+1} is given as the slope of the line between a point on the equilibrium curve and F. The slope of the line OA is the initial concentration of solute in liquid on the solid, and the slope of the line FA is the concentration of the solute in the liquid leaving the first stage. This concentration must be the same as that of the liquid retained in the solid as the line OB is drawn parallel to FA. The line FB has a slope equal to the concentration of the liquid leaving the second stage, so OC is drawn parallel to FB and the construction continued until the point along the equilibrium curve is reached corresponding to the desired solute concentration in the liquid on the solid.

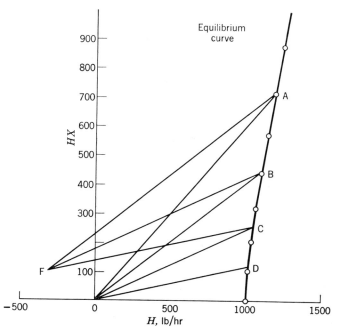

Fig. 5. Graphical stagewise calculations for liquid extraction of a solid with a variable amount of adhering solution (15). Courtesy *Chemical Engineering Progress*.

This technique can be extended to adsorption operations if the amount of solute adsorbed on the solid is included in the value of HX when plotting the equilibrium curve, and the treatment will be rigorous.

The close analogy between liquid–liquid and liquid–solid extraction makes it possible to apply all the techniques of the previous section to this process. In all cases the additional solid can be treated as an inert solid which passes through all stages with the heavy liquid phase H. It is obvious that if no solute is adsorbed on or trapped in the solid and the liquid can be completely removed from the solid, it will never be necessary to use more than one leaching stage. Alternatively, if some liquid is retained on the solid the solute can be completely removed by washing with fresh solvent, as is usually done in filtration. The continuous displacement is theoretically more efficient than the stagewise washing technique of countercurrent decantation and the two methods become identical only in the limiting case of an infinite number of stages with a differential amount of solvent.

Practical considerations frequently make countercurrent decantation expedient, as in the case where the solids are difficult to filter from solution or when the solid tends to contract after removal of the liquid so that channeling of the subsequent wash liquid occurs and washing efficiency is therefore poor.

On the other hand, if the solution of the solute in the solvent is controlled by the diffusion of the solute out of the solid or by the diffusion of solvent and reactant into the solid, the approach to equilibrium is slow and a long time is required for complete removal. Theoretically, even this can be handled most efficiently on a filter by introducing the fresh wash solvent at a sufficiently low rate. But in this case economic considerations clearly dictate the use of a countercurrent leaching operation because the loss in efficiency is small and the cost of a mixing-settling tank is considerably less than the cost of a filter which will provide the necessary residence time for the same amount of solids. The slower the approach to equilibrium, the greater is the reduction in equipment cost.

The efficient solvent extraction of vegetable oils such as linseed and cottonseed oils depends upon the diffusion of the solute through the cell walls of the seed pulp, and this process will be called "washing" even though solute and solvent are separated by a barrier. On the other hand, the economic leaching of low-grade ores depends upon diffusion of the solubilizing reactant through the inert solid to the desired product. Both of these operations approach equilibrium differently and must be considered separately.

Fractional Approach to Equilibrium in Washing

The simplest mechanism for the leaching of a porous solid results from the assumption that the solute is in the liquid phase throughout the solid. It has been found experimentally by Boucher, Brier, and Osburn (2) and proved theoretically by Ruth (14) that the fraction of a solute removed by diffusion at any time is a constant independent of the actual concentration if the solvent outside the solid contains no solute. The situation would be approximated if this solute concentration were small with respect to the solute concentration in the solvent retained in the solid.

It is also possible to postulate a stage efficiency analogous to the Murphree efficiency in distillation column design (11). Thus

$$e = (X_n - X_{n+1})/(X_n - X_{n+1}{}^*) \qquad (10)$$

where X_{n+1} is the average concentration of the solute in the liquid adhering to the solid leaving the $n + 1$ stage, $X_{n+1}{}^*$ is the concentration if solute actually were to come to equilibrium with the liquid in the same stage, and X_n is the average concen-

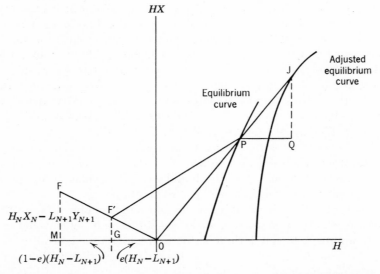

Fig. 6. Graphical stagewise calculations for liquid–solid extraction with a fractional stage efficiency.
Courtesy *Chemical Engineering Progress*.

tration of solute in the liquid adhering to the solid leaving the n stage and entering the $n + 1$ stage.

If the free liquid in the stage and the liquid retained on the solid are both of uniform concentration and the residence time in each stage is the same, it can be shown that the stage efficiency will be constant in all stages. The graphical technique developed by Scheibel and previously discussed can be readily applied to this type of system (15).

Solving equation 10 for X_{n+1} and substituting equation 9 for X_{n+1}^* and rearranging gives

$$X_{n+1} = \frac{[H_n - (1 - e)(H_N - L_{N+1})]X_n - e(H_N X_N - L_{N+1} Y_{N+1})}{H_n - (1 - e)(H_N - L_{N+1}) - e(H_N - L_{N+1})} \qquad (11)$$

In Figure 6, if point F is located as before, a point F′ is located at a fractional distance e along OF. An adjusted equilibrium curve is constructed by extending line OP between the origin and any point on the equilibrium curve a distance PQ equal to the distance MG to locate points on the adjusted equilibrium curve. Stagewise calculations are then carried out as previously described in Figure 5, using F′ and the adjusted equilibrium curve to satisfy the conditions of equation 11.

Figure 6 illustrates the application to the general case where the liquid retention of the solids varies with solute concentration. If this retention is constant, all values of H and L are constant in the column and the equilibrium curve in Figure 6 would be vertical. For this special case Scheibel (15) developed a similar graphical technique utilizing the actual equilibrium curve but locating F′ at a different fractional distance along OF. This is illustrated in Figure 7.

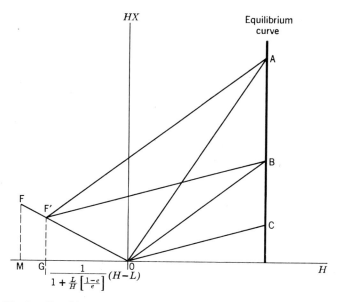

Fig. 7.   Graphical stagewise calculations for liquid–solid extraction with fractional stage efficiency when solution adhering to solid is constant, Courtesy *Chemical Engineering Progress.*

For conditions of constant H and L equation 10 can be rearranged to give

$$X_n = \frac{HX_n - \dfrac{1}{1 + (L/H)\,(1 - e)/e}\,(HX_N - LY_N)}{H - \dfrac{1}{1 + (L/H)\,(1 - e)/e}\,(H - L)} \tag{12}$$

The fractional distance of F' along line OF is $1/[1 + (L/H)(1 - e)/e]$ and graphical calculations are carried out between F' and the equilibrium curve as indicated in Figure 7.

For systems represented by either Figures 6 or 7 the stage efficiency can be determined from actual operating data by a trial and error technique analogous to that used to evaluate the Murphree efficiency of distillation columns. In either figure the point F' is located by trial so the observed degree of solute removal is obtained in the given number of stages and the stage efficiency is then calculated from the location of this point. It can be recognized that when the equilibrium curve corresponds to Figure 7 the technique is more convenient than the conventional procedure for Murphree efficiency in distillation.

If the stage efficiency is not constant this technique would give only an average value when applied to multistage data. If data are available to give the variation of efficiency in the different stages, the graphical method can be applied to design by varying the location of F' appropriately for each stage.

When the basic mechanism for transfer of solute from within a solid to the main body of the liquid is considered, it is apparent that the assumption of constant stage efficiency is highly empirical. The fractional removal with time is constant only if the concentration gradient in the solid at the start is in the proper relationship, as for example, if the concentration is uniform in all cases. Under these conditions the rate constant for material transferred to the main body liquid will vary inversely as the square root of the time and diffusion coefficient as long as the concentration gradient does not penetrate to the center of the solid. As the solid passes from one stage to the next the concentration of solute at the surface of the liquid changes stepwise but the gradient within the solid remains the same and then begins to change at a different rate in the next stage.

Fractional Approach to Equilibrium in Leaching

The concept of a constant stage efficiency has even less application when the solute is a solid and the liquid–solid interface recedes into porous media. Piret, Ebel, Kiang, and Armstrong (12) derived equations for the diffusion of a solid from a capillary tube when the rate of solution is so rapid that diffusion controls the rate process.

The leaching of an ore with an acid might also be classified in this category if a large excess of reactant is used and the reaction producing the soluble metal salt is rapid. However, most such processes involve reactions that liberate gas and thus insulate the solid from the reactant; in these cases the reaction is controlled by diffusion of the gas through the liquid away from the reacting area and could be extremely slow. In these cases, a few large agitated stages will provide the necessary residence time at a minimum cost.

It is thus apparent that for these cases the concepts of an equilibrium stage have no application and they must be considered on the basis of dynamic, nonequilibrium concepts. Bruniche-Olsen (3) studied liquid–solid extraction in the beet sugar industry and postulated several mechanisms, each giving different relationships and each of which might apply in certain cases. This particular phase of solid–liquid extraction does not lend itself readily to rigorous mathematical analysis, and the design of equipment generally is based on experimental pilot data with special attention to residence times in the scale-up to larger equipment.

Continuous Extraction Equipment

According to the foregoing discussion it would appear quite obvious that the way to obtain maximum extraction of a solute, whether solid or liquid, from an inert solid in the shortest time would be to grind the solid as fine as possible before leaching. In some instances this may not be desirable. If the extractable material is a minor fraction of initial material, as in the case of cottonseed and flaxseed, the disposal of the residual solids could present a problem. At the present time these residues are sold for animal feed, and if excessive grinding in the initial preparation or attrition in the subsequent extraction produces a solid residue unsuitable for this purpose, the economics of the extraction process will be adversely affected. Larger equipment can be justified to provide the greater residence time necessary for extraction of the coarser meal; alternatively, a lower degree of extraction might be acceptable to retain the value of the extracted residue. Excessively fine grinding can also make the separation of the solids from the extract solution difficult and present problems in the solids flow through the countercurrent extraction equipment. Thus, all industrial extraction processes depend upon the overall economic optimization and these con-

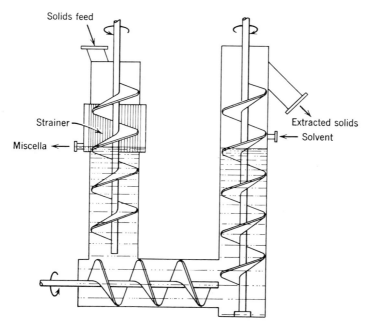

Fig. 8. Hildebrandt-type extractor.

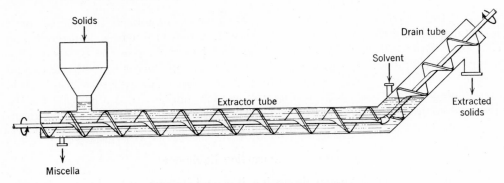

Fig. 9. Screw-conveyor type extractor.

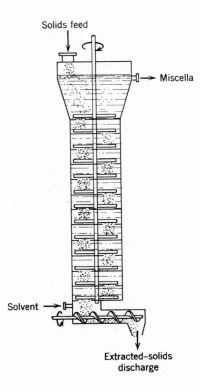

Fig. 10. Bonotto-type extractor.

ditions may be considerably different from the theoretical optimum based on only one factor.

Survey of the different types of extractors proposed and in use for the extraction of natural oils indicates that gentle action is the keynote rather than intense agitation. Most of the units operate by keeping the solids completely submerged as shown in Figures 8, 9, and 10.   Figure 8 shows an extractor in which the solids are moved through a U-bend by means of three separate screw conveyors.   Figure 9 shows a simpler arrangement utilizing one screw conveyor for the extraction and another one for the washing of the cake and draining.   Figure 10 shows another type of extractor in which the solid is pushed around on horizontal plates by rotating blades until it falls

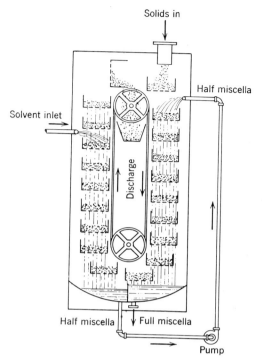

Fig. 11. Bollmann-type continuous extractor.

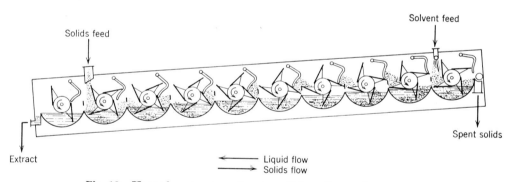

Fig. 12. Kennedy extractor. Courtesy *Vulcan Copper & Supply Co.*

through a hole to the plate below where the action is repeated. Holes in the plates are staggered so that the solid spends some time on all plates.

Another type of extractor operates by percolation; Figure 11 shows one of the earliest designs. On the solids inlet side the two phases flow cocurrently to achieve the best equilibrium and thus maximum solute concentration in the miscella. On the solids discharge side they are washed by a solvent stream falling countercurrently to the rising solids. The weak solution from this operation constitutes the feed to the first step.

The Kennedy extractor (9) shown in Figure 12 also works on the percolation principle but utilizes a truly countercurrent process. However, the solids are sub-

jected to more mechanical action than in the Bollmann extractor in Figure 11.
Thus in Figure 12 the solids are lifted out of the solvent in each stage by the slow
counterclockwise rotation of the agitators. They are then scraped automatically into
the next stage as shown so they flow countercurrent to the solvent through the extractor. The stage at the extreme left permits settling of the fines for return to the
extraction operation and thus reduces the load on the final clarification of the rich extract. Residence time of the solid is directly proportional to the time of rotation of
the agitator and must be adequate for the diffusion of the solute out of the solids.

The Rotocel extractor (7) shown in Figure 13 combines all the advantages of the
countercurrent process with the mild action of the basket-type extractors and is
one of the most popular of the recent developments of continuous leaching equipment.

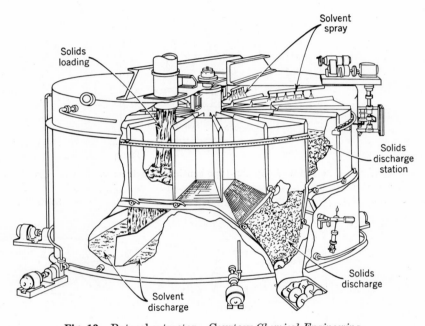

Fig. 13. Rotocel extractor. Courtesy *Chemical Engineering.*

One of the most significant advantages of this equipment is in the small overall size.
It requires much less space and can be housed in a building one-fourth the height
required by the earlier basket-type extractors of the type shown in Figure 11.

The rotor shown in Figure 13 contains separate compartments which are filled
continuously at one location and washed by successive streams as they rotate slowly.
A countercurrent flow is maintained by washing the solid in each location with the
liquid effluent from the cake in the previous compartment, and after the final wash
with fresh solvent the bottom of the compartment falls away, as shown in the figure,
and the extracted solids are discharged. As the rotor moves further, the bottom closes
and a new charge is deposited. The relatively small overall size of the unit can be
appreciated by noting that the rotor itself is only 5 ft high in this case. This extractor
is simple, efficient, and low in cost.

Applications of Liquid–Solid Extraction

Some of the most significant applications of liquid–solid extraction are leaching of uranium from the ore with acids or soda ash solutions, leaching of phosphoric acid from phosphate rock with sulfuric acid, and leaching of iodine from seaweed with sulfuric acid. Important washing operations are the extraction of turpentine and rosin from tree stumps and the extraction of vegetable oils from the natural seeds, such as linseed oil from flaxseed and cottonseed oil from cottonseed by the use of hydrocarbon solvents.

Some of the more recent developments are in the extraction of caffein from the green coffee beans for the production of caffein free coffee; also, the general acceptance of instant coffee has brought about the extraction of the roasted coffee beans on a commercial scale to obtain the concentrated solution for the spray-drying of the soluble coffee extract.

From these typical applications it is apparent that liquid extraction is still the most popular method for recovering valuable products from their natural sources and can be applied to all such problems, from the large-scale recovery of millions of pounds per day to the extremely small scale recovery of rare and exotic essences and flavors or unique biologically active and medicinal compounds.

Bibliography

"Liquid–Solid Extraction" under "Extraction" in *ECT* 1st ed., Vol. 6, pp. 91–122, by Frank Lerman, The Vulcan Copper & Supply Co.

1. E. M. Baker, *Chem. & Met. Eng.* **42**, 699 (1935); *Trans. Am. Inst. Chem. Engrs.* **32**, 62 (1936).
2. D. F. Boucher, J. C. Brier, and J. O. Osburn, *Trans. Am. Inst. Chem. Engrs.* **38**, 967 (1942).
3. H. Bruniche-Olsen, *Solid–Liquid Extraction*, NYT Nordisk Forlag, Arnold Busch, Copenhagen, 1962.
4. N. H. Chen, *Chem. Eng.* **71**, 125 (Nov. 23, 1964).
5. J. A. Grosberg, *Ind. Eng. Chem.* **42**, 1, 154 (1950).
6. J. Hawley, *Ind. Eng. Chem.* **9**, 866 (1917).
7. G. Karnofsky, *Chem. Eng.* **57**, 109 (Aug. 1950).
8. A. Kremser, *Natl. Petrol. News* **22** (21), 42 (May 21, 1930).
9. F. Lerman, A. B. Kennedy, and J. Loshin, *Ind. Eng. Chem.* **40**, 1753 (1948).
10. W. L. McCabe and V. Smith, *Unit Operations in Chemical Engineering*, McGraw-Hill Book Co., Inc., New York, 1956, p. 769.
11. E. V. Murphree, *Ind. Eng. Chem.* **17**, 747, 960 (1925).
12. E. L. Piret, R. A. Ebel, C. J. Kiang, and W. P. Armstrong, *Chem. Eng. Progr.* **47**, 405, 628 (1951).
13. R. N. Rickles, *Chem. Eng.* **72**, 157 (March 15, 1965).
14. B. F. Ruth, *Chem. Eng. Progr.* **44**, 71 (1948).
15. E. G. Scheibel, *Chem. Eng. Progr.* **49**, 355 (July 1953).
16. M. Souders and G. G. Brown, *Ind. Eng. Chem.* **24**, 519 (1932).
17. A. J. V. Underwood, *Ind. Chemist* **10**, 129 (1934).

E. G. Scheibel
The Cooper Union for the
Advancement of Science and Art

EYE LOTIONS. See Cosmetics.

F

FACE POWDER. See Cosmetics.

FAST COLOR SALTS. See under Azo dyes, Vol. 2, p. 891.

FATS AND FATTY OILS

Fats and oils are water-insoluble substances of plant or animal origin which consist predominantly of glyceryl esters of fatty acids, or triglycerides. They constitute one of the three main kinds of foodstuffs (carbohydrate, protein, and fat) and are widely distributed in nature. Common usage considers as "fats" triglycerides that are solid or semisolid at room temperature and as "oils" triglycerides that are liquid under the same conditions. Actually, the distinction is not clear-cut; therefore, the term "fats" will be used in this chapter to cover glycerides regardless of their physical state.

Triglycerides contain approximately 95% fatty acids and 5% glycerol, combined as esters. Triglycerides have the general formula (**1**). If R = R′ = R″, the triglyceride can be named from the parent acid by means of the termination "-in"; thus, for acetic acid (R = R′ = R″ = CH_3) the triglyceride is *triacetin*. The acids in the fats are fatty acids (qv), which are long-chain aliphatic acids, both saturated and unsaturated. *Tristearin* and *tripalmitin* are examples of fats that contain only one fatty acid; a structure such as (**2**) can be referred to as *sym-oleodipalmitin*.

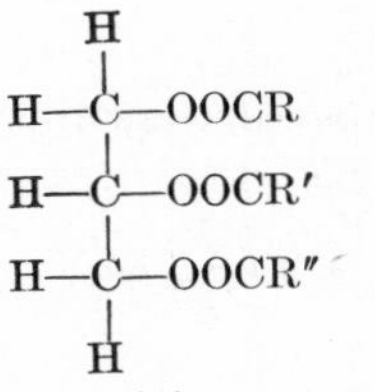

$$
\begin{array}{ll}
\text{H} & \\
\text{H}-\overset{|}{\underset{|}{\text{C}}}-\text{OOCR} & \\
\text{H}-\overset{|}{\underset{|}{\text{C}}}-\text{OOCR}' & \\
\text{H}-\overset{|}{\underset{|}{\text{C}}}-\text{OOCR}'' & \\
\text{H} & \\
\quad (\mathbf{1}) &
\end{array}
\qquad
\begin{array}{l}
\text{H} \\
\text{H}-\overset{|}{\underset{|}{\text{C}}}-\text{OOC}(CH_2)_{14}CH_3 \\
\text{H}-\overset{|}{\underset{|}{\text{C}}}-\text{OOC}(CH_2)_7CH{=}CH(CH_2)_7CH_3 \\
\text{H}-\overset{|}{\underset{|}{\text{C}}}-\text{OOC}(CH_2)_{14}CH_3 \\
\text{H} \\
\textit{sym-oleodipalmitin} \ (\mathbf{2})
\end{array}
$$

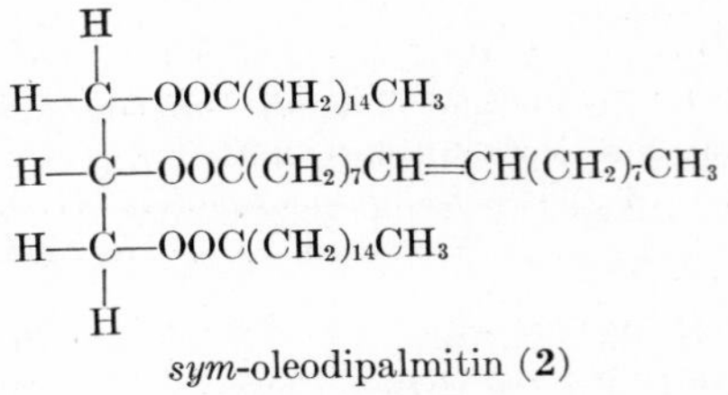

Waxes (qv) differ from fats in that they are fatty acid esters of certain higher monohydric alcohols rather than glycerol. Wool grease or fat, also called degras, is chiefly a wax, as is also sperm oil.

Because the fatty acid radicals constitute the greater part of the glyceride molecule, and also the reactive portion, the chemical and physical properties of a fat are determined largely by the properties of its component fatty acids. In general, fats become progressively higher melting and more easily solidified as the average molecular weight of the fatty acids increases and as their average unsaturation (number of double bonds) decreases. Fatty oils are sometimes called fixed oils to distinguish them from volatile, ethereal, or essential oils.

Naturally occurring fats contain minor amounts of soluble impurities such as pigments and sterols. These are removed to some extent during processing. Fats also contain small quantities of phospholipids (lecithin, cephalin, and sphingomyelin) in which glycerol, fatty acids, phosphoric acid, and a nitrogen base are combined. Associated with phospholipids are glycolipids which are carbohydrate–fatty acid compounds containing nitrogen but no phosphoric acid. Because of their occurrence in nerve tissue, particularly in the brain, they are referred to as cerebrosides.

In the human diet, large quantities of fat are consumed as natural fatty foods and many edible prepared fat products. Fats are the most concentrated source of energy in the diet, yielding 9.3 kg-cal/g as compared to 4.1 kg-cal/g from protein and carbohydrates. They are also important sources of oil-soluble vitamins and of certain essential fatty acids.

The considerably smaller (about $\frac{1}{3}$ of the total) technical or nonedible use of fat is based mainly upon the property of the more unsaturated members of polymerizing to form elastic but durable protective coatings, and the long-chain character of the fatty acids, which confers surface activity upon many of their derivatives. In the manufacture of soap as well as of many other surface-active materials, fats are important not as such but as a source of fatty acids. Where the fatty acids alone are utilized, glycerol is a valuable by-product. In certain industrial applications and for edible use as well, the lubricating or plasticizing properties of fats or fatty acids are important.

Composition

Fatty Acids and Glycerides. Owing to the complexity of glyceride structure and the enormous experimental difficulties in attempting to accurately determine the composition of a fat in terms of all the component glycerides, chemical analysis of fats normally shows only the relative proportions of the different fatty acids. Actually, the characteristics and particularly the physical properties of the fat are considerably dependent upon how the fatty acids are distributed within the glyceride molecules (see formula (**2**) for a typical triglyceride). Hilditch and co-workers (1) have shown that in vegetable fats and particularly in seed fats there is a marked tendency for any given fatty acid to be distributed as evenly as possible among the different glycerides so that simple triglycerides (containing a single fatty acid) do not usually occur in any quantity unless the molar proportion of any one acid exceeds $\frac{2}{3}$ of the whole, whereas any acid comprising more than $\frac{1}{3}$ of the total will tend to appear in all the glycerides. Since trisaturated glycerides have much higher melting points than glycerides containing one or more unsaturated fatty radicals, the even distribution theory is consistent with the fact that vegetable fats generally have lower melting points than animal fats of equivalent fatty acid composition. However, several researchers have amassed a considerable body of data pointing out exceptions and offering other theories (2). It now appears that more work must be done and more refined methods of separation of glycerides must be developed before final and positive conclusions on the theories of fatty acid distribution can be made.

Phospholipids. Phospholipids are fat-soluble and, being associated with fats in many plant and animal tissues, are often found in crude fats (for example, to the extent of 2–3% in soybean and corn oils). They are removed from oil by "degumming" (hydration) or by acid or alkali refining. Commercial "lecithin" is now prepared from soybean oil, particularly in the U.S., by hydration of the oil followed by cen-

Table 1. Iodine and Saponification Values and Fatty Acid Compositions of Representative Samples of Common Vegetable and Land Animal Fats and Oils

Fat or oil	Iodine value	Saponification value	Saturated acids					Monoethenoid acids		Diethenoid acids, C18	Triethenoid acids, C18	Other acids
			C12	C14	C16	C18	C20	C16	C18			
almond oil	95	190		1.2	4.5	1.2			77.0	17.3		
apricot kernel oil	108.7	190			2.6	1.2			64.4	31.8		
babassu oil	16.1	249	44.1	15.4	8.5	2.7	0.2		16.1	1.4		caproic, 0.2; caprylic 4.8; capric, 6.6
Borneo tallow	33.2	193			18.0	43.3	1.1		37.4	0.2		
butterfat (cow)	25–42	233–240	4	12	29	11	2	4	25	2		butyric, 3; caproic, 1; caprylic, 1; capric, 3; satd above C18, 2; monoethenoid, C10–C14, 2; unsatd C20–C22, 1
butterfat (goat)	28.8	240	6.0	12.3	27.9	6.0		2.6	21.1	3.6		butyric, 3.0; caproic, 2.5; caprylic, 2.8; capric, 10.0; satd above C18, 0.6; monoethenoid C10–C14, 1.4
candlenut (lumbang) oil	164.3	191			5.5	6.7			10.5	48.5	28.5	
castor oil[a]	81–91	176–187			2.0	1.0			7.0	3.0		ricinoleic, 87.0; dihydroxystearic, 0.6
Chinese vegetable tallow[a]	16–29	200–218	0–2.5	0.5–3.7	58–72	1.2–7.6			20–35	0–1.6		
cocoa butter	35–40	190–198			24.4	35.4			38.1	2.1		
coconut (copra) oil[a]	7.5–10.5	250–264	48.0	17.5	9.0	2.1			5.7	2.6		caprylic, 7.9; capric, 7.2
cohune oil	9.8	251	46.4	16.1	9.3	3.3			9.9	0.9		caprylic, 7.5; capric, 6.6
corn oil[a]	103–128	187–193			13	4			29	54		

Oil	iodine value	saponification value	lauric	myristic	palmitic	stearic	arachidic	oleic	linoleic	linolenic	other acids
cottonseed oil[a]	99-113	189-198		1	29	4	2		24	40		tetradecenoic, trace
grapefruitseed oil	100.8	197		1.2	27.5	2.9	2.1		21.1	39.3	5.9	
hempseed oil	140-175	190-193			5-10				7-14	46-69	16-28	
kapok oil[a]	86-110	189-197		3	10.5-10.8	4.9-8.6	1		46.1-56.6	27.7-34.6		
lard (prime steam, U.S.)	53-77	190-202			24	18	3		42	9		
linseed oil	177 min	189-195			6	4			22	16	52	
mowrah (illipé) fat	63.9	194			23.7	19.3			43.3	13.7		
murmuru oil	11.0	242	42.5	36.9	4.6	2.1			10.8	0.4		caprylic, 1.1; capric, 1.6
mustard seed oil	103	175			8	3			28	35	8	erucic, 18
neatsfoot oil[a]	66-76	190-199		0.7	16.9	2.7			64.4	2.3	0.7	tetradecenoic, 1.2; unsatd C_{20}-C_{22}, 1.6
oiticica oil	205-220[b]	188-193			10-12	0.1						licanic, 73-83; nonconjugated unsatd, 5-16
olive oil[a]	80-88	188-196		trace	15.6	2.0	1.6		64.6	15.0		
orangeseed oil	97.6	196			23.8	8.3			24.8	37.1	5.3	
ouricuri oil	14.7	257	45.8	9.0	7.7	2.3			13.1	2.2		caproic, 1.8; caprylic, 9.8; capric, 8.2
palm oil[a]	44-58	195-205		1	48	4			38	9		
palm kernal oil[a]	14-22	245-255	45	17	9	3			13	3		caprylic, 6; capric, 4
peanut oil[a]	84-100	188-195		trace	6	5	trace		61	22		behenic, 3; lignoceric, 1
perilla oil[a]	193-208	188-197			7	2			13	14	64	
poppyseed oil	133.4	197			7.2	2			28.3	58.5		
rapeseed (colza) oil[a]	97-108	170-180			4		trace		19	15.8	8	eicosenoic, 13; erucic, 40
ravison oil	108.5	178		2.1	4.3	1.8	0.6		15.5	20.9	9.9	behenic, 0.5; lignoceric, 0.6; eicosenoic, 4.1; erucic, 38.7; docosadienoic, 1.0

(continued)

Table 1 (*continued*)

Fatty acid composition, % by wt

Fat or oil	Iodine value	Saponification value	Saturated acids C12	C14	C16	C18	C20	Monoethenoid acids C16	C18	Diethenoid acids, C18	Triethenoid acids, C18	Other acids
rice bran oil	99.9	185	0.5		11.7	1.7	0.5	trace	39.2	35.1		lignoceric, 0.4
safflower oil[a]	140–150	188–194	trace		8	3	trace		13	75	1	
sesame oil[a]	103–116	188–195			10	5	0.5		40	43		
shea fat	59.1	184			5.7	41.0			49.0	4.3		
sorghum oil	119.0	191	0.2		8.3	5.8		0.1	36.2	49.4		
soybean oil[a]	120–141	189–195	trace		11	4			25	51	9	satd C20–C24, trace
stillingia oil	185.8	207	.... 9						20	25–30	40	conjugated decadienoic, 3–6
sunflowerseed oil[a]	125–136	188–194			11	6			29	52		
tallow (beef)[a]	35–48	193–202	0.2	3.1	24.9	24.1	0.8	2.4	41.8	1.8	0.5	tetradecenoic, 0.4; unsatd C20–C22, 0.5
tallow (goat)	33.5	199	2.1	3.5	25.5	28.1	2.4		38.4	4.3		
tallow (mutton)	41.2	197		4.6	24.6	30.5			36.0	7.4		
teaseed oil	86.3	192	0.3		7.6	0.8	0.6		83.3	2.5		
tucum oil	15.8	241	48.9	21.6	6.4	1.7			13.2			caprylic, 1.3; capric, 4.4
tung (China wood) oil[a]	160–175[b]	189–195			4	1			8	4		eleostearic, 80
ucuhuba butter	9.9	228	14.8	72.5	4.9				6.3			capric, 0.5
walnut (English) oil	155.7	190	.... 8.1						19.1	65.9	6.9	
wheat germ oil	128.6	184			11–16	1–6			8–30	44–65	4–10	C20–C22, satd, 0–1

[a] Iodine numbers and saponification value ranges recommended by the American Oil Chemists' Society.

[b] Due to incomplete halogen absorption, iodine values for conjugated acid oils by the usual methods (Wijs, Hanus, etc) are both low and variable. The true iodine value of fresh tung oil, as determined by special methods (5), is 248–252; that of oiticica oil is 205–220.

trifugation and vacuum drying. Lecithin is used extensively in margarine, chocolate, cooking fats, paints, and in many other applications in which a natural emulsifying agent is preferred.

Antioxidants (qv). Most vegetable fats contain minor proportions (0.05–0.20%) of antioxidants which serve to inhibit atmospheric oxidation, the cause of rancidity in fats. In animal fats, antioxidants are generally almost entirely absent. The common antioxidants of vegetable fats are tocopherols; in a few cases, antioxidants peculiar to specific fats are known. Antioxidants are not removed to any large extent by refining or other common (edible oil) processing treatment.

Antioxidants approved by the U.S. Department of Agriculture for use in meat fats (in specific maximum concentrations) include butylated hydroxyanisole (BHA), butylated hydroxytoluene (BHT), tocopherols, propyl gallate, citric acid, phosphoric acid, monoisopropyl citrate, guaiac resin, nordihydroguaiaretic acid, lecithin, and glycine (2).

Pigments. The characteristic yellow-red color of most vegetable fats and of some animal fats is derived principally from carotenoid pigments. Palm oil, which is unusually high in color, contains about 0.20% beta-carotene. Olive oil and some seed oils (for example, soybean oil) may contain sufficient chlorophyll or related compounds to produce a greenish tinge. Cottonseed oil is strongly colored by pigments of the gossypol type. All of these pigments are readily reduced to low levels by alkali refining of the oil and adsorption bleaching. However, brownish or reddish pigments found in oils derived from damaged materials, which are probably in part protein and carbohydrate decomposition products, are relatively resistant to refining treatments.

The content of carotenoid pigments is lowered by oxidation or by heat treatment, but vegetable oils containing gamma-tocopherol darken with limited oxidation, due to the formation of chroman-5,6-quinones (derivatives of 5,6-chromandione).

Vitamins. Vitamin A occurs as such in butterfat (see Milk and milk products) and fish body oils and in high concentrations in certain fish liver oils. The precursor of vitamin A (carotene) occurs in butterfat, in unbleached palm oil, and in traces in other fats. Vitamin D is found in fish-liver oils, fish-body oils, and to some extent in butterfat. As a source of vitamins, the common vegetable oils are important only with respect to their content of tocopherols, which possess vitamin E activity.

Sterols. Most of the 0.5–1.5% unsaponifiable material commonly found in both vegetable and animal fats consists of sterols. The sterols of animal fats, consisting principally of cholesterol, are sufficiently different from the mixture of sitosterols, stigmasterols, etc, in vegetable oils to permit the two classes of fats to be distinguished through the difference in melting points of their sterol acetates (3).

Sterols are colorless, odorless, and generally inert insofar as the practical applications of fats are concerned. A portion of the sterols in crude oils is removed by alkali refining; the soap stock or residue from refining serves as a commercial source of sterols for the manufacture of pharmaceuticals.

Free Fatty Acids. The free fatty acid content of a crude fat is usually dependent upon the degree to which the fat has been subjected to enzymic hydrolysis in the parent oil-bearing material before extraction. In fats of good quality it is not ordinarily greater than about 1%, although in fats obtained from damaged materials, it may be much higher. Palm oil and inedible tallows and greases are characteristically high in free fatty acids (3–30%).

Other minor constituents of fats and oils include traces of hydrocarbons, ketones,

Table 2. Iodine and Saponification Values and Fatty Acid Compositions of Representative Samples of Marine Oils

Oil	Iodine value	Saponification value	Saturated acids, % by wt					Unsaturated acids, % by wt[a]					
			C_{12}	C_{14}	C_{16}	C_{18}	C_{20}–C_{22}	C_{14}	C_{16}	C_{18}	C_{20}	C_{22}	C_{24}
cod-liver	118–190	182–191		5.8	8.4	0.6	0.6	0.2	20.0 (2.3)	29.1 (2.8)	25.4 (6.0)	9.6 (6.9)	
herring	115–160	180–192	0.1	7.0	11.7	0.8	0.1	1.2 (2.0)	11.8 (2.4)	19.6 (3.5)	25.9 (5.2)	21.6 (4.3)	0.1 (3.8)
menhaden	150–185	185–195		5.9	16.3	0.6	1.4		15.5 (2)	29.6 (4)	19.0 (10)	11.7 (10)	
sardine, California (pilchard)	170–188	188–199		5.1	14.4	3.2			11.7 (2.0)	17.7 (3.3)	17.9 (4.1)	13.8 (8.5)	15.2 (10.9)
sardine, Japanese	160–190	185–195		5.8	9.7	2.3			13.0 (2)	14.2 (2)[c]	26.0 (5)	19.0 (5)	
seal, gray	162.2	191		4.7	12.1	2.0	0.1	3.3 (2.0)	19.2 (2.2)	31.8 (2.7)	12.9 (6.2)	13.4 (10.0)	0.5 (11.0)
whale[b]	110–135	185–202		9.2	15.6	1.9	0.6	2.5 (2.0)	13.9 (2.1)	37.2 (2.4)	12.0 (7.1)	7.1 (9.4)	

[a] Values in parentheses represent unsaturation of fraction in terms of deficiency of hydrogen.

[b] Iodine value and saponification equivalent ranges recommended by the American Oil Chemists' Society.

[c] Other values: 10.0 (4); trace (6).

and other unidentified materials which give the individual members their distinctive odors and flavors. In addition, mono- and diglycerides, resulting from hydrolysis of triglycerides, may be present, particularly in fats obtained from damaged materials.

CHARACTERISTICS OF INDIVIDUAL FATS AND OILS

The iodine and saponification values (see below under Analysis and testing) and fatty acid compositions reported for representative samples of vegetable and land-animal fats and oils are listed in Table 1. In the case of some oils, detailed analyses, including estimates of minor fatty acids, are not available, and contents of minor acids are included with those of related acids, for example, palmitoleic (hexadecenoic) with oleic, and arachidic with stearic. In a few cases, the portions of acids originally reported have been adjusted to make them conform with later and more accurate but incomplete data. Most of the iodine and saponification values listed are observed values, but a few are calculated. The original literature should be consulted for detailed analyses on any of these oils where detailed information is important.

It must be remembered that until the 1950s fatty acid analyses were based largely on the fractional distillation of fatty acid esters and analysis of the fractions by such methods as saponification value, iodine value, thiocyanogen value, etc. Improvements in gas–liquid chromatography since its introduction to fat analysis by James and Martin (4) indicate it will amost entirely replace ester fractionation and other methods as a procedure for the determination of fatty acids.

Corresponding data for marine oils are given in Table 2. In these oils, the wide variety of unsaturated fatty acids makes it impossible to determine the proportions of individual acids; and hence, only the average degree of unsaturation of the acids of each chain length has been recorded. The average unsaturation is given in each case in terms of deficiency of hydrogen atoms. For monoethenoid acids, for example, it is 2.0; for diethenoid acids, 4.0; etc.

Classification

On the basis of their unsaturation and consequent drying or polymerizing properties, fats and oils are commonly classified as *nondrying* (iodine value below about 90), *semidrying* (iodine value about 90–130), and *drying* (iodine value above about 130) (see Drying oils). A more rational classification (2), based upon chemical composition and industrial applications, places the commercially important fats and oils in the groups shown below (see Table 3).

Milk fats are distinguished by low unsaturation and the presence of a wide variety of saturated fatty acids of short chain length. *Butter fat* (of the cow) is the only important member; it is relatively expensive and is used only for edible purposes.

Lauric acid oils are distinguished by very low unsaturation and a high content of lauric acid as well as other short-chain acids. They melt sharply at relatively low temperatures and are relatively light colored and low in nonglyceride constituents. Lauric acid oils are derived from seeds of cultivated or noncultivated palms. The important members are coconut and palm-kernel oils; they are normally cheap and are used for soapmaking and also for edible products.

Vegetable butters are low in unsaturation and contain principally 14- to 18-carbon acids. The relatively low melting points and very sharp melting of these

Table 3. Classification, Sources, and Production of Commercially Important Vegetable Oils

Fat or oil	Type or group	Botanical name of plant[a]	Principal geographical sources	Normal world production[b]
almond oil[c]	oleic–linoleic acid	*Prunus amygdalus*	Europe, Africa, U.S.	very small
apricot kernel oil[c]	oleic–linoleic acid	*Prunus armeniaca*	U.S., Europe	very small
babassu oil	lauric acid	*Orbignya (Attalea) speciosa*	Brazil	small
borneo tallow	vegetable butter	*Shorea stenoptera*	East Indies, Malaya	probably very small
candlenut (lumbang) oil	linolenic acid	*Aleurites moluccana*	Philippines, South Pacific region	probably very small
castor oil	hydroxy acid	*Ricinus communis*	Brazil, India, U.S.S.R., Manchuria	large
Chinese vegetable tallow	vegetable butter	*Stillingia sebifera*	China	probably very small
cocoa butter[c]	vegetable butter	*Theobroma cacao*	Africa, Brazil, Central America	small
coconut (copra) oil	lauric acid	*Cocos nucifera*	Philippines, East Indies, other South Pacific Islands, Ceylon	very large
cohune oil	lauric acid	*Attalea cohune*	Central America	very small
corn oil[c]	oleic–linoleic acid	*Zea mays*	U.S., Europe, Argentina	large
cottonseed oil[c]	oleic–linoleic acid	*Gossypium hirsutum, Gossypium barbadense*	U.S., India, Brazil, U.S.S.R., China, Egypt, and others	very large
grapefruitseed oil[c]	linolenic acid	*Citrus paradisi*	U.S.	very small
hempseed oil[c]	linolenic acid	*Cannabis sativa*	Europe, Asia	probably small
kapok oil[c]	oleic–linoleic acid	*Eriodendron anfractuosum*	Indonesia	probably very small
linseed oil	linolenic acid	*Linum usitatissimum*	Argentina, U.S., Canada, U.S.S.R., India	very large
mowrah (illipé) fat	vegetable butter	*Bassia longifolia, Bassia latifolia*	India	probably very small
murumuru oil	lauric acid	*Astrocaryum murumuru*	Brazil	very small
mustardseed oil	erucic acid	*Brassica nigra*	Europe, India	probably small
oiticica oil	conjugated acid	*Licania rigida*	Brazil	very small
olive oil	oleic–linoleic acid	*Olea europaea*	Spain, Italy, North Africa, Greece	very large
orangeseed oil[c]	linolenic acid	*Citrus sinensis*	U.S.	very small
ouricuri oil	lauric acid	*Syagrus coronata*	Brazil	very small
palm oil	oleic–linoleic acid	*Elaeis guineensis*	Africa, Indonesia, Malaya	very large

Oil	Fatty acid/type	Source	Region	Production
palm kernel oil	lauric acid	*Elaeis guineensis*	Africa, Indonesia, Malaya	large
peanut oil	oleic–linoleic acid	*Arachis hypogaea*	Africa, India, China, U.S., and others	very large
perilla oil	linolenic acid	*Perilla ocymoides*	Manchuria, Korea, Japan, India	very small
poppyseed oil	oleic–linoleic acid	varieties of *Papaveraceae*	Europe, U.S.S.R., Asia	probably small
rapeseed (colza) oil	erucic acid	*Brassica campestris*	Europe, India, China, Japan	very large
ravison oil	erucic acid	varieties of *Brassica campestris*	Black Sea region	probably small
rice bran oil[c]	oleic–linoleic acid	*Oryza sativa*	Japan, U.S., China	probably very small
safflower oil	oleic–linoleic acid	*Carthamus tinctorius*	India, Egypt, U.S.S.R., U.S.	probably small
sesame oil	oleic–linoleic acid	*Sesamum indicum*	China, India, Africa, Mexico, and others	large
shea fat	vegetable butter	*Butyrospermum parkii*	Africa	probably very small
soybean oil	linolenic acid	*Soja max*	U.S., China, Manchuria	very large
stillingia oil	conjugated acid	*Stillingia sebifera*	China	probably very small
sunflowerseed oil	oleic–linoleic acid	*Helianthus annus*	Argentina, U.S.S.R., Baltic region, Canada	very large
teaseed oil	oleic–linoleic acid	*Thea susanqua*	China	very small to small
tucum oil	lauric acid	*Astrocaryum tucuma*	Brazil	very small
tung (China wood) oil	conjugated acid	*Aleurites fordii, Aleurites montana*	China, small production in U.S. and South America	large
ucuhuba butter	vegetable butter	*Virola sebifera, Virda surinamensis*	Brazil	very small
walnut (English) oil[c]	linolenic acid	*Juglans regia*	Central Europe, Asia, U.S.	probably very small
wheat germ oil[c]	linolenic acid	varieties of *Triticum*	U.S., Canada, and others	very small

[a] All of the oils listed are derived from the seed kernels of the plants, with the exception of Chinese vegetable tallow, olive oil, and palm oil, which are fruit-coat oils.

[b] Production of the different oils is rated approximately as follows (per annum basis): over 1 billion pounds, very large; 200 million to 1 billion pounds, large; 50–200 million pounds, small; under 50 million pounds, very small.

[c] Plant cultivated or processed primarily for products other than oil.

butters are due to the even distribution of saturated and unsaturated fatty acids, rather than to the presence of low-molecular-weight acids as in lauric acid oils. Vegetable butters are derived from seeds of tropical trees. *Cocoa butter* is the most important member; it is expensive and is used principally in confectionery (see Chocolate and cocoa).

Land-animal fats are relatively low in unsaturation and contain principally 16- and 18-carbon acids. The unsaturated acids consist almost entirely of oleic and linoleic acid. With saturated and unsaturated acids evenly distributed, they exhibit gradual melting and relatively high melting points. If derived from undamaged materials, they are light colored and low in nonglyceride constituents; inedible grades are often dark colored. *Lard* (from hogs) and *tallow* (from cattle and sheep) are derived principally from the body fat as the by-product of meat packing (see Meat and meat products). They are relatively cheap and are used as edible fats, as a source of commercial fatty acid (see Manufacture from fats under Fatty acids), and for soap making. The term "grease" refers to the softer inedible fats used principally by soap makers; a fat with a titer (see p. 790) below 40°C is considered a grease, and a fat with a titer over 40°C is classed as an inedible tallow.

Oleic–linoleic acid oils are of medium, but rather variable unsaturation (iodine value varies from about 50 for palm oil to about 120 for corn oil), with no fatty acids more unsaturated than linoleic (2 double bonds); the fatty acids are predominantly of 18 carbons. These oils are normally liquid in the raw form, but are frequently hydrogenated to produce plastic fats. The crude seed oils are relatively high in nonglyceride substances. They are derived principally from fruit pulp of perennial plants, (palm, olive), and seed of cultivated annual plants (for example, cottonseed, peanut, corn, safflower, sesame, and sunflowerseed). The oils are of medium price and are used principally for edible purposes (palm oil is used considerably in soapmaking).

Erucic acid oils resemble in composition the oleic–linoleic acid oils, except that the predominant unsaturated fatty acid is a 22-carbon monoethenoid acid, erucic, and there is a minor proportion (6–10%) of linolenic acid. The commercially important members, rapeseed (colza), ravison, and mustardseed are used in Europe and in Asia as edible oils; but in the United States they are used mainly for technical purposes, that is, for sulfonation (see Surfactants) and in the manufacture of lubricants (see Lubrication and lubricants). They are derived from the seeds of cultivated annual plants.

Linolenic acid oils, derived almost wholly from the seeds of cultivated annual plants, are generally similar to the oleic–linoleic acid oils but are distinguished from the latter by containing a more highly unsaturated acid, linolenic (3 double bonds). The most important members are soybean and linseed, which are medium-priced oils. Soybean is used both in edible products and as a drying oil, but linseed is used exclusively as a drying oil (except in the Baltic region, where it is also used as an edible oil). Linolenic acid oils or other oils containing a substantial proportion of unsaturated acids with more than 2 double bonds are less desirable than other fats for the manufacture of edible products because of their flavor instability or tendency toward "flavor reversion" after deodorization.

Conjugated acid oils are used only as drying oils (qv) for which they are particularly suited because of their high content of unsaturated fatty acids with conjugated double bonds. The commercially important members, tung and oiticica, are derived from the seeds of subtropical trees. They are relatively high-priced.

Marine oils are distinguished by their considerable content of fatty acids, which vary considerably in chain length ranging both above and below 18 carbons, and by the presence of highly unsaturated acids (4 or more double bonds) together with a considerable content of saturated acids (as much as 25% of the total acids). Although used for edible purposes, as drying oils, and, after hydrogenation, for soapmaking (including the manufacture of metallic soap) (see Driers and metallic soaps), the diversity of their component fatty acids prevents them from being the most highly desirable products for any particular purpose. They are generally the cheapest of all fats and oils. Large quantities are used in the fatliquoring of leather (qv).

Unlike the land-animal fats, marine oils are not a by-product of food processing. The commercially important members are derived from the whale and from small oily fishes, such as the California sardine (pilchard), menhaden, and herring, which are taken principally for their oil. (Sperm whale oils are actually in large part liquid waxes.) The body and head oils are composed of approximately 65 and 75% of esters of normal, higher monohydric alcohols, and 35 and 26% of esters of glycerol, respectively. Fish-liver oils, derived from an entirely different species of fish (since oily fish generally have livers with a low oil content and vice versa), were formerly important as a source of natural vitamin A.

Hydroxy acid oils are represented by castor oil which consists principally of glycerides of ricinoleic (12-hydroxyoleic) acid. Castor oil is used (after "dehydration") as a drying oil of the conjugated type, and for the manufacture of a number of specialty products.

Miscellaneous fats include three of unusual fatty acid composition that have been investigated recently (2).

Sterculia oil which contains a 19-carbon cyclopropenyl fatty acid ($CH_3(CH_2)_7$-$C=C(CH_2)_7COOH$) as a major component, is found in the kernels of the tropical $\overset{\diagdown\diagup}{CH_2}$

tree *Sterculia foetida*.

Isano (boleko) oil contains an 18-carbon fatty acid either with 2 acetylenic bonds and 1 double bond (isanic acid, $CH_2=CH(CH_2)_4C\equiv CC\equiv C(CH_2)_7COOH$) or with 2 acetylenic bonds, 1 double bond, and 1 hydroxyl group (isanolic, 8-hydroxyoctadeca-17-en-9,11-diynoic acid, or bolekic acid). This oil is obtained from the kernel of the Isano (Boleko) tree in the Congo.

Vernonia oil contains over 70% of 12,13-epoxyoleic acid, 12,13-epoxy-octadeca-*cis*-9-enoic acid. This is obtained from the purple fleabane grown in India and in the United States.

Properties

PHYSICAL AND THERMAL PROPERTIES

Viscosity. On a log–log scale, the viscosity–temperature relationship of a fatty oil approaches a straight line, with a slope less than that of mineral oils. The curves for hydrogenated cottonseed oil at three different iodine values (6,7) and for oleic acid (Fig. 1) are representative of oils containing principally C_{16} and C_{18} acids. As the viscosity is somewhat dependent upon the average molecular weight as well as the unsaturation, coconut oil, for example, is about one-third less viscous than hydrogenated cottonseed oil of the same iodine value, and rapeseed oil is about one-third more viscous. Because of its content of hydroxy acids, castor oil is much more viscous than

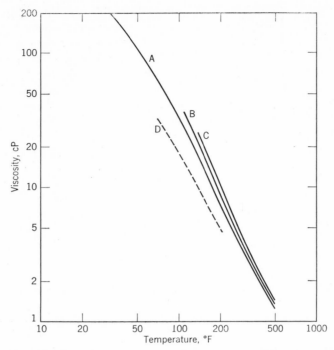

Fig. 1. Viscosity–temperature curves: **A,** cottonseed oil (iodine value, 110); **B,** partially hydrogenated cottonseed oil (iodine value, 66); **C,** highly hydrogenated cottonseed oil (iodine value, 6); and **D,** oleic acid.

ordinary oils (600–800 cP at 25°C and 15–20 cP at 100°C). The viscosity of an oil is increased markedly by polymerization. In the range 25–100°C, the viscosity of an oil is roughly twice that of the corresponding free fatty acids.

Surface and Interfacial Tensions. The surface tension of a refined oil such as cottonseed oil is about 35 dyn/cm and the interfacial tension against water is about 30 dyn/cm at 60–70°C. Both decrease slowly with increasing temperature; for example, the surface tension at 200°C is about 30 dyn/cm.

Crystal Formation. Most natural fats contain a great diversity of high- and low-melting glycerides, which melt or solidify over a wide range of temperatures. Limited cooling of a liquid fat results in the deposition of the higher-melting glycerides in the form of needlelike crystals, which interlace and cohere to form a plastic material with the lower-melting liquid glycerides. The plasticity of fats, which thus changes progressively with temperature, is a highly important property of many industrial fat products (see Margarine; Shortenings). To a large degree, the size of the crystals and the plasticity are dependent upon the rate of cooling, the smallest crystals being produced by rapid cooling. Marked supercooling is characteristic of fats.

Pure triglycerides are polymorphic, that is, they are capable of existing in more than one crystal form, each of which has a distinctive melting point, density, heat of fusion, etc (8). Tristearin, for example, crystallizes in three forms, α, β', and β, with melting points of 65, 70, and 72°C, respectively. The lower-melting metastable forms, which tend to crystallize from rapidly cooled melts, transform irreversibly to the stable highest-melting form when heated slowly, however, rapid heating may cause melting

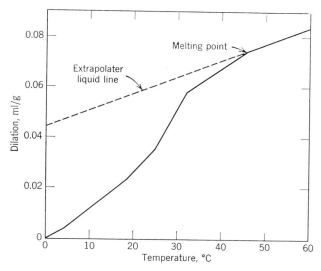

Fig. 2. Dilatometric curve of prime steam lard. Distance of dilatometric curve from extrapolated liquid line is a measure of the amount of solid or crystalline material.

before transformation can occur. Polymorphism is not ordinarily observed in the complex glyceride mixtures comprising most commercial fats; it may be prominent, however, in fats that consist predominantly of one glyceride or class of glycerides, for example, cocoa butter, oleo oil (expressed from oleostock, a high grade of edible tallow), and in highly hydrogenated vegetable oil, where it may produce "double melting" and other anomalous effects.

Melting and Solidification Points. In general, triglycerides reflect the melting points of their constituent fatty acids. Therefore, a low degree of unsaturation, a high molecular weight, and the presence of trans rather than cis isomers of unsaturated acids, all contribute to a relatively high melting point. The melting points (of the stable form) of representative pure triglycerides are given in Table 4. The final melting point of a commercial fat that melts over a range of temperatures is difficult to determine by the ordinary capillary tube method; in addition, it is not always a highly important characteristic, as the practical fat processor or user is often more concerned with the consistency of the fat at some temperature short of that representing complete liquefaction. Most of the melting point methods for commercial fats, including the widely used *Wiley melting point method* (9), actually determine the temperature at which there is an arbitrarily established degree of softening or near-melting. The melting behavior of a typical plastic fat, as revealed by dilatometric measurements, is shown in Figure 2 (5).

The final melting point at which all crystals disappear from the fat is a useful characteristic of hard butters, highly hydrogenated fats, and other fats in which melting occurs with reasonable abruptness, rather than gradually. The final melting points of average samples of certain of these and other fats are given in Table 5.

The solidification point of a commercial fat or other mixture is characteristic only if the determination is carried out under carefully standardized conditions. The solidification point is not often determined on fats as such, except in some cases, for the control of commercial hydrogenation (the so-called *congeal point*), but it is a useful

Table 4. Melting Points of Pure Triglycerides

Triglyceride	Mp, °C	Triglyceride	Mp, °C
tristearin	73.0	*sym*-palmitodistearin	68
tripalmitin	65.5	*unsym*-palmitodistearin	65
trimyristin	57.0	*unsym*-stearodipalmitin	62.5
trilaurin	46.4	palmitomyristolaurin	49.0
triolein	5.5	*sym*-oleodistearin	43.5
trielaidin	42.0	*sym*-oleodipalmitin	37.5
trilinolein	−13	*unsym*-stearodiolein	23.5
trilinolenin	−24	*unsym*-palmitodiolein	19.0

Table 5. Final Melting Points of Average Samples of Fats

Fat or oil	Mp, °C	Fat or oil	Mp, °C
babassu oil	26	palm oil (refined)	40
beef tallow	50	palm kernel oil	29
Borneo tallow	38	peanut oil	13
butterfat	37		
cocoa butter	36	castor oil[a]	87
coconut oil	26	cottonseed oil[b]	60.0
cottonseed oil	11	sardine oil[b]	57.5
lard, prime steam, U.S.	45	soybean oil[b]	66.5

[a] Hydrogenated oil; iodine value, 0.5.   [b] Hydrogenated oil; iodine value, 10.

characteristic of the separated fatty acids when the fat is to be used for soapmaking or fatty acid manufacture. The solidification point of the mixed fatty acids, or the maximum temperature to which the acids are carried by heat of crystallization when a sample of given size is solidified under specified conditions, is known as the *titer* of the fat. The usual ranges of titers for different fats are given in Table 6.

Density. There are no great differences in the densities of different fats and oils in the liquid state, although both the degree of unsaturation (as measured by the iodine value) and the average molecular weight (as measured by the saponification value) affect this property slightly. The following relationship may be derived from the correlation given by Lund (10): $d^{15} = 0.8467 + 0.00030$ (saponification value) +

Table 6. Ranges of Titers for Different Fats

Fat or oil	Titer range, °C	Fat or oil	Titer range, °C
babassu oil	22–23	palm kernel oil	20–28
beef tallow	40–47	peanut oil	26–32
castor oil	2–4	rapeseed oil	11–15
coconut oil	20–24	sardine oil	27–28
corn oil	14–20	sesame oil	20–25
cottonseed oil	30–37	soybean oil	21–23
greases, inedible	36–40	sunflowerseed oil	16–20
lard	32–43	whale oil	22–24
linseed oil	19–21		
menhaden oil	30–34	sardine oil[a]	53.5
olive oil	17–26	soybean oil[a]	64.5
palm oil	40–47	tallow[a]	58.5

[a] Hydrogenated oil; iodine value, 6.

Table 7. Densities of Representative Samples of Fats at 60°C

Fat or oil	d^{60}	Fat or oil	d^{60}
castor oil	0.932	lard[a]	0.889
coconut oil	0.895	linseed oil[a]	0.903
cottonseed oil	0.895	rapeseed oil[a]	0.886
cottonseed oil[a]	0.880	tung oil[a]	0.912

[a] Hydrogenated oil; iodine value, 6.

0.00014 (iodine value). Because of the unusual structure of their fatty acids, conjugated acid oils and hydroxy acid oils do not conform to this relationship. The density of most oils, over the range of temperatures to which oils are ordinarily heated in processing (about 50–500°F), varies linearly with temperature at the rate of about 0.00064/°C or 0.000355/°F. Representative values for the density at 60°C are given in Table 7.

Fats when melted are considerably less dense than if present in the solid state. When a fat sample is melted, there is an accompanying sizable increase in specific volume resulting from both thermal expansion and melting dilation (Fig. 2). Consequently, the solids content of a fat may be estimated from melting dilation data. This dilatometric technique finds application in the control of blending of margarine oil to ensure the desired low-temperature characteristics. It is also useful as an aid in controlling hydrogenation and, generally, in the blending of fats. For these purposes, this technique is likely to replace some of the physical tests now employed.

Specific Heat and Heat of Fusion. The specific heat of liquid fats increases slightly with decrease in the iodine value and varies almost linearly with the temperature. Values reported for different fats are approximately as given in Table 8 (11).

The heat of fusion is a function of the compactness of the fat crystals, being higher for fats of high molecular weight than for those of low molecular weight, higher for simple than for mixed saturated triglycerides, and higher for saturated than for unsaturated glycerides. Heats of fusion of pure trilaurin, trimyristin, tripalmitin, and tristearin are 46.2, 50.3, 53.1, and 54.5 g-cal/g, respectively (12). Reported values for raw cottonseed oil, partially hydrogenated cottonseed oil (iodine value = 59.5), and highly hydrogenated cottonseed oil (iodine value = 0.9) are 20.6, 27.4, and 44.3 g-cal/g, respectively (13). For data for calculations involving melting of these materials, the original articles should be consulted, as plastic fats are not completely solidified except at very low temperatures, and the calculated heat of fusion varies according to the temperature at which melting is assumed to occur.

Vapor Pressure. The vapor pressures of triglycerides are very low. Reported values, in mm Hg, include the following (14): tristearin, 0.001 at 253°C and 0.050

Table 8. Specific Heats of Representative Samples of Oils

Oil	Specific heat	
	40°C	200°C
castor oil	0.52	0.59
cottonseed oil, hydrogenated[a]	0.50	0.60
soybean oil and linseed oil	0.48	0.58
tung oil	0.46	0.55

[a] Iodine value, 6.5

at 313°C; trilaurin, 0.001 at 188°C and 0.050 at 244°C; soybean oil and olive oil, 0.001 at 254°C and 0.050 at 308°C.

Heat of Combustion. Bertram (15) has given the following formula for calculating the approximate heat of combustion of fatty oils, in g-cal/g, in terms of constant volume at 15°C: heat of combustion = 11,380 — iodine value — 9.15 × saponification value. A value of 9500 g-cal/g is ordinarily taken for common edible fats such as lard and cottonseed oil.

Smoke, Fire, and Flash Points. The smoke, fire, and flash points of a fat depend primarily on its content of free fatty acids. "Smoke point" is the temperature at which, in a standardized test (52), a sample gives off a thin, continuous stream of bluish smoke. "Flash point" is the temperature at which a flash appears at any point on the surface of the sample. "Fire point" is the temperature at which application of the test flame to the sample causes burning for a period of at least five seconds. Average values for common fats containing principally C_{16} and C_{18} acids are approximately as given in Table 9.

Table 9. Smoke, Fire, and Flash Points of Common Fats Containing Principally C_{16} and C_{18} Acids

Free fatty acids, %	Smoke pt, °F	Flash pt, °F	Fire pt, °F
0.01	450	625	685
0.10	390	620	680
1.0	315	600	675
10.0	240	470	550

Thermal Conductivity. Fats are relatively poor conductors of heat. The thermal conductivity varies little for different oils, and ranges from about 0.00040 cal/(sec)(sq cm)(°C/cm) at 20°C to 0.00039 at 100°C.

Solubility and Miscibility. Fats and oils are freely miscible with most organic solvents except alcohols at temperatures above their melting points. Castor oil exhibits the peculiarity of free miscibility with alcohols and limited miscibility with hydrocarbons at atmospheric temperatures. At temperatures far below their melting points, fats are only very slightly soluble in solvents. Near their critical temperatures and pressures, organic solvents exhibit an anomalous behavior with respect to their miscibility with fats. Thus, for example, liquid propane becomes incompletely miscible and may be used as an agent for liquid–liquid extraction.

Ordinary refined liquid oils dissolve about 0.07% of their own weight of water at −1°C and about 0.14% at 32°C. The solubility of liquid oils in water is extremely low. Liquid oils dissolve about 92% of their own volume of carbon dioxide at 64°C and about 62% at 140°C. The solubility of other gases, such as nitrogen, oxygen, hydrogen, and carbon monoxide *increases* with increasing temperature of the oil (2). Air dissolves in liquid oils to the extent of about 8 vol/100 vol oil at 30°C and 13 vol/100 vol at 150°C. In all cases there is a linear relationship between solubility and temperature.

Refractive Index. The refractive index of an ordinary fat is dependent upon its average molecular weight (and to a minor degree upon its glyceride structure), as well as its degree of unsaturation, but is useful for estimating the iodine value because of the ease and rapidity with which it can be determined and because there is little variation in the average molecular weight among many common fats. De-

Table 10. Iodine Value Versus Refractive Index for Common Fats and Hydrogenated Fats

Iodine value	n_D^{60}	Iodine value	n_D^{60}
0	1.4468	125	1.4597
25	1.4490	150	1.4628
50	1.4512	175	1.4657
75	1.4540	200	1.4687
100	1.4568		

terminations of the refractive index are particularly useful in the control of fatty-oil hydrogenation.

A curve drawn through the points given in Table 10 will usually indicate the iodine value of an oil or hydrogenated oil such as soybean, sesame, corn, sunflower, or sardine, with fair accuracy (2–3 units), provided the oil is substantially neutral and has not suffered oxidation. In oils high in free fatty acids, the refractive index will be lower than indicated, and in oxidized oils it will be higher.

For oils with saponification values (average molecular weights) different from the oils mentioned above, corrections to the refractive indexes listed should be made as follows: for cottonseed oil, lard, etc, subtract 0.0005; for tallow, palm oil, etc, subtract 0.0010; for palm-kernel oil, subtract 0.0055; for coconut oil, subtract 0.0060; for rapeseed oil, add 0.0008. Castor oil and tung oil, which have fatty acids of unusual structure, have much higher refractive indexes: 1.4730–1.4750 and 1.5170–1.5200, respectively, at 25°C (unhydrogenated oil). The refractive index decreases to the extent of about 0.00038 for each increase in temperature of 1°C.

REACTIONS

The reactions of fats are to a large degree reactions of the component fatty acids. The autoxidation of fats and oils is a reaction of particular importance because of its role in drying oils and in fat rancidification. In general, the readiness with which a fat undergoes oxidation is dependent upon its unsaturation. Spoilage in fat products is almost always a result of atmospheric oxidation rather than the action of microorganisms; although in fatty products of appreciable moisture content, ketonic rancidity, due to the peroxidase activity of molds, may occur. For reactions peculiar to fats, as distinguished from fatty acids, see Ester interchange; Manufacture from fats under Fatty acids; and Soap.

Analysis and Testing

The two most important chemical characteristics of fats are the *iodine value* (the number of grams of iodine or equivalent halogen absorbed under standard conditions by 100 g of fat), which indicates the average degree of unsaturation, and the *saponification value* (the number of milligrams of potassium hydroxide required to saponify 1 g of fat), which is indicative of the average molecular weight. European workers commonly calculate saponification values in terms of the *saponification equivalent* (the number of grams of fat saponified by one mole, 56.1 g, of potassium hydroxide).

Unsaturated fatty acids absorb thiocyanogen in a manner that is different from the absorption of iodine and different according to the number and position of the double bonds; hence, the *thiocyanogen value* (which is calculated in terms of iodine on a percentage basis under standardized conditions), taken together with the iodine value, gives an indication of the fatty acid composition of a fat (9). In recent years, the thiocyanogen value has been largely replaced by ultraviolet measurements on alkali isomerized oils.

Characteristics sometimes determined in dealing with special oils include the Reichert-Meissl, Polenske, and Kirschner values, which depend upon the content of low-molecular-weight fatty acids and, hence, are useful in detecting adulteration in butterfat. The *Reichert-Meissl value* is expressed as the number of milliliters of $0.1N$ alkali required to neutralize the water-soluble volatile fatty acids (largely butyric, caproic, and caprylic) obtained from 5 g of the fat or oil by a specified method of saponification and distillation. The value for butter is relatively high, 21–34; for coconut oil and other lauric acid oils, 3–8; and for most other edible fats and oils, less than 1. Similarly, the *Polenske value* is a measure of water-insoluble, volatile fatty acids (largely capric and lauric). The value for butter is 1.5–3 and for coconut oil, 15–18. The *Kirschner value* indicates the content of water-soluble volatile fatty acids having soluble silver salts (butyric acid). For special oils, such as castor oil, a measure of the free hydroxyl groups is the *acetyl value*, the number of milligrams of potassium hydroxide required to neutralize the acetic acid produced by hydrolysis of 1 g of acetylated fat.

Determinations are often made of the percentage of *unsaponifiable matter*, those components that do not form sodium or potassium soaps, but are soluble in the common oil solvents. In most refined fats, the content of unsaponifiable matter (largely sterols) is 0.5–1.0%; although in high-grade animal fats and coconut oil and other lauric acid oils, it is often lower, and in a few fats (for example, rice-bran oil and shea fat) it may be substantially higher. Determinations are also often made of the percentage of *free fatty acids*, which is calculated as lauric acid for coconut and palm-kernel oils and as oleic acid for most other oils. The free fatty acids can also be expressed in terms of the *acid value*, the number of milligrams of potassium hydroxide required to neutralize the free fatty acids in one gram of fat. The relationship between acid value and percent free fatty acids (calculated as oleic acid) is that 1 unit of acid value = 0.503% free fatty acids.

A number of color tests are used for the detection of specific oils in mixtures, of which only the Halphen test for cottonseed, kapok, or baobab oil, and the Baudouin or Villavecchia tests for sesame oil are altogether reliable. The *Halphen test* depends upon the development of a rich red color when cottonseed oil (or kapok or baobab oil) is heated with amyl alcohol and carbon disulfide containing 1% of sulfur. The reaction is ineffective if the cottonseed oil has been hydrogenated to any considerable degree; however, unhydrogenated oil can be detected if only 1% is present in a mixture of oils. The *Baudouin test* depends upon the development of a persistent rose-red color when sesame oil or hydrogenated sesame oil is treated with a mixture of concentrated hydrochloric acid and cane sugar; it will detect 2% of sesame oil. The *Villavecchia test*, a modification of the Baudouin test, uses furfural instead of cane sugar.

The resistance of a fat to atmospheric oxidation is usually determined by subjecting samples to conditions that greatly accelerate their normal course of oxidation, and noting the time required for a specific high peroxide value (corresponding to rancidity or near-rancidity) to develop. Standard methods include the *A.O.M.* or *Swift stability test* (aeration test) (16,17) in which the samples are aerated at 97.7°C or, in a modification of this test, at 110°C, and the values (times) are reported in hours.

A recent development has been the *ASTM oxygen bomb method* as modified by Gearhart et al. (18), which is more rapid than the A.O.M. method and possesses good precision. For control purposes, a rapid oxygen bomb method (19) is also available. In both of these methods the oxygen absorption is measured on the fat in a bomb under oxygen pressure. This technique appears to be supplanting the standard A.O.M. test in many research laboratories in the United States.

In the *Schaal* or *oven test* (20) samples are incubated in an oven at 60°C and the values are reported in days. Some laboratories determine the stability of a fat by measuring the time required for it to absorb a specific volume of oxygen at an elevated temperature (21). Where some degree of oxidation has occurred before testing the fat, a determination of the *peroxide value* is usually depended upon to evaluate the extent of oxidation. The peroxide value is a determination of the ability of compounds produced by oxidation to liberate iodine from potassium iodide in glacial acetic acid and is expressed in terms of millimoles of peroxide or milliequivalents of oxygen per 1000 grams of fat. There are a number of tests for advanced deterioration or incipient rancidity based upon the presence of aldehydes, of which the *Kreis test* (development of a red color with hydrochloric acid and phloroglucinol) is perhaps the best known. A qualitative test for aldehydes that can also be used is the *Schiff test*, which depends upon the formation of a violet-red color when aldehydes are treated with Schiff reagent (a solution of fuchsin that has been decolorized by passing sulfur dioxide through the solution).

In recent years, several new analytical techniques have been successfully employed in determining the composition of fats, including those listed below.

Chromatography. This involves selective adsorption from solution in a column packed with solid adsorbent. Separations may be based on degree of unsaturation or on chain length. Also, nonfatty constituents may be separated and, if desired, isolated in a highly purified form. Phosphatides can be separated as well as mixtures of mono-, di-, and triglycerides, and cis and trans isomers of fatty acids. Column, paper, thin layer, and GLC (gas–liquid chromatography) are among the types used. The latter is now used widely, in preference to fractional distillation, for determining the chain length and degree of unsaturation of fatty acids. With this technique, small quantities of fatty acids are measurable, making obsolete many of the fatty acid analyses reported by the earlier methods. Details will be found in a recent short course on new lipid analyses (22).

Countercurrent distribution. This makes use of the differing solubilities of fatty acids in two immiscible solvents (23).

In dealing with hydrogenated oils, *nickel*, which may be present as an impurity, is sometimes determined.

For special tests applied in the grading of oils for trading purposes, including refining tests and tests for evaluation of oils on the basis of their depth of color, see Cottonseed. The physical characteristics of importance in the analysis and testing of fats were discussed under Physical and thermal properties, above. As sources of detailed information on analytical and testing methods, the publications of the American Oil Chemists' Society (9) and Jamieson (3) are recommended.

Extraction of Fats and Oils

The commercially important oil-bearing materials include oilseeds, the pulp of certain fruits, and fatty animal tissues. In oilseeds, the oil is concentrated in the kernel, which may contain as little as 16–20% oil in the case of soybeans or as much as 65–70% oil in the case of copra or babassu kernels. The important oil-bearing fruits are the olive and the oil palm, the pulps of which contain about 25–35% oil and 40–50% oil, respectively. The fat content of fatty animal tissues ranges usually from about 60 to 90%. Fat from land animals such as cattle, sheep, and hogs, and from the whale, is recovered largely from fatty tissues that have been trimmed from other portions of the carcass; but fish oils are usually obtained by processing whole fish that contain 10–20% oil. Residues from the processing of oilseeds or animal tissues for oil recovery are high in protein content and are widely used as animal feeds (see Feeds, animal). In the United States, cottonseed, soybean, linseed, peanut, copra, and fish meals or "cake" and animal "tankage" (see Vol. 3, p. 569) are, in particular, important articles of commerce, which are sold at prices based principally upon their protein content. Certain of the residues find some use as plant foods or fertilizers and there is a limited use of certain oilseed residues (principally soybean) as a source of human food or industrial protein products.

Methods for the recovery of fat or oil from oilseeds or other oil-bearing materials will be treated in more detail in special articles dealing with individual fats (see Fish; Soybeans).

Oil-bearing materials that are to be extracted are first pretreated mechanically to facilitate the separation of the oils from the solids. These pretreatments include cleaning, decortication (for large oilseeds), and size reduction or crushing (for almost all oil-bearing materials).

Except in the recovery of olive oil and a small quantity of "cold-pressed" oil from oilseeds, the mechanical expression of oil-bearing materials is invariably preceded by heat treatment, to coagulate proteins and make the parent material permeable to oil flow, to decrease the affinity of the oil for the tissue solids, to cause coalescence of small oil droplets, and to increase the fluidity of the oil. While in the case of oilseeds, such treatment (called cooking) is purely a preparatory operation, in the case of animal tissues, separation of the oil is largely accomplished during the course of the heat treatment (called dry or wet rendering).

Mechanical expression (by batch pressing, continuous pressing, or centrifugal expression) is utilized to recover the major portion of the oil from many oilseeds with a high oil content and from fruit pulp. It is also utilized to recover oil from rendering residues. For maximum recovery of the oil from oilseeds with a low oil content, solvent extraction (batch or continuous) is more efficient than mechanical expression; recently, it has also been used for a few oilseeds of high oil content. Solvent extraction is also utilized for final recovery of oil from residue from mechanical expression. See Centrifugal separation; Extraction.

PROCESSING OF OILSEEDS

Mechanical pretreatment of oilseeds includes cleaning to remove foreign material, decortication (in the case of the larger oilseeds), and reduction of the kernels. Representative practices applicable to most oilseeds are described in detail in the article on Cottonseed. Special *decortication* methods are required for large oilseeds with thick hulls, such as coconuts and palm nuts. Coconuts are split and dried either by exposure to the sun or by forced heating to detach the hulls and produce the copra of commerce. The preliminary decortication and drying of coconuts and of the various palm nuts is carried out in the producing regions, often by hand labor. Other oilseeds are generally shipped in an undecorticated form and are processed all together at the oil mills.

Reduction of oilseeds to relatively small particles or to thin flakes is a necessary preliminary to oil recovery by any means. Reduction methods for small oilseeds are described in connection with the processing of cottonseed and soybeans. In the processing of copra or other large oilseeds, preliminary reduction is often accomplished by the use of hammer mills.

Cooking of oilseeds before mechanical pressing is essentially the same for other oilseeds as for cottonseed and soybeans. Somewhat different practices are followed according to whether the seeds are to be hydraulically pressed or pressed in continuous screw presses. As considerable mechanical heat is generated in the latter, less preliminary heat treatment is required. An important part of the cooking operation is adjustment of the moisture content to give the seed mass the proper plasticity for efficient pressing. Castor beans are virtually the only oilseed pressed in quantity in the United States without preliminary heat treatment (see Castor oil).

Mechanical expression of oilseeds can be carried out by means of open hydraulic presses, or by continuous expellers or screw presses (2). The *cage press*, which consists of a vertical perforated cage in which oil is expelled from the seed by the action of a ram, has been little used in the United States except for the cold pressing of castor beans and the processing of copra; for the latter it is now largely replaced by the screw press. Although relatively expensive and cumbersome in operation, it has the advantage of requiring no press cloths and of being able to handle high-oil materials which are difficult to retain in cloths. As it permits the generation of very high pressures (5000–6000 psi), it is particularly suitable for pressing uncooked seeds. The *pot press*, a steam-heated modification of the cage press, with multiple cages or pots and bottom rather than side drainage, is widely used for the processing of cocoa beans or other oilseeds containing a fat of high melting point (see Vol. 5, p. 381).

In Europe, pressing, either continuous or discontinuous, is often conducted in successive stages at increasingly higher pressures, a practice uncommon in the U.S.

Solvent extraction is a highly efficient means of oil recovery which is capable of reducing the oil content of oilseed residues to about 0.5% as compared with 3–6% by mechanical expression. It is particularly advantageous in the processing of seeds of low oil content and for this reason has in the past found application in the United States principally in the soybean industry. Recently, however, it has been extended to the processing of other oilseeds, including cottonseed, flaxseed, and corn germs. As solvent extraction becomes mechanically complicated in proportion to the oil content of the seed (high oil seeds tend to disintegrate during extraction), it is common practice to "pre-press" seeds of high oil content in low-pressure screw presses (to about 10% residual oil) before extraction.

The design and operation of the continuous extractors used in all large plants has been summarized by Bailey (2). Batch extractors are used to a considerable extent for the extraction of castor bean pomace or residue from mechanical expression. The usual solvents are a light petroleum fraction (so-called extraction naphthas), such as a grade consisting chiefly of *n*-hexane.

RECOVERY OF OIL FROM FRUIT PULPS

Olives, after being crushed in edge-runner or other types of mills, are pressed in open hydraulic presses or, occasionally, pot presses or screw presses. In European practice, relatively low pressure (500–1000 psi) open presses are used and pressing is conducted in two or three stages with segregation of the oil from each stage. The product of the first pressing is so-called "virgin" olive oil. Separation of oil from the aqueous material that is expressed is carried out by prolonged settling. As olive oil is relatively expensive, the residue or "marc" from pressing which contains 8–10% oil is commonly solvent-extracted with a hydrocarbon solvent to produce an oil that is salable as an edible oil after refining. So-called "sulfur olive oil," obtained by solvent extraction with carbon disulfide according to older European practice, is not edible.

Bunches of *palm* fruits are first "sterilized" to stop enzyme action and loosen the fruit from the stalks by a short steam treatment in an autoclave. The fruits are then stripped off and cooked or "digested" in open steam-heated kettles. The digested and partially dried material is pressed in special steam-heated cage presses and, after the addition of water, the extract is separated into an oil layer and a water and solids layer by settling or centrifuging. By an alternative method, dehydration of the fruits during sterilization and digestion is avoided and the oil is separated in an atmosphere of steam in a basket centrifuge. The two methods are said to be equally efficient.

RENDERING OF ANIMAL FATS

For a description of the wet-rendering and dry-rendering methods used in the United States packing houses for the recovery of lard, tallow, and greases see Meat and meat products. Rendering methods for other animal fats, including marine oils, are essentially similar; however, whale and fish oils are invariably wet-rendered, often continuously, with centrifugal separation of the fatty and aqueous phases. Open hydraulic presses, cage presses, and continuous screw presses are all used for the final recovery of oil from rendering residues, and the latter are often solvent-extracted after pressing.

Processing

The following discussion of oil processing will cover only those methods that are applied to fats and oils generally and will exclude special methods for individual products.

REFINING

Crude fats or oils are refined to remove free fatty acids and phosphatides and other gummy or mucilaginous materials and to improve the color.

Alkali Refining. Refining is generally carried out by treating the fat with a strong (10–20°Bé) solution of caustic soda. The process involves the following steps: (*1*) emulsifying the fat with a considerable excess of the aqueous alkali solution; (*2*) heating to break the emulsion; and (*3*) separating the refined oil from the precipitated soap and miscellaneous associated impurities. The precipitated material known in the trade as "foots" or "soapstock" is a commodity that usually contains 30–50% free and combined fatty acids; this material, with or without acidulation to decompose the soap and remove excess water, is sold for use in soapmaking and the manufacture of commercial fatty acids.

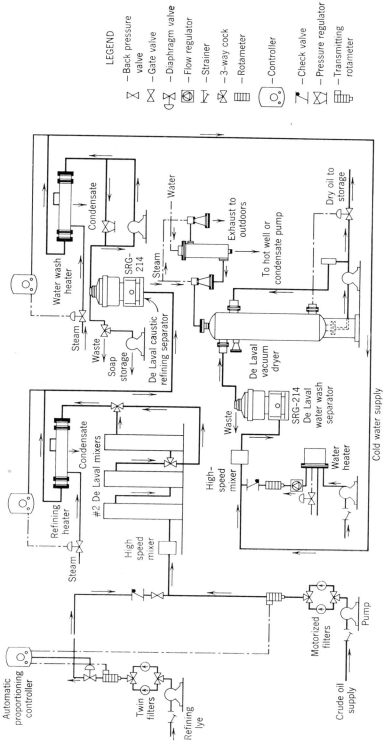

Fig. 3. Continuous oil refining. Courtesy The De Laval Separator Co.

By means of refining, crude oils, which seldom contain less than 0.5% free fatty acids and often much more, are reduced to a free fatty acids content of 0.01–0.03%.

Batch caustic soda refining is carried out in open kettles equipped with cone bottoms, heating coils, and variable-speed mechanical agitators in which separation of the refined oil and soapstock is effected by prolonged gravity settling. In the batch refining of animal fats and vegetable fats of the lauric acid type which are almost free of phosphatides, relatively little neutral oil is lost by saponification or occlusion in the soapstock. However, in refining vegetable oils, such as cottonseed and soybean, the presence of phosphatides or other surface-active materials leads to considerable neutral oil losses. Cottonseed oil, for example, which contains 1.0% free fatty acids and 2.0% phosphatides and other nonglyceride impurities, will often have a refining loss by the batch method as high as 7–8%. Consequently, there has been widespread adoption, particularly in the United States where cottonseed and soybean oil processing predominates, of a continuous caustic soda refining process (24–27), which reduces the refining loss (usually by 25–30%) by shortening the contact time between caustic and oil and by separating the oil and soapstock very efficiently in high-speed centrifuges. Continuous caustic soda refining was introduced in the United States in about 1933, and, in succeeding years, largely replaced batch refining for the treatment of vegetable oils. A flow diagram of the continuous caustic refining process is shown in Figure 3.

There have been many attempts to reduce refining losses by minimizing the saponification that occurs with neutral oil and alkali, especially where stronger alkalies are needed to obtain sufficiently light-colored oil. In the well-known Clayton continuous soda ash–caustic soda process (28–30) refining is carried out in two stages and with two reagents. In the first stage, the oil is largely neutralized, and the phosphatides and other gums are removed by treatment with a 20°Bé soda ash solution; in the second stage, neutralization is completed and color bodies are taken out by treatment with 20°Bé caustic soda solution. Although theoretically sound, carbonate neutralization has often been found difficult to apply in practice, especially in view of the extra equipment needed and problems resulting from the CO_2 formed. In view of this, U.S. suppliers of continuous refining systems currently prefer to offer straight caustic refining, and the expected replacement of caustic by soda ash–caustic soda systems has not taken place.

Hydration or "degumming" of crude vegetable oils with water or a weak aqueous solution to precipitate phosphatides, is often practiced before alkali refining, particularly in dealing with solvent-extracted soybean oil where the phosphatides or gums form the raw material for the production of commercial lecithin (qv). Hydration is usually carried out continuously, separation of the gums being effected in high-speed centrifuges.

Acid Refining. Drying oils intended for technical use are sometimes acid-refined, that is, treated with a small amount of strong (60°Bé or about 78%) sulfuric acid, to char and precipitate phosphatides and similar impurities.

Steam Refining. Lard or other high-grade animal fats and vegetable oils substantially free of phosphatides can be successfully steam-refined or deacidified by steam stripping at high temperatures under a vacuum.

Solvent Refining. The Solexol process (53) of liquid–liquid extraction with propane is very effective for the removal of color bodies from low-grade fats and is used to some extent for refining inedible tallows and greases for soapmaking.

BLEACHING OR DECOLORIZATION

For many products, including shortening, margarine, high-grade soaps, and light varnishes and enamels, alkali refining alone does not produce a sufficiently light-colored oil, and additional bleaching treatment is required.

Adsorption. Bleaching is usually effected by treating the refined oil with an absorbent in powder form. Both natural (fuller's earth) and acid-activated bleaching earths (or clays) are used as adsorbents. The latter are more expensive, but have greater adsorptive power for fat pigments, particularly for chlorophyll or related compounds. Activated carbon is used in bleaching to some extent but usually only as an adjunct to a bleaching earth and in much smaller quantity; it tends to take up impurities as well as pigments, including traces of soap left from refining.

Bleaching is usually carried out at a temperature of 220–240°F (104–116°C) under atmospheric pressure; in bleaching under vacuum, slightly lower temperatures may be employed. More than about 1% of activated earth is seldom used in bleaching good edible oils although considerably more may be required if a natural earth of lower activity is used or if the oil is of poor grade and highly colored. Equilibrium between unadsorbed pigments in the oil and adsorbed pigments on the earth is quickly established (within about 5 min) when the latter is vigorously agitated with the oil. In the common practice of batch bleaching, the oil and adsorbent are heated and mixed together in a kettle of about 30,000-lb capacity, after which the kettle charge is pumped through a filter press. The press cake of spent adsorbent is blown with air, or steam and air, to reduce its entrained oil content to a minimum of 30–40% and is discarded, in some cases after solvent extraction or other treatment for further oil recovery.

To avoid oxidation, which is injurious to the stability, the operation is preferably carried out in a closed system under vacuum, although the use of open kettles is not uncommon. Continuous and semicontinuous closed bleaching systems, in which the oil or oil–earth slurry is pumped into an evacuated chamber for deaeration, are now finding widespread acceptance in the industry. Such a continuous system has been described by Singleton and McMichael (31). Preference for continuous or semi-continuous plants depends largely upon the variety of fats processed, semicontinuous often being preferred where several different fats are bleached and where any mixing is undesirable.

Chemical bleaching methods (using such reagents as sodium dichromate or chlorine dioxide) depend upon the oxidation of fat pigments to colorless forms. As they also involve hazard of oxidation of the oil, they are not used in processing edible fats and are applied on but a limited scale in the treatment of fats for technical use. The Solexol process of extraction with liquid propane constitutes an effective bleaching method, particularly for fats that contain pigments difficult to remove by adsorption. A considerable bleaching effect (principally through the reduction or heat destruction of carotenoid pigments) is incidental to the hydrogenation process and also, to a lesser degree, to steam deodorization or other heat treatment of vegetable oils.

HYDROGENATION

Hydrogenation is a highly important process of the fatty oil industry, particularly in the manufacture of edible fat products (see Margarine; Shortenings), where it is used to convert liquid oils, such as cottonseed and soybean oils, to plastic fats. It is also used in the manufacture of soaps. In addition to its effect upon the melting point

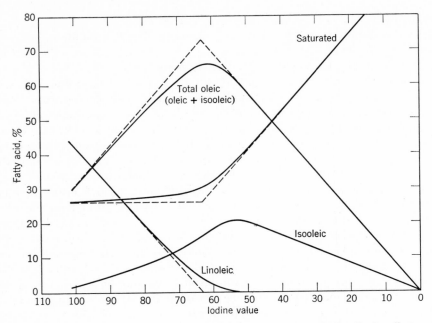

Fig. 4. Effect of hydrogenation on the composition of cottonseed oil. Broken lines represent theoretical contents of saturated, oleic, and linoleic acids, with complete selectivity of hydrogenation.

and consistency of oils and fats, hydrogenation improves the resistance of the edible fat products to atmospheric oxidation. The stability of a partially hydrogenated fat depends principally upon its decreased content of linoleic or other polyunsaturated acids as these acids oxidize much more readily than oleic acid (32,33). As defined here, hydrogenation refers to the reduction of ethylenic linkages in fatty acid chains; for hydrogenation at the carboxyl group to produce fatty alcohols, see Alcohols, higher, fatty.

As carried out commercially, the hydrogenation of fats, fatty acids, or other fatty esters is a liquid-phase process in which gaseous hydrogen is dispersed and caused to dissolve in the heated fat, where, under the influence of a solid catalyst (almost invariably nickel), it combines with unsaturated fatty acid radicals. Although continuous hydrogenation with a fixed catalyst has been practiced on a limited scale (34), the process has inherent disadvantages, and virtually all present-day hydrogenation is carried out batchwise with a powder catalyst, which is removed from the fat by filtration at the conclusion of the reaction and is generally reused a number of times. The rate of reaction, as well as the course of the reaction and the composition of the hydrogenated product, is profoundly influenced by the nature of the catalyst and also by the conditions under which hydrogenation is conducted, including the temperature, pressure, thoroughness of dispersion of hydrogen in the oil, and catalyst concentration. The present process is not essentially different from that originated by Normann (35) and placed in large-scale operation in the period about 1905–1915; improvements in hydrogenation practice have resulted chiefly from the development of improved catalyst, more efficient methods of dispersing the hydrogen in the oil, and better understanding of the effects of the different operating variables.

Principles. The typical effect of hydrogenation on the composition of an oleic–linoleic acid oil is illustrated in Figure 4. Hydrogen absorbed by the oil is used principally in converting linoleic acid to oleic acid, rather than in converting oleic acid to the saturated (stearic) acid. However, the oleic acid formed during the course of hydrogenation is not wholly normal oleic acid (*cis*-9-octadecenoic acid), but consists in part of trans forms of oleic acid and its isomers. As these so-called "isooleic" acids are higher melting than the normal acid, the consistency and melting point of the hydrogenated fat depend to a considerable degree upon the extent to which they are formed, as well as the degree to which linoleic acid is hydrogenated, in preference to oleic acid. In general, isooleic acids increase the hardness of the fat at lower temperatures (up to about 35°C) but have relatively little effect upon the consistency at higher temperatures (35–45°C), whereas saturated acids formed during the reaction contribute to the consistency in both ranges of temperature (36). The technology of fat hydrogenation (for the manufacture of margarine and shortening) is largely concerned with control of the reaction to provide the proportions of saturated, isooleic, normal oleic, and linoleic acids that are required to provide specific consistency and stability characteristics in the hydrogenated products.

The term *selectivity* is applied in reference to the preferential hydrogenation of linoleic acid in fats where both linoleic and oleic acids are present. In general, selectivity is associated with the formation of relatively large amounts of isooleic acids, and is promoted by a high temperature, a high catalyst concentration, a low hydrogen pressure, and a low degree of hydrogen dispersion in the oil. It appears that the factors of catalyst concentration, pressure, hydrogen dispersion, and possibly also temperature, all affect the selectivity through their influence upon the concentration of hydrogen in the reaction zone (that is, adsorbed on the catalyst), with selectivity being favored by a low concentration (37). With very high selectivity, the rate at which hydrogen reacts with linoleic acid may be as much as fifty times as great as its rate of reaction with oleic acid; under conditions leading to very low selectivity, the reaction rate of linoleic acid may be no more than four times that of oleic acid (37). In the hydrogenation of cottonseed oil the isooleic acid content (as determined by the usual lead soap–alcohol method) may rise to a maximum as high as 25–30% with very selective hydrogenation, or as low as 3–4% with very nonselective hydrogenation.

Selectivity appears to be largely a matter of a difference in reactivity between double bonds separated by an active methylene group (as in linoleic acid) and double bonds more widely separated (38); hence, if the double bonds are widely separated, polyethenoid acids are not highly reactive. Furthermore, as the number of double bonds in a fatty acid is increased beyond two, further increase in reactivity is not comparable to the difference between linoleic and oleic acids. An "isolinoleic" acid (9,15-octadecadienoic acid), for example, hydrogenates only about 2.5–4.0 times as readily as oleic acid, and linolenic acid only about 1.5–2.5 times as readily as linoleic acid, the exact ratio in each case being relatively little dependent upon hydrogenation conditions (37).

Different catalysts vary considerably with respect to the amount of isooleic acids produced at a given level of saturated acid formation. In the industry, catalysts that tend to suppress the formation of both saturated and isooleic acids are termed selective.

Hydrogenation Reactors. The reactors in common use in the United States are of two types. The *hydrogen-recirculation type* consists of a tall cylindrical vessel that often has no mechanical agitator but is provided with a hydrogen distributor in the

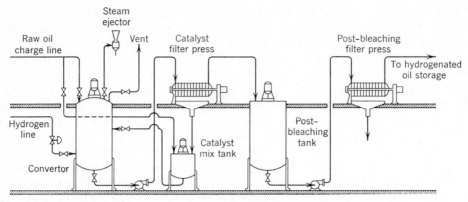

Fig. 5. Simplified flow diagram of hydrogenation plant, dead-end system.   Courtesy Votator Division, Chemetron Corp.

bottom through which hydrogen in excess of the amount required for reaction is blown during the course of reaction; the hydrogen not absorbed is recirculated from the headspace by means of a blower.   The vessel is usually designed for pressures only slightly in excess of atmospheric and is supplied with hydrogen from a low-pressure holder.   Internal steam and water coils are provided for heating the charge of oil and catalyst and for carrying away the heat of reaction, but the finished batch is usually cooled by pumping it out through an external heat exchanger as agitation within the vessel ceases when hydrogen flow is stopped at the conclusion of the reaction.

The newer *dead-end system* employs a vertical, cylindrical, pressure vessel with a mechanical agitator of the gas-dispersion type and is supplied from high-pressure storage tanks with only as much hydrogen as is absorbed by the oil.   It is provided with internal coils for both heating and cooling and often with a steam ejector for maintaining the vessel under vacuum during periods when hydrogenation is not progressing.   The recirculation reactor is kept filled with hydrogen at all times.   A complete hydrogenation plant employing the dead-end system is illustrated in Figure 5.

There is no great difference between the two systems with respect to the reaction rate, and preference for one or the other is based upon consideration of such factors as installed cost, operating economy, and ease of hydrogenation control.   The usual range of capacities for either is 10,000–40,000 lb/batch.

In practice, hydrogenation is usually carried out with maximum hydrogen dispersion and a fairly constant concentration of catalyst (0.05–0.15% nickel), and adjustments of the temperature and pressure are depended upon to give the variations in selectivity that are required for different products.   The usual ranges of temperature and pressure are about 250–375°F (120–190°C) and 0–100 psig, respectively.   In general, margarine oils are hydrogenated very selectively at relatively low pressures and high temperatures to produce a firm but low-melting product, whereas shortening stocks are hydrogenated with moderate selectivity at lower temperatures and higher pressures to obtain the minimum iodine value and maximum stability consistent with proper low- and high-temperature consistency.   In the hydrogenation of edible hard stocks for blending with soft oils, or in the hydrogenation of inedible fats for manufacture of fatty acids, such as stearic acid, or for soapmaking, the selectivity of the reaction is unimportant; thus, a combination of high temperature and high pressure is used to make the reaction as rapid as possible. Margarine or shortening stocks are generally hydrogenated within 1–2 hr. A somewhat longer time is usually required for the hydrogenation of hard stocks or inedible fats.

Catalysts. Hydrogenation catalysts are prepared either by "wet reduction," that is, by thermal decomposition of nickel formate or other heat-labile nickel salt in a fatty oil at about 425–450°F (218–232°C), or sometimes by "dry reduction" with hydrogen of nickel carbonate or nickel hydroxide precipitated on a diatomaceous earth carrier at about 800–900°F (427–482°C). Wet-reduced catalysts are often copper-promoted to facilitate reduction (39); the promotion of nickel catalysts with other metals is uncommon. There is a limited use of catalysts of the Raney or nickel alloy type. Platinum and palladium are effective hydrogenation catalysts, but offer no advantages over the much cheaper nickel and, hence, find no commercial use. The most desirable catalysts are highly active, as selective as they can be made without undue sacrifice of ruggedness or activity, and uniform with respect to both activity and selectivity. A large part of the catalysts consumed in the United States is now made by chemical companies specializing in catalyst manufacture, rather than by oil processors (see also Catalysis).

Catalysts are readily inactivated or rendered nonselective by a variety of poisons which may be present in either the oil or the hydrogen. The oil to be hydrogenated must be free of phosphatides or other gums, and also soap and sulfur or halogen compounds. The common gaseous catalyst poisons from which the hydrogen must be rigorously purified include sulfur compounds (hydrogen sulfide, carbon disulfide, organic sulfur compounds) and carbon monoxide. Poisoning of the catalyst with carbon monoxide has the peculiarity of being reversible when the catalyst–oil mixture is subjected to reduced pressure and of being most pronounced at the lower hydrogenation temperatures. Carbon dioxide, nitrogen, methane, and water vapor are not catalyst poisons although they may be undesirable hydrogen diluents.

DEODORIZATION

With the exception of olive oil, which is prized for its natural flavor and odor, virtually all of the vegetable oil entering edible fat products in Occidental countries is subjected to deodorizing treatment for flavor and odor removal. Although lard is largely consumed in its natural form, there is now a significant and growing production of deodorized lard products in the United States; and the considerable amount of lard and edible tallow incorporated into compound-type shortenings is also deodorized. All hydrogenated fats intended for edible use must be deodorized to free them of the typical flavor and odor imparted by hydrogenation.

The identity and concentrations of the odoriferous materials in fats and oils are still under active investigation. Among the materials discovered to date are ketones (40), terpenoid hydrocarbons (41), and unsaturated aldehydes (42). They generally constitute less than 0.1% of the total weight of the oil.

Deodorization is a process of steam distillation in which the relatively nonvolatile oil is maintained at a high temperature and under reduced pressure while it is stripped of the relatively volatile constituents responsible for flavor and odor. Free fatty acids in the oil are usually reduced to 0.01–0.03% if originally present in greater amount, and vegetable oils and their products also ordinarily undergo a considerable reduction in color. In the manufacture of edible products, deodorization is almost invariably the last step in processing before finishing and packaging.

Rather drastic treatment is required to produce the completely bland and odorless fats that are demanded by consumers in the United States and many other countries. Even at elevated temperatures and low pressures, prolonged stripping with a considerable quantity of steam is required for satisfactory flavor and odor removal. In modern installations, three-stage steam ejectors with barometric intercondensers are usually used for maintaining a vacuum on the oil; with these, depending upon the temperature of the condenser water, 3–4 lb of motive steam are required for each pound of steam used for stripping. Hence, steam requirements of the process are relatively high. As the volatility of the odoriferous components of an oil appears to increase with increase in the temperature at roughly the same rate as the vapor pressures of the common fatty acids (doubling with each increment of about 30°F. (or 17°C.), and as stripping-stem requirements at a fixed temperature are in direct proportion to the absolute pressure (43), the importance of high temperature and high vacuum in the interest of steam economy is manifest. Modern developments in deodorization have been primarily a matter of working toward higher vacuums and, more particularly, higher temperatures, which are now generally in the range of 425–475°F (218–246°C), and at the same time effecting mechanical improvements in the equipment. The effective use of higher temperatures has made mechanical design more exacting as the deleterious effect of accidental air leakage is greatly magnified, as is also that of metallic contamination of the oil. In modern deodorizing practice, the rigorous exclusion of oxygen from the oil in process may be regarded as absolutely essential.

The common batch deodorizer is a vertical cylindrical vessel usually designed to hold 20,000–30,000 lb of oil. To accommodate rolling and splashing of the oil charge without excessive carry-over, a headspace approximately equivalent to the depth of oil is usually provided. Stripping steam at the rate of about 500–1000 lb/hr is injected into a distributor at the bottom of the vessel and, after passing upward through the oil, is taken off at the top through a large vapor line communicating with the ejector system. Most modern installations operate at an absolute pressure of 5–6 mm, which is the practical limit of three-stage steam-ejector equipment. A few four-stage ejector systems are in operation that produce a pressure of 1–2 mm, but it is generally considered that the advantages gained with the lower pressure are not commensurate with the increased motive-steam consumption.

Practice varies in heating and cooling the oil charge. Some deodorizers contain no heating or cooling coils; the charge is heated before deodorization by recirculation through an external heater and is pumped out through a cooler after it is deodorized. In other installations, the oil is heated in the deodorizer and cooled externally; in still others, internal coils are provided for both heating and cooling. In any case, it is necessary to reduce the temperature of the oil to 120–140°F (49–60°C) before it is exposed to the atmosphere to avoid injury to its flavor or flavor stability. Some processors withdraw deodorized shortening under nitrogen and likewise plasticize and package under nitrogen.

Batch deodorizers are generally built of ordinary carbon steel although, recently, increasing use has been made of nickel or stainless steel. In laboratory tests, Ziels and Schmidt (44) have demonstrated that at deodorizing temperatures nickel and aluminum are the only common metals of construction that are completely free of proxidant effect on oils. The refluxing of easily condensible materials from the cool surfaces of the upper shell and vapor lines is a source of considerable trouble in batch deodorizers. To prevent refluxing, these are sometimes provided with a heating jacket (45).

For rapid and efficient deodorization, somewhat higher temperatures are required than are obtainable with steam at ordinary boiler pressures. In the older high-temperature deodorization plants, the oil was heated by circulation through a direct-fired heater (the Wesson system) or by the circulation of mineral oil through a similar heater and then through coils in the deodorizer (the Merrill system). Some modern installations have employed high-pressure steam for heating, but preference has generally been given to the use of Dowtherm (diphenyl–diphenyl oxide) vaporizers (see Heat transfer media), which provide sufficiently high vapor temperatures at pressures of 10–20 psig.

In batch deodorization, stripping is carried out for periods ranging from about 2–10 hr; the total weight of stripping steam used per 100 lb oil usually ranges from about 15–50 lb, with an average of perhaps 25 lb.

Two types of continuous deodorizers have found considerable use in the United States. The first of these, the *Foster-Wheeler deodorizer* (46–48), introduced in about 1936, employs a stainless-steel tower with trays and bubble caps down which deaerated oil, after heat exchange with hot effluent oil and Dowtherm vapors, is passed in counter-current flow to stripping steam. The usual amount of stripping steam used is 10 lb/100 lb oil. Capacities of standard units are 2500–30,000 lb/hr. A number of units are in operation in the United States and in South America.

The second type, the *Votator "semicontinuous" deodorizer*, of The Girdler Corporation (49) employs a series of superimposed shallow nickel trays (interconnected with drop lines and automatically operated drop valves) which are suspended inside a tall cylindrical shell and in which the oil is heated (with steam and Dowtherm vapor), stripped, and cooled as it drops intermittently from one tray to another. The shell and tray construction provides a double wall between the oil and the atmosphere that renders it impossible for air accidentally leaking into the apparatus to come into contact with the hot oil. The oil is deodorized for one hour, and stripping steam requirements are 4.5 lb/100 lb oil. The capacities of standard units are 2000–15,000 lb/hr or more. Introduced in 1948, it has been adopted by a number of United States and Canadian processors.

Sources and Production

Most oils (60%) are obtained from plants, with animals next (36%), and marine life last (4%).

In order of world production, in 1962 (50) the most common fats and oils ranked as follows (production in billions of pounds given in parentheses after each oil): butter (8.70), lard (8.36), soybean oil (8.22), tallows and greases (7.55), peanut oil (5.10), cottonseed oil (4.89), sunflower oil (4.34), coconut oil (4.28), olive oil (2.89), rapeseed oil (2.84), palm oil (2.80), and linseed oil (2.07).

Butterfat, from cow's milk, is produced mostly in the United States, Australia, New Zealand, and Western Europe. The largest lard-producing sections of the world are essentially those in which quantities of corn are available for hog feeding, and include particularly the United States and the Danube Valley. Soybean oil is produced mainly in the United States and China. United States production of soybean oil has risen strikingly in the last thirty years and particularly in the last ten years, increasing from 2.7 billion lb in 1954 to 5.1 billion lb in 1964. Beef and mutton tallow production is concentrated in the United States, South America, Australia, and New Zealand. The sources and approximate world production of the commercially important vegetable oils are given in Table 3. Special note should be made of safflower oil which in the last few years has had limited use in this country in several margarines as a result of the interest in polyunsaturated fats. Production of safflower oil in 1962–1963 averaged 116 million lb.

Of the marine oils, whale oil production exceeded that of fish (including liver) oils until 1961 when fish oils took the lead. Unlike animal fats, marine oils are not usually by-products of the preparation of carcasses for meat but come from fish taken for oil. Fish oils are derived mainly from small oily fish, such as sardines, herring, and menhaden, which are caught in the North Atlantic and North Pacific oceans. The whole fish is processed to yield oils as the primary product, and the residue remaining after extraction of the oil is used for animal feed or as a fertilizer. Whales, normally taken in the Antarctic regions, yield whale oil together with some by-products.

The production of fish-liver oils, of which cod-liver oil is the most plentiful, is not large, but is important because of the vitamin content of the oils. The largest producers are the United States, Canada, and Norway.

Economic Aspects

The factory consumption of the principal fats and oils in different classes of products in the United States in 1963 is shown in Table 11. In this connection it should be noted that there are pronounced differences in the utilization of fats as food material

Table 11. Factory Consumption, in Millions of Pounds, of Fats and Oils in Different Classes of Products in the United States in 1963 (51)

Fat or oil	Edible product	Soap	Paints	Miscellaneous[a]
cottonseed	1145			4
soybean	3636		88	133
corn	352			
peanut	69			4
lard	709			19
edible tallow	392			11
safflower	53		7	1
coconut	225	152		350
linseed			312	72
inedible tallow and grease		684		1550
tall oil			18	905
castor			24	101
tung			23	9
palm				44
palm kernel				55
fish				53
marine mammal				36
other				46

[a] Includes miscellaneous inedible uses where edible use figures are given and includes all uses where no separate figures are available for edible and inedible uses.

here and abroad. The vegetable shortening industry, for example, furnishes a considerable proportion of the edible fat consumed in the United States but is relatively unimportant in almost all other countries. On the other hand, margarine is the most popular fat product in the northern European countries, and olive oil or other liquid fats are preferred in the Mediterranean region. Cottonseed and soybean oils, which dominate the North American vegetable oil field, are secondary to such oils as peanut, palm, palm kernel, rapeseed, and whale oils in Europe. Rapeseed, sesame, and sunflowerseed oils are important edible oils in Eastern Europe and the Orient. Sunflowerseed oil is the most important vegetable oil in the Soviet Union and is very important in South America.

Only the United States and the Soviet Union are relatively self-sufficient in oil and fat supplies. The vegetable oil supplies of Western Europe are normally derived in large part from oilseeds imported from Africa, India, China, Manchuria, the East Indies, and other islands of the South Pacific. Butter for the United Kingdom and

Table 12. Wholesale Prices of Different Fats and Oils in the United States, 1950–1963

Fat or oil	Grade	Container	Place of sale	Wholesale price average, $\not c/lb^{a,b}$		
				1950–1954	1960	1963
butter	92 score		Chicago	66.4	59.9	58.0
castor oil	no. 3	tanks	New York	25.2	19.3	18.5
coconut oil	crude	tanks	Pacific coast	17.1	14.3	11.2
cod-liver oil	USP XIII	barrels	New York	21.4	18.2	16.9
corn oil	crude	tank cars	Midwestern mills	15.3	13.1	14.5
cottonseed oil	crude	tank cars	Southeastern mills	14.9	9.9	10.1
grease	A white	tank cars	Chicago	7.4	5.4	4.8
lard	prime steam	loose	Chicago	13.1	8.8	8.2
linseed oil	raw	tank cars	Minneapolis	16.2	13.1	12.7
olive oil	edible	drums	New York	33.5	30.8	54.7
palm oil	crude	drums	New York	15.0	14.2	14.0
peanut oil	crude	tank cars	mills	18.7	15.1	12.6
rapeseed oil	refined, denatured	bulk	New York	19.2	13.0	13.5
safflower oil	nonbreak	tanks	East coast	15.8	15.5	20.0
soybean oil	crude	tank cars	Midwestern mills	13.5	8.8	9.2
tallow	edible	tank cars	Chicago	9.8	8.5	8.2
tung oil		drums	New York	32.1	24.1	42.2

[a] U.S. Department of Agriculture, *Agricultural Statistics, 1963.*
[b] U.S. Department of Agriculture, Bureau of Agricultural Economics, *The Fats & Oils Situation,* March 1964.

Germany is largely imported from Australia, New Zealand, Denmark, and the Netherlands. Tallows come largely from the United States, South America, Australia, and New Zealand. Large quantities of vegetable oils and oilseeds come from South America, with Brazil the largest producer of castor beans (and the only producer of babassu and oiticica oils) and Argentina the largest producer of flaxseed and sunflowerseed. China produces almost all the tung oil. In general, there is a heavy importation of fats or oilseeds by industrialized nations from more agricultural and less industrialized parts of the world.

The prices of fats and oils are characterized by greater variation than those of most commodities. Prices of selected fats and oils during the period 1950–1963 are given in Table 12.

Bibliography

"Fats and Fatty Oils" in *ECT* 1st ed., Vol. 6, pp. 140–172, by A. E. Bailey, The Humko Co.

1. T. P. Hilditch and P. N. Williams, *The Chemical Constitution of Natural Fats*, 4th ed., John Wiley & Sons, Inc., New York, 1964.
2. D. Swern, *Bailey's Industrial Oil and Fat Products*, 3rd ed., John Wiley & Sons, Inc., New York, 1964.
3. G. S. Jamieson, *Vegetable Fats and Oils*, 2nd ed., Reinhold Publishing Corp., New York, 1943.
4. A. T. James and A. J. P. Martin, *Biochem. J.* **50,** 679 (1950).
5. L. Klee and G. H. Benham, *J. Am. Oil Chemists' Soc.* **27,** 130–133 (1950).
6. F. C. Magne and E. L. Skow, *Ind. Eng. Chem.* **37,** 1097–1101 (1945).
7. H. Wakeham and F. C. Magne, *Ind. Eng. Chem.* **36,** 568–570 (1944).
8. A. E. Bailey, *Melting and Solidification of Fats*, Interscience Publishers, Inc., New York, 1950.
9. *American Oil Chemists' Society Official and Tentative Methods*, 2nd ed., 1964 revision, Chicago, Ill.
10. J. Lund, *Z. Untersuch. Nahr. u. Genussm.* **44,** 113–187 (1922).
11. P. E. Clark, C. R. Waldeland, and R. P. Cross, *Ind. Eng. Chem.* **38,** 350–353 (1946).
12. G. H. Charbonnet and W. S. Singleton, *J. Am. Oil Chemists' Soc.* **24,** 140–142 (1947).
13. G. D. Oliver, W. S. Singleton, S. S. Todd, and A. E. Bailey, *Oil & Soap* **21,** 297–300 (1944).
14. E. S. Perry, W. H. Weber, and B. F. Daubert, *J. Am. Chem. Soc.* **71,** 3720–3726 (1949).
15. S. H. Bertram, *Chem. Tech. (Dordrecht)* **1,** 101–102 (1946).
16. A. E. King, H. L. Roschen, and W. H. Irwin, *Oil & Soap* **10,** 204–207 (1933).
17. V. C. Mehlenbacher, *Oil & Soap* **19,** 137–139 (1942).
18. W. M. Gearhart, B. N. Stuckey, and J. J. Austen, *J. Am. Oil Chemists' Soc.* **34,** 427 (1957).
19. W. D. Pohle, R. L. Gregory, and B. van Giessen, *J. Am. Oil Chemists' Soc.* **40,** 603 (1963).
20. N. T. Joyner and J. E. McIntyre, *Oil & Soap* **15,** 184–186 (1938).
21. E. W. Eckey, *Oil & Soap* **23,** 38–40 (1946).
22. *J. Am. Oil Chemists' Soc.* **38,** 538–562, 565–588, 625–636, 708–727 (1961).
23. V. C. Mehlenbacher, *The Analysis of Fats and Oils*, The Garrard Press, Champaign, Ill., 1960, pp. 575–582.
24. E. M. James, *Oil & Soap* **11,** 137–138 (1934).
25. L. D. Tyler, *Food Inds.* **20,** 1456–1459 (1948).
26. U.S. Pat. 2,050,844 (Aug. 11, 1936), E. M. James (to Sharples Specialty Co.).
27. U.S. Pats. 2,100,274; 2,100,275 (Nov. 23, 1937), B. Clayton, W. B. Kerrick, and H. M. Stadt (to Refining, Inc.); 2,100,276; 2,100,277 (Nov. 23, 1937), B. Clayton (to Refining, Inc.).
28. M. Mattikow, *Oil & Soap* **19,** 83–87 (1942).
29. M. Mattikow, *J. Am. Oil Chemists' Soc.* **25,** 200–203 (1948).
30. U.S. Pats. 2,190,593; 2,190,594; and succeeding pats. (Feb. 13, 1940), B. Clayton (to Refining, Inc.).
31. W. A. Singleton and C. E. McMichael, *J. Am. Oil Chemists' Soc.* **32,** 1–6 (1955).
32. G. S. Fisher, W. G. Bickford, and F. G. Dollear, *J. Am. Oil Chemists' Soc.* **24,** 379–382 (1947).
33. F. D. Gunstone and T. P. Hilditch, *J. Chem. Soc.* **1945,** 836–841.
34. E. R. Bolton, *J. Soc. Chem. Ind. (London)* **46,** 444–446T (1927).
35. Brit. Pat. 1,515 (Jan. 21, 1930), W. Normann.
36. A. E. Bailey, *J. Am. Oil Chemists' Soc.* **26,** 596–601 (1949).
37. A. E. Bailey, *J. Am. Oil Chemists' Soc.* **26,** 644–648 (1949).
38. T. P. Hilditch, *Nature* **157,** 586 (1946).
39. U.S. Pats. 1,268,692 (June 4, 1918); 1,275,405 (Aug. 13, 1918), J. Dewar and A. Liebmann (to Proctor & Gamble Co.).
40. A. H. Solway, *J. Chem. Soc.* **111,** 407–410 (1917).
41. H. Jasperson and R. Jones, *J. Soc. Chem. Ind.* **66,** 13–17 (1947).
42. S. Patton, I. J. Barnes, and L. E. Evans, *J. Am. Oil Chemists' Soc.* **36,** 280–283 (1959).
43. A. E. Bailey, *Ind. Eng. Chem.* **33,** 404–408 (1941).
44. N. W. Ziels and W. H. Schmidt, *Oil & Soap* **22,** 327–330 (1945).

45. U.S. Pat. 2,407,616 (Sept. 10, 1946), G. W. Phelps and H. C. Black (to Industrial Patents Corp.).
46. E. H. Chapin and D. K. Dean, *Oil & Soap* **17,** 217–222 (1940).
47. D. K. Dean and E. H. Chapin, *Oil & Soap* **15,** 200–202 (1938).
48. U.S. Pat. 2,280,896 (April 28, 1942), D. K. Dean (to Foster Wheeler Corp.).
49. A. E. Bailey, *J. Am. Oil Chemists' Soc.* **26,** 166–170 (1949).
50. U.S. Dept. of Agriculture, *Agricultural Statistics*, Washington D. C., *1963*.
51. "Fats & Oils, Production, Consumption, & Factory & Warehouse Stocks,— *Series M20K (63)-13*, U.S. Bureau of the Census, Current Industrial Reports, Washington, D.C., 1965.
52. *Official and Tentative Methods of the American Oil Chemists' Society*, 2nd ed., revised 1964, The American Oil Chemists' Society, Chicago, Ill.
53. U.S. Pat. 2,631,157 (1953), A. W. Hixson and R. Miller.

F. A. Norris
Swift & Company

FATTY ACIDS

Introduction

The fatty acids are a large group of aliphatic monocarboxylic acids, many of which occur as glycerides (esters of glycerol, qv) in natural fats and oils (see also Acids, carboxylic; Fats and fatty oils). Some of them also occur as other esters in waxes (qv) and essential oils (see Oils, essential), and as free acids in tall oil (qv). See also Formic acid; Ethanoic acid; Propionic acid; Butyric acid.

Although the term "fatty acids" has been restricted by some to the saturated acids of the acetic acid series, $C_nH_{2n+1}COOH$, both normal and branched-chain, it is now generally used to include also related unsaturated acids, certain substituted acids (hydroxy and keto), and even aliphatic acids containing alicyclic substituents, as the chaulmoogra oil acids. See Tables 1–4. Certain other alicyclic acids (naphthenic acids, qv) which contain no aliphatic chain, have also sometimes been loosely termed fatty acids and their salts called soaps (see Driers and metallic soaps).

The naturally occurring fatty acids (also called "fat acids") with a few exceptions are higher straight-chain unsubstituted acids containing an even number of carbon atoms. Although only a few branched-chain, hydroxy, and keto acids have been detected in naturally occurring fatty substances in appreciable amounts, a considerable number of these and also of odd-numbered acids have been prepared synthetically.

The unsaturated fatty acids can be divided, on the basis of the number of double bonds in the hydrocarbon chain, into *monoethenoid, diethenoid, triethenoid,* etc (or *monoethylenic* etc). The *polyethenoid* acids may also be classified as nonconjugated or conjugated, depending upon the relative positions of the double bonds. If these

Table 1. Saturated Fatty Acids

Common name	Synonyms	Formula	Formula weight	Mp, °C	Bp, °C	d_4^{20}	n_D^{20}	Neutraliza-tion value
formic	methanoic	HCOOH	46.03	8.4	100.5	1.220	1.3714	1218.96
acetic	ethanoic	CH_3COOH	60.05	16.6	118.1	1.049	1.3718	934.26
propionic	propanoic	C_2H_5COOH	74.08	-22	141.1	0.992	1.3874	757.36
butyric	butanoic	C_3H_7COOH	88.10	-7.9	163.5	0.959	1.39906	636.79
valeric	pentanoic	C_4H_9COOH	102.13	-34.5	187.0	0.942	1.4086	549.34
caproic	hexanoic	$C_5H_{11}COOH$	116.15	-3.4	205.8	0.929	1.4170	483.00
enanthic	heptanoic	$C_6H_{13}COOH$	130.18	-10.5	223.0	0.922	1.4230	430.96
caprylic	octanoic	$C_7H_{15}COOH$	144.21	16.7	239.7	0.910	1.4280	389.05
pelargonic	nonanoic	$C_8H_{17}COOH$	158.23	12.5	255.6	0.907	1.4322	354.56
capric	decanoic	$C_9H_{19}COOH$	172.26	31.6	270.0	0.895^{30}	1.4169^{70}	325.69
n-undecylic	undecanoic; hendecanoic	$C_{10}H_{21}COOH$	186.29	29.3	284.0	0.9905^{25}	1.4202^{70}	301.17
lauric	dodecanoic	$C_{11}H_{23}COOH$	200.31	44.2	298.9	0.883	1.4230^{70}	280.08
n-tridecylic	tridecanoic	$C_{12}H_{25}COOH$	214.34	41.5	312.4	0.8458^{80}	1.4252^{70}	261.75
myristic	tetradecanoic	$C_{13}H_{27}COOH$	228.36	53.9	326.2	0.858^{60}	1.4273^{70}	245.68
n-pentadecylic	pentadecanoic	$C_{14}H_{29}COOH$	242.39	52.3	339.1	0.8423^{80}	1.4292^{70}	231.46
palmitic	hexadecanoic	$C_{15}H_{31}COOH$	256.42	63.1	351.5	0.8534^{62}	1.4309^{70}	218.80
margaric	heptadecanoic	$C_{16}H_{33}COOH$	270.44	61.3	363.8	0.853^{60}	1.4324^{70}	207.45
stearic	octadecanoic	$C_{17}H_{35}COOH$	284.47	69.6	376.1	0.847^{693}	1.4337^{70}	197.23

Common name	Systematic name	Formula	Mol wt	mp	bp	d	n	
n-nonadecylic	nonadecanoic	$C_{18}H_{37}COOH$	298.49	68.6		0.8771^{24}	1.4512^{25}	187.96
arachidic	eicosanoic; arachic	$C_{19}H_{39}COOH$	312.52	75.3	299_{100}	0.8240^{100}	1.4250^{100}	179.52
n-heneicosoic	heneicosanoic	$C_{20}H_{41}COOH$	326.55	74.3	$203–205_{1}$			171.81
behenic	docosanoic	$C_{21}H_{43}COOH$	340.57	79.9	306_{60}	0.8221^{100}	1.4270^{100}	164.73
n-tricosoic	tricosanoic	$C_{22}H_{45}COOH$	354.60	79.1				158.22
lignoceric	tetracosanoic	$C_{23}H_{47}COOH$	368.62	84.2		0.8207^{100}	1.4287^{100}	152.20
n-pentacosoic	pentacosanoic	$C_{24}H_{49}COOH$	382.65	83.5				146.62
cerotic	hexacosanoic	$C_{25}H_{51}COOH$	396.68	87.7	dec	0.8198^{100}	1.4301^{100}	141.44
n-heptacosoic	heptacosanoic	$C_{26}H_{53}COOH$	410.70	87.6				136.60
montanic	octacosanoic	$C_{27}H_{55}COOH$	424.73	90.0		0.8191^{100}	1.4313^{100}	132.09
n-nonacosoic	nonacosanoic	$C_{28}H_{57}COOH$	438.75	90.3				127.87
melissic	triacontanoic	$C_{29}H_{59}COOH$	452.78	93.6			1.4323^{100}	123.91
n-hentriacontoic	hentriacontanoic	$C_{30}H_{61}COOH$	466.80	93.1				120.19
n-dotriacontoic	dotriacontanoic	$C_{31}H_{63}COOH$	480.83	96.2				116.68
n-tetratriacontoic	tetratriacontanoic	$C_{33}H_{67}COOH$	508.88	98.4				110.24
ceroplastic	pentatriacontanoic	$C_{34}H_{69}COOH$	522.91	98.3–98.5				107.28
n-hexatriacontoic	hexatriacontanoic	$C_{35}H_{71}COOH$	536.94	99.9				104.49
n-octatriacontoic	octatriacontanoic	$C_{37}H_{75}COOH$	564.99	101.6				99.30
n-hexatetracontoic	hexatetracontanoic	$C_{45}H_{91}COOH$	677.20	106.8				82.85

Table 2. Monoethenoid Fatty Acids

Common name	Synonyms	Formula	Mp, °C	Bp, °C	d_4^{20}	n_D^{20}	Neutralization value	Theoret. iodine value
obtusilic	4-decenoic	$CH_3(CH_2)_4CH=CH(CH_2)_2COOH$		$148\text{-}150_{13}$	0.9197	1.4497	329.55	149.10
caproleic	*cis*-9-decenoic	$CH_2=CH(CH_2)_7COOH$		142_4	0.9238^{15}	1.4488	329.55	149.10
10-undecylenic	10-undecenoic; 10-hendecenoic	$CH_2=CH(CH_2)_8COOH$	24.5	275	0.9072^{24}			
lauroleic	*cis*-9-dodecenoic	$CH_3CH_2CH=CH(CH_2)_7COOH$			0.9130^{15}	1.4535^{15}	282.93	128.01
physeteric	5-tetradecenoic	$CH_3(CH_2)_7CH=CH(CH_2)_3COOH$			0.9046	1.4552	247.87	112.15
myristoleic	*cis*-9-tetradecenoic	$CH_3(CH_2)_3CH=CH(CH_2)_7COOH$			0.9018	1.4549	247.87	112.15
palmitoleic	*cis*-9-hexadecenoic	$CH_3(CH_2)_5CH=CH(CH_2)_7COOH$	−0.5 to 0.5		0.86369^{70}	1.44103^{70}	220.53	99.78
petroselinic	*cis*-6-octadecenoic	$CH_3(CH_2)_{10}CH=CH(CH_2)_4COOH$	30		0.8681^{40}	1.4533^{40}	198.63	89.87
petroselaidic	*trans*-6-octadecenoic	$CH_3(CH_2)_{10}CH=CH(CH_2)_4COOH$	54				198.63	89.87
oleic	*cis*-9-octadecenoic	$CH_3(CH_2)_7CH=CH(CH_2)_7COOH$	13.4 (α-) 16.3 (β-)	$234\text{-}235_{15}$	0.8905	1.45823	198.63	89.87
elaidic	*trans*-9-octadecenoic	$CH_3(CH_2)_7CH=CH(CH_2)_7COOH$	46.5	234_{15}	0.85682^{70}	1.44053^{70}	198.63	89.87
vaccenic	*trans*-11-octadecenoic	$CH_3(CH_2)_5CH=CH(CH_2)_9COOH$	42.5		0.85637^{70}	1.4406^{70}	198.63	89.87
gadoleic	*cis*-9-eicosenoic	$CH_3(CH_2)_9CH=CH(CH_2)_7COOH$					180.69	81.75
cetoleic	11-docosenoic	$CH_3(CH_2)_9CH=CH(CH_2)_9COOH$					165.72	74.98
erucic	*cis*-13-docosenoic	$CH_3(CH_2)_7CH=CH(CH_2)_{11}COOH$	34.7	281_{30}	0.85321^{70}	1.44438^{70}	165.72	74.98
brassidic	*trans*-13-docosenoic	$CH_3(CH_2)_7CH=CH(CH_2)_{11}COOH$	61.9	265_{15}	0.85002^{70}	1.44349^{70}	165.72	74.98
selacholeic	*cis*-15-tetracosenoic; nervonic	$CH_3(CH_2)_7CH=CH(CH_2)_{13}COOH$	42.5				153.04	69.24
ximenic	17-hexacosenoic	$CH_3(CH_2)_7CH=CH(CH_2)_{15}COOH$					142.16	64.32
lumequoic	21-triacontenoic	$CH_3(CH_2)_7CH=CH(CH_2)_{19}COOH$					124.46	56.31

Table 3. Di-, Tri-, and Other Polyethenoid Fatty Acids

Common name	Synonyms	Formula	Mp, °C	Bp, °C	d_4^{20}	n_D^{20}	Neutralization value	Theoret. iodine value
sorbic	2,4-hexadienoic	$CH_3CH=CHCH=CHCOOH$	134.5	228 (dec)			500.37	226.39
linoleic	cis-9,cis-12-octadecadienoic; linolic	$CH_3(CH_2)_4CH=CHCH_2CH=CH(CH_2)_7COOH$	−5.0 to −5.27	$202_{1.4}$	0.9038^{18}	1.4699	200.06	181.03
linolelaidic	trans-9,trans-12-octadecadienoic	$CH_3(CH_2)_4CH=CHCH_2CH=CH(CH_2)_7COOH$	28–29				200.06	181.03
hiragonic	6,10,14-hexadecatrienoic	$CH_3CH=CH(CH_2)_2CH=CH(CH_2)_2CH=CH(CH_2)_4COOH$			0.9288	1.4855	224.08	304.16
α-eleostearic	cis-9,cis-11,trans-13-octadecatrienoic (?)	$CH_3(CH_2)_3CH=CHCH=CHCH=CH(CH_2)_7COOH$	48–49	235_{12}	0.9028^{30}	1.5112^{50}	201.51	273.51
β-eleostearic	trans-9,cis-11,cis-13-octadecatrienoic (?)	$CH_3(CH_2)_3CH=CHCH=CHCH=CH(CH_2)_7COOH$	71.5		0.8909^{75}	1.5022^{75}	201.51	273.51
punicic	9,11,13-octadecatrienoic	$CH_3(CH_2)_3CH=CHCH=CHCH=CH(CH_2)_7COOH$	43.5–44				201.51	273.51
linolenic	cis-9,cis-12,cis-15-octadecatrienoic	$CH_3CH_2CH=CHCH_2CH=CHCH_2CH=CH(CH_2)_7COOH$	−11.0 to −11.3	$157{-}158_{0.001}$	0.9046	1.4780	201.51	273.51
elaidolinolenic	trans-9,trans-12,trans-15-octadecatrienoic (?)	$CH_3CH_2CH=CHCH_2CH=CHCH_2CH=CH(CH_2)_7COOH$	29–30				201.51	273.51
psuedoeleostearic	trans-10,trans-12,trans-14-octadecatrienoic	$CH_3(CH_2)_2CH=CHCH=CHCH=CH(CH_2)_8COOH$	79				201.51	273.51
moroctic	4,8,12,15-octadecatetraenoic	$CH_3CH_2CH=CHCH_2CH=CH(CH_2)_2CH=CH(CH_2)_2CH=CH(CH_2)_2COOH$			0.9297	1.4911	202.98	367.34
α-parinaric	9,11,13,15-octadecatetraenoic	$CH_3CH_2CH=CHCH=CHCH=CHCH=CH(CH_2)_7COOH$	85–86				202.98	367.34
β-parinaric	9,11,13,15-octadecatetraenoic	$CH_3CH_2CH=CHCH=CHCH=CHCH=CH(CH_2)_7COOH$	95–96				202.98	367.34
arachidonic	5,8,11,14-eicosatetraenoic	$CH_3(CH_2)_4CH=CHCH_2CH=CHCH_2CH=CHCH_2CH=CH(CH_2)_3COOH$	−49.5			1.4824	184.28	333.50
clupanodonic	4(?),8,12,15,19-docosapentaenoic	$CH_3CH_2CH=CH(CH_2)_2CH=CHCH_2CH=CH(CH_2)_2CH=CH(CH_2)_2CH=CH(CH_2)_2COOH$			0.9356	1.5020	169.76	384.03
nisinic	4(?),8,12,15,18,21-tetracosahexaenoic	$CH_3CH_2CH=CHCH_2CH=CHCH_2CH=CH(CH_2)_2CH=CH(CH_2)_2CH=CH(CH_2)_2COOH$					157.36	427.19

Table 4. Ethynoid and Substituted Ethenoid Fatty Acids

Common name	Synonyms	Formula	Mp, °C	Bp, °C	d_4^{20}	n_D^{20}	Neutral-ization value	Theoret. iodine value
Ethynoid acids								
propiolic	2-propynoic; propargylic	$HC{\equiv}CCOOH$	9	144	$1.139_{1.5}^{5}$	1.4146^{15}	800.96	724.78
tetrolic	2-butynoic	$CH_3C{\equiv}CCOOH$	76	203			667.33	603.86
4-pentynoic		$HC{\equiv}C(CH_2)_2COOH$	57	$203{-}204_{766}$			571.92	517.51
dehydroun-decylenic	10-undecynoic	$HC{\equiv}C(CH_2)_8COOH$	43	175_{15}			307.83	278.55
tariric	6-octadecynoic	$CH_3(CH_2)_{10}C{\equiv}C(CH_2)_4COOH$	51.5				200.06	181.03
stearolic	9-octadecynoic	$CH_3(CH_2)_7C{\equiv}C(CH_2)_7COOH$	48	260			200.06	181.03
behenolic	13-docosynoic	$CH_3(CH_2)_7C{\equiv}C(CH_2)_{11}COOH$	57				166.71	150.85
isanic	octadec-17-enedi-9,11(?)-ynoic; erythrogenic	$CH_2{=}CH(CH_2)_4C{\equiv}CC{\equiv}C(CH_2)_7COOH$	39.5		0.9309^{45}	1.49148^{50}	204.47	462.55
Substituted acids								
ricinoleic	12-hydroxy-*cis*-9-octa-decenoic; ricinolic	$CH_3(CH_2)_5CHOHCH_2CH{=}CH(CH_2)_7{-}COOH$	4–5		$0.940_{1.5}^{1.5}$	1.4716	187.98	85.05 4
licanic	4-oxo-9,11,13-octadeca-trienoic; couepic	$CH_3(CH_2)_3CH{=}CHCH{=}CHCH{=}CH{-}(CH_2)_4CO(CH_2)_2COOH$	74–75 (α-) 99.5 (β-)				191.87	260.3

bonds are separated by one or more single-bonded carbon atoms, $-C=C-C_n-C=C-$, the acid is said to be *nonconjugated*. When double-bonded carbon atoms are adjacent to one another, $-C=C-C=C-$, the acid is referred to as *conjugated*. An acid containing one or more triple-bonded carbon atoms is referred to as an *acetylenic* or *ethynoid* acid.

NOMENCLATURE

Of the three principal types of names for carboxylic acids (see Vol. 1, p. 225), common names and IUPAC-modified Geneva names are most used for fatty acids. Thus, palmitic acid, $CH_3(CH_2)_{14}COOH$, so named from its occurrence in palm oil among other sources, is systematically called hexadecanoic acid from the corresponding hydrocarbon, hexadecane, $CH_5(CH_2)_{14}CH_3$; stearic acid, $CH_3(CH_2)_{16}COOH$, from Greek *stear*, tallow, is octadecanoic acid from octadecane, $CH_3(CH_2)_{16}CH_3$. (Names like *n*-hexadecoic acid and *n*-hexadecylic acid are also still used to some extent.) Similarly, oleic acid, $CH_3(CH_2)_7CH=CH(CH_2)_7COOH$, from Latin *oleum*, oil, is an octadecenoic acid; linoleic acid, $CH_3(CH_2)_4CH=CHCH_2CH=CH(CH_2)_7COOH$, which occurs in linseed and other oils, is an octadecadienoic acid; and linolenic acid, $CH_3CH_2CH=CHCH_2CH=CHCH_2CH=CH(CH_2)_7COOH$, is an octadecatrienoic acid. Tariric acid, $CH_3(CH_2)_{10}C\equiv C(CH_2)_4COOH$, is an octadecynoic (octadecinoic) acid.

The positions in the higher fatty acids are usually designated for convenience by numbers instead of Greek letters, although α, β, and γ are frequently used and only Greek letters are employed with common names by *Chemical Abstracts*. For example:

$$CH_3CH_2CH_2CH_2CH_2CH_2CH_2CH_2CHOHCH_2CH_2CH_2CH_2CH_2CH_2CH_2COOH$$

18	17	16	15	14	13	12	11	10	9	8	7	6	5	4	3	2	1
ρ	π	σ	ξ	ν	μ	λ	κ	ι	θ	η	ζ	ϵ	δ	γ	β	α	

     usual name: 10-hydroxystearic acid
     CA name: ι-hydroxystearic acid
     IUPAC Geneva name: 10-hydroxyoctadecanoic acid

It should be noted that α corresponds to 2, not 1. The Greek letter ω is often used to designate the terminal carbon atom (farthest from the carboxyl group) in any chain.

The positions of double and triple bonds in unsaturated acids are similarly indicated, the number indicating the lower-numbered of the two carbon atoms of the unsaturated linkage. Formerly (and still to some extent), the Greek letter Δ was used to designate double and sometimes triple bonds, usually with two numbers to specify both attachments of each bond. Thus, oleic acid is 9-octadecenoic or $\Delta^{9,10}$-octadecenoic acid, linoleic acid is 9,12- or $\Delta^{9,10,12,13}$-octadecadienoic acid, and stearolic acid is 9- or $\Delta^{9,10}$-octadecynoic acid.

Since, like other ethylenic compounds, fatty acids containing one or more double bonds exhibit geometric isomerism, the cis and trans forms are also indicated when known. With systematic names it is necessary to designate the isomers by the use of the prefixes *cis* and *trans*. However, in the case of naturally occurring acids and certain synthetic acids with a common name, this name alone is sufficient if it refers specifically to one form, usually the common natural or normal isomeric form; oleic acid, for example, is the cis form and elaidic acid the corresponding trans form:

          $HC(CH_2)_7CH_3$ $CH_3(CH_2)_7CH$
            ‖   ‖
          $HC(CH_2)_7COOH$ $HC(CH_2)_7COOH$
             oleic acid   elaidic acid

In other common names containing -oleic and -elaidic (or elaido-), the former usually denotes a cis form and the latter a trans form: myristoleic is thought to be *cis*-9-tetradecenoic and petroselaidic is *trans*-6-octadecenoic. Again, if two or more double bonds are present, the isomeric forms resulting from each such bond must be indicated in systematic names but not usually in common names. Thus linoleic denotes specifically *cis*-9,*cis*-12-octadecadienoic, and linolelaidic, *trans*-9,*trans*-12-octadecadienoic.

Because of the large number of possible isomeric unsaturated acids (both positional and geometric isomers) and the difficulty of isolating and identifying them, there is still great confusion in the names of many of the acids in the literature. Common names have been extended to include other isomers: *trans*-oleic has been used as a synonym for elaidic, and linoleic sometimes denotes any unsaturated straight-chain fatty acid containing 18 carbon atoms and two double bonds. On the other hand, the prefix iso has sometimes been used broadly to designate any isomers of well-known acids, as isooleic acids. Greek letters have also been employed in an attempt to distinguish between isomers, as α- and β-eleostearic acids.

Optical isomerism, resulting from the presence of one or more asymmetric carbon atoms, occurs only in branched-chain and substituted fatty acids, as ricinoleic acid and chaulmoogra oil acids. Various systems of naming the stereoisomers have been used, including (+) and (−) to indicate direction of rotation, and carbohydrate prefixes such as D-*threo*- and L-*erythro*- and D-*ribo*- and L-*xylo*- (see Vol. 4, p. 137) as in dihydroxystearic acid. The prefixes cis- and trans- have also often been used erroneously to denote such configurations.

The conventional way to name acyl radicals has been to change the ending "-ic acid" to "-yl," as in formyl from formic acid. Geneva names involve this same change of -ic to -yl (or -oic to -oyl): heptanoyl from heptanoic. The unfortunate use of the same name for related alkyl and acyl radicals in a few instances has caused ambiguity. Lauryl, for example, may mean $C_{12}H_{25}$— or $C_{11}H_{23}CO$—. Palmityl and stearyl are similar offenders. To meet this situation, Geneva names are recommended for these alkyl radicals: dodecyl, hexadecyl, and octadecyl, and adoption of -oyl rather than -yl for the acyl radicals, eg, lauroyl, palmitoyl, stearoyl.

Industrially Important Reactions

ESTERIFICATION

Production of fatty esters is the most important phase in the industrial chemistry of fatty acids. The esters produced are of several types and include those resulting from reaction with monohydric alcohols, polyhydric alcohols, ethylene or propylene oxide, and acetylene or vinyl acetate (1–3) (see also Esterification).

The principal *monohydric alcohols* used are methanol, 1-propanol, 2-propanol, and 1-butanol. Esterification is an equilibrium reaction, and water is a product:

$$RCOOH + R'OH \rightleftharpoons RCOOR' + H_2O$$

The reaction is catalyzed by an acid, usually 1–3% of sulfuric acid or of hydrogen chloride. The equilibrium can be shifted toward completion by various means. With short-chain alcohols, weight ratios of alcohol to fatty acid of from 2–4 to 1 are used, corresponding to molar ratios of from 10–20 to 1. At such high molar ratios, the equilibrium is shifted in accordance with the law of mass action, and yields of 95% or better are obtained. With alcohols of intermediate chain length which are not miscible with water, such as hexyl and higher alcohols, stoichiometric quantities of acid and alcohol can be used, and water is removed by azeotropic distillation with toluene or xylene. With long-chain fatty alcohols, removal of water may be done by azeotropic distillation, by sparging with an inert gas, or by subjecting the reaction to reduced pressure. Esters may also be prepared by alcoholysis of an animal fat or vegetable oil in the presence of an alkaline or acidic catalyst:

$$
\begin{array}{c}
\text{RCOOCH}_2 \qquad\qquad \text{HOCH}_2 \\
| \qquad\qquad\qquad\qquad | \\
\text{RCOOCH} \ + \ 3\,\text{R}'\text{OH} \rightarrow \text{HOCH} \ + \ 3\,\text{RCOOR}' \\
| \qquad\qquad\qquad\qquad | \\
\text{RCOOCH}_2 \qquad\qquad \text{HOCH}_2
\end{array}
$$

Esters of monohydric alcohols are used for plasticizers (qv) and in cosmetics (qv).

The principal *polyhydric alcohols* include ethylene, propylene, diethylene, and polyethylene glycols (see Glycols), glycerol, pentaerythritol, and certain carbohydrates. Esterification with polyols is a more complex reaction than that with simple alcohols because polyols are immiscible with the fatty acid or ester. Temperatures of 230–235°C and vigorous agitation are required for a good reaction, in contrast to the milder conditions used for the simple alcohols. Temperatures higher than 235°C cause polyols to condense to ethers and to decompose. Nearly stoichiometric quantities of glycol and fatty acid are needed to make either monoesters or diesters. Product water may be removed as usual by reduced pressure, azeotropic distillation, or sparging. With volatile glycols, appropriate temperatures and pressures must be used to avoid loss of glycol. Monoesters are preferably formed by reaction of *ethylene* or *propylene oxide* with the fatty acid:

$$
\text{RCOOH} + n\,\text{CH}_2\!\!-\!\!\text{CH}_2 \rightarrow \text{RCOO}\!\!-\!\!(\text{CH}_2\text{CH}_2\text{O})\!\!-\!\!_n\text{H}
$$
$$
\underset{\text{O}}{\diagdown\diagup}
$$

The product is a mixture having varying polyoxyethylene chain lengths. Glycol diesters are used as vinyl plasticizers; the monoesters, as surface-active agents and as viscosity modifiers for alkyd resins.

Glycerol esterifications are even more complex (4). Even with excess glycerol, a mixture of mono-, di-, and triglycerides is formed because of the limited solubility of glycerol in the reaction product. Compositions of the reaction mixture can be calculated on a statistical basis, if equivalence of the three hydroxyl groups and no isomer formation are assumed (5). The mixture results from the preferential, homogeneous reaction of free fatty acid with monoglyceride and diglyceride in the lipid phase. Various metal salts or oxides may be used as catalysts; the chlorides of zinc and tin(II) or tin(IV) have been reported to be most effective (6). The maximum yield of monoglyceride is about 60%, of diglyceride, about 49%. Molecular distillation of the mixture gives monoglyceride fractions with a purity of more than 90%. Relatively pure diglyceride fractions may also be obtained by molecular distillation. Glycerolysis, an interesterification process, also gives the same mixture of products and is the preferred commercial route:

$$
\begin{array}{c}
\text{RCOOCH}_2 \quad \text{HOCH}_2 \qquad \text{RCOOCH}_2 \qquad \text{RCOOCH}_2 \\
| \qquad\qquad | \qquad\qquad\quad | \qquad\qquad\qquad | \\
\text{RCOOCH} \ + \ \text{HOCH} \ \rightleftharpoons \ \text{RCOOCH} \ + \quad \text{HOCH} \\
| \qquad\qquad | \qquad\qquad\quad | \qquad\qquad\qquad | \\
\text{RCOOCH}_2 \quad \text{HOCH}_2 \qquad \text{HOCH}_2 \qquad \text{HOCH}_2
\end{array}
$$

The amount of 2-monoglyceride in commercial monoglycerides is no more than 5–8%; accordingly, isomers of the monoglycerides and the diglycerides are neglected in the equation. Basic catalysts (caustic soda or sodium methoxide) are used for the interesterification process. Higher yields of mono- or diglycerides have been obtained by the use of a sulfonic acid catalyst and of phenol as a solvent in which all reactants and products are soluble. Higher yields may also be obtained by removal of the water of esterification by azeotropic distillation with a hydrocarbon such as hexane (7). Glycerides are important as surface-active agents; triolein is used to some extent as a plasticizer.

Pentaerythritol (see Vol. 1, p. 589) with its four primary hydroxyl groups is used for the preparation of tetraesters and presents little difficulty except for its high melting point (263°C, when pure). Pentaerythritol tetraesters are used in alkyds and in synthetic drying oils. Esters derived from trimethylolalkanes (see Vol. 1, pp. 594, 595) and dipentaerythritol are also used in alkyds. Esterification may also take place in situ during preparation of the alkyd.

Of the higher polyols used in direct esterification of fatty acids, *sorbitol* (see Vol. 1, p. 573) is most important. It has two primary and four secondary hydroxyl groups, but these are not necessarily all available for reaction with fatty acid. Dehydration occurs during esterification to give sorbitans having one primary and three secondary hydroxyl groups. Esters of the sorbitans and of sorbitans modified with ethylene oxide are extensively used as surface-active agents.

Vinyl esters are prepared by the reaction of a fatty acid with acetylene in direct condensation or with vinyl acetate by acidolysis. The reaction of a fatty acid with acetylene, which was discovered by Reppe, is carried out at 169–180°C and 200 psig pressure with diluted acetylene and with the zinc or cadmium salt of the fatty acid as a catalyst:

$$RCOOH + HC{\equiv}CH \rightarrow RCOOCH{=}CH_2$$

Acidolysis of vinyl acetate is carried out in the presence of a mercuric salt as catalyst:

$$RCOOH + CH_3COOCH{=}CH_2 \rightarrow RCOOCH{=}CH_2 + CH_3COOH$$

POLYMERIZATION

Treatment of soybean or tall oil fatty acids, and even oleic acid, with a clay catalyst at 220°C gives dimer and trimer acids (8). Dimer acid is a cyclic dicarboxylic acid having a total of 36 carbon atoms. Trimer acid is a tricarboxylic acid having a total of 54 carbon atoms. These two acids are formed by isomerization of two double bonds in linoleic acid to a conjugated system followed by a Diels-Alder addition to an isolated double bond of a second fatty acid molecule (see below under Polybasic acids).

Oleic acid can be used in this preparation because the clay catalyst apparently acts as a dehydrogenating catalyst as well as an isomerization catalyst; the mechanism has not been established. Without a catalyst, thermal treatment of linoleic acid, but not oleic, also gives a dimer acid. Dimer acid has a molecular weight of 560, does not crystallize, and has isolated double bonds that do not conjugate readily but do react with sulfur and oxygen. Dimer acid esters may be distilled in a molecular still. The unsymmetrical cyclic structure is the reason for the lack of crystallinity and it contributes to flexibility in polymers derived from it.

Vinyl esters of saturated fatty acids readily form homopolymers when the polymerization is initiated by peroxide, but their main use is in copolymerizations with vinyl acetate or vinyl chloride (9–11). Vinyl esters of unsaturated fatty acids retard copolymerizations because of participation of the unsaturation in chain transfer reactions. See Vinyl compounds and polymers. Several studies have been carried out on copolymerization of conjugated fatty acids or esters with styrene, but the polymerization is complicated by Diels-Alder and chain transfer reactions which reduce the extent of copolymerization. At 70°C, Diels-Alder adducts are not significant, but participation of the unsaturated fatty acid in the peroxide-initiated copolymerization with styrene is quite small. At temperatures above 100°C, increasing proportions of the undesired Diels-Alder adducts are formed.

OXIDATION

Two oxidation reactions of fatty acids are industrially important, both involving cleavage of the long carbon chain at points of unsaturation: (*1*) the action of ozone (qv) on oleic acid: (*2*) the oxidative, alkaline cleavage of ricinoleic acid (12).

Ozonolysis of oleic acid is carried out in two steps (13). In the first, an approximately 1:1 mixture of oleic acid and pelargonic acid is introduced continuously into a reactor through which is passed a countercurrent stream of oxygen containing about 2% of ozone. The slightly exothermic reaction is carried out at 25–40°C. Pelargonic acid is added as a diluent to reduce the viscosity of the ozonolysis product solution. The solution is then introduced continuously into another reactor, where the ozonolysis products are oxidized to azelaic and pelargonic acids by a countercurrent stream of oxygen containing traces of ozone. The general reaction is the following:

$$CH_3(CH_2)_7CH{=}CH(CH_2)_7COOH \rightarrow HOOC(CH_2)_7COOH + CH_3(CH_2)_7COOH$$

       oleic acid   azelaic acid   pelargonic acid

The oxidation is exothermic and is carried out at about 95°C. The oxidized products are fed to a still for removal of pelargonic acid at 230°C and 25 mm of mercury. Azelaic acid is removed by a second distillation at 270°C and 3–4 mm of mercury. The distilled azelaic acid is treated with water at 95°C to dissolve it and thereby separate it from other, water-insoluble acids. Water is removed from the solution to give azelaic acid of 85% purity (see also Vol. 1, p. 250). Attack of ozone at the 9,10 double bond of oleic acid results first in an unstable intermediate according to the Criegee mechanism for ozonolysis (14):

$$CH_3(CH_2)CH{=}CH(CH_2)_7COOH + O_3 \rightarrow [CH_3(CH_2)_7CH{-}CH(CH_2)_7COOH]$$
$$O_3$$

This intermediate immediately breaks down into 9-carbon cleavage products: zwitterions ($RCHOO^-$) and carbonyl compounds ($RHCO$). The zwitterions are extremely reactive and react with the carbonyl compounds, with themselves, or with the solvent (if an acid or an alcohol) to give a mixture of ozonolysis products including ozonides, cyclic peroxides, aldehydes, and acyloxy (or alkoxy) hydroperoxides. The mixture of ozonolysis products, when oxidatively decomposed with heat and oxygen, gives pelargonic and azelaic acids. Both of these acids are used in the manufacture of synthetic lubricants and vinyl plasticizers.

Nonamethylene diamine, $H_2N(CH_2)_9NH_2$, may be obtained from oleic acid in a multistep synthesis involving a similar ozonization process and has been used to make the Japanese experimental polyurea fiber, Urylon (15).

The second oxidation process of major chemical import is the preparation of sebacic acid from ricinoleic acid, a major constituent of castor oil (see Vol. 1, p. 251).

Ricinoleic acid also undergoes a unique internal oxidation-reduction reaction when pyrolyzed:

$$CH_3(CH_2)_5CHCH_2CH{=}CH(CH_2)_7COOH \xrightarrow{heat} CH_3(CH_2)_5HC{=}O + CH_2{=}CH(CH_2)_8COOH$$
$$\underset{OH}{|}$$

The products of this reaction are heptaldehyde and undecylenic acid. Undecylenic acid is used on a large scale in France as an intermediate for Rilsan (nylon-11).

A minor commercial reaction is the preparation of peroxy acids from saturated fatty acids for use as free radical polymerization initiators (1,16):

$$CH_3(CH_2)_{10}COOH + H_2O_2 \rightarrow CH_3(CH_2)_{10}COOOH + H_2O$$

The reaction may be catalyzed by sulfuric acid, boron trifluoride, and similar compounds.

HYDROGENOLYSIS

Fatty alcohols are prepared from fatty acids, such as tallow acids, by hydrogenation over a copper chromite catalyst at high temperatures (325°C) and pressures (3500 psig) (1,17):

$$RCOOH + 4 H_2 \rightarrow RCH_2OH + H_2O$$

The yield of fatty alcohol is on the order of 90%. Fatty alcohols may also be prepared by high-pressure catalytic hydrogenolysis of either a glyceride or a methyl ester:

$$RCOOCH_3 + 2 H_2 \rightarrow RCH_2OH + CH_3OH$$

A copper chromite catalyst is used at 270–300°C and 5000 psig of hydrogen pressure. If a glyceride is used, the yield of glycerol is relatively low because of hydrogenolysis to to propylene glycol and isopropyl alcohol. The saturated fatty alcohols thus produced find use primarily in the production of detergents (See Alcohols, higher fatty, Vol. 1, pp. 542–557).

Reduction of glycerides or other esters with sodium and a secondary alcohol such as cyclohexanol or 4-methyl-2-pentanol is a second method for producing fatty alcohols:

$$RCOOR' + 4 Na + 2 R''OH \rightarrow RCH_2ONa + R' ONa + 2 R''ONa$$

$$RCH_2ONa \xrightarrow{H_2O} RCH_2OH + NaOH$$

This method costs more than hydrogenolysis but gives a high yield of glycerol and an unsaturated fatty alcohol if the original fatty ester was unsaturated. The method is of minor importance today, although it was used for large-scale production of coconut fatty alcohols for a period after World War II. It was also used for a short time for the production of unsaturated fatty alcohols.

A route leading to unsaturated alcohols is the selective hydrogenation of the carboxyl or ester group in preference to the olefinic unsaturation. Copper-cadmium and zinc-chromium oxides have seemed to give most selectivity (18). Copper chromite catalysts are not selective.

SALT FORMATION

The saponification of fats and oils with caustic soda or potash gives water-soluble soaps useful as detergents. Water-insoluble, metallic soaps are prepared by fusion, by precipitation, or by direct solution of metal. Fusion gives fine, dense, but slightly off-color metallic soaps useful as driers by the reaction of metallic oxides, carbonates, or acetates with a fatty acid. This method is illustrated for a zinc soap:

$$2 \, RCOOH + ZnO \rightarrow (RCOO)_2Zn + H_2O$$

The reactants are heated at elevated temperatures (180–300°C) with vigorous agitation to drive off water and ensure complete reaction. The molten product is then cooled, crushed, and powdered. The precipitation method forms fluffy, finely divided soaps of excellent color provided the original fatty acid is of good quality. The reaction is carried out in aqueous solution of about 10% concentration with a sodium soap and a metal salt. This method is most important for producing metallic stearates. In the direct solution method, a finely divided metal reacts directly with the fatty acid in the presence of a catalyst with evolution of hydrogen (see Driers and metallic soaps).

α-SULFONATION

The α-sulfo fatty acids are prepared industrially only to a minor extent for use as surface-active agents. They are prepared by the action of sulfur trioxide on a fatty acid (20):

$$RCH_2COOH + SO_3 \rightarrow \underset{\underset{SO_3H}{|}}{RCHCOOH}$$

Either the acid or the monosodium salt can be used to make esters, which are unusually stable to hydrolysis:

$$\underset{\underset{SO_3H}{|}}{RCHCOOH} + n\text{-}C_4H_9OH \rightarrow \underset{\underset{SO_3H}{|}}{RCHCOOC_4H_9} + H_2O$$

The sulfonic acid group is more strongly acidic than the carboxylic acid group, so that the monosodium salt, as well as the disodium, may occur. The monosodium salt has sharply reduced solubility compared to the free sulfo fatty acid; the disodium salt is somewhat more soluble than the monosodium salt.

OTHER REACTIONS

Fatty acid chlorides are used for preparing *amides* from ammonia or amines (see Vol. 2, p. 72) and have a number of other interesting reactions (21). The acid chlorides are prepared by the action of phosphorus trichloride or thionyl chloride, $SOCl_2$, on a fatty acid:

$$3 \, RCOOH + PCl_3 \rightarrow 3 \, RCOCl + H_3PO_3$$

Fatty amines are prepared by treatment of fatty acid with ammonia, forming the nitrile, followed by catalytic hydrogenation (see Vol. 2, p. 127):

$$RCOONH_4 \rightarrow RCN + 2 \, H_2O \qquad RCN + H_2 \rightarrow RCH_2NH_2$$

Thiols, particularly 1-dodecanethiol (lauryl mercaptan), are used in the manufacture of styrene–butadiene rubber (1). 1-Dodecanethiol may be formed by the action of hydrogen sulfide and hydrogen on lauric acid under pressure:

$$RCOOH + H_2S + 2 \, H_2 \rightarrow RCH_2SH + 2 \, H_2O$$

Unsaturated fatty acids and oils react with sulfur and sulfur chlorides to give adducts useful as cutting oils, special lubricants, and rolling oils.

Reactions of the fatty acid carboxyl group that do not have commercial importance at present include pyrolysis of calcium or magnesium salts to form ketones, reductive coupling of esters with sodium to form acyloins, and dehydration to anhydrides and ketones (22).   Reactions of the hydrocarbon chain that have no major industrial significance include halogenation (23), reaction with hypohalous acids, Friedel-Crafts alkylation of aromatic hydrocarbons, and addition of hydrogen cyanide (24).

Bibliography

"Reactions" under "Fatty Acids (Survey)" in *ECT* 1st ed., Vol. 6, pp. 208–221, by K. S. Markley, U.S. Department of Agriculture.

1. M. W. Formo, "General Chemical Reactions of Fatty Acids" in E. S. Pattison, ed., *Industrial Fatty Acids and Their Applications*, Reinhold Publishing Corp., New York, 1959, Chap. 6.
2. K. S. Markley, "Esters and Esterification" in K. S. Markley, ed., *Fatty Acids—Their Chemistry, Properties, Production, and Uses*, Part 2, 2nd ed., Interscience Publishers, a division of John Wiley & Sons, Inc., New York, 1961, Chap. 9.
3. A. W. Ralston, *Fatty Acids and Their Derivatives*, John Wiley & Sons, Inc., New York, 1948, Chap. 7.
4. R. O. Feuge, *J. Am. Oil Chemists' Soc.* **39**, 521–527 (1962).
5. R. O. Feuge and A. E. Bailey, *Oil & Soap* **23**, 259–264 (1946).
6. R. O. Feuge, E. A. Kraemer, and A. E. Bailey, *Oil & Soap* **22**, 202–207 (1945).
7. A. T. Gros and R. O. Feuge, *J. Am. Oil Chemists' Soc.* **41**, 727–731 (1964).
8. J. C. Cowan, *J. Am. Oil Chemists' Soc.* **39**, 534–545 (1962).
9. F. R. Mayo and H. Haff, "Polymerization and Copolymerization of Unsaturated Fatty Acids and Their Esters—A Survey of the Literature," *U.S. Dept. Agr. Bull. ARS-71-30* (May 1963).
10. W. S. Port, "Polymers and Copolymers from Vinyl Esters of Fatty Acids" in E. S. Pattison, ed., *Industrial Fatty Acids and Their Application*, Reinhold Publishing Corp., New York, 1959, Chap. 14.
11. H. M. Teeter, *J. Am. Oil Chemists' Soc.* **40**, 143–156 (1963).
12. R. L. Logan and A. Maggiolo, "Ozone and Other Cleavage Processes" in E. S. Pattison, ed., *Industrial Fatty Acids and Their Application*, Reinhold Publishing Corp., New York, 1959, Chap. 5.
13. U.S. Pat. 2,813,113 (Nov. 12, 1957), C. G. Goebel, A. C. Brown, H. F. Oehlschlager, and R. P. Rolfes (to Emery Industries, Inc.).
14. R. Criegee, *Record Chem. Progr. (Kresge-Hooker Sci. Lib.)* **18**, 110–120 (1957).
15. A. Maggiolo, *J. Am. Oil Chemists' Soc.* **40**, 161–164 (1963).
16. L. S. Silbert, *J. Am. Oil Chemists' Soc.* **39**, 480–487 (1962).
17. K. S. Markley, "Hydrogenation" in K. S. Markley, ed., *Fatty Acids—Their Chemistry, Properties, Production, and Uses*, Part 2, 2nd ed., Interscience Publishers, a division of John Wiley & Sons, Inc., New York, 1961, Chap. 12.
18. H. Bertsch, H. Reinheckel, and K. Haage, *Fette, Seifen, Anstrichmittel* **66**, 763–773 (1964).
19. K. S. Markley, "Salts of Fatty Acids" in K. S. Markley, ed., *Fatty Acids—Their Chemistry, Properties, Production, and Uses*, Part 2, 2nd ed., Interscience Publishers, a division of John Wiley & Sons, Inc., New York, 1961, Chap. 8.
20. A. J. Stirton, *J. Am. Oil Chemists' Soc.* **39**, 490–496 (1962).
21. N. O. V. Sonntag, *Chem. Rev.* **52**, 237–416 (1953).
22. N. O. V. Sonntag, "Dehydration, Pyrolysis, and Polymerization" in K. S. Markley, ed., *Fatty Acids—Their Chemistry, Properties, Production, and Uses*, Part 2, 2nd ed., Interscience Publishers, a division of John Wiley & Sons, Inc., New York, 1961, Chap. 10.
23. N. O. V. Sonntag, *J. Am. Oil Chemists' Soc.* **40**, 199–203 (1963).
24. H. J. Harwood, *Chem. Rev.* **62**, 99–154 (1962).

E. H. Pryde
U.S. Department of Agriculture

Manufacture

FAT SPLITTING

The preparation of fatty acids from a glyceride fat or oil may be accomplished by one of several "splitting" or hydrolytic processes. In all cases the hydrolysis reaction may be summarized as follows:

$$
\begin{array}{c}
\text{H} \\
| \\
\text{H—COOCR} \\
| \\
\text{H—COOCR} \\
| \\
\text{H—COOCR} \\
| \\
\text{H}
\end{array}
\;+\; 3\,\text{H}_2\text{O} \;\rightarrow\; 3\,\text{RCOOH} \;+\;
\begin{array}{c}
\text{H} \\
| \\
\text{HC—OH} \\
| \\
\text{HC—OH} \\
| \\
\text{HC—OH} \\
| \\
\text{H}
\end{array}
$$

fat or oil   water   fatty acids   glycerol

Historically, various batch processes such as caustic splitting and subsequent acidulation, the Twitchell process, and autoclave splitting with or without catalyst, have been employed. In modern fatty acid plants, however, this process is carried out by continuous high-pressure, high-temperature hydrolysis of the fat.

Batch Processes. The earliest method used for splitting fat involves complete saponification using caustic, either sodium or potassium hydroxide. This process, one of the oldest chemical reactions known, is widely applied in soapmaking. Fat, placed in a large steel kettle, is blown with steam until the temperature reaches 80°C. Concentrated aqueous caustic is added gradually with continued addition of steam and with efficient agitation of the mass. Hydrolysis proceeds in stages, one fatty acid splitting off at a time until all three have been removed from the triglyceride molecule. The reaction is reversible and to prevent reesterification the aqueous glycerol is periodically drawn off and replaced with fresh water and more caustic. The product, sodium or potassium soaps, must be acidified to free the fatty acid. This additional step and expense have relegated this method to laboratory use for the preparation of fatty acids.

The development by Twitchell in 1890 of a compound to catalyze the aqueous hydrolysis of fat led the way to the evolution of the method which was for many years the most popular of the fat-splitting processes. Stocks containing impurities that are catalyst poisons, gums, proteinaceous material, calcium and iron soaps, should be acid-washed. Acid washing is generally performed in lead-lined or other suitably resistant tanks. A charge of melted fat is treated at about 140°F with 2–4% of sulfuric acid in a fairly dilute (30–50%) solution, with good agitation, for about an hour, after which the charge is further heated to about 200°F with live steam. After settling, the acid water is drawn off and the charge thoroughly washed with water to remove the mineral acid. Bleaching treatment with acid clays is effective not only in reducing color bodies but also in removing oxidized acids and other impurities which hinder splitting and hydrogenation. The fat is then mixed with 25–50% by wt of water and 0.75–1.25% of a Twitchell catalyst (originally benzenestearosulfonic acid, C_6H_4-$(SO_3H)C_{18}H_{35}O_2$, but most commonly a sulfonated petroleum product today). Sulfuric acid to the extent of about 0.5% based on the weight of fat is usually added with the Twitchell reagent. The mixture is boiled with steam for 20–48 hr. The splitting is carried out, usually in covered tanks, in 2–4 stages, at the end of each of which the glycerol "sweet water" is withdrawn and replaced with fresh water or a less concen-

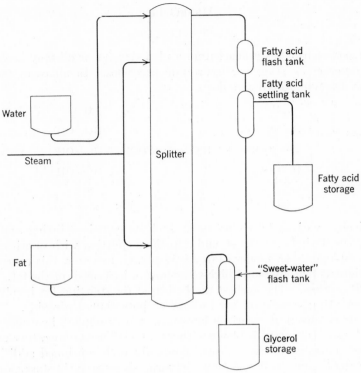

Fig. 1. Fat splitter.

trated "sweet water" from a previous run. The effectiveness of the Twitchell reagent in bringing about the splitting is not entirely catalytic, but depends also on the emulsifying action of the substance. Its surface-active properties greatly increase the mutual solubility of the oil and water phases, and the establishment of an extensive oil–water interface accelerates the splitting reaction. Fatty acids produced by the Twitchell method are somewhat darker than those produced by continuous or batch high-pressure autoclave splitting. Moreover, the glycerol is more difficult to purify since the sweet water contains acid and catalyst residues.

Batch autoclave splitting either with or without catalyst is practiced to some degree, especially in Europe. It has certain advantages over the processes already described, primarily in the great reduction in the time required as well as in the production of lighter-colored fatty acids.

The reaction is accomplished in a copper, or better, in a stainless-steel autoclave into which is charged the fat, 30–60% water, and, if desired, 1–2% catalyst, usually an oxide of calcium, magnesium, barium, or zinc. Steam is then admitted to achieve the desired pressure of 75–150 psi and a temperature of 300–350°F. Hydrolysis is complete in 5–10 hr, after which the contents of the autoclave are blown into a separating tank where the glycerol is withdrawn from the fatty acid. An acid wash is essential to remove the catalyst, which is in combination with the fatty acid. Noncatalytic splitting requires a high-pressure autoclave, the temperature being increased to 450°F and the pressure to 425–450 psi. The reaction time is lowered considerably in this manner, requiring only 2–3 hr to effect 95–98% hydrolysis. This is possible because the reaction has a positive temperature coefficient and because the solubility of water in oil increases with temperature.

Fat splitting by means of *lipolytic enzymes* has been carried out on a commercial scale in the past, but has no present industrial importance. The enzyme preparation for commercial fat splitting has usually been obtained from castor beans.

Selective enzymic splitting is used effectively in modern glyceride analysis. Mattson (1) in this country and Desnuelle (2) in France have used pig pancreatic lipase because of its selective cleavage of glycerides at the α, α' positions.

Continuous Process. The process which currently finds the widest application for the production of fatty acids from glyceride stocks is continuous, countercurrent, high-temperature, high-pressure splitting. Adaptions of this method were developed during the 1940s by Colgate-Palmolive-Peet, Procter & Gamble, and Emery Industries. They make use of fatty acid-resistant, high-pressure, stainless-steel alloys.

In the operation of a typical continuous fat-hydrolysis plant (see Fig. 1), fat stock, which has been pretreated as for the Twitchell splitting, is pumped first through a deaerator to prevent darkening of the oil by oxidation during splitting. The feed stock is then pumped into the reaction chamber through a sparge ring, which breaks the fat into droplets. These droplets begin their rise through the aqueous glycerol in the sweet water accumulating section at the bottom of the column. As the oil rises it effectively sweeps entrained and dissolved fatty acid and oil from the countercurrent flow of sweet water. Simultaneously, deaerated water sparged into the top of the column is heated by contact with the fatty acids in the accumulator section at the top of the column. As the droplets of water fall through the fatty acid layer, dissolved sweet water is swept out and carried downward.

After the fat and water have left the contacting regions at the top and bottom of the column, they are brought to hydrolysis temperature in the middle of the column by the direct injection of steam at 240–250°C and 650–700 psi. Hydrolysis occurs in the emulsion or continuous-phase layer in the reaction zone of the column.

The sweet water collected at the bottom of the column is automatically discharged into a flash tank where a portion of the water is removed. It is then piped to a settling tank and subsequently to a concentrator for processing to commercial glycerol.

Discharge of the split acids from the top of the column is automatically controlled by a back-pressure valve, which also maintains proper operating pressure in the tower. The fatty acids pass into a flash tank where part of the entrained water is removed, and from there to a settling tank where further separation is effected.

Units may be operated catalytically with an increase in capacity, using magnesium, zinc, or calcium oxide. In such case the product must be acid-washed to break down the soap. Hydrolysis of fat by continuous methods is capable of producing a 97–99% split and a 10–25% sweet water.

PURIFICATION AND FRACTIONATION OF FATTY ACIDS

Starting materials most commonly used for the production of fatty acids include coconut oil, palm oil, inedible animal fats, fish oils, and the foots of the commonly used vegetable oils, soybean, cottonseed, and corn. The composition of the fatty acids obtained from the "splitter" is dependent on the fat or oil from which they are made. Rarely will the composition of the fatty acid mixture be ideal or even satisfactory for most uses. Hence fractionation is used almost universally to prepare products more desirable for specific end uses than the mixtures obtained from the splitter. Fractionation according to the degree of unsaturation present is usually effected by a crystallization process, whereas fractionation according to molecular weight is best accomplished by fractional distillation. These fractionation processes are used to separate fractions having improved value for specific end uses and are generally not used commercially for the preparation of pure compounds other than lauric acid.

Fractionation by Crystallization. One of the oldest processes, now falling into disfavor, involves the fractional crystallization of fatty acids without use of solvent. This process is most readily adaptable for use on fatty acid mixtures such as tallow fatty acids which solidify readily at or near room temperature. The molten fatty acid mixture is run into flat pans and cooled to a specified temperature. The resulting solid cakes are removed, wrapped in bags, and pressed in a suitable press. This expression removes the liquid unsaturated acids, that is, the "red oil," which constitutes the oleic acid of commerce. The residue from the pressing is single-pressed stearic acid. Pressing under more drastic conditions yields "double-pressed" or "triple-pressed" acid.

Fractional crystallization from solvents is more frequently practiced by fatty acid processors. By comparison with "panning and pressing," the use of solvents facilitates better fractionation, and since the process is well adapted to continuous operation, important economies can result. In practice, a solution of mixed fatty acids, usually in methanol or acetone, is passed through crystallization tubes and then to continuous filters. From there, both fractions are fed separately to stripping stills for solvent removal.

Distillation. Overcoming the difficulties encountered in distilling an organic substance having a molecular weight up to about 300 and hence having a boiling point at atmospheric pressure, well above its decomposition temperature, has posed difficult engineering problems. These problems are augmented by the acidic nature of the fatty acids and their resulting corrosive action, particularly at elevated temperatures. Nevertheless, distillation has been used as a means of purifying fatty acids for many years.

The simplest major objective to be achieved by distillation is that of removing high-boiling color bodies, oxidized and polymeric materials, sterols, unsplit glycerides, and other high-boiling impurities. Simple distillation will achieve this objective and their removal by a pretreatment is not necessary. Other impurities may decompose or volatilize and contaminate the distillate acid and hence should be removed. Water-soluble salts will deposit on heating surfaces. Mineral acid will attack the equipment when present. Water-washing and drying of feedstocks containing these impurities is essential.

If considerable amounts of odor bodies and low-boiling unsaponifiable matter remain in the fatty acids some means of fractionally concentrating these "low boilers" either by fractional condensation or fractional distillation is required. If the component acids must be separated by chain length an efficient fractionating column still is necessary.

Batch Stills. The oldest of the stills in current use are probably of the semicontinuous batch type. These are usually direct-fired, and sparging steam is used together with vacuum. As bottoms accumulate in the still pot, the end of the run is indicated by a reduction in distillation rate and a darkening of the product. At this time feeding of the still is discontinued, and the product is switched to a secondary receiver, the temperature of the still being increased to reduce the contents to *pitch*. When sampling shows that a suitable pitch has been obtained, firing of the furnace is stopped. After equalizing the vacuum on the pitch receiver, the pitch is withdrawn. The vacuum on the system is relieved, and the still is cleaned out and made ready for the next run. The pitch has certain uses, but it has suffered in recent years by competition from tall oil pitch, which has become available in large quantities (see below under Fatty acids from tall oil).

Units for performing *continuous* straight distillation have largely replaced the semicontinuous types. Stills of this type are made by numerous manufacturers, both American and European; several which might be noted are Wurster and Sanger, Foster-Wheeler, Wecker, and Lurgi. Each of these has certain distinguishing features and offers its own advantages under certain conditions. Moreover, each is a continuous still with constant feed and constant removal of distillate and residue. All distillations are carried out under vacuum and steam is also used in all cases.

Fractionating Distillation. There is marked difference in the volatility of any two fatty acids of different chain length, and in practice, the utility of fractional distillation is enhanced by the absence of odd-membered acids in the natural fats, so that 2 carbon atoms is nearly always the minimum difference in chain length of the fatty acids present in a mixture. The first fractionating still for use with fatty acids was put into operation by Armour and Company, and incorporated the work pioneered by Potts and his co-workers (3). Fractionating stills now in operation are capable of producing fatty acids of 95% purity or better from the viewpoint of chain length. It is not possible to separate unsaturated acids from each other or from saturated acids by commercial fractional distillation when all have the same chain length.

Fatty acid fractionation is frequently used to separate lauric acid from coconut oil for use in detergents. It may also be used to prepare a linoleic acid concentrate from cottonseed oil fatty acids by fractionation removal of the palmitic acid. The linoleic acid concentrate obtained in this way is useful in nonyellowing alkyds. Fatty acids from marine oils or hydrogenated marine oils may also be fractionated, either to give individual acids, or to give fractions having greater utility than the unfractionated materials.

The preferred method for heating fatty acids for distillation is by indirect means, usually Dowtherm vapor. In the Lurgi stills, however, high-pressure steam is used as the heating medium. All fatty acid distillations are carried out at very low absolute pressures, frequently in the range of 5–25 mm Hg. Steam is universally injected since it assists in the distillation and minimizes decomposition of the fatty acids.

HYDROGENATION

The hydrogenation of fatty acids is generally similar to the hydrogenation of fats and oils to produce hard fats, but exceptions are to be noted in several details. Hydrogenation is relatively difficult; 0.2–0.5% of nickel is required, and the catalyst is largely inactivated with one usage. The temperatures used are generally lower than in the case of neutral fats, rarely being above about 305°F and sometimes being as low as 300°F, or even lower; high pressures are depended upon to accelerate the reaction. The converters, which must be built of molybdenum-stabilized stainless steel or other alloy resistant to fatty acids at elevated temperatures, are usually designed for a working pressure of 200–300 lb/in².

It has been reported that the hydrogenation of free fatty acids takes place much less selectively than the hydrogenation of corresponding esters (4). The lessened selectivity is explained upon the basis of the strong polarity of the free carbonyl groups which compete with the active methylene groups in the process of adsorption on the catalyst. There is evidence that hydrogenation of fatty acids or stock containing substantial amounts of fatty acids will give products containing significant quantities of heavy-metal soaps unless careful provisions are made for their removal (5,6).

Bibliography

"Manufacture from Fats" under "Fatty Acids (Survey)" in *ECT* 1st ed., Vol. 6, pp. 231–236, by H. J. Harwood and E. F. Binkerd, Armour and Company.

1. F. H. Mattson and E. S. Lutton, *J. Biol. Chem.* **233**, 868–871 (1958).
2. P. Savary, J. Flauzy, and P. Desnuelle, *Rev. Franç. Corps Gras* **5**, 493–498 (1958); P. Desnuelle and P. Savary, *Fette, Seifen, Anstrichmittel* **61**, 871–876 (1959).
3. U.S. Pats. 2,054,096 (Sept. 15, 1936) and 2,224,984 (Dec. 17, 1940), R. H. Potts and J. E. McKee (to Armour and Co.,); U.S. Pats. 2,322,056 (June 15, 1943) 2,674,570 (April 6, 1954), R. H. Potts (to Armour and Co.).
4. T. P. Hilditch and C. W. Moore, *J. Soc. Chem. Ind.* **42**, 15–16T (1923).
5. B. A. Brice, C. Ricciuti, C. O. Willits, M. L. Swain, and W. C. Ault, *J. Am. Oil Chemists' Soc.* **28**, 85–87 (1951).
6. *Baileys Industrial Oil and Fat Products*, Interscience Publishers, a division of John Wiley & Sons, Inc., New York, 1964, pp. 885–886.

W. C. AULT
U.S. Department of Agriculture

Analysis and Standards

COMPOSITION AND CHEMICAL PROPERTIES

The determinations relating to composition most often made on fatty acids, and reported in some of the following tables, are titer, iodine value, acid value (neutralization value), and saponification value.

Titer: This is the solidification point of fatty acids in degrees Celsius as measured in a specified manner, for example by AOCS (American Oil Chemists' Society) Tentative Method Cc12-59.

Iodine value: This is the number of grams of iodine or equivalent halogen absorbed under standard conditions by 100 g of fatty acid.

Acid value: This is the number of milligrams of potassium hydroxide required to neutralize 1 gram of fatty acid.

Saponification value: This is, as with fats, the number of milligrams of potassium hydroxide consumed on hydrolysis of the sample. For a pure fatty acid, this would be equal to the acid value; the excess over the acid value indicates the amount of unsaponified fat.

Acid composition is not normally a specification of fatty acids, although many suppliers give typical fatty acid compositions of their products. However, composition is important since the specifications usually described are by no means a precise indication of fatty acid composition. Iodine number is certainly a measure of the total amount of unsaturation present, but it provides no sure indication of which unsaturated acids are present in a mixture. For example, an essentially pure oleic acid will

Table 1. Approximate Composition of Distilled Fatty Acids

Source of fatty acid	Saturated acids, %						Unsaturated acids, %			
	C_8	C_{10}	C_{12}	C_{14}	C_{16}	C_{18}	Palmitoleic	Oleic	Linoleic	Linolenic
animal				3	29	18	4	40	4	1
coco	6	7	50	19	9	2			6	1
coco (stripped)		2	56	21	10	3			6	1
corn				1	18	3		26	50	2
cottonseed				1	25	4		26	43	1
linseed				1	7	2		23	17	51
soya				1	16	4				

have an iodine number of 90, while a composition consisting of approximately equal parts of stearic acid (no unsaturation) and linoleic acid (2 double bonds) will have about the same iodine number. As may be expected, the titer of the two materials will be different.

In the same way, acid number is an indication of chain length, since it increases as average molecular weight decreases. Again, however, composition factors such as unsaponifiable content make it virtually impossible to derive precise information about fatty acid composition from acid number.

Although some specifications are related to end use, undoubtedly the use of most acids arose before it was possible to determine chemical composition by any reasonable method; now, however, this is readily done. Historically, this has been possible since the mid 1940s by use of a good fractionating still and an ultraviolet spectrophotometer. More recently, the very rapid gas–liquid chromatographic (GLC) method of separation and analysis is coming into almost universal use. In the hands of a skilled operator, complete and precise information concerning the fatty acid composition of most fatty materials can be obtained in a few minutes (1). The method has even been used for materials containing hydroxy-, acetoxy-, and oxostearic acid methyl esters (2).

Thin-layer chromatography (TLC), which requires much less elegant and sophisticated equipment than GLC, is a more recently developed method of analysis which can be used to analyze fatty acids. It is capable of giving valuable qualitative and semiquantitative information in the hands of an experienced person. Mangold has published a comprehensive review and bibliography of TLC (3).

Relatively few fatty acids of high chemical purity are available commercially. Therefore the composition of nearly all commercial fatty acids will reflect their source and the method used in their preparation. Important exceptions to this occur in the case of the saturated acids, most of which are available in a purity of above 95%.

Important markets exist for fatty acids which have not been fractionated in any way. Such fatty acids invariably will have the same component fatty acid composition as the fats from which they are derived. Normally, the splitting of edible whole oils, such as soybean, cottonseed, or corn oils, is not economically justified. In the alkali refining of these oils, however, soaps of the free fatty acids present are removed along with emulsified glycerides and impurities from the treated oils. These so-called soapstocks, when acidulated and concentrated, are a source of the same acids which characterize the oil. Recently, limitations to the wider use of soapstocks for fatty acid production have arisen. Improvements in the methods of oil extraction and refining lower the amount of recoverable acid therein, in proportion to the original oil, and

Table 2. Approximate Specifications of Distilled Fatty Acids

Source of fatty acid	Titer, °C		Iodine value		Acid value		Saponification value		Color, max	Heat stability	Moisture, %	Unsaponifiable, %
	Min	Max	Min	Max	Min	Max	Min	Max				
animal	40	43	50	60	200	206	201	207	2.0R-15Y			1
coco	22	26	8	12	260	270	261	272	2.0R-10Y			
coco (stripped)	25	30	8	15	250	260	250	262	2.0R-10Y		0.3	0.5
corn	26	32	105	120	195	203	198	210	8 Gardner			
cottonseed	32	38	95	110	195	208	198	210	8 Gardner			
linseed	17	20		180	197	204	197	204	3 Gardner	10 Gardner		
soya	24	29	120	126	195	205	198	207	5 Gardner	10 Gardner		

moreover, some acidulated soapstocks have been found acceptable for animal feeding, thus creating competition for a limited raw material. At the same time, a new source for drying-type acids having approximately the same composition as the linoleic acid oils such as soya oil has originated in the Kraft paper industry, with the increased availability of tall oil fatty acids.

Among those fatty acids which are marketed without substantial fractionation and usually named to indicate their source may be included, soya, corn, cottonseed, coconut, linseed, and animal. Approximate composition and specifications are shown in Tables 1 and 2, but the exact composition will vary with variations in the raw material and in the methods of processing.

Fatty acids other than those in Tables 1 and 2 which are available in unfractionated form include tung acids, having about 85–90% oleostearic acid; octadecatrienoic acid with the double bonds conjugated; and dehydrated castor oil acids, having about 75–85% isomeric octadecadienoic acids, a substantial part of which are conjugated.

The unsaturated component acids of almost all commercial fatty acids are complex mixtures of both positional and stereoisomers. This results not only from the presence of a great variety of isomers in the raw material, but also from the considerable isomerization which takes place during the storage and processing of commercial fats.

Animal fats, principally in the form of inedible tallow but also including inedible greases and marine oils, continue to be large sources of fatty acids, and almost wholly the source of the saturated or monoethenoid (oleic acid) types. Although a variety of processes may now be used to prepare the acids from animal fats, they are frequently designated by names indicative of earlier methods of preparation. Thus, for example, stearic acid from animal fats may be referred to as single, double, or triple pressed, even though it is now prepared by methods which do not involve the old three-step conventional pressing procedures.

The production of commercial stearic acid from animal fats by either a panning and pressing operation or by solvent crystallization leads to a co-product, red oil or the "oleic" acid of commerce.

Typical composition and specification data for several of the more common grades of stearic acid as prepared from animal fats are shown in Tables 3 and 4. As an aside, it is of interest to note that "stearic acid" of commerce frequently contains more palmitic acid than stearic acid.

Stearic acid may also be prepared from vegetable sources by processes involving hydrogenation. Reference to the composition of the vegetable fatty acids shows that

Table 3. Approximate Composition of Stearic Acids

Grades of stearic acid	Saturated acids, %					Unsaturated acids, %	
	C_{14}	C_{15}	C_{16}	C_{17}	C_{18}	Oleic	Linoleic
commercially pure, 97%			3		97		
commercially pure, 90%			8	2	90	trace	
triple pressed	2	1.0	52	2	43	1.0	
double pressed	1	1.0	51	2	42	4	
single pressed	2	1.0	50	2	38	7	1
hydrogenated tallow	4	1.0	30	1	63	1	

Table 4. Approximate Specifications of Commercial Grades of Stearic Acid

Grades of stearic acid	Titer, °C		Iodine value		Acid value		Saponification value		Color, Lovibond, max	Heat stability, Lovibond	Moisture, %	Unsaponifiable, %
	Min	Max	Min	Max	Min	Max	Min	Max				
commercially pure, 97%	66	69	0.5	1.0	196	200	197	201	0.5R-1.5Y	1.5R-5.0Y	0.2	0.5
commercially pure, 90%	65	68	0.7	1.0	196	200	197	201	1.0R-15Y	3.5R-20Y	0.2	0.5
triple pressed	54.5	56		0.5	205	210	206	212	0.5R-2.0Y	1.5R-7Y	0.5	0.5
double pressed	54	54.5	5.0	7.0	205	211	206	212	0.5R-2.0Y	3.0R-20Y		0.5
single pressed	53	54	5.0	10.0	207	210	207	211	2.0R-10Y			
hydrogenated tallow	57	60		2	200	206	201	207	1.0R-5Y	2.5R-20Y		0.5

Table 5. Approximate Composition of Commercial Saturated Acids other than Stearic

Acid	Saturated acids, %							
	C_6	C_8	C_9	C_{10}	C_{12}	C_{14}	C_{16}	C_{18}
caprylic	5	92		3				
pelargonic		4	94	2				
capric		1		97	2			
lauric				1	97	2.0		
myristic					1	96	3	
palmitic 90%						1	94	5
palmitic eutectic[a]						1	70	28

[a] Also contains 1% oleic acid.

soybean oil contains about 90% C_{18} acids, most of which are unsaturated. If these acids are fully hydrogenated, the result is products containing about 90% stearic acid; by additional processing, this yield can be enriched even further. For example, fractional distillation can be used to eliminate acids other than stearic acid or solvent treatment can be used to remove lower-melting materials.

Saturated acids other than stearic acid are also available commercially. Most of these are available from the fractional distillation of coconut oil or to a lesser degree from hydrogenated fish oil. The acids available from these sources include caprylic, capric, lauric, myristic, arachidic, and behenic. Of these, the only one which is manufactured and sold on any substantial scale is lauric acid. Typical specifications and composition data for these saturated acids are shown in Tables 5 and 6. For unsaturated acids, see Tables 7 and 8.

Pelargonic acid, a saturated acid containing 9 carbon atoms, is also commercially available as a result of the ozone cleavage of oleic acid. The commercial product has a pelargonic acid content of at least 90% and an iodine value below 0.5. The principal impurities are capric and caprylic acids. It is a clear, almost water-white liquid (color, Gardner 1 max) with a mild characteristic odor.

Complex mixtures of saturated fatty acids are made commercially by hydrolysis of hydrogenated fish oils. The fatty acid composition of these may be judged from the composition of crude menhaden oils; the most unusual characteristic of these oils is the relatively large amount of C_{20} and C_{22} material present.

Rapeseed oil or its acidulated foots may also serve as a source of fatty acids having 20 carbon atoms in the chain because of the characteristic presence of about 55% erucic acid. Rapeseed oil is not an important oil in the United States, however. Its significant culture is confined to Poland, Canada, and other countries having a climate too harsh for soybean production.

PHYSICAL AND CHEMICAL PROPERTIES

The physical and chemical properties of fatty acids are of great practical importance and hence certain of these properties are a part of their specifications for use in trading and describing commercial products. The most commonly used methods are standardized and are described in well-recognized publications such as the *Official and Tentative Methods of the American Oil Chemists' Society* (4), *Methods of the American Society for Testing and Materials, Standard Methods for the Analysis of Fats and Oils* (5), and the *Methods of the Association of Official Agricultural Chemists* (AOAC).

Table 6. Approximate Specifications of Commercial Saturated Acids other than Stearic

Acid	Titer, °C Min	Titer, °C Max	Iodine value, max	Acid value Min	Acid value Max	Saponification value Min	Saponification value Max	Color, Lovibond, max	Heat stability, Lovibond	Moisture, %	Unsaponifiable, %
caprylic	8	12	0.5	387	392	388	394	1.5R-7.0Y	4.0R-40Y	0.2	0.2
pelargonic	8	11	0.5	345	355			0.5R-1.5Y			0.2
capric	29	32	0.5	323	329	323	330	1.0R-5.0Y	2.5R-10Y	0.2	0.2
lauric	40	44	1.0	275	282	278	284	0.5R-4.0Y		0.2	0.2
myristic	50	54	0.5	244	249	245	250	0.5R-2.0Y	1.5R-8Y	0.2	0.2
palmitic 90%	58	62	0.5	216	219	217	220	0.5R-2.0Y	1.5R-8Y	0.2	0.3
palmitic eutectic	53	55	1.0	210	214	211	215	1.0R-5.0Y	2.0R-10Y		0.3

Table 7. Approximate Composition of Commercial Unsaturated Acids

Acid	Saturated acids, %				Unsaturated acids, %			
	C_{14}	C_{15}	C_{17}	C_{18}	Palmitoleic	Oleic	Linoleic	Linolenic
low polyunsaturated oleic	3	4	1		10	77	4	1
oleic, white	3	4	1		8	73	8	1
oleic, red oil	3	5	1	1	7	71	8	1
linoleic acid	1	4			1	33	60	1

Table 8. Approximate Specifications of Commercial Unsaturated Acids

Acid	Titer, °C		Iodine value		Acid value		Saponification value		Color, max	Moisture, %	Unsaponifiable, %
	Min	Max	Min	Max	Min	Max	Min	Max			
low polyunsaturated oleic	2	6	85	90	200	204	200	205	0.5R-5.0Y	0.4	1.0
oleic, white	0	5	85	95	197	204	198	205	1.0R-8Y	0.5	1.0
oleic, red oil	8	11	85	95	197	204	199	205	dark	0.4	1.5
linoleic acid		5	140	145	195	200	195	201	3 Gardner	0.5	1.0

Standard methods are not all uniform and hence at times it is very important to know the specific method which is being used to examine a fatty acid. Moreover, methods of a research character or those which are in a stage of development are not found in the standardized methods. This follows from the nature and amount of work necessary to the process of standardization. Tables 1–8 show the specifications and chemical composition of most of the fatty acids now commercially available in the United States. The fatty acid composition of some fats and oils is given in Table 9. Standard methods, with or without slight modifications, are used in specification work; most of the fatty acid compositions shown have been determined by methods based on gas–liquid chromatography.

Table 9. Approximate Fatty Acid Composition of Selected Fats and Oils

Acid	Designation[a]	Composition, %						
		Coconut	Corn	Cottonseed	Soya	Linseed	Lard	Tallow
caprylic	8:0	8						
capric	10:0	7						
lauric	12:0	48						
myristic	14:0	17	1	1			2	4
palmitic	16:0	9	12	24	11	6	27	29
hexadecenoic	16:1			26	1		2	1
stearic	18:0	2	3	4	3	3	14	23
octadecanoic	18:1	7	29		21	20	44	41
octadecadienoic	18:2	2	55	55	52	18	9	2
octadecatrienoic	18:3				8	53	2	

[a] Number of carbon atoms and number of double bonds.

RESISTANCE TO DETERIORATION

The deterioration occurring in commercial fatty acids manifests itself chiefly as changes in color and odor. Assuming that the handling and packaging have been performed satisfactorily, the chemical reactions involved are almost solely oxidation and oxidative polymerization and cleavage. These reactions, however, are quite complex and for details reference 6 should be consulted.

From a practical standpoint, the oxidative deterioration of fatty acids is most closely related to the development of rancidity in fats and oils. Actually, development of rancid colors and flavors can be of great importance in the case of fatty acids which are to be used in foods, ie, food-grade acids, and in cosmetics. In other cases, odor development itself may be of importance chiefly as an indication that a certain amount of oxidative deterioration has taken place. The autoxidation of the unsaturated components of fats proceeds by a free-radical chain mechanism in which hydroperoxide formation and decomposition are the principal reactions.

The rate of autoxidation of linoleate and other methylene-interrupted systems is much higher than that of monounsaturated systems because a methylene group is activated by surrounding double bonds. In turn, the autoxidation of a monounsaturated acid is much more rapid than that of a saturated acid. The relative rates of oxidation of several fatty acids at 100°C has been shown by Stirton, et al. (7) to be as follows: stearic, 1; oleic, 10; linoleic, 100; and linolenic, 100.

Gunstone and Hilditch (8) have found the unsaturated acids to have approximately the same relative rates of oxidation at 20°C as those reported by Stirton, et al.

This information points to the conclusion that stability will be related inversely to unsaturation. However, polyunsaturates are much more undesirable in saturated acids than monounsaturates and will lead more quickly to rancidity and color degradation. From a practical point of view it therefore becomes of interest to know not only the unsaturation, as measured by the iodine number, but also the chemical nature of the unsaturates present. There also appears to be some difference between the relative ease of oxidation of cis and trans double bonds, but this is not as well documented and differences are of considerably lesser magnitude than the effects of methylene groups.

There are several methods available for measuring the expected stability of fatty acids. The most commonly used is AOCS Tentative Method L15a58. This method measures the color stability of fatty acids by measuring the change in color after heating under the specified conditions of the test; it is usually described in a specification as the maximum allowable color of the sample after it has been subjected to the prescribed heating conditions.

Another simple and commonly used accelerated method for determining stability of fats or fat products is the oven or Schall test (9). The sample is simply incubated in a loosely closed container in an oven at about 60–70°C until it develops a specific peroxide number or rancid odor and flavor. No standards for this method have been adopted; hence no strict comparisons can be made among results from different laboratories. An experienced worker can, however, often obtain information of value by use of this extremely simple method.

Bibliography

"Separation and Analysis" under "Fatty Acids (Survey)" in *ECT* 1st ed., Vol. 6, pp. 228–231, by T. H. Hopper, U.S. Department of Agriculture.

1. L. D. Metcalfe, *J. Am. Oil Chemists' Soc.* **41**, 4 (1964).
2. A. P. Tulloch, *J. Am. Oil Chemists' Soc.* **41**, 833–836 (1964).
3. H. K. Mangold, *J. Am. Oil Chemists' Soc.* **41**, 762–773 (1964).
4. *Official and Tentative Methods of the American Oil Chemists' Society*, 2nd ed., American Oil Chemists' Society, Chicago, Ill. (Issued continuously.)

5. *Standard Methods for the Analysis of Fats and Oils*, Fat Commission, International Union of Pure and Applied Chemistry, Paris, 1954.
6. W. O. Lundberg, ed., *Autoxidation and Antioxidants*, 2 vols., Interscience Publishers, a division of John Wiley & Sons, Inc., New York, 1961 and 1922.
7. A. J. Stirton, J. Turer, and R. W. Riemenschneider, *Oil & Soap* **22**, 81–83 (1945).
8. F. D. Gunstone and T. P. Hilditch, *J. Chem. Soc.* **1945**, 836–841.
9. N. T. Joyner and J. E. McIntyre, *Oil & Soap* **15**, 184 (1938).

General References

Daniel Swern, ed., *Bailey's Industrial Oil and Fat Products*, 3rd ed., Interscience Publishers, a division of John Wiley & Sons, Inc., New York, 1964.
E. Scott Pattison, ed., *Industrial Fatty Acids*, Reinhold Publishing Corp., New York, 1964.
V. C. Mehlenbacher, *Analysis of Fats and Oils*, The Garrard Press, Champaign, Ill., 1960.
Klare S. Markley, ed., *Fatty Acids*, 2nd ed., Part I, 1960; Part II, 1961; Part III, 1964, Interscience Publishers, a division of John Wiley & Sons, Inc., New York.
E. W. Eckey, *Vegetable Fats and Oils*, Reinhold Publishing Corp., New York, 1954.
T. P. Hilditch and P. N. Williams, *The Chemical Constitution of Natural Fats*, 4th ed., John Wiley & Sons, Inc., New York, 1964.
M. E. Stansby, ed., *Industrial Fishery Technology*, Reinhold Publishing Corp., New York, 1963.

W. C. AULT
U.S. Department of Agriculture

Economic Aspects

Total fatty acid production has increased by more than 80% in the twelve-year period since 1953, when figures became available for the first time (Fig. 1) (1,2).

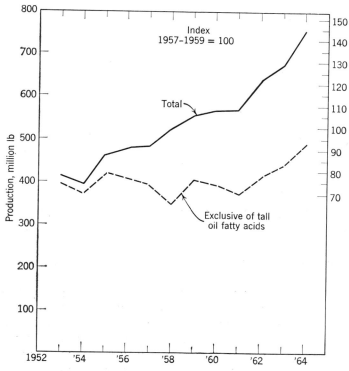

Fig. 1. Total fatty acid production, and fatty acid production exclusive of tall oil fatty acids, in million pounds, 1953–1964. Index figures are for total fatty acid production only.

Table 1. Fatty Acid Production and Disposition, 1954 vs 1964 (in million pounds)

FAPC category	Fatty acid[a]	1954	1964
	Production		
	saturated		
1	stearic acid, 40–50% stearic content	50.2	71.1
2a	hydrogenated fatty acids having a maximum titer of 60°C and a minimum IV of 5		85.9
		85.	
2b	hydrogenated fatty acids having a minimum titer of 57°C and a maximum IV of 5		80.2
3	palmitic acid, more than 60% palmitic content, maximum IV of 12	4.4	6.2
4	hydrogenated fish and marine mammal fatty acids	12.5	10.3
5	coconut-type acids having IV of 5 or more, including palm kernel, babassu, and hydrogenated coconut acids	18.1	23.0
6	fractionated short-chain fatty acids having IV below 5, including caprylic, capric, lauric, and myristic acids	14.4	21.2
	unsaturated		
7	oleic acid (red oil)	87.8	108.9
8	animal fatty acids other than oleic (IV 36 to 80)	30.7	42.5
9	vegetable or marine fatty acids having a maximum IV of 115	24.1	10.1
10	fatty acids having IV 116 to 130	21.4	17.4
11	fatty acids having IV more than 130	22.5	12.4
12	tall oil fatty acids containing less than 2% rosin acids and more than 95% fatty acids	[b]	129.9
13	tall oil fatty acids containing 2–6% rosin acids and more than 90% fatty acids	[c]	136.2
	total	371.5	755.3
	Disposition		
	domestic shipments	315.5	628.0
	captive consumption	46.2	97.1
	export shipments	22.3	53.2
	total	384.0	778.3

[a] IV = iodine value.

[b] Statistics not available. Production in 1958 was 66.9 million pounds and in 1959 was 83.2 million pounds.

[c] Statistics not available. Production in 1959 was 66.4 million pounds.

SOURCE: Fatty Acid Producers' Council (FAPC).

Comparison of the production indexes (1957–1959 = 100) shows that total fatty acid production for the period 1961–1964 increased (from 109.7 to 144.7) at a slightly greater rate than total industrial production (from 109.7 to 131.9). Totals for fatty acid production include estimated values for tall oil fatty acids from 1953 to 1957. Accurate census figures for vegetable and animal fatty acids have been available since 1952, but for tall oil fatty acids only since 1958. The rapid growth in overall fatty acid production is due mainly to the growth in tall oil fatty acids, as illustrated in both Figures 1 and 2, the latter showing the growth of individual classes. Production of

Table 2. Production of Fatty Acid Derivatives as Plasticizers (in thousand pounds)

Fatty acid derivative	Year of production						1963 unit value, $/lb
	1950	1955	1960	1961	1962	1963	
azelaic acid esters			7,295	7,335	13,090	16,254	0.30
complex linear polyesters and polymeric plasticizers			16,474	33,731	35,740		0.42
epoxidized esters, total				15,887	53,998	58,752	0.29
epoxidized soya oils					37,725	39,965	0.29
octyl epoxy tallates					14,611	15,915	0.28
all other					1,662	2,872	0.43
glycerol monoricinoleate		287	298	367	175	237	0.39
isopropyl myristate						1,833	0.33
isopropyl palmitate						892	0.31
oleic acid esters, total	7,401	11,545	6,219	8,939	6,073	10,037	0.24
butyl oleate		1,999	1,822	1,827	2,022	2,999	0.20
glycerol trioleate					1,618	3,480	0.20
isopropyl oleate						536	0.23
n-propyl oleate					513	480	0.20
all other		9,546	4,397	7,112	1,920	1,369	0.40
sebacic acid esters, total	2,258	9,305	13,781	11,500	12,944	11,856	
dibutyl sebacate		3,435	3,596	3,499	3,847	4,276	0.63
di(2-ethylhexyl) sebacate			9,178	7,434	8,864	7,580	0.57
stearic acid esters, total	17,158	9,628	12,288	7,366	6,371	7,433	0.24
n-butyl stearate	1,904	6,368	3,501	3,150	3,003	2,739	0.24
all other	15,254	3,260	8,787	4,216	3,368	4,694	0.24
triethylene glycol di-(caprylate–caprate)		2,031	2,009	2,223	2,601	2,022	0.32

SOURCE: United States Tariff Commission Reports, Synthetic Organic Chemicals.

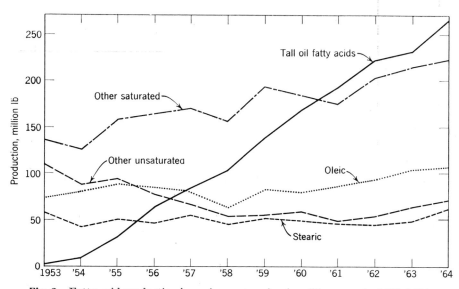

Fig 2. Fatty acid production in various categories, in million pounds, 1953–1964.

Table 3. Production of Selected Fatty Acid Derivatives as Surface-Active Agents (in thousand pounds)

Fatty acid derivative	Year of production						1963 unit value, $/lb
	1950	1955	1960	1961	1962	1963	
amides, amines, and quaternary ammonium salts, total	28,373[a]	65,353[a]	110,999	120,625	141,339	146,683	0.44
acyclic quaternary ammonium salts						22,039	0.43
amine salts				2,708	2,724	2,581	0.41
amines, alkoxylated				5,152[c]	7,002	9,886	0.35
benzenoid (benzylated)		1,445	1,459	2,092	1,042	926	0.95
fatty acid–alkanolamine condensates				86,945	82,506	67,245	0.38
fatty acid–polyamine condensates				2,173	9,603	11,027	0.28
fatty acid–polyamine condensates, ethoxylated					6,383	7,539	0.70
other amides, amines, and quaternary ammonium salts			69,802	18,951	24,326	18,447	0.44
carboxylic acid esters, total				90,115	113,843	112,031	0.33
diethylene glycol esters				1,800	1,999	2,675	0.34
ethylene glycol esters				558	1,624	1,402	0.32
glycerol esters				48,776	60,722	61,458	0.26
polyethylene glycol esters				17,168	20,924	20,494	0.35
other carboxylic acid esters				21,501	32,197	26,002	0.45
ethers, total	20,363	101,227	177,430	85,918	100,908	109,486	0.26
castor oil, ethoxylated				1,801	1,631	2,129	0.35
n-dodecyl alcohol, ethoxylated				1,402[c]	1,535[c]	51,343	0.48
lanolin, ethoxylated					470	63	0.43
9-octadecenyl alcohol, ethoxylated					1,966	1,629	0.48
n-octadecyl alcohol, ethoxylated				49	116	168[c]	0.41
other				25,750	58,191	46,736	0.24

							%
dodecyl mercaptan	6,371	7,774	9,488	11,295	9,624	8,963	0.46
fatty acids, potassium and sodium salts, total	2,668	23,094	11,275	12,893	11,640	13,807	0.23
fats, oils, and waxes, sulfated and sulfonated, total	53,989	53,173	30,986	28,201	30,252	29,286	0.19
animal fats and oils (including fish and marine animal oils)	34,533	23,218	15,968	16,110	18,511	17,938	
vegetable oils	17,765	13,355	10,368	10,348	10,423	5,810[c]	0.28
other fats, oils, and waxes	1,691	16,600	4,650	1,743	1,318	1,244	0.28
other nonbenzenoid surface-active agents, sulfated and sulfonated, total	34,533[b]	197,816[b]	254,758	233,654	234,738	250,900	0.21
n-butyl sulfo-oleate						686	0.27
coconut oil acids–ethanolamine condensate, sulfated, potassium salt		113	95	91	47	44	1.07
n-dodecyl sulfate, ammonium salt			420	864	923	1,436	0.55
n-dodecyl sulfate, sodium salt		13,598	11,665	12,752	13,365	13,151	0.52
n-dodecyl sulfate, triethanolamine salt		4,035	3,881	5,468	5,736	6,714	0.31
isopropyl sulfo-oleate	766	870	606	1,031	1,152	828	0.30
N-methyl-N-oleyltaurine				2,340	2,943	2,993	0.54
oleic acid, sulfonated	2,157	2,520	2,632	2,378	2,193	2,910	0.32
n-propyl sulfo-oleate		1,510	1,298	781	1,288	1,031	0.24
other				207,215	208,943	220,331	0.18

[a] Listed as nitrogen-containing surface-active agents, nonsulfonated.
[b] Listed as acyclic surface-active agents, sulfated and sulfonated.
[c] Sales.

SOURCE: United States Tariff Commission Reports, Synthetic Organic Chemicals.

Table 4. Production of Selected Fatty Acid Derivatives (in thousand pounds)

Fatty acid derivative	Year of production						1963 unit value, $/lb
	1950	1955	1960	1961	1962	1963	
alcohols							
dodecyl alcohol (lauryl alcohol) (95%)					10,911^c	17,854	0.31
1-hexadecanol (cetyl alcohol) (95%)	685	556	1,026		1,090	1,452	0.18
1-octadecanol (stearyl alcohol) (95%)				12,594	4,214^c	5,254^c	
amines							
coconut oil amine			980	892	943	859	0.54
dodecyl amine				1,280	1,886^c	1,034^c	0.64
octadecyl amine			381	582	916	1,048	0.46
oleyl amine					1,016	998	0.36
tallow amine				2,057	2,089	3,191	0.36
tallow amine, dihydrogenated and hydrogenated			3,540	3,047	2,087	4,203	0.32
dilauryl 3,3'-thiodipropionate				432	352	728	0.99
fatty acid esters^a	1,223	3,813	3,195	3,254	5,028	13,384	0.31
lauroyl chloride			9,984				
linoleic acid salts, total	1,442	1,080	466	492	437	409	0.34
calcium linoleate	726	463^c	149	145	135	105	
cobalt linoleate	387	234	101		112	158	
oleic acid salts^b	381	237	198	329	213	329	0.80
palmitic acid salts	401	407	264		327	274	
palmitoyl chloride		66			136	163	
stearic acid salts, total^b	24,369	23,346	25,246	27,299	30,573	30,885	0.35
aluminum stearates, total	9,317	7,360	5,108	5,298	5,066	4,971	0.38
aluminum distearate	8,060	5,091	3,951	4,273	3,990	3,693	0.37
aluminum stearate, other	1,257	2,269	1,157	1,025	1,076	1,278	0.41
calcium stearate	4,169	4,538	7,432	8,433	10,083	10,836	0.28
lead stearate	629	701	302	441	611	646	0.36
lithium stearate		126	161	261	259	279	0.52
magnesium stearate	574	772	1,008	1,088	1,265	1,235	0.40
zinc stearate	6,976	7,411	7,296	7,705	8,538	8,567	0.38
all other	2,704	2,438	3,939	4,073	4,751	4,351	0.45
tallow amide, hydrogenated				1,382	1,235		0.34

^a Including isopropyl myristate and palmitate not entered under plasticizer or surface-active agents.

^b Exclusive of potassium and sodium salts which are listed under surface-active agents.

^c Sales.

stearic, oleic, and other unsaturated acids remained at a fairly steady rate from 1953 to 1964, whereas total production of other saturated acids (as defined in Table 1) increased from 142 to 227 million pounds, and production of tall oil fatty acids from 18 (estimated) to 266 million pounds. Table 1 shows the production of 13 categories of fatty acids as defined by the Fatty Acid Producers' Council, as well as disposition for all fatty acids for the years 1954 and 1964.

Outstanding uses for fatty acids and their derivatives are in plasticizers (qv) and surface-active agents (see Surfactants) (3). Production figures of some fatty acid derivatives for plasticizer use are given in Table 2. Noteworthy is the emergence since 1960 of esters of azelaic acid (see Vol. 1, p. 250; Esters), polymeric polyesters (see Polyesters), and epoxidized fatty derivatives (see Epoxidation).

In spite of the surge to petroleum-based detergents in the last decade, fatty acid-based surface-active agents have managed to hold their own (Table 3). Recent emphasis on biodegradable detergents may increase demand for fatty acid-based products.

Fatty acid derivatives other than those used for plasticizers or surface-active agents are listed in Table 4. The most important of these derivatives are the stearic acid salts, used in lubricating greases and paints; as internal lubricants, heat stabilizers, and light stabilizers; and as catalysts. Fatty alcohols, fatty amines, and lauroyl chloride are also high-volume production items. About 40 million pounds annually of stearic acid is consumed by the rubber industry, half for compounding and the other half in the emulsion copolymerization of styrene and butadiene.

Bibliography

1. *Fatty Acid Production, Disposition, and Stocks Census*, Fatty Acid Producers' Council, Division of the Soap and Detergent Association, New York, N.Y.
2. *Fatty Acids—Building Blocks for Industry*, Fatty Acid Producers' Council, Division of the Soap and Detergent Association, New York, N.Y.
3. *Synthetic Organic Chemicals, United States Production and Sales*, United States Tariff Commission, *Annual Reports*, U.S. Government Printing Office, Washington, D.C.

E. H. PRYDE
U.S. Department of Agriculture

Fatty Acids from Tall Oil

Tall oil is a nonglyceride oil obtained from the pine wood used in making wood pulp (see Pulp). In making wood pulp by the sulfate process, all fats, fatty acids, and rosin acids in the wood are converted into soaps. These soaps are washed out of the pulp and collect in the waste black liquor from which they are subsequently separated as skimmings. Tall oil plants convert the skimmings into tall oil by acidulation with sulfuric acid. See also Tall oil; Rosin.

Crude tall oil is a mixture of rosin acids related to abietic acid and fatty acids related to oleic acid, together with varying proportions of unsaponifiable material comprised of sterols, alcohols, and hydrocarbons. Whole tall oil from any one source does not vary much in composition. However, comparisons of whole tall oils from various pulp mills often show marked differences. Surveys of commercial whole tall oils have shown compositions with ranges of 38–58% rosin acids, 54–36% fatty acids, and 5–15% unsaponifiables.

Much of the whole tall oil produced is processed further to improve its color and odor, or to alter its composition. A variety of methods may be used for refining and modifying tall oil but fractional distillation is the method used commercially for the production of tall oil fatty acids. These acids are commercially available in a variety of grades which vary in color, color stability, and content of rosin acid and unsaponifiable material. Commercial tall oil fatty acids usually contain a minimum of 90% fatty acids, the remainder being rosin acids and unsaponifiable matter. Within this limit of over 90% fatty acid content there are a large number of fatty acid products from tall oil on the market, some specifying over 99% fatty acid content.

The residue from fractional distillation is a pitch, which is used in applications where resinous materials are required which are economical in price and where color is not a handicap. Specific fields of use therefore include industrial paints and finishes, tar and asphalt extenders and emulsifiers, sealing compounds, etc.

The fatty acids of tall oil consist of a mixture of dienoic, monoenoic, and saturated acids. Anderson and Wheeler (1) reported the composition of the fatty acids of six samples of American tall oil using modern methods of analysis (see Table 1). Although the total fatty acid content of their six samples varied widely, they reported the fatty acids to be remarkably uniform in composition. They found average composition of the six samples of fatty acids to be 48% linoleic, including 11% conjugated dienoic acids; 45% oleic (possibly 1% palmitoleic); and 45% saturated acids, chiefly palmitic acid.

Table 1. Composition of Tall Oil Fatty Acids—Spectrophotometric Method (1)

Sample	Conjugated linoleic, %	Linoleic, %	Oleic, % by difference	Saturated, % determined
A	9	45	48	7
		42	51	
B	10	47	47	6
		44	50	
C	12	49	43	8
		46	46	
D	12	49	44	7
		46	47	
E	13	52	41	7
		48	45	
F	9	45	48	7
		42	51	
a*v*	11	48	45	7

Table 2. Annual Production of Tall Oil and Tall Oil Fatty Acid

Year	Crude tall oil, million lb/yr	Tall oil fatty acid, million lb/yr
1950	310	5.0
1955	584	47.4
1960	789	
1961	826	
1962	880	
1963	990	240.0[a]
1964	1050[b]	

[a] Estimate (2).   [b] Estimate (3).

The annual production of both tall oil and tall oil fatty acid has increased very rapidly, as shown in Table 2.

According to trade estimates, nine companies in the United States operated thirteen tall oil fractionating plants in 1963. At the end of the year, the plants had capacities of nearly 1.2 billion pounds and further plant additions were planned at the time.

The fraction of the tall oil that is most readily marketable is the rosin. It finds substantial ready outlet in the manufacture of paper size. Hence, tall oil fatty acids have competed effectively with other fatty acids available from the animal fat and vegetable oil industries. Because of their composition, tall oil fatty acids have been especially effective competitors of soy and linseed fatty acids, but after partial or complete hydrogenation their composition also permits use interchangeably with animal fatty acids for many purposes.

Tall oil fatty acid production in 1963 totaled 240,000,000 lb. Its use was distributed as follows: coatings, 54,000,000 lb; detergents, soaps, and disinfectants, 27,000,000 lb; intermediate chemicals, 64,000,000 lb; flotation, 13,800,000 lb; tallate driers, 4,200,000 lb; hard-floor coverings, 7,000,000 lb; other, inventory and exports, 69,400,000 lb.

Bibliography

1. R. H. Anderson and D. H. Wheeler, *J. Am. Oil Chemists' Soc.* **22**, 137–141 (1945).
2. *Oil Paint Drug Reptr.* **184** (26), 1 (Dec. 23, 1963).
3. *Fats and Oils Situation* **221**, 32 (1964).

W. C. AULT
U.S. Department of Agriculture

Polybasic Acids

Heating polyunsaturated acids such as linoleic acid in the absence of a catalyst (1) or in the presence of a catalyst such as clay produces low polymers consisting predominantly of *dimers*, *trimers*, and *tetramers*. Variation of the starting materials and

Table 1. Dimer Acids—Composition, Specifications and Characteristics

	Grade				
	1014	1016	1018	1022	1024
Composition					
dimer acid, wt %	95	87	83	75	75
trimer acid, wt %	4	13	17	22	25
Specifications					
acid value	191–195	190–198	188–196	186–194	186–194
saponification value	195–199	194–200	192–198	191–199	191–199
neutr. value	288–294	284–295	287–299	289–301	289–301
unsaponifiable, %, max	1	0.5		2	2
color, Gardner, max	8	7	8	9	9
Characteristics					
specific gravity, 100/20°C	0.90	0.90	0.90	0.90	0.90
refractive index, n_D^{20}	1.4706	1.4671	1.4704	1.4738	1.4755
viscosity, Gardner-Holdt	Z-3	Z-3	Z-4	Z-4	Z-5

of the conditions under which the reaction is carried out will alter the ratio of the various polymers to each other but conditions have not been reported which lead to dimers exclusively.

The first reaction is believed to be the isomerization of the polyunsaturated acid to a conjugated acid which then undergoes a Diels-Alder-type addition with a double bond in a second molecule. The reaction may be depicted as follows:

$$CH_3(CH_2)_4CH=CHCH_2CH=CH(CH_2)_7COOH \qquad \text{linoleic acid}$$

$$\downarrow$$

$$\overset{\displaystyle CH-CH}{\underset{CH_3(CH_2)_3CH \qquad CH(CH_2)_7COOH}{}} \qquad \text{conjugated linoleic acid}$$

$$+$$

$$CH_3(CH_2)_4CH=CHCH_2CH=CH(CH_2)_7COOH$$

$$\downarrow$$

$$\text{dimer acid}$$

Because triglycerides crosslink to form gels before polymerization is far advanced, oils as such are not suitable raw materials for the manufacture of dimer acids. Polymerization is preferably carried out on free fatty acids or monoesters.

The reaction takes place at ordinary pressures and at temperatures in the range of 255–325°C. At the most useful upper portion of this range decarboxylation may become significant. This undesirable side reaction can be minimized by the proper choice of temperature and possibly more significantly by the use of both steam and pressure (2).

Dimer Acids. These may be obtained commercially at prices which usually make them more expensive than phthalic anhydride but considerably cheaper than other dibasic acids of relatively high molecular weight, such as azelaic and sebacic acids. The dimer acids are available in a variety of grades varying from 75 to 90% dimer and 25 to 4% trimer. Monobasic acid content will usually vary from trace amounts to a maximum of 3%. The commercial products are light yellow in color (7–9, Gardner). They are viscous liquids which increase gradually in viscosity as the temperature is lowered especially below room temperature.

Specifications and characteristics for a number of the Empol dimer acids as presented by their manufacturer are shown in Table 1 (3).

Commercial dimer acids are useful in the manufacture of polyesters (4), alkyd resins (5), polyamide resins (6), polyurethan resins (7), and gasoline additives (8). An extensive bibliography on the uses of dimer acids has been prepared (9).

Bibliography

1. T. F. Bradley and W. B. Johnson, *Ind. Eng. Chem.* **32**, 802 (1940); T. F. Bradley and W. B. Johnson, *Ind. Eng. Chem.* **33**, 86 (1941).
2. C. G. Goebel, *J. Am. Oil Chemists' Soc.* **24**, 65 (1947).
3. Emery Industries Inc., Technical Bulletin No. 431, *Empol Dimer Acid in Alkyd-Oil Paints*, April 1963; Technical Bulletin No. 442, *Empol 1016 Dimer Acid*, July 1964.
4. U.S. Pat. 2,373,015 (April 3, 1945), J. C. Cowan and W. C. Ault (to U.S. Dept. of Agriculture); J. C. Cowan, et al., *Ind. Eng. Chem.* **38**, 1138 (1946).
5. J. C. Cowan and L. B. Falkenburg, *J. Am. Oil Chemists' Soc.* **20**, 153–157 (1943).
6. J. C. Cowan et al., *J. Am. Oil Chemists' Soc.* **21**, 101 (1944). L. B. Falkenburg, *J. Am. Oil Chemists' Soc.* **22**, 143 (1945).
7. U.S. Pat. 2,776,194 (Jan. 1, 1957), W. W. Scheumann (to Cities Service Research and Development Company).
8. *Empol Dimer Acids in Urethane Coatings*, Technical Bulletin No. 433, Emery Industries Inc., Oct. 1962.
9. *Abstracts of Dimer Acid Use Patents and Journal References*, Technical Bulletin No. 412 A. Emery Industries Inc., July 1962.

W. C. AULT

U.S. Department of Agriculture

Branched-Chain Acids

The branched-chain fatty acids contain one or more branching alkyl groups. A branch frequently, but not always, is attached at the carbon atom alpha to the carboxyl group. Numerous branched-chain acids have been synthesized but only the low- and medium-weight ones have found any significant industrial outlet. Their synthesis usually involves an aldol condensation or use of the oxo process to yield aldehydes which are then oxidized to the corresponding acids.

More or less typical is a route for the preparation of 2-ethylhexanoic acid (2-ethylhexoic acid) from butyraldehyde. This preparation may be outlined as follows:

$$CH_3CH_2CH_2CHO \xrightarrow{OH^-} CH_3CH_2CH_2CHOHCHCHO \xrightarrow{-H_2O}$$

n-butyraldehyde
(butanal)

with C_2H_5 branch

$$CH_3CH_2CH_2CH{=}CCHO \xrightarrow{H_2, Ni} CH_3CH_2CH_2CH_2CHCHO \xrightarrow{[O]} CH_3CH_2CH_2CH_2CHCOOH$$

with C_2H_5 branches

2-ethyl-2-hexenal   2-ethylhexanal   2-ethylhexanoic acid

The properties of several branched-chain acids characteristic of those available commercially are shown in Table 1.

The branched-chain acids have a wide variety of industrial uses, those for 2-ethylhexanoic acid being typical. Commercially important salts of 2-ethylhexanoic acid which are utilized as varnish driers are those of lead, cobalt, and manganese. These salts usually are made by double decomposition (1a,2). See Driers and metallic soaps. Other ethylhexanoates find uses similar to those of the metallic soaps of other acids. The basic lead salt and the barium salt are heat stabilizers for vinyl resins, and the salts of light metals such as aluminum are useful in greases and as thickening agents in certain lacquers and paints (3). Certain ethylhexanoates such as those of cobalt, nickel, zinc, and magnesium can be used to inhibit sludge and varnish deposition in mineral oils (4).

Table 1.   Branched-Chain Acids (1)

Acid	Sp gr 20/20	Bp, °C 760 mm	n_D^{20}	Fp, °C	Solubility in water, at 20°C, % by wt	Ionization constant, 25°C	Viscosity, cP, at 20°C
2-ethylbutyric	0.9245	194	1.4133	−15	1.6	1.80×10^{-5}	3.3
"isopentanoic" (mixed isomers)	0.9388	183	1.4076	−44	3.24	1.75×10^{-5}	2.2
2-methyl-pentanoic	0.9242	196	1.4135	−85	1.3	1.57×10^{-5}	2.9
2-ethylhexanoic	0.9077	227	1.4252	−118.4	0.25	1.54×10^{-5}	7.7

Certain derivatives of 2-ethylhexanoic acid are used as plasticizers (qv). For example, polyethylene glycol bis(2-ethylhexanoate) is suggested for smooth vinyl films and sheets (5), the diester amide of 2-ethylhexanoic acid and diethanolamine (6), and the products from 2-ethylhexanoic acid and various amino resins for vinyl resins (7). 2-Ethylhexanoic acid can also be used as a plasticizer for zein compositions employed for impregnating and coating (8).

Certain thio derivatives of 2-ethylhexanoic acid have been reported to have value as oil additives (9). The acid itself has been suggested as an insect repellent (10) and for use in the extraction of acetic acid from dilute aqueous solutions (11). The aluminum salt is reported to be useful in the preparation of a gelable scintillator plate (12). Vinyl 2-ethylhexanoate may be used in preparing copolymers useful for treating polyethylene films (13).

Bibliography

"Branched-Chain Saturated Acids" under "Fatty Acids (Branched-Chain)" in *ECT* 1st ed., Vol. 6, pp. 259–262, by Mabel D. Reiner (in part); and J. A. Field (in part), Union Carbide and Carbon Corporation.

1. *Acids and Acid Anhydrides*, Union Carbide Corp., Chemicals Div., New York, 1958, 1960.
1a. G. Fearnley, *Offic. Dig. Federation Paint Varnish Prod. Clubs* **290**, 137–143 (1949).
2. C. A. Klebstattel, *Paint Varnish Production Mfg.* **28**, 332–340 (1948).
3. U.S. Pat. 2,274,675 (March 3, 1942), C. E. Earle.
4. U.S. Pat. 2,384,551 (Sept. 11, 1945), L. Jehle (to Carbide and Carbon Chemicals Company).
5. U.S. Pat. 2,229,222 (Jan. 21, 1941), G. H. Reid (to Carbide and Carbon Chemicals Company).
6. U.S. Pat. 2,472,900, 2,472,901 (June 4, 1949), F. Johnston, and W. H. Hensley (to Carbide and Carbon Chemicals Company).
7. U.S. Pat. 2,437,657 (March 9, 1948), H. J. West and H. M. Enterline (to American Cyanamid Co.).
8. U.S. Pat. 2,410,124 (Oct. 29, 1946), W. L. Morgan (to E. A. Staley Manufacturing Co. and American Maize Products Co.).
9. U.S. Pat. 2,435,071 (Jan. 27, 1948), T. W. Evans and E. C. Shokal (to Shell Development Co.).
10. U.S. Pat. 2,396,012 (March 5, 1946), H. A. Jones and B. V. Travis (dedicated to public).
11. D. F. Othmer, *Ind. Eng. Chem.* **41**, 1030 (1949).
12. J. C. Roncayrol and P. Taillandier, *Compt. Rend.* **256**, 4653–4654 (1963).
13. U.S. Pat. 3,041,208 (Jan. 26, 1962), P. M. Hay, G. R. Mitchell, and P. Salatiello (to Olin-Mathieson Chemical Corp.).

W. C. Ault
U.S. Department of Agriculture

TRIALKYLACETIC ACIDS

None of the trialkylacetic acids has been reported to occur naturally. Since the early 1960s commercial quantities of some of these acids have been available, as shown in Table 1. The first member of the series, trimethylacetic acid, is known as pivalic acid. Other commercial products are known as neo-acids (Enjay Chemical Co.); Versatic acids (Shell Chemical Co.). The unique properties of these acids have led to widespread applications studies in industry. Some of the applications have already reached commercial status.

The unique properties of these acids arise mainly because the carboxyl group is sterically hindered, resulting in generally lower reactivity than straight-chain fatty acids but in enhanced stability of the derivatives, particularly esters. Also, physical properties of the acids differ significantly from the corresponding straight-chain fatty acids. For example, neo-decanoic acid has a melting point below $-40°C$ compared with $+30.4°C$ for capric acid, a straight-chain C_{10} acid.

Physical Properties. Physical properties of the trialkylacetic acids which are commercially available in the U.S. are listed in Table 1. Most of the acids are made from feedstocks which are mixtures of isomers, or isomers and homologs, and therefore are not single compounds.

Chemical Properties. The trialkylacetic acids listed in Table 1 are all weak acids. They are characterized by their generally low reactivity. Contrary to published reports, however, esterification can be readily carried out by simply using higher reaction temperatures and catalyst concentrations than normally used in the esterification of straight-chain fatty acids. Table 2 illustrates the conditions for esterification of several of the acids with a primary alcohol (1). Table 3 illustrates the relative hydrolytic stability of certain trialkylacetic acid esters vs conventional unhindered esters in basic media (2). The greatly enhanced stability of the trialkylacetic acid esters is apparent. Stability in acidic media is also greatly enhanced (2).

Metal salts can be prepared without difficulty via conventional routes, such as metathesis, hydrocarbon solvent reflux, or direct fusion of the metal oxide with the acid. Ethylene oxide adducts can be prepared in the laboratory by direct addition of ethylene oxide using 0.5 g NaOH catalyst per mole of acid at 200°C. Acid chlorides are made by the addition of excess thionyl chloride at 60°C. Heat is necessary to initiate and maintain the reaction, as opposed to cooling as required with typical fatty acids. Amides and substituted amides can be made by bubbling ammonia gas or amines (eg, methylamine) into the acid chloride at 0–25°C. Higher-molecular-weight substituted amides (eg, N-dodecyl neo-tridecanoamide) are made by pyrolysis of the corresponding amine salt at 260–320°C. The high temperature required to effect this pyrolysis suggests the enhanced stability of this salt as well as the amide. Hindered alcohols can be made by the reduction of the corresponding acid using lithium aluminum hydride catalyst. The ease of reduction decreases rapidly with increasing molecular weight. Reduction of pivalic acid to neo-pentyl alcohol goes readily with LiAlH₄.

Manufacture. The chemistry for making pivalic acid by various routes has long been well known; ie, carboxylation of isobutylene with carbon monoxide in aqueous sulfuric acid (3), oxidation of diisobutylene in the presence of potassium hydroxide (4), reaction of acetone with carbon monoxide and steam in the presence of potassium hydroxide (5), oxidation of pinacolone; and reaction of *tert*-butylmagnesium halides with carbon dioxide (6).

Table 1. Typical Physical Properties of Commercial Trialkylacetic Acids

Acid	Color, Pt–Co (APHA)	Acid value, mg KOH/g	Melting pt, °C	Distillation range, °C	Sp gr	Refractive index n_D^{20}	Viscosity, CS 20°C	Viscosity, CS 60°C
pivalic acid (trimethylacetic acid)	20 (melted)	550	35.3	163–165	0.874 (70/4°C)	1.3927	(solid)	1.7
2,2-dimethylpentanoic acid (neo-heptanoic acid)[a]	10	424	<−40	204–213	0.920 (20/20°C)	1.4212	7.6	3
Versatic 9 acid[b]	<100	348	liquid with small amount of crystals at 20°C		0.930 (20/4°C)	1.4418	72	10
neo-decanoic acid[c]	60	315	<−40	147–152/20 mm	0.906 (20/20°C)	1.4385	35.7	7
Versatic 911 acid[d]	60	300	<−30	140–162/20 mm	0.92 (20/4°C)	1.447	42.5	7
neo-tridecanoic acid[e]	30	255	<−40	156–168/10 mm	0.908 (20/20°C)	1.4471	240	4
Versatic 1519 acid[f]	160	207	<−40		0.926 (20/4°C)		555	47

Typical Composition

[a] 95% 2,2-dimethylpentanoic acid + 5% 2-methyl-2-methylbutanoic acid.

[b] 56% 2,2,4,4-tetramethylvaleric acid, 27% 2-isopropyl-2,3-dimethylbutyric acid, 17% other isomers.

[c] Mixture of C_{10} trialkylacetic acids.

[d] Mixture of C_9, C_{10}, and C_{11} tertiary (90%) and secondary (10%) monocarboxylic acids.

[e] Mixture of C_{13} trialkylacetic acids.

[f] Mixture of highly branched principally tertiary C_{15}–C_{19} monocarboxylic acids.

Table 2. Typical Conditions for Producing Hexyl[a] Esters of Trialkylacetic Acids

Trialkylacetic acid	Entrainer	Catalyst, wt% on total charge	Max temp, °C	Time, hr	Percent completion
pivalic	toluene	0.33 toluenesulfonic acid	140	4	99.0
neo-decanoic	mixed xylenes	2.0 conc H_2SO_4	169	3.5	99.7
neo-tridecanoic	mixed xylenes	2.0 conc H_2SO_4	175	3.3	100.0

[a] The hexyl alcohol is a commercially available alcohol made by the Enjay Chemical Company by the oxo process; it consists of a mixture of about one-third 1-hexanol, the remainder being 2-, 3-, and 4-methyl-1-pentanol. One mole of acid and 1.2 mole of the hexyl alcohol are heated under the conditions shown with an entrainer to remove the water formed (see Vol. 2, p. 857).

Table 3. Relative Hydrolytic Stability of Hexyl[a] Esters of Hindered vs Unhindered Acids in Basic Solution[b]

Acid	k_2[c] (liter/(mole)(sec)) $\times 10^5$	Relative rates[d]
pivalate (C_5 hindered)	55	32
valerate (C_5 unhindered)	9260	5400
pelargonate (C_9 unhindered)	2960	1700
neo-decanoate (C_{10} hindered)	3.2	2
laurate (C_{12} unhindered)	2285	1300
neo-tridecanoate (C_{13} hindered)	1.7	1

[a] See footnote [a], Table 2.

[b] $0.1N$ NaOH in 10% aqueous ethylene glycol monoethyl ether at 50°C.

[c] k_2 (second-order rate constant) $= (1/t(B - E)) \ln (E(B - X))/(B(E - X))$; where $t =$ time (sec), $B =$ concn of base ($t = 0$), $E =$ concn of ester ($t = 0$), $X =$ amount reacted at time t.

[d] Neo-tridecanoate rate arbitrarily set at 1.00.

Although these techniques were known, there was no substantial commercial production of pivalic acid or other trialkylacetic acids until recently when commercial plants in both Europe and the U.S. went onstream. Trialkylacetic acids are made commercially in the U.S. by a process (7) involving the addition of carbon monoxide to olefins in the presence of an acidic catalyst to produce a CO–catalyst–olefin complex. This is followed by hydrolysis of the complex to a crude carboxylic acid which is then further purified.

The complexing reaction mechanism is believed to involve the formation of a carbonium ion by olefin–hydrogen ion interactions. The CO then reacts with the carbonium ion to form an acyl carbonium ion. Equations 1–3 illustrate the production of pivalic acid from isobutylene by this method.

$$CH_2{=}\underset{\underset{CH_3}{|}}{\overset{\overset{CH_3}{|}}{C}} + H^+ \rightarrow CH_3{-}\underset{\underset{CH_3}{|}}{\overset{\overset{CH_3}{|}}{C}}{}^+ \qquad (1)$$

isobutylene   catalyst   carbonium ion

$$CH_3{-}\underset{\underset{CH_3}{|}}{\overset{\overset{CH_3}{|}}{C}}{}^+ + CO \rightarrow \left[CH_3{-}\underset{\underset{CH_3}{|}}{\overset{\overset{CH_3}{|}}{C}}{-}CO \right]^+ \qquad (2)$$

acyl carbonium ion

Hydrolysis then leads to the trialkylacetic acid and regenerates the catalyst:

$$\begin{bmatrix} & CH_3 \\ & | \\ CH_3-C-CO \\ & | \\ & CH_3 \end{bmatrix}^+ + HOH \rightarrow \underset{\text{pivalic acid}}{\underset{CH_2}{\underset{|}{CH_3-C-COOH}}} \overset{CH_3}{\overset{|}{}} + \underset{\text{catalyst}}{H^+} \tag{3}$$

Note that in the complexing step, a tertiary carbonium ion is needed to obtain a trialkylacetic acid. In general, the carboxyl group selectively adds to the carbon with the fewest hydrogen atoms. For instance, isobutylene feed will yield almost exclusively pivalic acid.

The simplified flow diagram shown in Figure 1 illustrates the basic process steps. Olefin feed and catalyst are pumped to reaction pressure and fed to the complexing reactor while a gas, rich in CO, is compressed and bubbled into the reaction mixture. After degassing, the complex proceeds to hydrolysis where water is added to spring the catalyst for reuse. The crude acid is then treated to remove the last traces of catalyst and is distilled to remove light and heavy ends.

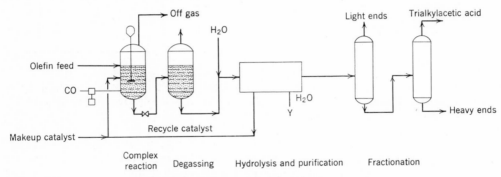

Fig. 1. Flowsheet for trialkylacetic acids process.

Economic Aspects. The trialkylacetic acids, having been commercially available a relatively short time, have not yet become large volume chemicals. Total free world production in 1964 was probably only a few million pounds. Current prices range from about 25 to 45¢/lb but are expected to decrease as large-volume uses develop; for example, pivalic acid, which was \$2.00/lb in 1963 dropped from 75¢/lb to 38¢/lb in 1964.

Storage and Handling. The trialkylacetic acids are all weak acids. However, like straight-chain fatty acids they attack ordinary steel; hence this must be considered in the selection of storage tanks and equipment. The flash points of the acids are shown in Table 4.

Toxicity. There are no undue hazards with regard to toxicity of the trialkylacetic acids listed, although all are irritating to the skin and are capable of causing skin damage. Hence, precautions should be taken to keep these materials off the skin and to remove them promptly from the skin by washing with plenty of soap and water if accidental contact does occur.

Applications (Current and Potential). One of the most interesting of the current commercial uses of the trialkylacetic acid derivatives is tertiary butyl peroxypivalate

Table 4. Flash Points of Acids

Acid	Flash point, °F (Cleveland open cup)	Acid	Flash point, °F (Cleveland open cup)
pivalic acid	165	versatic 911 acid	240
2,2-dimethylpentanoic acid		neo-tridecanoic acid	320
(neo-heptanoic acid)	225	Versatic 1519 acid	338
Versatic 9 acid	240		
neo-decanoic acid	305		

(TBPP) as an initiator for olefinic polymerizations. TBPP is more resistant to hydrolysis than other aliphatic peroxyesters such as *t*-butyl peroxyacetate. Because it is more resistant to hydrolysis it will operate more efficiently under varying pH conditions in aqueous systems. Economic rates of polymerization are achieved at low temperatures using low initiator concentrations. Hence TBPP can produce polymers exhibiting good color and heat stability, exceptional electrical properties, high molecular weight and increased linearity, according to the manufacturer (8).

Metal salt paint driers are commercially available based on neo-decanoic acid. Increased hydrolytic stability in aqueous systems, low odor and color, and increased tolerance for mineral spirits and linseed oil are advantages claimed (9).

The glycidyl (2,3-epoxy-1-propyl, $CH_2\!\!-\!\!CH\!\!-\!\!CH_2\!\!-$) ester of Versatic 911 acid is

commercially available under the trademark Cardura E (10). This ester is low in viscosity and is completely soluble in all common solvents. It is only slightly miscible with water. The reactions of Cardura E involve the epoxide group and are in many respects analogous to the reactions of epichlorohydrin.

In alkyd cooking, Cardura E may generally be regarded as a fatty acid monoglyceride. It is highly stable, but the epoxide group in the molecule confers a high degree of reactivity with carboxyl. Therefore, Cardura E, during alkyd processing with acids such as phthalic anhydride, reacts rapidly, performing as a diol.

The resistance to breakdown, characteristic of trialkylacetic acid ester groups, and high reactivity of the epoxide group with acids make alkyd resins derived from Cardura E more resistant to chemical attack than even the best-quality alkyds derived from unhindered acids. Since the reaction rate between epoxide and carboxyl groups is rapid, the overall cooking time to low acid values is reduced over conventional alkyds. In addition, other benefits are claimed.

Polyvinyl chloride stabilizers, such as the cadmium salt of neo-heptanoic acid, with barium phenoxide and a phosphite, show excellent performance in accelerated aging tests.

Complex esters of trialkylacetic acids are considerably more stable than comparable derivatives of unhindered acids, and merit evaluation as plasticizers for polyvinyl chloride, cellulosics, etc.

A number of pleasant fruity, floral, and winey aromas and flavors have been obtained by esterifying pivalic and neo-heptanoic acids with lower alcohols, oxo alcohols, benzyl alcohol, etc. Toxicological data to support these applications have not been obtained at this time.

Comparative tests have shown that neo-decanoic acid has excellent plant defoliant characteristics (11). Field tests are in progress on tributyltin neo-decanoate as a rodent repellent (12).   The complex of pivalohydroxamic acid, $(CH_3)_3CCONHOH$, with Fe^{3+} is claimed for use in iron-deficient soils (13).

Tributyltin neo-decanoate is reported to exhibit a broad spectrum of biostatic activity which is derived from the tributyltin moiety.   Potential applications include paints, wood preservation, textiles, and sanitizers (14).

Lithium salts of pivalic acid and other trialkylacetic acids are claimed as anti-knock additives in gasoline (15).   Stable esters of pivalic acid and polyols, such as pentaerythritol, were prepared as lubricants for gas-turbine engines (16).   Pivalic acid is claimed as a plasticizing agent for zein compositions used in adhesives, inks, etc. (17).

Bibliography

1. *Technical Information Sheet C41*, Enjay Chemical Company, New York.
2. *Technical Information Sheet C42A*, Enjay Chemical Company, New York.
3. U.S. Pat. 2,419,131 (April 15, 1947), T. A. Ford (to Du Pont).
4. R. W. Bost and L. B. Lockhart, *J. Am. Chem. Soc.* **63**, 2790–2792 (1941).
5. D. V. N. Hardy, *J. Chem. Soc.* **1938**, 464–468.
6. S. V. Puntambecker and E. A. Zoellner, in H. Gilman and A. H. Blatt, eds., *Organic Syntheses*, 2nd ed., JohnWiley & Sons, Inc., New York, Coll. Vol. I, 1941, 524.
7. W. J. Ellis and C. Roming, *Hydrocarbon Processing* **44** (6), 139–141 (1965).
8. Product Bulletin 6.501, *Lupersol 11*, Wallace & Tiernan, Lucidol Division, Buffalo, N.Y.
9. Technical Bulletin, *Ten-Cem*, Mooney Chemicals, Inc., Cleveland, Ohio.
10. Technical Bulletin, IC-63-16R, Shell Chemical Company, New York, N.Y.
11. U.S. Pat. 2,988,440 (June 13, 1961), J. H. Bartlett and I. Kirshenbaum (to Esso Research & Engineering Company).
12. Technical Bulletin D-114, Carlisle Chemical Works, Reading, Ohio.
13. Brit. Pats. 894,119 and 894,120 (April 18, 1962), (to Imperial Chemical Industries).
14. Technical Bulletin D-113, Carlisle Chemical Works, Reading, Ohio.
15. U.S. Pat. 3,013,869 (December 19, 1961), Erik Kissa (to Du Pont).
16. U.S. Pat. 3,115,519 (December 24, 1963), B. F. Crouse and W. W. Reynolds (to Shell Oil Company).
17. U.S. Pat. 2,410,124 (October 29, 1946), W. L. Morgan (to A. E. Staley Manufacturing Company and American Maize Products Company).

E. J. WICKSON
Enjay Laboratories

FD&C DYES.   See Colors for foods, drugs, and cosmetics.

FEEDS, ANIMAL

The term "feed" is used to designate plant and animal products available for livestock consumption, whereas food is the usual term applied to products used for human consumption. Feed consists for the most part of materials that man cannot utilize directly, or, those that he prefers to have concentrated into a more palatable product. Animal feeding should be regarded as a practice of condensing relatively coarse materials into meat, milk, eggs, wool, or other products.

Animal feeds consist largely of plant products, and nearly all pasture and forage are fed to livestock. Whole or ground cereals form a substantial portion of the rations of animals or birds. Although feeds may vary in composition because of soil and other environmental conditions, the quantity of the plant material seems to be more easily influenced than the quality (21). According to U.S. Department of Agriculture statistics, of the major cereals, corn leads as a livestock feed: Approx 84% of that grain tonnage crop was fed to livestock in the three-year period from 1959 to 1961. In addition to this portion of our major feed grain crop, approx 86% of the oats, 54% of the barley, 79% of the grain sorghums, and 4% of the wheat were used as feed. In addition to the enormous quantity of cereals fed before technological processing, a very substantial tonnage of by-products from industrially processed cereals is also fed to livestock. The approximate tonnages of the more common by-product feeds fed to livestock are given in Table 1.

Table 1. The Estimated Disappearance of Individual By-product Feeds, 1961[a]

Various types of feed	Tons fed, in 1000's
Mill products	
wheat millfeeds	4932
gluten feed and meal	1237
rice millfeeds	315
brewers' dried grains	266
distillers' dried grains	380
dried and molasses beet pulp	765
alfalfa meal	1502
Oilseed cake and meal	
cottonseed	2622
soybean	9232
linseed	330
peanut	53
copra	139
Animal proteins	
tankage and meat meal	1752
fish meal	614
dried milk	165

[a] From *Agricultural Statistics, 1964.*

Detailed analyses of various livestock feeds and their digestibility coefficients and total digestible nutrient values have been summarized by Morrison (16) and others (5,8,17). The analyses of some of the more common by-products used in feeds are given in Table 2 (18). Rarely does one feed make up the sole ration of an animal. Feeding standards have been prepared to aid in compounding rations suitable for

Table 2. Approximate Chemical Composition of Various By-product Feeds and the Parent Seed

Feedstuff	Dry matter, %	Ash, %	Crude protein, %	Ether extract, %	Fiber, %	Calcium, %	Phosphorus, %	Gross calories, lb
barley, U.S.—all analyses	89	2.7	11.6	1.9	5	0.09	0.47	2086
brewers' dried grains	92	3.6	25.9	6.2	15	0.27	0.50	2111
corn, dent—all analyses	86	1.3	9.0	3.9	2	0.03	0.31	2001
corn gluten meal	91	2.4	42.9	2.3	4	0.16	0.40	
cottonseed meal, solvent	91	6.5	41.6	1.6	11	0.15	1.10	1920
distillers' dried grain (corn)	92	2.6	27.1	9.3	12	0.04	0.37	2268
linseed meal, solvent	91	5.8	35.1	1.7	9	0.40	0.83	1917
molasses, cane	75	8.1	3.2	0.1	0	0.89	0.08	
oats, U.S.—all analyses	89	3.6	11.8	4.5	11	0.11	0.39	2138
oat groats	91	2.2	16.7	5.8	3	0.07	0.43	
oat hulls	93	6.1	3.8	1.3	30	0.10	0.11	
peanut meal, solvent	92	4.5	47.4	1.2	13	0.20	0.65	
rice bran	91	10.9	13.5	15.1	11	0.06	1.82	
rice hulls	92	19.2	2.8	0.8	40	0.09	0.06	
sorghum grain, all analyses	89	2.0	11.1	3.0	2	0.05	0.35	2005
soybean meal, solvent	89	5.8	45.8	0.9	6	0.32	0.67	1908
wheat, U.S.—all analyses	89	1.8	12.7	1.2	3	0.06	0.41	2043
wheat bran	89	6.1	16.0	4.1	10	0.14	1.17	1842
wheat brown, shorts	89	3.9	15.5	4.2	5	0.08	0.74	

various levels of production, and the most commonly used of these is the Morrison standard (16).

Cereals and Their By-Products

In general, the cereals and their by-products are very palatable to livestock (see Grains, cereal). Because of their relatively high price, the quantity used is often restricted (except in feeding swine) to that amount that gives optimum economy of production. In recent years, it has been found that the optimum level of concentrates is much higher when modern feeding techniques involving automation are used, than was the case with former methods of feeding. The cereals as a class of feed represent a high concentration of energy, but the cereals as individual grains are often lacking in both quantity and quality of protein, or in the proper proportion of the so-called essential amino acids (15,16,19). Cereal by-products often have a high protein concentration, but are usually deficient in the quality of protein needed for optimum performance when fed as the only supplementary source to poultry and swine.

The cereals are characteristically low in calcium but are a fair source of phosphorus unless produced on soils deficient in the element. Apart from yellow corn, which has an appreciable carotene content, the cereals are low in vitamin A or its precursor carotene. In addition, the cereals are very low in vitamin D. The water-soluble vitamins are much more abundant than the fat-soluble ones. Most of the cereal by-products vary considerably in analysis from the parent grain.

Barley is a hard-seeded grain that should be ground, rolled, or crimped for nearly all livestock except sheep; steeped or cooked barley is often used as an appetizer in fitting cattle for exhibition. The use of barley has been increasing as a feed for fattening cattle in North Dakota, California, and other states with appreciable barley production. Nearly all the barley by-products, except those of the brewery industry, result from the manufacture of pearl barley or barley flour for human consumption.

Barley Feed. In the manufacture of pearl barley, the hull and outer coats of the kernel are removed in milling and the resulting product is sold as barley feed.

Barley Mixed Feed. When barley is processed into flour, the entire offal consisting of barley hulls and barley middlings is sold as the mixed feed. Middlings consist of germ, bran, and coarse flour.

Barley Hulls. This product consists of the outer covering of barley after the groats have been removed; sometimes it is mistakenly referred to as barley bran. It is a coarse and bulky feed and should be regarded as a roughage instead of a concentrate.

Corn or maize is considered the standard fattening grain for livestock, and most other grains are usually compared with it in experiments comparing different livestock feeds for fattening meat animals (16). In addition, it is widely used in dairy and poultry rations. Corn grain is usually fed as whole-ear corn or shelled corn to hogs, and as shelled grain to sheep, but it is usually ground as shelled or as ear corn for cattle past one year of age. When finely ground it is usually called corn meal and when more coarsely divided it is referred to as cracked corn, ground corn, or corn chop. Corn and its by-products are lacking in quality of protein to even a greater extent than most of the other cereals (13).

Corn bran consists of the outer coating of the kernel and kernel tip but has very little of the starch or germ.

Corn Gluten Feed. In the wet milling of cornstarch or for syrup, kernel residues remain that consist of germ, gluten, bran, and corn solubles. A mixture of corn gluten meal and corn bran constitutes a by-product feed sold as corn gluten feed; it may or may not contain corn solubles or corn oil meal. The amount of corn gluten meal is regulated to keep the protein content of the preparation in a range of 25–27%. Gluten feed is fed primarily to dairy cows and is considered most valuable when mixed with more palatable feeds.

Corn Gluten Meal. It is a common commercial practice to refrain from mixing corn bran into what would be gluten feed, and the product, containing very little of the outer and coarser part of the corn kernel, is then sold as the gluten meal. Corn solubles and corn oil meal may be mixed into gluten meal. Corn gluten meal has been a common constituent of commercial dairy feeds but is usually not fed as the sole protein supplement. In recent years, the amount of corn gluten meal available for livestock feeding has been greatly reduced since the meal is used in the production of monosodium glutamate (see Vol. 1, p. 724).

Corn Oil Cake or Meal. In the wet milling of corn for the production of cornstarch or corn syrup, the germs are floated from the shredded corn kernels. Pressing the oil from the germs leaves a residue of corn oil cake, but often this is ground and the product is sold as corn oil meal. Occasionally germs are separated in the dry-milling process, and, after the oil is expressed, the germ cake obtained is usually ground to corn germ meal.

Hominy Feed. When hominy grits, pearl hominy, or corn meal is prepared for human consumption, the corn bran, germ, and a portion of the starch are removed from the kernel by dry milling, and the mixture is sold as hominy feed. The product sold must contain at least 5% fat (1). In composition and feeding value, it closely resembles the corn grain from which it originates.

Grain Sorghums. These consist principally of the milos and kaffirs and are grown extensively in the great high plains area east of the Rocky Mountains and in California. In recent years, dwarf or "combine" types of plant growth that lend themselves to mechanical harvesting have been introduced. In composition and feeding value the various sorghum grains resemble corn; usually the grain is fed as ground or chopped grain to cattle and hogs, but is fed whole to sheep. *Grain sorghum, gluten feed, and meal* are produced in the same manner as the corresponding products are produced from corn. They are not common but are available when corn is comparatively high or scarce, and the grain sorghums are used as a replacement in making alcohol or distilled liquors.

Oats are held in high esteem as livestock feed particularly for dairy cows and growing stock. They are highly palatable, bulky enough to help prevent bolting and overeating, and contain more minerals than the other common feed grains. Oats are usually fed whole to sheep and young cattle but as oat chop or ground oats to other livestock; sometimes, they are crushed or rolled. Oats are too bulky to be used to make up a substantial part of the fattening ration for swine.

Oat Groats and Oatmeal. In the process of making oatmeal, the hull is removed and the remaining portion of the kernel is the groat. The broken groats may be rolled, flour resulting from oatmeal manufacture added, and the product sold as "feeding oatmeal." It is considered particularly valuable for starting young chicks or pigs because of its low fiber content which must not exceed 4% (1).

Oat Hulls. This product is the outer covering of the oat produced in the milling of oats for their groats. Hulls are extremely bulky, have little nutritive value, and contain so much fiber that they should be regarded as a low-grade roughage rather than as a concentrate. Oat hulls are usually sold in mixed feeds and are regarded as an adulterant to the extent that some state feed officials require special labeling when they are used in a mix.

Rice produced in the United States is grown in Louisiana, Texas, Arkansas, and California, and most of the grain is processed for human consumption. When the whole grain is cheap or damaged, it may be ground and fed to livestock and as such is called ground rough rice.

Rice Bran. When table rice is being milled, the pericarp or bran layer is removed and a certain portion of hull fragments cling to the bran. Rice bran contains over 12% ether extract and hence will turn rancid more rapidly than most other milled products; the product is similar in most other respects to wheat bran, for which it is often used as a substitute in cattle rations.

Rice Hulls. These hulls represent the outer covering of rough rice. Although they are fed to livestock and are often included in mixed feeds, such use is not recommended. They are very high in fiber, are quite indigestible, and may cause mechanical injury to the digestive tract. Some states now prohibit their sale in livestock feeds.

Rice Polish. In manufacturing table rice the grain is brushed to polish the kernel after the hull and bran have been removed. The refuse thus obtained is high in niacin and thiamine but is low in riboflavin and has its highest value in the fattening of swine (16).

Rye. Rye is used very little as livestock feed. Its feeding value is low as compared to most of the other farm grains; it lacks in palatability; and its commercial price is usually above its feeding value because of its value in industry, particularly to distilleries. Some rye is milled for household use, and when so processed it yields the same mill products as the other grains milled for flour.

Wheat is raised as a grain for human consumption; unless there is an unusual price relationship with the other grains or it is damaged, it is not fed extensively to livestock and poultry. When fed to cattle or hand-fed to hogs, the grain is usually ground, but, when fed to poultry or self-fed to hogs, the whole grain is most commonly used. By-products from the milling of wheat are palatable and valued livestock feeds; many tons of these by-products are incorporated into mixed feeds.

Wheat bran is the coarse outer coat of the wheat kernel that has been washed and milled. It is one of the most highly regarded of the mill feeds and is valued for its palatability, bulk, and slightly laxative influence on the animal. Some small mills do not have adequate separation facilities and some flour may be included in the bran; in such case, the product is often referred to as "mill run."

Wheat-Germ Oil Meat and Cake. The germs of wheat are pressed to remove a portion of the wheat-germ oil and the resulting cake is available as livestock feed but must contain 29% protein (1); the cake may be ground, and merchandised as meal.

Wheat Middlings. Two kinds of wheat middlings are commercially produced, and, of these, the standard middlings contain bran, germ, and some fibrous mill offal but must not contain more than 9.5% crude fiber (1). On the other hand, flour middlings have wheat red dog added to the standard middlings and cannot contain over 6.0% crude fiber (1). Both products are obtained from milling spring wheat.

Wheat Red Dog. This product is obtained in regular milling of spring wheat and consists predominantly of aleurone but contains fine bran particles and traces of coarse flour. It must not exceed 4.0% crude fiber (1). It is not usually sold as a separate feed but is more commonly sold in middlings or in mixed feeds. A corresponding product called wheat white shorts is produced from hard red winter wheat.

Wheat Shorts. Products corresponding to middlings, both standard and flour, are obtained in milling hard red winter wheat and are called wheat brown shorts and wheat gray shorts, respectively. Both shorts and middlings are valued as hog feeds, particularly by feeders who prefer to feed wet feed or a "slop."

Cereal By-Products

Brewers' Products. These are produced by the brewery industry in malting grain and in brewing beer (see Beer and brewing; Malt.) Usually, they are fed near the producing plant or are dried and incorporated into mixed feeds.

Brewers' Grains. The residue remaining at the close of the malting process is referred to as *brewers' grains*. Primarily, the product consists of barley that has been sprouted, the sprouts removed, and the remainder subjected to the enzymic action of diastase (amylase), which changes most of the starch to sugar. Other grains may be added in the manufacture of the wort. Brewers' grains contain approx 75% water when removed from the vat. They spoil readily if not fed within one or two days. Usually the grains are dried; the common designation is *brewers' dried grains.*

Brewers' Dried Yeast. This is a product obtained by drying the yeast filtered from beer after fermentation is completed, and it must contain 45% protein on a dry-matter basis (1). It is used in poultry and livestock feeds to only a limited extent for its protein content but is often added because it contains a wide variety of the water-soluble vitamins. When irradiated with ultraviolet rays, it is sold as irradiated yeast.

Malt Sprouts. This material consists of the sprouts removed from barley sprouted in the malting process. It unavoidably contains hulls, some malt, and other material. The sprouts are dried and usually sold for inclusion in mixed feeds; they must contain a minimum of 24% crude protein (1). In case other grains are malted their sprouts are sold with the prefix name of the grain.

Distillers' Products. These are obtained when common cereals are fermented for the production of industrial alcohol or distilled liquors (see Ethanol; Alcoholic beverages, distilled).

Distillers' Dried Grains. These products are the dried residue obtained by screening the stillage from the manufacture of alcohol and distilled liquors. The name of the grain that predominated in the mixture is prefixed (eg, corn distillers' dried grains). The most common and most valuable of the distillers' grains is produced from corn and a large part of the production finds its way into dairy-cattle feeds where bulk is considered undesirable.

Distillers' Solubles. Distillers' solubles are obtained by condensing screened stillage from the manufacture of alcohol or distilled liquors. The name prefixed corresponds to the predominating grain. If the product is condensed to a syrupy consistency, it is sold as a semisolid product, or it may be dried and merchandised as the dried product (eg, dried corn distillers' solubles).

Distillers' Dried Grains with Solubles. When condensed screened stillage is dried and added to distillers' dried grains, the mixture is sold as containing the solubles. The latter product is rich in the water-soluble vitamins and makes the feed more valuable in poultry feeding but does not materially improve it for sheep or cattle. If the product is not dried, it can be sold in a syrupy condition as semisolid distillers' dried grains with solubles.

Oil-Bearing Seeds and Their By-Products

Oil-bearing seeds are not commonly fed whole to livestock although most of them can be safely fed as protein supplements. Occasionally, there is some objection to them as feeds because of their high oil content, but the chief objection to feeding them whole is that the oil is too valuable commercially. The high protein residue remaining after expressing the oil is used extensively to supply needed protein to livestock and poultry rations. Proteins obtained from oilseeds are usually not as well balanced in amino acid content as those obtained from animal sources; hence oilseeds should not be the chief source of protein for animals critical to protein quality (13,15). See Fats and fatty oils.

Cottonseed (qv) can be fed as a protein supplement, but usually the price of cottonseed oil makes this practice unwise. Occasionally the whole seed with hull attached is pressed without cooking to remove the oil and the residue sold as whole pressed cottonseed.

Cottonseed Meal and Cake. Each ton of cottonseed yields approx 950 lb of cottonseed meal or cake, and is sold on a guaranteed protein content, most commonly 41% crude protein. After the hulls are removed by mechanical separation, the seed is treated by the hydraulic expeller, or solvent methods to remove most of the oil (see Vol. 4, pp. 584–585). Pressure meals usually contain more than 6% ether extract while the solvent production has less than one-half that amount. Solvent meals are not as palatable but have been shown to be as useful in balancing the rations of cattle

(9). Cottonseed meals vary not only in method of preparation, but also in the amount of hull remaining with the seed. In commercial practice, the meals or cake are sold subject to well-defined sizes and quality grades (1). Under most economic conditions, cottonseed meal or cake is fed in amounts only adequate to balance the rations of fattening cattle or dairy cattle, but when cheaper than grain it may be fed to replace corn grain, pound for pound (16). Usually cottonseed meal is not considered safe for hogs in excess of 10% of the ration because of its possible gossypol content (16). When manufacturers include enough hull in cottonseed meal to exceed the allowable crude fiber limits specified by respective state feed control officials, the product is marked as cottonseed feed at a stipulated protein content.

Cottonseed Hulls. The mechanically removed cottonseed hull is a low-protein roughage not unlike other nonlegume roughages. It is usually used to replace hay in the ration, partially or entirely, and is particularly useful when concentrates are to be mixed into and fed with the roughage as a complete ration for ruminants.

Linseed and Flax Products. Flax is grown principally in the North Central States, and the two principal uses of the crop are to produce linseed oil, widely used in paint, and linseed meal, valued as a protein supplement for livestock.

Linseed Meal and Cake. The oil may be removed from flaxseed by the same methods as cottonseed oil. When obtained by the hydraulic process the resulting meal or cake is referred to as "old process." When flaxseed is extracted by solvents, the resulting cake or meal is called "new process"; this procedure results in a less palatable product and one that has less favor with feeders. Linseed cake is graded into various sizes, and when ground it is called meal and as such is most usually fed to livestock. Linseed meal and cake are particularly valued by cattle feeders because these products produce a gloss in the coat of the animal that results in sales appeal at market. In addition, these feeds are very palatable and are good appetizers in cattle rations.

Peanut Products (see Nuts). The product resulting from the extraction of a portion of the oil from peanut kernels is *peanut oil meal or cake*. It is produced, sold, and used in a manner similar to that for cottonseed meal. *Unhulled peanut oil feed* is the name for the residue left after oil is extracted from the whole unshelled peanut.

Soybean Products. Soybeans have played an important role in livestock feeding only since about 1920. Today it is a widely used source of protein supplements for livestock feeding, and these supplements are considered to be among the best-quality proteins available from plant sources. Since soybeans are competitive acreage with corn as a cash crop, the supply of soya products is dependent upon the price of soybean oil. The whole beans can be ground and fed as a protein supplement, and they are so used when the price of oil does not justify the sale of beans and the purchase of meal. Usually this is an economic waste and is avoided. Feeding beans to swine may result in soft or oily pork because the melting point of the pork fat is raised by the high melting point of the ingested oil.

Soybean Oil Meal and Cake. These products are, in general, produced like the cottonseed products, but a much higher percent of the total production is by the solvent method because the ether extract content can be reduced to less than 1.0% as compared to more than 5% for the pressure-produced meals. Nearly all the increase in production facilities since 1940 has been for the production of solvent meal, and as worn-out equipment is replaced, extraction methods are being installed. Solvent meals are satisfactory as protein supplements for cattle and sheep (8) and can be used as satisfactorily for poultry and swine as the pressure-produced meals if the meal is heated sufficiently to make the cystine and possibly other essential amino acids available. Most pressure meals exceed 41% in crude protein content while solvent meals usually exceed 45% crude protein.

Other Oil Feeds, Coconut (Copra) Oil Meal or Cake. Coconut meal or, as it is sometimes called, copra meal, is obtained by extracting part of the oil from the dried meat of the coconut. Its preparation is similar to that of the other oilseed meals, but it usually contains only about 21% protein; little of it is sold through retail channels since most of the production is included in mixed feeds.

Palm-Kernel Oil Meal. This is a low-protein meal, containing less than 20% crude protein, that represents the residue when palm oil is extracted from the kernel by pressure or solvents.

Sesame Oil Meal. A product very similar in composition and feeding value to cottonseed meal is obtained when most of the oil is removed from the sesame seed.

Forages and Their By-Products

Few forages are processed commercially and hence they are not an important item in manufacturing. However, they are extremely important as livestock feeds and form a most important part of the rations of growing and mature ruminants. Even the simple-stomached animal can make excellent use of certain types of forage.

Alfalfa is the forage crop that most commonly becomes an item of commerce after it is processed. If merely chopped before sale it is sold as chopped alfalfa. Occasionally chopped alfalfa hay or chopped stems are treated with blackstrap or other molasses and sold to cattle feeders for their appetizing value.

Alfalfa Meal. This product is obtained by grinding alfalfa hay into meal, but it must not contain more than 33% crude fiber (1); hence most of the leaves must be present. Alfalfa meal may be made from sun-cured hay or from alfalfa that is dried by artificial heat in a rotary dryer. The latter method preserves carotene but produces a product with lower vitamin D potency. Feed manufacturers like to obtain meals high in carotene, but the content declines with storage unless the meals are treated with chemical additives to stabilize the carotene. Artificially dried meals may exceed 175 ppm of carotene when first made, but lower values are more common. Most alfalfa meals are used in mixed feeds because of their value in correcting common nutritive deficiencies.

Alfalfa Leaf Meal. When the leaves of alfalfa are separated and ground, the product is called alfalfa leaf meal, provided it contains no less than 20% crude protein and no more than 18% crude fiber. This product is used largely in poultry feeds and in feeds for starting young calves and pigs, where the maximum corrective properties of alfalfa are desired and yet the fiber content of the ration needs to be held at a minimum.

Alfalfa stem meal represents the ground residue from the production of alfalfa leaf meal. It is coarse, of low feeding value, and is valued mostly as a carrier for liquid feeds such as molasses.

Lespedeza products are similar in major aspects to alfalfa products but are much less commonly produced.

Straw Meal. Any ground residue that remains after seed is separated from the mature plants may be marketed as straw meal, provided the originating plant name is used as a prefix. Its presence in a feed should be regarded as a filler.

Animal By-Products

The various animal by-products are almost without exception highly desirable feeds and as a result are relatively scarce and high in price. Thus, they are used almost exclusively for those animals and poultry that are considered most critical in their requirements, or where high levels of digestibility and assimilation are essential. Although animal by-products were first used to supply protein in the ration, they have been found to be excellent sources of preventive and corrective nutrients. Their use is not necessarily indicated for grown animals or species that are not critical in their requirements.

Milk (qv) is considered the near-perfect food for growing young animals. Its principal dietary deficiency is iron but it contains an abundance of nearly all other required nutrients (14). The value of cows' milk for human food precludes its use for nearly all livestock except nursing young. Milk products that enter directly into commerce originate from creameries and processing plants that obtain cream or whole milk from producers. Farms that sell cream use skim milk, resulting from centrifugal separation, as feed for growing calves, poultry, and swine to supply partially or entirely the supplementary protein needed to balance a diet that contains low-protein cereals. Only small amounts of skim milk from processing plants are available as livestock feed, because it can be more advantageously sold for human consumption. Dried milk products contain only 8% or less water.

Buttermilk and Its Derivatives. Buttermilk is the watery residue that remains after butter has been removed from the churn. Unless water has been added in excess, it has a similar composition and feeding value to skim milk. It is too bulky for transportation and hence is usually sold as the dried or condensed product. It must not contain more than 8% water or more than 13% mineral matter (1). It is especially used in poultry mixed feeds and for preparing feeds for young calves and pigs. In manufacturing evaporated or condensed buttermilk, water is removed until the product contains at least 27% total solids and a minimum of 0.055% butterfat and a maximum of 0.14% for each percent of solids (1). The condensed or semisolid products are most widely used in poultry and swine feeding where maximum feed consumption and performance are of greater importance than economy.

Casein. This is a high-protein product containing at least 80% crude protein that is obtained by the acid or rennet precipitation of skim milk. It is fed only to experimental animals where purity of diet is a consideration.

Cheese Rind. In preparing processed cheeses, the rind is removed, cooked, and most of the fat removed. The product is a high-quality meal used like the other animal proteins.

Skim Milk and Its Derivatives. Skim milk may be processed and sold similarly to buttermilk, but it is usually merchandised as the dry powder. It may be condensed, or condensed and cultured with suitable bacteria; the cultured product may also be dried. Skim-milk products are sold for the most part for inclusion in commercial poultry feeds where they are particularly valued for their riboflavin content and quality of protein, but a smaller quantity is used in the better grades of calf and pig starters.

Whey and Its Derivatives. Whey is the liquid remaining in the cheese vat after the curd has been removed, and it may be dried or condensed in a similar manner to buttermilk and skim milk. The dried product must contain at least 65% lactose (1) and usually contains only about 12% protein. It is even higher in riboflavin than skim milk and is included in mixed feeds as a source of water-soluble fractions.

Enormous tonnages of packing-house by-products (see Meat) are produced in the processing of meat in modern packing plants, where every effort is made to salvage all that can be utilized from the animal carcass. Some by-products result from the disposal of offal and are often sold below the cost of manufacture to assure sanitary disposal at the least net cost to the plant. Most by-products, however, have sufficient value for the net profit from such products often to represent the source of packing-house profits. Efficient by-product production and sales make it possible for the large packer to compete successfully with a local butcher who has lower freight and labor charges.

Blood Meal. Packing-house blood (see Blood, animal) is collected and heated to produce coagulation, after which moisture is drained and then pressed from the coagulate. After drying, the blood is ground into blood meal. It is a product having usually over 80% protein, but it is not so digestible or high in quality of protein as most of the other animal by-products.

Bone Meal. The bones from slaughtered animals are cooked with steam under pressure, and extra fat and protein are removed before the residue is dried and ground to sell as steam bone meal. The bones are sometimes charred in retorts and sold as bone black for clarifying sugar, and, after serving this purpose, they may be recharred and sold as spent bone black for livestock feeding. Bone ash is obtained by burning clean bones without charring.

Liver Meal. Most of the wholesome animal liver obtained is sold in the fresh state for human food, but other animal livers are dried and ground into meal which must contain at least 27 mg of riboflavin per lb (1). Animal liver and glandular meal may be sold but no more than one-half of the material may be of glandular origin, and it must contain 18 mg riboflavin per lb (1). Liver meal is an excellent source of known and unknown nutritional substances. Numerous workers have reported noticeable response in poultry and young swine when 2% or less of liver meal was added to the ration. The scarcity and high price of such meal prohibits its use merely as a protein supplement.

Meat Meal or Meat Scraps. In the preparation of meat meal or scraps, animal tissue exclusive of hair, hoof, and blood is dry-rendered in an open kettle heated by steam. The excess water is driven off, the fat removed, and the residue dried and ground. The product usually contains over 50% protein, but, if it contains more than 4.4% phosphorus, it must be labeled as meat and bone meal (or scrap). Although lower in protein than tankage, it is usually preferred by swine and poultry raisers because of its higher quality of protein.

Tankage. A product referred to as digester tankage or meat meal tankage is prepared from the same source of material as meat scraps. The cooking is done under steam in pressure tanks, the fat and liquid are removed, and the residue is pressed to remove additional fat. The liquid is evaporated to form "stick," which is added to the solid residue, and the mixture is dried and ground. Often tankage is standardized to 60% protein by the addition of blood meal. Most tankage is used in swine feeds, but the tonnage produced is declining because of the more efficient methods employed in dry-rendering meat scraps and the higher quality of protein in the resulting product.

Marine Products

Marine products (see Fish) have come into much more general use since 1930 than before that date. Some marine by-products are produced when edible fish are processed for human consumption, whereas other marine products are made by processing inedible fish for feeding purposes (16). They are considered very valuable sources of growth factors especially in poultry and swine rations.

Condensed Fish Solubles. Many species of fish are caught for their oil content, and the oil is extracted by hydraulic pressure. Condensation of the water resulting from such pressing produces condensed fish solubles which are regarded as an excellent source of nutrients commonly lacking in the rations of poultry and swine fed in dry lot or under confinement, where green growing plant food is not available.

Crab Meal. The undecomposed waste of the crab consisting of shell, viscera, and varying amounts of flesh is ground and dried. The product is high in mineral matter and it must contain at least 25% protein (1). It is not as palatable as most other marine products.

Fish Liver and Glandular Meal. This product is made by drying the complete coelomic contents of fish; at least 50% of the dried weight must have originated from fish livers (1).

Fish Meal. Fish meal may be produced by drying and grinding undecomposed fish or fish offal from which the oil may or may not have been expressed. In modern practice the excess water is often removed by partial vacuum at lower temperatures than formerly used. This results in a more digestible and higher-quality product. The demand for fish meal has increased rapidly since swine raisers and poultry producers have found it produces excellent growth response when making up only a portion of the supplementary protein requirement. The protein content varies with the source material from which the meal is made.

Fish Residue Meal. In the process of manufacturing glue from nonoily fish, a residue remains that can be dried, ground, and sold as a fish meal residue. It is a much less common product than fish meal.

Shrimp Meal. Shrimp meal may consist of ground dried shrimp waste, such as the head and hull, and may or may not contain whole shrimp. Shrimp meal often contains less than 40% protein but can replace fish meal if enough more is fed to supply the same protein intake.

Whale Meal. Whale meal can be used to replace other meat meals in livestock feeding if the whale is processed before it starts to decompose. In preparing such meal, the fat is pressed out and the residue dried and ground. The mineral and protein contents depend on the amount of bone in the processed material. Greater care in processing material while fresh would improve the consumer acceptance of the product and provide an increased supply of animal protein suitable for livestock feeding.

Miscellaneous Feeds

Beet pulp (see Sugar manufacture) is a residue feed obtained from the sugar beet in the manufacture of beet sugar. It may be fed directly as it comes from the plant, as wet beet pulp, or it may be ensiled and fed as beet pulp silage. If the product is to be shipped, it is dried and sold as dried beet pulp or dried and mixed with molasses and called dried molasses beet pulp. The dried pulps are palatable but bulky, and resemble oats in feeding value except that they contain appreciably less protein and are low in phosphorus.

Buckwheat Middlings. In the milling of buckwheat as flour for human consumption such by-products as middlings and hulls are produced which correspond in origin to similar products produced from oats. Middlings are used in preparing dairy feeds but the hulls have little feeding value. The middlings and hulls may be combined and sold as buckwheat feed (1), providing the crude fiber content does not exceed 30%.

Dried Citrus Pulp. Citrus pulp is the residue remaining after citrus juice is extracted, and it may or may not contain cull fruit. In some cases, oil is expressed from the peel before it is dried or ground, and the product is then sold as citrus meal.

Dried Sweet Potatoes. Before World War II, workers in Alabama (10) and others had shown that sweet potatoes could be fed to livestock, but during the war, interest was renewed in the possibility of using dried sweet potatoes as a carbohydrate concentrate to replace scarce grain in livestock feeding. It was found that they had approximately 90% the value of corn in fattening cattle (3,6). Sweet potatoes may be dried after slicing by spreading in the sun on a suitable slab, or they may be sliced and dried in a drum-type dryer similar to that used for alfalfa and other crops.

Dried Pomace. Dried apple and dried tomato pomaces are produced when juice is pressed from the respective fruits. The products are dried and form a satisfactory bulky addition to dairy rations. Either pomace can be fed wet, but as such must be utilized locally.

Mungbeans. Mungbeans are a low-fat bean, of oriental origin, used by sprouters to produce commercial bean sprouts for human consumption. Cracked beans or other damaged beans that will not sprout can be ground and fed to beef or dairy cattle to replace other protein supplements (20) for they contain about 25% protein, but they are not very palatable to sheep or hogs.

Molasses (qv). Three kinds of feeding molasses are available to livestock feeders and feed mixers, but cane or blackstrap molasses is by far the most commonly used. Blackstrap is obtained in the manufacture of cane sugar and is the thick syrupy molasses left after as much sugar as feasible has been crystallized and the excess water removed by evaporation. It must contain at least 48% or more of total sugar expressed as invert sugars (1), and it is a very appetizing and valuable feed when not used in such excessive amounts as to reduce the utilization of other feeds (4). "Feeding beet molasses" is a similar product obtained in the manufacture of beet sugar. "Feeding corn molasses" is obtained in making sugar from corn and must contain 48% or more reducing sugars expressed as dextrose, and must contain at least 60% total carbohydrates (1). Neither is as palatable as blackstrap molasses. Molasses feeds are all low in protein and, when fed beyond their optimum appetizing ability, which is usually no more than 10% of the mix, are less valuable than the common grains because of their lower dry-matter content. When low enough in price, so that extra dry matter can be purchased for less per lb than corn or other grain, molasses feeds may be used to supply large parts of the concentrate in the ration of beef or dairy cattle.

Urea (qv). When adequate supplies of naturally occurring proteins are not available or are exceedingly high in price, urea can be fed to ruminants to supply a portion of the nitrogen required, provided readily available carbohydrates are also supplied (7,11–13). This synthetic product should not, according to present nutrition knowledge, be used to supply more than 25–30% of the protein of the concentrate. Urea should be thoroughly incorporated in a feed mix to avoid danger of alkalosis.

Compounded Feeds

The suitability of compounded feeds for various classes of livestock and poultry depends upon the intelligence and integrity used in their processing. Most feed manufacturers attempt to acquaint themselves with problems of nutrition and produce a satisfactory product for the purpose intended. The economy of a livestock or poultry feeder using compounded feeds will depend upon the ability of the manufacturer to supply him with as good a feed at the same or less cost than he can obtain by compounding his own rations. Often, especially in the case of poultry feeds, the high price and difficulty experienced in obtaining expensive ingredients that may be needed in small quantities indicate the use of a factory-prepared product.

It is much easier for a feed mixer to add small amounts of certain substances to a mixed feed than it is for the feeder to incorporate such in the ration. Some nutrients are required in larger amounts for some animals or birds than for others, and the mixer can consider these requirements in compounding rations. Choline, for instance, has been shown to be required in relatively larger amounts in chick and poultry rations to prevent perosis in the growing chick and to prevent mortality and low hatchability in hens. Some feeds suitable in most respects for poultry or other critical animals may or may not be good sources of choline and other known nutritional substances (16), and these may be added if the total ration lacks the amount required to adequately nourish the animal or bird. In recent years vitamin B_{12} has been found to have great value when added to certain feeds or combinations of feeds. The factor is now added as routine mixing procedure by most feed manufacturers in preparing certain chick and pig rations to ensure the presence of enough of the substance for optimum growth. Vitamin B_{12} is a nutritional factor which is absolutely essential for normal growth, and the minimum requirements have been carefully determined for young pigs and chicks.

Commercial feeds are usually prepared under "closed" formulas but may be sold under "open" formulas. In the three-year period 1959–1961, an average of 23,348,000 tons of commercial feeds was manufactured and sold annually. In the case of closed formula feeds, the ingredients are listed, but their respective proportions are not given on the feed tag; in open formulas, the amounts of the ingredients are listed. There is no one best ration that can be prepared to meet all existing conditions, and the ingredients in a mixed feed can be varied considerably to take care of economic conditions, if minimum allowances of certain essential nutrients are provided. Mixers must constantly be alert to variations in price of alternate ingredients that might be used if they are to compete with whole natural feeds and with other feed mixers. The use of electronic computers has become very common in arriving at a desired formulation at a minimum cost. Mixed feeds must be sold on the basis of guaranteed minimum protein, fat, and nitrogen-free extract contents, and guaranteed maximum crude fiber and ash contents. Violations of these requirements are punishable within states where the feeds are sold and federal laws are involved if feed enters interstate commerce.

Most large feed manufacturers use highly automated mixing procedures, while batch mixers are used in preparing small volumes. In the former the ingredients are added at controlled rates as the mix is augered along a line; when feed molasses is added its temperature is regulated to control consistency. Batch mixes are usually prepared by adding all ingredients to a specially constructed hopper and augering the mix until it is uniform. Minor additions or special ingredients are usually premixed with some feed before being added for the final mixing. It is a very common practice to process a mixed feed further by using a special machine to press it into pellets or other specially desired size or shapes.

Mineral feed mixes are prepared and sold for various classes of livestock and may give an economic response if added to rations deficient in some essential element they carry. However, the minerals most likely to be lacking in livestock rations are sodium chloride and phosphorus and calcium compounds, and these can be cheaply supplied as common salt, steam bone meal, defluorinated rock phosphate (see Fertilizers), and ground limestone.

In recent years other elements such as cobalt, iron, copper, iodine, selenium, and zinc have been found lacking in certain localities (16). When a ration is deficient in any mineral element, it may prove not only to be a depressing factor in the response of the animal to feed, but may result in appearances of malnutrition or poor performance even though an abundance of feed is supplied and other nutritional requirements are satisfied. Often a purchaser of a mineral mixture buys many ingredients and even trace elements already present in abundant quantities in the rations he feeds. A feeder can easily learn from unbiased sources of possible deficiencies in rations or probable trace mineral deficiencies in crops grown in a specified area. Condiments or conditioners are widely prepared and sold for livestock feeding. These should be used only upon the advice of a veterinarian or trained nutritionist not interested in the sale of the product (2). Their addition to well-balanced rations that are fed in ample quantities is seldom indicated.

Bibliography

"Feeds, Animal" in *ECT* 1st ed., Vol. 6, pp. 299–312, by H. M. Briggs, Oklahoma Agricultural and Mechanical College.

1. Assoc. Am. Feed Control Officials, *Official Pub.*, College Park, Md., 1960.
2. Blaxter, K. L., Reinke, E. P., Crampton, E. W., and Peterson, W. E., *J. Animal Sci.* **8,** 307 (1949).
3. Briggs, H. M., Gallup, W. D., Heller, V. G., Darlow, A. E., and Cross, F. B., *Oklahoma Agr. Expt. Sta. Tech. Bull.* **T-28** (1947).
4. Briggs, H. M., and Heller, V. G., *J. Agr. Research* **71,** 81 (1945).
5. Crampton, E. W., *Applied Animal Nutrition*, W. H. Freeman & Co., San Francisco, Calif., 1956.
6. Darlow, A. E., Ross, O. B., Stephens, D. F., McVicar, R. W., Cross, F. B., and Thompson, D. P., *Oklahoma Agr. Expt. Sta. Bull.* **B342** (1950).
7. Dinning, J. S., Briggs, H. M., and Gallup, W. D., *J. Animal Sci.* **8,** 24 (1949).
8. "Food and Life," *Yearbook Agr. U.S. Dept. Agr.* **1937**.
9. Gallup, W. D., Briggs, H. M., and Hatfield, E. E., *J. Animal Sci.* **9,** 194–200 (1950).
10. Grimes, J. C., *Alabama Polytech. Inst. Agr. Expt. Sta. Rept.* **1941**.
11. Harris, L. E., and Mitchell, H. H., *J. Nutr.* **22,** 183 (1941).
12. Hart, E. B., Bohstedt, G., Deebald, H. J., and Webner, M. L., *J. Dairy Sci.* **22,** 785 (1939).
13. Loosli, J. K., and McCay, C. M., *J. Nutr.* **25,** 197 (1943).
14. Maynard, L., and Loosli, J. K., *Animal Nutrition*, McGraw-Hill Book Co., Inc., New York, N.Y., 1962.
15. Mitchell, H. H., *J. Animal Sci.* **2,** 263 (1943).
16. Morrison, F. B., *Feeds and Feeding*, 22nd ed., Morrison, Ithaca, N.Y., 1956.
17. "Natl. Research Council, Recommended Nutrient Allowances for Domestic Animals: I, Poultry, 1960; II, Swine, 1959; III, Dairy Cattle, 1958; IV, Beef Cattle, 1963; V, Sheep, 1957; VI, Horses, 1961," *Natl. Acad Sci.—Natl. Res. Council Publ.*
18. "Joint, United States–Canadian Tables of Feed Composition," *Natl. Acad. Sci.—Natl. Res. Council Publ.* **659** (1959).
19. Rose, W. C., *Physiol. Revs.* **18,** 109 (1938).
20. "Science Serving Agriculture," *Oklahoma Agr. Expt. Sta. Repts.* **1942, 1948**.
21. Webb, R. J., Lewis, J. M., Kammlade, W. G., Fuelleman, R. F., and Hamilton, T. S., *J. Animal Sci.* **7,** 159 (1948).

H. M. BRIGGS
South Dakota State University

FELT.   See Nonwoven fabrics.

FERMENTATION

In the classical sense, the word fermentation refers to the anaerobic breakdown of organic compounds by the action of microorganisms (qv) or their extracts to products simpler than the starting substrate. The broader definition of the word fermentation, and perhaps the more useful one, is that of microbial action which is controlled by man to make products useful to man. Some of the materials produced from carbohydrates by anaerobic dissimilation would be ethanol, lactic acid, acetic acid, and products containing these materials, such as wine, vinegar, pickles, and sauerkraut. Products of the latter definition, that is, the more broadly applicable definition of the word "fermentation," include the more sophisticated products, such as antibiotics, vitamins, and steroids which have emerged since World War II as important products of the fermentation industry. A more descriptive term defining the process would perhaps be microbial synthesis, which is the prime source of perhaps one hundred products for the food, chemical, and pharmaceutical industries (1). Fermentation has emerged as a partner, and occasionally a competitor, of chemical synthesis.

Microbial forms of life responsible for the fermentation processes now in use are yeasts, molds, bacteria, and actinomycetes. Although intact microbial cells are generally used, they are merely sources of catalysts. The reactions are truly catalytic and could, in general, be carried out by chemical means. The advantages of the biological catalysts are the greater efficiency obtained and the fact that less drastic conditions are usually called for to complete the reactions. The microbial biocatalysts are enzymes (qv). Some of the advantages of microbial synthesis over chemical synthesis are as follows: (1) Microbial synthesis may be the only practical means of synthesizing a complex compound. (2) It may achieve in one step a molecular change which could only be achieved by a long chemical synthesis. (3) Cheaper starting material may be used. (4) The enzymes of microorganisms may be used to replace the drastic, sometimes expensive, conditions required by a chemical process. (5) Microbial synthesis may remove unwanted components from a product (2).

A general equation for the fermentation process is as follows:

$$\text{microorganism} + \text{substrate} \rightarrow \text{more microorganisms} + \text{metabolic products}$$

These metabolic products, which are by-products of the organisms' growth, constitute the complement of materials containing the fermentation product useful to man. Hence, it is inefficient to grow microorganisms in this process when microbial cells are not the desired end product. But, if it is intended to produce microbial cells, then the metabolic by-products can be considered as materials which detract from the prime product of the reaction.

Historical Development of the Fermentation Industry

The first products made by industrial fermentation in any form of purity were ethanol, acetic acid, and lactic acid. These products were made in large volumes prior to 1915 and were separated from their reaction mixtures in relatively good purity. In the following twenty-five years, acetone, 1-butanol, citric acid, enzymes, particularly the amylases and proteases, and a few other products, such as gluconic acid, were introduced into the market by fermentation processes. Subsequently more complex molecules, such as antibiotics, vitamins, amino acids, and steroids, became the major products of industrial microbial synthesis. To indicate the progress in the chemical industry which parallels that in the fermentation industry, many of the products which were first introduced via fermentation are now produced synthetically from petrochemicals. For example, acetone, 1-butanol, and lactic acid, all fairly simple molecules, are now mainly made by chemical synthesis. Competition has gradually forced the shift to production of complex, rather than simple, molecules by microbial synthesis. Presently, a major share of research effort in this country is directed toward the development of products that are too complicated to make by ordinary chemical means, and there is much less effort aimed at improving production or increasing efficiency of the processes for producing small, simple molecules.

Presently, microbial synthesis is a major industrial operation for some thirty United States companies (1). It is, in general, a thriving industry with production increasing yearly in many areas. In addition, there are few areas left in the current fermentation industries which are vulnerable to competition from chemical synthesis. Products which are growing yearly in volume include antibiotics, steroids, vitamins, and other growth factors, and amino acids. Products which are losing ground to synthetic processes are solvents and organic acids. The shift from fermentation to synthetic production of simpler molecules may be due to the high cost of substrates for the fermentation process, rather than inefficiency of the process. Another limitation to the widespread use of fermentative processes is the fact that there are, in general, aqueous systems in which the product and reactants occur in low concentrations; this necessarily complicates the recovery process used to purify the final product.

Microbiological Aspects of Fermentation Technology

An important consideration in industrial fermentation is the selection of the proper microorganism to carry out the desired reaction efficiently. The proper microorganism is able to maintain its activity from generation to generation and thus lend reproducibility to the process. It is also able to combat infections or invasion and competition from strange microorganisms (3). Stock cultures of bacteria, yeasts, molds, and actinomycetes used in industrial processes are generally maintained in culture collections in the manufacturing plants or in universities or other institutional collections (4,5). Individual organisms desired to carry out specific reactions can also be isolated from natural sources, such as soil, pond water, and so forth, if a method for screening the desired reaction is known. Although it is relatively simple to isolate a microorganism capable of carrying out a desired reaction, it is much more difficult to find a microorganism capable of carrying out that reaction on an industrially feasible scale.

The best examples of large-scale screening processes were those carried on for the discovery of new, useful antibiotics in the early 1940s. It is no exaggeration to state that millions of cultures of new microorganisms were tested for their ability to produce antibiotics. The results of these programs are the relatively few commercially successful antibiotics now in use. The chances for the discovery of new, clinically useful antibiotics from such a program appear to be very slim. The dilemma of such a situation to industrial concerns engaged in the pharmaceutical business is readily apparent. They can hardly afford to carry out the extensive program required, and yet, in order to remain competitive, they cannot afford not to screen for new antibiotics.

The first step in obtaining a practically useful microorganism is the isolation of an organism which carries out the type of reaction desired. The second step, often a lengthy one, is the improvement, development, and adaptation of the organism to industrial use. The improvement process consists of modifications to the medium and fermentation conditions used, so as to increase the yields of the end product. However, the greatest advances are generally made in the performance of the organism itself. Strain improvement depends chiefly on the selection of improved cultures which are obtained by natural means or by the induction of mutation. In recent years, the possibility of using genetic methods has become more practical. There is little doubt that significant advances in the clarification of genetic coding in the future will allow more organisms to be "tailor-made" for chosen processes.

Perhaps the best example of process improvement through the selection of more efficient microorganisms is the classical development of the penicillin process. Yields have increased from about one hundred to perhaps twenty thousand units since penicillin was discovered, due mainly to improvement in the strain of microorganism used. Generally speaking, improvements in fermentation conditions, nutrient supply, etc, may double yields, whereas strain improvement and selection of more efficient microorganisms can increase yields tenfold or even one hundredfold.

The most widely used method for strain improvement is mutation. A typical mutation procedure involves the exposure of spores of the organism to the action of a mutagen and extensive killing of 99% of the parent organism. The surviving population, which consists of surviving parents, morphological variants, and some true mutants, is then screened (as was the original parent stock isolate) to determine the suitability of new mutants to produce more of the desired product. The best strains, surviving the first screen, are retained for further testing and further mutation work. Variant organisms, usually difficult to handle, which produce large amounts of by-product, or which are not improved over the parent strain, are, of course, rejected from the screen. Mutagenic agents frequently used are ultraviolet radiation, x rays, and chemicals such as nitrogen mustard and colchicine. Mutagenic agents disrupt the genetic material of the cells which are being treated. The results are completely random; the only control which can be exercised is the extent of lethality.

The application of microbial genetics to directed strain improvement awaits further elucidation of the genetic code. It is quite probable that in the near future tailor-made strains of organisms will result from further description and elucidation of the genetic coding of industrially useful microorganisms.

An obvious precaution in the fermentation industries is the preservation of microorganisms so as to ensure their viability and reproducibility from batch to batch. When fermentation was still an art, cultures were stored in a haphazard manner and repetitive processes, such as wine making, brewing, bread baking, etc, were carried out by transferring inoculum from batch to batch of product. This procedure selected organisms which were uniquely adapted to the process being carried out. It also selected organisms which were among the most stable varieties available in nature. However, the most stable form is not necessarily the most efficient form for industrial processes. During the past few decades, newer scientific methods of preserving microorganisms have been introduced and allow the preservation of the more useful microorganisms without loss of vitality (6). In general, microorganisms are preserved as spores surrounded by a dry, nonnutritive milieu. If water is present, it is generally frozen. Common means of storage are as lyophilized pellets, as soil stocks, or as agar slants covered with nonmetabolizable substances such as paraffin. Freeze-dried preparations are usually preferred. The phenomenon of culture run-down is being experienced less frequently as more is learned about the preservation of microorganisms. Occasionally, a culture remains in good condition for a considerable period of time and then suddenly deteriorates from apparently unknown causes. Such rundown is probably due to genetic instability of the parent culture. Means for avoiding such spontaneous genetic alteration have not been investigated adequately as yet.

Fermentation Raw Materials

The microorganisms used are unicellular plants requiring certain nutrients for growth, such as carbohydrates, nitrogen, growth factors, and minerals. Microbes used in industry can grow and form products from a variety of substrates ranging from synthetic chemicals to complex agricultural by-products. Generally, the raw materials of the fermentation industry are commercially available items, reasonably priced. They are usually of plant origin, such as molasses, sulfite liquor, corn steep liquor, stillage, and various sugars. Because of their relatively higher price, little use is made of animal materials except in the pharmaceutical industries where items of higher cost per unit are produced. Factors which govern the selection of raw materials include low price, high yield, availability, close market, and purity. In the production of foods and beverages, the taste and aroma of the raw material are important, because they may affect the final product. In the case of pharmaceuticals which have to be of high purity, the ease of purification of the product and its separation from the residual raw materials become highly important. Hence, the choice of raw materials is dictated by the use of the end product as well as by the other considerations mentioned previously.

Microbial nutrients supplied by the raw materials occasionally need supplementation with vitamins, minerals, or other growth factors to render the final fermentation efficient. Nitrogen can be provided in the form of liquid ammonia, ammonium salts, urea, or, more generally, crude agricultural products containing relatively large amounts of assimilable nitrogen. Generally, trace quantities of elements such as manganese, iron, cobalt, nickel, copper, and magnesium are added to the fermentation.

The Fermentation Process

In order to ensure the metabolic activity of only the desired organism in the material which is being converted by fermentation, the nutrient solution is first subjected to sterilization to inactivate or kill extraneous microorganisms which may be present. The sterilization process is generally accomplished by applying heat. Yeasts and molds and their spores are usually destroyed within a few minutes of exposure to a temperature of 80–90°C. Bacterial spores, on the other hand, may resist exposure to temperatures above 100°C (7). Therefore, the normal sterilization cycle in a batch process takes place at a temperature from 120–130°C for approx 15 min. Heat is often supplied by introducing live steam into the nutrient liquid contained in the fermentor. Continuous flow sterilization is usually carried out at much higher temperatures for a much shorter time. In this method, the nutrient solution is pumped through a sterilizer into a previously sterilized fermentor. There are some fermentation processes in which the desired organism is so vigorous that it outgrows possible contaminants, and only partial sterilization or pasteurization is needed. Processes of this nature are the acetic acid or vinegar fermentation, the lactic acid fermentation, and fermentations with yeasts for beverage alcohol production. Other means of sterilization, which have been used only to a very limited extent, are ultraviolet radiation (for certain clear liquids), ionizing radiation, the addition to the media of chemicals that inhibit the growth of undesired organisms, and filtration through micropore filters. Any material which enters the fermentation during the process must also be sterilized. This includes air, antifoam agents, and other fermentation adjuncts. Air is sterilized by passing through a previously sterilized filter packed with glass wool or carbon particles. Other materials are generally kept in holding-vessels which were previously sterilized for use during the fermentation cycle.

The next step in a typical fermentation process is the addition of a suitable inoculum to the sterilized and cooled fermentation medium. The seed, or inoculum, constitutes 1–10% by vol of the final fermentation batch. Inocula for the final commercial fermentation are usually produced in several multiple stages beginning in the laboratory with a small test tube culture. Between the laboratory and the production-scale fermentor, the inoculum may be transferred to new batches of substrate several times to increase the volume of the seed available. The size of inoculum chosen for each stage of the fermentation is selected in order to accelerate the process time. It is, of course, desirable to keep final processing time in the large fermentation vessel at a minimum. Also, the number of transfers made between the laboratory culture and the final inoculum is kept as low as possible in order to reduce the chances for contamination. Usually, organisms actively growing in the logarithmic phase of their life cycle are used for seeding the next stage of the fermentation. This practice assures a negligible lag-phase in the succeeding stage and minimizes the chances for contamination.

The desired changes of microbial catabolism taking place during a typical fermentation process have a fairly narrow optimum temperature range. Also, the heat generated by the oxidative action of growing microorganisms is significant. Hence, commercial fermenting vessels are equipped with temperature-controlling devices. Generally, they are cooled by submerged coils through which cold water circulates. The fermenting temperature is kept constant within a range of $\pm 1°C$ by automatic temperature control devices. In some processes, the optimum temperature for the growth of the microorganism is not the same as the optimum temperature for the formation of product. Therefore, the temperature may be programmed to different levels at different times during the fermentation cycle.

Products of microbial action frequently have a different hydrogen-ion concentration than the raw materials from which they are formed. This, of course, causes a change in the pH of the fermenting medium. In order to keep the acidity of the fermenting substrate in the optimum range for maximum yield, it is frequently necessary to control the pH or buffer the fermenting liquid extensively. The pH can be controlled readily by metering in sterile acid or base with automatic control devices. It is now common practice to control pH to within one-tenth of a unit in large-scale commercial fermentations.

In aerobic fermentation processes, the presence of air (oxygen) is necessary for the microorganisms to carry out the desired metabolic steps. Therefore an ample supply of sterile air to the fermenting vessel is needed. However, several commercial processes are anaerobic; ie, the microorganism does not require air, and oxygen may even be toxic. In these processes it is necessary to exclude air from the fermenting vessel.

In the aerobic fermentation processes, oxygen actually takes part in the chemical reaction which transforms the substrate to the final product. Air may be supplied to the fermenting liquid in several different ways (8), the simplest by surface contact. On a laboratory scale, this is accomplished by placing fermenting vessels on a shaking machine which continually disrupts the surface and increases the interfacial area between the liquid and the air. Oxygen can also be dissolved in the liquid by spreading it in thin layers, as is done in tray culture. By far, the most universally used method of obtaining dissolved oxygen in a fermentation liquid is by bubbling air through the liquid and distributing the air throughout the fermentation vessel by means of an agitator and a baffling system. In many aerobic fermentations, the rate of product formation is proportional to the amount of oxygen supplied to the fermenting organism. Hence, it is important to dissolve the largest possible amount of oxygen in the liquid. It is not uncommon to supply several hundred cubic feet of sterilized air per minute to a normal-sized industrial fermentor.

Vessels in which commercial fermentation processes are carried out may be of many different sizes and shapes and are made of many different materials of construction. The typical submerged pure culture aerobic fermentation process is carried out in a closed fermentor under pressure, so that a pressure vessel must be used for the fermentation. Connecting pipelines are generally made of stainless steel because of the corrosion problem and the necessity for cleanliness and sterility. These tanks are also provided with automatic temperature control, pH control, agitation, air sparger, devices for automatic cleaning, and steam sterilization. Auxiliary equipment includes inoculum and nutrient tanks. In order to follow the fermentation, devices such as sample cocks, thermometers, pressure meters, etc, are also connected to the fermentation vessel. Fermentors may be of any size depending upon the scale of production. In general, commercial fermentors range from 5000 to 50,000 gal in size.

After the microbial action has been completed, it is necessary to separate the product from the impurities contained in the typical fermentation mash. The final whole culture contains the desired product in dilute solution along with similar metabolic products. Product concentration seldom exceeds 10% and is often much below 1%. The purification process consists of removing the 5% desired product from the 95% extraneous materials. This is generally accomplished by a series of physical and chemical treatments such as chilling, heating, distillation, extraction, evaporation, and crystallization. The recovery and purification process may cost considerably more than the entire preceding fermentation process, particularly in the case of fine pharmaceuticals like antibiotics and vitamins. After recovery and purification of the desired product, the bulk of the material still remains and this is marketed or disposed of as a by-product. Frequently, the unreacted raw material adds to the economy of a microbial process; but often it becomes a burden on the entire process and must be disposed of at a cost.

Contemporary Fermentation Processes

The annual fermentation review in *Biotechnology and Bioengineering* gives a survey of current fermentation products. The fermentation industry is based upon a wide variety of products which arise from microbial metabolism. Some products, derived from very simple carbohydrate oxidation, may be obtained at relatively high concentrations of 10–20%, while others, such as vitamin B_{12}, are measured in parts per million.

Undoubtedly, the major segment of the fermentation industry in the 1960s is the production of antibiotics. These materials have been in production for approximately twenty-five years. In addition to the over one thousand antibiotics described during this period, there were many more which were encountered and not described. Fifty-three antibiotic substances have been produced on a commercial scale in the last twenty-five years by various firms in the world. In 1961, for example, a total of thirty-two antibiotics were produced by sixteen manufacturers (1). By far the largest number of antibiotics are used in human and animal therapy. Several, however, are used in feed only for their growth-promoting effects on animals. One is used as an anthelmintic in hog feeds; another is used to control plant pathogens; and several antibiotics have multiple uses. See also Antibiotics; Macrolide antibiotics; Polyene antibiotics; Polypeptide antibiotics; Penicillin; Tetracyclines.

The major products of carbohydrate metabolism are those which started the fermentation industry. Historically, the most important part of the fermentation industry has been the production of organic acids and solvents. This was the natural result from the use of fermentation in food preservation and in the production of beverages. The major organic acids produced by fermentation can be listed as lactic acid (qv), acetic acid (see Ethanoic acid), citric acid (qv), gluconic acid, and glutamic acid. Other acids which are produced commercially in lesser volume are 2-ketogluconic acid and itaconic acid. These acids are all major products of carbohydrate metabolism and are formed from a series of very simple reactions by microorganisms acting on sugars. The industrial solvents produced in good yields from sugars, namely acetone, butanol, and ethanol, are now produced nearly entirely by synthetic processes for economic reasons.

In the past few years, there has been a great deal of interest in the production of amino acids (qv) by microbial fermentations centered on glutamic acid because it is a standard item of commerce. In addition, processes now in use for the production of lysine have been described in the technical literature (1,9). Glutamic acid, marketed as its monosodium salt, is produced in large amounts in the Orient from raw materials, such as cane molasses, beet molasses, and potato starches. Yields as high as 90%, based on the glucose consumed, have been reported. Processes for the biosynthesis of many other amino acids (qv) have been reported in the literature. Some of the amino acids include trytophan, isoleucine, threonine, homoserine, valine, aspartic acid, alanine, and homolanthionine. At present, none of these processes is commercially used, either because of lack of demand for the amino acid or the prohibitively high cost of its production.

Another important segment of the fermentation industry is based on the conversion of steroids to medicinally useful compounds (10). This technique has been developed in the past decade and makes use of microorganisms to carry out transformation of steroids. Well over one thousand publications have appeared since the work on steroids began in the early 1950s. Compared with other fermentation processes, the changes brought about by the microorganism used in steroid conversions are minor. However, these changes are subtle in nature and compete favorably with chemical reactions because of their high degree of specificity for carrying out the chosen transformation. Desired transformations include hydroxylation in the 11α, 11β, and 16α positions as well as several other hydroxylations and dehydrogenations. See Steroids and steroidal hormones.

Enzymes (qv) are another family of substances produced by industrial fermentation processes. These biocatalysts are used in medicinal fields, in food preservation and preparation, and in industrial reactions. In medicine, enzymes are used for debridement of wounds, for clearing of blood clots, and as digestive aids. Because of their narrow specificity, enzymes also find use as qualitative and quantitative analytical tools in laboratories. Perhaps the largest use of microbial enzymes is in the enzymatic conversion of starch to simple sugar. Yields by this process are almost 100%, and products result which have greater purity than those obtained by acid hydrolysis of starch. For many years, microbial enzyme preparations have also been used to catalyze a variety of reactions in the production of food products (11). The following enzymes are used in the food industry: proteases, which hydrolyze protein to peptides or amino acids; pectinases or pectinolytic enzymes, used in the clarification of fruit juices; and lipolytic enzymes, which hydrolyze fats and are used in producing food flavors. Enzymes which hydrolyze or partially hydrolyze both cellulose and hemicelluloses also find industrial application. In addition, a great many highly specific enzymes are used in research studies. Most of the commercial enzymes now in use are derived from strains of the *Aspergillus* mold or from the large family of the *Bacillus* bacteria. Highly evolved techniques of submerged fermentations are used in the production of enzymes for industrial uses.

All biosynthetic reactions are catalyzed by enzymes. Some of these enzymes appear externally from the microbial cells and can be used to catalyze desired reactions in the absence of the cells. Other enzymes are located either in or on the cells and cannot be practically separated from the cells; hence, the whole microorganism is used to carry out reactions. New techniques of freeing the enzyme protein from microbial cells have recently been developed, and it is quite conceivable that cell-free preparations of enzymes will find wider application in the near future.

Microorganisms also have the ability to biosynthesize vitamins (qv). Two vitamins which are produced commercially by microbial fermentations are vitamin B_{12} and riboflavin (qv). Vitamin B_{12} is used in pharmaceuticals and for animal feed supplementation. Riboflavin also finds use in these two areas; it may also be manufactured by chemical synthesis. Unidentified vitamins or growth factors are produced and used in animal feeds without separation and purification. Some of these materials are actually complex mixtures of water-soluble vitamins and cellular material which is left as a byproduct after the primary fermentation is completed. Another growth factor, namely, gibberellin, a growth stimulator for plants, is produced commercially and for use in malting where it increases the enzyme complement of the germinating barley. A carotenoid has also been produced by fermentation. Although this material is not a true vitamin, it is used in animal feeds to enhance the pigmentation of poultry and poultry products.

Microbial cells, another product of microbial metabolism, are also used commercially. Yeasts (qv) are used in foods and feed; mushrooms grown commercially by submerged fermentation are used in food flavoring; and certain bacteria are used as microbial insecticides. Much of the yeast now used in animal feed is a by-product from the paper industry. Manufacturers, using a sulfite process, can grow a "torula" type yeast in their waste liquors and produce a salable product while solving a waste disposal problem. The yeast grown by conventional fermentation means is dried and sold to feed blenders. The use of certain microorganisms as specific insecticides is a novel fermentation development which has taken place within the past few years. Residue problems created by the use of broad-spectrum chemical insecticides make it desirable to use microbial insecticides in certain applications. The microbial materials are pathogenic only for certain classes of insects and, therefore, are advantageous where the ecology of nature should not be disturbed by the use of broad-spectrum material.

Future Growth of the Fermentation Industry

The emphasis of commercial fermentation has gradually shifted from the production of simple molecules to the production of more complex molecules. This change results from the increased sophistication and newer knowledge of fermentation and from the competition of the synthetic chemical routes to the simpler molecules. Efforts currently spent in fermentation research indicate that this trend will continue. The newer techniques of mutation, that is, the tailor-making of microorganisms to carry out a specific job, indicate that this method will be used more widely in the future. Elucidation of the genetic coding is only in its beginning and holds a great potential for use in the fermentation industry. It is conceivable that any product found in an organism's metabolic pathway could be produced in commercial amounts by suitable selection of mutants. Another promising area for gains in the fermentation field is the use of nonaqueous, high-energy, hydrocarbon raw materials for biosynthesis. These substrates are essentially unoxidized, whereas the carbohydrate materials previously used are approximately half-oxidized. This advantage can be fully exploited in the production of bulk commodities such as acids, proteins, and similar materials. It is not inconceivable that a 100% weight yield of protein or organic acid may be obtained from fermentation of a hydrocarbon substrate. Moreover, certain hydrocarbon raw materials are appreciably cheaper than bulk carbohydrate sources.

An area of growing importance is the use of continuous fermentation processes, which in effect increase plant capacity without installation of additional equipment. Continuous processes are potentially more efficient than batch operations, but the technology is much more complicated. Certain simple processes have been developed for continuous methods, such as the manufacture of yeast and vinegar. Technical reports on continuous processes for the production of ethanol, polyols, penicillin, vitamin B_{12}, enzymes, 1-butanol, acetone, and various amino acids have appeared (12). Continuous operation furthers the development of continuous automatic analyzers and other monitoring and control equipment. For an efficient continuous fermentation process, it is mandatory that an efficient, steady state be reached and maintained. Therefore sophisticated control mechanism is needed. Also, the problem of continuous sterilization and harvesting becomes apparent. It is safe to say that continuous fermentation will become an important aspect of the fermentation industry in the coming decade.

Bibliography

"Fermentation" in *ECT* 1st ed., Vol. 6, pp. 317–375, by George I. de Becze, Schenley Distillers, Inc.

1. D. Perlman and C. Kroll, *Chem. Week* **90**, 98 (1962).
2. S. J. Pirt, *Chem. Ind. (London)* **1964**, (43), 1772–1777.
3. C. T. Calam in D. J. D. Hockenhull, ed., *Progress in Industrial Microbiology*, Vol. 5, Gordon & Breach, Science Publishers, Inc., New York, N.Y., 1964.
4. R. J. Davis, *J. Bacteriol.* **85**, 486–487 (1963).
5. A. P. Harrison, Jr., and M. J. Pelczar, Jr., *J. Gen. Microbiol.* **30**, 395–400 (1963).
6. W. C. Haynes, L. J. Wickerham, and C. W. Hesseltine, *Appl. Microbiol.* **3**, 361–368 (1963).
7. J. J. Shull, G. T. Carso, and R. R. Ernst, *Appl. Microbiol.* **11**, 485–487 (1963).
8. J. H. Rushton, *Ind. Eng. Chem.* **55** (8), 55–56, 58 (1963).

9. J. R. De Zeeuw, *Abstracts of Papers*, 10P, 145th Meeting, American Chemical Society, Division of Microbial Chemistry and Technology, New York, N.Y., Sept. 1963.

10. D. H. Peterson in C. Rainbow and A. H. Rose, eds., *Biochemistry of Industrial Micro-organisms*, Academic Press, Inc., New York, N.Y., 1963.

11. E. J. Beckhorn, M. D. Labbee, and L. A. Underkofler, *J. Agr. Food Chem.* **13**, 30–34 (1965).

12. R. I. Mateles, D. Perlman, A. E. Humphrey, and F. H. Deindoerfer, *Biotechnol. Bioeng.* **7**, 1–90 (1965).

Fermentation Reviews

H. E. Silcox and S. B. Lee, *Ind. Eng. Chem.* **40**, 1602–1608 (1948).

S. B. Lee, *Ind. Eng. Chem.* **41**, 1868–1879 (1949).

Ibid., **42**, 1672–1690 (1950).

Ibid., **43**, 1948–1969 (1951).

D. Perlman, W. E. Brown, and S. B. Lee, *Ind. Eng. Chem.* **44**, 1996–2012 (1952).

D. Perlman, A. E. Tempel, Jr., and W. E. Brown, *Ind. Eng. Chem.* **45**, 1944–1969 (1953).

D. Perlman and C. L. Kroll, *Ind. Eng. Chem.* **46**, 1809–1826 (1954).

S. C. Beesch and G. M. Shull, *Ind. Eng. Chem.* **47**, 1857–1875 (1955).

Ibid., **48**, 1585–1603 (1956).

Ibid., **49**, 1491–1508 (1957).

S. C. Beesch and F. W. Tanner, Jr., *Ind. Eng. Chem.* **50**, 1341–1354 (1958).

Society for Industrial Microbiology, *Developments in Industrial Microbiology*, distributed by Plenum Press, New York 1960–1962; later published by American Institute of Biological Sciences, Washington, D.C., 1963–1964.

K. V. Thimann, *The Life of Bacteria*, The Macmillan Company, New York, N.Y., 1955.

W. W. Umbreit, ed., *Advances in Applied Microbiology*, Academic Press, Inc., New York, N.Y., 1959–1964.

L. A. Underkofler and R. J. Hickey, eds., *Industrial Fermentations*, Chemical Publishing Company, Inc., New York, 1954.

General References

D. J. D. Hockenhull, ed., *Progress in Industrial Microbiology*, Interscience Publishers, Inc., New York; later published by Gordon & Breach, Science Publishers, Inc., New York, N.Y., 1959–1964.

H. T. Huang in D. J. D. Hockenhull, ed., *Progress in Industrial Microbiology*, Vol. 5, Gordon & Breach, Science Publishers, Inc., New York, N.Y., 1964.

M. W. Miller, *The Pfizer Handbook of Microbial Metabolites*, McGraw-Hill Book Co., Inc., New York, N.Y., 1961.

J. R. Porter, *Bacterial Chemistry and Physiology*, John Wiley & Sons, Inc., New York, N.Y., 1946.

S. C. Prescott and C. G. Dunn, *Industrial Microbiology*, 3rd ed. rev., McGraw-Hill Book Co., Inc., New York, N.Y., 1959.

C. Rainbow and A. H. Rose, eds., *Biochemistry of Industrial Micro-organisms*, Academic Press, Inc., New York, N.Y., 1963.

A. H. Rose, *Industrial Microbiology*, Butterworth & Co., Ltd., London, 1961.

C. E. Skinner, C. W. Emmons, H. M. Tsuchiya, *Henrici's Molds, Yeasts, and Actinomycetes*, 2nd ed., John Wiley & Sons, Inc., New York, N.Y., 1947.

S. C. Beesch and F. W. Tanner, Jr., *Ind. Eng. Chem.* **51**, 1086–1098 (1959).

A. E. Humphrey and F. H. Deindoerfer, *Ind. Eng. Chem.* **53**, 934–946 (1961).

A. E. Humphrey and F. H. Deindoerfer, *Appl. Microbiol.* **10**, 359–385 (1962).

A. E. Humphrey, F. H. Deindoerfer, and R. I. Mateles, *Ind. Eng. Chem., Ann. Rev. Suppl.* **54a**, 66–76 (1962).

F. H. Deindoerfer, R. I. Mateles, and A. E. Humphrey, *Appl. Microbiol.* **11**, 273–303 (1963).

R. I. Mateles, F. H. Deindoerfer, and A. E. Humphrey, *Biotechnol. Bioeng.* **5**, 1–84 (1964).

R. I. Mateles, D. Perlman, A. E. Humphrey, and F. H. Deindoerfer, *Biotechnol. Bioeng.* **7**, 1–90 (1965).

RALPH F. ANDERSON
International Minerals &
Chemical Corporation,
Bioferm Division

FERRICYANIDES; FERROCYANIDES.　See Iron compounds.

FERRITES

The word "ferrite" has been variously used.　As a chemical term it refers to salts $MFeO_2$ or MFe_2O_4 (for a mono or divalent metal, M), in which iron is in the oxidation state +3.　However, the approved chemical term for these salts is ferrates(III).　See Iron compounds.

Many of these ferrites have remarkable magnetic properties and are in wide use for a number of components in a variety of electronic equipment.　The term "ferrite" has therefore been extended to all magnetic oxides containing iron as a major metallic component; in this usage, the term can include certain spinels, perovskites, magnetoplumbites, and garnets.

In actual usage in the electronics industry, the word "ferrite" has become a term that does not denote any particular chemical composition or structure but simply refers to a given property; in this sense it is used for any technically useful magnetic oxide.　See Magnetic properties; Magnetic materials.　Table 1 lists some magnetic ferrites found in nature.

Table 1.　Some Naturally Occurring Magnetic Ferrites

Mineral	Approximate formula	Color	Melting point,[a] °C
magnetite	Fe_3O_4	black	1540 dec[b]
maghemite	γ-Fe_2O_3	black	150 dec[b]
jacobsite	$(Fe,Mn)_3O_4$ includes $MnFe_2O_4$	gray-black	1570
franklinite	$(Fe,Mn,Zn)Fe_2O_4$	gray-black	1590
magnesioferrite	$MgFe_2O_4$	orange-brown	1780
magnetoplumbite	$PbMn_{3.5}Fe_{7.5}Al_{0.5}Ti_{0.5}O_{19}$	gray-black	1540

[a] Approximate values.　Melting point will be affected by the exact composition involved.

[b] Decomposition occurs either with the loss of oxygen (for Fe_3O_4) or to a new crystal form (for γ-Fe_2O_3).

(The term "ferrite" is also used in metallurgy for an important phase in iron, α-Fe; this is an entirely different sense of the term.)

As the electrical era made itself felt early in the twentieth century, the artificial production of ferrites was started.　Hilpert in Germany worked in this field but was not successful because of the lack of reproducibility and the limited need for the material at that time.　Just before World War II, the Japanese, Kato and Takie and their associates, did much to bring these materials to a higher degree of development.　After the war the Dutch under Snoek (1), at the Philips Co., brought them to the degree of maturity needed for proper utility.　Philips Co. personnel have devoted an entire volume, *Ferrites* (2), to covering this topic in great detail.　It is used quite extensively in this review, and any topic not specifically referenced to it can be found therein. Advances in the use of high frequencies, especially commercial television, made the development of ferrites essential. Today magnetic ferrites are a very important ceramic material in electronic technology and science.

Crystal Chemistry of Ferrites

Although ferromagnetism is often thought of as a property exclusively of certain metals, it can also occur, and for the same fundamental reason, in certain compounds of metals, such as the ferrites. Metallic cations with unpaired $3d$ electrons in the oxide framework of the ferrites can give rise to a net magnetic moment. For an understanding of this behavior the physical arrangement of the lattice structure involved must be examined.

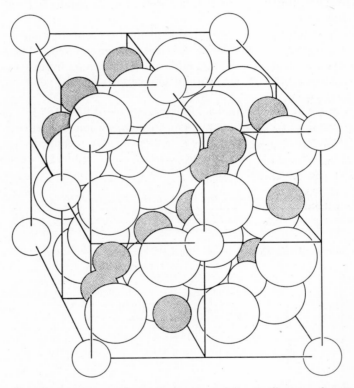

Fig. 1. Spinel unit cell; large open spheres are oxygen anions, small open spheres are tetrahedral cations, and small solid spheres are octahedral cations.

The ferrites, or ferrospinels (3) (these names are used interchangeably), have the structure of the mineral spinel (4,5), $MgAl_2O_4$, in Figure 1. This is a face-centered cubic array of oxygen anions containing interstices only partially filled with the metallic cations. The unit cell, the basic repetitive unit, consists of 32 oxygen anions (the large open spheres). In this block of 32 oxygens, there exist two types of interstitial positions: 32 octahedral (6 oxygens around a central location) and 64 tetrahedral (4 oxygens around a central location). Of these 96 interstices, only 24 are occupied:

8 tetrahedral (the solid spheres) and 16 octahedral (the small open spheres). Electronic charge compensation necessitates that this ratio exist: one divalent ion and two trivalent ions for every four oxygens, ie $(Mg^{2+} + 2Al^{3+}):4O^{2-}$. Other combinations are also possible, but these are not of prime importance in this discussion. Closer examination shows that two possible extremes of cation distribution exist. If all the divalent ions (M) of spinel go into the tetrahedral positions and the trivalent ions into the octahedral positions, a logical, well-balanced lattice results. This is called the "normal" configuration. It does occur for some ferrites, ie, $ZnFe_2O_4$ and $CdFe_2O_4$, but the result is a nonmagnetic material. The "inverse" configuration is the magnetic one. Here, the trivalent ions first fill all available tetrahedral positions. The remaining ions, the rest of the trivalent and all of the divalent ions, go randomly into the octahedral positions. Using accepted convention, nickel ferrite is written as $Fe^{3+}(Ni^{2+}Fe^{3+})O_4^{2-}$; the parenthesis designates the octahedral positions. An understanding of these distributions is important for the discussion of the origin of the magnetization in the ferrites.

Ferrimagnetism in Ferrites

In 1949, Néel (6) was able to explain in simple terms the origin of the observed magnetic moments in ferrites. He showed that an antiparallel spin alignment exists for the cations in the two lattice sites, octahedral and tetrahedral. The term "ferri" is adopted for this "anti" arrangement of the spins as opposed to the "ferro" in ferromagnetism, where only one spin direction is involved. The discussion that follows describes in more detail the origin of the net magnetic moment of ferrimagnetism. The transition metal atoms' third and fourth orbitals have unpaired $3d$ electrons in the ions they form, as shown in Table 2. These ions go into respective positions, "normal" or "inverse," as explained above. Exchange forces cause the spins of the ions in the tetrahedral lattice sites to line up parallel to each other but antiparallel to the aligned spins of the ions in the octahedral positions. Table 3 shows this sche-

Table 2. Atomic and Ionic Electron Spin Alignment of the Third and Fourth Orbitals in Some Transition Metals

Metal	Valence	Electrons ($3s$)	Electrons ($3p$)	Electrons ($3d$)	Electrons ($4s$)	Uncompensated cation electrons
Mn	0	↓↑	↓↑ ↓↑ ↓↑	↓ ↓ ↓ ↓ ↓	↓↑	
	2+	↓↑	↓↑ ↓↑ ↓↑	↓ ↓ ↓ ↓ ↓	□	5
	3+	↓↑	↓↑ ↓↑ ↓↑	↓ ↓ ↓ ↓ □	□	4
	4+	↓↑	↓↑ ↓↑ ↓↑	↓ ↓ ↓ □ □	□	3
Fe	0	↓↑	↓↑ ↓↑ ↓↑	↓↑ ↓ ↓ ↓ ↓	↓↑	
	2+	↓↑	↓↑ ↓↑ ↓↑	↓↑ ↓ ↓ ↓ ↓	□	4
	3+	↓↑	↓↑ ↓↑ ↓↑	↓□ ↓ ↓ ↓ ↓	□	5
Co	0	↓↑	↓↑ ↓↑ ↓↑	↓↑ ↓↑ ↓ ↓ ↓	↓↑	
	2+	↓↑	↓↑ ↓↑ ↓↑	↓↑ ↓↑ ↓ ↓ ↓	□	3
Ni	0	↓↑	↓↑ ↓↑ ↓↑	↓↑ ↓↑ ↓↑ ↓ ↓	↓↑	
	2+	↓↑	↓↑ ↓↑ ↓↑	↓↑ ↓↑ ↓↑ ↓ ↓	□	2
Cu	0	↓↑	↓↑ ↓↑ ↓↑	↓↑ ↓↑ ↓↑ ↓↑ ↓↑	↓	
	1+	↓↑	↓↑ ↓↑ ↓↑	↓↑ ↓↑ ↓↑ ↓↑ ↓↑	□	0
	2+	↓↑	↓↑ ↓↑ ↓↑	↓↑ ↓↑ ↓↑ ↓↑ ↓□	□	1
Zn	0	↓↑	↓↑ ↓↑ ↓↑	↓↑ ↓↑ ↓↑ ↓↑ ↓↑	↓↑	
	2+	↓↑	↓↑ ↓↑ ↓↑	↓↑ ↓↑ ↓↑ ↓↑ ↓↑	□	0

Table 3. Magnetic Spin Alignment in Some Ferrites at $0°K$

| Ferrite | Unpaired $3d$ electrons | | Net moment, n_B/mol | |
	Tetrahedral, Fe^{3+}	Octahedral, Fe^{3+} and M^{2+}	Calculated	Observed
$Fe^{3+}(Fe^{3+}Mn^{2+})O_4^{2-}$ †	↓ ↓ ↓ ↓ ↓	↑ ↑ ↑ ↑ ↑ ↑ ↑ ↑ ↑ ↑	5	4.6
$Fe^{3+}(Fe^{3+}Fe^{2+})O_4^{2-}$	↓ ↓ ↓ ↓ ↓	↑ ↑ ↑ ↑ ↑ ↑ ↑ ↑ ↑	4	4.1
$Fe^{3+}(Fe^{3+}Co^{2+})O_4^{2-}$	↓ ↓ ↓ ↓ ↓	↑ ↑ ↑ ↑ ↑ ↑ ↑ ↑	3	3.7
$Fe^{3+}(Fe^{3+}Ni^{2+})O_4^{2-}$	↓ ↓ ↓ ↓ ↓	↑ ↑ ↑ ↑ ↑ ↑ ↑	2	2.3
$Fe^{3+}(Fe^{3+}Cu^{2+})O_4^{2-}$	↓ ↓ ↓ ↓ ↓	↑ ↑ ↑ ↑ ↑ ↑	1	1.3
$Fe^{3+}(Fe^{3+}Mg^{2+})O_4^{2-}$ ‡	↓ ↓ ↓ ↓ ↓	↑ ↑ ↑ ↑ ↑	0	1.1
$Zn^{2+}(Fe^{3+}Fe^{3+})O_4^{2-}$	none	random	10 ††	0

† Neutron diffraction studies show that this is not entirely true. There is an 80% observed deviation toward the "normal" configuration, but it does not affect the example shown above.

‡ The distribution in $MgFe_2O_4$ is temperature-dependent and does not achieve the ideal case shown here. Mg^{2+} has no $3d$ electrons.

†† Theoretical.

Table 4. Net Magnetic Spin Alignment in Some "Mixed" Nickel-Zinc Ferrites and Calculated Moments

| Ferrite | Tetrahedral Fe^{3+} | Octahedral | | Net moment,[a] n_B/mol |
		Fe^{3+}	Ni^{2+}	
$Fe(FeNi)O_4$	↓ ↓ ↓ ↓ ↓ (1.0)	↑ ↑ ↑ ↑ ↑ (1.0)	↑ ↑ (1.0)	2.0
$Zn_{0.1}Fe_{0.9}(Fe_{1.1}Ni_{0.9})O_4$	↓ ↓ ↓ ↓ ↓ (0.9)	↑ ↑ ↑ ↑ ↑ (1.1)	↑ ↑ (0.9)	2.8
$Zn_{0.2}Fe_{0.8}(Fe_{1.2}Ni_{0.8})O_4$	↓ ↓ ↓ ↓ ↓ (0.8)	↑ ↑ ↑ ↑ ↑ (1.2)	↑ ↑ (0.8)	3.6
$Zn_{0.3}Fe_{0.7}(Fe_{1.3}Ni_{0.7})O_4$	↓ ↓ ↓ ↓ ↓ (0.7)	↑ ↑ ↑ ↑ ↑ (1.3)	↑ ↑ (0.7)	4.4

[a] Simple computed values; ie, for a 10% zinc ferrite substitution in nickel ferrite, the net moment from the aligned octahedral spins less the aligned tetrahedral spins is $1.1\ (5) + 0.9\ (2) - 0.9\ (5) = 2.8\ n_B$.

matically and lists the calculated and observed magnetic moments. This is the state at $0°K$ where the disrupting influence of temperature is not present. Above and beyond the simple cases shown above, the magnetization of the ferrites can be further enhanced. Mixing a nonmagnetic ferrite (ie, $ZnFe_2O_4$) with a magnetic one, as in Table 4, shows how this is accomplished on a theoretical basis. Figure 2 plots some observed values. It must be remembered that this is a lattice substitution and not a physical mixture as such. The increased net moment results from the decrease in the total number of spins in the octahedral positions (more Fe); zinc preferentially fills tetrahedral positions first. The deviation from ideal behavior observed at higher concentrations of substitution (solid line in Figure 2) is due to the weakening of the exchange forces by the nonmagnetic constituent. Theoretically, ten Bohr magnetons would result in $ZnFe_2O_4$ if the "normal" ferrospinel configuration could maintain complete spin alignment in this compound.

Magnesium ferrite ($MgFe_2O_4$) is a hybrid case. As the compound is heated to higher and higher temperatures, the cations tend to approach a random distribution; the random case would yield $Mg_{1/3}Fe_{2/3}(Mg_{2/3}Fe_{1/3})O_4$. This behavior gives the varied magnetic moment shown in Figure 2. The value is dependent upon which cation configuration was frozen in. The magnetic moment is theoretically at 3.33 n_B for the random distribution of the high-temperature form. Gamma-ferric oxide

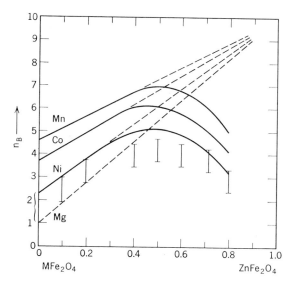

Fig. 2. Magnetic moment change (in Bohr magnetons, n_B) of various zinc-substituted ferrites; M = Mn, Co, Ni, and Mg in $Zn_\delta M_{1-\delta}Fe_2O_4$.

(γ-Fe_2O_3) is another special case (7). This iron oxide is a ferrospinel having all the iron ions in the +3 valence state. As in magnetite (Fe_3O_4), the close-packed oxygen superstructure is present, but vacancies occur in the "magnetite"-type lattice to satisfy electroneutrality. The respective "ferrite" formulas are $Fe^{3+}(Fe^{3+}Fe^{2+})O_4$ for magnetite and $Fe^{3+}(Fe_{1\frac{2}{3}} \square_{\frac{1}{3}})^{3+}O_4$ for gamma-ferric oxide with one-sixth of the normally occupied octahedral sites left vacant. One method of preparing this material is by a controlled low-temperature oxidation of magnetite:

$$4\,Fe_3O_4 + O_2 \xrightarrow[150°C]{\Delta} 6\,\gamma\text{-}Fe_2O_3$$

If the compound is heated to higher temperatures, it changes crystallographic form (no oxygen needed) from the cubic ferrospinel to the hexagonal α-ferric oxide hematite, the stable high-temperature form. Gamma-ferric oxide is, of course, primarily of academic interest. The compound by itself cannot be maintained at the high temperatures needed to get a useful sintered product. Some question does exist, however, as to whether or not it is "stabilized" by additives and whether or not it does, in fact, exist as a solid solution in some mixed ferrites having excess iron oxide.

Magnetic Behavior of Ferrites

The ferromagnetic hysteresis loop (8,9) shows many of the useful technical properties of the ferrites. A short review of this behavior will aid in understanding the response of ferrites to an applied field. Close examination of a small crystallite (0.1 μ or less) would, in the simplest case, show configurations as in Figure 3. It was stated above that in the ferrite lattice a net spontaneous electron spin alignment (arrows) exists along a specific crystallographic axis. If condition A exists, a large external field results (magnetostatic energy) which is energetically unstable; this is found only in a single domain particle. State B reduces the energy involved, but state C is the low-

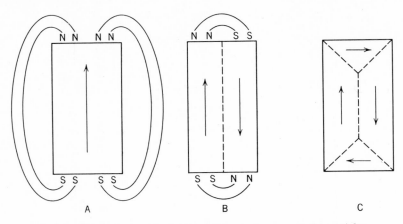

Fig. 3. Magnetic domain configurations in ferromagnetic particles.

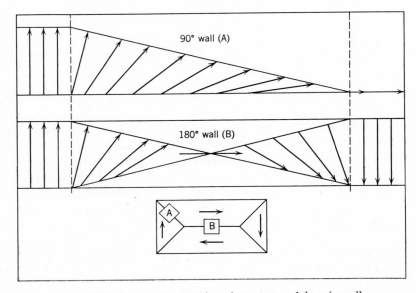

Fig. 4. Schematic representation of two types of domain walls.

energy form. That is, each domain is "head-to-toe" along equivalent axes, and compensating field closure is essentially complete within the crystallite. A careful look at the boundaries between these areas, called walls, reveals two types: 90° walls (A) and 180° walls (B), as in Figure 4. There is a gradual transition of the magnetic spin alignment from one preferred crystallographic axis to another, shown schematically in Figure 4. Energy required to form these walls is derived from that saved by reducing the magnetostatic energy.

It is the action of an applied field on this multidomain structure that gives rise to the hysteresis loop. In fact, in normal ferrite shapes there is an array of these crystallites randomly oriented throughout the piece. Each domain, regardless of orientation in the polycrystalline ceramic, is governed by the same conditions and responds similarly. The application of a slowly increasing external field (H_{applied}) on an "unmagnetized"

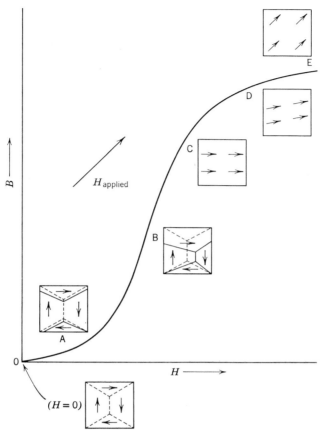

Fig. 5. Initial magnetization curve for a ferromagnetic material. Inserts show approximate domain configurations at various values of $H_{applied}$.

crystallite causes the response shown in Figure 5, the initial magnetization curve. The initial low field moves the walls in such a manner as to tend to increase the induction, B, in the field direction (H at a 45° angle to the cube axis in the example shown), as in A. This action is completely reversible and is linear up to a certain point, called the *initial permeability*, $\mu_0 = B/H$ in Figure 6 (also written as μ'). Further increases in the applied field will cause the wall to proceed, but no longer reversibly. The walls move through the domains in a rather discontinuous manner as they jump past crystalline imperfections, impurities, gross defects, voids, grain boundaries, etc. This is the Barkhausen effect. It is directly observable by "Bitter pattern" (10) techniques. By placing a search coil on the specimen, blips can be seen on an oscilloscope or sharp clicks heard on an audio amplifier. These are caused by sudden emf changes which occur as the "hung up" wall is suddenly released from the obstruction. The normal hysteresis loop needs considerable magnification to show these directly. A point is reached at D where the wall has finally moved through the crystallite and all spin vectors point into a crystallographic axis closest to the applied field direction. The crystallites are now saturated, or single domains. Additional increases in the applied field can now turn the spin vectors only into the field direction. The last increment of

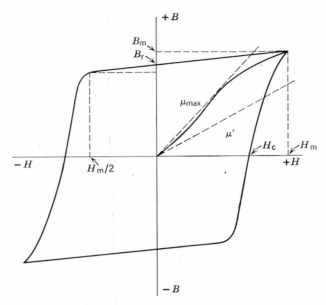

Fig. 6. The ferromagnetic hysteresis loop showing some technically important magnetic characteristics.

magnetization increase is pictured in E. This final action is reversible because the spins cannot stay in this unstable location between favored positions. Any further increases in the applied field will have no effect. The core now acts as an air core with a differential permeability of unity: $dB/dH = 1$ where the core material contributes nothing to the magnetization process at B_m in Figure 6. It must be understood that the processes described above are not discrete but that some overlap exists between successive mechanisms.

It is obvious that a reduction in the applied field from the "saturating field," approximately at D in Figure 5, will cause the induction, B, to follow a different return path. The imperfections and other impediments to wall motion will leave some residual induction when the field is removed, as point B_r, the remanent induction (or retentivity). A reverse field is needed to push the walls back and a field H_c, the coercive force, is needed to bring the induction to zero. Field reversal to $-H_m$ completes the excursion in the opposite direction. To return the material to its original state, it is necessary to subject it to an ac field of successively diminishing strength until the hysteresis loop disappears; the material is now demagnetized. Another method is to heat it above its Curie temperature, then cool it with no applied field so that a normal equilibrium domain structure is achieved.

The Curie temperature, T_c, is a very important property of ferrites. It is the temperature at which thermal energy is sufficient to overcome the aligning influence of the exchange forces. At this point, the material loses its ferrimagnetism as shown by the magnetization curves in Figure 7. Table 5 lists some of these, together with some other typical magnetic data. Note that at the Curie temperature the thermal effect causes the magnetic response to drop off rapidly. In most instances this is a good direct measure of the strength of the exchange forces. Its effect can also be observed in other magnetic characteristics. The weakening of the exchange forces is shown

Table 5. Typical Room-Temperature Magnetic Data and Curie Temperatures of Some Ferrites

Ferrite	B_s	Initial permeability, μ'	Curie temperature, °C
$MnFe_2O_4$	4500	250	300
Fe_3O_4	6100	70	575
$NiFe_2O_4$	3000	10	590
$CuFe_2O_4$	3600	70	455
$MgFe_2O_4$	1800	10	310
$CoFe_2O_4$	5000	>1	520

very markedly by the substitution of zinc ferrite in nickel ferrite (11) in Figure 8. Note how the magnetization at 0°K (−273°C) increases with substitutions up to 50 mole % as expected from the previous discussion of Table 4 and Figure 2. (It decreases, however, at 65% substitution.) The continuous decrease in T_c represents the weakening of the exchange forces. This same effect for various ferrites is shown in Figure 9.

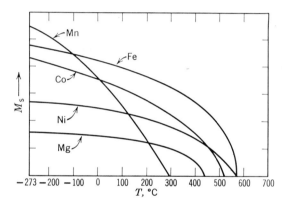

Fig. 7. Saturation magnetization of some ferrites as affected by temperature variations.

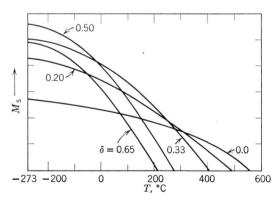

Fig. 8. Saturation magnetization in $Zn_\delta Fe_{1-\delta}(Ni_{1-\delta}Fe_{1+\delta})O_4$ as affected by temperature variations; δ is the amount of zinc substituting for nickel in the lattice.

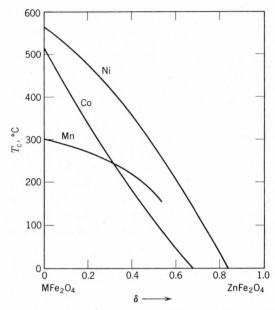

Fig. 9. Curie temperature change in some ferrites by zinc ferrite substitutions; δ = degree of substitution.

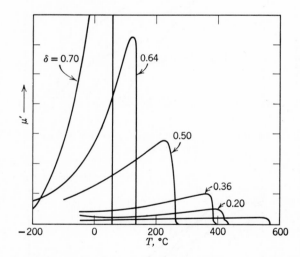

Fig. 10. Temperature response of initial permeability (μ') for some nickel–zinc ferrites: $Zn_\delta Fe_{1-\delta}(Ni_{1-\delta}Fe_{1+\delta})O_4$.

Another example of the thermal effect is shown in Figure 10. A spectacular increase in the initial permeability is found just before the Curie temperature. The loosened, but not completely disrupted, alignment permits easy response to the applied frequency. It is obvious that most commercial compositions must have Curie temperatures considerably above room temperature in order to utilize effectively the magnetic characteristics available. The frequency response of the initial permeability μ' in substituted ferrites must also be considered. Ferrites with higher Curie temperatures

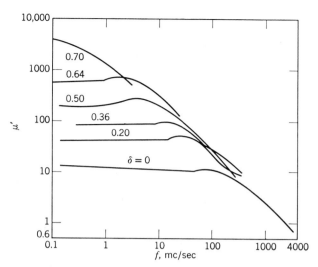

Fig. 11. Frequency response of initial permeability (μ') for some nickel–zinc ferrites: $Zn_\delta Fe_{1-\delta}(Ni_{1-\delta}Fe_{1+\delta})O_4$.

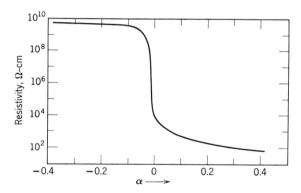

Fig. 12. Resistivity change in $NiFe_{2-\alpha}O_4$ with small deviations (α) from stoichiometry.

respond better to higher applied frequencies (12), as shown in Figure 11 for the zinc-substituted nickel ferrite series. Here, too, the nature of the aligning forces is apparent. Applications of ferrites at higher frequencies generally call for materials with high Curie temperatures. An extension of the useful frequency range is possible by the addition of nonmagnetic components, such as Al_2O_3 substituted for some of the Fe_2O_3 in the basic ferrite. In such compositions, the octahedral site is preferentially occupied by the nonmagnetic cation (Al), giving rise to a decreased magnetic moment but a higher frequency response. This is in direct contrast with zinc, which prefers the tetrahedral sites.

The important feature of ferrites that is borne out in the preceding discussion is the wide range of properties available for the technical applications. Compositional variations seem to have no end. Mixed ferrites of all varieties, including those between magnetic end members, can meet the specific and exacting requirements of industry. In addition to these possibilities are the variations that result from the technology of preparation and manufacture. Pronounced changes can be effected in these materials, often by very small variations. An illustration of this is the resistivity change in nickel ferrite caused by small deviations from the stoichiometric content of iron, as shown in Figure 12 (13). In effect, dissociation of the excess Fe_2O_3 takes place at sintering temperatures to form magnetite in solid solution:

$$6\,Fe_2O_3 \overset{\Delta}{\rightarrow} 4\,Fe_3O_4 + O_2\uparrow$$

Electronic conduction, characteristic of magnetite, becomes possible between the iron ions in the octahedral sites: $Fe^{3+} + e^- \rightleftharpoons Fe^{2+}$. Other parameters, such as grain size, density, homogeneity, induced strains, etc (14), all can affect the properties of the manufactured component. These variations are put to use daily to meet the varied needs of an ever-changing industry. Thus the limitations found in conventional metallic systems have been pushed aside and new areas of utility opened.

"Hard Ferrites"

"Hard ferrites" (that is to say, "hard" in magnetic properties) (15) are derivatives of the mineral magnetoplumbite (see Table 1), ideally $PbFe_{12}O_{19}$ (or $PbO.6Fe_2O_3$). Commercially, the barium derivative, magnetobarite ($BaFe_{12}O_{19}$), is the most important, with magnetostrontite ($SrFe_{12}O_{19}$) recently getting some attention. The magnetobarite structure can best be visualized, to a first approximation, as an extended magnetite structure with no ferrous ions. In addition, the oxygen arrangement is altered

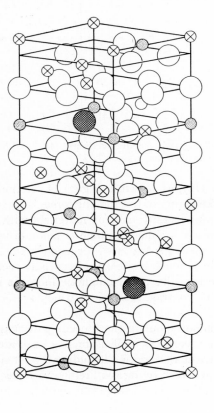

Fig. 13. Schematic representation of the magnetobarite ($BaFe_{12}O_{19}$) unit cell: large open circle, O^{2-}; large hatched circle, Ba^{2+}; small solid circle, Fe^{3+} (tetrahedral); small circle with X, Fe^{3+} (octahedral).

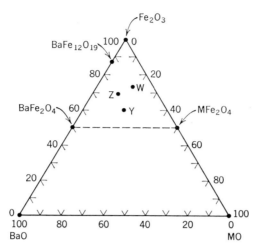

Fig. 14. The system BaO–MO–Fe₂O₃ showing the relationship between various "ferrites"; MFe_2O_4 = ferrospinel, Ba-Fe₁₂O₁₉ = magnetobarite, and W, Y, and Z are some intermediate compositions.

to the hexagonal arrangement. At specific intervals a barium cation (large hatched sphere) substitutes for an oxygen anion, as shown schematically in Figure 13. Magnetization occurs in a manner similar to that described for the ferrites. The structural difference that exists (hexagonal instead of cubic as found in the soft ferrites) has a direct bearing on the magnetic behavior. In the hexagonal arrangement, the magnetic interactions between the cations cause the net magnetic spins to point only toward the c axis of this lattice. This behavior is in contrast to that of the ferrospinels which are cubic and in which all faces are equivalent. Changing the magnetic spin direction from one crystallographic axis to another in the ferrospinels is quite easy, whereas in magnetobarite it is very difficult. Much energy is required to get the hysteresis loop response. The coercive force, H_c, is often three orders of magnitude higher than with soft ferrites. This difference in behavior is utilized very effectively in commercial products; it also explains the "hard" aspect of the magnetization.

There have also come into existence hybrid combinations between the ferrospinels and the magnetobarites called "ferroxplana" (16) and "ferroxcona"; W, Y, and Z in Figure 14 show the composition of some examples. Properties achieved in these are intermediate between the two basic types, but closer to the hard. Their crystallography is similar to that of magnetoplumbite. In contrast to the latter type, the equilibrium spin directions in the ferroxcona materials is at some angle, or cone, out of the c direction. This deviation can continue until the ferroxplana materials are reached. In these the spin directions are in the c plane. No extensive use has been found for these hybrids, so they have made no real impact in the field as yet.

There is one true ferrite, however, that exhibits hard magnetic properties, $CoFe_2O_4$. It is a ferrospinel which shows a marked magnetic anisotropy, or change in magnetization with crystallographic direction. The theoretical aspects of this behavior will not be considered here. Suffice it to say that cobalt ferrite (17) finds utility as a hard magnet where properties between the hard and soft are desired, especially where they are closer to that of soft magnetic materials.

Other "Ferrites"

To include the rare earth iron garnets with the ferrites is also not truly valid, but common usage apparently includes them. The technology for all these magnetic oxide materials is similar, and there is therefore a plausible reason for discussing all these related magnetic materials together. These compounds have a structure similar to the mineral garnet ($Ca_3Fe_2Si_3O_{12}$). Their general formula is $Re_3Fe_5O_{12}$ (or $3Re_2O_3$.- $5Fe_2O_3$), where Re is a rare earth cation (also yttrium). The lattice configuration (18) is very complex (not shown). It has, in addition to the octahedral and tetrahedral interstices in a cubic oxygen lattice, an eightfold coordinated position. This last position may or may not contribute to the overall magnetic performance, depending upon the magnetic moment of the rare earth cation occupying it.

Magnetic perovskites do not contain iron. The basic structure is similar to that of cubic $SrTiO_3$. In this lattice, the strontium and oxygen ions form a close-packed system (they are about the same size) with the tetravalent cation (Ti) occupying an octahedral position formed by oxygens alone. Lanthanum manganite ($La^{3+}Mn^{3+}O_3$) is one compound having this basic structure (19); the manganese ion occupies the octahedral site. It is nonmagnetic, but with substitutions of divalent calcium for some of the trivalent lanthanum, a magnetic compound results. These substitutions cause the valence of some of the manganese ions to change to the tetravalent state in order to satisfy the required electroneutrality. The interactions between the trivalent and tetravalent manganese in equivalent lattice sites gives the observed magnetic effects. In contrast with the ferrites, this behavior is ferromagnetic, not ferrimagnetic.

Ferrite Manufacture

The fundamental reaction in the formation of a simple ferrite is

$$MO + Fe_2O_3 \xrightarrow{\Delta} MFe_2O_4$$

Whether or not the oxides are used is not important. The result will remain the same as long as somewhere in the reaction process the proper amount of oxygen can be picked up or decomposition products given off to yield the end compound (20–22). Two other simple reactions that may be mentioned are the following:

$$\text{hydroxide:} \quad M^{2+} + 2\,Fe^{3+} + 8\,OH^- \rightarrow M(OH)_2 + 2\,Fe(OH)_3$$
$$\downarrow \Delta$$
$$MFe_2O_4 + 4\,H_2O \uparrow$$

$$\text{carbonate:} \quad MCO_3 + Fe_2O_3 \xrightarrow{\Delta} MFe_2O_4 + CO_2 \uparrow$$

A combination of the carbonate reaction and the oxide reaction is employed commercially, incorporating rather complex combinations of components. Even achieving a stoichiometric ratio of the cations is not always desired. In fact, the oxygen content might also be deficient. Various combinations of cations are arrived at. Theoretical computations and systematic empirical studies produce formulations needed to give the desired end properties in a useful component shape. In industry it is this last feature that is the ultimate goal. A typical modern ferrite manufacturing flow pattern (20,23) is shown in Figure 15. The major tasks accomplished are (1) formation of the compound; (2) preparation of a powder, to be formed by ceramic pressing techniques; and (3) component fabrication (see Ceramics).

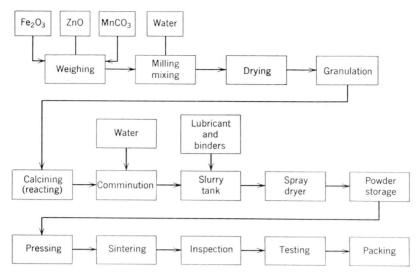

Fig. 15. A typical ferrite component manufacturing process flowsheet.

Compound Formation. The raw materials (usually of cp grade) are weighed according to set formulations to better than a half percent accuracy. Corrections are included to account for tolerable impurities, moisture content, etc, variations that are encountered from lot to lot of raw materials. These materials are milled, either wet or dry, primarily to get an intimate blending and homogenizing. This physical mixture is then granulated to a rather uniform granule size or pressed into blocks, then heated to a reaction temperature of about 1000°C. The temperature is held for a specific length of time to achieve the desired degree of reaction. The conversion may or may not go to completion. The extent of this reaction is determined by the amount of non-reacted components remaining and the degree of crystallinity in the ferrite formed. There is no necessity that a liquid phase be present in any of these reactions. Solid-state diffusion in a well-mixed, small-particle aggregate will cause the reaction to proceed rapidly at these temperatures.

Preparation of Pressing Powder. The rather coarse and hard reacted ferrite product must next be ground to a small particle size. The component pressing operation and final sintering that are to follow will be improved if the interacting particles are small, usually less than 1 μ. Grinding is done in various types of closed mills using water and steel balls as the grinding media. The mill speed, load, ball size and density, viscosity of the slurry, etc, all determine the length of time needed. Just prior to the end of the milling operation, organic lubricants and binders can be added to the slurry and blended in. The object here is to introduce a lubricating material so that pressing of the dry powder will be more efficient. Binders give added strength to the pressed part for ease of handling in this "green" state.

Slurry drying is accomplished in various ways: drum drying, pan drying, filtering and drying, spray drying (24), etc. In all these methods, except for the spray drying, it is necessary to granulate the dried "cake" to the desired granule size. This granule size will be determined by the size of the piece to be formed, the shape of the piece, the compaction ratio desired, etc. Spray drying yields spherical granules directly. Some factors governing the size of the granules formed by this process are the density of the

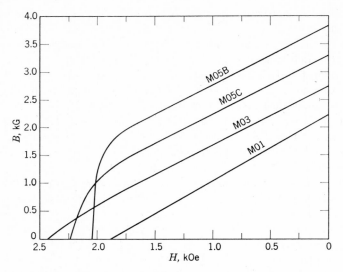

Fig. 16. Demagnetization curves of some commercial hard ferrite materials.
Courtesy Allen-Bradley Co.

slurry used, speed of the spraying head, diameter and height of the drying chamber, and the temperature and volume of the dry air going into the dryer. Classification of these granules gives a more uniform size range for more effective control of the pressed part.

Component Fabrication. The powder thus formed is ready for pressing. The type of compaction used will vary with the shape being molded. Injection molding, extrusion, isostatic pressing, and hot pressing can be mentioned but do not find extensive use in ferrite component fabrication. Certain special shapes are best formed by these techniques, but the bulk of the commercial shapes are formed by *compaction presses* using the dry, granular powder. These compaction presses, either hydraulic or mechanical, can have complex pressing cycles to yield an optimum output and uniform density in rather intricate parts. "Green" ferrite parts are next loaded on refractory plates, usually an aluminum oxide material, and carefully stacked on cars going into a high-temperature tunnel kiln. Temperatures of 1200°C and over are needed. Varied heating cycles are employed, depending upon the composition and the end effects wanted. Heating and cooling rates of 100°C/hr with a 2–6 hr soak period in the peak temperature zone are common. Air, oxygen-enriched, or oxygen-deficient atmospheres are needed in the entire sintering cycle, or some portion of it, according to the composition being fired. The densified parts emerging from the tunnel kiln are inspected for physical defects, usually touched up if needed, and then subjected to electrical testing. These tests ensure proper quality control and that the material will meet the set electrical and magnetic specifications. Careful packaging is needed to protect these fragile ceramic parts during shipment.

Special Processing for Hard Ferrites. The manufacturing sequence described above is also applicable to the hard ferrites. Certain permanent magnet properties can be enhanced in a component by variations in processing techniques. Specifically, the anisotropic magnetic behavior of the basic crystal that was pointed out earlier can be utilized. It is obvious that if no care is taken to attain an orientation of the individual crystallites in a polycrystalline matrix (as is found in a normal ceramic part), magnetic response in a part so fabricated will be nearly equal in all directions. If knowledge of the crystallite anisotropy (platy structure) and the magnetic anisotropy (magnetization is easiest in the c axis) is utilized, parts can be fabricated showing a highly anisotropic behavior similar to that of the crystallites.

The commonest way to accomplish this is to prepare the milled ferrite powder as a slurry, then subject it to a magnetic field just prior to compaction (25,26). Special porous dies with an applied magnetic field permit an orientation of the particles as the water is being drawn out from the slurry. Compaction in these porous dies can be either parallel or perpendicular to the applied field direction, depending upon the type of part involved. The effect of this orienting process in some commercial materials is shown in the demagnetization curves in Figure 16. The isotropic material is labeled M01; parts made of it show about equal permanent magnet properties in all directions. Successively more highly oriented materials are also shown, with the M05B material having about an 85% net orientation of the crystallites in one direction on the part. Unlike metallic permanent magnets, orientation in these parts must be done prior to pressing. The sintering temperatures required to get material flow are considerably higher than the Curie temperature. At these temperatures the material is nonmagnetic, so that the application of an external field has no effect on the magnetic orientation.

Applications of Ferrites

Technological advances in ferrite manufacture and property control have permitted the electronics industry to go far in effectively applying their versatile properties (27). New applications are constantly being reported in publications and patents.

Table 6. Typical Ferrite Applications

Application	Ferrite property	Typical ferrite[a]
filter inductor	high μ, low loss	Mn–Zn
transformer	low loss, temperature stability, high μ	Ni–Zn; Mn–Zn
antenna rod	high μ, low loss	
adjustable inductors	high μ, low loss	Mn–Zn; Ni–Zn
flyback transformers	low loss, good temperature coefficient	Mn–Zn; Ni–Zn
deflection yoke	low loss, high skin resistance	
suppression beads	high loss at specific frequency	Mn–Zn; Ni–Zn
recording heads	low loss, mechanically strong	Ni–Zn; Mn–Zn
memory cores	hysteresis loop rectangularity, moderately low H_c	Mg–Mn
switching cores	hysteresis loop rectangularity, moderately low H_c	Mg–Mn
multiaperture cores	hysteresis loop rectangularity, moderately low H_c	Mg–Mn
magnetic amplifiers	hysteresis loop rectangularity, moderately low H_c	Mg–Mn
isolators, attenuators, modulators, switches	Faraday rotation, ferromagnetic resonance	Mg–Mn
delay lines	high magnetostriction	Ni–Zn
filters and oscillators		Ni–Zn
temperature controls	low Curie temperature, steep temperature coefficient	Ni–Zn

[a] This refers to major constituents only.

Fig. 17. Typical soft ferrite shapes. Courtesy of Allen-Bradley Co.

Owens (28) categorized soft ferrite applications as linear B–H curve, nonlinear B–H curve, rectangular hysteresis loop, microwave, and magnetostrictive. A part of his tabulation is in Table 6. Typical commercial shapes are shown in Figure 17. Pot cores, transformer cores (segments and rings), a television deflection yoke, some rods, and recording heads are included. These shapes account for a major part of today's soft ferrite production.

In the high-speed digital computer field, soft ferrites have taken a prominent position. Their rectangular hysteresis loop characteristic, low coercive force, high resistivity, low energy loss, high speed response, high flux output, reproducibility, stability, and low cost are features utilized. The basic principle employed is their ability to respond as coincident current elements (29). Three wires passing through a toroid can be used to illustrate the application. Basically, the arrangement can be regarded as a one- or two-turn transformer, two wires for input and the third for sensing the output flux. A toroid (or core) is first cycled so that it is in one of its remanent states, B_r or $-B_r$. This is information storage. A current pulse of magnitude $-H/2$ will not materially change the state of magnetization; see Figure 6. The output flux, dB/dH, sensed by the third wire, is very small. Doubling this input current to $-H_m$, half carried by each wire, will cause the core to switch into the opposite remanent state, $-B_r$. The output flux is high because the core has traversed half the hysteresis loop. This output triggers impulses in appropriate circuits, telling whether the core was in the "zero" or "one" state and constitutes information retrieval. High-speed digital computers have thousands, even millions, of these cores in their "memory" banks. Information is stored in binary code; "yes" or "no," "plus" or "minus," and "one" or "zero" are some of the names given to the two states of magnetization. A typical experimental memory consisting of 256 (2^8) cores of 0.080 in. OD, 0.050 in. ID, and 0.025 in. in height is shown in Figure 18. Operating times of about 1 μsec are possible. A memory bank of one million bits (one million cores) can be examined for its information in about one second. Magnetic amplifiers, switching devices, and circuits using multiaperture ceramic shapes and other applications make use of this loop rectangularity (30).

The Faraday rotation (31) effect is a high-frequency (microwave) characteristic of ferrites now used extensively. A plane-polarized electromagnetic wave passing through a magnetized ferrite undergoes a rotation of its axis of polarization. The extent of this rotation is dependent upon the distance the wave travels in the ferrite. A unique feature is that a reflected wave reentering the circuit (and the ferrite) is rotated in the same direction. Interference is thus eliminated. Isolators, gyrators, phase shifters, etc, are designed around this property. Ferromagnetic resonance

Fig. 18. Coincident current memory plane of ferrite cores (about 1 in. square).

absorption in the microwave frequency range limits the utility of ferrites. Attenuators, on the other hand, utilize this effect. At specific frequencies, energy absorption occurs in the ferrite. It is shown by a sharp rise in the energy loss versus applied field curve. The amount of this absorption is governed by inherent crystallographic factors that cannot be altered except by compositional changes. There are, however, a number of internal structural features of a ceramic nature that can be controlled (32). Ferrites are, therefore, specially prepared for microwave applications to minimize the width and height of the absorption peak. High crystallinity, homogeneity, purity of composition, highest oxidation state of the iron oxide, and high density are criteria for fabrication.

Fig. 19. Typical ceramic permanent magnet shapes in extensive use today. Courtesy Allen-Bradley Co.

For some time now, hard ferrites have had only a limited market. Primary applications were for latching purposes, magnetic particle separation in filtering, loudspeaker magnets, and in small engine magnetos. Limited application has been for dc motor fields. Some of these typical shapes are shown in Figure 19. At the top are motor stator segments and rings. In the center are loudspeaker magnets and gasoline engine magneto magnets. On the bottom are various latching magnets. Through an extensive educational program by manufacturers such as the Allen-Bradley Co. (33) and with the rise in popularity of "cordless" appliances, hard ferrites have reached maturity. Their high coercive force is especially attractive. It makes them less susceptible to demagnetizing influences and temperature effects. High efficiency, low heat generation, small package size, less weight, and overall cost savings are available to the design engineer. Manufacturers of conventional fractional horsepower motors are now aware of the advantages of this "new" material. In the automotive field alone, windshield wiper motors, alternators, air conditioner and heater motors, and window lift and actuator motors of all types are in use or are being developed. Cordless appliances offer a large market. From small toothbrush motors, electric shaver motors, and electric knife motors, to the larger battery-operated vacuum cleaners, lawn mowers, and hedge trimmers yet to come, ceramic hard ferrite applications appear limitless. Advances in both compositional and manufacturing technologies are keeping abreast with commercial demands. As shown earlier in Figure 16, variations in available properties make possible a wide variety of designs.

Commercial production figures for ferrites are not available. A reasonable estimate can be computed. The production figures for television, the largest consumer of soft ferrites, show that over seven million sets were manufactured in the United States in 1964. Since there is about half a pound of ferrite in each set (deflection yoke, flyback transformer core, and antenna rod, if used), the total amount is about 3.5 million pounds of soft ferrites. All other applications could well increase this figure by fifty percent to give an overall total of over 5 million pounds in 1964. With color television gaining in popularity, another fifty percent increase in tonnage is possible in the next few years; heavier pieces are used in color television sets. Hard ferrite production of about 2 million pounds appears to be a reasonable current production estimate. Anticipated future applications as stated above could rapidly swell this figure. A six- to tenfold increase in the next few years is not improbable.

Bibliography

1. J. L. Snoek, *Philips Tech. Rev.* **8**, 353 (1946).
2. J. Smit and H. P. J. Wijn, *Ferrites*, John Wiley & Sons, Inc., New York, 1959.
3. R. L. Harvey, I. J. Hegyi, and H. W. Leverenz, *RCA Rev.* **11**, 321 (1950).
4. A. F. Wells, *Structural Inorganic Chemistry*, 3rd ed., The Clarendon Press, Oxford, 1962, pp. 487–494.
5. E. J. W. Verwey and E. I. Heilmann, *J. Chem. Phys.* **15**, 174–180 (1947).
6. L. Néel, *Ann. Phys.* **3**, 137–198 (1948).
7. G. W. van Oosterhaut and C. J. M. Rooijmans, *Nature* **181**, 44 (1958).
8. R. M. Bozorth, *Ferromagnetism*, D. Van Nostrand Co., Inc., Princeton, N.J., 1951.
9. G. T. Rado and H. Suhl, eds., *Magnetism*, Vols. 1–3, Academic Press Inc., New York, 1963.
10. F. Bitter, *Phys. Rev.* **41**, 507 (1932).
11. E. W. Gorter, *Philips Res. Rept.* **9**, 295–320, 321–365, 403–443 (1954).
12. H. P. J. Wijn, M. Gevers, and C. M. van der Burgt, *Rev. Mod. Phys.* **25**, 91–92 (1953).
13. L. G. Van Uitert, *Proc. I.R.E.* **44**, 1294–1303 (1956).
14. G. Economos, "Effect of Microstructure on the Electrical and Magnetic Properties of Ceramics," in W. D. Kingery, ed., *Ceramic Fabrication Processes*, M.I.T. Technology Press and John Wiley & Sons, Inc., New York, 1958, Chap. 21.
15. J. J. Went, G. W. Ratheman, E. W. Gorter, and G. W. Oosterhout, *Philips Tech. Rev.* **13**, 194–208 (1952).
16. G. H. Jonker, H. P. J. Wijn, and P. B. Braun, *Philips Tech. Rev.* **18**, 145–154 (1956).
17. A. Feiner, C. A. Lovell, T. N. Lowry, and P. G. Ridinger, *Bell System Tech. J.* **39**, 1–30 (1960).
18. G. S. Gellor and M. A. Gilleo, *Acta Cryst.* **10**, 239 (1957).
19. G. H. Jonker and J. H. van Santen, *Physica* **16**, 337–349 (1950).
20. G. Economos, *J. Am. Ceram. Soc.* **38**, 241–244, 292–297, 335–340 (1956); **42**, 628–632 (1959).
21. G. Economos and T. R. Clevenger, Jr., *J. Am. Ceram. Soc.* **43**, 48–52 (1960).
22. G. Economos, "Solid Reactions in Ferrites," in W. D. Kingery, ed., *Kinetics of High-Temperature Processes*, M.I.T. Technology Press and John Wiley & Sons, Inc., New York, 1959, Chap. 29.
23. G. Economos, *J. Electrochem. Soc.* **106**, 465–467 (1959).
24. J. Motyl, *The Western Electric Engineer* **7**, 2–10 (July, 1963).
25. A. L. Stuijts, *Trans. Brit. Ceram. Soc.* **55**, 57–74 (1956).
26. U.S. Pat. 2,980,617 (April 18, 1961), J. R. Ireland (to Indiana General Corp.).
27. R. F. Soohoo, *Theory and Applications of Ferrites*, Prentice-Hall Inc., Englewood Cliffs, N.J., 1960.
28. C. D. Owens, *Proc. I.R.E.* **44**, 1234–1248 (1956).
29. J. W. Forrester, *J. Appl. Phys.* **21**, 44–48 (1951); U.S. Pat. 3,069,608 (Dec. 18, 1962), J. W. Forrester et al. (to Parsons Corp.).
30. B. R. Budny, *Proc. Electron. Components Conf.* **1959**, 122–127.
31. B. Lax and K. Button, *Microwave Ferrites and Ferrimagnetics*, McGraw-Hill Book Co., Inc. New York, 1962.
32. S. L. Blum, J. E. Zniemer, and H. Z. Zlotnick, *J. Am. Ceram. Soc.* **40**, 143 (1957).
33. J. B. Gollhardt, *Paper 64-305, I.E.E.E., 15th Annual Appliance Technical Conf., May 20, 1964, Philadelphia, Pa.*

GEORGE ECONOMOS
Allen-Bradley Company